LOCAL ANALYTIC GEOMETRY

PURE AND APPLIED MATHEMATICS

A Series of Monographs and Textbooks

Edited by

PAUL A. SMITH and SAMUEL EILENBERG
Columbia University, New York

LOCAL ANALYTIC GEOMETRY

SHREERAM SHANKAR ABHYANKAR

Division of Mathematical Sciences
Purdue University
Lafayette, Indiana

1964

ACADEMIC PRESS New York and London

ACADEMIC PRESS INC.
111 FIFTH AVENUE, NEW YORK, New York 10003

United Kingdom Edition published by
ACADEMIC PRESS INC. (London) LTD.
BERKELEY SQUARE HOUSE, LONDON W.1

Library of Congress Catalog Card Number: 64–24650

PRINTED IN THE UNITED STATES OF AMERICA

Dedicated to

Professor Shankar Keshav Abhyankar

and

Mrs. Umabai Abhyankar

by their son

Preface

This book is written in the spirit of Weierstrass: power series play the dominant role.

As algebraic geometry is the study of algebraic equations, so analytic geometry is the study of analytic equations. An analytic function on an open set D in the space $\mathbf{C}^n$ of n complex variables is a complex valued function which can be locally expanded in a convergent power series. An analytic set in D is a subset of D which is locally the set of common zeroes of a finite number of analytic functions. A complex space is obtained by patching together analytic sets. In all this, $\mathbf{C}$ can be replaced by any complete valued field K. There results the notion of an analytic space over K or an analytic K-space. In addition to the real and complex fields, some other complete valued fields are: p-adic number fields, complete algebraic closures of p-adic number fields, and the field of formal power series in one indeterminate with coefficients in a field of any characteristic. It should be noted that whereas the real and complex fields are connected, every other complete valued field is totally disconnected. The term analytic geometry as meaning the theory of complex spaces, especially in its relationship with algebraic geometry, goes back at least to Serre's 1956 paper (Serre **[2]***). It becomes all the more appropriate when one is dealing, as is the case in this book, with analytic spaces over general K.

In connection with his Normalization Theorem for complex spaces, Oka proved a lemma to the effect that if a complex space X is a hypersurface in $\mathbf{C}^n$ then: X is normal if and only if the dimension of the singular locus of X is less than the dimension of X by at least two (Oka **[8]**). In the summer of 1959, Professor Remmert asked me whether this could be generalized from the hypersurface case to the case of a complete intersection. Drawing on the analogy with the corresponding situation in algebraic geometry, I could easily give a simple proof for complete intersections which consisted of showing the invariance of "rank" and "embedding dimension", deducing from this the analytic analogue of Zariski's criterion for a simple subvariety in algebraic geometry, and then using some elementary local algebra. The only nonelementary algebraic

* Boldface numbers within brackets refer to the Bibliography at the end of the book.

result which I needed was the regularity of the quotient ring of a regular local ring with respect to a prime ideal. At the request of Professor Remmert, I found a simple proof for convergent power series rings which amounted to reducing to the polynomial case by using the Weierstrass Preparation Theorem. This work on the generalization of Oka's lemma was published in Abhyankar [**3**]; although not needed for the Oka lemma, I included a proof of "invariance of order along a simple subspace". When I wrote this paper, I became convinced that the entire local theory of complex spaces can be treated quite simply by first invoking the Preparation Theorem and then using the technique of local rings initiated by Krull and the method of algebraic geometry as developed by Zariski; at the same time it would extend the theory from the complex case to the case of any algebraically closed complete valued field. This project was carried out during 1960; the results were first announced in a lecture at the American Mathematical Society meeting in October 1960 at Worcester; part of the material was then included in courses given at Harvard and Johns Hopkins during 1961–1962. Initially I was planning to publish this work in one or more papers. However, as I felt that even in the complex case there was no easily accessible exposition of the subject, I thought that it would be more useful to write a self-contained book giving an elementary exposition of the theory of analytic spaces over any K and at the same time including the special features of the complex case arising out of the connectedness of the complex field.

Professor Zariski taught me whatever algebraic geometry I know. For the classical theory of complex spaces my sources were the works of Behnke, Cartan, Grauert, Oka, Osgood, Remmert, Rückert, Stein, and Thullen, and above all some lectures given to me by Professor Remmert in the summer of 1959. My sole contribution has been to put the two subjects together.

Instead of describing the contents of the various chapters systematically, I shall make a number of comments. Except when I say "complex case", it is to be understood that I am in the "general case", i.e., the case of any algebraically closed complete valued field K (part of the considerations apply without the assumption of K being algebraically closed).

Impressed by the power of the Preparation Theorem—indeed, it prepares us so well!—I considered "Weierstrass Preparation Theorem and its immediate consequences" as a possible title for the entire book. In any case, I have tried to bring out this power. For instance the following things are deduced from the Preparation Theorem and the resulting proofs seem to be simpler than some of the customary proofs: Hensel's lemma (§12 and §20), continuity and analyticity of algebroid functions (§11 and §12), open map theorem (§11 and §32), regularity of quotient rings of power series rings (§25), dimension of an intersection (§27), and so on. As far as Chapter IV is concerned, the Preparation Theorem is the cornerstone and owing to it I could treat formal power series rings and convergent power series rings in a unified manner.

Another reason for the similarity between formal power series rings and convergent power series rings is that although the latter are not complete they are nevertheless Henselian, and Henselian rings do share many properties with complete local rings (§20).

In a sense, Chapter IV deals with the "punctual" and hence formal theory of analytic sets; in Chapter V this is extended "locally", and then in Chapter VII analytic sets are glued together to form analytic spaces by using the language of sheaves. Most of our considerations being of a local nature, the use of sheaves is quite rudimentary. Thus on the one hand most of Chapter VII could have been written without using the language of sheaves, and on the other hand analytic spaces could have been introduced at the beginning of Chapter V. The significance of sheaves lies more in the global aspects of complex spaces, in particular in the theory of Stein manifolds which are the natural generalization of domains of holomorphy (§7). It is hoped to give an exposition of the elementary theory of Stein manifolds and other topics in complex analysis in a possible second volume.

The transition from "punctual" to "local" is to a large extent concentrated in the proposition proved in §31 to the effect that if an analytic set is irreducible at a point then it is pure dimensional in some neighborhood of that point. The proof of this proposition and the treatment of many other topics in Chapter V are facilitated by the use of what may be called "normic forms" (§28) and the most elementary case of intersection multiplicity (§30). In the same vein, upon analyzing an argument given by Osgood, I introduce the concept of the Osgoodian of a pair of elements and formulate the main property (purely formal) of the Osgoodian as Osgood's lemma (§35). The Osgoodian is a function of the same type as the norm and the trace and it should be useful also in field theory. Using Osgood's lemma and the classical Riemann extension theorem (in $\mathbf{C}^n$) one obtains the following proposition which explains the significance of the notions of integral dependence and integral closure in complex analysis: a point of a complex space is normal (i.e., the ring of analytic function germs at that point is integrally closed in its total quotient ring) if and only if the Riemann extension theorem holds at that point (§36).

The coherence of the structure sheaf and other local properties of analytic sets proved in §33 are recapitulated in §44 in the context of analytic spaces. With this at hand, the results in Abhyankar [**3**] carry over *verbatim* to the general case (§45). It turned out that the "invariance of order along a simple subspace" was exactly what was needed to replace certain analysis arguments used in Oka's proof of his Normalization Theorem. Together with some ideas taken from Zariski's theory of normalization in algebraic geometry, this now swiftly leads to the Normalization Theorem and hence also to the analyticity of the nonnormal locus in the general case (§46).

The key to the various connectivity properties of complex spaces is the connectedness of an irreducible algebroid hypersurface which in turn is proved by using the Riemann extension theorem in $\mathbf{C}^n$ (§14).

The work on this book was partly supported by National Science Foundation research grants at The Johns Hopkins University, in the earlier stages of the book under NSF-G7030 and in the latter stages under NSF-G25225. I would like to express my appreciation for this support. Also I would like to thank G. Fischer and V. Güntzer for help in proof reading.

July, 1962 S. S. A.

Instructions to the Reader

Propositions traditionally known as "lemma" (e.g., Hensel's lemma) or "theorem" (e.g., Weierstrass preparation theorem) are called as such. Most of the remaining propositions are merely designated by a decimal number.

In cross reference, the chapters play no role. Sections are numbered consecutively throughout the book as §1, §2,... . Parts of §x are numbered as (x.1), (x.2),... and they are cited as ($x.y$). Items in ($x.y$) are labeled 1), 2),..., 1°), 2°),..., i), ii),..., etc. In ($x.y$), z) refers to item z) of ($x.y$) and ($x'.y'.z'$) refers to item z') of $(x'.y') \neq (x.y)$.

The book need not be read in consecutive order. Here is the approximate interdependence of the various chapters.

Chapter I and the complex case: §1 and §2 are used throughout the book. §8 is used only in §37. §9 is used only in §10. §3 to §7 form one unit; from this only §4 is used in the rest of the book and that only in the portion dealing with special features of the complex case. Except for some isolated places, this portion consists of §§13, 14, 16, 34, 36, 37, 38, 39, 44C. The rest of the book in no way depends on this portion. After reaching the end of §35, §36 to §39 may be read in any order.

Chapter II: §10, §11, §12 are basic. §15 is used only in §26, §33C, §42. §16 is not used elsewhere in the book.

Chapter III: The reader may choose to read this chapter only as needed except that (17.1) to (17.5) and (19.1) to (19.9) should be read before proceeding to Chapters IV and V.

Chapter IV: §23 (except 23.11 and 23.12), §25, (26.1), (26.2), and §28 should be read before proceeding to Chapter V. §27 is not used elsewhere in the book.

Chapter VI: This is mostly independent of the previous chapters.

Chapter VII: Although proofs here depend on Chapter V, still it is possible to read this before Chapter V. Chapter VI is needed here.

Instructions to the Reader

Propositions, traditionally known as "lemmas" [illegible] (or "theorems" [illegible]) are called [illegible] [illegible] [illegible] propositions [illegible] numbered [illegible]

In [illegible] chapters play no role [illegible] are numbered consecutively throughout the book as [illegible] are numbered as (x.1), (x.2), [illegible] and these are [illegible] [illegible] refers to (x,y) and (x.y) [illegible] refers [illegible]

The book need not be read in [illegible] order [illegible] the approximate [illegible] of the [illegible]

[illegible]

[illegible] this only [illegible] and that [illegible]

[illegible]

[illegible] 140. The [illegible]

[illegible] may be read in any order.

Chapter [illegible] 11, 12 are [illegible]

[illegible]

Chapter III [illegible] reader may [illegible] except that [illegible] should be read before proceeding to Chapters IV and V.

Chapters [illegible] II and [illegible] should be read before proceeding to Chapter [illegible]

[illegible]

Chapter VI [illegible] of the previous chapters.

Chapter VII [illegible] proofs [illegible] depend on Chapter V [illegible] possible [illegible] Chapter V [illegible]

Contents

CHAPTER I

Elementary Theory in $\mathbf{C}^n$

CHAPTER II

Weierstrass Preparation Theorem

CHAPTER III

Review from Local Algebra

CHAPTER IV

Parameters in Power Series Rings

CHAPTER V

Analytic Sets

CHAPTER VI

Language of Sheaves

CHAPTER VII

Analytic Spaces

LOCAL ANALYTIC GEOMETRY

CHAPTER I

Elementary Theory in $\mathbf{C}^n$

§1. NOTATION AND TERMINOLOGY

(**1.1**) By a ring we mean a commutative ring with identity (denoted by 1). Unless otherwise stated, a ring homomorphism is assumed to carry identity into identity, and subring and overring are assumed to have the same identity element. A ring R is a null ring means $R = 0$, i.e., R contains only the zero element, i.e., $1 = 0$ in R. An integral domain is a nonnull ring without zerodivisors. All modules are unitary.

Let R be a ring. For any subset B of an R-module $\mathfrak{A}$, the submodule of $\mathfrak{A}$ generated by B is denoted by BR; if $B = \emptyset$ then $BR = \{0\}$. For any ideal $\mathfrak{a}$ in R we set

$$\text{rad}_R\mathfrak{a} = \{r \in R\colon r^p \in \mathfrak{a} \text{ for some integer } p > 0\}.$$

$\mathfrak{a}$ is a proper ideal means $\mathfrak{a} \neq R$. $\mathfrak{a}$ is a prime ideal means $R/\mathfrak{a}$ is an integral domain; $\mathfrak{a}$ is then necessarily proper. $\mathfrak{a}$ is a maximal ideal means $R/\mathfrak{a}$ is a field. An element r in R is said to be a unit in R provided $rr' = 1$ for some r' in R. Two elements in R are said to be R-associates if and only if they differ by unit factors in R. The subscript or prefix R may be dropped when it is clear from the context. Thus we may write "rad $\mathfrak{a}$" for "$\text{rad}_R\mathfrak{a}$", and "associate" for "R-associate". This applies to all other concepts which we shall introduce, i.e., qualifying subscripts, superscripts, and prefixes may be dropped when reference to them is clear from the context.

(**1.2**) Let R be a ring. By definition, R is a quasisemilocal ring $\Leftrightarrow$ the set of maximal ideals in R is a nonempty finite set; note that R is then necessarily a nonnull ring. R is a quasilocal ring $\Leftrightarrow$ R has a unique maximal ideal $\mathfrak{m}$; we indicate this by writing $(R, \mathfrak{m})$. Note that R is quasilocal $\Leftrightarrow$

the set of all nonunits in R is an ideal, which is then the maximal ideal in R. R is a semilocal ring $\Leftrightarrow$ R is noetherian and quasisemilocal. R is a local ring $\Leftrightarrow$ R is noetherian and quasilocal. If $(R, \mathfrak{m})$ is a local ring, then by Krull's theorem[1] $\bigcap_{i=1}^{\infty} \mathfrak{m}^i = \{0\}$. More generally, a quasilocal ring $(R, \mathfrak{m})$ is said to be a quasilocal Hausdorff ring provided $\bigcap_{i=1}^{\infty} \mathfrak{m}^i = \{0\}$. For then R is a Hausdorff space in the *Krull topology* given by taking powers of $\mathfrak{m}$ for a vicinity basis of zero. R is said to be *complete* if it is complete in the Krull topology. Equivalently: $a_n \to a \Leftrightarrow a - a_n \in \mathfrak{m}^{i(n)}$ with $\lim_{n\to\infty} i(n) = \infty$; (a_n) is a Cauchy sequence $\Leftrightarrow a_n - a_{n+1} \in \mathfrak{m}^{i(n)}$ with $\lim_{n\to\infty} i(n) = \infty$; R is complete $\Leftrightarrow$ every Cauchy sequence in R is convergent.

(1.3) Let R be a nonnull ring. We put

$R[[x_1,\ldots, x_n]]$ = ring of formal power series in indeterminates $x_1,\ldots, x_n$ with coefficients in R.

Note that this is naturally isomorphic to $R[[x_1,\ldots, x_{n-1}]][[x_n]]$. For $R_1 \subset R$ we write $R_1[[x_1,\ldots, x_n]]$ for the set of all elements in $R[[x_1,\ldots, x_n]]$ all of whose coefficients are in R_1. Let

$$f = \sum f_{i_1\ldots i_n} x_1^{i_1}\ldots x_n^{i_n} \in R[[x_1,\ldots, x_n]]; \qquad f_{i_1\ldots i_n} \in R.$$

Then f is a unit in $R[[x_1,\ldots, x_n]] \Leftrightarrow$ the constant term $f_{0\ldots 0}$ is a unit in R. "$\Rightarrow$" is obvious. If $f_{0\ldots 0}$ is a unit in R then dividing f by it we may assume that $f_{0\ldots 0} = 1$. Then $f = 1 - g$ where

$$g = \sum_{i_1,\ldots,i_n > 0} g_{i_1\ldots i_n} x_1^{i_1}\ldots x_n^{i_n}; \qquad g_{i_1\ldots i_n} \in R.$$

Now $h = 1 + g + g^2 + \ldots \in R[[x_1,\ldots,x_n]]$, and $fh = (1 - g)(1 + g + g^2 + \ldots) = 1$.

For any field K, $K[[x_1,\ldots,x_n]]$ is an integral domain and we put

$$K((x_1,\ldots,x_n)) = \text{quotient field of } K[[x_1,\ldots,x_n]].$$

[1] Northcott [**1**: Theorem 3 on p. 50], or Zariski-Samuel [**1**: Corollary 2 on p. 217].

(1.4) Let K be a field. Then $K[[x_1,..., x_n]]$ is a complete Hausdorff quasilocal integral domain with maximal ideal generated by $x_1,..., x_n$. Consequently, nonunits $g_1,..., g_n \in K[[y_1,..., y_m]]$ can be "substituted" for $x_1,..., x_n$ in $f(x_1,..., x_n) \in K[[x_1,..., x_n]]$ with convergence in the Krull topology of $K[[y_1,..., y_m]]$. In particular, we can make a nonsingular (homogeneous) K-linear transformation on $x_1,..., x_n$; i.e., if we substitute

$$\sum_{j=1}^{n} a_{ij}y_j \quad \text{for} \quad x_i \qquad (i = 1,..., n),$$

where $a_{ij} \in K$ with $\det((a_{ij})) \neq 0$, then we get an isomorphism of $K[[x_1,..., x_n]]$ onto $K[[y_1,..., y_n]]$. We may consider this as giving an "identification" between $K[[x_1,..., x_n]]$ and $K[[y_1,..., y_n]]$. In other words, we may take $y_1,..., y_n$ as "new variables".

For any

$$f = \sum f_{i_1...i_n} x_1^{i_1}...x_n^{i_n} \in K[[x_1,..., x_n]]; \qquad f_{i_1...i_n} \in K,$$

we set

$$\mathbf{o}f = \textit{leading degree of } f = \begin{cases} \min i \text{ such that } f_{i_1...i_n} \neq 0 \text{ with } i = i_1 + ... + i_n, & \text{if } f \neq 0 \\ \infty, & \text{if } f = 0; \end{cases}$$

and

$$\textit{leading form of } f = \begin{cases} \sum_{i_1+...+i_n=\mathbf{o}f} f_{i_1...i_n} x_1^{i_1}...x_n^{i_n}, & \text{if } f \neq 0 \\ 0, & \text{if } f = 0. \end{cases}$$

Note that leading degrees are preserved under the above isomorphism.

(1.5) Recall that a valued field is a field K with a nonnegative real valued function $a \to |a|$ such that:

$$|a| = 0 \Leftrightarrow a = 0; \qquad \text{and}$$

$$|ab| = |a|\,|b| \quad \text{and} \quad |a + b| \leqq |a| + |b| \qquad \text{for all } a, b \in K.$$

Calling $|a - b|$ to be the distance between a and b, K becomes a metric space. The adjectives "complete" and "nondiscrete" refer to K as a metric space. Then K is nondiscrete $\Leftrightarrow |a| \neq 0, 1$ for some $a \in K$. Calculus properties of real series—absolute convergence, uniform convergence, etc. —go over *verbatim* to series in a valued field. Note that if K is nondiscrete valued then it is necessarily infinite.

(1.6) When it is clear from the context, without explicit mention, for an element in a cartesian product $X_1 \times \ldots \times X_n$, subscripts will indicate components: $a \in X_1 \times \ldots \times X_n$, $a = (a_1, \ldots, a_n)$, $a_j \in X_j$. For $Y \subset X_1 \times \ldots \times X_n$, writing $Y\{x_1, \ldots, x_n\}$ will mean that we are considering $x_1, \ldots, x_n$ as "variables" in $X_1, \ldots, X_n$, respectively. $X^n = X \times \ldots \times X = n$-fold cartesian product of X. For a field K, when it is clear from the context: $(0) = (0, \ldots, 0) =$ origin in K^n.

$\mathbf{Z}$ = ring of ordinary integers.
$\mathbf{R}$ = real field.
$\mathbf{R}_+$ = nonnegative reals.
$\mathbf{R}_{++}$ = positive reals.
$\mathbf{C}$ = complex field.

When we think of $\mathbf{C}$ (or $\mathbf{R}$) as space of a variable (rather than a field) then we shall usually use the superscript 1: $\mathbf{C}^1\{x\}$. For any complex number a, the real and imaginary parts of a are denoted by $\mathbf{Re}\, a$ and $\mathbf{Im}\, a$, respectively. When inequality signs, $\leqq$, $<$, $\geqq$, $>$ are used, it will usually be understood that we are dealing with real numbers.

Let $\varphi : X \to Y$ be a map of a set X into a set Y. For any $X' \subset X$ and $Y' \subset Y$ with $\varphi(X') \subset Y'$ we get a map $\psi : X' \to Y'$ of X' into Y' by taking $\psi(a) = \varphi(a)$ for all $a \in X'$; the map ψ is said to be *induced by* φ. For any $X' \subset X$, the map $X' \to Y$ induced by φ is called the *restriction of* φ *to* X' and is denoted by $\varphi|X'$. For any $X' \subset X$, the *canonical injection of* X' *into* X is the map $i : X' \to X$ given by taking $i(a) = a$ for all $a \in X'$. The canonical injection of X into X is called the *identity map of* X.

(1.7) Let X be a topological space and let $A \subset X$. We write:

$$\begin{aligned} \mathrm{cl}_X A &= \text{closure of } A \text{ in } X, \\ \mathrm{int}_X A &= \text{interior of } A \text{ in } X, \\ \mathrm{bd}_X A &= \text{boundary of } A \text{ in } X = (\mathrm{cl}_X A) - (\mathrm{int}_X A) \\ &= (\mathrm{cl}_X A) \cap (\mathrm{cl}_X (X - A)); \end{aligned}$$

again the subscript X may be omitted. A *vicinity* of A in X is a subset V of X such that $A \subset \mathrm{int}\, V$; *neighborhood* = open vicinity. A *vicinity basis* of A in X is a set Ω of vicinities of A such that every vicinity of A contains a member of Ω. Similarly for a *neighborhood basis*.

Let X be a topological space and let $A \subset X$. A is said to be *locally closed* in X provided any one of the following three equivalent conditions holds:

1°) Given $a \in A$ there exists a neighborhood U of a in X such that $U \cap A$ is closed in U.

2°) A is open in $\mathrm{cl}_X A$.

3°) A is the intersection of an open set in X and a closed set in X.

1°) ⇔ 2°) ⇐ 3°) is obvious. Concerning 1°) ⇒ 3°) we actually have the following: assume 1°) and let $B = X - \text{bd}_{\text{cl}_X A} A$, then B is the largest open set in X containing A in which A is closed; and we have $A = (\text{cl}_X A) \cap B$.

REMARKS. Any open set in X is locally closed in X. Any closed set in X is locally closed in X. If X^* is an open set in X, then any locally closed set in X^* is locally closed in X.

Let φ be a map of a topological space X into a topological space Y. φ is *open* at $a \in X$ means: for any neighborhood N of a in X, we have $\varphi(a) \in \text{int}_Y \varphi(N)$; or equivalently, given a neighborhood N of a in X, there exists a neighborhood N' of a in N such that $\varphi(a) \in \text{int}_Y \varphi(N')$. φ is *open* (on X) means: φ is open at each point of X; or equivalently, for any open set N in X, $\varphi(N)$ is open in Y. φ is *closed* means: for any closed set N in X, $\varphi(N)$ is closed in Y. In case X and Y are Hausdorff, φ is *proper* means: for any compact set M in Y, $\varphi^{-1}(M)$ is compact.

By a domain in a topological space X we mean an open connected subset of X.

Let X and Y be metric spaces (more generally, uniform spaces) and let P be a sequence of functions from X into Y. P is said to be locally uniformly convergent on X provided every point in X has a neighborhood on which P is uniformly convergent. P is said to be compactly convergent on X provided P is uniformly convergent on every compact subset of X. Note that if X is an open set in $\mathbf{C}^n$ (or $\mathbf{R}^n$) then these two notions coincide.

(1.8) Let K be a valued field. $A_j^{(-1)} < A_j^{(1)} > 0$. *Open annular polycylinder* in K^n:

$$\{x \in K^n : A_j^{(-1)} < |x_j| < A_j^{(1)};\ j = 1,\dots, n\}.$$

Closed annular polycylinder in K^n:

$$\{x \in K^n : A_j^{(-1)} \leqq |x_j| \leqq A_j^{(1)};\ j = 1,\dots, n\}.$$

These are products over j, respectively, of:

$$\{A_j^{(-1)} < |x_j| < A^{(1)}\}; \qquad \{A_j^{(-1)} \leqq |x_j| \leqq A_j^{(1)}\}.$$

When $A_j^{(-1)} < 0$ for $j = 1,\dots, n$; the adjective "annular" may be dropped. For $K = \mathbf{C}$,

$$\{A_j^{(-1)} < |x_j| < A_j^{(1)}\}$$

is an open annulus or open disk in $\mathbf{C}^1\{x_j\}$ according as $A_j^{(-1)} \geqq 0$ or $A_j^{(-1)} < 0$.

Mostly we shall use annular polycylinders of the above type, i.e., around the origin. However for any $a \in K^n$ one can consider annular polycylinders around a by translation:

Open:

$$\{x \in K^n: A_j^{(-1)} < |x_j - a_j| < A_j^{(1)}; j = 1, \ldots, n\}.$$

Closed:

$$\{x \in K^n: A_j^{(-1)} \leqq |x_j - a_j| \leqq A_j^{(1)}; j = 1, \ldots, n\}.$$

(**1.9**) Unless otherwise stated: K will denote a field; x, y, z with or without subscripts will denote indeterminates as well as variables; T with or without subscripts will denote an indeterminate. Whenever we talk of $K[\langle\ \rangle]$ or $K(\langle\ \rangle)$, (see §2A), it is to be understood that K is complete nondiscrete valued.

§2. CONVERGENT POWER SERIES

§2A. *Domain of convergence*

Let K be a complete nondiscrete valued field. Let

$$f = \sum f_{i_1 \ldots i_n} x_1^{i_1} \ldots x_n^{i_n} \in K[[x_1, \ldots, x_n]]; \qquad f_{i_1 \ldots i_n} \in K.$$

If at $x = a \in K^n$ the above series is absolutely convergent then its value is uniquely determined and we denote it by $f(a)$.[1] We put

$$\mathbf{E}^*(f) = \{A \in \mathbf{R}_+^n: \exists D \in \mathbf{R}_+ \text{ such that } |f_{i_1 \ldots i_n}| A_1^{i_1} \ldots A_n^{i_n} \leqq D \text{ for all } i_1, \ldots, i_n\};$$

$$\mathbf{E}(f) = \text{interior of } \mathbf{E}^*(f) \text{ in } \mathbf{R}_+^n;$$

and

$$\mathbf{D}(f) = \textit{domain of convergence of } f = \{a \in K^n: (|a_1|, \ldots, |a_n|) \in \mathbf{E}(f)\};$$

[1] This "substitution" in the topology of K does not clash with "substitution" in the Krull topology of $K[[x_1, \ldots, x_n]]$, because they are not defined for the same objects except when we are substituting $(0, \ldots, 0)$ and in that case both the meanings of $f(0, \ldots, 0)$ give the same element $f_{0 \ldots 0}$ of K.

i.e.,

$$\mathbf{D}(f) = \{a \in K^n : \exists A \in \mathbf{R}_+^n,\ D \in \mathbf{R}_+ \text{ such that } |a| < A_1, \ldots, |a_n| < A_n, \text{ and } |f_{i_1 \ldots i_n}| A_1^{i_1} \ldots A_n^{i_n} \leqq D \text{ for all } i_1, \ldots, i_n\}.$$

Given a as above, we can find $B \in \mathbf{R}_+^n$ such that

$$|a_1| < B_1 < A_1, \ldots, |a_n| < B_n < A_n, \quad \text{and then the series}$$

$$\sum f_{i_1 \ldots i_n} a_1^{i_1} \ldots a_n^{i_n}$$

is "majorized" by the power series expansion of

$$D(1 - B_1/A_1)^{-1} \ldots (1 - B_n/A_n)^{-1}.$$

Therefore f is absolutely uniformly convergent in the polycylinder $\{|x_j| < B_j; j = 1, \ldots, n\}$ which is a neighborhood of a in K^n.[2] Consequently, $\mathbf{D}(f)$ is an open set in K^n, f is absolutely locally uniformly convergent in $\mathbf{D}(f)$, and hence $a \to f(a)$ is a K-valued continuous function on $\mathbf{D}(f)$. We shall say: f is *convergent* $\Leftrightarrow \mathbf{D}(f) \neq \emptyset$; f is *convergent at* $a \in K^n \Leftrightarrow a \in \mathbf{D}(f)$; and more generally f is *convergent in* $X \subset K^n \Leftrightarrow X \subset \mathbf{D}(f)$. *We put*

$$K[\langle x_1, \ldots, x_n \rangle] = \{f \in K[[x_1, \ldots, x_n]] : \mathbf{D}(f) \neq \emptyset\}.$$

It is immediate that $K[\langle x_1, \ldots, x_n \rangle]$ is a subring of $K[[x_1, \ldots, x_n]]$. *We put*

$$K(\langle x_1, \ldots, x_n \rangle) = \text{quotient field of } K[\langle x_1, \ldots, x_n \rangle].$$

By majorization and rearrangement of absolutely convergent multiple series we get: *If* $g_1, \ldots, g_n$ *are elements in* $K[\langle y_1, \ldots, y_m \rangle]$ *which are nonunits in* $K[[y_1, \ldots, y_m]]$ *and if* f *is an element of* $K[\langle x_1, \ldots, x_n \rangle]$, then $f(g_1, \ldots, g_n) \in K[\langle y_1, \ldots, y_m \rangle]$, *and for all* a *in a certain neighborhood of the origin in* K^n *the two meanings of* $f(g_1(a), \ldots, g_n(a))$ *coincide.* In particular, the isomorphism of $K[[x_1, \ldots, x_n]]$ onto $K[[y_1, \ldots, y_n]]$ given by a nonsingular K-linear transformation $x_i = \Sigma a_{ij} y_j$ maps $K[\langle x_1, \ldots, x_n \rangle]$ onto $K[\langle y_1, \ldots, y_n \rangle]$, and hence we may then "identify" $K[\langle x_1, \ldots, x_n \rangle]$ with $K[\langle y_1, \ldots, y_n \rangle]$. Via the equality $(1 - z)(1 + z + z^2 + \ldots) = 1$ in $K[\langle z \rangle]$ we deduce that:

$$\begin{aligned} & f \in K[\langle x_1, \ldots, x_n \rangle] \text{ is a unit in } K[\langle x_1, \ldots, x_n \rangle] \\ \Leftrightarrow & f \text{ is a unit in } K[[x_1, \ldots, x_n]] \\ \Leftrightarrow & f(0, \ldots, 0) \neq 0. \end{aligned}$$

[2] When there is no confusion, the same letters $x_1, \ldots, x_n$ may be used for indeterminates as well as "variables".

We shall have occasion to use the following remarks. Let

$$f = \sum f_q x_n^q = \sum f_{i_1 \ldots i_n} x_1^{i_1} \ldots x_n^{i_n} \in K[[x_1, \ldots, x_n]];$$
$$f_q \in K[[x_1, \ldots, x_{n-1}]]; \qquad f_{i_1 \ldots i_n} \in K.$$

If $f \in K[\langle x_1, \ldots, x_n \rangle]$ then $f_q \in K[\langle x_1, \ldots, x_{n-1} \rangle]$ for all q; (the converse is obviously false). Let

$$g = \sum g_{i_1 \ldots i_n} x_1^{i_1} \ldots x_n^{i_n} \in K[[x_1, \ldots, x_n]]$$

where $g_{i_1 \ldots i_n} = f_{i_1 \ldots i_n}$ for certain values of $i_1, \ldots, i_n$ and $g_{i_1 \ldots i_n} = 0$ for the remaining values of $i_1, \ldots, i_n$. Then $\mathbf{D}(f) \subset \mathbf{D}(g)$. In particular if f is convergent then so is g.

Let $f, g \in K[[x_1, \ldots, x_n]]$, $a \in K^n$. By majorization and rearrangement of absolutely convergent series we get: If f and g are convergent at a then so are fg and $f + g$, and we have

$$(fg)(a) = f(a)g(a) \qquad \text{and} \qquad (f + g)(a) = f(a) + g(a).$$

Definition of Analytic Functions and Analytic Sets. Let X be an open set in K^n and let $a \in X$. A K-valued function φ on X is said to be *analytic at a* if there exist

$$f = \sum f_{i_1 \ldots i_n} x_1^{i_1} \ldots x_n^{i_n} \in K[\langle x_1, \ldots, x_n \rangle]; \qquad f_{i_1 \ldots i_n} \in K;$$

and a neighborhood Y of the origin in $\mathbf{D}(f)$ such that for all b in Y, $(a_1 + b_1, \ldots, a_n + b_n)$ is in X and $\varphi(a_1 + b_1, \ldots, a_n + b_n) = f(b_1, \ldots, b_n)$. Later on (2.3, 10.5.1) we shall show that f is uniquely determined (by φ and a). f is called the *Taylor expansion of φ around a*. Considering $x_1, \ldots, x_n$ as variables, in

$$\{x: (x_1 - a_1, \ldots, x_n - a_n) \in Y\}$$

we then have

$$\varphi(x_1, \ldots, x_n) = \sum f_{i_1 \ldots i_n} (x_1 - a_1)^{i_1} \ldots (x_n - a_n)^{i_n}.$$

Consequently, by abuse of language, the above expression may also be called the Taylor expansion of φ around a. φ is said to be *analytic on X* provided φ is analytic at each point in X. Especially when $K = \mathbf{C}$, the term *holomorphic function* is used as a synonym to the term analytic function.

$V \subset K^n$ is said to be *analytic at a* if there exists a neighborhood X^* of a in K^n and a finite number of analytic functions $\varphi_1, \ldots, \varphi_u$ on X^* such that

$$V \cap X^* = \{x \in X^*: \varphi_1(x) = \ldots = \varphi_u(x) = 0\}.$$

$V \subset X$ is said to be *analytic* (resp: *locally analytic*) *in* X provided V is analytic at each point in X (resp: at each point in V). It is then clear that: V is locally analytic in $X \Rightarrow V$ is locally closed in X; and V is analytic in $X \Leftrightarrow V$ is locally analytic in X and V is closed in X.

Examples. 1°) Any open set V in X is locally analytic in X but is not necessarily analytic in X, e.g., $X = \mathbf{C}^1$ and $V =$ any nonempty open set in $\mathbf{C}^1$ different from $\mathbf{C}^1$.

2°) For V take a sequence $a^{(1)}, a^{(2)}, \ldots$ of distinct points in K^n such that $a^{(p)} \to a \in K^n$. Then V is locally analytic in K^n, but is not analytic at a.

§2B. *The translation operator* τ_a

Let

$$Q(i; j; k) = Q(i_1, \ldots, i_n; j_1, \ldots, j_n; k_1, \ldots, k_n)$$

be the ordinary integers defined by the polynomial identity

$$(x_1 + y_1)^{j_1} \ldots (x_n + y_n)^{j_n} = \sum_{i, k} Q(i; j; k) x_1^{i_1} \ldots x_n^{i_n} y_1^{k_1} \ldots y_n^{k_n}$$

in indeterminates $x_1, \ldots, x_n, y_1, \ldots, y_n$ over the ring $\mathbf{Z}$ of ordinary integers. Let $\bar{Q}(i; j; k)$ be the image of $Q(i; j; k)$ under the natural homomorphism $\mathbf{Z} \to K$. Let

$$P(i; j)(y) = P(i_1, \ldots, i_n; j_1, \ldots, j_n)(y)$$

be the polynomials in $y = (y_1, \ldots, y_n)$ with coefficients in K defined by the polynomial identity

$$(x_1 + y_1)^{j_1} \ldots (x_n + y_n)^{j_n} = \sum_{i} P(i; j)(y) x_1^{i_1} \ldots x_n^{i_n}$$

in $K[x_1, \ldots, x_n, y_1, \ldots, y_n]$. Then

$$P(i; j)(y) = \sum_{k} \bar{Q}(i; j; k) y_1^{k_1} \ldots y_n^{k_n}.$$

Let

$$f = \sum_{j} f_{j_1 \ldots j_n} x_1^{j_1} \ldots x_n^{j_n} \in K[\langle x_1, \ldots, x_n \rangle]; \qquad f_{j_1 \ldots j_n} \in K;$$

and $a \in \mathbf{D}(f)$ be given. We can find $B \in \mathbf{R}_{++}^n$ such that

$$(B_1 + |a_1|, \ldots, B_n + |a_n|) \in \mathbf{E}(f).$$

For any such B, we can find $\bar{B} \in \mathbf{R}_{++}^n$ such that $B_1 < \bar{B}_1, \ldots, B_n < \bar{B}_n$, and

$(\bar{B}_1 + |a_1|, \ldots, \bar{B}_n + |a_n|) \in \mathbf{E}(f)$. Now

$$\begin{aligned}\infty &> \sum_j |f_{j_1 \ldots j_n}|(\bar{B}_1 + |a_1|)^{j_1} \ldots (\bar{B}_n + |a_n|)^{j_n} \\ &= \sum_{i,j,k} |f_{j_1 \ldots j_n}| Q(i; j; k) \bar{B}_1^{i_1} \ldots \bar{B}_n^{i_n} |a_1|^{k_1} \ldots |a_n|^{k_n} \\ &\geqq \sum_i |g_{i_1 \ldots i_n}| \bar{B}_1^{i_1} \ldots \bar{B}_n^{i_n}\end{aligned}$$

where

$$\begin{aligned}g_{i_1 \ldots i_n} &= \sum_{j,k} f_{j_1 \ldots j_n} \bar{Q}(i; j; k) a_1^{k_1} \ldots a_n^{k_n} \\ &= \sum_j f_{j_1 \ldots j_n} P(i; j)(a).\end{aligned}$$

Putting

$$\boldsymbol{\tau}_a f = \sum_i g_{i_1 \ldots i_n} x_1^{i_1} \ldots x_n^{i_n} \in K[[x_1, \ldots, x_n]]; \qquad g_{i_1 \ldots i_n} \in K;$$

we thus have that $\boldsymbol{\tau}_a f$ is convergent and $B \in \mathbf{E}(\boldsymbol{\tau}_a f)$. Let $b \in K^n$ with $|b_1| \leqq B_1, \ldots, |b_n| \leqq B_n$ be given. Consider

$$1') \qquad \sum_{i,j,k} f_{j_1 \ldots j_n} \bar{Q}(i; j; k) b_1^{i_1} \ldots b_n^{i_n} a_1^{k_1} \ldots a_n^{k_n}.$$

Now

$$\begin{aligned}&\sum_{i,j,k} |f_{j_1 \ldots j_n}| \, |\bar{Q}(i; j; k)| \, |b_1|^{i_1} \ldots |b_n|^{i_n} |a_1|^{k_1} \ldots |a_n|^{k_n} \\ &\leqq \sum_{i,j,k} |f_{j_1 \ldots j_n}| Q(i; j; k) |b_1|^{i_1} \ldots |b_n|^{i_n} |a_1|^{k_1} \ldots |a_n|^{k_n} \\ &= \sum_j |f_{j_1 \ldots j_n}|(|b_1| + |a_1|)^{j_1} \ldots (|b_n| + |a_n|)^{j_n} \\ &< \infty.\end{aligned}$$

Thus 1′) is absolutely convergent. Summing 1′) in two ways we get

$$\begin{aligned}&f(a_1 + b_1, \ldots, a_n + b_n) \\ &= \sum_j f_{j_1 \ldots j_n}(b_1 + a_1)^{j_1} \ldots (b_n + a_n)^{j_n} \\ &= \sum_{i,j,k} f_{j_1 \ldots j_n} \bar{Q}(i; j; k) b_1^{i_1} \ldots b_n^{i_n} a_1^{k_1} \ldots a_n^{k_n} \\ &= \sum_{i,j} f_{j_1 \ldots j_n} P(i; j)(a) b_1^{i_1} \ldots b_n^{i_n} \\ &= \sum_i g_{i_1 \ldots i_n} b_1^{i_1} \ldots b_n^{i_n} \\ &= (\boldsymbol{\tau}_a f)(b).\end{aligned}$$

The remaining parts of (2.1) below also follow by majorization and rearrangement.

(2.1) *If $f \in K[[x_1,\ldots, x_n]]$ is convergent at a then $\boldsymbol{\tau}_a f$ is convergent and for all b in a certain neighborhood of the origin we have $(\boldsymbol{\tau}_a f)(b) = f(a_1 + b_1,\ldots, a_n + b_n)$. For any subset X of K^n containing the origin, $\{f \in K[[x_1,\ldots, x_n]]\colon X \subset \mathbf{D}(f)\}$ is a subring of $K[\langle x_1,\ldots, x_n \rangle]$. For $a \in K^n$, $f \to \boldsymbol{\tau}_a f$ is a homomorphism of the ring $\{f \in K[[x_1,\ldots, x_n]]\colon a \in \mathbf{D}(f)\}$ into the ring $K[\langle x_1,\ldots, x_n \rangle]$.*[3] *In a natural manner, the operation $\boldsymbol{\tau}_a$ is compatible with nonsingular K-linear transformations on $x_1,\ldots, x_n$. Note that $\boldsymbol{\tau}_a f$ is the Taylor expansion around a of the analytic function $\mathbf{D}(f) \to K$ associated with f.*

For a matrix $h = ((h^{(ij)}))$ with $h^{(ij)} \in K[[x_1,\ldots, x_n]]$, we set

$$\mathbf{D}(h) = (\textit{domain of convergence of } h) = \bigcap_{i,j} \mathbf{D}(h^{(ij)}).$$

We shall say: h is *convergent* $\Leftrightarrow \mathbf{D}(h) \neq \emptyset$; h is *convergent at* $a \in K^n \Leftrightarrow a \in \mathbf{D}(h)$; more generally h is *convergent in* $X \subset K^n \Leftrightarrow X \subset \mathbf{D}(h)$. For $a \in \mathbf{D}(h)$ we set $\boldsymbol{\tau}_a h = ((\boldsymbol{\tau}_a h^{(ij)}))$, and $h(a) = ((h^{(ij)}(a)))$. All this applies in particular then to any vector $h = (h^{(1)},\ldots, h^{(u)})$ with $h^{(1)},\ldots, h^{(u)}$ in $K[[x_1,\ldots, x_n]]$.

§2C. *Derivatives*

Let F be a K-valued function on an open set X in $K^n\{x_1,\ldots, x_n\}$. Let $a \in X$. Since K is nondiscrete valued, it contains elements of arbitrarily small nonzero absolute value. Hence we may talk of

$$\lim_{\substack{\delta \to 0 \\ \delta \neq 0}} \frac{F(a_1 + \delta, a_2,\ldots, a_n) - F(a_1,\ldots, a_n)}{\delta}.$$

When the above limit exists, we denote it by $(\partial F/\partial x_1)(a)$. If $(\partial F/\partial x_1)(a)$ exists for all $a \in X$, then we get the function $\partial F/\partial x_1\colon X \to K$. Similarly we can define $\partial F/\partial x_u$ for $u = 1,\ldots, n$, and also the various iterated partial derivatives. We shall only deal with situations where the order of differentiation does not matter. Usual calculus rules—derivatives of sums, products, polynomials, etc.—hold. Let

$$f = \sum f_{i_1\ldots i_n} x_1^{i_1}\ldots x_n^{i_n} \in K[[x_1,\ldots, x_n]]; \qquad f_{i_1\ldots i_n} \in K.$$

We define

$$\frac{\partial f}{\partial x_1} = \sum_i i_1 f_{i_1\ldots i_n} x_1^{i_1 - 1} x_2^{i_2}\ldots x_n^{i_n} \in K[[x_1,\ldots, x_n]].$$

[3] In (9.3) we shall show that $\boldsymbol{\tau}_a$ is actually a monomorphism.

Similarly for $\partial f/\partial x_u$ and the various iterated "formal partials". We want to show that if f is convergent then so is $\partial f/\partial x_1$. Let $A_1,\ldots, A_n$, D be positive real numbers such that

$$|f_{i_1\ldots i_n}|A_1^{i_1}\ldots A_n^{i_n} \leqq D \qquad \text{for all} \quad i_1,\ldots, i_n.$$

Let $0 < B_j < A_j$. For any integer i, $|i| \leqq i$ where in $|i|$, i is considered as an element of K. Hence

$$\begin{aligned}
&|i_1 f_{i_1\ldots i_n}|B_1^{i_1-1}B_2^{i_2}\ldots B_n^{i_n}\\
&\leqq |f_{i_1\ldots i_n}|i_1 B_1^{i_1-1}B_2^{i_2}\ldots B_n^{i_n}\\
&\leqq |f_{i_1\ldots i_n}|(i_1+\ldots+i_n)(1/B_1)B_1^{i_1}\ldots B_n^{i_n}\\
&= |f_{i_1\ldots i_n}|A_1^{i_1}\ldots A_n^{i_n}(1/B_1)(i_1+\ldots+i_n)(B_1/A_1)^{i_1}\ldots(B_n/A_n)^{i_n}\\
&\leqq (D/B_1)(i_1+\ldots+i_n)(B_1/A_1)^{i_1}\ldots(B_n/A_n)^{i_n}\\
&\leqq (D/B_1)(i_1+\ldots+i_n)B^{i_1+\ldots+i_n}
\end{aligned}$$

where $B = \max(B_1/A_1,\ldots, B_n/A_n)$. Now $0 < B < 1$ and hence $1/B = 1 + C$ with $C > 0$. For any nonnegative integer m we get

$$(1/B)^m = (1+C)^m \geqq mC, \qquad \text{i.e.,} \qquad mB^m \leqq 1/C.$$

Therefore for all $i_1,\ldots, i_n \geqq 0$ we have

$$|i_1 f_{i_1\ldots i_n}|B_1^{i_1-1}B_2^{i_2}\ldots B_n^{i_n} \leqq D/B_1 C.$$

Since $B_1,\ldots, B_n$ are arbitrary with $0 < B_j < A_j$, we conclude that $\partial f/\partial x_1$ is convergent and $\mathbf{D}(f) \subset \mathbf{D}(\partial f/\partial x_1)$.

Let $a \in \mathbf{D}(f)$. *We assert that* $\partial(\boldsymbol{\tau}_a f)/\partial x_1 = \boldsymbol{\tau}_a(\partial f/\partial x_1)$. We have

$$\boldsymbol{\tau}_a f = \sum_i \{\sum_j f_{j_1\ldots j_n}[P(i_1,\ldots, i_n; j_1,\ldots, j_n)(a)]\}x_1^{i_1}\ldots x_n^{i_n}$$

and hence

$$\frac{\partial(\boldsymbol{\tau}_a f)}{\partial x_1} = \sum_i \{(i_1+1)\sum_j f_{j_1\ldots j_n}[P(i_1+1, i_2,\ldots, i_n; j_1,\ldots, j_n)(a)]\}x_1^{i_1}\ldots x_n^{i_n}.$$

Next

$$\frac{\partial f}{\partial x_1} = \sum_j j_1 f_{j_1\ldots j_n}x_1^{j_1-1}x_2^{j_2}\ldots x_n^{j_n}$$

and hence

$$\boldsymbol{\tau}_a\left(\frac{\partial f}{\partial x_1}\right) = \sum_i \{ \sum_j j_1 f_{j_1\ldots j_n}[P(i_1,\ldots, i_n; j_1 - 1, j_2,\ldots, j_n)(a)]\} x_1^{i_1}\ldots x_n^{i_n}.$$

Thus our assertion is equivalent to this: For all $i_1,\ldots, i_n$:

$$\begin{aligned}&(i_1 + 1) \sum_j f_{j_1\ldots j_n} P(i_1 + 1, i_2,\ldots, i_n; j_1,\ldots, j_n)(a)\\ &= \sum_j j_1 f_{j_1\ldots j_n} P(i_1,\ldots, i_n; j_1 - 1, j_2,\ldots, j_n)(a).\end{aligned}$$

Our assertion is trivially verified when f is a monomial, i.e., when $f = x_1^{j_1}\ldots x_n^{j_n}$. Consequently, the above equality holds with $f_{j_1\ldots j_n} = 1$ and $f_{k_1\ldots k_n} = 0$ whenever $(k_1,\ldots, k_n) \neq (j_1,\ldots, j_n)$, i.e.,

$$\begin{aligned}&(i_1 + 1)P(i_1 + 1, i_2,\ldots, i_n; j_1,\ldots, j_n)(a)\\ &= j_1 P(i_1,\ldots, i_n; j_1 - 1, j_2,\ldots, j_n)(a).\end{aligned}$$

This being true for all $j_1,\ldots, j_n$ we get the desired.

Let F be the function $\mathbf{D}(f) \to K$ associated with f: $F(a) = f(a)$ for all $a \in \mathbf{D}(f)$. We can write

$$f = g(x_2,\ldots, x_n) + f_{10\ldots 0}x_1 + x_1 h(x_1,\ldots, x_n)$$

where

$$g(x_2,\ldots, x_n) \in K[\langle x_2,\ldots, x_n \rangle], \qquad h(x_1,\ldots, x_n) \in K[\langle x_1,\ldots, x_n \rangle],$$

and

$$h(0,\ldots, 0) = 0.$$

Consequently for $(\delta, 0,\ldots, 0) \in \mathbf{D}(f)$ with $\delta \neq 0$, we get

$$\frac{f(\delta, 0,\ldots, 0) - f(0,\ldots, 0)}{\delta} = f_{10\ldots 0} + h(\delta, 0,\ldots, 0).$$

The function H associated with h being continuous, we have $h(\delta, 0,\ldots, 0) \to 0$ as $\delta \to 0$. Therefore $(\partial F/\partial x_1)(0,\ldots, 0)$ exists and equals $f_{10\ldots 0}$. Now let $a \in \mathbf{D}(f)$. Then for all b in some neighborhood of the origin in K^n we have $F(a_1 + b_1,\ldots, a_n + b_n) = (\boldsymbol{\tau}_a f)(b)$. Therefore $(\partial F/\partial x_1)(a)$ exists and equals the coefficient of $x_1^1 x_2^0\ldots x_n^0$ in $\boldsymbol{\tau}_a f$. From what we have proved so far we thus get

$$\frac{\partial F}{\partial x_1}(a) = \frac{\partial(\boldsymbol{\tau}_a f)}{\partial x_1}(0) = \left(\boldsymbol{\tau}_a \frac{\partial f}{\partial x_1}\right)(0) = \frac{\partial f}{\partial x_1}(a).$$

Consequently in $\mathbf{D}(f)$, $\partial F/\partial x_1$ exists and is the function associated with $\partial f/\partial x_1$. In particular, we can "differentiate term by term". Relabeling $x_1, \ldots, x_n$ we get the corresponding statements for differentiation with respect to any x_u, and by induction we get them for all the iterated derivatives. We summarize.

(2.2) *Let $f \in K[\langle x_1, \ldots, x_n \rangle]$. Let F be the function associated with f: $F(a) = f(a)$ for all a in $\mathbf{D}(f)$. Let $i_1, \ldots, i_n \geqq 0$. Then*

$$\mathbf{D}(f) \subset \mathbf{D}\left(\frac{\partial^{i_1+\ldots+i_n} f}{\partial^{i_1} x_1 \ldots \partial^{i_n} x_n}\right),$$

and

$$\boldsymbol{\tau}_a\left(\frac{\partial^{i_1+\ldots+i_n} f}{\partial^{i_1} x_1 \ldots \partial^{i_n} x_n}\right) = \frac{\partial^{i_1+\ldots+i_n}(\boldsymbol{\tau}_a f)}{\partial^{i_1} x_1 \ldots \partial^{i_n} x_n} \qquad \text{for all} \quad a \in \mathbf{D}(f).$$

In $\mathbf{D}(f)$,

$$\frac{\partial^{i_1+\ldots+i_n} F}{\partial^{i_1} x_1 \ldots \partial^{i_n} x_n}$$

exists, does not depend on the order of differentiation, and can be obtained by term by term differentiation, i.e., by formal differentiation, i.e., it is the function associated with

$$\frac{\partial^{i_1+\ldots+i_n} f}{\partial^{i_1} x_1 \ldots \partial^{i_n} x_n}.$$

In particular

$$\frac{\partial^{i_1+\ldots+i_n} F}{\partial^{i_1} x_1 \ldots \partial^{i_n} x_n}(0) = i_1! \ldots i_n! f_{i_1 \ldots i_n}.$$

(2.3) In case K is of characteristic zero, as a corollary of (2.2), we get the *uniqueness of Taylor expansion*: Let f and g be convergent power series; if $f(a) = g(a)$ for all a in some neighborhood of the origin in K^n then $f = g$. A proof of this, independent of the characteristic of K, will be given in (10.5.1). In view of this uniqueness theorem we can make the

(2.4) Definition. Let φ be an analytic function on an open set X in K^n. Let $a \in X$. *We set*

$$\mathbf{o}_a \varphi = \text{leading degree of the Taylor expansion of } \varphi \text{ around } a.$$

We shall say that φ has a zero of order $\mathbf{o}_a\varphi$ at a, or that a is a root of $\varphi = 0$ of multiplicity $\mathbf{o}_a\varphi$. We shall say that a is a zero of φ provided $\mathbf{o}_a\varphi > 0$, i.e., provided $\varphi(a) = 0$. In (10.6) we shall show that there exists a neighborhood X^* of a in X such that for all b in X^*: $\mathbf{o}_b\varphi \leqq \mathbf{o}_a\varphi$. In case K is of characteristic zero, this is a corollary of (2.2), because then:

$$\mathbf{o}_a\varphi = \min m \text{ such that } \frac{\partial^{i_1+\ldots+i_n}\varphi}{\partial^{i_1}x_1\ldots\partial^{i_n}x_n}(a) = 0$$

$$\text{for all } \quad i_1 + \ldots + i_n < m;$$

and by continuity

$$\frac{\partial^{i_1+\ldots+i_n}\varphi}{\partial^{i_1}x_1\ldots\partial^{i_n}x_n}(a) \neq 0 \Rightarrow \frac{\partial^{i_1+\ldots+i_n}\varphi}{\partial^{i_1}x_1\ldots\partial^{i_n}x_n}(b) \neq 0$$

for all b in some neighborhood of a.

Let $n = 1$, $x = x_1$. *Then the zeroes of* φ *are all isolated*, i.e., if every neighborhood of a in X contains a point at which the value of φ is nonzero, then there exists a neighborhood X^* of a in X such that $\varphi(b) \neq 0$ whenever $b \in X^*$ and $b \neq a$. This follows from the following observation: For the Taylor expansion $f(x)$ of φ around a we have $f(x) = x^m g(x)$ where $m = \mathbf{o}_a\varphi$ and $g(x)$ is a unit in $K[\langle x \rangle]$.

For any $f \in K[\langle x_1,\ldots, x_n \rangle]$ and $a \in \mathbf{D}(f)$ we set $\mathbf{o}_a f = \mathbf{o}_a F$ where F is the function associated with f; in other words $\mathbf{o}_a f = \mathbf{o}(\boldsymbol{\tau}_a f)$.

(2.5) From the semicontinuity of $\mathbf{o}$ proved above we deduce the following.

1) IDENTITY THEOREM. *Assume that* K *is connected.*[4] *Let* φ *and* ψ *be analytic functions on a domain* X *in* K^n. *If* $\varphi|X^* = \psi|X^*$ *for a nonempty open subset* X^* *of* X *then* $\varphi = \psi$ *on* X.

Replacing φ by $\varphi - \psi$ it suffices to show that if $\varphi \equiv 0$ on X^* then $\varphi \equiv 0$ on X. By (2.2), for any $a \in X$ we have: $\mathbf{o}_a\varphi = \infty \Leftrightarrow \varphi \equiv 0$ on some neighborhood of a. Fix $a \in X^*$. Let if possible $b \in X$ be such that $\mathbf{o}_b\varphi < \infty$. Take an arc γ: $[0, 1] \to X$, $\gamma(0) = a$, $\gamma(1) = b$. Let

$$s = \inf\{t \in [0, 1]: \mathbf{o}_{\gamma(t)}\varphi < \infty\}.$$

Then $\mathbf{o}_{\gamma(s)}\varphi < \infty$. Hence $\mathbf{o}_{\gamma(s-\delta)}\varphi < \infty$ for all small positive δ. Contradiction.

[4] **R** and **C** are obviously connected and locally arcwise connected. Conversely, if K is connected then it is topologically isomorphic either to **R** or to **C** (see §9); [two valued fields are topologically isomorphic means: there is a field isomorphism between them which is at the same time a homeomorphism of the underlying topological spaces]. Consequently, K is connected $\Rightarrow$ K^n is locally arcwise connected $\Rightarrow$ every domain in K^n is arcwise connected.

2) *Assume that K is connected.*[4] *Then for any $a \in K^n$, $f \to \boldsymbol{\tau}_a f$ is a monomorphism of $\{f \in K[\langle x_1, \ldots, x_n \rangle]: a \in \mathbf{D}(f)\}$ into $K[\langle x_1, \ldots, x_n \rangle]$.*

In virtue of 1) it suffices to prove that for any $f \in K[\langle x_1, \ldots, x_n \rangle]$, $\mathbf{D}(f)$ is connected. Let $\mu: K \to \mathbf{R}$(resp: $\mathbf{C}$) be a topological isomorphism. For any $u \in K$: $|u| < 1 \Leftrightarrow u^p \to 0 \Leftrightarrow \mu(u)^p \to 0 \Leftrightarrow |\mu(u)| < 1$; and $|u| > 1 \Leftrightarrow u \neq 0$ and $|1/u| < 1$. Hence for any $u, v \in K$ we have: $|u| \leqq |v| \Leftrightarrow |\mu(u)| \leqq |\mu(v)|$. Therefore for any $b \in K^n$, μ induces a homeomorphism of $P = \{\alpha \in K^n: |\alpha_1| \leqq |b_1|, \ldots, |\alpha_n| \leqq |b_n|\}$ onto $Q = \{\beta \in \mathbf{R}^n(\text{resp: } \mathbf{C}^n): |\beta_1| \leqq |\mu(b_1)|, \ldots, |\beta_n| \leqq |\mu(b_n)|\}$. Obviously Q is connected and hence so is P. Now it is enough to note that if $b \in \mathbf{D}(f)$ then $P \subset \mathbf{D}(f)$.

(2.6) Definition. For any $f_1, \ldots, f_p \in K[[x_1, \ldots, x_n]]$, $m \leqq n$, we define

$$\frac{J(f_1, \ldots, f_p)}{J(x_1, \ldots, x_m)} = \textit{Jacobian matrix of } f_1, \ldots, f_p \text{ with respect to } x_1, \ldots, x_m$$

$$= \text{the } p \times m \text{ matrix } \left(\left(\frac{\partial f_i}{\partial x_j}\right)\right) \text{ with entries in } K[[x_1, \ldots, x_n]].$$

If K is complete nondiscrete valued then for any $a \in K^n$ at which $f_1, \ldots, f_p$ are convergent we have

$$\begin{aligned}\frac{J(f_1, \ldots, f_p)}{J(x_1, \ldots, x_m)}(a) &= \text{the } p \times m \text{ matrix } \left(\left(\frac{\partial f_i}{\partial x_j}(a)\right)\right) \text{ with entries in } K \\ &= \left(\left(\frac{\partial \boldsymbol{\tau}_a f_i}{\partial x_j}(0)\right)\right) \\ &= \left(\left(\boldsymbol{\tau}_a \frac{\partial f_i}{\partial x_j}\right)\right)(0) \\ &= \left(\boldsymbol{\tau}_a \frac{J(f_1, \ldots, f_p)}{J(x_1, \ldots, x_m)}\right)(0).\end{aligned}$$

If $m = p$ then we define

$$\frac{\partial(f_1, \ldots, f_p)}{\partial(x_1, \ldots, x_p)} = \textit{Jacobian determinant of } f_1, \ldots, f_p \text{ with respect to } x_1, \ldots, x_p$$

$$= \det\left(\left(\frac{\partial f_i}{\partial x_j}\right)\right);$$

for any $a \in K^n$ at which $f_1,\ldots, f_p$ are convergent we then have

$$\frac{\partial(f_1,\ldots, f_p)}{\partial(x_1,\ldots, x_p)}(a) = \det\left(\left(\frac{\partial f_i}{\partial x_j}(a)\right)\right).$$

Note that in the general case

$$\operatorname{rnk}\frac{J(f_1,\ldots, f_p)}{J(x_1,\ldots, x_m)} = \max r \quad \text{such that} \quad \frac{\partial(f_{i_1},\ldots, f_{i_r})}{\partial(x_{j_1},\ldots, x_{j_r})} \neq 0 \qquad \text{for some}$$

$$i_1 < i_2 < \ldots < i_r \leqq p, \qquad j_1 < j_2 < \ldots < j_r \leqq m;$$

and similarly for any $a \in K^n$ at which $f_1,\ldots, f_p$ are convergent.

Now assume that K is complete nondiscrete valued. For any analytic functions $F_1,\ldots, F_p$ on an open set X in $K^n\{x_1,\ldots, x_n\}$, and $m \leqq n$, we define

$$\frac{J(F_1,\ldots, F_p)}{J(x_1,\ldots, x_m)} = \textit{Jacobian matrix} \text{ of } F_1,\ldots, F_p \text{ with respect to } x_1,\ldots, x_m$$

$$= \text{the } p \times m \text{ matrix } \left(\left(\frac{\partial F_i}{\partial x_j}\right)\right) \text{ whose entries are analytic functions on } X.$$

If $m = p$ then we define

$$\frac{\partial(F_1,\ldots, F_p)}{\partial(x_1,\ldots, x_p)} = \textit{Jacobian determinant} \text{ of } F_1,\ldots, F_p \text{ with respect to } x_1,\ldots, x_p$$

$$= \det\left(\left(\frac{\partial F_i}{\partial x_j}\right)\right).$$

§3. LAURENT SERIES

Let K be a complete nondiscrete valued field. Let $x = (x_1,\ldots, x_n)$ be coordinates in K^n. Let μ: $K^n \to \mathbf{R}^n_+$ be given by $\mu(x) = (|x_1|,\ldots, |x_n|)$. Consider the "Laurent series"

$$f(x_1,\ldots, x_n) = \sum_{-\infty<i_1,\ldots,i_n<\infty} f_{i_1\ldots i_n} x_1^{i_1}\ldots x_n^{i_n}; \qquad f_{i_1\ldots i_n} \in K.$$

Let

$$\mathbf{E}^*(f) = \{A \in \mathbf{R}^n_+ \colon A_j \neq 0 \text{ if } f_{i_1\ldots i_n} \neq 0 \text{ for some } (i_1, \ldots, i_n) \text{ with } i_j < 0; \text{ and } \exists\, D > 0 \text{ such that } |f_{i_1\ldots i_n}| A_1^{i_1}\ldots A_n^{i_n} \leqq D \text{ for all } i_1,\ldots, i_n\}.$$

The condition "$A_j \neq 0$ if $f_{i_1 \dots i_n} \neq 0$ for some $(i_1, \dots, i_n)$ with $i_j < 0$" means that it makes sense to talk about $|f_{i_1 \dots i_n}| A_1^{i_1} \dots A_n^{i_n}$. Let

$$\mathbf{E}(f) = \text{interior of } \mathbf{E}^*(f) \text{ in } \mathbf{R}_+^n.$$

Define

$$\begin{aligned} \mathbf{D}(f) &= \textit{domain of convergence of } f \\ &= \mu^{-1}\mathbf{E}(f). \end{aligned}$$

Then for any $x \in \mathbf{D}(f)$ the above series makes sense. Since μ is continuous, $\mathbf{D}(f)$ is an open set in K^n.

Definition. $X \subset K^n$ is a *Reinhardt set* if and only if: $[a \in X, b \in K^n; |a_j| = |b_j| \text{ for } j = 1, \dots, n] \Rightarrow b \in X$; i.e., if and only if $X = \mu^{-1}\mu(X)$. Note that for $K = \mathbf{C}$, $X \subset \mathbf{C}^n$ is a Reinhardt set if and only if X has a "faithful picture" in the absolute, i.e., in the nonnegative n-space of $|x_1|, \dots, |x_n|$. A Reinhardt set $X \subset K^n$ is *relatively complete* if and only if: $[a, b \in X, c \in K^n, a_j = 0, c_i = b_i \text{ for all } i \neq j \text{ and } |c_j| \leqq |b_j|] \Rightarrow c \in X$. A Reinhardt set $X \subset K^n$ is *complete* if and only if: X is relatively complete and contains the origin. Thus $\emptyset \neq X \subset K^n$ is a complete Reinhardt set if and only if: $[a \in X, b \in K^n, |b_j| \leqq |a_j| \text{ for } j = 1, \dots, n] \Rightarrow b \in X$. From the definition of $\mathbf{D}(f)$ we at once get

(3.1) $\mathbf{D}(f)$ *is a relatively complete Reinhardt open set in* K^n. $\mathbf{D}(f)$ *is complete* $\Leftrightarrow$ $[\mathbf{D}(f) \neq \emptyset$ *and* $f_{i_1 \dots i_n} = 0$ *whenever* $i_j < 0$ *for some* $j] \Leftrightarrow f$ *is a convergent power series.*

Next we prove

(3.2) $\{(\log A_1, \dots, \log A_n) : (A_1, \dots, A_n) \in \mathbf{E}(f) \cap \mathbf{R}_{++}^n\}$ *is a convex set in* $\mathbf{R}^n$.

$V \subset \mathbf{R}^n$ is convex $\Leftrightarrow$ $[p, q \in V \Rightarrow (\text{segment joining } p \text{ and } q) \subset V]$; also V is convex $\Rightarrow$ interior of V in $\mathbf{R}^n$ is convex; (see §5). Now

$$(A_1, \dots, A_n) \to (\log A_1, \dots, \log A_n)$$

is a homeomorphism of $\mathbf{R}_{++}^n$ onto $\mathbf{R}^n$; and clearly

$$\mathbf{E}(f) \cap \mathbf{R}_{++}^n = \text{interior of } \mathbf{E}^*(f) \cap \mathbf{R}_{++}^n \text{ in } \mathbf{R}_{++}^n.$$

Therefore it suffices to show that

$$\{(\log A_1, \dots, \log A_n) : (A_1, \dots, A_n) \in \mathbf{E}^*(f) \cap \mathbf{R}_{++}^n\}$$

is convex. Let $A, \bar{A}, B \in \mathbf{R}_{++}^n$ be such that $(\log B_1, \dots, \log B_n)$ is on the segment joining $(\log A_1,\dots, \log A_n)$ and $(\log \bar{A}_1,\dots, \log \bar{A}_n)$. Then there exist $\alpha, \bar{\alpha} \in \mathbf{R}_+$ with $\alpha + \bar{\alpha} = 1$ such that

$$\log B_j = \alpha \log A_j + \bar{\alpha} \log \bar{A}_j \qquad \text{for} \quad j = 1,\dots, n.$$

Then $B_j = A_j^{\alpha} \bar{A}_j^{\bar{\alpha}}$. If $A, \bar{A} \in \mathbf{E}^*(f)$ then there exist $D, \bar{D} > 0$ such that for all $i_1,\dots, i_n$ we have $|f_{i_1\dots i_n}| A_1^{i_1}\dots A_n^{i_n} \leqq D$ and $|f_{i_1\dots i_n}| \bar{A}_1^{i_1}\dots \bar{A}_n^{i_n} \leqq \bar{D}$; consequently

$$\begin{aligned} &|f_{i_1\dots i_n}| B_1^{i_1}\dots B_n^{i_n} \\ &= |f_{i_1\dots i_n}|^{\alpha} |f_{i_1\dots i_n}|^{\bar{\alpha}} (A_1^{\alpha} \bar{A}_1^{\bar{\alpha}})^{i_1}\dots (A_n^{\alpha} \bar{A}_n^{\bar{\alpha}})^{i_n} \\ &= [|f_{i_1\dots i_n}| A_1^{i_1}\dots A_n^{i_n}]^{\alpha} [|f_{i_1\dots i_n}| \bar{A}_1^{i_1}\dots \bar{A}_n^{i_n}]^{\bar{\alpha}} \\ &\leqq D^{\alpha} \bar{D}^{\bar{\alpha}}; \end{aligned}$$

whence $B \in \mathbf{E}^*(f)$.

(3.3) *The given Laurent series f is absolutely locally uniformly convergent on $\mathbf{D}(f)$, and $a \to f(a)$ is analytic on $\mathbf{D}(f)$.*

PROOF. Let $a \in \mathbf{D}(f)$ be given. Relabel $x_1,\dots, x_n$ so that $a_j \neq 0$ for $j \leqq m$ and $a_j = 0$ for $j > m$. Then $f_{i_1\dots i_n} = 0$ if $i_j < 0$ for some $j > m$. Since $(|a_1|,\dots, |a_m|, 0,\dots, 0) \in$ interior of $\mathbf{E}^*(f)$ in $\mathbf{R}_+^n$, and $|a_1| \neq 0,\dots, |a_m| \neq 0$, we can find real numbers $A_j^{(-1)}, A_j^{(1)}$ such that $0 < A_j^{(-1)} < |a_j| < A_j^{(1)}$ for $j \leqq m$, $0 = |a_j| < A_j^{(1)}$ for $j > m$, and

$$\{u \in \mathbf{R}_+^n : A_j^{(-1)} \leqq u_j \leqq A_j^{(1)} \text{ for } j \leqq m \text{ and } u_j \leqq A_j^{(1)} \text{ for } j > m\} \subset \mathbf{E}(f).$$

Let

$$\begin{aligned} \Lambda &= \{\lambda = (\lambda_1,\dots, \lambda_n) : \lambda_j = -1, 1 \text{ for } j \leqq m; \lambda_j = 1 \text{ for } j > m\} \\ &= \text{a set of } 2^m \text{ vectors.} \end{aligned}$$

Let Z_λ and Z be the annular polycylinders:

$$Z_\lambda = \{x \in K^n : |x_j| < A_j^{(\lambda_j)} \text{ if } \lambda_j = 1 \text{ and } |x_j| > A_j^{(\lambda_j)} \text{ if } \lambda_j = -1\};$$

$$Z = \{x \in K^n : A_j^{(-1)} < |x_j| < A_j^{(1)} \text{ for } j \leqq m \text{ and } |x_j| < A_j^{(1)} \text{ for } j > m\}.$$

Then $Z = \bigcap_{\lambda \in \Lambda} Z_\lambda$, and Z is a neighborhood of a in $\mathbf{D}(f)$. For any $\lambda \in \Lambda$, we have $(A_1^{(\lambda_1)},\dots, A_n^{(\lambda_n)}) \in \mathbf{E}(f)$ and hence there exists $D_\lambda > 0$ such that

$$|f_{i_1\dots i_n}| [A^{(\lambda_1)}]^{i_1}\dots [A^{(\lambda_n)}]^{i_n} \leqq D_\lambda \qquad \text{for all} \quad i_1,\dots, i_n;$$

whence in particular

$$|f_{\lambda_1 i_1,\dots,\lambda_n i_n}|[A_1^{(\lambda_1)}]^{\lambda_1 i_1}\dots[A_n^{(\lambda_n)}]^{\lambda_n i_n} \leqq D_\lambda \qquad \text{for all} \quad i_1,\dots, i_n \geqq 0.$$

Therefore the power series

$$\sum_{\substack{0 \leqq i_j < \infty \text{ if } \lambda_j = 1 \\ 0 < i_j < \infty \text{ if } \lambda_j = -1}} f_{\lambda_1 i_1,\dots,\lambda_n i_n} \bar{x}_1^{i_1}\dots\bar{x}_n^{i_n}$$

is absolutely locally uniformly convergent on

$$\{\bar{x} \in K^n : |\bar{x}_j| < [A^{(\lambda_j)}]^{\lambda_j}; j = 1,\dots, n\}$$

and defines an analytic function there.

Via the transformation $\bar{x}_j = x_j^{\lambda_j}$ we then get that

$$\sum_{\substack{0 \leqq i_j < \infty \text{ if } \lambda_j = 1 \\ -\infty < i_j < 0 \text{ if } \lambda_j = -1}} f_{i_1\dots i_n} x_1^{i_1}\dots x_n^{i_n}$$

is absolutely locally uniformly convergent on Z_λ and defines an analytic function there. Now it is enough to note that in Z we have

$$\sum_{-\infty < i_1,\dots, i_n < \infty} f_{i_1\dots i_n} x_1^{i_1}\dots x_n^{i_n} = \sum_{\lambda \in \Lambda} \sum_{\substack{0 \leqq i_j < \infty \text{ if } \lambda_j = 1 \\ -\infty < i_j < 0 \text{ if } \lambda_j = -1}} f_{i_1\dots i_n} x_1^{i_1}\dots x_n^{i_n}.$$

The following useful elementary property of $\mathbf{C}^n$ is not valid in general K^n.

(3.4) *μ is an open map of $\mathbf{C}^n$ onto $\mathbf{R}_+^n$. Equivalently, for any $X \subset \mathbf{C}^n$, μ(interior of X in $\mathbf{C}^n$) $\subset$ interior of $\mu(X)$ in $\mathbf{R}_+^n$. If X is Reinhardt then the above inclusion is an equality.*

DEFINITION. $X \subset \mathbf{C}^n$ is *logarithmically convex* if and only if

$$\{(\log|x_1|,\dots, \log|x_n|) : x \in X; x_1 \neq 0,\dots, x_n \neq 0\}$$

is a convex set in $\mathbf{R}^n$.

(3.5) *Let $K = \mathbf{C}$. Let*

$\mathbf{D}^*(f) = \{a \in \mathbf{C}^n :$ the Laurent series f makes sense at $x = a$, i.e., $a_j \neq 0$ if $f_{i_1\dots i_n} \neq 0$ for some $(i_1,\dots, i_n)$ with $i_j < 0$; and f converges at a in the weakest sense, i.e., some simple ordering (depending on a) of f converges at $a\}$.

Then $\mathbf{D}(f)$ = *interior of* $\mathbf{D}^*(f)$ *in* $\mathbf{C}^n$. *The Laurent series is absolutely locally uniformly convergent on* $\mathbf{D}(f)$ *and defines an analytic function there.* $\mathbf{D}(f)$ *is a logarithmically convex relatively complete Reinhardt domain.*

PROOF. By (3.3), $\mathbf{D}(f) \subset \operatorname{int} \mathbf{D}^*(f)$. Next, $a \in \mathbf{D}^*(f) \Rightarrow$ [absolute values of the terms of the Laurent series are uniformly bounded at a] $\Rightarrow$ $\mu(a) \in \mathbf{E}^*(f)$. Thus $\mu(\mathbf{D}^*(f)) \subset \mathbf{E}^*(f)$; whence by (3.4), $\mu(\operatorname{int} \mathbf{D}^*(f)) \subset \mathbf{E}(f)$. Therefore $\operatorname{int} \mathbf{D}^*(f) \subset \mathbf{D}(f)$ by the definition of $\mathbf{D}(f)$. Thus $\mathbf{D}(f) = \operatorname{int} \mathbf{D}^*(f)$.

In the present situation ($K = \mathbf{C}$) obviously for any set Y in $\mathbf{R}_+^n$ we have that $\mu\mu^{-1}(Y) = Y$. Therefore $\mu(\mathbf{D}(f)) = \mathbf{E}(f)$. Hence by (3.2) we deduce that $\mathbf{D}(f)$ is logarithmically convex. It only remains to be shown that $\mathbf{D}(f)$ is connected. This follows from

(3.6) *Any logarithmically convex Reinhardt open set* X *in* $\mathbf{C}^n$ *is connected.*

PROOF. Let $a \in X$ be given. Since X is open, there exists $u \in \mathbf{R}_+$ such that the arc $(a_1 + t, \ldots, a_n + t)$, $0 \leqq t \leqq u$, is in X, and $a_i' = a_i + u \neq 0$ for $i = 1, \ldots, n$. Let $A_i = |a_i'|$ and $\Gamma = \{x \in \mathbf{C}^n : |x_i| = A_i \text{ for } i = 1, \ldots, n\}$. Then Γ being a product of circles is arcwise connected, and $\Gamma \subset X$ since X is Reinhardt. Hence $(a_1', \ldots, a_n')$ can be joined to $A = (A_1, \ldots, A_n)$ by an arc in X. Similarly, given $b \in X$, there is an arc in X joining b to a point $B = (B_1, \ldots, B_n) \in \mathbf{R}_{++}^n$. Since X is logarithmically convex and $\mu^{-1}\mu(X) = X$, A can be joined to B by the arc in X given by:

$$(\exp[(1 - t)\log A_1 + t \log B_1], \ldots, \exp[(1 - t)\log A_n + t \log B_n]),$$
$$0 \leqq t \leqq 1.$$

(3.7) EXAMPLES. Annular polycylinder (open or closed) in K^n is always a relatively complete Reinhardt set; it is complete if and only if it is actually a polycylinder. Now let $K = \mathbf{C}$. Let $X \subset \mathbf{C}^n\{x_1, \ldots, x_n\}$ be a product set, i.e., $X = X_1 \times \ldots \times X_n$ with $X_j \subset \mathbf{C}^1\{x_j\}$; then X is a Reinhardt domain $\Leftrightarrow X$ is an open annular polycylinder $\Rightarrow X$ is logarithmically convex. However, there are lots of Reinhardt domains which are not product domains. Let X = ball of radius $D > 0$ in $\mathbf{C}^n$: $|x_1|^2 + \ldots + |x_n|^2 < D$; show that X is a logarithmically convex complete Reinhardt domain, but X is not a product domain. An indirect proof of the logarithmic convexity of the ball will follow from the theory of domains of holomorphy (§7). More generally, from that theory, it will follow that: [X relatively complete Reinhardt domain in $\mathbf{C}^n$, and X convex (in $\mathbf{R}^{2n} = \mathbf{C}^n$)] $\Rightarrow$ [X logarithmically convex]; (see 6.5.3).

(3.8) DEFINITION. Let $X^{(i)}$, $i \in I$, be a family of Reinhardt sets in K^n and let

$$X^* = \bigcap_{i \in I} X^{(i)}.$$

It is clear that X^* is a Reinhardt set, and if each $X^{(i)}$ is relatively complete then so is X^*. Also

1°) $\mu(X^*) = \bigcap_{i \in I} \mu(X^{(i)})$.

Now let $K = \mathbf{C}$. Let $\ln : \mathbf{R}^n_{++} \to \mathbf{R}^n$ be given by $\ln(A_1, \ldots, A_n) = (\log A_1, \ldots, \log A_n)$. Let X be a (nonempty) *relatively complete Reinhardt open set in* $\mathbf{C}^n$. Take $X^{(i)}$, $i \in I$, to be the family of all relatively complete logarithmically convex Reinhardt sets in $\mathbf{C}^n$ containing X. This family is not empty since it contains $\mathbf{C}^n$.

2°) In $\mathbf{R}^n$, the intersection of any convex sets is convex and the interior of any convex set is convex (see §5).

3°) ln is a homeomorphism of $\mathbf{R}^n_{++}$ onto $\mathbf{R}^n$.

4°) For any set V in $\mathbf{R}^n_{+}$ we have:

$$(\text{interior of } V \text{ in } \mathbf{R}^n_{+}) \cap \mathbf{R}^n_{++} = \text{interior of } V \cap \mathbf{R}^n_{++} \text{ in } \mathbf{R}^n_{++}.$$

From these observations we get

$$\begin{aligned}
&\ln[\mu(\text{interior of } X^* \text{ in } \mathbf{C}^n) \cap \mathbf{R}^n_{++}] \\
&= \ln[(\text{interior of } \mu(X^*) \text{ in } \mathbf{R}^n_{+}) \cap \mathbf{R}^n_{++}] && \text{by (3.4)} \\
&= \ln[\text{interior of } \mu(X^*) \cap \mathbf{R}^n_{++} \text{ in } \mathbf{R}^n_{++}] && \text{by 4°)} \\
&= \ln[\text{interior of } \bigcap_{i \in I} \{\mu(X^{(i)}) \cap \mathbf{R}^n_{++}\} \text{ in } \mathbf{R}^n_{++}] && \text{by 1°)} \\
&= \text{interior of } \bigcap_{i \in I} \ln[\mu(X^{(i)}) \cap \mathbf{R}^n_{++}] \text{ in } \mathbf{R}^n && \text{by 3°)} \\
&= \text{a convex set in } \mathbf{R}^n. && \text{by 2°)}
\end{aligned}$$

Now X^* is a relatively complete Reinhardt set in $\mathbf{C}^n$ and hence by (3.4) so is int X^*. Since X is open, we get $X \subset \text{int } X^*$. Therefore $X^* \subset \text{int } X^*$, i.e., X^* is open. *Thus X^* is the smallest logarithmically convex relatively complete Reinhardt set containing X; and X^* is open.* (Note that if X is complete then so is X^*). We define

$$\textit{logarithmic convex hull of } X = X^*.$$

From (3.5) it follows that for any Laurent series f (in $\mathbf{C}^n$):

1) $X \subset \mathbf{D}(f) \Rightarrow$ (logarithmic convex hull of X) $\subset \mathbf{D}(f)$.

§4. CAUCHY THEORY

(4.1) Review from Calculus. A circle in $\mathbf{C}^1\{x\}$ of radius $D \geqq 0$ around a point a is to be thought of as having parametrization $x = a + De^{i\theta}$, θ going from 0 to 2π. For a circle Γ_j in $\mathbf{C}^1\{x_j\}$ of radius D_j around a_j, $\Gamma = \Gamma_1 \times \ldots \times \Gamma_n$, $f\colon \Gamma \to \mathbf{C}$, the integral

$$\int_\Gamma f(x)dx = \int_{\Gamma_1\times\ldots\times\Gamma_n} f(x_1,\ldots, x_n)dx_1\ldots dx_n$$

is to be interpreted as the complex valued Riemann integral

$$\int f(a_1 + D_1e^{i\theta_1},\ldots, a_n + D_ne^{i\theta_n})(iD_1e^{i\theta_1})\ldots(iD_ne^{i\theta_n})d\theta_1\ldots d\theta_n$$

over the cube $[0, 2\pi] \times \ldots \times [0, 2\pi] \subset \mathbf{R}^n\{\theta_1,\ldots, \theta_n\}$;

$$(x_j = a_j + D_je^{i\theta_j} \Rightarrow dx_j = iD_je^{i\theta_j}d\theta_j).$$

1) *Repeated integral = multiple integral.* If $f\colon \Gamma \to \mathbf{C}$ is continuous then

$$\int_{\Gamma_1} [\ldots[\int_{\Gamma_n} f(x_1,\ldots, x_n)dx_n]\ldots]dx_1 \quad \text{and} \quad \int_\Gamma f(x)dx$$

both exist and are equal. Hence in particular, the value of the repeated integral does not depend on the order of integration.

2) *Term by term integration.* Let $f^{(p)}\colon \Gamma \to \mathbf{C}$ be continuous. If $f^{(p)} \to f$ uniformly on Γ, then f is continuous on Γ and

$$\int_\Gamma f^{(p)}(x)dx \to \int_\Gamma f(x)dx.$$

If $f = \Sigma f^{(p)}$ uniformly on Γ, then f is continuous on Γ and

$$\int_\Gamma f(x)dx = \sum \int_\Gamma f^{(p)}(x)dx.$$

3) *Continuity under integral.* If $Y\{y\}$ is a metric space and $f\colon Y \times \Gamma \to \mathbf{C}$ is continuous, then

$$g(y) = \int_\Gamma f(y, x)dx$$

is continuous on Y.

4) *Differentiation under integral.* Let Y be an open set in $\mathbf{C}^1\{y\}$ and let $f: Y \times \Gamma \to \mathbf{C}$ be continuous such that $f_y = \partial f/\partial y$ exists and is continuous on $Y \times \Gamma$. Then on Y,

$$\frac{d}{dy}\int_\Gamma f(y, x)dx$$

exists and equals

$$\int_\Gamma f_y(y, x)dx.$$

1) follows exactly as in the theory of real valued Riemann integrals in $\mathbf{R}^n$ or can be deduced from it by splitting

$$[f(a_1 + D_1 e^{i\theta_1}, \ldots, a_n + D_n e^{i\theta_n})(iD_1 e^{i\theta_1})\ldots(iD_n e^{i\theta_n})]$$

into real and imaginary parts. 2) and 3) are straightforward. 4) can be proved thus. Let $\bar{y} \in Y$ be given. For any $A > 0$ let $Z\langle A\rangle = \{y \in \mathbf{C}^1 : |y - \bar{y}| \leqq A\}$. Since Y is open, $Z\langle A_0\rangle \subset Y$ for some $A_0 > 0$. Since $Z\langle A_0\rangle \times \Gamma$ is compact, f_y is uniformly continuous there; whence the compactness of Γ yields: Given $B > 0$, there exists $0 < A < A_0$ such that $|\Delta(y, x)| \leqq B$ for all $(y, x) \in Z\langle A\rangle \times \Gamma$, where $\Delta(y, x) = f_y(y, x) - f_y(\bar{y}, x)$. Let Ω be the segment from $\bar{y}$ to $\bar{y} + y^*$, (y^* small). Then Ω is of length $|y^*|$. Expressing

$$\int_\Omega \ldots dy$$

as an integral on a real segment we get

$$f(\bar{y} + y^*, x) - f(\bar{y}, x) = \int_\Omega f_y(y, x)dy = \int_\Omega [f_y(\bar{y}, x) + \Delta(\bar{y} + y^*, x)]dy;$$

$$\int_\Omega f_y(\bar{y}, x)dy = y^* f_y(\bar{y}, x);$$

and

$$\left|\int_\Omega \Delta(\bar{y} + y^*, x)dy\right| \leqq |y^*| \sup|\Delta(\bar{y} + y^*, x)| \leqq |y^*|B \quad \text{for all } |y^*| < A.$$

Therefore

$$|f(\bar{y} + y^*, x) - f(\bar{y}, x) - y^* f_y(\bar{y}, x)| \leqq |y^*|B \quad \text{for all } |y^*| < A, x \in \Gamma.$$

Hence, for all $0 < |y^*| < A$, we get

$$\left|\frac{1}{y^*}\left[\int_\Gamma f(\bar{y} + y^*, x)dx - \int_\Gamma f(\bar{y}, x)dx\right] - \int_\Gamma f_y(\bar{y}, x)dx\right| \leqq vB$$

where v is the volume of Γ; and $vB \to 0$ as $A \to 0$.

(4.2) *Cauchy theory in* $\mathbf{C}^1$. From this we need the following simple cases.

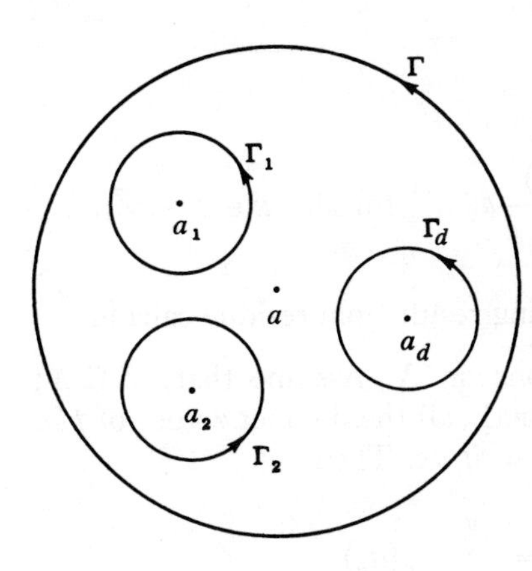

Case 1.

$a, a_1, \ldots, a_d \in \mathbf{C}^1\{x\}$.
$A > 0; A_1, \ldots, A_d \geqq 0$.
$Z = \{x: |x - a| < A\}$,
$\bar{Z} = \{x: |x - a| \leqq A\}$,
$Z_p = \{x: |x - a_p| < A_p\}$,
$\bar{Z}_p = \{x: |x - a_p| \leqq A_p\}$.
$\bar{Z}_p \subset Z$ for all p.
$\bar{Z}_p \cap \bar{Z}_q = \emptyset$ for all $p \neq q$.
Γ = circle of radius A around a.
Γ_p = circle of radius A_p around a_p.
X = open set in $\mathbf{C}^1\{x\}$.

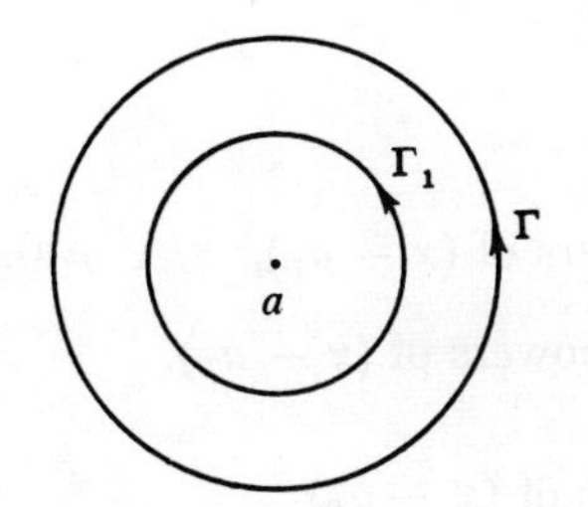

Case 2.

$d = 1, a_1 = a$.

In 1) to 5), $f: X \to \mathbf{C}$ is such that df/dx exists in X.

1) (*Case* 1). $\quad \bar{Z} - \bigcup_{p=1}^{d} Z_p \subset X \Rightarrow \int_\Gamma f(x)\, dx = \sum_{p=1}^{d} \int_{\Gamma_p} f(x)\, dx.$

In particular

2) (*Case* 2). $\quad \bar{Z} - Z_1 \subset X \Rightarrow \int_\Gamma f(x)\, dx = \int_{\Gamma_1} f(x)\, dx.$

In particular

3)
$$\bar{Z} \subset X \Rightarrow \int_{\Gamma} f(x)\, dx = 0.$$

Next

4)
$$\bar{Z} \subset X \Rightarrow f(x) = \frac{1}{2\pi i} \int_{\Gamma} \frac{f(\xi)}{\xi - x}\, d\xi \qquad \text{for all } x \in Z.$$

More generally

5) (*Case* 2). $\bar{Z} - Z_1 \subset X \Rightarrow$

$$f(x) = \frac{1}{2\pi i} \int_{\Gamma} \frac{f(\xi)}{\xi - x}\, d\xi - \frac{1}{2\pi i} \int_{\Gamma_1} \frac{f(\xi)}{\xi - x}\, d\xi \qquad \text{for all} \quad x \in Z - \bar{Z}_1.$$

As an application, we have the following result from residue calculus.

6) Let f and φ be analytic functions on X. Assume that: $\bar{Z} \subset X$; f is nowhere zero on Γ; $a_1, \ldots, a_p$ are exactly all the distinct zeroes of f in Z and their orders are $e_1, \ldots, e_p$. Let $f' = df/dx$. Then

$$\frac{1}{2\pi i} \int_{\Gamma} \frac{\varphi(x) f'(x)}{f(x)}\, dx = \sum_{p=1}^{d} e_p \varphi(a_p).$$

PROOF.

$$f(x) = c(x - a_p)^{e_p} + \text{higher powers of } (x - a_p), \qquad c \neq 0.$$

$$f'(x) = ce_p(x - a_p)^{e_p - 1} + \text{higher powers of } (x - a_p).$$

$$\frac{f'(x)}{f(x)} = \frac{e_p}{(x - a_p)} + \text{higher powers of } (x - a_p).$$

Therefore

$$\frac{\varphi(x) f'(x)}{f(x)} = \frac{e_p \varphi(a_p)}{(x - a_p)} + \text{higher powers of } (x - a_p).$$

Hence by 3),

$$\int_{\Gamma_p} \frac{\varphi(x) f'(x)}{f(x)}\, dx = \int_{\Gamma_p} \frac{e_p \varphi(a_p)}{(x - a_p)}\, dx.$$

By direct computation,

$$\int_{\Gamma_p} \frac{1}{x - a_p}\, dx = 2\pi i.$$

By 1),

$$\int_{\Gamma} \frac{\varphi(x) f'(x)}{f(x)}\, dx = \sum_{p=1}^{d} \int_{\Gamma_p} \frac{\varphi(x) f'(x)}{f(x)}\, dx.$$

Taking $\varphi \equiv 1$ in 6) we get

7) Let $f\colon X \to \mathbf{C}$ be analytic such that $\bar{Z} \subset X$ and f has no zeroes on Γ. Then

$$\frac{1}{2\pi i} \int_{\Gamma} \frac{f'(x)}{f(x)}\, dx = \text{number of zeroes of } f \text{ in } Z \text{ counted with their orders.}$$

Cauchy theory in $\mathbf{C}^n$

Notation for (4.3) *to* (4.7). Let X be an open set in $\mathbf{C}^n\{x\} = \mathbf{C}^n\{x_1, \ldots, x_n\}$ and let $f\colon X \to \mathbf{C}$ be continuous such that $\partial f / \partial x_j$ exists in X for $j = 1, \ldots, n$. Let $a \in \mathbf{C}^n$ and $A_1 > 0, \ldots, A_n > 0$ be such that $\bar{Z} \subset X$ where

$$\bar{Z} = \{x \in \mathbf{C}^n\colon |x_j - a_j| \leqq A_j \text{ for } j = 1, \ldots, n\}.$$

Let

$$Z = \{x \in \mathbf{C}^n\colon |x_j - a_j| < A_j \text{ for } j = 1, \ldots, n\},$$
$$\Gamma_j = \text{circle in } \mathbf{C}^1\{\xi_j\} \text{ of radius } A_j \text{ around } a_j,$$
$$\Gamma = \Gamma_1 \times \ldots \times \Gamma_n.$$

For $x \in Z$, by repeated applications of (4.2.4) we get

$$\begin{aligned} f(x_1, \ldots, x_n) &= \frac{1}{2\pi i} \int_{\Gamma_1} \frac{f(\xi_1, x_2, \ldots, x_n)}{\xi_1 - x_1}\, d\xi_1 \\ &= \frac{1}{(2\pi i)^2} \int_{\Gamma_1} \left[\int_{\Gamma_2} \frac{f(\xi_1, \xi_2, x_3, \ldots, x_n)}{(\xi_1 - x_1)(\xi_2 - x_2)}\, d\xi_2 \right] d\xi_1 \\ &= \frac{1}{(2\pi i)^n} \int_{\Gamma_1} \left[\cdots \left[\int_{\Gamma_n} \frac{f(\xi_1, \ldots, \xi_n)}{(\xi_1 - x_1) \ldots (\xi_n - x_n)}\, d\xi_n \right] \cdots \right] d\xi_1. \end{aligned}$$

$f(\xi_1,\ldots,\xi_n)$ is given to be continuous on Γ and the denominator is obviously continuous and nonzero there. Hence by (4.1.1) we get:

(4.3) CAUCHY FORMULA. *For all $x \in Z$*

$$f(x_1,\ldots,x_n) = \frac{1}{(2\pi i)^n} \int\limits_{\Gamma_1 \times \ldots \times \Gamma_n} \frac{f(\xi_1,\ldots,\xi_n)}{(\xi_1 - x_1)\ldots(\xi_n - x_n)} d\xi_1 \ldots d\xi_n$$

Repeatedly differentiating under the integral sign we get

(4.4) CAUCHY FORMULA. *For all $x \in Z$, for all $k_1,\ldots,k_n \geqq 0$,*

$$\frac{\partial^{k_1+\ldots+k_n} f(x_1,\ldots,x_n)}{\partial^{k_1} x_1 \ldots \partial^{k_n} x_n}$$

exists, does not depend on the order of differentiation, and equals

$$\frac{k_1!\ldots k_n!}{(2\pi i)^n} \int\limits_{\Gamma_1 \times \ldots \times \Gamma_n} \frac{f(\xi_1,\ldots,\xi_n)}{(\xi_1 - x_1)^{k_1+1}\ldots(\xi_n - x_n)^{k_n+1}} d\xi_1 \ldots d\xi_n.$$

Next, $|\xi_1 - a_1|^{k_1+1}\ldots|\xi_n - a_n|^{k_n+1} = A_1^{k_1+1}\ldots A_n^{k_n+1}$, and the volume of $\Gamma_1 \times \ldots \times \Gamma_n$ is $(2\pi)^n A_1 \ldots A_n$. Therefore,

(4.5) CAUCHY INEQUALITY. *For all $k_1,\ldots,k_n \geqq 0$,*

$$\left| \frac{\partial^{k_1+\ldots+k_n} f}{\partial^{k_1} x_1 \ldots \partial^{k_n} x_n}(a) \right| \leqq \frac{k_1!\ldots k_n!}{A_1^{k_1}\ldots A_n^{k_n}} \sup |f(\Gamma)|.$$

(4.6) THULLEN'S LEMMA. *Let Y be a compact subset of X. For any $D > 0$ let*

$$Y_D = \bigcup_{y \in Y} \{x \in \mathbf{C}^n : |x_1 - y_1| \leqq D,\ldots, |x_n - y_n| \leqq D\}.$$

Now $Y \cap (\mathbf{C}^n - X) = \emptyset$, Y is compact, and $\mathbf{C}^n - X$ is closed. Taking $\max(|x_1 - y_1|,\ldots,|x_n - y_n|)$ as a metric in $\mathbf{C}^n$ *we deduce that* $Y_D \subset X$ *for all small* $D > 0$. *Let* $D > 0$ *be any such.* Now Y_D is compact and hence $\sup|f(Y_D)| < \infty$. Given $y \in Y$ let Γ_j' be the circle in $\mathbf{C}^1\{x_j\}$ of radius D around y_j. Then by (4.5)

$$\left| \frac{\partial^{k_1+\ldots+k_n} f}{\partial^{k_1} x_1 \ldots \partial^{k_n} x_n}(y) \right| \leqq \frac{k_1!\ldots k_n!}{D^{k_1+\ldots+k_n}} \sup |f(\Gamma_1' \times \ldots \times \Gamma_n')|,$$

and obviously $\sup|f(\Gamma_1' \times \ldots \times \Gamma_n')| \leqq \sup|f(Y_D)|$. *Thus for all* $k_1, \ldots, k_n \geqq 0$ *we have*

$$\sup\left|\frac{\partial^{k_1+\ldots+k_n}f}{\partial^{k_1}x_1\ldots\partial^{k_n}x_n}(Y)\right| \leqq \frac{k_1!\ldots k_n!}{D^{k_1+\ldots+k_n}}\sup|f(Y_D)|.$$

Resume the notation before (4.3). Fix $x \in Z$. $f(\xi)$ being continuous on compact Γ, $|f(\xi)|$ is bounded there. $|x_j - a_j| < |\xi_j - a_j|$ for all $\xi_j \in \Gamma_j$ and hence by geometric series expansion

$$\frac{1}{\xi_j - x_j} = \frac{1}{\xi_j - a_j}\,\frac{1}{1 - \dfrac{x_j - a_j}{\xi_j - a_j}} = \sum_{k_j=0}^{\infty}\frac{(x_j - a_j)^{k_j}}{(\xi_j - a_j)^{k_j+1}}$$

with absolute uniform convergence on $\Gamma_j\{\xi_j\}$. Multiplying out these series for $j = 1,\ldots, n$, and then multiplying both sides by $f(\xi)/(2\pi i)^n$ we get

$$\frac{1}{(2\pi i)^n}\,\frac{f(\xi)}{(\xi_1 - x_1)\ldots(\xi_n - x_n)}$$

$$= \frac{1}{(2\pi i)^n}\sum_{0\leqq k_1,\ldots,k_n<\infty}\frac{f(\xi)}{(\xi_1 - a_1)^{k_1+1}\ldots(\xi_n - a_n)^{k_n+1}}(x_1 - a_1)^{k_1}\ldots(x_n - a_n)^{k_n}$$

with absolute uniform convergence on $\Gamma(\xi)$. Integrating term by term we get

$$\frac{1}{(2\pi i)^n}\int_\Gamma \frac{f(\xi)}{(\xi_1 - x_1)\ldots(\xi_n - x_n)}\,d\xi$$

$$= \sum_{0\leqq k_1,\ldots,k_n<\infty}\left[\frac{1}{(2\pi i)^n}\int_\Gamma \frac{f(\xi)}{(\xi_1 - a_1)^{k_1+1}\ldots(\xi_n - a_n)^{k_n+1}}\,d\xi\right]$$

$$\times\,(x_1 - a_1)^{k_1}\ldots(x_n - a_n)^{k_n}$$

where for each $x \in Z$, the right-hand side converges for some simple ordering. The right hand side is a power series and Z is an open polycylinder; consequently we have absolute local uniform convergence on $Z\{x\}$. By (4.3), the left-hand side equals $f(x)$. By (2.2 or 4.4), the "coefficient" of

$$(x_1 - a_1)^{k_1}\ldots(x_n - a_n)^{k_n} \quad \text{equals} \quad \frac{1}{k_1!\ldots k_n!}\,\frac{\partial^{k_1+\ldots+k_n}f}{\partial^{k_1}x_1\ldots\partial^{k_n}x_n}(a).$$

Thus we have proved

(**4.7**) TAYLOR EXPANSION

$$f(x_1,\dots,x_n) = \sum_{0 \leq k_1,\dots,k_n < \infty} f_{k_1\dots k_n}(x_1 - a_1)^{k_1}\dots(x_n - a_n)^{k_n}$$

with absolute local uniform convergence on $Z\{x\}$, *where*

$$f_{k_1\dots k_n} = \frac{1}{(2\pi i)^n} \int_\Gamma \frac{f(\xi)}{(\xi_1 - a_1)^{k_1+1}\dots(\xi_n - a_n)^{k_n+1}} d\xi$$

$$= \frac{1}{k_1!\dots k_n!} \quad \frac{\partial^{k_1+\dots+k_n} f}{\partial^{k_1} x_1 \dots \partial^{k_n} x_n}(a).$$

(**4.8**) REMARK. Let f be a complex valued function on an open set in $\mathbf{C}^n\{x_1,\dots,x_n\}$. We have shown that: f is analytic $\Leftrightarrow f$ is continuous and $\partial f/\partial x_1,\dots,\partial f/\partial x_n$ exist. In our proof, continuity of f was used in converting the repeated integral

$$\int_{\Gamma_1} \dots \int_{\Gamma_n} \quad \text{into the multiple integral} \quad \int_{\Gamma_1 \times \dots \times \Gamma_n} .$$

A result of Hartogs says that "$\Leftarrow$" holds without assuming f continuous, or equivalently: f is analytic in each variable $\Rightarrow f$ is analytic in all the variables simultaneously. As we shall have no occasion to use this, for proofs we refer to Bochner-Martin [**1**: Chapter VII] or Carathéodory [**1**: Chapter 1 of Part 7].

Another consequence of what we have proved above is this.

1) *Let f be an analytic function on an open set X in* $\mathbf{C}^n$ *and let* $a \in X$. *Then the Taylor expansion of f around a,* [which is unique by (2.3)], *is valid in every open polycylinder around a in X.*

From 1) we get

2) *Let f and g be analytic functions on an open set X in* $\mathbf{C}^n$. *If* $f = g$ *on a neighborhood of* $a \in X$ *then* $f = g$ *on every open polycylinder around a in X.*

From 2) we deduce

3)[1] IDENTITY THEOREM. *Let f and g be analytic functions on a domain X in* $\mathbf{C}^n$. *If* $f|X^* = g|X^*$ *for a nonempty open subset* X^* *of X then* $f = g$ *on X.*

Fix $a \in X^*$. Given $b \in X$, join a to b by an arc γ in X. By compactness of γ we can find a finite number of points $a^{(1)},\dots, a^{(p+1)}$ in X and an open

[1] A proof of this which does not use the Cauchy Theory and is valid for $\mathbf{C}^n$ as well as $\mathbf{R}^n$ has already been given in (2.5).

polycylinder Z_q around $a^{(q)}$ in X such that: $a = a^{(1)}$, $b = a^{(p+1)}$, and $a^{(q+1)} \in Z_q$ for $q = 1,\ldots, p$. Since $f = g$ on a neighborhood of $a^{(1)}$, by 2) we get $f = g$ on Z_1. In particular $f = g$ on a neighborhood of $a^{(2)}$. Hence $f = g$ on Z_2; and so on.

(4.9) TERM BY TERM DIFFERENTIATION. *Let $f^{(p)}$ be analytic on open set X in $\mathbf{C}^n\{x_1,\ldots, x_n\}$.*

1) *$f^{(p)} \to f$ locally uniformly on $X \Rightarrow f$ is analytic on X and for all $k_1,\ldots, k_n \geqq 0$,*

$$\frac{\partial^{k_1+\ldots+k_n} f^{(p)}}{\partial^{k_1} x_1 \ldots \partial^{k_n} x_n} \to \frac{\partial^{k_1+\ldots+k_n} f}{\partial^{k_1} x_1 \ldots \partial^{k_n} x_n} \qquad \textit{locally uniformly on } X.$$

2) $$\sum_p f^{(p)} = f$$

locally uniformly on $X \Rightarrow f$ is analytic on X and for all $k_1,\ldots, k_n \geqq 0$,

$$\sum_p \frac{\partial^{k_1+\ldots+k_n} f^{(p)}}{\partial^{k_1} x_1 \ldots \partial^{k_n} x_n} = \frac{\partial^{k_1+\ldots+k_n} f}{\partial^{k_1} x_1 \ldots \partial^{k_n} x_n} \qquad \textit{locally uniformly on } X.$$

3) *Let*

$$f = \prod_{p=1}^{\infty} f^{(p)}, \text{ i.e., } \prod_{p=1}^{q} f^{(p)} \to f \qquad \textit{as} \quad q \to \infty.$$

Assume that: Given $a \in X$ there exists $r > 0$ and a neighborhood X^* of a in X such that for all $p \geqq r$, $f^{(p)}$ is nowhere zero in X^*, and

$$\sum_{p=r}^{\infty} |f^{(p)}(x) - 1|$$

is uniformly convergent in X^*. Then f is analytic on X, and

$$\mathbf{o}_a f = \sum_{p=1}^{\infty} \mathbf{o}_a f^{(p)}$$

for all $a \in X$.

First we prove 1). Given $a \in X$, fix $A > 0$ such that

$$\{x \in \mathbf{C}^n \colon |x_j - a_j| \leqq A; j = 1,\ldots, n\} \subset X.$$

Let $X^* = \{x \in \mathbf{C}^n \colon |x_j - a_j| < A/2; j = 1,\ldots, n\}$; Γ_j = circle of radius A around a_j; and $\Gamma = \Gamma_1 \times \ldots \times \Gamma_n$. Since Γ is compact and $f^{(p)} \to f$ locally uniformly, we have: Given $D > 0$ there exists q such that for all $p \geqq q$,

$|f(\xi) - f^{(p)}(\xi)| \leqq D$ on $\Gamma\{\xi\}$. For all $x \in X^*$ and $\xi \in \Gamma$ we get

$$\left| \frac{f(\xi) - f^{(p)}(\xi)}{(\xi_1 - x_1)^{k_1+1} \ldots (\xi_n - x_n)^{k_n+1}} \right| \leqq \frac{D}{(A/2)^{k_1+\ldots+k_n+n}}$$

and hence

$$\left| \int_\Gamma \frac{f(\xi)}{(\xi_1 - x_1)^{k_1+1} \ldots (\xi_n - x_n)^{k_n+1}} d\xi - \int_\Gamma \frac{f^{(p)}(\xi)}{(\xi_1 - x_1)^{k_1+1} \ldots (\xi_n - x_n)^{k_n+1}} d\xi \right.$$
$$\leqq \frac{(2\pi)^n A^n D}{(A/2)^{k_1+\ldots+k_n+n}}.$$

Therefore

$$\int_\Gamma \frac{f^{(p)}(\xi)}{(\xi_1 - x_1)^{k_1+1} \ldots (\xi_n - x_n)^{k_n+1}} d\xi \to \int_\Gamma \frac{f(\xi)}{(\xi_1 - x_1)^{k_1+1} \ldots (\xi_n - x_n)^{k_n+1}} d\xi$$

uniformly on X^*. Consequently, in view of (4.4), it suffices to show that $f(x)$ is analytic on X^*. Taking $k_1 = \ldots = k_n = 0$ in the above formula, and applying (4.3) to $f^{(p)}(x)$ which is given to be analytic we get:

$$\frac{1}{(2\pi i)^n} \int_\Gamma \frac{f(\xi)}{(\xi_1 - x_1) \ldots (\xi_n - x_n)} d\xi = f(x).$$

Differentiating under integral, we deduce that $\partial f(x)/\partial x_1, \ldots, \partial f(x)/\partial x_n$ exist in X^*. 2) follows by applying 1) to the partial sums.

The assumption in 3) implies that

$$\prod_{p=r}^{q} f^{(p)} \to \prod_{p=r}^{\infty} f^{(p)}$$

uniformly on X^* and

$$\prod_{p=r}^{\infty} f^{(p)}$$

is nowhere zero on X^*. Since $f^{(p)}$ is analytic on X^*, so is

$$\prod_{p=r}^{q} f^{(p)};$$

therefore by 1),

$$\prod_{p=r}^{\infty} f^{(p)}$$

is analytic on X^* and hence so is f.

(**4.10**) Analytic Continuation in $\mathbf{C}^n$. In view of (4.8.3), as in the one variable case, one can define direct analytic continuation and then define analytic continuation along an arc, and also prove uniqueness of analytic continuation in a simply connected domain. We need not go into details here especially because of the following. In the classical treatment of complex analytic sets (for example, Osgood [**1**] and Remmert-Stein [**1**]) frequent use is made of the method of analytic continuation. We shall however use this method only in (14.8′) where, to bring out the parallelism between the language of analytic continuation and the language of coverings, we give an alternative proof of (14.8); the proof in (14.8) uses elementary observations about coverings (14.6).[2] The reason for not having to use analytic continuation elsewhere is on a somewhat different level. It is something like this. Classically, in a certain situation, making analytic continuations and forming symmetric functions, etc., an expression Φ is found; this holds outside an exceptional set $\boldsymbol{\Delta}$; by Riemann Extension Theorem (14.3) the functions occurring in Φ are extended in $\boldsymbol{\Delta}$ and Φ is shown to have the required properties also in $\boldsymbol{\Delta}$. Now one can realize the algebraic meaning of Φ; frequently Φ is expressible in terms of norms, traces, coefficients of field polynomials etc. So define Φ algebraically to begin with. It is then easy to show that Φ has the required properties everywhere. As we have obtained Φ at once everywhere, analytic continuation and Riemann Extension Theorem are not needed.[3] Besides making things simpler and clearer, this also makes the result (or a part of it) valid over an arbitrary algebraically closed complete nondiscrete valued ground field K.[4]

(**4.11**) Later on we shall prove the several variable case of the Riemann Extension Theorem (or theorem on removable singularities). For the sake of completeness, here we recall the classical one variable case. Let X be an open set in $\mathbf{C}^1\{x\}$ and let Y be a discrete subset of X, i.e., every point of Y has a neighborhood in X which contains no other point of Y.

1) One Variable Riemann Extension Theorem (Strong Form). *Let $f\colon (X - Y) \to \mathbf{C}$ be analytic. If f (i.e. $|f|$) is bounded in the neighborhood of each point of Y, then f has a unique analytic extension to X.*

Uniqueness follows from the Identity Theorem. Existence can be shown thus. Let $a \in Y$ be given. Fix $A > 0$ such that $\bar{Z} = \{x\colon |x| \leqq A\} \subset X$,

[2] This would give the reader some facility in studying the classical literature.

[3] For instance compare Osgood [**1**] and Remmert-Stein [**1**] with our Chapter V.

[4] As a rule, some use of the Riemann Extension Theorem has to be made in proving a statement which is valid only for $K = \mathbf{C}$. See §9.

and $\bar{Z} \cap Y = \{a\}$. Let $Z = \{x: |x| < A\}$. For any $B > 0$ let Γ_B be the circle in $\mathbf{C}^1\{\xi\}$ around a of radius B. Let $\Gamma = \Gamma_A$. Let

$$g(x) = \int_\Gamma \frac{f(\xi)}{\xi - x} d\xi.$$

By continuity and differentiation under integral, $g(x)$ is analytic on Z. It suffices to show that $g = f$ on $Z - \{a\}$; for then we can put $f(a) = g(a)$. Let $x \in Z - \{a\}$ be given. By Cauchy formula (4.2.5)

$$f(x) = \frac{1}{2\pi i} \int_\Gamma \frac{f(\xi)}{\xi - x} d\xi - \frac{1}{2\pi i} \int_{\Gamma_B} \frac{f(\xi)}{\xi - x} d\xi$$

for all $0 < B < |x - a|$. Since $|f|$ is bounded near a, we deduce that

$$\left| \int_{\Gamma_B} \frac{f(\xi)}{\xi - x} d\xi \right| \to 0 \qquad \text{as} \quad B \to 0, \qquad (x \text{ fixed}).$$

Therefore

$$f(x) = \int_\Gamma \frac{f(\xi)}{\xi - x} d\xi = g(x).$$

As a special case of 1) we have

2) One Variable Riemann Extension Theorem (Weak Form). *Let $f: X \to \mathbf{C}$ be continuous. If f is analytic on $X - Y$ then f is analytic on X.*

(4.12) We end this section with a remark on the maximum principle. Let X be a domain in $\mathbf{C}^1\{x\}$ and let $f: X \to \mathbf{C}$ be analytic.

1) *Maximum principle.* $[\{x: |x - a| \leqq A\} \subset X, Z = \{x: |x - a| < A\}, \Gamma = \{x: |x - a| = A\}$, f nonconstant on $Z] \Rightarrow |f(x)| < \sup|f(\Gamma)|$ for all $x \in Z$.

2) *Maximum principle.* $[M \in \mathbf{R}$ such that $|f(x)| \leqq M$ for all $x \in X$ and $|f(a)| = M$ for some $a \in X] \Rightarrow f(x) = f(a)$ for all $x \in X$.

3) *Open map theorem.* f nonconstant on $X \Rightarrow f: X \to \mathbf{C}$ is an open map.

Various proofs of these statements, either directly using Cauchy formula or using residue calculus can be found in standard textbooks. In any case, any one of the above statements can at once be deduced from any other. Later on we shall give a proof of the following:

4) *General open map theorem.* X = open set in K^n where K is any algebraically closed complete nondiscrete valued field. $f: X \to K$ analytic. $a \in X$ such that f is nonconstant near a. Then there exists a neighborhood X^* of a in X such that $f|X^*$ is an open map of X^* into K.

In view of the identity theorem, 4) yields 3) and hence 2) for $X \subset \mathbf{C}^n$. Note that for $K = \mathbf{C}$, maximum principle follows from open map theorem because $y \to |y|$ is an open map: $\mathbf{C} \to \mathbf{R}_+$ and hence $x \to |f(x)|$ is an open map: $X \to \mathbf{R}_+$. This does not hold for general K.

§5. CONVEXITY IN $\mathbf{R}^n$ [1]

In §3 we have seen that the domain of convergence of a complex Laurent series is logarithmically convex. The significance of the various notions of convexity in complex analysis goes much deeper. For purposes of motivation, here we analyse the usual notion of convexity in $\mathbf{R}^n$.

Notation. $x = (x_1, \ldots, x_n)$ are coordinates in $\mathbf{R}^n$. Unless otherwise stated, closure, interior and boundary are with respect to $\mathbf{R}^n$. ρ denotes distance in $\mathbf{R}^n$. Note that if A is a closed set in $\mathbf{R}^n$ and B is a compact set in $\mathbf{R}^n$ such that $A \cap B = \emptyset$ then $\rho(A, B) > 0$. For $a \in \mathbf{R}^n$, $b \in \mathbf{R}^n$, let

$$\operatorname{seg}(a, b) = \{(1-\lambda)a + \lambda b = ((1-\lambda)a_1 + \lambda b_1, \ldots, (1-\lambda)a_n + \lambda b_n): 0 \leqq \lambda \leqq 1\}.$$

$\boldsymbol{l}$ = the set of all functions of the form:

$$l(x) = \alpha_1 x_1 + \ldots + \alpha_n x_n + \alpha_{n+1}; \quad \alpha_1, \ldots, \alpha_{n+1} \in \mathbf{R}, \quad \alpha_j \neq 0 \text{ for some } j \leqq n.$$

For $l \in \boldsymbol{l}$ put

$$L^{(-)} = \{x \in \mathbf{R}^n : l(x) < 0\},$$
$$L = \{x \in \mathbf{R}^n : l(x) = 0\},$$
$$L^{(+)} = \{x \in \mathbf{R}^n : l(x) > 0\}.$$

L is then a hyperplane in $\mathbf{R}^n$. $L^{(+)}$ and $L^{(-)}$ are called the two sides of L in $\mathbf{R}^n$. If $l_1 \in \boldsymbol{l}$ is such that $L_1 = L$ then $L_1^{(+)}, L_1^{(-)}$ is a permutation of $L^{(+)}, L^{(-)}$.

Let $l \in \boldsymbol{l}$, $a \neq b \in \mathbf{R}^n$; $u_\lambda = (1-\lambda)a + \lambda b$, $0 \leqq \lambda \leqq 1$, $\varphi(\lambda) = l(u_\lambda)$. Then $\varphi(\lambda) = \alpha\lambda + \beta$ with $\alpha, \beta \in \mathbf{R}$. $\varphi(\lambda)$ is monotonic (increasing or decreasing) in λ. Hence

$$\begin{aligned} a, b \in L^{(+)} &\Rightarrow \varphi(0), \varphi(1) > 0 \\ &\Rightarrow \varphi(\lambda) > 0 \text{ for all } \lambda \in [0, 1] \\ &\Rightarrow \operatorname{seg}(a, b) \subset L^{(+)}. \end{aligned}$$

[1] Behnke-Stein [**1**].

Similarly,

$$a, b \in L^{(-)} \Rightarrow \operatorname{seg}(a, b) \subset L^{(-)}.$$

Now suppose $a \in L^{(+)}$ and $b \in L^{(-)}$, $\gamma: [0, 1] \to \mathbf{R}^n$ continuous, $\gamma(0) = a$, $\gamma(1) = b$. Let $\psi(t) = l(\gamma(t))$. Then $\psi(t)$ is continuous, $\psi(0) > 0$, $\psi(1) < 0$. By intermediate value theorem, there exists $0 < t < 1$ such that $\psi(t) = 0$, i.e., $\gamma(t) \in L$. Thus we have proved

(5.1) *$L^{(+)}$ and $L^{(-)}$ are the connected components of $\mathbf{R}^n - L$. For $a \neq b \in \mathbf{R}^n - L$, $\operatorname{seg}(a, b) \cap L \neq \emptyset \Leftrightarrow a$ and b are on opposite sides of L. If X is a connected subset of $\mathbf{R}^n - L$ then $X \subset L^{(+)}$ or $X \subset L^{(-)}$.*

Note that $|l(x)|$ is a constant multiple of the perpendicular distance from x to L, and the sign of $l(x)$ determines on which side of L, x lies.

From now on until the end of §5B, X will denote a subset of $\mathbf{R}^n$.

DEFINITION. Let $l \in \boldsymbol{l}$.

X lies on one side of $L \Leftrightarrow X \subset L^{(+)}$ or *$X \subset L^{(-)}$.*
X lies weakly on one side of $L \Leftrightarrow X \subset L^{(+)} \cup L$ or *$X \subset L^{(-)} \cup L$.*
X lies strictly on one side of $L \Leftrightarrow \inf l(X) > 0$ or *$\sup l(X) < 0$.*

Note that

X lies strictly on one side of L

$\Leftrightarrow$ cl X lies strictly on one side of L

$\Leftrightarrow \exists$ a hyperplane L' parallel to L and different from L such that X lies on the side of L' which is contained in a side of L; (take L' on the same side of L as X and at a distance of $\frac{1}{2}\rho(X, L)$ from L).

We put

$$J_i(X) = \{y \in \mathbf{R}^n: \exists\, l \in \boldsymbol{l} \text{ such that } l(y) < \inf l(X)\},$$

$$J_s(X) = \{y \in \mathbf{R}^n: \exists\, l \in \boldsymbol{l} \text{ such that } l(y) > \sup l(X)\},$$

$$J_h(X) = \{y \in \mathbf{R}^n: \exists \text{ a hyperplane } L \text{ such that } y \text{ and } X \text{ lie on opposite sides of } L\}.$$

By suitable parallel translations as above, we see that

$$J_h(X) = \{y \in \mathbf{R}^n: \exists \text{ a hyperplane } L \text{ through } y \text{ such that } X \text{ lies strictly on one side of } L\}.$$

Replacing l by $-l$ we see that $J_i(X) = J_s(X)$.

Replacing l by $l - l(y)$ we see that $J_i(X) = J_h(X)$. Put

$$H_i(X) = \mathbf{R}^n - J_i(X) = \{y \in \mathbf{R}^n : \forall\, l \in \boldsymbol{l},\ l(y) \geqq \inf l(X)\},$$
$$H_s(X) = \mathbf{R}^n - J_s(X) = \{y \in \mathbf{R}^n : \forall\, l \in \boldsymbol{l},\ l(y) \leqq \sup l(X)\},$$
$$H_h(X) = \mathbf{R}^n - J_h(X).$$

Then $H_i(X) = H_s(X) = H_h(X)$. We also define

$$J_I(X) = \{y \in \mathbf{R}^n : \exists\, l \in \boldsymbol{l} \text{ such that } |l(y)| < \inf |l(X)|\},$$
$$J_S(X) = \{y \in \mathbf{R}^n : \exists\, l \in \boldsymbol{l} \text{ such that } |l(y)| > \sup |l(X)|\},$$

and

$$H_I(X) = \mathbf{R}^n - J_I(X) = \{y \in \mathbf{R}^n : \forall\, l \in \boldsymbol{l},\ |l(y)| \geqq \inf |l(X)|\},$$
$$H_S(X) = \mathbf{R}^n - J_S(X) = \{y \in \mathbf{R}^n : \forall\, l \in \boldsymbol{l},\ |l(y)| \leqq \sup |l(X)|\}.$$

Recall that by definition: X is convex $\Leftrightarrow [a, b \in X \Rightarrow \operatorname{seg}(a, b) \subset X]$. We define:

$$H^*(X) = \text{intersection of all convex sets in } \mathbf{R}^n \text{ containing } X,$$
$$\bar{H}(X) = \text{intersection of all closed convex sets in } \mathbf{R}^n \text{ containing } X.$$

Now the intersection of any convex sets is convex and hence: $H^*(X)$ is the smallest convex set containing X, and $H^*(X) \subset \bar{H}(X)$. Finally, for $X_1, X_2 \subset \mathbf{R}^n$ we put

$$K(X_1, X_2) = \bigcup_{a \in X_1,\, b \in X_2} \operatorname{seg}(a, b).$$

Note that if $X_1, X_2 \subset X$ then $K(X_1, X_2) \subset H^*(X) \subset \bar{H}(X)$.

In the above definitions, the letter H is meant to suggest convex hull.

§5A. *Convex and hyperplane convex*

DEFINITION. X is *hyperplane convex* $\Leftrightarrow [a \in \operatorname{bd} X \Rightarrow \exists$ a hyperplane L through a such that $L \cap \operatorname{int} X = \emptyset]$. L is called a supporting hyperplane of X. X is *locally convex* $\Leftrightarrow [a \in \operatorname{bd} X \Rightarrow \exists$ a neighborhood N of a in $\mathbf{R}^n$ and a hyperplane L through a such that $N \cap (L \cap \operatorname{int} X) = \emptyset]$.

(5.2) *If X is a hyperplane convex domain then X is convex.*

PROOF. Otherwise there exist $a, b \in X$ with $a \neq b$ such that $\operatorname{seg}(a, b) \not\subset X$. Then $\Lambda = \{\lambda \in [0, 1] : (1 - \lambda)a + \lambda b \notin X\}$ is nonempty. Let $\lambda = \inf \Lambda$, $c = (1 - \lambda)a + \lambda b$. Then $c \in \operatorname{seg}(a, b)$, $a \neq c \neq b$, $c \in \operatorname{bd} X$. By assumption there exists a hyperplane L through c such that $L \cap X = \emptyset$. By (5.1), a and b lie on opposite sides of L while X lies on one side of L. Contradiction.

REMARK. (5.2) is false if X is not connected, e.g.,

$$X = \text{union of two parallel disjoint open cubes}$$
$$= \{x: |x_j| < \epsilon\} \cup \{x: |x_1 - 1| < \epsilon, |x_j| < \epsilon \text{ for } j > 1\}; \quad (0 < \epsilon \leqq \tfrac{1}{2}).$$

(5.3) *If X is a convex domain then X is hyperplane convex.*

REMARK. Let S be an affine subspace of $\mathbf{R}^n$ and M a hyperplane in S such that $M \cap X = \emptyset$.[2] By (5.1), X convex $\Rightarrow X \cap S$ lies on one side of M in S.

First proof of (5.3). Induction on n. Trivial for $n = 1$. Let $n > 1$ and assume true for $n - 1$. Given a point in bd X, by a translation bring this point to the origin. Suppose if possible that every line through the origin meets X. Then: Given $x \in \mathbf{R}^n$, either $\lambda x = (\lambda x_1, \ldots, \lambda x_n) \in X$ for some $\lambda > 0$ or $\lambda x \in X$ for some $\lambda < 0$. Therefore

$$\mathbf{R}^n - \{(0)\} = \left[\bigcup_{\lambda>0} \lambda X\right] \cup \left[\bigcup_{\lambda<0} \lambda X\right].$$

Since X is convex and $(0) \notin X$, we must have

$$\left[\bigcup_{\lambda>0} \lambda X\right] \cap \left[\bigcup_{\lambda<0} \lambda X\right] = \emptyset.$$

For each $\lambda \neq 0$, $x \to \lambda x$ is a homeomorphism of $\mathbf{R}^n - \{(0)\}$ onto itself. Hence, X is open $\Rightarrow \lambda X = \{\lambda x: x \in X\}$ is open

$$\Rightarrow \bigcup_{\lambda>0} \lambda X \text{ and } \bigcup_{\lambda<0} \lambda X \text{ are open.}$$

This contradicts the easily verifiable fact that $\mathbf{R}^n - \{(0)\}$ is connected, $(n > 1)$. Consequently, some line through the origin does not meet X. Make a linear transformation so that this line becomes: $x_1 = \ldots = x_{n-1} = 0$. Let $\mathbf{R}^{n-1}$: $x_n = 0$. Then π: $(x_1, \ldots, x_n) \to (x_1, \ldots, x_{n-1})$ is an open map of $\mathbf{R}^n$ onto $\mathbf{R}^{n-1}$. Therefore $\pi(X)$ is open in $\mathbf{R}^{n-1}$. Also $(0) \in$ closure of X in $\mathbf{R}^n \Rightarrow (0) \in$ closure of $\pi(X)$ in $\mathbf{R}^{n-1}$; and obviously $(0) \notin \pi(X)$. Therefore $(0) \in$ boundary of $\pi(X)$ in $\mathbf{R}^{n-1}$. Also X convex $\Rightarrow \pi(X)$ convex. By induction hypothesis, we can find a hyperplane L^* in $\mathbf{R}^{n-1}$ through (0) such that $L^* \cap \pi(X) = \emptyset$. Now $\pi^{-1}(L^*)$ is a hyperplane in $\mathbf{R}^n$ through the origin and $\pi^{-1}(L^*) \cap X = \emptyset$.

Second proof of (5.3). Let $a \in \text{bd } X$ be given. By induction on m we shall show that for all $0 \leqq m \leqq n - 1$ there exists an affine subspace E

[2] An affine subspace of a vector space is a translate of a linear subspace.

of dimension m such that $a \in E$ and $E \cap X = \emptyset$. For $m = 0$ take $E = a$. Now let $0 < m \leqq n - 1$ and let F be an affine subspace of dimension $m - 1$ such that $a \in F$ and $F \cap X = \emptyset$. Let T be an affine subspace of dimension $m + 1$ containing F. Then $T = F \times P$ where $P\{y, z\}$ is a plane. If $(F \times \{z = 0\}) \cap X = \emptyset$ then we can take $F \times \{z = 0\}$ for E. Now assume the contrary. Replacing y by $-y$ if necessary, arrange that $(F \times \{z = 0, y > 0\}) \cap X \neq \emptyset$. Let

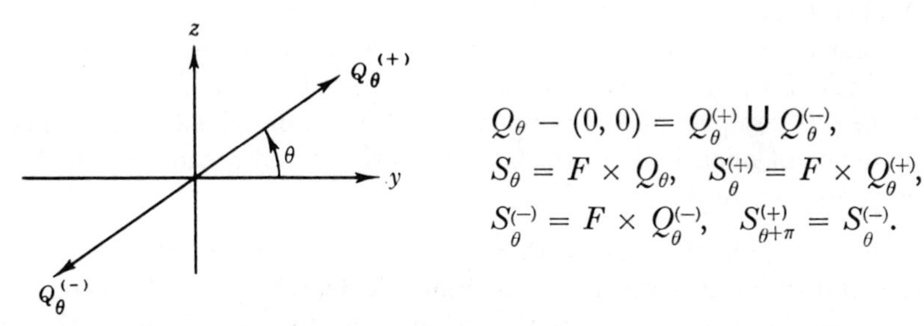

$$Q_\theta - (0, 0) = Q_\theta^{(+)} \cup Q_\theta^{(-)},$$
$$S_\theta = F \times Q_\theta, \quad S_\theta^{(+)} = F \times Q_\theta^{(+)},$$
$$S_\theta^{(-)} = F \times Q_\theta^{(-)}, \quad S_{\theta+\pi}^{(+)} = S_\theta^{(-)}.$$

Then $S_\theta^{(+)}$ and $S_\theta^{(-)}$ are the two sides of $F \times (0, 0)$ in S_θ. Hence for any θ, at most one of the two sets $S_\theta^{(+)}$ and $S_\theta^{(-)}$ meets X. Let $\Theta = \{\theta \geqq 0: S_\theta^{(+)} \cap X = \emptyset\}$. Then $\pi \in \Theta$ and hence $\Theta \neq \emptyset$. Let $\varphi = \inf \Theta$. Suppose $u \times (v, w) \in X \cap S_\theta^{(+)}$ with $u \in F$ and $(v, w) \in P$; since X is open, there exists $\epsilon > 0$ such that $u \times V \subset X$ where $V = \{(y, z) \in P: (y - v)^2 + (z - w)^2 < \epsilon^2\}$; and hence $X \cap S_{\theta+\delta}^{(+)} \neq \emptyset$ for all δ with small $|\delta|$. Thus

$$1°) \quad X \cap S_\theta^{(+)} \neq \emptyset \Rightarrow X \cap S_{\theta+\delta}^{(+)} \neq \emptyset \text{ for all } \delta \text{ with small } |\delta|.$$

Similarly

$$2°) \quad X \cap S_\theta^{(-)} \neq \emptyset \Rightarrow X \cap S_{\theta+\delta}^{(-)} \neq \emptyset \text{ for all } \delta \text{ with small } |\delta|.$$

By assumption, $X \cap S_0^{(+)} \neq \emptyset$. Hence taking $\theta = 0$ in 1°) we get that $X \cap S_\delta^{(+)} \neq \emptyset$ for all small nonnegative δ; whence $\varphi > 0$. Taking $\theta = \varphi$ in 1°) we have:

$$\begin{aligned}[X \cap S_\varphi^{(+)} \neq \emptyset &\Rightarrow X \cap S_{\varphi+\delta} \neq \emptyset \text{ for all small } \delta \geqq 0 \\ &\Rightarrow \varphi \neq \inf \Theta; \text{ contradiction}].\end{aligned}$$

Therefore $X \cap S_\varphi^{(+)} = \emptyset$. Taking $\theta = \varphi$ in 2°) we have:

$$\begin{aligned}[X \cap S_\varphi^{(-)} \neq \emptyset &\Rightarrow X \cap S_{\varphi-\delta}^{(-)} \neq \emptyset \text{ for all small } \delta \geqq 0 \\ &\Rightarrow X \cap S_{\varphi-\delta}^{(+)} = \emptyset \text{ for all small } \delta \geqq 0 \\ &\Rightarrow \varphi > \inf \Theta; \text{ contradiction}].\end{aligned}$$

Therefore $X \cap S_\varphi^{(-)} = \emptyset$. Thus $X \cap S_\varphi = \emptyset$ and we can take S_φ for E.

(5.4) *If X is a domain then: X is convex $\Leftrightarrow$ X is locally convex.*

In view of (5.2) and (5.3), here convexity can be interpreted as hyperplane convexity. "$\Rightarrow$" is then obvious. "$\Leftarrow$" follows from the following stronger assertion.

(5.5) *Assume that X is a locally convex domain. Let $a \in \operatorname{bd} X$, L a hyperplane through a, and N a neighborhood of a in $\mathbf{R}^n$ such that $N \cap (L \cap X) = \emptyset$. Then $L \cap X = \emptyset$.*

First note that any two points p, q in X can be joined by a polygonal arc in X. For, since X is a domain, p and q can be joined by an arc γ in X. Since γ is compact and X is open, p and q can be joined by a connected sequence of open balls in X. Consequently, p and q can be joined by a polygonal arc in X.

Proof of (5.5). Otherwise there exists $b \in L \cap X$. Since $a \in \operatorname{bd} X$, we can find $a^{(m)} \in X$ with $a^{(m)} \to a$. Since $N \cap (L \cap X) = \emptyset$, there exists $c \in \operatorname{seg}(a, b)$, $a \neq c \neq b$, $c \notin X$. For large m, the angle between the lines $a^{(m)}c$ and ac is acute. Choose $b^{(m)}$ on the line $a^{(m)}c$ such that the triangles $aa^{(m)}c$ and $bb^{(m)}c$ are similar. Then $\rho(b, b^{(m)}) = [\rho(b, c)/\rho(a, c)]\rho(a, a^{(m)})$. Hence $a^{(m)} \to a \Rightarrow b^{(m)} \to b$. Since $b \in X$ and X is open, $b^{(m)} \in X$ for large m. For some large m, let $p = a^{(m)}$ and $q = b^{(m)}$.

Thus we have found $p, q \in X$ with $p \neq q$, and $c \in \operatorname{seg}(p, q)$ with $c \notin X$. Take polygonal arc $\gamma: [0, 1] \to X$, $\gamma(0) = q$, $\gamma(1) = p$. Let

$$\Lambda = \{\lambda \in [0, 1]: \operatorname{seg}(p, \gamma(\lambda')) \subset X \text{ for all } \lambda' \in [\lambda, 1]\}.$$

Then $0 \notin \Lambda$, $1 \in \Lambda$. Let $\lambda = \inf \Lambda$. Let $u = \gamma(\lambda)$. Then $u \neq p$. Let v be the vertex of γ next to u, $(u \neq v)$. Then $\operatorname{seg}(p, u) \not\subset X$; and $\operatorname{seg}(p, w) \subset X$ for all $w \in \operatorname{seg}(u, v)$ with $w \neq u$. Let T be the triangle formed by p and the "open" segment uv, i.e., $T = K(p, \operatorname{seg}(u, v) - \{u\} - \{v\})$. Then $T \subset X$. Since p, $u \in X$ and $\operatorname{seg}(p, u) \not\subset X$, we can find $r \in \operatorname{seg}(p, u)$ with $p \neq r \neq u$ such that $\operatorname{seg}(p, r) - \{r\} \subset X$, and $r \in \operatorname{bd} X$. Since X is

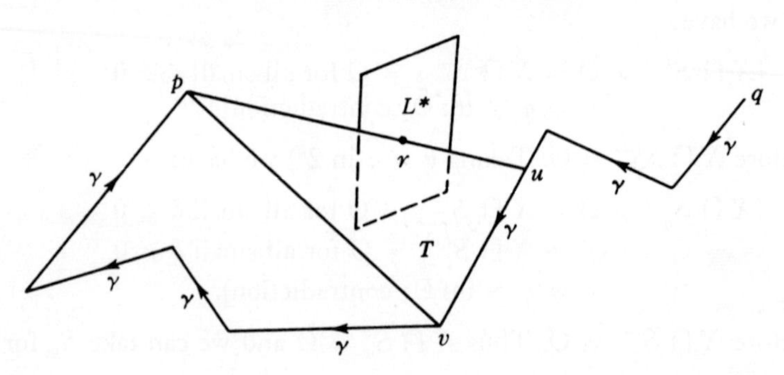

locally convex and $r \in \operatorname{bd} X$, there exists a neighborhood N^* of r in $\mathbf{R}^n$ and a hyperplane L^* through r such that $N^* \cap (X \cap L^*) = \emptyset$. Since $\operatorname{seg}(p, r) - \{r\} \subset X$, L^* cannot contain the line pu; whence $(L^* \cap N^*) \cap T \neq \emptyset$. This contradicts the fact that $T \subset X$.

(5.6) *If X is convex then* $\operatorname{cl} X$ *is convex. Hence in particular, without assuming X convex,* $\bar{H}(X) = \operatorname{cl} H^*(X)$.

PROOF. $[a^{(m)} \to a, b^{(m)} \to b, c \in \operatorname{seg}(a, b)] \Rightarrow \exists\, c^{(m)} \in \operatorname{seg}(a^{(m)}, b^{(m)})$ such that $c^{(m)} \to c$.

(5.7) *If X is convex then* $\operatorname{int} X$ *is convex.*

PROOF. Let $a, b \in \operatorname{int} X$. Take $\epsilon > 0$ such that $A = \{x \in \mathbf{R}^n: \rho(x, a) < \epsilon\} \subset X$ and $B = \{x \in \mathbf{R}^n: \rho(x, b) < \epsilon\} \subset X$. Then $K(A, B) \subset X$ since X is convex, and obviously $\operatorname{seg}(a, b) \subset \operatorname{int} K(A, B)$.

(5.8) *If X is convex then we have the following.*

1) $\operatorname{int} X \neq \emptyset \Rightarrow \operatorname{bd} X = \operatorname{bd}(\operatorname{int} X)$.

2) $\operatorname{int} X = \emptyset \Leftrightarrow$ *X is contained in some hyperplane.*

Proof of 1). Take $b \in \mathbf{R}^n$ and $\epsilon > 0$ such that $B = \{x \in \mathbf{R}^n: \rho(x, b) < \epsilon\} \subset X$. For any $a \in X$ we have: $a \in \operatorname{cl}(\operatorname{int} K(a, B))$ and $K(a, B) \subset X$.

Proof of 2). "$\Leftarrow$" is obvious. To prove "$\Rightarrow$" let M be a highest dimensional affine subspace of $\mathbf{R}^n$ such that $\operatorname{int}_M(X \cap M) \neq \emptyset$. Take $b \in M$ and $\epsilon > 0$ such that $B = \{x \in M: \rho(x, b) < \epsilon\} \subset X \cap M$. Let if possible $a \in X$ with $a \notin M$. Let N be the affine subspace spanned by M and a. Then $\dim N = (\dim M) + 1$, $K(a, B) \subset X \cap N$, and $\operatorname{int}_N K(a, B) \neq \emptyset$. Contradiction.

(5.9) *If X is convex then we have the following.*

1) $y \in \operatorname{bd} X \Rightarrow \exists$ *a hyperplane L through y such that* $\operatorname{int} X$ *is on one side of L and* $\operatorname{cl} X$ *is weakly on one side of L. Hence in particular, X is hyperplane convex.*

2) $y \in \mathbf{R}^n - \operatorname{cl} X \Rightarrow \exists$ *a hyperplane L through y such that* $\operatorname{cl} X$ *is strictly on one side of L.*

PROOF. 1) follows from (5.3, 5.7, 5.8). We prove 2) by induction on n. Trivial for $n = 1$. So let $n > 1$ and assume for $n - 1$.

Case 1$'$: $\operatorname{int} X \neq \emptyset$. Take $y' \in \operatorname{int} X$. Then there exists $y^* \in \operatorname{seg}(y, y')$ such that $y^* \in \operatorname{bd} X$. By 1) there is a hyperplane L^* through y^* such that int X is on one side of L^* and cl X is weakly on one side of L^*. Take L to be the hyperplane through y parallel to L^*.

Case 2′: int $X = \emptyset$. By (5.8), cl X is contained in a hyperplane M. If $y \notin M$ then take L to be the hyperplane through y parallel to M. If $y \in M$ then by induction hypothesis there exists an affine subspace N of $\mathbf{R}^n$ such that: dim $N = n - 2$, $y \in N \subset M$, and cl X is strictly on one side of N in M. Take L to be any hyperplane in $\mathbf{R}^n$ such that $N \subset L$ and $L \neq M$.

§5B. *Comparison of various convex hulls in* $\mathbf{R}^n$

(5.10) $H_I(X) \subset H_i(X) = H_h(X) = \bar{H}(X) = H_s(X) \subset H_S(X)$.

PROOF. We know that $H_i = H_h = H_s$. Hence enough to show that:

1°) $H_h(X) = \bar{H}(X)$, 2°) $J_i(X) \subset J_I(X)$, and 3°) $J_S(X) \subset J_h(X)$.

1°) Suppose $y \notin \bar{H}(X)$. By (5.9.2) there exists a hyperplane L through y such that $\bar{H}(X)$ is strictly on one side of L. Whence $y \notin H_h(X)$.

Suppose $y \notin H_h(X)$. Then there exists a hyperplane L such that y and X are on opposite sides of L. Say $y \in L^{(-)}$ and $X \subset L^{(+)}$. Then $L^{(+)} \cup L$ is a closed convex set containing X and hence $\bar{H}(X) \subset L^{(+)} \cup L$. Since $y \notin L^{(+)} \cup L$, we get that $y \notin \bar{H}(X)$.

2°) Let $y \in J_i(X)$. Then there exists $l \in \boldsymbol{l}$ such that $l(y) < \inf l(X)$. Let $l_1 = l - l(y)$. Then $l_1(y) = 0 < \inf |l_1(X)|$. Hence $y \in J_I(X)$.

3°) Let $y \in J_S(X)$. Then there exists $l \in \boldsymbol{l}$ such that $|l(y)| > \sup|l(X)|$. Let L: $l(x) = l(y)$. Then L is a hyperplane through y and X lies strictly on one side of L. Therefore $y \in J_h(X)$.

(5.11) *If X is connected then* $H_I(X) = H_i(X)$.

PROOF. In view of (5.10) it suffices to show that $J_I(X) \subset J_h(X)$. Given $y \in J_I(X)$, there exists $l \in \boldsymbol{l}$ such that $|l(y)| < \inf |l(X)|$. Let $l_1 = l - l(y)$. Then L_1 is a hyperplane through y, $X \cap L_1 = \emptyset$, $X \cap L_1^{(+)}$ lies strictly on one side of L_1, and $X \cap L_1^{(-)}$ lies strictly on one side of L_1. Since X is connected, $X \subset L_1^{(+)}$ or $X \subset L_1^{(-)}$. Therefore $y \in J_h(X)$.

REMARK. (5.11) is false if X is not connected (even if X is bounded), e.g. $X =$ two points.

(5.12) *If X is bounded then* $H_s(X) = H_S(X)$.

PROOF. In view of (5.10) it suffices to show that $J_s(X) \subset J_S(X)$. Given $y \in J_s(X)$ there exists $l \in \boldsymbol{l}$ such that $l(y) > \sup l(X)$. Let $l_1 = l - l(y)$, and $k = -\sup l_1(X)$. Then $l_1(y) = 0 > \sup l_1(X)$, and hence $k > 0$. Since X is bounded, there exists $u \geqq k$ such that $-u < \inf l_1(X)$. For all $x \in X$ we have:

$$l_1(y) = 0 > -k \geqq l_1(x) \geqq -u, \quad \text{i.e.,} \quad l_1(y) + u > u - k \geqq l_1(x) + u \geqq 0.$$

Let $l_2 = l_1 + u \in \boldsymbol{l}$. Then $|l_2(y)| = l_2(y) > \sup |l_2(X)|$, and hence $y \in J_S(X)$.

REMARK. (5.12) is false if X is unbounded (even if X is connected), e.g.,: X = lower half space $= \{x \in \mathbf{R}^n : x_1 \leqq 0\}$; and y = any point in the upper half space, i.e., $y_1 > 0$.

(5.13) *Let H' stand for any one of H_i, H_h, $\bar{H}$, H_s, H_S. Let H stand for any one of H_I, H_i, H_h, $\bar{H}$, H_s, H_S. Then we have the following.*

1) *$H(X)$ is closed.*

2) *If X is bounded then $H(X)$ is compact.*

3) *If X is open and convex and Y is any compact subset of X, then $H(Y)$ is compact and $H(Y) \subset X$.*

4) *Let X be open. If $H'(Y) \cap X$ is compact for every compact subset Y of X, then X is convex.*

5) *Let X be a domain. If $H(Y) \cap X$ is compact for every compact subset Y of X, then X is convex.*

PROOF. 1) is obvious. In view of 1) and (5.10, 5.12), to prove 2) it suffices to show that, if X is bounded then $\bar{H}(X)$ is bounded. Let A be a closed ball (of finite radius) containing X. Then A is a convex closed set and hence $\bar{H}(X) \subset A$. Therefore $\bar{H}(X)$ is bounded.

In view of 2) and (5.10, 5.12), to prove 3) it suffices to show that $\mathbf{R}^n - X \subset J_h(Y)$. Let $y \in \mathbf{R}^n - X$ be given. By (5.9), we can find a hyperplane L through y such that X is on one side of L. Since $Y \subset X$, Y is also on one side of X. Since Y is compact and L is closed, we get $\rho(Y, L) > 0$. Thus Y is strictly on one side of L. Therefore $y \in J_h(Y)$.

To prove 4), suppose that X is not convex. Take $a, b \in X$ such that $\text{seg}(a, b) \not\subset X$. Then there exist $c^{(m)} \in \text{seg}(a, b) \cap X$ such that $c^{(m)} \to c$, $c \notin X$. Take $Y = \{a\} \cup \{b\}$. Then Y is compact $\subset X$. Now $c^{(m)} \in \text{seg}(a, b) = \bar{H}(Y) = H'(Y)$ by (5.10, 5.12). Hence $H'(Y) \cap X$ is not compact.

To prove 5), let a, b, $c^{(m)}$ be as above. For Y take an arc joining a and b in X. Then by (5.10, 5.11), $c^{(m)} \in \text{seg}(a, b) \subset \bar{H}(Y) = H_I(Y)$. Hence $H_I(Y) \cap X$ is not compact.

§5C. *Monomial convex and logarithmically convex. Convex and holomorphically convex*

Let $X \subset \mathbf{R}^n$ be fixed. For any $Y \subset X$ let

$$\mathbf{H}_I(Y), \ldots, \mathbf{H}_S(Y) = H_I(Y) \cap X, \ldots, H_S(Y) \cap X.$$

Then

$$\mathbf{H}_I(Y) = \{x \in X\colon \forall\, l \in \boldsymbol{l},\ |l(x)| \geqq \inf |l(Y)|\},$$
$$\mathbf{H}_i(Y) = \{x \in X\colon \forall\, l \in \boldsymbol{l},\ l(x) \geqq \inf l(Y)\},$$
$$\ldots$$
$$\mathbf{H}_S(Y) = \{x \in X\colon \forall\, l \in \boldsymbol{l},\ |l(x)| \leqq \sup |l(Y)|\}.$$

Part of (5.13) can be restated as

(**5.14**) Proposition. *Let $X \subset \mathbf{R}^n$ be open. Then X is convex* $\Leftrightarrow \mathbf{H}(Y)$ *is compact for every compact subset Y of X, where $\mathbf{H}$ stands for any one of* $\mathbf{H}_i, \mathbf{H}_h, \bar{\mathbf{H}}, \mathbf{H}_s, \mathbf{H}_S$. *If X is a domain then $\mathbf{H}$ may also stand for $\mathbf{H}_I$.*

(**5.15**) Definition. **1**) Thus we have characterized convexity of X in terms of a set of functions on X. In the future we shall use the analogs of $\mathbf{H}_S$. Thus quite generally, for any topological space X and for any set Φ of continuous functions on X with values in a valued field, for any $Y \subset X$ *we can put*

$$\mathbf{H}^{\Phi}(Y) = \Phi\text{-}convex\ hull\ of\ Y \text{ (in } X) = \{x \in X\colon \forall\, \varphi \in \Phi,\ |\varphi(x)| \leqq \sup |\varphi(Y)|\},$$

and then define:

X is Φ-convex $\Leftrightarrow \mathbf{H}^{\Phi}(Y)$ *is compact for every compact subset Y of X.*

2) Note that $\mathbf{H}^{\Phi}(Y)$ is always closed. Consequently, if $\Psi \subset \Phi$ and if X is Ψ-convex then X is Φ-convex.

3) Let *X be a domain in* $\mathbf{C}^n\{x_1,\ldots, x_n\}$. Taking Φ = set of all holomorphic functions on X we get the notions of *holomorphic convex hull of $Y \subset X$*, and of *holomorphic convexity of X*. Taking Ψ = set of all monomials $\alpha x_1^{m_1}\ldots x_n^{m_n}$, $\alpha \in \mathbf{C}$, $m_j \geqq 0$ in case X contains a point a with $a_j = 0$, we get the notions of *monomial convex hull of $Y \subset X$*, and of *monomial convexity of X*.

From 2) we at once deduce

4) *Let $X \subset \mathbf{C}^n$. If X is monomial convex then X is holomorphically convex.*

Next we prove

(**5.16**) Proposition. *Let X be a relatively complete Reinhardt domain in* $\mathbf{C}^n\{x_1,\ldots, x_n\}$. *If X is logarithmically convex then X is monomial convex.*

PROOF. Induction on n. Take $n = 1$. Since X is logarithmically convex, $\{\log|x|: 0 \neq x \in X\}$ is a segment. Since log is monotonic, $\{|x|: 0 \neq x \in X\}$ is also a segment, and hence so is $\{|x|: x \in X\}$. Therefore:

Case 1°): $X = \{x \in \mathbf{C}^1: |x| < B\}$ with $0 < B \leqq \infty$, or:

Case 2°): $X = \{x \in \mathbf{C}^1: A < |x| < B\}$ with $0 \leqq A < B \leqq \infty$.

Let Y compact $\subset X$. In case 1°), $Y \subset Y^* = \{x \in \mathbf{C}^1: |x| \leqq B_1\}$ with $0 < B_1 < B$. Using the monomial x we see that $\mathbf{H}^{\Psi}(Y) \subset Y^*$. In case 2°), $Y \subset Y^* = \{x \in \mathbf{C}^1: A_1 \leqq |x| \leqq B_1\}$ with $A < A_1 < B_1 < B$. Using the monomials x and x^{-1} we see that $\mathbf{H}^{\Psi}(Y) \subset Y^*$.

Take $n > 1$ and assume true for $n - 1$. Let Y compact $\subset X$. Suppose if possible that $\mathbf{H}^{\Psi}(Y)$ is not compact. Then there exists a sequence $(y^{(m)})$ in $\mathbf{H}^{\Psi}(Y)$ having no limit point there. Since Y is compact, there exist $A_j \in R_{++}$ such that

$$Y \subset Z = \{x \in \mathbf{C}^n: |x_j| \leqq A_j \text{ for } j = 1,\dots, n\}.$$

Taking the monomials $x_1,\dots, x_n$ we see that $\mathbf{H}^{\Psi}(Y) \subset Z$; whence $\mathbf{H}^{\Psi}(Y)$ is bounded. Replacing $(y^{(m)})$ by a subsequence, we may thus assume that $y^{(m)} \to y \in \mathbf{C}^n$. Since $\mathbf{H}^{\Psi}(Y)$ is closed in X, y must lie in the boundary of X in $\mathbf{C}^n$. *Suppose if possible that $y_j = 0$ for some j.* Say $y_n = 0$. Let $\pi: \mathbf{C}^n\{x_1,\dots, x_n\} \to \mathbf{C}^{n-1}\{x_1,\dots, x_{n-1}\}$ be given by $\pi(x_1,\dots, x_n) = (x_1,\dots, x_{n-1})$. As a subset of $\mathbf{C}^n$, $\mathbf{C}^{n-1}$ is given by: $x_n = 0$.

Case 1′): $X \cap \mathbf{C}^{n-1} = \emptyset$. Then the monomial $\psi(x) = x_n^{-1}$ is in Ψ. Since Y is compact and the continuous function $|x_n|$ is nonzero on Y, it has a positive minimum δ there. Hence $|\psi(Y)| \leqq \delta^{-1}$. However, $y^{(m)} \to y$ and $y_n = 0$ imply that $|\psi(y^{(m)})| > \delta^{-1}$ for large m. This is a contradiction since $y^{(m)} \in \mathbf{H}^{\Psi}(Y)$.

Case 2′): $X \cap \mathbf{C}^{n-1} \neq \emptyset$. Since X is a relatively complete Reinhardt set in $\mathbf{C}^n$, $\pi(X)$ is a relatively complete Reinhardt set in $\mathbf{C}^{n-1}$. Since π is continuous, $\pi(X)$ is connected and $\pi(Y)$ is compact. Since π is open, $\pi(X)$ is open in $\mathbf{C}^{n-1}$. Let $(a_1,\dots, a_{n-1}), (b_1,\dots, b_{n-1}) \in \pi(X)$ with $a_1,\dots, a_{n-1}, b_1,\dots, b_{n-1} \neq 0$. Since X is open in $\mathbf{C}^n$, there exist $a_n \neq 0 \neq b_n$ such that $(a_1,\dots, a_n)$ and $(b_1,\dots, b_n)$ are in X. Since X is logarithmically convex, there exists $X^* \subset X$ such that $x_1^*,\dots, x_n^* \neq 0$ for all $x^* \in X^*$, and such that

$$\{(\log|x_1^*|,\dots, \log|x_n^*|): x^* \in X^*\}$$

is the segment joining $(\log |a_1|,\dots, \log |a_n|)$ and $(\log |b_1|,\dots, \log |b_n|)$. Now $\pi(X^*) \subset \pi(X)$, and

$$\{(\log|x_1^*|,\dots, \log|x_{n-1}^*|): x^* \in \pi(X^*)\}$$

is the segment joining $(\log|a_1|,\ldots,\log|a_{n-1}|)$ and $(\log|b_1|,\ldots,\log|b_{n-1}|)$. This shows that $\pi(X)$ is a relatively complete logarithmically convex Reinhardt domain in $\mathbf{C}^{n-1}$ and $\pi(Y)$ compact $\subset \pi(X)$. Now $y_n = 0$, X is relatively complete, and $X \cap \mathbf{C}^{n-1} \neq \emptyset$. Hence $y \in \pi(X)$ would imply that $y \in X$. Therefore $y \notin \pi(X)$. Also $y^{(m)} \to y$ yields that $\pi(y^{(m)}) \to \pi(y)$. Therefore $\pi(y)$ must lie in the boundary of $\pi(X)$ in $\mathbf{C}^{n-1}$. By the induction hypothesis, the monomial convex hull of $\pi(Y)$ in $\pi(X)$ is compact; hence for some large m, $y^{(m)}$ cannot belong to this hull. Therefore, there exists $\psi(x) = \alpha x_1^{m_1}\ldots x_{n-1}^{m_{n-1}}$ with $\alpha \in \mathbf{C}$ and $m_j \geqq 0$ in case $\pi(X)$ contains a point x^* with $x_j^* = 0$, such that $|\psi(\pi(y^{(m)}))| > \sup|\psi(\pi(Y))|$. Obviously $\psi \in \Psi$ and $\psi(x) = \psi(\pi(x))$ for all $x \in X$. Therefore $|\psi(y^{(m)})| > \sup|\psi(Y)|$, which contradicts the fact that $y^{(m)} \in \mathbf{H}^{\Psi}(Y)$.

This shows that in both the cases 1′) and 2′) we must have $y_j \neq 0$ for $j = 1,\ldots, n$. Note that the induction hypothesis will not be needed any more and the notation used in the proof thus far may now be abandoned.

Summarizing: X is a relatively complete logarithmically convex Reinhardt domain in $\mathbf{C}^n\{x_1,\ldots, x_n\}$. Y compact $\subset X$; $y^{(m)} \in \mathbf{H}^{\Psi}(Y)$; $y^{(m)} \to y \in$ (boundary of X in $\mathbf{C}^n$); $y_j \neq 0$ for $j = 1,\ldots, n$. We want to show that this situation leads to a contradiction.

Omitting a finite number of terms in the sequence $(y^{(m)})$ we may assume that $y_j^{(m)} \neq 0$ for all m, for all j. Let

$$\mathbf{C}_{++}^n = \{x \in \mathbf{C}^n : x_j \neq 0 \text{ for } j = 1,\ldots, n\}.$$

Then $X \cap \mathbf{C}_{++}^n$ is open in $\mathbf{C}_{++}^n$ and $y \in$ (boundary of $X \cap \mathbf{C}_{++}^n$ in $\mathbf{C}_{++}^n$). Let $\ln : \mathbf{C}_{++}^n \to \mathbf{R}^n\{v_1,\ldots, v_n\}$ be given by $v_i = \log|x_i|$. Let $V = \ln(X \cap \mathbf{C}_{++}^n)$, and $w = \ln(y)$. Now $x \to (|x_1|,\ldots, |x_n|)$ is an open map of $\mathbf{C}_{++}^n$ onto $\mathbf{R}_{++}^n$ and $(|x_1|,\ldots, |x_n|) \to \ln x$ is a homeomorphism of $\mathbf{R}_{++}^n$ onto $\mathbf{R}^n$. Consequently, V is open in $\mathbf{R}^n$. Hence by assumption, V is a convex domain in $\mathbf{R}^n$. ln being continuous we get that $\ln(y^{(m)}) \to w$ and hence $w \in$ (closure of V in $\mathbf{R}^n$). Finally, X Reinhardt and $y \notin X$ imply that $w \notin V$. Therefore

$$w \in \operatorname{bd} V = (\text{boundary of } V \text{ in } \mathbf{R}^n).$$

By (5.3), V is hyperplane convex and hence there exist $\alpha_1,\ldots, \alpha_{n+1} \in \mathbf{R}$, with $\alpha_j \neq 0$ for some $j \leqq n$, such that

$$\alpha_1 w_1 + \ldots + \alpha_n w_n + \alpha_{n+1} = 0,$$

and

$$\alpha_1 v_1 + \ldots + \alpha_n v_n + \alpha_{n+1} < 0 \qquad \text{for all} \quad v \in V.$$

Let

$$p(x) = \alpha|x_1|^{\alpha_1}\ldots|x_n|^{\alpha_n}, \qquad \alpha = e^{\alpha_{n+1}}.$$

Then $p(y) = 1$; and $p(x) < 1$ for all $x \in X \cap \mathbf{C}^n_{++}$. Suppose if possible that $\alpha_1 < 0$ and there exists $(a_1,\dots, a_n) \in X$ with $a_1 = 0$. Since X is open and relatively complete Reinhardt, there exist $D_1,\dots, D_n > 0$ such that

$$(D_1^*, D_2,\dots, D_n) \in X \cap \mathbf{R}^n_{++} \qquad \text{for all } 0 < D_1^* < D_1.$$

Now $p(D_1^*, D_2,\dots, D_n) \to +\infty$ as $D_1^* \to 0$; hence for some D_1^*, $(D_1^*, D_2,\dots, D_n) \in X \cap \mathbf{C}^n_{++}$ and $p(D_1^*, D_2,\dots, D_n) > 1$. Contradiction.

This shows that $[a \in X,\ a_j = 0 \Rightarrow \alpha_j \geqq 0]$. Consequently, $p(x)$ is defined for all $x \in X$. Let $x \in X$ be given. Since X is a relatively complete Reinhardt open set, we can find $x^* \in X \cap \mathbf{C}^n_{++}$ such that $x_j^* = x_j$ if $x_j \neq 0$ and $0 < |x_j^*| < 1$ if $x_j = 0$. Then $p(x) \leqq p(x^*) < 1$. Thus $p(x) < 1$ for all $x \in X$. In particular, $p(x) < 1$ for all $x \in Y$. Since Y is compact, there exists $0 < E < 1$ such that $p(x) < E$ for all $x \in Y$. Again since Y is compact, there exists $A > 0$ such that $|x_j| \leqq A$ for $j = 1,\dots, n$ for all $x \in Y$. Let

$$p_1(x) = \alpha|x_1|^{\alpha_1+\delta_1}\dots|x_n|^{\alpha_n+\delta_n}; \qquad \delta_1,\dots, \delta_n \geqq 0.$$

Then $p_1(x)$ is defined for all $x \in X$, and for all $x \in Y$ we have

$$p_1(x) = p(x)|x_1|^{\delta_1}\dots|x_n|^{\delta_n} \leqq p(x)A^{\delta_1+\dots+\delta_n};$$

also

$$p_1(y) = |y_1|^{\delta_1}\dots|y_n|^{\delta_n}.$$

As $\delta_1,\dots, \delta_n \to 0$: $A^{\delta_1+\dots+\delta_n} \to 1$, $|y_1|^{\delta_1} \to 1,\dots, |y_n|^{\delta_n} \to 1$. Therefore, given $\epsilon > 0$ there exists $\delta > 0$ such that:

$$A^{\delta_1+\dots+\delta_n} \leqq 1 + \epsilon \quad \text{and} \quad p_1(y) \geqq 1 - \epsilon$$
$$\text{whenever} \quad 0 \leqq \delta_1 \leqq \delta,\dots, 0 \leqq \delta_n \leqq \delta.$$

Choose $\epsilon > 0$ small so that $(1 + \epsilon)E < 1 - \epsilon$. Choose $0 \leqq \delta_1 \leqq \delta,\dots, 0 \leqq \delta_n \leqq \delta$ so that $\beta_j = \alpha_j + \delta_j$ is rational for $j = 1,\dots, n$. Let

$$\beta = \alpha/p_1(y), \qquad F = (1 + \epsilon)E/p_1(y), \qquad \text{and} \qquad q(x) = p_1(x)/p_1(y).$$

Then

$$q(x) = \beta|x_1|^{\beta_1}\dots|x_n|^{\beta_n} \quad \text{is defined for all} \quad x \in X;$$
$$q(y) = 1; \quad 0 < F < 1; \quad \text{and} \quad q(x) \leqq F \quad \text{for all} \quad x \in Y.$$

Now $\beta_j = \gamma_j/t$ where $\gamma_1,\dots, \gamma_n, t$ are integers and $t > 0$. Let

$$r(x) = (q(x))^t, \qquad \gamma = \beta^t, \qquad G = F^t.$$

Then

$$r(x) = \gamma|x_1|^{\gamma_1}\dots|x_n|^{\gamma_n} \quad \text{is defined for all} \quad x \in X;$$

$$r(y) = 1; \qquad 0 < G < 1; \qquad \text{and} \qquad r(x) \leqq G \qquad \text{for all} \quad x \in Y.$$

Since $y^{(m)} \to y$, we get that $r(y^{(m)}) > G$ for large m. Let $\psi(x) = \gamma x_1^{\gamma_1}\dots x_n^{\gamma_n}$. Then $\psi \in \Psi$. Also $|\psi| = r$ and hence for large m

$$|\psi(y^{(m)})| > G \geqq \sup|\psi(Y)|.$$

This is a contradiction since $y^{(m)} \in \mathbf{H}^{\Psi}(Y)$. Hence our supposition that $\mathbf{H}^{\Psi}(Y)$ is not compact must be false.

REMARK. Actually the converse of (5.16) is also true. An indirect proof of this will be given in the next section. We leave it to the reader to give a simple direct proof of (5.16) and its converse, at least under the assumption: $[a \in X \Rightarrow a_j \neq 0 \quad \text{for} \quad j = 1,\dots, n]$.

Finally we prove

(5.17) *Let X be a domain in $\mathbf{C}^n\{x_1,\dots, x_n\}$. If X is convex* (as a subset of $\mathbf{R}^{2n} = \mathbf{C}^n$) *then X is holomorphically convex.*

PROOF. Let Y compact $\subset X$ be given. Let $Y^* = \mathbf{H}_s(Y)$ and $Y' = \mathbf{H}^{\Phi}(Y)$. Then Y' is closed in X, and by assumption Y^* is compact. Hence it suffices to show that $Y' \subset Y^*$. Let $y \in X$, $y \notin Y^*$. Then there exist $\alpha_1,\dots, \alpha_n$, $\beta_1,\dots, \beta_n, \gamma \in \mathbf{R}$ such that for

$$l(x) = \alpha_1 \mathbf{Re}\, x_1 + \beta_1 \mathbf{Im}\, x_1 + \dots + \alpha_n \mathbf{Re}\, x_n + \beta_n \mathbf{Im}\, x_n + \gamma$$

we have $l(y) > \sup l(Y)$.

Let

$$m(x) = (\alpha_1 - i\beta_1)x_1 + \dots + (\alpha_n - i\beta_n)x_n + \gamma; \qquad \text{and} \qquad \varphi(x) = e^{m(x)}.$$

Then $\mathbf{Re}\, m(x) = l(x)$ and hence $|\varphi(y)| > \sup|\varphi(Y)|$. Since $\varphi \in \Phi$, we conclude that $y \notin Y'$.

§6. LAURENT EXPANSION IN $\mathbf{C}^n$

To continue the discussion of §3 in the complex case, consider the Laurent series

$$f = \sum_{-\infty < i_1,\dots,i_n < \infty} f_{i_1\dots i_n} x_1^{i_1}\dots x_n^{i_n}; \qquad f_{i_1\dots i_n} \in \mathbf{C}.$$

Let $A_1 > 0,\dots, A_n > 0$ be such that $(A_1,\dots, A_n) \in \mathbf{D}(f)$. Let Γ_j be the circle in $\mathbf{C}^1\{x_j\}$ of radius A_j around the origin. Let $\Gamma = \Gamma_1 \times \dots \times \Gamma_n$.

Then the above series is absolutely uniformly convergent on Γ. Let $k_1, \ldots, k_n$ be any integers. Then

$$\frac{f(x)}{x_1^{k_1+1} \ldots x_n^{k_n+1}} = \sum_{-\infty < i_1, \ldots, i_n < \infty} f_{i_1 \ldots i_n} x_1^{i_1-k_1-1} \ldots x_n^{i_n-k_n-1}$$

with absolute uniform convergence on Γ. Integrating term by term we get

$$\int_\Gamma \frac{f(x)}{x_1^{k_1+1} \ldots x_n^{k_n+1}} dx$$

$$= \sum_{-\infty < i_1, \ldots, i_n < \infty} f_{i_1 \ldots i_n} \int_{\Gamma_1 \times \ldots \times \Gamma_n} \prod_{j=1}^n x_j^{i_j-k_j-1} dx_1 \ldots dx_n$$

$$= \sum_{-\infty < i_1, \ldots, i_n < \infty} f_{i_1 \ldots i_n} \prod_{j=1}^n \int_{\Gamma_j} x_j^{i_j-k_j-1}\, dx_j$$

$$= (2\pi i)^n f_{k_1 \ldots k_n}$$

because

$$\int_{\Gamma_j} x_j^p\, dx_j = \begin{cases} 0 & \text{if } p \neq -1 \\ 2\pi i & \text{if } p = -1. \end{cases}$$

Thus we have proved

(6.1) *For all $i_1, \ldots, i_n$,*

$$f_{i_1 \ldots i_n} = \frac{1}{(2\pi i)^n} \int_\Gamma \frac{f(x)}{x_1^{i_1+1} \ldots x_n^{i_n+1}} dx.$$

Consequently, if

$$g = \sum_{-\infty < i_1, \ldots, i_n < \infty} g_{i_1 \ldots i_n} x_1^{i_1} \ldots x_n^{i_n}; \qquad g_{i_1 \ldots i_n} \in \mathbf{C},$$

is another Laurent series such that $f(a) = g(a)$ for all a in a nonempty open annular polycylinder in $\mathbf{D}(f) \cap \mathbf{D}(g)$ then $f_{i_1 \ldots i_n} = g_{i_1 \ldots i_n}$ for all $i_1, \ldots, i_n$.

Next we prove

(6.2) *Let Z be a nonempty open annular polycylinder in $\mathbf{C}^n\{x_1, \ldots, x_n\}$ and let $\bar{Z}$ be the closure of Z in $\mathbf{C}^n$. Let F be a holomorphic function on a neighborhood of $\bar{Z}$ in $\mathbf{C}^n$. Then F has a Laurent expansion in Z, i.e., there exists a Laurent series f such that $Z \subset \mathbf{D}(f)$ and $f(a) = F(a)$ for all $z \in Z$.*

PROOF. There exist $0 \leqq A_j^{(-1)} < A_j^{(1)}$ such that

$$\bar{Z} = \{x \in \mathbf{C}^n: A_j^{(-1)} \leqq |x_j| \leqq A_j^{(1)};\ \ j = 1,..., n\}.$$

Relabel $x_1,..., x_n$ so that $A_j^{(-1)} \neq 0$ for $j \leqq m$, and $A_j^{(-1)} = 0$ for $j > m$. Since F is holomorphic on a neighborhood of $\bar{Z}$, we may replace Z by the interior of $\bar{Z}$. Then

$$Z = \{x \in \mathbf{C}^n: A_j^{(-1)} < |x_j| < A_j^{(1)} \text{ for } j \leqq m,\ \ |x_j| < A_j^{(1)} \text{ for } j > m\}.$$

Let $\Gamma_j^{(-1)}$ and $\Gamma_j^{(1)}$ be the circles in $\mathbf{C}^1\{\xi_j\}$ around the origin of radii $A_j^{(-1)}$ and $A_j^{(1)}$, respectively. Let

$$\Lambda = \{\lambda = (\lambda_1,..., \lambda_n): \lambda_j = \pm 1 \text{ for } j \leqq m \quad \text{and} \quad \lambda_j = 1 \text{ for } j > m\}$$
$$= \text{a set of } 2^m \text{ vectors.}$$

Let $\Gamma^{(\lambda)} = \Gamma_1^{(\lambda_1)} \times ... \times \Gamma_n^{(\lambda_n)}$. Repeatedly applying the one variable Cauchy formulas (4.2.4, 4.2.5) and then converting the repeated integrals into multiple integrals, we get

$$1°) \qquad F(x) = \frac{1}{(2\pi i)^n} \sum_{\lambda \in \Lambda} \lambda_1 ... \lambda_n \int_{\Gamma^{(\lambda)}} \frac{F(\xi)}{(\xi_1 - x_1)...(\xi_n - x_n)}\, d\xi$$

for all $x \in Z$. Fix $x \in Z$. By geometric series expansion we get

$$2°) \qquad \frac{1}{\xi_j - x_j} = \sum_{0 \leqq k_j < \infty} \frac{x_j^{k_j}}{\xi_j^{k_j + 1}}$$

with absolute uniform convergence on $\Gamma_j^{(1)}$; and

$$3°) \qquad \frac{1}{\xi_j - x_j} = \sum_{-\infty < k_j < 0} \frac{-x_j^{k_j}}{\xi_j^{k_j + 1}}$$

with absolute uniform convergence on $\Gamma_j^{(-1)}$. Let $\lambda \in \Lambda$ be given. Since $F(\xi)$ is continuous on the compact set $\Gamma^{(\lambda)}$, its absolute value is bounded there. Take 2°) if $\lambda_j = 1$ and 3°) if $\lambda_j = -1$. Multiplying out these n series, and then multiplying both sides by $\lambda_1 ... \lambda_n F(\xi)/(2\pi i)^n$ we get

$$\frac{\lambda_1 ... \lambda_n}{(2\pi i)^n} \frac{F(\xi)}{(\xi_1 - x_1)...(\xi_n - x_n)}$$
$$= \frac{1}{(2\pi i)^n} \sum_{\substack{0 \leqq k_j < \infty \text{ if } \lambda_j = 1 \\ -\infty < k_j < 0 \text{ if } \lambda_j = -1}} \frac{F(\xi)}{\xi_1^{k_1 + 1} ... \xi_n^{k_n + 1}} x_1^{k_1} ... x_n^{k_n}$$

with absolute uniform convergence on $\Gamma^{(\lambda)}$. Integrating term by term, then summing over all λ in Λ, and then applying 1°) to the left-hand side we get

$$F(x) = \frac{1}{(2\pi i)^n} \sum_{\lambda \in \Lambda} \sum_{\substack{0 \leq k_j < \infty \text{ if } \lambda_j = 1 \\ -\infty < k_j < 0 \text{ if } \lambda_j = -1}} f^{(\lambda)}_{k_1 \dots k_n} x_1^{k_1} \dots x_n^{k_n}.$$

where

$$f^{(\lambda)}_{k_1 \dots k_n} = \int_{\Gamma^{(\lambda)}} \frac{F(\xi)}{\xi_1^{k_1+1} \dots \xi_n^{k_n+1}} \, d\xi.$$

By §3, this expansion is absolutely locally uniformly convergent on $Z\{x\}$.

(6.3) LAURENT EXPANSION IN A REINHARDT DOMAIN. *Let X be a Reinhardt domain in $\mathbf{C}^n\{x_1, \dots, x_n\}$ and let F be a holomorphic function on X. Then F has a unique Laurent expansion in X, i.e., there exist unique elements $f_{i_1 \dots i_n}$ in $\mathbf{C}$ such that for the Laurent series*

$$f = \sum_{-\infty < i_1, \dots, i_n < \infty} f_{i_1 \dots i_n} x_1^{i_1} \dots x_n^{i_n}$$

we have that $X \subset \mathbf{D}(f)$ and $f(a) = F(a)$ for all $a \in X$. Hence in particular, $f_{i_1 \dots i_n} = 0$ if for some j: $i_j < 0$ and there exists $a \in X$ with $a_j = 0$. Let $A_1 > 0, \dots, A_n > 0$ be such that $(A_1, \dots, A_n) \in X$. Let Γ_j be the circle in $\mathbf{C}^1\{x_j\}$ of radius A_j around the origin. Let $\Gamma = \Gamma_1 \times \dots \times \Gamma_n$. Then

$$f_{i_1 \dots i_n} = \frac{1}{(2\pi i)^n} \int_{\Gamma} \frac{f(x)}{x_1^{i_1+1} \dots x_n^{i_n+1}} \, dx.$$

PROOF. Since X is Reinhardt, for any $y \in X$ there exists an open annular polycylinder $Z(y)$, (always around the origin), such that $y \in Z(y) \subset X$. By (6.2) there exists a Laurent series

$$f^{(y)} = \sum_{-\infty < i_1, \dots, i_n < \infty} f^{(y)}_{i_1 \dots i_n} x_1^{i_1} \dots x_n^{i_n}; \qquad f^{(y)}_{i_1 \dots i_n} \in \mathbf{C};$$

such that $Z(y) \subset \mathbf{D}(f^{(y)})$ and $f^{(y)}(a) = F(a)$ for all $a \in Z(y)$. Let $f = f^{(A)}$. Uniqueness and the formula for $f_{i_1 \dots i_n}$ follow by applying (6.1) to F in $Z(A)$. To prove the existence, it is enough to show that for all $y \in X$, $f^{(y)}_{i_1 \dots i_n} = f_{i_1 \dots i_n}$ for all $i_1, \dots, i_n$. Given $y \in X$, join A to y by an arc γ in X. γ being compact, we can find $y^{(0)}, \dots, y^{(p)} \in X$ such that $A = y^{(0)}$, $y = y^{(p)}$, and $Z(y^{(q)}) \cap Z(y^{(q+1)}) \neq \emptyset$ for $q = 0, \dots, p-1$. By (6.1) it follows that for $q = 0, \dots, p-1$:

$$f^{(y^{(q)})}_{i_1\ldots i_n} = f^{(y^{(q+1)})}_{i_1\ldots i_n} \quad \text{for all} \quad i_1,\ldots, i_n.$$

Therefore $f^{(y)}_{i_1\ldots i_n} = f_{i_1\ldots i_n}$ for all $i_1,\ldots, i_n$.

(6.4) DEFINITION. **1)** In the situation of (6.3) let $\tilde{X}$ denote the logarithmically convex hull of X. Then $\tilde{X} \subset \mathbf{D}(f)$ by (3.8.1), and hence f defines a holomorphic function F^* on $\tilde{X}$ such that $F^*|X = F$. Let F' be any holomorphic function on $\tilde{X}$. By (6.3), F' has a Laurent expansion in $\tilde{X}$; if $F'|X = F|X$ then by (6.1) $F' = F^*$ on entire $\tilde{X}$. To state this result we introduce the following definition.

2) *Let X be any domain in* $\mathbf{C}^n$. Then X is a *domain of holomorphy* $\Leftrightarrow$ there exists a holomorphic function F on X which cannot be extended, i.e., if F^* is a holomorphic function on a domain X^* in $\mathbf{C}^n$ with $X \subset X^*$ and $F^*|X = F$ then necessarily $X^* = X$.

X is a weak domain of holomorphy
$\Leftrightarrow$ [$y \in \operatorname{bd} X \Rightarrow$ there exists a holomorphic function F on X which cannot be extended near y, i.e., if F^* is a holomorphic function on a domain X^* in $\mathbf{C}^n$ with $X \subset X^*$ and $F^*|X = F$ then necessarily $y \notin X^*$].

Note that obviously: X domain of holomorphy $\Rightarrow X$ weak domain of holomorphy. In the next section we shall show that the converse is also true. Here bd X denotes the boundary of X in $\mathbf{C}^n$.

What we have proved in 1) is this.

(6.4) *Let X be a Reinhardt domain in* $\mathbf{C}^n$. *Let $\tilde{X}$ be the logarithmically convex hull of X. Every holomorphic function F on X can uniquely be extended to a holomorphic function on $\tilde{X}$. If $\tilde{X} \neq X$, i.e., either if X is not relatively complete or if X is not logarithmically convex, then X is not a domain of holomorphy.*

Let us anticipate the following which will be proved in the next section.

Theorem of Cartan-Thullen. A domain X in $\mathbf{C}^n$ is a domain of holomorphy $\Leftrightarrow X$ is holomorphically convex.

Using the "$\Leftarrow$" part of this, we can now characterize domains of convergence of Laurent series and in particular of power series. In any case we know that such a domain is necessarily a relatively complete Reinhardt domain.

(6.5) *Let X be a relatively complete Reinhardt domain in $\mathbf{C}^n$.*

1) *The following five conditions are equivalent.*

i) *X is the domain of convergence of a Laurent series.*
ii) *X is a logarithmically convex.*
iii) *X is monomial convex.*
iv) *X is holomorphically convex.*
v) *X is a domain of holomorphy.*

2) *X is the domain of convergence of a power series if and only if X is complete and satisfies any one of the conditions* ii), iii), iv), v).

3) *If X is convex* (as a subset of $\mathbf{R}^{2n} = \mathbf{C}^n$) *then conditions* i) *to* v) *hold.*

PROOF. 2) follows from 1). By (5.17), X convex $\Rightarrow$ X holomorphically convex and hence 1) yields 3). Thus it suffices to prove 1). In (3.5), (5.16), (5.15) we have, respectively, proved that i) $\Rightarrow$ ii), ii) $\Rightarrow$ iii), iii) $\Rightarrow$ iv). By "$\Leftarrow$" of Cartan-Thullen we have iv) $\Rightarrow$ v). Thus it suffices to show that v) $\Rightarrow$ i). In proving that v) $\Rightarrow$ i) we shall also get a direct proof of v) $\Rightarrow$ ii).

So assume that there exists a holomorphic function F on X which cannot be extended. Let $\tilde{X}$ be the logarithmically convex hull of X. By (6.4), F can be extended on $\tilde{X}$ and hence $X = \tilde{X}$, i.e., X is logarithmically convex. Let f be the Laurent series of F in X. Then the function defined by f on $\mathbf{D}(f)$ is an extension of F. Hence $X = \mathbf{D}(f)$.

As a corollary of (6.3) or (6.4) we get

(6.6) *Let Z be an open set in $\mathbf{C}^n\{x_1,..., x_n\}$ and let $a \in Z$. Let $V = \{x \in Z: x_j = a_j$ for $j = 1,..., d\}$ where $2 \leqq d \leqq n$. Let F be a holomorphic function on $Z - V$. Then F has a unique holomorphic extension to Z.*

PROOF. Uniqueness is obvious since Z = closure of $Z - V$ in Z. Let $b \in V$ be given near which we want to extend F. By a translation, bring b to the origin. Then $V = \{x \in Z: x_1 = ... = x_d = 0\}$. Take $A > 0$ such that $\tilde{X} = \{x \in \mathbf{C}^n: |x_j| \leqq A$ for $j = 1,..., n\} \subset Z$. Let $X = \tilde{X} - V$. By (6.3), F has a Laurent expansion

$$f = \sum f_{i_1...i_n} x_1^{i_1}...x_n^{i_n}$$

in X. Since $d \geqq 2$, for any $j \leqq n$ we have: X contains a point $y^{(j)}$ with $y_j^{(j)} = 0$, whence $f_{i_1...i_n} = 0$ whenever $i_j < 0$. Thus f is a power series and defines a holomorphic function F^* on $\tilde{X}$. F^* is obviously a holomorphic extension of $F|X$ to $\tilde{X}$.

Aliter. Since $d \geqq 2$, we have: if X' is a relatively complete Reinhardt set in $\mathbf{C}^n$ with $X \subset X'$, then $\tilde{X} \subset X'$. Obviously $\tilde{X}$ is a relatively complete logarithmically convex Reinhardt domain, whence $\tilde{X}$ = logarithmically convex hull of X. Hence by (6.4), $F|X$ has a holomorphic extension to $\tilde{X}$.

Taking $d = n$ in (6.6) we get

(6.7) *A holomorphic function of more than one complex variable cannot have an isolated singularity, i.e.: Let Z be a domain in $\mathbf{C}^n$, $n > 1$, $a \in Z$, and F holomorphic on $Z - \{a\}$. Then there exists a unique holomorphic function F^* on Z such that $F^*|(Z - \{a\}) = F$.*

(6.8) Remark. Whatever we have said about Laurent series and Reinhardt domains (around the origin) is valid for Laurent series and Reinhardt domains around an arbitrary point x^*. To do this, either replace x_j by $x_j - x_j^*$, $(j = 1, \ldots, n)$, everywhere in the statements and proofs, or bring x^* to the origin by a translation and use the results around the origin.

(6.9) Examples. We end this section by illustrating (6.4) by pictures in the absolute plane of $|x_1|$, $|x_2|$, $(n = 2)$.

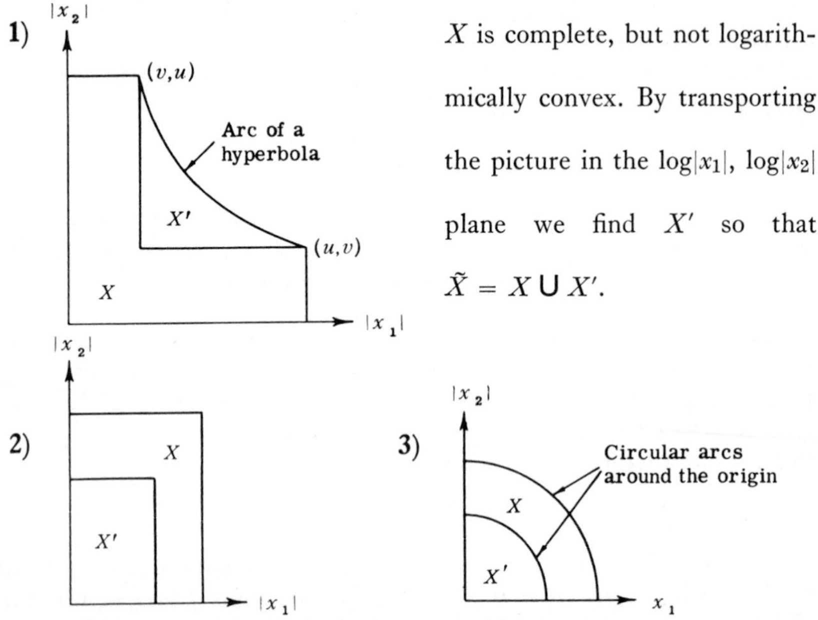

1) X is complete, but not logarithmically convex. By transporting the picture in the $\log|x_1|$, $\log|x_2|$ plane we find X' so that $\tilde{X} = X \cup X'$.

In 2) and 3): X is not relatively complete; $X \cup X'$ is the smallest relatively complete Reinhardt domain containing X; $X \cup X'$ is convex (in $\mathbf{R}^4 = \mathbf{C}^2$)

and hence by (6.5), $\tilde{X} = X \cup X'$. In 1), 2), and 3): X has points on $x_1 = 0$ and on $x_2 = 0$; hence the Laurent expansion of F in X is a power series.

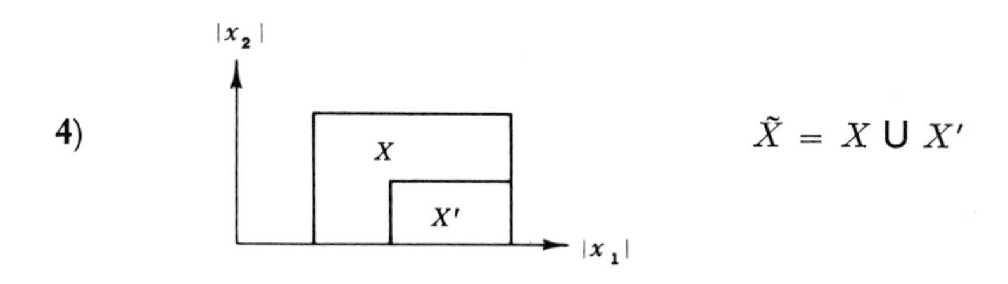

§7. DOMAINS OF HOLOMORPHY

(7.1) THEOREM OF CARTAN-THULLEN.[1] *For any domain X in $\mathbf{C}^n\{x_1,\ldots, x_n\}$ the following three conditions are equivalent.*

i) *X is a domain of holomorphy.*
ii) *X is a weak domain of holomorphy.*
iii) *X is holomorphically convex.*

Obviously i) $\Rightarrow$ ii). Hence enough to show that ii) $\Rightarrow$ iii) and iii) $\Rightarrow$ i). Let Φ denote the set of all holomorphic functions on X. For any $Y \subset X$ let $\tilde{Y}$ denote the holomorphic convex hull of Y in X, i.e.,

$$\tilde{Y} = \{x \in X: \forall\ \varphi \in \Phi,\ |\varphi(x)| \leqq \sup|\varphi(Y)|\}.$$

Recall that, by definition, X is holomorphically convex $\Leftrightarrow$ $\tilde{Y}$ is compact for every compact subset Y of X.

Proof of ii) $\Rightarrow$ iii). Otherwise there exists Y compact $\subset X$ such that $\tilde{Y}$ is not compact. Since Y is compact, we can find $A > 0$ such that $|x_j| \leqq A$ for $j = 1,\ldots, n$, for all $x \in Y$. Since $x_j \in \Phi$, we deduce that $|x_j| \leqq A$ for $j = 1,\ldots, n$, for all $x \in \tilde{Y}$. Therefore $\tilde{Y}$ is bounded. Since $\tilde{Y}$ is not compact, we can find a sequence in $\tilde{Y}$ having no limit point there. Since $\tilde{Y}$ is bounded, this sequence has a subsequence converging to $y \in \mathbf{C}^n$. Since $\tilde{Y}$ is closed in X, y must be on the boundary of X in $\mathbf{C}^n$. Hence by assumption, we can find $f \in \Phi$ such that f cannot be continued near y. Choose $D > 0$ such that

$$Y_D = \bigcup_{y \in Y} \{x \in \mathbf{C}^n: |x_1 - y_1| \leqq D,\ldots, |x_n - y_n| \leqq D\} \subset X.$$

Then Y_D is compact and hence $M = \sup|f(Y_D)| < \infty$. By Thullen's lemma (4.6), for all $k_1,\ldots, k_n \geqq 0$,

[1] Cartan-Thullen [**1**].

$$\sup \left| \frac{\partial^{k_1+\dots+k_n} f}{\partial^{k_1} x_1 \dots \partial^{k_n} x_n} (Y) \right| \leqq \frac{k_1! \dots k_n! M}{D^{k_1+\dots+k_n}}.$$

Now

$$\frac{\partial^{k_1+\dots+k_n} f}{\partial^{k_1} x_1 \dots \partial^{k_n} x_n} \in \Phi$$

and hence

$$\sup \left| \frac{\partial^{k_1+\dots+k_n} f}{\partial^{k_1} x_1 \dots \partial^{k_n} x_n} (\tilde{Y}) \right| = \sup \left| \frac{\partial^{k_1+\dots+k_n} f}{\partial^{k_1} x_1 \dots \partial^{k_n} x_n} (Y) \right|.$$

Since y is in the closure of $\tilde{Y}$ in $\mathbf{C}^n$, we can find $y^* \in \tilde{Y}$ such that

$$y \in Z = \{x \in \mathbf{C}^n : |x_j - y_j^*| < D; j = 1, \dots, n\}.$$

For the Taylor series

$$f(x_1, \dots, x_n) = \sum_{k_1, \dots, k_n \geqq 0} f_{k_1 \dots k_n} (x_1 - y_1^*)^{k_1} \dots (x_n - y_n^*)^{k_n}$$

of f around y^* we have

$$f_{k_1 \dots k_n} = \frac{1}{k_1! \dots k_n!} \frac{\partial^{k_1+\dots+k_n} f}{\partial^{k_1} x_1 \dots \partial^{k_n} x_n} (y^*)$$

and hence

$$|f_{k_1 \dots k_n}| D^{k_1+\dots+k_n} \leqq M \qquad \text{for all} \quad k_1, \dots, k_n \geqq 0.$$

Therefore Z is contained in the domain of convergence of the Taylor series and hence the latter defines a holomorphic function f' on Z such that $f'|Z \cap X = f|Z \cap X$. Thus

$$f^* = \begin{cases} f & \text{on } X \\ f' & \text{on } Z \end{cases}$$

is a holomorphic extension of f to $X \cup Z$, and $y \in Z$. Contradiction.

Proof of iii) $\Rightarrow$ i). We want to prove the existence of $f \in \Phi$ such that f cannot be extended to a holomorphic function on any larger domain. If $X = \mathbf{C}^n$ then we may take $f \equiv 0$. Now assume that $X \neq \mathbf{C}^n$. Fix a sequence $(x^{(p)})$ which is everywhere dense in X, [for instance all points in X with rational coordinates]. Let $A_p > 0$ be maximum such that

$$Z_p = \{x \in \mathbf{C}^n : |x_j - x_j^{(p)}| < A_p; j = 1, \dots, n\} \subset X.$$

Since $X \neq \mathbf{C}^n$, we must have $A_p < \infty$. Fix a sequence of compact sets $Y_1 \subset Y_2 \subset \ldots \subset X$ such that

$$X = \bigcup_{p=1}^{\infty} \operatorname{int} Y_p$$

and $\operatorname{int} Y_1 \neq \emptyset$; [for instance, let

$$Y_p = \bigcup_{q=1}^{p} \{x \in \mathbf{C}^n : |x_j - x_j^{(q)}| \leqq A_q/2; j = 1, \ldots, n\}].$$

Since A_p is maximal and $\tilde{Y}_p$ is compact, we get that $Z_p \not\subset \tilde{Y}_p$. Fix $y^{(p)} \in Z_p, y^{(p)} \notin \tilde{Y}_p$. By the definition of $\tilde{Y}_p$, there exists $g^{(p)} \in \Phi$ such that

$$|g^{(p)}(y^{(p)})| > \sup|g^{(p)}(Y_p)|.$$

Fix a large enough positive integer N_p such that for

$$f^{(p)}(x) = [g^{(p)}(x)/g^{(p)}(y^{(p)})]^{N_p}$$

we have

$$|[1 - f^{(p)}(x)]^p - 1| < 2^{-p} \qquad \text{for all} \quad x \in Y_p.$$

Then $f^{(p)} \in \Phi$ and $f^{(p)}(y^{(p)}) = 1$. Let

$$f(x) = \prod_{p=1}^{\infty} [1 - f^{(p)}(x)]^p.$$

For all $p \geqq r \geqq 1$ we have $Y_r \subset Y_p$ and hence:

$$[1 - f^{(p)}(x)]^p \qquad \text{is nowhere zero on } Y_r,$$

and

$$\sum_{p=r}^{\infty} |[1 - f^{(p)}(x)]^p - 1| \qquad \text{is uniformly convergent on } Y_r.$$

Therefore by (4.9.3), f is holomorphic on X, and

$$\mathbf{o}_{y^{(p)}} f(x) \geqq \mathbf{o}_{y^{(p)}} [1 - f^{(p)}(x)]^p \geqq p.$$

Suppose if possible that f has a holomorphic extension f^* to a domain $X^* \supset X$ with $X^* \neq X$. Since X^* is a domain, a point a of X can be joined to a point b of X^*, $b \notin X$, by an arc γ in X^*. The "first point" y of γ which is not in X is then a boundary point of X. Let $N = \mathbf{o}_y f^*$. Now f and hence f^* is nowhere zero in Y_1, and $\operatorname{int} Y_1 \neq \emptyset$. Therefore by the identity theorem (2.5), $N < \infty$. By (2.4), $\mathbf{o}_z f^* \leqq N$ for all z in some neighborhood of y in X^*. Since $\mathbf{o}_{y^{(p)}} f^* \geqq p$, we shall reach a contradiction if we show that

y is a limit point of the sequence $(y^{(p)})$, i.e., if we show that: given $B > 0$, there exists p such that $|y_j - y_j^{(p)}| < B$ for $j = 1,\dots, n$. Since $y \in \operatorname{bd} X$ and the sequence $(x^{(p)})$ is everywhere dense in X, there exists p such that $|y_j - x_j^{(p)}| < B/2$ for $j = 1,\dots, n$. Since $y \notin X$, we must have $A_p < B/2$. Since $y^{(p)} \in Z_p$, we then get

$$|y_j - y_j^{(p)}| \leqq |y_j - x_j^{(p)}| + |x_j^{(p)} - y_j^{(p)}| < B/2 + B/2 = B$$

for $j = 1,\dots, n$. Q.E.D.

(7.2) REMARKS.

1) COROLLARY. *Every domain X in $\mathbf{C}^1\{x\}$ is a domain of holomorphy (and is hence holomorphically convex).* In view of the Theorem (7.1), it is enough to show that X is a weak domain of holomorphy. Given $a \in \operatorname{bd} X$, the function $1/(x - a)$ is holomorphic on X and cannot be continued near a.

2) Classical proof of the above corollary is thus: Take a sequence $(y^{(p)})$ in X which has no limit point in X but has every boundary point of X as a limit point. By Weierstrass' theorem on zeroes, there exists a holomorphic function f on X whose zeroes are exactly at the points $(y^{(p)})$. Obviously f cannot be extended outside X. Note the resemblance of the usual proof of the said theorem of Weierstrass and the proof of iii) $\Rightarrow$ i) given above.

3) Contrary to the one variable case, already by examples of Reinhardt domains we have shown (§6) that a domain in $\mathbf{C}^n$, $n > 1$, need not be a domain of holomorphy. Historically this was one point of departure for investigations in the theory of several complex variables.

4) One application and hence motivation of (7.1) has been given in §6 in characterizing domains of convergence of Laurent series. The significance of (7.1) goes much deeper. From the point of view of function theory, domains of holomorphy are natural objects of study as they are the *exact* domains of definition of holomorphic functions. However, their definition is relative to the embedding space $\mathbf{C}^n$. On the other hand, holomorphic convexity is an intrinsic property. It is also the basic axiom in the definition of a Stein manifold. Very approximately speaking, a Stein manifold is a complex manifold on which generalizations of the theorem of Weierstrass (existence of holomorphic functions with prescribed zeroes) and of the theorem of Mittag–Leffler (existence of meromorphic functions with prescribed principal parts, i.e., negative parts of

Laurent expansions) usually hold. Stein manifolds are generalizations of domains of holomorphy. For the theory of Stein manifolds see the works of Cartan and Oka listed in the Bibliography. We hope to give an introduction to this theory in the second volume of this book.

§8. A THEOREM OF RADÓ

In 1924, Radó [**1**] proved the following very useful theorem.

(**8.1**) *Let X be an open set in $\mathbf{C}^1$ and let $f\colon X \to \mathbf{C}$ be continuous such that f is holomorphic when it is not zero, i.e., f is holomorphic on $X - f^{-1}(0)$. Then f is holomorphic on X.*

Since a continuous function of n complex variables is holomorphic if it is holomorphic in each variable, from (8.1) we at once get

(**8.2**) *Let X be an open set in $\mathbf{C}^n$ and let $f\colon X \to \mathbf{C}^n$ be continuous such that f is holomorphic on $X - f^{-1}(0)$. Then f is holomorphic on X.*

In 1956, Heinz [**1**] gave a simple proof of (8.1) using harmonic functions. We shall follow his proof.

Notation. As we have to split the complex variable into real and imaginary parts, we shall denote it by z; $z = x + iy$, $x = \mathbf{Re}\, z$, $y = \mathbf{Im}\, z$, $\bar{z} = (\text{conjugate of } z) = x - iy$. Partial derivatives will be indicated by subscripts. For any $A \subset \mathbf{R}^2\{x, y\} = \mathbf{C}^1\{z\}$, $\hat{A}$ will denote the closure of A in $\mathbf{R}^2$, and $\mathring{A}$ will denote the boundary of A in $\mathbf{R}^2$.

$$Z = \{z\colon |z| < 1\}, \qquad \hat{Z} = \{z\colon |z| \leqq 1\}.$$
$$X = \text{a nonempty open set in } \mathbf{C}^1\{z\}.$$

Initial remark on (8.1). Let $a \in X$ be given near which we want to show f to be holomorphic. By a translation, bring a to the origin. Replacing f by $f(\alpha z)$ where α is a suitable nonzero complex constant, we may assume that $\hat{Z} \subset X$. Then $|f|$ is bounded on $\hat{Z}$. Replacing f by βf, where β is a suitable nonzero complex constant, we may assume that $\sup |f(\hat{Z})| \leqq 1$. Thus it suffices to prove

(**8.3**) *Let $f\colon \hat{Z} \to \mathbf{C}$ be continuous such that $f|(Z - f^{-1}(0))$ is holomorphic. Then $f|Z$ is holomorphic.*

For the sake of completeness we start with a résumé on harmonic functions. $F\colon X \to \mathbf{R}$ is harmonic $\Leftrightarrow$ (def) F has continuous partials of order $\leqq 2$ on X and $F_{xx} + F_{yy} \equiv 0$ on X. $f\colon X \to \mathbf{C}$ is harmonic $\Leftrightarrow$ (def) $\mathbf{Re}\, f$ and $\mathbf{Im}\, f$ are harmonic on X. Note that obviously, f is harmonic $\Leftrightarrow \bar{f}$ is harmonic. The following is well known.

(8.4) *Let $f: X \to \mathbf{C}$ have continuous partials of order $\leqq 2$. Let $f = u + iv$, $u = \mathbf{Re}\, f$, $v = \mathbf{Im}\, f$. Then* (Cauchy-Riemann equations): *f is holomorphic on $X \Leftrightarrow u_x = v_y$ and $u_y = -v_x$ on X; and hence: f is holomorphic on $X \Rightarrow u$ and v are harmonic on X. Conversely, given u: $X \to \mathbf{R}$ harmonic, there exists v: $X \to \mathbf{R}$ harmonic such that $f = u + iv$ is holomorphic on X.*

For $f = u + iv$ we have $f_x = u_x + iv_x$, $f_y = u_y + iv_y$, and hence $f_x + if_y = (u_x - v_y) + i(u_y + v_x)$. Thus the Cauchy-Riemann equations can be expressed as

(8.5) *Let f: $X \to \mathbf{C}$ have continuous partials of order $\leqq 2$. Then: f is holomorphic on $X \Leftrightarrow f_x + if_y \equiv 0$ on X.*

Now let

$$h = \overline{f_x + if_y}\ ;$$

then

$$h_x = \overline{f_{xx} + if_{xy}}$$

and

$$ih_y = i(\overline{f_{xy} + if_{yy}}) = \overline{-if_{xy} + f_{yy}}\ ;$$

whence

$$h_x + ih_y = \overline{f_{xx} + f_{yy}}\,.$$

Therefore (8.5) yields

(8.6) *If f: $X \to \mathbf{C}$ is harmonic then $\overline{f_x + if_y}$ is holomorphic on X.*

Since every real valued harmonic function is the real part of a holomorphic function, and since $w \to \mathbf{Re}\, w$ is an open map of $\mathbf{C}$ onto $\mathbf{R}$, from the open map theorem for holomorphic functions (4.12.3), we get

(8.7) Open Map Theorem. *If F: $X \to \mathbf{R}$ is harmonic, X is connected, and F is nonconstant on X, then F is an open map of X into $\mathbf{R}$.*

Now the continuous image of a connected set is connected, and the only open connected subsets of $\mathbf{R}$ are open segments. Therefore (8.7) yields

(8.8) Maximum Principle. *If F: $X \to \mathbf{R}$ is harmonic, X is connected, and $F(a) = \sup F(X)$ for some $a \in X$, then F is constant on X.*

From this we deduce

(8.9) MAXIMUM PRINCIPLE. *Let $F\colon X \to \mathbf{R}$ be harmonic, X bounded, $M \in \mathbf{R}$. Assume that:*

i) $$a_n \in X,\ a_n \to a \in \mathring{X} \Rightarrow \limsup_{n\to\infty} F(a_n) \leqq M.$$

Then $\sup F(X) \leqq M$.

First we claim that for any connected component Y of X we have: Y is open and bounded, and

1′) $$a_n \in Y,\ a_n \to a \in \mathring{Y} \Rightarrow \limsup_{n\to\infty} F(a_n) \leqq M.$$

X being bounded so is Y; X being locally arcwise connected, Y is open. In view of assumption i), to prove 1′) it suffices to show that $\mathring{Y} \subset \mathring{X}$. Let $t \in \mathring{Y}$. Since $Y \subset X$, we must have $t \in \hat{X}$. Suppose if possible that $t \notin \mathring{X}$. Then $t \in X$. Consequently, X contains an open disk H around t. Since H and Y are both connected and $H \cap Y \neq \emptyset$, we get that $H \cup Y$ is connected. Since Y is a connected component of X, we must have $H \subset Y$ and hence $t \in Y$. Contradiction.

Suppose we have proved (8.9) for the case when X is connected. Then in view of the above observation, $\sup F(Y) \leqq M$ for each connected component Y of X; hence $\sup F(X) \leqq M$. Thus we may assume that X is connected to begin with.

Since X is bounded, we have that $\hat{X}$ is compact and $\mathring{X} \neq \emptyset$. Let $N = \sup F(X)$. We want to show that $N \leqq M$. Suppose if possible that $N > M$. Since $N = \sup F(X)$, we can find $b_n \in X$ such that $F(b_n) \to N$. Since $\hat{X}$ is compact, replacing (b_n) by a subsequence, we may assume that $b_n \to b \in \hat{X}$. Since $F(b_n) \to N > M$, by assumption i) we must have $b \notin \mathring{X}$. Thus $b \in X$. Since F is continuous on X, we get $N = F(b) < \infty$. Since $N = \sup F(X)$, (8.8) now yields that $F \equiv N$ on X. Since $\mathring{X} \neq \emptyset$ we can find $a_n \in X$ such that $a_n \to a \in \mathring{X}$, and then by i), $\limsup F(a_n) \leqq M$. However since $F \equiv N$ on X we get that $\limsup F(a_n) = N > M$. Contradiction.

Applying (8.9) to $-F$ we get

(8.10) MINIMUM PRINCIPLE. *Let $F\colon X \to \mathbf{R}$ be harmonic, X bounded, $M \in \mathbf{R}$. Assume that:*

i′) $$a_n \in X,\ a_n \to a \in \mathring{X} \Rightarrow \liminf_{n\to\infty} F(a_n) \geqq M.$$

Then $\inf F(X) \geqq M$.

(8.11) DIRICHLET PROBLEM. *Given* $\tilde{F}: \mathring{Z} \to \mathbf{R}$ *continuous, there exists* $F: \hat{Z} \to \mathbf{R}$ *continuous such that* $F|Z$ *is harmonic and* $F|\mathring{Z} = \tilde{F}$.

For a proof using Poisson formula, see for instance Behnke-Sommer [**1**, p. 158]. Applying (8.11) to real and imaginary parts we get

(8.12) DIRICHLET PROBLEM. *Given* $\tilde{f}|\mathring{Z} \to \mathbf{C}$ *continuous, there exists* $f: \hat{Z} \to \mathbf{C}$ *continuous such that* $f|Z$ *is harmonic and* $f|\mathring{Z} = \tilde{f}$.

Finally, let $f: X \to Y$ be holomorphic where Y is an open set in $\mathbf{C} = \mathbf{R}^2\{u, v\}$; $f = u + iv$. Let $g(u, v): Y \to \mathbf{R}$ be harmonic. Using the Cauchy-Riemann equations "$u_x = v_y$, $u_y = -v_x$", by direct computation involving chain rule, one can show that $g(u(x, y), v(x, y)): X \to \mathbf{R}$ is harmonic. In particular, since $g(u, v) = \frac{1}{2}\log(u^2 + v^2)$ is obviously harmonic on $R^2\{u, v\} - (0, 0)$ we conclude with the following.

(8.13) *Let* $f: X \to \mathbf{C}$ *be holomorphic and nowhere zero on* X. *Then* $\log|f(z)|: X \to \mathbf{R}$ *is harmonic.*

Now we shall restate and prove (8.3).

Let $f: \hat{Z} \to \mathbf{C}$ *be continuous such that:* f *is holomorphic on* $D = Z - f^{-1}(0)$; $f \not\equiv 0$ *on* Z, *i.e.,* $D \neq \emptyset$; *and* $\sup |f(\hat{Z})| \leqq 1$. *Then* f *is holomorphic on* Z.

By (8.12), there exists $g: \hat{Z} \to \mathbf{C}$ continuous such that $g|Z$ is harmonic and $g|\mathring{Z} = f|\mathring{Z}$. Now the proof is in three steps.

Step 1) $f|D = g|D$.
Step 2) $g|Z$ is holomorphic.
Step 3) $f|Z = g|Z$.

Proof of Step 3). By Step 2), g is holomorphic on Z and by Step 1), g is not $\equiv 0$ on Z. Consequently $E = Z - g^{-1}(0)$ is a nonempty arcwise connected set. Fix $a \in D$. By Step 1), $f(a) = g(a) \neq 0$ and hence $a \in E$. Suppose if possible that $f(b) \neq g(b)$ for some $b \in Z$. By Step 1), $f(b) = 0$ and hence $g(b) \neq 0$, i.e., $b \in E$. Consequently we can join a to b by an arc $\gamma: [0, 1] \to E$, $\gamma(0) = a$, $\gamma(1) = b$. Let

$$t' = \inf\{t: 0 \leqq t \leqq 1, \quad f(\gamma(t)) = 0\}.$$

Since f is continuous, we must have $0 < t'$ and $f(\gamma(t')) = 0$. Now $f(\gamma(t)) \neq 0$ for all $t < t'$. Since f and g are continuous, we can take limits as $t \to t'$, $t < t'$. This gives $f(\gamma(t')) = g(\gamma(t'))$ which is a contradiction since $f(\gamma(t')) = 0$ and $g(\gamma(t')) \neq 0$.

Proof of step 2). Let $h = \overline{g_x + ig_y}$ on Z. Since $g|Z$ is harmonic, $h|Z$ is holomorphic by (8.6). Now $f|D$ is holomorphic and hence by Step 1),

$g|D$ is holomorphic; hence $h \equiv 0$ on D by (8.5). Now [$h|Z$ is holomorphic and $h \equiv 0$ on the nonempty open subset D of Z] $\Rightarrow h \equiv 0$ on $Z \Rightarrow$ (by 8.5) $g|Z$ is holomorphic.

Proof of Step 1). Let

$$\varphi(z, t) = \mathbf{Re}[g(z) - f(z)] + t \log|f(z)|, \quad t \in \mathbf{R}, \quad z \in D.$$

Then for all t, $\varphi(z, t)$ is harmonic in $D\{z\}$. Let $s > 0$. Let $a_n \in D$, $a_n \to a \in \mathring{D}$.

Case 1°): $f(a) = 0$. Then $f(a_n) \to 0$ and hence $s \log|f(a_n)| \to -\infty$. Also $\mathbf{Re}[g(z) - f(z)]$ is bounded on $\hat{Z}$. Consequently

$$\limsup_{n\to\infty} \varphi(a_n, s) \leqq 0.$$

Case 2°): $f(a) \neq 0$. Then $a \in \mathring{Z}$. Since $f|\mathring{Z} = g|\mathring{Z}$, we get $\mathbf{Re}[g(a) - f(a)] = 0$. Since $\sup|f(\hat{Z})| \leqq 1$, we get that

$$s \log|f(a)| = p \quad \text{with} \quad -\infty < p \leqq 0.$$

Thus

$$\mathbf{Re}[g(a_n) - f(a_n)] \to 0 \quad \text{and} \quad s \log|f(a_n)| \to p \leqq 0.$$

Consequently,

$$\limsup_{n\to\infty} \varphi(a_n, s) \leqq 0.$$

Thus in either case

$$\limsup_{n\to\infty} \varphi(a_n, s) \leqq 0.$$

This is true whenever $a_n \in D$ and $a_n \to a \in \mathring{D}$. Hence by (8.9), for all $z \in D$: $\varphi(z, s) \leqq 0$. Replacing s by $-s$ and (8.9) by (8.10) we also get that for all $z \in D$: $\varphi(z, -s) \geqq 0$. Therefore for all $z \in D$ we have:

$$\log|f(z)| \leqq 0;$$

and

$$s \log|f(z)| \leqq \mathbf{Re}[g(z) - f(z)] \leqq -s \log|f(z)|; \quad s > 0.$$

Since this is so for all $s > 0$, we must have

$$\mathbf{Re}[g(z) - f(z)] = 0.$$

Replacing **Re** by **Im** we similarly get that

$$\mathbf{Im}[g(z) - f(z)] = 0 \quad \text{for all} \quad z \in D.$$

Therefore $f(z) = g(z)$ for all $z \in D$. Q.E.D.

(8.14) REMARK. Radó's theorem for several variables is a significant step in the proof of the Remmert–Stein–Thullen theorem on essential singularities of analytic sets which we shall give later on. As an application of the one variable case of Radó's theorem we can deduce the following.

1) $\mathbf{P}^1$ *is the only compactification of* $\mathbf{C}^1$. Here $\mathbf{P}^1$ denotes the complex projective line, i.e., the Riemann sphere. A compactification of a connected complex manifold X is a compact connected complex manifold $\hat{X}$ such that X is an open submanifold of $\hat{X}$.

In fact we can prove more.

2) *Let S be a one dimensional connected complex manifold such that $\mathbf{C}^1\{z\}$ is an open submanifold of S. Then either $S = \mathbf{C}^1$, or*

$$S = \mathbf{C}^1 \cup \{\infty\} = P^1.$$

First note that Radó's theorem being local, it applies to any one dimensional complex manifold. Assume that $S \neq \mathbf{C}^1$. Let o be the origin of $\mathbf{C}^1$. Let

$$f = \begin{cases} 1/z & \text{on} \quad \mathbf{C}^1 - \{o\} \\ 0 & \text{on} \quad S - \mathbf{C}^1. \end{cases}$$

Then f is continuous on $T = S - \{o\}$ and holomorphic on $\mathbf{C}^1 - \{o\}$. Hence by Radó's theorem, f is holomorphic on T. Since $f \not\equiv 0$, $T - \mathbf{C}^1 = f^{-1}(0)$ is a discrete set. Consequently (by open map theorem), in the neighborhood of each point of $T - \mathbf{C}^1$, f takes every value with small absolute value at least once. From the definition of f it is clear that f takes each non zero value exactly once in T. Therefore $T - \mathbf{C}^1$ is a single point which we denote by ∞. From the definition of f it is then clear that f maps T biholomorphically onto $\mathbf{C}^1\{w\}$, $w = f(z)$. Therefore $S = \mathbf{P}^1$.

Finally, we note that (8.1) can also be stated thus:

(8.15) *Let X be an open set in $\mathbf{C}^1$ and let $f\colon X \to \mathbf{C}$ be continuous. Assume that for each $a \in X$ we can find a neighborhood X_a of a in X and a discrete subset Y_a of $\mathbf{C}$ such that f is holomorphic on $X_a - f^{-1}(Y_a)$. Then f is holomorphic on X.*

By continuity, we can find a neighborhood X_a^* of a in X_a such that f is holomorphic on $X_a^* - f^{-1}(f(a))$. Applying (8.1) to $f^*|X_a^*$ where $f^*(z) = f(z) - f(a)$ we see that f^* is holomorphic on X_a^* and hence so is f.

§9. COMMENTS ON TOTALLY DISCONNECTED FIELDS

(9.1) Let K be a nondiscrete valued field.

1) By definition: K is archimedean $\Leftrightarrow |n| > 1$ for some integer n in K; K is nonarchimedean $\Leftrightarrow K$ is not archimedean; K is ultrametric $\Leftrightarrow |a + b| \leqq \max(|a|, |b|)$ for all $a, b \in K$. It can easily be checked that K is ultrametric $\Leftrightarrow K$ is nonarchimedean $\Leftarrow K$ is of nonzero characteristic.

2) It is obvious that **R** and **C** are archimedean. Conversely, it is a classical theorem of Ostrowski [**1**] that if K is archimedean and complete then K is topologically isomorphic either to **R** or to **C**; for a proof see also Hasse [**1**: §13].

3) Let K be nonarchimedean. From the ultrametric property one can at once deduce the following:

For $a, b \in K$ with $|a| < |b|$ we necessarily have $|a + b| = |b|$.
For $a, b \in K$; $A, B > 0$; the disks

$$\{x \in K: |x - a| < A\} \qquad \text{and} \qquad \{x \in K: |x - b| < B\}$$

are either disjoint or one contains the other.
For $a \in K^n$ $(n > 0)$, $A \in \mathbf{R}^n_{++}$, each of the polycylinders

$$\{x \in K^n: |x_j - a_j| < A_j \text{ for } j = 1,\dots, n\},$$
$$\{x \in K^n: |x_j - a_j| \leqq A_j \text{ for } j = 1,\dots, n\},$$

is open and closed (in K^n). Consequently, every point in K^n has a basis of neighborhoods which are open and closed. Thus K^n (in particular K) is totally disconnected and in particular not connected.

4) Thus if K is complete then:

K is topologically isomorphic either to **R** or to **C**
$\Leftrightarrow K$ is connected
$\Leftrightarrow K$ is not totally disconnected
$\Leftrightarrow K$ is not ultrametric.

In particular if K is complete and algebraically closed then:

K is not topologically isomorphic to **C**
$\Leftrightarrow K$ is ultrametric.

(9.2) Let K be complete nondiscrete valued, ultrametric, and algebraically closed. Take $a \in K$ such that $0 < |a| < 1$. Let $w \in K$ be a root of unity different from 1. Fix $D > 0$ such that $D < |a|$ and $D < |1 - w|$.

Let

$$X_i = \{x: |x - a^i| < D^{i+1}\}, \qquad Y_i = \{x: |x - wa^i| < D^{i+1}\},$$

$$Z = K - \bigcup_{i=1}^{\infty} X_i - \bigcup_{i=1}^{\infty} Y_i.$$

Then $X_1, X_2, \ldots, Y_1, Y_2, \ldots, Z$ are pairwise disjoint; $0 \in Z$; int $Z = Z - \{0\}$; $a^i \to 0$; and $wa^i \to 0$. Let m be any positive integer such that $m <$ characteristic of K in case this is nonzero. Let

$$f(x) = \begin{cases} (a^i/m!)x^m & \text{if} \quad x \in X_i \\ (a^{2i}/m!)x^m & \text{if} \quad x \in Y_i \\ 0 & \text{if} \quad x \in Z. \end{cases}$$

Let $f_q(x) = d^q f(x)/d^q x$. Then for all $x \in K$, $f_q(x)$ exists for all $q \leqq m$, and

$$f_q(x) = \begin{cases} [a^i/(m - q)!]x^{m-q} & \text{if} \quad x \in X_i \\ [a^{2i}/(m - q)!]x^{m-q} & \text{if} \quad x \in Y_i \\ 0 & \text{if} \quad x \in Z. \end{cases}$$

In particular,

$$f_m(x) = \begin{cases} a^i & \text{if} \quad x \in X_i \\ a^{2i} & \text{if} \quad x \in Y_i \\ 0 & \text{if} \quad x \in Z. \end{cases}$$

Consequently $f_{m+1}(x) = 0$ if $x \neq 0$. However

$$\frac{f_m(a^i) - f_m(0)}{a^i} = 1$$

and

$$\frac{f_m(wa^i) - f_m(0)}{wa^i} = \frac{a^i}{w} \to 0 \qquad \text{as} \quad i \to \infty.$$

Therefore $f_{m+1}(0)$ does not exist.

Thus f has continuous derivatives of order $\leqq m$, but $f_{m+1}(0)$ does not exist and hence f is not analytic at 0. However f is obviously analytic on $K - \{0\}$.

This shows that Riemann's theorem on removable singularities, even in the weak form (4.11.2), is not valid in K; consequently none of the stronger statements [e.g.: Radó's theorem, theorem on essential singularities of analytic sets,[1] etc.] are valid in K. Thus we may state

1) *Let K be an algebraically closed complete nondiscrete valued field. Then*

K is not totally disconnected
$\Leftrightarrow$ K is connected
$\Leftrightarrow$ Riemann's theorem holds
$\Leftrightarrow$ Radó's theorem holds
$\Leftrightarrow$ etc.

It would be interesting to get direct proofs of these statements. For instance, prove Riemann's theorem (or Radó's theorem) as a direct consequence of $\mathbf{C}$ being connected, and not using the Cauchy theory.

(9.3) Let K be complete nondiscrete valued. Let $R = K[\langle x_1,\ldots, x_n\rangle]$. For $a \in K^n$, let $S_a = \{f \in R\colon a \in \mathbf{D}(f)\}$. For $a, b \in K^n$, write $a + b$ for $(a_1 + b_1,\ldots, a_n + b_n)$, and $-a$ for $(-a_1,\ldots, -a_n)$. In (10.5.1′) we shall prove

1*) *Uniqueness of Taylor expansion*: $[f, g \in R; f(\alpha) = g(\alpha)$ for all α in some neighborhood of the origin$] \Rightarrow f = g$.

Using 1*) we want to prove the following:

1) *For any $a \in K^n$, $\boldsymbol{\tau}_a$ is a monomorphism of S_a into R.*

2) *For any $a \in K^n$, $\boldsymbol{\tau}_a$ leaves K elementwise fixed.*

3) *Let $f \in R$ be such that $f \notin K$; then for all $a \in \mathbf{D}(f)$ we have that $\boldsymbol{\tau}_a f \notin K$. Consequently, if φ is an analytic function on an open set X in K^n such that φ is nonconstant in the neighborhood of $a \in X$, then there exists a neighborhood X^* of a in X such that φ is nonconstant in the neighborhood of each point in X^*.*[2]

2) is obvious and 3) follows from 1*), 1), and 2). In (2.5) we have already proved 1) in case K is connected. Thus it only remains to prove 1) when K is ultrametric.

[1] Let $X = \bigcup_{i=1}^{\infty} X_i$. Then $K - X - \{0\}$ is open and hence X is closed in $K - \{0\}$. Thus X is a pure one dimensional analytic set in $K - \{0\}$. Let $\hat{X} = \mathrm{cl}_K X$. Then $\hat{X} = X \cup \{0\}$. Now $a^i \in \hat{X}$ and $a^i \to 0$; hence 0 is not an isolated point of $\hat{X}$. However $wa^i \to 0$ and $wa^i \notin \hat{X}$. Therefore $\hat{X}$ is not analytic at 0.

[2] φ is nonconstant in the neighborhood of a means: in every neighborhood of a, φ takes at least two distinct values.

LEMMA. *Assume that K is ultrametric. Let $f \in R$. Let $A \in \mathbf{E}^*(f)$, $a \in K^n$, $b \in K^n$ be such that $|a_k| < A_k$ and $|b_k| < A_k$ for $k = 1,\ldots, n$.*

Then

$$1') \quad a \in D(f), \qquad a + b \in D(f), \qquad b \in D(\boldsymbol{\tau}_a f), \qquad f(a + b) = (\boldsymbol{\tau}_a f)(b);$$

and

$$2') \qquad \boldsymbol{\tau}_{a+b} f = \boldsymbol{\tau}_b(\boldsymbol{\tau}_a f).$$

Suppose we have proved 1'). By (2.1) there exists $D > 0$ such that for all $\alpha \in K^n$ with $|\alpha_1| < D,\ldots, |\alpha_n| < D$ we have:

$$a + b + \alpha \in D(f), \qquad \alpha \in D(\boldsymbol{\tau}_{a+b} f), \qquad f(a + b + \alpha) = (\boldsymbol{\tau}_{a+b} f)(\alpha);$$

and

$$b + \alpha \in D(\boldsymbol{\tau}_a f), \qquad \alpha \in D(\boldsymbol{\tau}_b(\boldsymbol{\tau}_a f)), \qquad (\boldsymbol{\tau}_a f)(b + \alpha) = (\boldsymbol{\tau}_b(\boldsymbol{\tau}_a f))(\alpha).$$

Choose $D > 0$ such that furthermore $|b_k| + D < A_k$ for $k = 1,\ldots, n$. Then for all α as above, by 1'): $f(a + b + \alpha) = (\boldsymbol{\tau}_a f)(b + \alpha)$ and hence $(\boldsymbol{\tau}_{a+b} f)(\alpha) = (\boldsymbol{\tau}_b(\boldsymbol{\tau}_a f))(\alpha)$. Therefore $\boldsymbol{\tau}_{a+b} f = \boldsymbol{\tau}_b(\boldsymbol{\tau}_a f)$ by 1*). This proves 2'). For any $a \in K^n$ taking $b = -a$ in the Lemma we get that for any $f \in R$, $a \in \mathbf{D}(f) \Rightarrow -a \in \mathbf{D}(\boldsymbol{\tau}_a f)$ and $f = \boldsymbol{\tau}_{-a}(\boldsymbol{\tau}_a f)$. Therefore $\boldsymbol{\tau}_a$ is a monomorphism. This completes the proof of 1). Now it only remains to prove 1').

Proof of 1'). Obviously $a \in \mathbf{D}(f)$. Since K is ultrametric, $|a_k + b_k| < A_k$ for $k = 1,\ldots, n$ and hence $a + b \in \mathbf{D}(f)$. Take $B = (B_1,\ldots, B_n) \in \mathbf{R}^n$ such that $A_k > B_k > \max(|a_k|, |b_k|)$ for $k = 1,\ldots, n$. Let

$$f = \sum f_{j_1\ldots j_n} x_1^{j_1}\ldots x_n^{j_n}; \qquad f_{j_1\ldots j_n} \in K;$$

and let

$$F = \sum F_{j_1\ldots j_n} x_1^{j_1}\ldots x_n^{j_n} \in \mathbf{R}[[x_1,\ldots, x_n]] \quad \text{where} \quad F_{j_1\ldots j_n} = |f_{j_1\ldots j_n}|.$$

Then $B \in \mathbf{D}(F)$ and hence

$$1^\circ) \qquad \sum F_{j_1\ldots j_n} B_1^{j_1}\ldots B_n^{j_n} = F(B) < \infty.$$

Let $G = x_1\ldots x_n F \in \mathbf{R}[[x_1,\ldots, x_n]]$. Then obviously $B \in \mathbf{D}(G)$ and hence by (2.2),

$$B \in \mathbf{D}\left(\frac{\partial^n G}{\partial x_1\ldots\partial x_n}\right).$$

Now

$$\frac{\partial^n G}{\partial x_1 \dots \partial x_n} = \sum (j_1 + 1) \dots (j_n + 1) F_{j_1 \dots j_n} x_1^{j_1} \dots x_n^{j_n}$$

and hence

$$2°) \qquad \sum (j_1 + 1) \dots (j_n + 1) F_{j_1 \dots j_n} B_1^{j_1} \dots B_n^{j_n} < \infty.$$

Let

$$(1 + T)^u = \sum_{v=0}^{u} p(u, v) T^v$$

be the polynomial identity in the polynomial ring in an indeterminate T over $\mathbf{Z}$, i.e., $p(u, v) \in \mathbf{Z}$ is the ordinary binomial coefficient. Let

$$(\tau_a f) = g = \sum g_{i_1 \dots i_n} x_1^{i_1} \dots x_n^{i_n}.$$

Then

$$g_{i_1 \dots i_n} = \sum_{\substack{j_1 \geqq i_1 \\ \dots \\ \dots \\ j_n \geqq i_n}} f_{j_1 \dots j_n} \prod_{k=1}^{n} p(j_k, i_k) a_k^{j_k - i_k}.$$

K being ultrametric we get

$$|p(j_k, i_k) a_k^{j_k - i_k}| \leqq |a_k|^{j_k - i_k} \leqq B_k^{j_k - i_k}$$

and hence for all $i_1, \dots, i_n$,

$$\begin{aligned} &|g_{i_1 \dots i_n}| B_1^{i_1} \dots B_n^{i_n} \\ &\leqq \sum_{\substack{j_1 \geqq 0 \\ \dots \\ \dots \\ j_n \geqq 0}} F_{j_1 \dots j_n} B_1^{j_1} \dots B_n^{j_n} \\ &< \infty \qquad \text{by } 1°). \end{aligned}$$

Therefore $b \in \mathbf{D}(g)$. Next we want to show that the multiple series

$$3°) \qquad \sum_{\substack{j_1 \geqq 0 \\ \dots \\ \dots \\ j_n \geqq 0}} \sum_{\substack{0 \leqq i_1 \leqq j_1 \\ \dots \\ \dots \\ 0 \leqq i_n \leqq j_n}} f_{j_1 \dots j_n} \prod_{k=1}^{n} p(j_k, i_k) a_k^{j_k - i_k} b_k^{i_k}$$

is absolutely convergent. K being ultrametric we get

$$|p(j_k, i_k)a_k^{j_k-i_k}b_k^{i_k}| \leqq |a_k|^{j_k-i_k}|b_k|^{i_k} \leqq B_k^{j_k}$$

and hence

$$\begin{aligned}&\sum_{\substack{j_1\geqq 0\\ \cdots\\ \cdots\\ j_n\geqq 0}} \sum_{\substack{0\leqq i_1\leqq j_1\\ \cdots\\ \cdots\\ 0\leqq i_n\leqq j_n}} |f_{j_1\ldots j_n}\prod_{k=1}^{n} p(j_k, i_k)a_k^{j_k-i_k}b_k^{i_k}|\\ \leqq &\sum_{\substack{j_1\geqq 0\\ \cdots\\ \cdots\\ j_n\geqq 0}} (j_1+1)\ldots(j_n+1)F_{j_1\ldots j_n}B_1^{j_1}\ldots B_n^{j_n}\\ < &\ \infty \qquad \text{by } 2°).\end{aligned}$$

Thus 3°) is absolutely convergent. Summing 3°) in two ways we get that $f(a+b) = g(b)$.

CHAPTER II

Weierstrass Preparation Theorem

§10. WEIERSTRASS PREPARATION THEOREM. IDENTITY THEOREM. FINITE IDEAL BASES AND UNIQUE FACTORIZATION IN POWER SERIES RINGS. IMPLICIT FUNCTION THEOREM

(10.1) NOTATION. Let R be a nonnull ring. Let

$$f = \sum f_i x^i \in R[[x]]; \qquad f_i \in R.$$

We put

$$\deg_{x,R} f = \textit{degree of } f \textit{ in } x \textit{ relative to } R$$

$$= \begin{cases} \text{degree of } f \text{ in } x, & \text{if } 0 \neq f \in R[x]; \\ -\infty & \text{if } f = 0; \\ \infty & \text{if } f \notin R[x]. \end{cases}$$

Now suppose that $(R, \mathfrak{m})$ is a quasilocal ring. We put

$$\operatorname{wideg}_{x,R} f = \textit{Weierstrass degree of } f \textit{ in } x \textit{ relative to } R$$

$$= \begin{cases} \min i \text{ such that } f_i \notin \mathfrak{m}, & \text{if } f \notin \mathfrak{m}[[x]]; \\ \infty & \text{if } f \in \mathfrak{m}[[x]]. \end{cases}$$

By the general convention made in §1, one or both the subscripts x and R will usually be dropped when reference to them is clear from the context. f is said to be $R[x]$-*distinguished* $\Leftrightarrow d = \operatorname{wideg} f < \infty$, $f_d = 1$, and $f_i = 0$ for all $i > d$; we may express this by saying that f is a *distinguished polynomial in x (of degree d) with coefficients in R*. If by $\bar{f}$ we denote the power series in x with coefficients in the field $R/\mathfrak{m}$ obtained from f by reducing its coefficients mod $\mathfrak{m}$, then $f \to \bar{f}$ is a ring epimorphism: $R[[x]] \to (R/\mathfrak{m})[[x]]$, and $\operatorname{wideg} f = \mathbf{o}\bar{f}$. From this observation we get the following.

For any elements f, g, h in $R[[x]]$ we have:

1) $\operatorname{wideg}(fg) = (\operatorname{wideg} f) + (\operatorname{wideg} g)$.

2) $h \in \mathfrak{m}[[x]] \Leftrightarrow \operatorname{wideg} h = \infty$.

3) *h is a unit in $R[[x]]$* $\Leftrightarrow \operatorname{wideg} h = 0$.

4) *If f and g are $R[[x]]$-associates then* $\operatorname{wideg} f = \operatorname{wideg} g$.

5) *f is distinguished* $\Leftrightarrow \deg f = \operatorname{wideg} f < \infty$ *and f is monic.*[1]

6) *If f is distinguished, g is a monic polynomial in x with coefficients in R and g divides f in $R[x]$, then g is distinguished.*

(10.2) Abstract Weierstrass Preparation Theorem.[2] *Let $(R, \mathfrak{m})$ be a complete Hausdorff quasilocal integral domain, and let $f, g \in R[[x]]$.*

1) *If* $\operatorname{wideg} f < \infty$ *then there exist unique elements $q, r \in R[[x]]$ such that $g = qf + r$ and* $\deg r < \operatorname{wideg} f$.

2) *If f and g are distinguished, then f and g are $R[[x]]$-associates $\Leftrightarrow f = g$.*

3) *If f is distinguished and $g \in R[x]$, then the equation $g = qf + r$* of 1) *is the division identity in $R[x]$, i.e., $q \in R[x]$. If furthermore g is also distinguished and $r = 0$, then q is distinguished.*

4) $f \notin \mathfrak{m}[[x]] \Leftrightarrow$ *f is an $R[[x]]$-associate of a distinguished element f^*, i.e., $f = \delta f^*$ where δ is a unit in $R[[x]]$; and then f^* and δ are uniquely determined by f.*

5) *If f is distinguished and $f = f_1 \dots f_p$ with $f_1, \dots, f_p \in R[[x]]$, then f_λ is an $R[[x]]$-associate of a distinguished polynomial f_λ^*, $(\lambda = 1, \dots, p)$, and $f = f_1^* \dots f_p^*$.*

Proof of 1). Let

$$f = \sum_{i \geqq 0} f_i x^i, \qquad f_i \in R; \qquad d = \operatorname{wideg} f.$$

Let

$$f' = \sum_{0 \leqq i < d} f_i x^i, \qquad \text{and} \qquad f^* = \sum_{i \geqq d} f_i x^{i-d}.$$

Then f^* is a unit in $R[[x]]$ and $f' \in \mathfrak{m}[[x]]$. Hence $F = -f'/f^* \in \mathfrak{m}[[x]]$, and $f = (x^d - F)f^*$. Taking $Q = f^* q$ and $G = g$, our assertion becomes equivalent to the following:

[1] A monic polynomial in an indeterminate is a *nonzero* polynomial in which the coefficient of the highest degree nonzero term is 1.

[2] The original algebraic treatment of the Preparation Theorem stems from Späth [**1**].

Given $G \in R[[x]]$ *and* $F \in \mathfrak{m}[[x]]$, *there exists unique* $Q \in R[[x]]$ *such that* $\deg[G - (x^d - F)Q] < d$.

Uniqueness. Enough to show that:

$$[Q = \sum_{i \geqq 0} Q_i x^i,\ Q_i \in R,\ \deg(x^d - F)Q < d] \Rightarrow Q = 0.$$

If $Q \in \mathfrak{m}^u[[x]]$, then for any $e \geqq 0$ we get $0 =$ [coefficient of x^{d+e} in $(x^d - F)Q] = Q_e +$ terms in $\mathfrak{m}^{u+1}$, and hence $Q_e \in \mathfrak{m}^{u+1}$. Hence by induction on u we can conclude that for all $e \geqq 0$: $Q_e \in \mathfrak{m}^u$ for all $u \geqq 0$ and hence $Q_e = 0$.

Existence. Using the fact that $F \in \mathfrak{m}[[x]]$, we successively try to find $Q^{(u)} \in \mathfrak{m}^u[[x]]$ such that

$$Q = Q^{(0)} + Q^{(1)} + Q^{(2)} + \ldots,$$

i.e.,

$$\deg[G - (Q^{(0)} + Q^{(1)} + Q^{(2)} + \ldots)x^d + (Q^{(0)} + Q^{(1)} + Q^{(2)} + \ldots)F] < d;$$

using $G - Q^{(0)}x^d$ get $Q^{(0)}$, put this in $-Qx^d + QF$ and from now on forget G; now get $Q^{(1)}$ by "solving" mod $\mathfrak{m}^2$, put this in and get $Q^{(2)}$ by "solving" mod $\mathfrak{m}^3$, and so on. Explicitly, let

$$G = \sum G_i x^i, \qquad G_i \in R; \qquad F = \sum F_i x^i, \qquad F_i \in \mathfrak{m};$$

and set (successively for $u = 0, 1, 2, \ldots$):

$$1°) \quad \begin{cases} Q_e^{(0)} = G_{d+e} & \text{for all } e \geqq 0; \\ Q_e^{(u+1)} = \sum_{j=0}^{d+e} F_j Q_{d+e-j}^{(u)} & \text{for all } u \geqq 0, \quad e \geqq 0; \\ Q^{(u)} = \sum_{e \geqq 0} Q_e^{(u)} x^e & \text{for all } u \geqq 0. \end{cases}$$

Then

$$\deg[G - Q^{(0)}x^d] < \text{d}; \text{ and } \deg[-Q^{(u+1)}x^d + Q^{(u)}F] < d \quad \text{for all } u \geqq 0.$$

Since $F \in \mathfrak{m}[[x]]$, by induction on u it follows that

$$2°) \qquad Q_e^{(u)} \in \mathfrak{m}^u \qquad \text{for all} \quad u \geqq 0, \quad e \geqq 0.$$

Now take

$$Q = \sum_{u \geqq 0} Q^{(u)},$$

i.e.,

$$Q = \sum_{e \geqq 0} Q_e x^e \qquad \text{where} \qquad Q_e = \sum_{u \geqq 0} Q_e^{(u)}.$$

Proof of 2). Assume that f and g are $R[[x]]$-associates. Then $g = \delta f$ where δ is a unit in $R[[x]]$. By (10.1) $\deg g = \operatorname{wideg} g = \operatorname{wideg} f = \deg f$. Since f and g are monic, we get $\deg(f - g) < \operatorname{wideg} f$. Since

$$(0)f + (f - g) = (1 - \delta)f + 0,$$

by the uniqueness part of 1) we get $f - g = 0$.

Proof of 3). The first assertion follows from the uniqueness part of 1) and then the second assertion follows from (10.1).

Proof of 4). "$\Leftarrow$" follows from (10.1). Now assume that $d = \operatorname{wideg} f < \infty$. Taking x^d for g in 1) we get $x^d = qf + r$ with $\deg r < d$. By (10.1), $r \in \mathfrak{m}[[x]]$. Let $f^* = x^d - r$. Then f^* is a distinguished polynomial of degree d in x, and $f^* = qf$. By (10.1), q is a unit. Uniqueness follows from 2).

Proof of 5). By (10.1), $f_\lambda \notin \mathfrak{m}[[x]]$ and hence by 4), f_λ is an associate of a distinguished polynomial f_λ^*. By (10.1), $f_1^* \dots f_p^*$ is distinguished and hence by 2), $f = f_1^* \dots f_p^*$.

(10.3) WEIERSTRASS PREPARATION THEOREM. *Let*

$$f = f(x_1, \dots, x_n) = \sum f_{i_1 \dots i_n} x_1^{i_1} \dots x_n^{i_n} \in K[[x_1, \dots, x_n]]; \qquad f_{i_1 \dots i_n} \in K.$$

Let

$$d = \begin{cases} \min i_n \quad \textit{such that} \quad f_{0 \dots 0 i_n} \neq 0 & \textit{if} \quad f_{0 \dots 0 i_n} \neq 0 \quad \textit{for some } i_n; \\ \infty & \textit{if} \quad f_{0 \dots 0 i_n} = 0 \quad \textit{for all } i_n. \end{cases}$$

1) *Assume that $d < \infty$, i.e., $f(0, \dots, 0, x_n) \neq 0$. Given $g \in K[[x_1, \dots, x_n]]$ there exist unique $q \in K[[x_1, \dots, x_n]]$ and unique $r \in K[[x_1, \dots, x_{n-1}]][x_n]$ with $\deg_{x_n} r < d$ such that $g = qf + r$. For fixed f, the map $g \to r$ of $K[[x_1, \dots, x_n]]$ into itself is K-linear and continuous in the Krull topology of $K[[x_1, \dots, x_n]]$. Now assume that K is complete nondiscrete valued. If f and g are convergent then so are q and r. More precisely, given convergent f and given a neighborhood X of the origin in K^n, there exists a neighborhood X^* of the origin in K^n such that, if g is convergent in X then q and r are convergent in X^*.*

2) *If $f(0, \dots, 0, x_n) \neq 0$ then there exist unique elements f^* and δ in $K[[x_1, \dots, x_n]]$ such that, f^* is a distinguished polynomial (of degree d) in x_n with coefficients in $K[[x_1, \dots, x_{n-1}]]$, δ is a unit in $K[[x_1, \dots, x_n]]$, and $f = \delta f^*$. If K is complete nondiscrete valued and f is convergent then so are f^* and δ.*

3) *If f is a distinguished polynomial in x_n with coefficients in $K[[x_1, \dots, x_{n-1}]]$, and $g \in K[[x_1, \dots, x_{n-1}]][x_n]$, then the equation $g = qf + r$ of 1) is the*

division identity in $K[[x_1,\ldots, x_{n-1}]][x_n]$, *i.e.*, $q \in K[[x_1,\ldots, x_{n-1}]][x_n]$. *If* K *is complete nondiscrete valued then the corresponding statement with* $[\langle\ \rangle]$ *replacing* $[[\ ]]$ *holds.*

4) *Two distinguished polynomials in* x_n *with coefficients in* $K[[x_1,\ldots, x_{n-1}]]$ *are* $K[[x_1,\ldots, x_n]]$*-associates if and only if they are equal. If* K *is complete nondiscrete valued then the corresponding statement with* $[\langle\ \rangle]$ *replacing* $[[\ ]]$ *holds.*

5) *If* f *is a distinguished polynomial in* x_n *with coefficients in* $K[[x_1,\ldots, x_{n-1}]]$ *and* $f = f_1\ldots f_p$ *with* $f_1,\ldots, f_p \in K[[x_1,\ldots, x_n]]$, *then* f_λ *is a* $K[[x_1,\ldots, x_n]]$*-associate of a distinguished polynomial* f^*_λ *with coefficients in* $K[[x_1,\ldots, x_{n-1}]]$, $(\lambda = 1,\ldots, p)$, *and* $f = f^*_1\ldots f^*_p$. *If* K *is complete nondiscrete valued then the corresponding statement with* $[\langle\ \rangle]$ *replacing* $[[\ ]]$ *holds.*

6) *Assume that* K *is infinite. Let* $f_\lambda(x_1,\ldots, x_n)$, $(\lambda = 1,\ldots, p)$, *be a finite number of nonzero elements in* $K[[x_1,\ldots, x_n]]$. *Then there exists a generic*[3] *nonsingular* K*-linear transformation*

$$y_i = \sum_{j=1}^{n} a_{ij}x_j, \qquad (i = 1,\ldots, n), \qquad a_{ij} \in K$$

with $\det((a_{ij})) \neq 0$, *such that upon putting* $\tilde{f}_\lambda(y_1,\ldots, y_n) = f_\lambda(x_1,\ldots, x_n)$, *for* $\lambda = 1,\ldots, p$ *we have:*

$$\begin{aligned} &\textit{Weierstrass degree of } \tilde{f}_\lambda(y_1,\ldots, y_n) \textit{ in } y_n \textit{ relative to } K[[y_1,\ldots, y_{n-1}]] \\ &= \textit{leading degree of } f_\lambda(x_1,\ldots, x_n) \\ &< \infty. \end{aligned}$$

[3] By "generic" we mean: given

$$0 \neq P(\ldots, A_{ij},\ldots) \in K[\ldots, A_{ij},\ldots],$$

where A_{ij}, $(i, j = 1,\ldots, n)$, are indeterminates, the transformation can be chosen so that $P(\ldots, a_{ij},\ldots) \neq 0$.

By a simple calculation with determinants, one can show the following. Given

$$0 \neq P(\ldots, A_{ij},\ldots) \in K[\ldots, A_{ij},\ldots]$$

there exists $0 \neq Q(\ldots, B_{uv},\ldots) \in K[\ldots, B_{uv},\ldots]$, where B_{uv}, $(u, v = 1,\ldots, n)$, are indeterminates, such that the following holds. For any $a_{ij} \in K$ with $\det((a_{ij})) \neq 0$ let $((b_{uv}))$ be the matrix of the inverse transformation

$$x_u = \sum_{v=1}^{n} b_{uv}y_v,$$

i.e., $((a_{ij}))((b_{uv})) = n$ by n unit matrix. Then $P(\ldots, a_{ij},\ldots) = 0 \Leftrightarrow Q(\ldots, b_{uv},\ldots) = 0$. Conversely, given $0 \neq Q(\ldots, B_{uv},\ldots) \in K[\ldots, B_{uv},\ldots]$, there exists $0 \neq P(\ldots, A_{ij},\ldots) \in K[\ldots, A_{ij},\ldots]$ such that....

Thus the above definition of "generic" is symmetric in x and y.

Furthermore $\tilde{f_\lambda}(y_1,\ldots, y_n)$ *is a* $K[[y_1,\ldots, y_n]]$*-associate of a distinguished polynomial*[4] *in* y_n *with coefficients in* $K[[y_1,\ldots, y_{n-1}]]$. *If* K *is complete nondiscrete valued then the corresponding statement with* $[\langle\ \rangle]$ *replacing* $[[\ ]]$ *holds.*

Initial Remark. Note that d is the Weierstrass degree of f in x_n relative to $K[[x_1,\ldots, x_{n-1}]]$. Assume that we have proved 1); and in (10.2) take $K[[x_1,\ldots, x_{n-1}]]$ for R and x_n for x. Then:

i) 4) follows from (10.2.2).
ii) 3) follows from the uniqueness part of 1).
iii) The existence part of 2) follows from the proof of (10.2.4) after replacing (10.2.1) by 1) there; and the uniqueness part of 2) follows from 4).
iv) 5) follows from 1) and (10.2.5).
v) Consider 6). Let $0 \neq Q(\ldots, B_{uv},\ldots) \in K[\ldots, B_{uv},\ldots]$ be given where B_{uv}, $(u, v = 1,\ldots, n)$, are indeterminates. Let d_λ be the leading degree of $f_\lambda(x_1,\ldots, x_n)$ and let $F_\lambda(x_1,\ldots, x_n)$ be the leading form of $f_\lambda(x_1,\ldots, x_n)$. Let

$$\begin{aligned} &F^*_\lambda(y_1,\ldots, y_n,\ldots, B_{uv},\ldots)\\ &= F_\lambda\left(\sum_{v=1}^{n} B_{1v}y_v,\ldots, \sum_{v=1}^{n} B_{nv}y_v\right)\\ &\in K[y_1,\ldots, y_n,\ldots, B_{uv},\ldots]. \end{aligned}$$

Let $F'_\lambda(\ldots, B_{uv},\ldots) \in K[\ldots, B_{uv},\ldots]$ be the coefficient of $y_n^{d_\lambda}$ in F^*_λ considered as a polynomial in $y_1,\ldots, y_n$. Then $F'_\lambda(\ldots, B_{uv},\ldots) = F_\lambda(B_{1n}, B_{2n},\ldots B_{nn}) \neq 0$. Since K is infinite, we can find $b_{uv} \in K$ such that $\det((b_{uv})) \neq 0$, $F'_\lambda(\ldots, b_{uv},\ldots) \neq 0$ for $(\lambda = 1,\ldots, p)$, and $Q(\ldots, b_{uv},\ldots) \neq 0$. To prove the first assertion, it thus suffices to make the transformation

$$x_u = \sum_{v=1}^{n} b_{uv}y_v, \qquad (u = 1,\ldots, n).$$

The second assertion now follows from 2).

Thus it suffices to prove 1).

Proof of 1). The first assertion in 1) follows from (10.2.1). For proving the rest of 1) we shall use the notation of the proof of (10.2.1). It is clear that $g \to r$ is K-linear. Let

$$\begin{aligned} Q &= \sum Q_{i_1\ldots i_n}x_1^{i_1}\ldots x_n^{i_n}, &\quad Q_{i_1\ldots i_n} &\in K;\\ G &= \sum G_{i_1\ldots i_n}x_1^{i_1}\ldots x_n^{i_n}, &\quad G_{i_1\ldots i_n} &\in K. \end{aligned}$$

[4] Whose degree in y_n equals the leading degree of $\tilde{f_\lambda}(y_1,\ldots, y_n)$ which in turn is the same as the leading degree of $f_\lambda(x_1,\ldots, x_n)$.

Formulas (10.2.1°) tell us that given $e \geqq 0$ and $u \geqq 0$, $Q_e^{(u)}$ is a linear combination of a finite number of G_i's with coefficients in R which are known from F, i.e., from f. Consequently, in view of (10.2.2°), each $Q_{j_1\dots j_n}$ depends only on a finite number of $G_{i_1\dots i_n}$'s. This yields the continuity of $g \to r$.

Now assume that f and g are convergent. It suffices to show that Q is convergent in a neighborhood of the origin in K^n which is determined by F and the domain of convergence of G. For any

$$t = \sum t_{i_1\dots i_{n-1}} x_1^{i_1}\dots x_{n-1}^{i_{n-1}} \quad \text{with} \quad t_{i_1\dots i_{n-1}} \text{ in } K, \quad \text{and} \quad A \geqq 0,$$

we shall denote the value[5] of

$$\sum |t_{i_1\dots i_{n-1}}| A^{i_1}\dots A^{i_{n-1}}$$

by $\bar{t}(A)$. For any

$$t = \sum t_{i_1\dots i_n} x_1^{i_1}\dots x_n^{i_n} \quad \text{with} \quad t_{i_1\dots i_n} \text{ in } K, \quad \text{and} \quad A \geqq 0, B \geqq 0,$$

we shall denote the value[5] of

$$\sum |t_{i_1\dots i_n}| A^{i_1}\dots A^{i_{n-1}} B^{i_n}$$

by $\bar{t}(A, B)$.

Since f is convergent, so is F. Hence there exists $A' > 0$ such that $\bar{F}(A', A') < \infty$. Since K is nondiscrete, there exists $0 \neq a \in K$ such that $|a| > 1/A'$. Via the automorphism $\varphi(x_1,\dots x_n) \to \varphi(x_1/a,\dots, x_n/a)$ of $K[[x_1,\dots, x_n]]$, without loss of generality *we may assume that* $\bar{F}(1, 1) < \infty$. Since G is convergent, there exists $A > 0$ such that $\bar{G}(A, A) < \infty$. Fix C such that

$$0 < C < 1 \qquad \text{and} \qquad C < A.$$

Fix B such that

$$0 < B < 1, \qquad B < A, \qquad \text{and}$$

1°) $$B\bar{F}(1, 1) < C^d(1 - C).$$

Obviously

2°) $$\bar{G}_e(B) \leqq \bar{G}(B, C)/C^e \qquad \text{for all} \quad e \geqq 0.$$

Also $\bar{F}_j(1) \leqq \bar{F}(1, 1)$. Since F_j has no constant term, this yields

3°) $$\bar{F}_j(B) \leqq B\bar{F}(1, 1) \qquad \text{for all} \quad j \geqq 0.$$

By induction on u we shall show that

4°) $$\bar{Q}_e^{(u)}(B) \leqq \frac{\bar{G}(B, C)}{C^{d+e}}\left[\frac{B\bar{F}(1, 1)}{C^d(1 - C)}\right]^u \qquad \text{for all} \quad u \geqq 0, \quad e \geqq 0.$$

[5] Which may be ∞.

For $u = 0$ this follows from 2°) and (10.2.1°). Let $u \geqq 0$ and assume true for u. Then

$$
\begin{aligned}
&\bar{Q}_e^{(u+1)}(B) \\
&\leqq \sum_{j=0}^{d+e} \bar{F}_j(B)\bar{Q}_{d+e-j}^{(u)}(B) && \text{by } (10.2.1°) \\
&\leqq B\bar{F}(1, 1)\sum_{j=0}^{d+e} \bar{Q}_{d+e-j}^{(u)}(B) && \text{by } 3°) \\
&\leqq B\bar{F}(1, 1)\sum_{j=0}^{d+e}\frac{\bar{G}(B, C)}{C^{d+d+e-j}}\left[\frac{B\bar{F}(1, 1)}{C^d(1 - C)}\right]^u && \text{by induction hypothesis} \\
&= \frac{\bar{G}(B, C)}{C^{d+e}}\left[\frac{B\bar{F}(1, 1)}{C^d(1 - C)}\right]^{u+1}\left[(1 - C)\sum_{j=0}^{d+e} C^j\right]
\end{aligned}
$$

and

$$
(1 - C)\sum_{j=0}^{d+e} C^j \leqq (1 - C)\sum_{j=0}^{\infty} C^j = 1 \qquad \text{because} \quad 0 < C < 1.
$$

This completes the proof of 4°).

Let $D = B\bar{F}(1, 1)/C^d(1 - C)$. Then D is the "ratio" of the geometric series whose u^{th} term is the right hand side of 4°). By 1°), $0 < D < 1$ and hence summing 4°) as u goes from 0 to ∞ we get

5°) $$\bar{Q}_e(B) \leqq \bar{G}(B, C)/C^{d+e}(1 - D).$$

Let C^* be any real number such that $0 < C^* < C$. In view of 5°) we then get

$$
\begin{aligned}
\bar{Q}(B, C^*) &= \sum_{e=0}^{\infty} \bar{Q}_e(B)C^{*e} \\
&\leqq [\bar{G}(B, C)/C^d(1 - D)]\sum_{e=0}^{\infty} (C^*/C)^e \\
&< \infty.
\end{aligned}
$$

Therefore Q is convergent. The proof is completed by noting that B and C depend only on A. Q.E.D.

(10.4) *Given $f \in K[\langle x_1, \ldots, x_n \rangle]$, we have $\mathbf{o}(\tau_a f) \leqq \mathbf{o}f$ for all a in some neighborhood of the origin in $\mathbf{D}(f)$.*

Proof. Trivial for $f = 0$. So let $f \neq 0$ and let $\mathbf{o}f = d$. In view of (10.3.6), via a K-linear transformation, we may assume that $f = \delta f^*$ where δ is a unit in $K[\langle x_1,\ldots, x_n\rangle]$ and f^* is a distinguished polynomial of degree d in x_n with coefficients in $K[\langle x_1,\ldots, x_{n-1}\rangle]$. Since $\delta(0) \neq 0$ and $a \to \delta(a)$ is continuous, we can find a neighborhood X of the origin in $\mathbf{D}(\delta) \cap \mathbf{D}(f^*)$ such that $\delta(a) \neq 0$ for all $a \in X$. Let $a \in X$ be given. Then $(\boldsymbol{\tau}_a\delta)(0) = \delta(a) \neq 0$ and hence $\boldsymbol{\tau}_a\delta$ is a unit in $K[\langle x_1,\ldots, x_n\rangle]$. Obviously $\boldsymbol{\tau}_a f^*$ is a monic polynomial of degree d in x_n with coefficients in $K[\langle x_1,\ldots, x_{n-1}\rangle]$. Therefore $\mathbf{o}(\boldsymbol{\tau}_a f) = \mathbf{o}(\boldsymbol{\tau}_a f^*) \leqq d$.

(10.5) IDENTITY THEOREM. *Let K be complete nondiscrete valued and let $f, g \in K[\langle x_1,\ldots, x_n\rangle]$.*

1) WEAK FORM. *If $f \neq g$ then there exists a neighborhood X of the origin in $\mathbf{D}(f) \cap \mathbf{D}(g)$ such that $\{b \in X: f(b) = g(b)\}$ is nowhere dense in X, and $\boldsymbol{\tau}_a f \neq \boldsymbol{\tau}_a g$ for all $a \in X$; hence in particular,* 1′) *if $f \neq g$ then each neighborhood of the origin in K^n contains a point b at which f and g are convergent and $f(b) \neq g(b)$. If $f \neq 0$ then there exists a neighborhood X of the origin in $\mathbf{D}(f)$ such that $\{b \in X: f(b) = 0\}$ is nowhere dense in X and $\boldsymbol{\tau}_a f \neq 0$ for all $a \in X$; hence in particular, if $f \neq 0$ then each neighborhood of the origin in K^n contains a point b at which f is convergent and $f(b) \neq 0$.*

2) STRONG FORM. *If $f \neq g$ then $\{b \in \mathbf{D}(f) \cap \mathbf{D}(g)\colon f(b) = g(b)\}$ is nowhere dense in $\mathbf{D}(f) \cap \mathbf{D}(g)$ and $\boldsymbol{\tau}_a f \neq \boldsymbol{\tau}_a g$ for all $a \in \mathbf{D}(f) \cap \mathbf{D}(g)$. If $f \neq 0$ then $\{b \in \mathbf{D}(f): f(b) = 0\}$ is nowhere dense in $\mathbf{D}(f)$ and $\boldsymbol{\tau}_a f \neq 0$ for all $a \in \mathbf{D}(f)$.*

3) SUPPLEMENT. *If $f \notin K$ then $\boldsymbol{\tau}_a f \notin K$ for all $a \in \mathbf{D}(f)$. Let $\varphi\colon X \to K$ be analytic where X is an open set in K^n. Let $a \in X$. If φ is nonconstant in the neighborhood of a then there exists a neighborhood X^* of a in X such that φ is nonconstant in the neighborhood of each point of X^*.*[6]

Initial remark. For most applications 1) is enough. Using the weakest conclusion of 1), namely 1′), in (9.3.3) we proved 3) and in (9.3.1) we proved: 2′) If $f \neq g$ then $\boldsymbol{\tau}_a f \neq \boldsymbol{\tau}_a g$ for all a in $\mathbf{D}(f) \cap \mathbf{D}(g)$. 2) follows from 1) and 2′). Hence it suffices to prove 1).

Proof of 1). The case $f \neq g$ follows from the case $f \neq 0$ by taking $f - g$ for f. So we consider the case of $f \neq 0$. In view of (10.3.6), via a K-linear transformation, we can arrange that $f = \delta f^*$ where $\delta \in K[\langle x_1,\ldots, x_n\rangle]$ with $\delta(0) \neq 0$, and f^* is a distinguished polynomial in x_n with coefficients in $K[\langle x_1,\ldots, x_{n-1}\rangle]$. Since $a \to \delta(a)$ is continuous, we can find a neighborhood X of the origin in $\mathbf{D}(\delta) \cap \mathbf{D}(f^*)$ such that for all $a \in X$ we have $\delta(a) \neq 0$ and hence in particular $\boldsymbol{\tau}_a\delta \neq 0$. Let

[6] φ is nonconstant in the neighborhood of a means: in every neighborhood of a, φ takes at least two distinct values.

$a \in X$ be given. Obviously $\boldsymbol{\tau}_a f^*$ is a monic polynomial in x_n with coefficients in $K[\langle x_1,\dots, x_{n-1}\rangle]$. Therefore $\boldsymbol{\tau}_a f^* \neq 0$ and hence $\boldsymbol{\tau}_a f \neq 0$. Let X^* be any neighborhood of a in X. Since $\boldsymbol{\tau}_a f^*$ is a monic polynomial, $(\boldsymbol{\tau}_a f^*)(0,\dots, 0, x_n) = 0$ has at most a finite number of roots in K. Since K is nondiscrete, we can find α in K having arbitrarily small absolute value such that $(\boldsymbol{\tau}_a f^*)(0,\dots, 0, \alpha) \neq 0$. Then $c = (a_1,\dots, a_{n-1}, a_n + \alpha)$ is in X^* and $f(c) \neq 0$. Obviously $\{b \in X^* : f(b) = 0\}$ is closed in X^* and hence we can find a neighborhood X' of c in X^* such that $f(b) \neq 0$ for all $b \in X'$. This shows that $\{b \in X : f(b) = 0\}$ is nowhere dense in X.

(10.4) and (10.5.1) at once yield

(10.6) *Let K be complete nondiscrete valued and let φ be an analytic function on an open set X in K^n. Given $a \in X$, there exists a neighborhood X^* of a in X such that $\mathbf{o}_b\varphi \leqq \mathbf{o}_a\varphi$ for all $b \in X^*$.*[7]

Next we consider the following

(10.7) PROPOSITION.

1) *$K[[x_1,\dots, x_n]]$ is an n dimensional regular local ring and a unique factorization domain.*

2) *Let f and g be coprime monic polynomials in $K[[x_1,\dots, x_{n-1}]][x_n]$.*[8] *Then f and g are coprime in $K[[x_1,\dots, x_n]]$.*
Now assume that K is complete nondiscrete valued.

3) *$K[\langle x_1,\dots, x_n\rangle]$ is an n dimensional regular local ring and a unique factorization domain; $K[[x_1,\dots, x_n]]$ is a completion of $K[\langle x_1,\dots, x_n\rangle]$.*

4) *2) holds with $[\langle\ \rangle]$ replacing $[[\ ]]$.*

5) *Let f and g be coprime monic polynomials in $K[\langle x_1,\dots, x_{n-1}\rangle][x_n]$. Then for all $a \in \mathbf{D}(f) \cap \mathbf{D}(g)$, $\boldsymbol{\tau}_a f$ and $\boldsymbol{\tau}_a g$ are coprime monic polynomials in $K[\langle x_1,\dots, x_{n-1}\rangle][x_n]$.*

6) *Let f and g be nonzero coprime elements in $K[\langle x_1,\dots, x_n\rangle]$. Then there exists a neighborhood X of the origin in $\mathbf{D}(f) \cap \mathbf{D}(g)$ such that for all $a \in X$, $\boldsymbol{\tau}_a f$ and $\boldsymbol{\tau}_a g$ are nonzero coprime elements in $K[\langle x_1,\dots, x_n\rangle]$.*

7) *Let $y = (y_1,\dots, y_e)$. Let $f(y, z)$ be a distinguished polynomial in z with coefficients in $K[\langle y\rangle]$ which are convergent at $b \in K^e$. Let $a = (b, c)$ with*

[7] See Definition (2.4).

[8] That is, f and g are monic polynomials in x_n with coefficients in $K[[x_1,\dots, x_{n-1}]]$, and f and g are coprime in $K[[x_1,\dots, x_{n-1}]][x_n]$.

$c \in K$. Assume that $f(y, 0) \neq 0$. Then z does not divide $\tau_a f$ in $K[\langle y \rangle][z]$. Consequently, if $f^*(y, z) \in K[[y, z]]$ divides $\tau_a f$ in $K[[y, z]]$ then $f^*(y, 0) \neq 0$.

Initial Remark. From local algebra we recall the following (see Chapter III). Let $(R, \mathfrak{m})$ be a local ring.

$$\dim R = \max e \quad \text{such that there exists a chain } \mathfrak{p}_0 \subset \mathfrak{p}_1 \subset \ldots \subset \mathfrak{p}_e = \mathfrak{m} \text{ of distinct prime ideals in } R.$$

$$\operatorname{emdim} R = \text{embedding dimension of } R = \min e \text{ such that } \mathfrak{m} \text{ can be generated by } e \text{ elements.}$$

Always $\operatorname{emdim} R \geqq \dim R$. R is regular $\Leftrightarrow$ (def) $\operatorname{emdim} R = \dim R$. R is regular $\Rightarrow$ R is an integral domain which is integrally closed in its quotient field. Let $\bar{R}$ be another local ring. $\bar{R}$ is a completion of R means: R is a subring of $\bar{R}$ and in the Krull topologies $\bar{R}$ is complete and R is a dense subspace of $\bar{R}$.

It is obvious that $\{x_1, \ldots, x_j\}$, $(j = 0, \ldots, n)$, generate distinct prime ideals in $K[[x_1, \ldots, x_n]]$, the last one being the maximal ideal. Thus

$$\operatorname{emdim} K[[x_1, \ldots, x_n]] \leqq n \leqq \dim R.$$

Hence $K[[x_1, \ldots, x_n]]$ is regular of dimension n, provided we show that it is noetherian. Same holds with $[\langle\ \rangle]$ replacing $[[\ ]]$. Thus it suffices to show that these rings are noetherian. For $K[[x_1, \ldots, x_n]]$ this can be proved without using the Preparation Theorem.[9] Also by a recent result of M. Auslander and D. Buchsbaum, any regular local ring is a unique factorization domain.[10] Here we shall prove these assertions under the assumption that K is infinite. Recall that by Hilbert basis theorem, over any noetherian ring R, any submodule of a finitely generated module is again finitely generated; in particular then any submodule of the v-fold direct sum R^v is finitely generated.

Proof of 1), 2), 3), 4). *$K[[x_1, \ldots, x_n]]$ is noetherian.* Induction on n. Trivial for $n = 0$. Let $n > 0$ and assume for $n - 1$. Let an ideal $\mathfrak{a}$ in $K[[x_1, \ldots, x_n]]$ be given. Fix $0 \neq f \in \mathfrak{a}$.[11] By (10.3.6), via a K-linear transformation, we may assume that f is a distinguished polynomial of some degree d in x_n with coefficients in $K[[x_1, \ldots, x_{n-1}]]$. By (10.3.1), for all g in $K[[x_1, \ldots, x_n]]$ there exist unique elements q_g and r_g in $K[[x_1, \ldots, x_n]]$ such that $g = q_g f + r_g$ and $\deg_{x_n} r_g < d$. Let $\mathfrak{b} = \{r_g : g \in \mathfrak{a}\}$. In a natural way, $\mathfrak{b}$ can be considered to be a $K[[x_1, \ldots, x_{n-1}]]$-submodule of the d-fold

[9] Indeed: if R is a noetherian ring then so is $R[[x_1, \ldots, x_n]]$; see §22.

[10] Zariski–Samuel [2: Appendix 7].

[11] If $\mathfrak{a} = \{0\}$ then there is nothing to show.

direct sum of $K[[x_1,\ldots, x_{n-1}]]$. By induction hypothesis, $\mathfrak{b}$ has a finite $K[[x_1,\ldots, x_{n-1}]]$-basis. Any such basis of $\mathfrak{b}$ together with f gives a finite ideal basis of $\mathfrak{a}$. In the above proof replacing $[[\ ]]$ by $[\langle\ \rangle]$ we get that $K[\langle x_1,\ldots, x_n\rangle]$ *is noetherian.*

$K[[x_1,\ldots, x_n]]$ *is a unique factorization domain.* Induction on n. Let $n > 0$ and assume for $n - 1$. Let f be a given nonzero element of $K[[x_1,\ldots, x_n]]$ which is to be factored. By (10.3.6), via a K-linear transformation, we may assume that f is a distinguished polynomial in x_n with coefficients in $K[[x_1,\ldots, x_{n-1}]]$. By induction hypothesis, $K[[x_1,\ldots, x_{n-1}]]$ is a unique factorization domain and hence so is $K[[x_1,\ldots, x_{n-1}]][x_n]$. By (10.1.6, 10.3.3, 10.3.4, 10.3.5), a factorization of f into irreducible factors in $K[[x_1,\ldots, x_{n-1}]][x_n]$ is one such in $K[[x_1,\ldots, x_n]]$, and any factorization of f into irreducible factors in $K[[x_1,\ldots, x_n]]$ corresponds to one in $K[[x_1,\ldots, x_{n-1}]][x_n]$. Thus $K[[x_1,\ldots, x_n]]$ is a unique factorization domain. Now let f and g be coprime monic polynomials in $K[[x_1,\ldots, x_{n-1}]][x_n]$. By (10.3.2, 10.3.3), $f = \delta f^*$ and $g = \bar{\delta} g^*$ where δ, $\bar{\delta}$, f^*, g^* are in $K[[x_1,\ldots, x_{n-1}]][x_n]$, f^* and g^* are distinguished in x_n, and δ and $\bar{\delta}$ are units in $K[[x_1,\ldots, x_n]]$. Let $f^* = f_1^* \ldots f_p^*$ and $g^* = g_1^* \ldots g_v^*$ be irreducible factorizations into monic polynomials in $K[[x_1,\ldots, x_{n-1}]][x_n]$. By (10.1.6, 10.3.3, 10.3.4, 10.3.5) these are then irreducible factorizations in $K[[x_1,\ldots, x_n]]$ and all the factors are distinguished in x_n. By assumption, f and g are coprime in $K[[x_1,\ldots, x_{n-1}]][x_n]$ and hence so are f^* and g^*. Consequently $f_i^* \neq g_j^*$ for all i, j. Hence by (10.3.4), f_i^* and g_j^* are not associates in $K[[x_1,\ldots, x_n]]$. This shows that f and g are coprime in $K[[x_1,\ldots, x_n]]$. This proves 2). Now assume that K is complete nondiscrete valued. Replacing $[[\ ]]$ by $[\langle\ \rangle]$ in the above proof we conclude that $K[\langle x_1,\ldots, x_n\rangle]$ is a unique factorization domain and that 2) holds with $[\langle\ \rangle]$ replacing $[[\ ]]$.

Since $K[[x_1,\ldots, x_n]]$ is obviously a completion of $K[\langle x_1,\ldots, x_n\rangle]$ this completes the proof of 1), 2), 3), 4).

Proof of 5). Let

$$f = \sum_{i=0}^{d} f_i(x_1,\ldots, x_{n-1})x_n^i, \qquad g = \sum_{i=0}^{e} g_i(x_1,\ldots, x_{n-1})x_n^i$$

with $f_i, g_i \in K[\langle x_1,\ldots, x_{n-1}\rangle]$, $f_d = 1$, $g_e = 1$. Then

$$\mathbf{D}(f) = \left[\bigcap_{i=0}^{d} \mathbf{D}(f_i)\right] \times K^1 \qquad \text{and} \qquad \mathbf{D}(g) = \left[\bigcap_{i=0}^{e} \mathbf{D}(g_i)\right] \times K^1.$$

Let h be the x_n-resultant of f and g. Then $h = H(f_0,\ldots, f_d, g_0,\ldots, g_e)$ where $H(T_0,\ldots, T_d, T'_0,\ldots, T'_e)$ is a polynomial in indeterminates $T_0,\ldots, T_d$,

$T'_0, \ldots, T'_e$ with integer coefficients which are completely determined by d and e.[12] Therefore

$$h \in K[\langle x_1, \ldots, x_{n-1} \rangle] \qquad \text{and} \qquad \left[\bigcap_{i=0}^{d} \mathbf{D}(f_i)\right] \cap \left[\bigcap_{i=0}^{e} \mathbf{D}(g_i)\right] \subset \mathbf{D}(h).$$

Since f and g are coprime in $K[\langle x_1, \ldots, x_{n-1} \rangle][x_n]$ and $K[\langle x_1, \ldots, x_{n-1} \rangle]$ is a unique factorization domain we know that f and g are coprime in $K(\langle x_1, \ldots, x_{n-1} \rangle)[x_n]$. Therefore $h \neq 0$. Let $a = (b, c) \in \mathbf{D}(f) \cap \mathbf{D}(g)$, $b = (b_1, \ldots, b_{n-1}) \in K^{n-1}$, $c \in K^1$, be given. Then

$$b \in \left[\bigcap_{i=0}^{d} \mathbf{D}(f_i)\right] \cap \left[\bigcap_{i=0}^{e} \mathbf{D}(g_i)\right].$$

It is obvious that, $\boldsymbol{\tau}_a f$ and $\boldsymbol{\tau}_a g$ are coprime in $K[\langle x_1, \ldots, x_{n-1} \rangle][x_n] \Leftrightarrow \boldsymbol{\tau}_{(b,0)} f$ and $\boldsymbol{\tau}_{(b,0)} g$ are coprime in $K[\langle x_1, \ldots, x_{n-1} \rangle][x_n]$. Now

$$\begin{aligned} \boldsymbol{\tau}_b h &= H(\boldsymbol{\tau}_b f_0, \ldots, \boldsymbol{\tau}_b f_d, \boldsymbol{\tau}_b g_0, \ldots, \boldsymbol{\tau}_b g_e) \\ &= x_n\text{-resultant of } \boldsymbol{\tau}_{(b,0)} f \text{ and } \boldsymbol{\tau}_{(b,0)} g. \end{aligned}$$

By (10.5.2), $\boldsymbol{\tau}_b h \neq 0$ and hence $\boldsymbol{\tau}_{(b,0)} f$ and $\boldsymbol{\tau}_{(b,0)} g$ are coprime.

Proof of 6). In view of (10.3.6), via a K-linear transformation, we may assume that $f = \delta f^*$ and $g = \bar{\delta} g^*$ where f^* and g^* are distinguished polynomials in x_n with coefficients in $K[\langle x_1, \ldots, x_{n-1} \rangle]$, and δ and $\bar{\delta}$ are units in $K[\langle x_1, \ldots, x_n \rangle]$. For all points a in some neighborhood of the origin in $\mathbf{D}(\delta) \cap \mathbf{D}(\bar{\delta}) \cap \mathbf{D}(f^*) \cap \mathbf{D}(g^*)$ we then have that $\boldsymbol{\tau}_a \delta$ and $\boldsymbol{\tau}_a \bar{\delta}$ are units in $K[\langle x_1, \ldots, x_n \rangle]$. Since f and g are coprime in $K[\langle x_1, \ldots, x_n \rangle]$, so are f^* and g^*. Hence f^* and g^* are coprime in $K[\langle x_1, \ldots, x_{n-1} \rangle][x_n]$ and hence by 5), $\boldsymbol{\tau}_a f^*$ and $\boldsymbol{\tau}_a g^*$ are coprime in $K[\langle x_1, \ldots, x_{n-1} \rangle][x_n]$. Therefore by 4), $\boldsymbol{\tau}_a f^*$ and $\boldsymbol{\tau}_a g^*$ are coprime in $K[\langle x_1, \ldots, x_n \rangle]$. Since $\boldsymbol{\tau}_a \delta$ and $\boldsymbol{\tau}_a \bar{\delta}$ are units in $K[\langle x_1, \ldots, x_n \rangle]$ and $\boldsymbol{\tau}_a f = (\boldsymbol{\tau}_a \delta)(\boldsymbol{\tau}_a f^*)$, $\boldsymbol{\tau}_a g = (\boldsymbol{\tau}_a \bar{\delta})(\boldsymbol{\tau}_a g^*)$, we conclude that $\boldsymbol{\tau}_a f$ and $\boldsymbol{\tau}_a g$ are coprime in $K[\langle x_1, \ldots, x_n \rangle]$.

Proof of 7). Let $g(y, z) = z - c$. Suppose if possible that g divides f in $K[\langle y \rangle][z]$; since f is distinguished in z, by (10.1.6) so is g; i.e., $c = 0$; hence z divides f in $K[\langle y \rangle][z]$ which contradicts the assumption that $f(y, 0) \neq 0$. Therefore g does not divide f in $K[\langle y \rangle][z]$. Obviously, g and $\boldsymbol{\tau}_a g = z$ are irreducible. Hence by 5), $\boldsymbol{\tau}_a g = z$ does not divide $\boldsymbol{\tau}_a f$ in $K[\langle y \rangle][z]$.

REMARK. Noetherian character is the basic result concerning finite generation in power series rings. Further results in that direction will be given in §15 and §16.

[12] See (17.10).

(10.8) IMPLICIT FUNCTION THEOREM. *Let* $y = (y_1, \ldots, y_m)$. *Let* $f_i(y, z_1, \ldots, z_n) \in K[[y, z_1, \ldots, z_n]]$, $(i = 1, \ldots, n)$, *be such that* $f_i(0, 0, \ldots, 0) = 0$ *for* $i = 1, \ldots, n$, *and*

$$\frac{\partial(f_1, \ldots, f_n)}{\partial(z_1, \ldots, z_n)}(0, 0, \ldots, 0) \neq 0.$$

Then there exist unique elements $\zeta_1(y), \ldots, \zeta_n(y)$ *in* $K[[y]]$ *such that* $\zeta_1(0) = \ldots = \zeta_n(0) = 0$ *and* $f_i(y, \zeta_1(y), \ldots, \zeta_n(y)) = 0$ *for* $i = 1, \ldots, n$. *Now assume that* $f_1, \ldots, f_n$ *are convergent. Then* $\zeta_1, \ldots, \zeta_n$ *are convergent. More precisely, there exist neighborhoods* Y *and* Z *of the origins in* K^m *and* K^n, *respectively, such that:* $f_1, \ldots, f_n$ *are convergent in* $Y \times Z$; $\zeta_1, \ldots, \zeta_n$ *are convergent in* Y; *and for all* $b \in Y$, $(\zeta_1(b), \ldots, \zeta_n(b))$ *is the unique solution of the "equations"*

$$f_i(b, z_1, \ldots, z_n) = 0, \qquad i = 1, \ldots, n,$$

in Z.

REMARK. Note that by continuity we may choose the neighborhood $Y \times Z$ so that

$$\frac{\partial(f_1, \ldots, f_n)}{\partial(z_1, \ldots, z_n)}(b, c_1, \ldots, c_n) \neq 0,$$

whenever $(b, c) \in Y \times Z$. For $n = 1$, this in particular means that $\mathbf{o}_{\zeta_1(b)} f_1(b, z_1) = 1$ for all $b \in Y$.

PROOF. Induction on n. *Take* $n = 1$. By (10.3.2),

$$f_1(y, z_1) = \delta(y, z_1)(z_1 - \zeta_1(y))$$

with $\zeta_1(y) \in K[[y]]$, $\zeta_1(0) = 0$, $\delta(y, z_1) \in K[[y, z_1]]$, $\delta(0, 0) \neq 0$, where ζ_1 and δ are convergent if f_1 is convergent. Obviously $f_1(y, \zeta_1(y)) = 0$. Let $\zeta_1'(y)$ be any element in $K[[y]]$ such that $\zeta_1'(0) = 0$ and $f_1(y, \zeta_1'(y)) = 0$. Then $\delta(y, \zeta_1'(y))(\zeta_1'(y) - \zeta(y)) = 0$. Since $\delta(0, 0) \neq 0$ and $\zeta_1'(0) = 0$ we get that $\delta(0, \zeta_1'(0)) \neq 0$ and hence $\delta(y, \zeta_1'(y)) \neq 0$. Therefore $\zeta_1'(y) = \zeta_1(y)$. Now suppose that f_1 is convergent. By continuity we can find neighborhoods Y and Z of the origins in K^m and K^1, respectively, such that f and δ are convergent in $Y \times Z$, $\delta(b, c) \neq 0$ whenever $(b, c) \in Y \times Z$, ζ_1 is convergent in Y, and $\zeta_1(b) \in Z$ whenever $b \in Y$. Since

$$f_1(b, c) = \delta(b, c)(c - \zeta_1(b)) \qquad \text{for all} \qquad (b, c) \in Y \times Z$$

we conclude that for all $b \in Y$, $\zeta_1(b)$ is the unique solution of the equation $f_1(b, z_1) = 0$ in Z.

Take $n > 1$ *and assume true for* $n - 1$. Relabeling $z_1, \ldots, z_n$ we can arrange that

$$\frac{\partial f_1}{\partial z_1}(0, 0, \ldots, 0) \neq 0.$$

By (10.3.2),

$$f_1(y, z_1,\dots, z_n) = \delta(y, z_1,\dots, z_n)(z_1 - \xi(y, z_2,\dots, z_n))$$

with

$$\xi(y, z_2,\dots, z_n) \in K[[y, z_2,\dots, z_n]], \qquad \xi(0, 0,\dots, 0) = 0,$$
$$\delta(y, z_1,\dots, z_n) \in K[[y, z_1,\dots, z_n]], \qquad \delta(0, 0,\dots, 0) \neq 0,$$

where ξ and δ are convergent if f_1 is convergent. For $i = 2,\dots, n$, let

$$h_i(y, z_2,\dots, z_n) = f_i(y, \xi(y, z_2,\dots, z_n), z_2,\dots, z_n).$$

Then $h_i(0, 0,\dots, 0) = 0$ for $(i = 2,\dots, n)$, and $h_2,\dots, h_n$ are convergent if $f_1,\dots, f_n$ are convergent. Letting (0) stand for the respective origins, by chain rule for formal differentiation we get

$$\frac{\partial h_i}{\partial z_j}(0) = \frac{\partial f_i}{\partial z_j}(0) + \frac{\partial f_i}{\partial z_1}(0)\frac{\partial \xi}{\partial z_j}(0) \qquad \text{for} \qquad i, j = 2,\dots, n;$$

$$\frac{\partial f_1}{\partial z_1}(0) = \delta(0);$$

$$\frac{\partial f_1}{\partial z_j}(0) = -\delta(0)\frac{\partial \xi}{\partial z_j}(0) \qquad \text{for} \qquad j = 2,\dots, n.$$

Consequently, computing with determinants we get

$$\begin{aligned}
0 &\neq \frac{1}{\delta(0)}\frac{\partial(f_1,\dots, f_n)}{\partial(z_1,\dots, z_n)}(0) \\
&= \det\begin{pmatrix} 1 & -\dfrac{\partial \xi}{\partial z_2}(0) & \cdots & -\dfrac{\partial \xi}{\partial z_n}(0) \\ \dfrac{\partial f_2}{\partial z_1}(0) & \dfrac{\partial f_2}{\partial z_2}(0) & \cdots & \dfrac{\partial f_2}{\partial z_n}(0) \\ \cdots & \cdots & \cdots & \cdots \\ \cdots & \cdots & \cdots & \cdots \\ \dfrac{\partial f_n}{\partial z_1}(0) & \dfrac{\partial f_n}{\partial z_2}(0) & \cdots & \dfrac{\partial f_n}{\partial z_n}(0) \end{pmatrix} \\
&= \det\left(\left(\frac{\partial f_i}{\partial z_j}(0) + \frac{\partial f_i}{\partial z_1}(0)\frac{\partial \xi}{\partial z_j}(0)\right)\right)_{i, j=2,\dots, n} \\
&= \frac{\partial(h_2,\dots, h_n)}{\partial(z_2,\dots, z_n)}(0).
\end{aligned}$$

Therefore by the existence part of the induction hypothesis, there exist elements $\zeta_2(y),\ldots, \zeta_n(y)$ in $K[[y]]$, which are convergent if $f_1,\ldots,f_n$ are convergent, such that $\zeta_2(0) = \ldots = \zeta_n(0) = 0$ and $h_i(y, \zeta_2(y),\ldots, \zeta_n(y)) = 0$ for $i = 2,\ldots, n$. Let $\zeta_1(y) = \xi(y, \zeta_2(y),\ldots, \zeta_n(y)) \in K[[y]]$. Then $\zeta_1(0) = \ldots = \zeta_n(0) = 0$; $f_i(y, \xi_1(y),\ldots, \xi_n(y)) = 0$ for $i = 1,\ldots, n$; and $\zeta_1,\ldots, \zeta_n$ are convergent if $f_1,\ldots, f_n$ are convergent. Let $\zeta_1'(y),\ldots, \zeta_n'(y)$ be any elements in $K[[y]]$ such that $\zeta_1'(0) = \ldots = \zeta_n'(0) = 0$ and $f_i(y, \zeta_1'(y),\ldots, \zeta_n'(y)) = 0$ for $i = 1,\ldots, n$. Now

$$
\begin{aligned}
0 &= f_1(y, \zeta_1'(y),\ldots, \zeta_n'(y)) \\
&= \delta(y, \zeta_1'(y),\ldots, \zeta_n'(y))(\zeta_1'(y) - \xi(y, \zeta_2'(y),\ldots, \zeta_n'(y)))
\end{aligned}
$$

and $\delta(y, \zeta_1'(y),\ldots, \zeta_n'(y)) \neq 0$ because $\delta(0, 0,\ldots, 0) \neq 0$ and $\zeta_1'(0) = \ldots = \zeta_n'(0) = 0$. Therefore we must have

$$\zeta_1'(y) = \xi(y, \zeta_2'(y),\ldots, \zeta_n'(y)).$$

Consequently for $i = 2,\ldots, n$ we get

$$h_i(y, \zeta_2'(y),\ldots, \zeta_n'(y)) = f_i(y, \zeta_1'(y),\ldots, \zeta_n'(y)) = 0.$$

Therefore by the uniqueness part of the induction hypothesis we get $\zeta_i'(y) = \zeta_i(y)$ for $i = 2,\ldots, n$.

Now suppose that $f_1,\ldots, f_n$ are convergent. By the induction hypothesis we can find a neighborhood $Y^* \times Z_{n-1}^*$ of the origin in $K^m \times K^{n-1}$ such that: $h_2,\ldots, h_n$ are convergent in $Y^* \times Z_{n-1}^*$; $\zeta_2,\ldots, \zeta_n$ are convergent in Y^*; and for all b in Y^*, $(\zeta_2(b),\ldots, \zeta_n(b))$ is the unique common solution of the equations $h_i(b, z_2,\ldots, z_n) = 0$, $(i = 2,\ldots, n)$, in Z_{n-1}^*. We can take neighborhoods Y and $Z = Z_1 \times Z_{n-1}$ of the origins in Y^* and $K^1 \times Z_{n-1}^*$, respectively, such that: $f_1,\ldots, f_n, \delta$ are convergent in $Y \times Z$; ξ is convergent in $Y \times Z_{n-1}$; ζ_1 is convergent in Y;

$$
\begin{aligned}
\delta(b, c_1,\ldots, c_n) &\neq 0 && \text{for all} \quad (b, c_1,\ldots, c_n) \in Y \times Z; \\
(\zeta_1(b),\ldots, \zeta_n(b)) &\in Z && \text{for all} \quad b \in Y; \\
\xi(b, c_2,\ldots, c_n) &\in Z_1 && \text{for all} \quad (b, c_2,\ldots, c_n) \in Y \times Z_{n-1}; \\
\zeta_1(b) &= \xi(b, \zeta_2(b),\ldots, \zeta_n(b)) && \text{for all} \quad b \in Y;
\end{aligned}
$$

and

$$h_i(b, c_2,\ldots, c_n) = f_i(b, \xi(b, c_2,\ldots, c_n), c_2,\ldots, c_n)$$

$$\text{for all} \quad (b, c_2,\ldots, c_n) \in Y \times Z_{n-1}, \qquad \text{for} \quad i = 2,\ldots, n.$$

Now it follows that, for all b in Y, $(\zeta_1(b),\ldots, \zeta_n(b))$ is the unique common solution of the equations

$$f_i(b, z_1,\ldots, z_n) = 0, \qquad (i = 1,\ldots, n), \qquad \text{in} \quad Z.$$

(10.9) DEFINITION. Let K be complete nondiscrete valued. Let X and Y be open sets in $K^n\{x_1,\ldots,x_n\}$ and $K^n\{y_1,\ldots,y_n\}$, respectively. A *bianalytic map* $g: X \to Y$ is a homeomorphism of X onto Y such that for any open subset X^* of X and any function $\beta: g(X^*) \to K$ we have that β is analytic on $g(X^*) \Leftrightarrow \beta \circ (g|X^*)$ is analytic on X^*. Let $g = (g_1,\ldots, g_n)$, and $g^{-1} = h = (h_1,\ldots, h_n)$. If g is bianalytic then obviously h is a bianalytic map of Y onto X; $g_1,\ldots, g_n$ are analytic functions on X; $h_1,\ldots, h_n$ are analytic functions on Y; and by chain rule

$$\frac{\partial(g_1,\ldots, g_n)}{\partial(x_1,\ldots, x_n)}(a) \cdot \frac{\partial(h_1,\ldots, h_n)}{\partial(y_1,\ldots, y_n)}(g(a)) = 1 \qquad \text{for all} \qquad a \in X,$$

whence in particular

1°) $$\frac{\partial(g_1,\ldots, g_n)}{\partial(x_1,\ldots, x_n)}(a) \neq 0 \qquad \text{for all} \qquad a \in X.$$

Conversely, from (10.10) it will follow that if $g = (g_1,\ldots, g_n): X \to Y$ is a homeomorphism such that $g_1,\ldots, g_n$ are analytic on X and 1°) holds then g is bianalytic.

If g is bianalytic, then via g we may "identify" X with Y; we may express this by saying that "$y_1,\ldots, y_n$ is an *analytic coordinate system in* X".

(10.10) INVERSION THEOREM. *Let* $x = (x_1,\ldots, x_n)$ *and* $y = (y_1,\ldots, y_n)$. *Let* $g_1(x),\ldots, g_n(x) \in K[[x]]$ *be such that* $g_1(0) = \ldots = g_n(0) = 0$ and

$$\frac{\partial(g_1,\ldots, g_n)}{\partial(x_1,\ldots, x_n)}(0) \neq 0.$$

Then there exist unique elements $h_1(y),\ldots, h_n(y)$ *in* $K[[y]]$ *such that* $h_1(0) = \ldots = h_n(0) = 0$ and

1°) $$g_i(h_1(y),\ldots, h_n(y)) = y_i \qquad \textit{for} \qquad i = 1,\ldots, n.$$ [13]

For any $\varphi(x) \in K[[x]]$ *let*

$$H(\varphi) = \varphi(h_1(y),\ldots, h_n(y)) \in K[[y]],$$

and for any $\psi(y) \in K[[y]]$ *let*

$$G(\psi) = \psi(g_1(x),\ldots, g_n(x)) \in K[[x]].$$

Then H *is an isomorphism of* $K[[x]]$ *onto* $K[[y]]$ *and* $G = H^{-1}$.

[13] By chain rule, from 1°) it follows that

$$\frac{\partial(g_1,\ldots, g_n)}{\partial(x_1,\ldots, x_n)}(0) \cdot \frac{\partial(h_1,\ldots, h_n)}{\partial(y_1,\ldots, y_n)}(0) = 1.$$

Now assume that $g_1,\dots, g_n$ are convergent. Then we have the following. $H(K[\langle x\rangle]) = K[\langle y\rangle]$ and $G(K[\langle y\rangle]) = K[\langle x\rangle]$; in particular $h_1,\dots, h_n$ are convergent. There exist neighborhoods X and Y of the origin in K^n such that: $g_1,\dots, g_n$ are convergent in X; $h_1,\dots, h_n$ are convergent in Y; the mapping

$$g: a \to (g_1(a),\dots, g_n(a))$$

is a bianalytic map of X onto Y; and the mapping

$$h: b \to (h_1(b),\dots, h_n(b))$$

is the inverse of g.

PROOF. Taking $z_i = x_i$ and $f_i(y, x_1,\dots, x_n) = y_i - g_i(x_1,\dots, x_n)$ in (10.8) we deduce that there exist unique elements $h_1(y),\dots, h_n(y)$ in $K[[y]]$ such that $h_1(0) = \dots = h_n(0) = 0$ and 1°) holds. If $g_1,\dots, g_n$ are convergent then by (10.8) we can find neighborhoods X' and Y of the origin in K^n such that: $g_1,\dots, g_n$ are convergent in X'; $h_1,\dots, h_n$ are convergent in Y; and for all $b \in Y$, $(h_1(b),\dots, h_n(b))$ is the unique point in X' which gets mapped onto b under the mapping $a \to ((g_1(a),\dots, g_n(a))$. Let

$$X = \{a \in X' : a = (h_1(b),\dots, h_n(b)) \text{ for some } b \in Y\}.$$

Then X is a neighborhood of the origin in K^n, $g: X \to Y$ is bianalytic and $h = g^{-1}$.

In the formal case, $H: K[[x]] \to K[[y]]$ and $G: K[[y]] \to K[[x]]$ are homomorphisms and by 1°) it follows that H is an epimorphism and $H \circ G$ = identity on $K[[y]]$. Now [$K[[x]]$ and $K[[y]]$ are local integral domains of the same dimension n and H is an epimorphism] $\Rightarrow$ H is an isomorphism and $G = H^{-1}$. Alternatively, in virtue of footnote 13, reversing the roles of $g_1,\dots, g_n$ and $h_1,\dots, h_n$ we find a homomorphism $G': K[[y]] \to K[[x]]$ such that $G' \circ H$ = identity on $K[[x]]$; since $H \circ G$ = identity on $K[[y]]$ we must then have $G' = G$ and hence $G \circ H$ = identity on $K[[x]]$; since H is an epimorphism we get that H is an isomorphism and $G = H^{-1}$.

If $g_1,\dots, g_n$ are convergent then by (10.8), $h_1,\dots, h_n$ are convergent and hence $H(K[\langle x\rangle]) = K[\langle y\rangle]$ and $G(K[\langle y\rangle]) = K[\langle x\rangle]$.

We end this section with some corollaries of (10.10).

Let $R = K[[x_1,\dots, x_n]]$ or $K[\langle x_1,\dots, x_n\rangle]$. Let $g_1(x),\dots, g_m(x) \in R$, $(m \leqq n)$, be given such that $g_1(0) = \dots = g_m(0) = 0$, and

$$\operatorname{rnk} \frac{J(g_1,\dots, g_m)}{J(x_1,\dots, x_n)}(0) = m.$$

Then we can find $g_{m+1}(x),\ldots, g_n(x) \in R$ so that $g_{m+1}(0) = \ldots = g_n(0) = 0$ and[14]

$$\frac{\partial(g_1,\ldots, g_n)}{\partial(x_1,\ldots, x_n)}(0) \neq 0.$$

By (10.10) we get an isomorphism H of R onto $K[[y_1,\ldots y_n]]$ or $K[\langle y_1,\ldots, y_n\rangle]$, respectively, such that $H(g_i) = y_i$ for $i = 1,\ldots, n$. Thus we get

(10.11) *Let $R = K[[x_1,\ldots, x_n]]$ or $K[\langle x_1,\ldots, x_n\rangle]$. Let $g_1(x),\ldots, g_m(x) \in R$, $(m \leqq n)$, be such that $g_1(0) = \ldots = g_m(0) = 0$ and*

$$\text{rnk}\,\frac{J(g_1,\ldots, g_m)}{J(x_1,\ldots, x_n)}(0) = m.$$

Let $\mathfrak{a} = \{g_1(z),\ldots, g_m(x)\}R$. Then $R/\mathfrak{a}$ is isomorphic to $K[[y_{m+1},\ldots, y_n]]$ or $K[\langle y_{m+1},\ldots, y_n\rangle]$, respectively; hence in particular $R/\mathfrak{a}$ is a regular local ring of dimension $n - m$.

Taking $R = K[\langle x_1,\ldots, x_n\rangle]$ by (10.10) we also get

(10.12) *Let $g_1(x),\ldots, g_m(x) \in K[\langle x_1,\ldots, x_n\rangle]$, $(m \leqq n)$, be such that $g_1(0) = \ldots = g_m(0) = 0$ and*

$$\text{rnk}\,\frac{J(g_1,\ldots, g_m)}{J(x_1,\ldots, x_n)}(0) = m.$$

Then there exists a bianalytic map g of a neighborhood X of the origin in $K^n\{x_1,\ldots, x_n\}$ onto a neighborhood Y of the origin in $K^n\{y_1,\ldots, y_n\}$ such that: $g_1,\ldots, g_m$ are convergent in X; and for any $a \in X$ letting $g(a) = b = (b_1,\ldots, b_n)$ we have $b_i = g_i(a)$ for $i = 1,\ldots, m$; and hence in particular

$$g(\{a \in X: g_1(a) = \ldots = g_m(a) = 0\}) = \{b \in Y: b_1 = \ldots = b_m = 0\}.$$

Now let $S = K[[x_1,\ldots, x_e]]$ or $K[\langle x_1,\ldots, x_e\rangle]$, respectively, where $e \leqq n$. Let $\mathfrak{a} = \{g_{e+1}(x),\ldots, g_n(x)\}R$ where $g_{e+i}(x)$ is a monic polynomial in x_{e+i} with coefficients in S and the wideg of g_{e+i} in x_{e+i} relative to S is one. Take $g_i(x) = x_i$ for $i = 1,\ldots, e$. Then $g_1(0) = \ldots = g_n(0) = 0$ and

$$\frac{\partial(g_1,\ldots, g_n)}{\partial(x_1,\ldots, x_n)}(0) \neq 0.$$

[14] $g_{m+1}(x),\ldots, g_n(x)$ can actually be chosen to be linear forms in $x_1,\ldots, x_n$ with coefficients in K.

Hence by (10.10) there is an isomorphism H of R onto $\tilde{R} = K[[y_1,\ldots,y_n]]$ or $K[\langle y_1,\ldots,y_n\rangle]$, respectively, such that $H(g_i) = y_i$ for $i = 1,\ldots, n$, and from the expression for the inverse isomorphism $G: \tilde{R} \to R$ we see that $G(\tilde{S}) = S$ where $\tilde{S} = K[[y_1,\ldots,y_e]]$ or $K[\langle y_1,\ldots,y_e\rangle]$, respectively. Let $\tilde{\mathfrak{a}} = H(\mathfrak{a})$. Then $\tilde{\mathfrak{a}} = \{y_{e+1},\ldots,y_n\}\tilde{R}$. Hence $\tilde{\mathfrak{a}} \cap \tilde{S} = \{0\}$, and given $q \in \tilde{R}$ there exists $q^* \in \tilde{S}$ such that $q - q^* \in \tilde{\mathfrak{a}}$. Applying G to $\tilde{R}$ we get: $\mathfrak{a} \cap S = \{0\}$, and given $p \in R$ there exists $p^* \in S$ such that $p - p^* \in \mathfrak{a}$. Thus we have proved

(10.13) *Let $e \leqq n$. Let $R = K[[x_1,\ldots, x_n]]$ or $K[\langle x_1,\ldots, x_n\rangle]$ and let $S = K[[x_1,\ldots, x_e]]$ or $K[\langle x_1,\ldots, x_e\rangle]$, respectively. Let $\mathfrak{a} = \{g_{e+1}(x),\ldots, g_n(x)\}R$ where $g_{e+i}(x)$ is a monic polynomial in x_{e+i} with coefficients in S such that the wideg of g_{e+i} in x_{e+i} relative to S is one. Let $\varphi: R \to R/\mathfrak{a}$ be the natural epimorphism. Then $\mathfrak{a} \cap S = \{0\}$ and $\varphi(R) = \varphi(S)$; and hence in particular $R/\mathfrak{a}$ is an e dimensional regular local ring.*

Finally, from (10.13) we immediately get

(10.14) *Let $e \leqq n$. Let $R = K[\langle x_1,\ldots, x_n\rangle]$ and $S = K[\langle x_1,\ldots, x_e\rangle]$. Let $a \in K^n$. Let $g_{e+i}(x) = g_{e+i}(x_1,\ldots, x_e, x_{e+i})$, $(i = 1,\ldots, n - e)$, be a monic polynomial in x_{e+i} with coefficients in S which are convergent at $(a_1,\ldots, a_e)$ such that a_{e+i} is a simple root of $g_{e+i}(a_1,\ldots, a_e, x_{e+i}) = 0$,* i.e., *$g_{e+i}(a_1,\ldots, a_e, x_{e+i}) = (x_{e+i} - a_{e+i})f_{e+i}(x_{e+i})$ where $f_{e+i}(x_{e+i})$ is a monic polynomial in x_{e+i} with coefficients in K and $f_{e+i}(a_{e+i}) \neq 0$. Let $\mathfrak{a} = \{\tau_a g_{e+i}(x),\ldots, \tau_a g_n(x)\}R$ and let $\varphi: R \to R/\mathfrak{a}$ be the natural epimorphism. Then $\mathfrak{a} \cap S = \{0\}$ and $\varphi(R) = \varphi(S)$; and hence in particular $R/\mathfrak{a}$ is an e dimensional regular local ring.*

§11. CONTINUITY OF ROOTS AND OPEN MAP THEOREM

(11.1) *Let K be valued. Let*

$$F(z_1,\ldots, z_d, y) = y^d + z_1 y^{d-1} + \ldots + z_d, \qquad d > 0.$$

Let $c_1,\ldots, c_d, b \in K$ be such that $|c_1| < 1,\ldots, |c_d| < 1$, $|b| > 2d$. Then $F(c_1,\ldots, c_d, b) \neq 0$.

PROOF. $|b| > 2d$ implies that $|b^i| > 2d$ for all $i > 0$; and this, in view of the inequality $|c_i| < 1$, implies that $|c_i/b^i| < 1/(2d)$ for $i = 1,\ldots, d$. Therefore

$$|(c_1/b) + \ldots + (c_d/b^d)| < 1/2.$$

Consequently

$$F(c_1,\ldots, c_d, b)/b^d = 1 + (c_1/b) + \ldots + (c_d/b^d) \neq 0.$$

Hence $F(c_1,\ldots, c_d, b) \neq 0$.

(11.2) *Let K be valued. Let*

$$F(z_1,\ldots, z_d, y) = y^d + z_1 y^{d-1} + \ldots + z_d, \quad d > 0.$$

Given $E > 0$, *there exists* $D > 0$ *such that*: *if* $c_1,\ldots, c_d, b \in K$, *with* $|c_1| < D,\ldots, |c_d| < D$, *and* $F(c_1,\ldots, c_d, b) = 0$, *then* $|b| < E$.

PROOF. Let $A = (2d)^{d-1} + (2d)^{d-2} + \ldots + 1$. Take D to be any positive real number such that $D < 1$ and $D < E^d/A$. Since $|c_1| < D < 1,\ldots, |c_d| < D < 1$, by (11.1) we get $|b| \leqq 2d$, and hence $|c_1 b^{d-1} + \ldots + c_d| \leqq AD$. Now

$$0 = F(c_1,\ldots, c_d, b) = b^d + c_1 b^{d-1} + \ldots + c_d.$$

Hence $|b^d| \leqq AD < A(E^d/A) = E^d$. Therefore $|b| < E$.

(11.3) *Let K be complete nondiscrete valued. Let* $x = (x_1,\ldots, x_m)$. *Let*

$$F(x, y) = y^d + F_{d-1}(x) y^{d-1} + \ldots + F_0(x), \qquad d > 0;$$

$F_i(x) \in K[\langle x \rangle]$ *with* $F_i(0) = 0$ *for* $i = 0,\ldots, d-1$. *Given* $E > 0$, *there exists* $D > 0$ *such that*: *if* $F_0,\ldots, F_{d-1}$ *are convergent at* $a \in K^m$ *with* $|a_1| < D,\ldots, |a_m| < D$, *and* $b \in K$ *with* $F(a, b) = 0$, *then* $|b| < E$.

PROOF. $a \to F_i(a)$ is continuous and $F_i(0) = 0$. Therefore $|F_0(a)|,\ldots, |F_{d-1}(a)|$ are "small" when $|a_1|,\ldots, |a_m|$ are "small". Hence we are reduced to (11.2).

(11.4) *Let K be complete nondiscrete valued and algebraically closed. Let* $n > 0$.

1) *Let* $H(x_1,\ldots, x_n, z)$ *be a distinguished polynomial in* z *with coefficients in* $K[\langle x_1,\ldots, x_n \rangle]$ *which are all convergent in a given neighborhood X of the origin in* K^n. *Assume that* $H(x_1,\ldots, x_n, 0) \neq 0$. *Let* $\Omega = \{c \in K\colon H(a_1,\ldots, a_n, c) = 0$ *for some* $(a_1,\ldots, a_n) \in X\}$. *Then* 0 *is an interior point of* Ω.

2) *Let* $f \in K[\langle x_1,\ldots, x_n \rangle]$, $f \notin K$. *Then the map* $\mathbf{D}(f) \to K$ *given by* $a \to f(a)$ *is open at the origin. Let* φ *be an analytic function on an open set* X *in* K^n, *and let* $a \in X$. *If* φ *is nonconstant in the neighborhood of* a *then* φ *is open at* a.

Proof of 1). Via a nonsingular K-linear transformation on $x_1,\ldots, x_n$, we can arrange that $H(x_1, 0,\ldots, 0, 0) \neq 0$. Let $h(y, z) = H(y, 0,\ldots, 0, z)$. Let Y be a neighborhood of the origin in K^1 such that $Y \times Y' \subset X$ for some neighborhood Y' of the origin in K^{n-1}. Let $\Gamma = \{c \in K\colon h(b, c) = 0$ for some $b \in Y\}$. Then obviously it suffices to show that 0 is an interior point of Γ. Now $0 \neq h(y, z) \in K[\langle y, z \rangle]$, $h(y, 0) \neq 0$ and $h(0, 0) = 0$. Hence by (10.3.2), $h(y, z) = \delta(y, z)F(y, z)$ with $\delta(y, z)$ and $F(y, z)$ in $K[\langle y, z\rangle]$ where

$$F(y, z) = y^d + F_1(z)y^{d-1} + \ldots + F_d(z)$$

with $d > 0$, $F_i(z) \in K[\langle z\rangle]$ with $F_i(0) = 0$ for $i = 1,\ldots, d$. Take $B > 0$, $C^* > 0$ such that

$$\{b \in K^1 \colon |b| < B\} \subset Y$$

and

$$\{(b, c) \in K^2 \colon |b| < B, |c| < C^*\} \subset \mathbf{D}(\delta) \cap \mathbf{D}(F).$$

By (11.3), we can find $0 < C < C^*$ such that: $[F(b, c) = 0$ and $|c| < C \Rightarrow |b| < B]$. Let $c \in K$ with $|c| < C$ be given. Since K is algebraically closed, we can find $b \in K$ such that $F(b, c) = 0$. Then $h(b, c) = \delta(b, c)F(b, c) = 0$ and $b \in Y$. This shows that 0 is an interior point of Γ.

Proof of 2). The second assertion follows from the first. To prove the first assertion, replacing f by $f - f(0)$, we may assume that $f(0) = 0$. By assumption, $f \neq 0$. Now apply 1) to $H(x_1,\ldots, x_n, z) = z - f(x_1,\ldots, x_n)$.

In view of the Identity Theorem (10.5), (11.4.2) yields

(11.5) Open Map Theorem. *Let K be complete nondiscrete valued and algebraically closed. Let $f \in K[\langle x_1,\ldots, x_n\rangle]$, $f \notin K$, $n > 0$. Then $a \to f(a)$ is an open map of $\mathbf{D}(f)$ into K. Let φ be an analytic function on an open set X in K^n and let $a \in X$. If φ is nonconstant in the neighborhood of a then there exists a neighborhood X^* of a in X such that $\varphi|X^*$ is an open map of X^* into K.*

In the complex case we get

(11.6) Open Map Theorem. *Let X be a domain in $\mathbf{C}^n$, $n > 0$, and $f\colon X \to \mathbf{C}$ analytic. Then the following twelve conditions are equivalent.*

α) (resp: $\alpha_1, \alpha_2, \alpha_3$). f (resp: $|f|$, $\mathbf{Re} f$, $\mathbf{Im} f$) *is nonconstant in the neighborhood of some point of X.*

β) (resp: $\beta_1, \beta_2, \beta_3$). f (resp: $|f|$, $\mathbf{Re} f$, $\mathbf{Im} f$) *is nonconstant on X.*[1]

γ) (resp: $\gamma_1, \gamma_2, \gamma_3$). f (resp: $|f|$, $\mathbf{Re} f$, $\mathbf{Im} f$) *is an open map of X into* $\mathbf{C}$ (resp: $\mathbf{R}_+$, $\mathbf{R}$, $\mathbf{R}$).

Proof. In view of the identity theorem (2.5), (11.5) yields the equivalence of α, β, γ. Obviously $\gamma_1 \Rightarrow \alpha_1 \Rightarrow \alpha$, $\gamma_1 \Rightarrow \beta_1 \Rightarrow \beta$; and since $x \to |x|$ is an open map $\mathbf{C}$ onto $\mathbf{R}_+$ we also have $\gamma \Rightarrow \gamma_1$. Again obviously $\gamma_2 \Rightarrow \alpha_2 \Rightarrow \alpha$, $\gamma_2 \Rightarrow \beta_2 \Rightarrow \beta$; and since $x \to \mathbf{Re}\, x$ is an open map of $\mathbf{C}$ onto $\mathbf{R}$ we also have $\gamma \Rightarrow \gamma_2$. Similarly for $\mathbf{Im}$. Q.E.D.

[1] That is, f (resp: $|f|$, $\mathbf{Re} f$, $\mathbf{Im} f$) takes at least two distinct values on X.

Now the continuous image of a connected set is connected and the only connected subsets of $\mathbf{R}$ are intervals. Consequently (11.6) yields

(**11.7**) MAXIMUM PRINCIPLE. *Let X be a domain in $\mathbf{C}^n$, $n > 0$, $f: X \to \mathbf{C}$ analytic. The following ten conditions are equivalent, and if any one of them is satisfied then f, $|f|$, $\mathbf{Re}\, f$, and $\mathbf{Im}\, f$ are constant on X.*

i) $|f(a)| = \sup|f(X)|$ *for some* $a \in X$.
ii) $|f(a)| = \sup|f(X^*)|$ *for some neighborhood* X^* *of some point* $a \in X$.
iii) $\mathbf{Re}\, f(a) = \sup \mathbf{Re}\, f(X)$ *for some* $a \in X$.
iv) $\mathbf{Re}\, f(a) = \inf \mathbf{Re}\, f(X)$ *for some* $a \in X$.
v) $\mathbf{Re}\, f(a) = \sup \mathbf{Re}\, f(X^*)$ *for some neighborhood* X^* *of some point* $a \in X$.
vi) $\mathbf{Re}\, f(a) = \inf \mathbf{Re}\, f(X^*)$ *for some neighborhood* X^* *of some point* $a \in X$.
iii′, iv′, v′, vi′): *same as* iii, iv, v, vi) *with* **Im** *replacing* **Re**.

Finally, exactly as in the proof of (8.9), (11.7) yields

(**11.8**) MAXIMUM PRINCIPLE. *Let X be a bounded open set in $\mathbf{C}^n$, $n > 0$, $f: X \to \mathbf{C}$ analytic. Let* bd X *denote the boundary of X in $\mathbf{C}^n$. Let $M \in \mathbf{R}$. Then we have the following.*

1) $[a^{(p)} \in X,\ a^{(p)} \to a \in \text{bd } X \Rightarrow \limsup_{p\to\infty} |f(a^{(p)})| \leqq M]$
$\Rightarrow \sup|f(X)| \leqq M.$

2) $[a^{(p)} \in X,\ a^{(p)} \to a \in \text{bd } X \Rightarrow \limsup_{p\to\infty} \mathbf{Re}\, f(a^{(p)}) \leqq M]$
$\Rightarrow \sup \mathbf{Re}\, f(X) \leqq M.$

3) $[a^{(p)} \in X,\ a^{(p)} \to a \in \text{bd } X \Rightarrow \liminf_{p\to\infty} \mathbf{Re}\, f(a^{(p)}) \geqq M]$
$\Rightarrow \inf \mathbf{Re}\, f(X) \geqq M.$

2′, 3′): *Same as* 2, 3) *with* **Im** *replacing* **Re**.

§12. HENSEL'S LEMMA. CONTINUITY OF ALGEBROID FUNCTIONS

§12A. *Hensel's lemma*

DEFINITION. Let $(R, \mathfrak{m})$ be a quasilocal ring. For any element r in R let $\bar{r}$ denote the residue class of r mod $\mathfrak{m}$. For any $F(y) \in R[y]$ let $\bar{F}(y)$ denote the polynomial in y obtained by reducing mod $\mathfrak{m}$ the coefficients of $F(y)$.

A *Henselian ring*[1] is a quasilocal ring $(R, \mathfrak{m})$ such that the following holds: If $F(y)$ is a monic polynomial in $R[y]$, and $\bar{F}(y) = G_1(y)...G_p(y)$ where $G_1(y),..., G_p(y)$ are pairwise coprime monic polynomials in $(R/\mathfrak{m})[y]$, then there exist monic polynomials $F_1(y),..., F_p(y)$ in $R[y]$ such that $F(y) = F_1(y)...F_p(y)$ and $\bar{F}_i(y) = G_i(y)$ for $i = 1,..., p$.

Now let R be either a complete Hausdorff quasilocal integral domain or $R = K[\langle x_1,..., x_n \rangle]$. Let $F(y) \in R[y]$ be given which is monic of degree $d > 0$ in y. Assume that $R/\mathfrak{m}$ is algebraically closed. Then

$$\bar{F}(y) = \prod_{j=1}^{p} (y - a_j)^{u_j}, \qquad u_j > 0,$$

where $a_1,..., a_p$ are distinct elements in $R/\mathfrak{m}$. Take $b_1 \in R$ such that $\bar{b}_1 = a_1$. Let $G(y) = F(y + b_1)$. Then $G(y)$ is a monic polynomial of degree d in y with coefficients in R and the wideg of $G(y)$ in y relative to R is u_1. By Preparation Theorem (resp: 10.2.3, 10.2.4; or 10.3.2, 10.3.3) we get $G(y) = \delta(y)G^*(y)$ where $\delta(y)$ and $G^*(y)$ are monic polynomials of degrees $d - u_1$ and u_1 in y with coefficients in R, $\delta(0)$ is a unit in R, and $\bar{G}^*(y) = y^{u_1}$. Let $F_1(y) = G^*(y - b_1)$ and $F^*(y) = \delta(y - b_1)$. Then $F_1(y)$ and $F^*(y)$ are monic polynomials in $R[y]$,

$$F(y) = F_1(y)F^*(y), \qquad \bar{F}_1(y) = (y - a_1)^{u_1}, \qquad \bar{F}^*(y) = \prod_{j=2}^{p} (y - a_j)^{u_j}.$$

Repeat the above argument with $F^*(y)$ replacing $F(y)$; and so on. There results the factorization of $F(y)$ into monic polynomials $F_1(y),..., F_p(y)$ in $R[y]$:

$$F(y) = F_1(y)... F_p(y); \qquad \bar{F}_j(y) = (y - a_j)^{u_j} \quad \text{for} \quad j = 1,..., p.$$

This shows that R is Henselian in case $R/\mathfrak{m}$ is algebraically closed. When $R/\mathfrak{m}$ is not necessarily algebraically closed, in the above argument taking $p = 2$, $a_1 = a$, $a_2 = 0$, $u_1 = 1$, $u_2 = e$, we get that: If $\bar{F}(y) = (y - a)y^e$, $0 \neq a \in R/\mathfrak{m}$, then $F(y) = (y - b)F^*(y)$ where $F^*(y)$ is a monic polynomial in $R[y]$ with $\bar{F}^*(y) = y^e$, and $b \in R$ with $\bar{b} = a$.

Thus we have proved (12.1) and (12.2).

(12.1) *Let* $(R, \mathfrak{m})$ *be either a complete Hausdorff quasilocal integral domain*[2] *or let* $R = K[\langle x_1,..., x_n \rangle]$.[3] *If* $F(y)$ *is a monic polynomial in* y

[1] This concept was introduced by Azumaya and was further studied by Nagata [**1**].

[2] This includes the case of $R = K[[x_1,..., x_n]]$.

[3] In case of $R = K[[x_1,..., x_n]]$ or $K[\langle x_1,..., x_n \rangle]$, $R/\mathfrak{m}$ is naturally isomorphic to K.

with coefficients in R, *such that* $\bar{F}(y) = (y - a)y^e$ *with* $0 \neq a \in R/\mathfrak{m}$, *then there exists* $b \in R$ *and a monic polynomial* $F^*(y)$ *in* $R[y]$ *such that* $F(y) = (y - b)F^*(y)$, $\bar{b} = a$, $\bar{F}^*(y) = y^e$.

(**12.2**) Hensel's Lemma. *Let* R *be as in* (12.1) *and assume that* $R/\mathfrak{m}$ *is algebraically closed. Then* R *is Henselian.*

§12B. *Algebroid functions—Continuity of roots*

Let K be algebraically closed complete nondiscrete valued. Let $y = (y_1, \ldots, y_e)$, and $S = K[\langle y \rangle]$. For any $\beta \in K^e$, $D > 0$, let

$$Y\langle D, \beta \rangle = \{b \in K^e : |b_i - \beta_i| < D; i = 1, \ldots, e\}.$$

For any $\gamma \in K$, $E > 0$, let

$$Z\langle E, \gamma \rangle = \{c \in K : |c - \gamma| < E\}.$$

Let

$$f(y, z) = \sum_{\nu=0}^{d} f_\nu(y) z^\nu, \qquad f_\nu \in S, \qquad f_d = 1, \qquad d > 0.$$

Let Y be a neighborhood of the origin in K^e in which $f_0, \ldots, f_d$ are convergent. For any $b \in Y$, $c \in K$, with $f(b, c) = 0$, let $l(b, c) > 0$ be the multiplicity of this root, i.e.,

$$f(b, z) = (z - c)^{l(b,c)} f^*(z) \qquad \text{with} \qquad f^*(z) \in K[z], \qquad f^*(c) \neq 0.$$

Obviously, $f(b, z)$ is a monic polynomial of degree d in z with coefficients in K and hence if $c^{(1)}, \ldots, c^{(N)}$ are the distinct roots of $f(b, z) = 0$ in K then

$$\sum_{\theta=1}^{N} l(b, c^{(\theta)}) = d.$$

(**12.3**) *Let* $\beta \in Y$ *be given. Let* $\gamma^{(\theta)}$, $(\theta = 1, \ldots, N)$, *be the distinct roots of* $f(\beta, z) = 0$ *in* K. *Let* $D^* > 0$, $E > 0$, *be given such that*

$$Y\langle D^*, \beta \rangle \subset Y, \qquad \text{and}$$

$$Z\langle E, \gamma^{(\theta)} \rangle \cap Z\langle E, \gamma^{(\theta')} \rangle = \emptyset \qquad \text{for all} \quad \theta \neq \theta'.$$

Then there exists $0 < D \leqq D^*$ *for which the following holds.*

Given $b \in Y\langle D, \beta \rangle$, *let* $c^{(\theta,\lambda)}$, $(\lambda = 1, \ldots, N^{(\theta)})$, *be the distinct roots of* $f(b, z) = 0$ *in* $Z\langle E, \gamma^{(\theta)} \rangle$. *Then*

$$\sum_{\lambda=1}^{N^{(\theta)}} l(b, c^{(\theta,\lambda)}) = l(\beta, \gamma^{(\theta)}) \qquad \text{for} \quad \theta = 1, \ldots, N.$$

Hence in particular, $c^{(\theta,\lambda)} \neq c^{(\theta',\lambda')}$ *if* $\theta \neq \theta'$ *or* $\lambda \neq \lambda'$; *and all the roots of* $f(b,z) = 0$ *in* K *are contained in*

$$\bigcup_{\theta=1}^{N} \langle E, \gamma^{(\theta)} \rangle.$$

If $l(\beta, \gamma^{(\theta)}) = 1$ *for a particular value of* θ, *then there exists* $\xi \in S$ *such that for all* $b \in Y\langle D, \beta \rangle$ *we have that* ξ *is convergent at* $(b_1 - \beta_1, \ldots, b_e - \beta_e)$ *and* $\xi(b_1 - \beta_1, \ldots, b_e - \beta_e)$ *is the (unique simple) root of* $f(b, z) = 0$ *in* $Z\langle E, \gamma^{(\theta)} \rangle$.

Proof. Replacing $f(y, z)$ by

$$\sum_{\nu=0}^{d} (\boldsymbol{\tau}_\beta f_\nu(y)) z^\nu,$$

we may assume that $\beta = (0) = (0, \ldots, 0) =$ the origin in K^e. Then by (12.2),

$$f(y, z) = \prod_{\theta=1}^{N} F^{(\theta)}(y, z - \gamma^{(\theta)})$$

where $F^{(\theta)}(y, z)$ is a distinguished polynomial of degree $l(\beta, \gamma^{(\theta)})$ in z with coefficients in S. By (11.3) we can find $0 < D_\theta \leqq D^*$ such that all the coefficients of $F^{(\theta)}(y, z)$ are convergent in $Y\langle D_\theta, (0) \rangle$, and for all $b \in Y\langle D_\theta, (0) \rangle$ all the roots of $F^{(\theta)}(b, z) = 0$ in K have absolute value less than E. It suffices to take $D = \min(D_1, \ldots, D_N)$. If $l((0), \gamma^{(\theta)}) = 1$ for a particular value of θ, then $F^{(\theta)}(y, z) = z - \bar{\xi}$ with $\bar{\xi} \in S$ which is convergent in $Y\langle D, (0) \rangle$, and it suffices to take $\gamma^{(\theta)} + \bar{\xi}$ for ξ.

§12C. *Algebroid polycylinders—Continuity of roots*

Let K be algebraically closed complete nondiscrete valued. Let $y = (y_1, \ldots, y_e)$, $S = K[\langle y \rangle]$, $z = (z_1, \ldots, z_m)$. Let $\pi: K^e \times K^m \to K^e$ be the natural projection. For any $\beta \in K^e$, $\gamma \in K^m$, $D > 0$, $E > 0$, let

$$Y\langle D, \beta \rangle = \{b \in K^e: |b_i - \beta_i| < D; \quad i = 1, \ldots, e\}$$
$$Z\langle E, \gamma \rangle = \{c \in K^m: |c_i - \gamma_i| < E; \quad i = 1, \ldots, m\}.$$

Let

$$g_i(y, z_i) = \sum_{\nu=0}^{d_i} g_{i\nu}(y) z_i^\nu, \quad g_{i\nu} \in S, \quad g_{id_i} = 1, \quad d_i > 0; \quad i = 1, \ldots, m.$$

Let Y be a neighborhood of the origin in K^e in which all the coefficients $g_{i\nu}$ are convergent. Let

$$W = \{(b, c) \in Y \times K^m: g_i(b, c_i) = 0 \text{ for } i = 1, \ldots, m\}.$$

For any $b \in Y$ and $c_i \in K$ let $l_i(b, c_i)$ be the order of zero of $g_i(b, z_i)$ at c_i, i.e.,

$$g_i(b, z_i) = (z_i - c_i)^{l_i(b,c_i)} g_i^*(z_i) \quad \text{with} \quad g_i^*(z_i) \in K[z_i], \quad g_i^*(c_i) \neq 0.$$

For any $a = (b, c) \in Y \times K^m$ let

$$l(a) = \prod_{i=1}^{m} l_i(b, c_i).$$

Then obviously $l(a)$ is a nonnegative integer; $l(a) > 0 \Leftrightarrow a \in W$; and for any $b \in Y$ we have

$$\sum_{a \in W \cap \pi^{-1}(b)} l(a) = d_1 \dots d_m.$$

(12.4) *Let $\beta \in Y$ be given. Let $\alpha^{(\theta)} = (\beta, \gamma^{(\theta)})$, $(\theta = 1, \dots, N)$, be the distinct points in $W \cap \pi^{-1}(\beta)$. Let $D^* > 0$, $E > 0$, be given such that*

$$Y\langle D^*, \beta\rangle \subset Y, \qquad \textit{and}$$

$$Z\langle E, \gamma^{(\theta)}\rangle \cap Z\langle E, \gamma^{(\theta')}\rangle = \emptyset \qquad \textit{for all} \qquad \theta \neq \theta'.$$

Then there exists $0 < D \leqq D^*$ such that the following holds.

i) $W \cap (Y\langle D, \beta\rangle \times K^m) = \bigcup_{\theta=1}^{N} [W \cap (Y\langle D, \beta\rangle \times Z\langle E, \gamma^{(\theta)}\rangle)]$.

ii) *For all* $b \in Y\langle D, \beta\rangle$ *we have*

$$\sum_{a \in W \cap (b \times Z\langle E, \gamma^{(\theta)}\rangle)} l(a) = l(\alpha^{(\theta)}) \qquad \text{for} \qquad \theta = 1, \dots, N;$$

and hence in particular

$$\pi[W \cap (Y\langle D, \beta\rangle \times Z\langle E, \gamma^{(\theta)}\rangle)] = Y\langle D, \beta\rangle \qquad \text{for} \qquad \theta = 1, \dots, N.$$

iii) *If $l(\alpha^{(\theta)}) = 1$ for a particular value of θ, then there exists $\xi = (\xi_1, \dots, \xi_m) \in S^m$ which is convergent in $Y\langle D, (0, \dots, 0)\rangle$ such that*

$$W \cap (Y\langle D, \beta\rangle \times Z\langle E, \gamma^{(\theta)}\rangle)$$
$$= \{(b, \xi(b_1 - \beta_1, \dots, b_e - \beta_e)) : b \in Y\langle D, \beta\rangle\}.$$

PROOF. For given i, take $g_i(y, z_i)$ for $f(y, z)$ in (12.3); then D^* and E satisfy the conditions of (12.3) and hence by (12.3) we can find $0 < D_i \leqq D^*$ such that the following holds: Given $b \in Y\langle D_i, \beta\rangle$, let $c_i^{(\theta,\lambda)}$, $(\lambda = 1, \dots, N_i^{(\theta)})$, be the distinct roots of $g_i(b, z_i) = 0$ in K for which $|c_i^{(\theta,\lambda)} - \gamma_i^{(\theta)}| < E$; then

$$1_i^\circ) \qquad \sum_{\lambda=1}^{N_i^{(\theta)}} l_i(b, c_i^{(\theta,\lambda)}) = l(\beta, \gamma_i^{(\theta)}) \qquad \text{for} \qquad \theta = 1, \dots, N;$$

if $l_i(\beta, \gamma^{(\theta)}) = 1$ for a particular value of θ then there exists $\xi_i \in S$ such that for all $b \in Y\langle D_i, \beta\rangle$ we have that ξ_i is convergent at $(b_1 - \beta_1,\ldots, b_m - \beta_m)$ and $\xi_i(b_1 - \beta_1,\ldots, b_m - \beta_m) = c_i^{(\theta,1)}$.

Take $D = \min(D_1,\ldots, D_m)$. Let $\theta \leqq N$ be given and assume that $b \in Y\langle D, \beta\rangle$. Let

$$a^{(\theta,\mu_1,\ldots,\mu_m)} = (b, c_1^{(\theta,\mu_1)},\ldots, c_m^{(\theta,\mu_m)}), \qquad (1 \leqq \mu_i \leqq N_i^{(\theta)}), \qquad (i = 1,\ldots, m).$$

Then these $N_1^{(\theta)}\ldots N_m^{(\theta)}$ points $a^{(\theta,\mu_1,\ldots,\mu_m)}$ are all distinct and they are exactly all the points in $W \cap (b \times Z\langle E, \gamma^{(\theta)}\rangle)$. Now

$$\begin{aligned}
&\sum_{1\leqq\mu_1\leqq N_1^{(\theta)},\ldots,1\leqq\mu_m\leqq N_m^{(\theta)}} l(a^{(\theta,\mu_1,\ldots,\mu_m)}) \\
&= \sum_{1\leqq\mu_1\leqq N_1^{(\theta)},\ldots,1\leqq\mu_m\leqq N_m^{(\theta)}} \prod_{i=1}^{m} l_i(b, c_i^{(\theta,\mu_i)}) \\
&= \prod_{i=1}^{m} \sum_{\lambda=1}^{N_i^{(\theta)}} l_i(b, c_i^{(\theta,\lambda)}) \\
&= \prod_{i=1}^{m} l_i(\beta, \gamma_i^{(\theta)}) \qquad \text{by } (1_1^\circ,\ldots, 1_m^\circ) \\
&= l(\alpha^{(\theta)}).
\end{aligned}$$

This proves ii) and also iii). Next, we have

$$\begin{aligned}
&\sum_{\theta=1}^{N} \sum_{1\leqq\mu_1\leqq N_1^{(\theta)},\ldots,1\leqq\mu_m\leqq N_m^{(\theta)}} l(a^{(\theta,\mu_1,\ldots,\mu_m)}) \\
&= \sum_{\theta=1}^{N} l(\alpha^{(\theta)}) \\
&= d_1\ldots d_m
\end{aligned}$$

and hence $a^{(\theta,\mu_1,\ldots,\mu_m)}$ for the various values of $\theta, \mu_1,\ldots, \mu_m$ give all the points in $W \cap \pi^{-1}(b)$. Therefore

$$W \cap (b \times K^m) = \bigcup_{\theta=1}^{N} [W \cap (b \times Z\langle E, \gamma^{(\theta)}\rangle)].$$

This proves i).

(12.5) *Let V be any nonempty closed subset of W,*[4] *and for any $m' \leqq m$, let $\pi' : K^e\{y\} \times K^m\{z\} \to K^e\{y\} \times K^{m'}\{z_1,\ldots, z_{m'}\}$ be the natural projection.*[5]

[4] For instance $V = W$.

[5] $\pi' = \pi$ if $m' = 0$.

Then we have the following.

1) *Let* $(a^{(p)})_{p=1,2,\ldots}$ *be any sequence of points in* V *such that the sequence* $(\pi' a^{(p)})$ *contains a subsequence converging to a point in* $Y \times K^{m'}$. *Then the sequence* $(a^{(p)})$ *contains a subsequence converging to a point in* V.

2) *The map* $V \to Y \times K^{m'}$ *induced by* π' *is proper and closed; in particular* $\pi'(V)$ *is a closed subset of* $Y \times K^{m'}$.

Proof of 1). The assumption implies that $(\pi a^{(p)})$ contains a subsequence converging to a point β in Y. Upon replacing $(a^{(p)})$ by a subsequence, we may assume that

$$\lim_{p\to\infty} b^{(p)} = \beta \qquad \text{where} \qquad b^{(p)} = \pi a^{(p)}.$$

Since V is closed in W, it suffices to show that $(a^{(p)})$ contains a subsequence converging to a point in W. Let $\alpha^{(\theta)} = (\beta, \gamma^{(\theta)})$, $(\theta = 1,\ldots, N)$, be the distinct points in $W \cap \pi^{-1}(\beta)$. By (12.4) we can find positive real numbers

$$D_1 > D_2 > \ldots, \quad D_p \to 0; \qquad E_1 > E_2 > \ldots, \quad E_p \to 0;$$

such that:

$$Y\langle D_1, \beta\rangle \subset Y;$$

$$Z\langle E_1, \gamma^{(\theta)}\rangle \cap Z\langle E_1, \gamma^{(\theta')}\rangle = \emptyset \qquad \text{for all} \qquad \theta \neq \theta';$$

and

$$W \cap \pi^{-1}(Y\langle D_p, \beta\rangle) = \bigcup_{\theta=1}^{N} [W \cap (Y\langle D_p, \beta\rangle \times Z\langle E_p, \gamma^{(\theta)}\rangle)] \qquad \text{for all} \qquad p > 0.$$

Since $b^{(p)} \to \beta$, upon replacing $(a^{(p)})$ by a subsequence, we can arrange that $b^{(p)} \in Y\langle D_p, \beta\rangle$ for all $p > 0$. Then in particular, $a^{(p)} \in W \cap \pi^{-1}(Y\langle D_1, \beta\rangle)$ for all $p > 0$. Now $W \cap \pi^{-1}(Y\langle D_1, \beta\rangle)$ equals the union of the finite number of pairwise disjoint sets

$$W \cap (Y\langle D_1, \beta\rangle \times Z\langle E_1, \gamma^{(\theta)}\rangle), \qquad (\theta = 1,\ldots, N).$$

Consequently we can find a value of θ and a sequence $p(1) < p(2) < \ldots$ of positive integers such that

$$a^{(p(n))} \in W \cap (Y\langle D_1, \beta\rangle \times Z\langle E_1, \gamma^{(\theta)}\rangle) \qquad \text{for all} \qquad n > 0.$$

Now for all $n > 0$ we have that $b^{(p(n))} \in Y\langle D_{p(n)}, \beta\rangle$ and

$$\begin{aligned} &W \cap (Y\langle D_{p(n)}, \beta\rangle \times Z\langle E_1, \gamma^{(\theta)}\rangle) \\ &= W \cap (Y\langle D_{p(n)}, \beta\rangle \times Z\langle E_{p(n)}, \gamma^{(\theta)}\rangle). \end{aligned}$$

Therefore

$$a^{(p(n))} \in Y(D_{p(n)}, \beta\rangle \times Z\langle E_{p(n)}, \gamma^{(\theta)}\rangle \qquad \text{for all} \qquad n > 0.$$

Therefore

$$\lim_{n\to\infty} a^{(p(n))} = (\beta, \gamma^{(\theta)}) \in W.$$

Proof of 2). Let V^* be any closed subset of V. Given β' in the closure of $\pi'(V^*)$ in $Y \times K^{m'}$ we can write

$$\beta' = \lim_{p\to\infty} \pi' a^{(p)}$$

with $a^{(p)} \in V^*$. By 1), $(a^{(p)})$ contains a subsequence converging to a point α in V. Since V^* is closed in V, we get $\alpha \in V^*$ and hence $\beta' = \pi'\alpha \in \pi'(V^*)$. Therefore $\pi'(V^*)$ is closed in $Y \times K^{m'}$. Now let Ω be any compact subset of $Y \times K^{m'}$. Let $(a^{(p)})$ be any sequence in $(\pi'|V)^{-1}(\Omega)$. Since Ω is compact, $(\pi' a^{(p)})$ contains a subsequence converging to a point in $Y \times K^{m'}$. Hence by 1), $(a^{(p)})$ contains a subsequence converging to a point α in V. Now $(\pi'|V)^{-1}(\Omega)$ is a closed subset of V and hence $\alpha \in (\pi'|V)^{-1}(\Omega)$. Therefore $(\pi'|V)^{-1}(\Omega)$ is compact.

§13. COMPLEX WEIERSTRASS PREPARATION THEOREM

In this section we shall present Weierstrass' original treatment of the preparation theorem in $\mathbf{C}^n$. In doing so we get a supplementary result giving bounds for the quotient q and the remainder r.[1] For notational convenience we write $(y, z) = (y_1,\dots, y_{n-1}, z)$ for $(x_1,\dots, x_n)$. For any $B \in \mathbf{R}^{n-1}_{++}$, by "$0 < D < B$" we mean "$D \in \mathbf{R}^{n-1}_{++}$ and $D_1 < B_1,\dots, D_{n-1} < B_{n-1}$" and by "$D > B$" we mean "$D \in \mathbf{R}^{n-1}_{++}$ and $D_1 > B_1,\dots, D_{n-1} > B_{n-1}$". For any $B \in \mathbf{R}^{n-1}_{++}$ and $C \in \mathbf{R}_{++}$ let

$$\begin{aligned}
Y\langle B\rangle &= \{y \in \mathbf{C}^{n-1} : |y_1| < B_1,\dots, |y_{n-1}| < B_{n-1}\},\\
\bar{Y}\langle B\rangle &= \{y \in \mathbf{C}^{n-1} : |y_1| \leqq B_1,\dots, |y_{n-1}| \leqq B_{n-1}\},\\
Z\langle C\rangle &= \{z \in \mathbf{C}^1 : |z| < C\},\\
\bar{Z}\langle C\rangle &= \{z \in \mathbf{C}^1 : |z| \leqq C\},\\
\Gamma\langle C\rangle &= \text{circle in } \mathbf{C}^1 \text{ of radius } C \text{ around the origin.}
\end{aligned}$$

(13.1) WEIERSTRASS DIVISION FORMULA. *Let*

$$F(y, z) = z^d + F_1(y)z^{d-1} + \dots + F_d(y), \qquad d \geqq 0,$$

$B \in \mathbf{R}^{n-1}_{++}$, $C \in \mathbf{R}_{++}$. *Assume that* $F_1(y),\dots, F_d(y)$ *are analytic on a neighborhood* Y *of* $\bar{Y}\langle B\rangle$ *in* $\mathbf{C}^{n-1}$ *and* $F(b, c) \neq 0$ *whenever* $(b, c) \in \bar{Y}\langle B\rangle \times \Gamma\langle C\rangle$.

[1] In reference to (10.3.1).

Let $g(y, z)$ be analytic on a neighborhood X of $\bar{Y}\langle B\rangle \times \bar{Z}\langle C\rangle$ in $\mathbf{C}^n$. Then there exist $B' > B$, $C' > C$, such that $Y\langle B'\rangle \subset Y$, $Y\langle B'\rangle \times \bar{Z}\langle C'\rangle \subset X$, and $F(b, c) \neq 0$ whenever $b \in Y\langle B'\rangle$ and $C \leqq |c| \leqq C'$. For any $(y, z) \in Y\langle B'\rangle \times Z\langle C'\rangle$ let

$$Q(y, z) = \frac{1}{2\pi i} \int_{\Gamma\langle C'\rangle} \frac{g(y, \zeta)}{F(y, \zeta)} \frac{d\zeta}{\zeta - z}$$

and

$$r(y, z) = g(y, z) - Q(y, z)F(y, z).$$

Then $Q(y, z)$ is analytic on $Y\langle B'\rangle \times Z\langle C'\rangle$; and

$$r(y, z) = \sum_{0 \leqq \nu < d} r_\nu(y) z^\nu$$

with $r_\nu(y)$ analytic on $Y\langle B'\rangle$.[2]

Furthermore

$$\sup|Q(\bar{Y}\langle B\rangle \times \bar{Z}\langle C\rangle)| \leqq M \sup|g(\bar{Y}\langle B\rangle \times \bar{Z}\langle C\rangle)|;$$
$$\sup|r(\bar{Y}\langle B\rangle \times \bar{Z}\langle C\rangle)| \leqq M \sup|g(\bar{Y}\langle B\rangle \times \bar{Z}\langle C\rangle)|;$$
$$\sup|r_\nu(\bar{Y}\langle B\rangle)| \leqq M \sup|g(\bar{Y}\langle B\rangle \times \bar{Z}\langle C\rangle)|, \qquad 0 \leqq \nu < d;$$

where M is a positive constant depending only on B, C, F and not on g.

PROOF. Existence of B', C' follows from the compactness of $\bar{Y}\langle B\rangle \times \Gamma\langle C\rangle$. Now the integrand in the definition of Q is continuous on $Y\langle B'\rangle \times Z\langle C'\rangle \times \Gamma\langle C'\rangle\{\zeta\}$ and for each $\zeta \in \Gamma\langle C'\rangle$ it has derivatives $\partial/\partial y_1, \ldots, \partial/\partial y_{n-1}, \partial/\partial z$ on $Y\langle B'\rangle \times Z\langle C'\rangle$. Therefore[3] Q is continuous on $Y\langle B'\rangle \times Z\langle C'\rangle$ and $\partial Q/\partial y_1, \ldots, \partial Q/\partial y_{n-1}, \partial Q/\partial z$ exist there. Hence Q is analytic on $Y\langle B'\rangle \times Z\langle C'\rangle$ and hence so is r. For fixed y, applying the one variable Cauchy formula (4.2.4) with respect to z we get

$$g(y, z) = \frac{1}{2\pi i} \int_{\Gamma\langle C'\rangle} \frac{g(y, \zeta)}{\zeta - z} d\zeta.$$

Hence

$$r(y, z) = \frac{1}{2\pi i} \int_{\Gamma\langle C'\rangle} \left(\frac{g(y, \zeta)}{F(y, \zeta)}\right)\left(\frac{F(y, \zeta) - F(y, z)}{\zeta - z}\right) d\zeta.$$

[2] Note that we are not assuming that $F_1(0) = \ldots = F_d(0) = 0$; and we do not claim that Q is the only analytic function such that $\deg_z(g - QF) < d$.

[3] By continuity and differentiation under integral, see (4.1.3, 4.1.4).

From the form of F we get

$$\frac{F(y,\zeta)-F(y,z)}{\zeta-z}=\sum_{0\leqq\nu<d}h_\nu(y,\zeta)z^\nu$$

where $h_\nu(y,z)$ is analytic on $Y\times\mathbf{C}^1\{z\}$. Hence for $(y,z)\in Y\langle B'\rangle\times Z\langle C'\rangle$ we have

$$r(y,z)=\sum_{0\leqq\nu<d}r_\nu(y)z^\nu$$

where

$$r_\nu(y)=\frac{1}{2\pi i}\int_{\Gamma\langle C'\rangle}\frac{g(y,\zeta)h_\nu(y,\zeta)}{F(y,\zeta)}d\zeta$$

is analytic on $Y\langle B'\rangle$.[3] Given $y\in Y\langle B'\rangle$, by compactness, $F(y,\zeta)$ is nowhere zero on a neighborhood of $\{\zeta: C\leqq|\zeta|\leqq C'\}$ and hence the above integrand is analytic on that neighborhood; whence by Cauchy formula (4.2.2) we get

$$1°)\quad r_\nu(\zeta)=\frac{1}{2\pi i}\int_{\Gamma\langle C\rangle}\frac{g(y,\zeta)h_\nu(y,\zeta)}{F(y,\zeta)}d\zeta\qquad\text{for all}\qquad y\in\bar{Y}\langle B\rangle.$$

Now $F(y,\zeta)$ is continuous and nowhere zero on the compact set $\bar{Y}\langle B\rangle\times\Gamma\langle C\rangle$ and hence $|F(y,\zeta)|$ is greater than a positive constant there; the functions $h_\nu(y,\zeta)$ are determined by F and they are continuous on the compact set $\bar{Y}\langle B\rangle\times\Gamma\langle C\rangle$; therefore by 1°) we get

$$\begin{aligned}\sup|r_\nu(\bar{Y}\langle B\rangle)|&\leqq N\sup|g(\bar{Y}\langle B\rangle\times\Gamma\langle C\rangle)|\\&\leqq N\sup|g(\bar{Y}\langle B\rangle\times\bar{Z}\langle C\rangle)|,\qquad 0\leqq\nu<d,\end{aligned}$$

and hence

$$\sup|r(\bar{Y}\langle B\rangle\times\bar{Z}\langle C\rangle)|\leqq N'\sup|g(\bar{Y}\langle B\rangle\times\bar{Z}\langle C\rangle)|$$

where N and N' are positive constants depending only on B, C, F. Now $|F(y,z)|$ is greater than a positive constant on $\bar{Y}\langle B\rangle\times\Gamma\langle C\rangle$ and hence at every point there we have

$$\begin{aligned}|Q|=|(g-r)/F|&\leqq|g/F|+|r/F|\\&\leqq N''\sup|g(\bar{Y}\langle B\rangle\times\Gamma\langle C\rangle)|\end{aligned}$$

where N'' is a positive constant depending only on B, C, F. By the one variable maximum principle (4.12.1), for any $y\in\bar{Y}\langle B\rangle$ we have

$$\sup|Q(y\times\bar{Z}\langle C\rangle)|\leqq\sup|Q(y\times\Gamma\langle C\rangle)|.$$

Therefore

$$\sup|Q(\bar{Y}\langle B\rangle \times \bar{Z}\langle C\rangle)| \leqq N'' \sup|g(\bar{Y}\langle B\rangle \times \bar{Z}\langle C\rangle)|.$$

Take $M = \max(N, N', N'')$. Q.E.D.

(13.2) *Let $f(y, z)$ be analytic on a neighborhood $\hat{X}$ of the origin in $\mathbf{C}^n$. Let $d = \mathbf{o}_0 f(0, z)$. Assume that $d < \infty$. Let $\hat{B} \in \mathbf{R}^{n-1}_{++}$ and $\hat{C} \in \mathbf{R}_{++}$ be given such that $Y\langle\hat{B}\rangle \times Z\langle\hat{C}\rangle \subset \hat{X}$. Then there exists $0 < C < \hat{C}$ such that $f(0, c) \neq 0$ whenever $0 < |c| \leqq C$. For any such C there exists $0 < B^{**} < \hat{B}$ such that $f(b, c) \neq 0$ whenever $(b, c) \in Y\langle B^{**}\rangle \times \Gamma\langle C\rangle$. For any such B^{**} and C we have the following.*

1) *There exist unique functions $F_1(y), \ldots, F_d(y)$ analytic on $Y\langle B^{**}\rangle$ such that upon putting*

$$F(y, z) = z^d + F_1(y)z^{d-1} + \ldots + F_d(y),$$

for any $(b, c) \in Y\langle B^{**}\rangle \times \mathbf{C}^1\{z\}$ we have:

i) $F(b, c) = 0 \Rightarrow |c| < C$; and
ii) $|c| < C \Rightarrow \mathbf{o}_c F(b, z) = \mathbf{o}_c f(b, z)$.

In particular $F_1(0) = \ldots = F_d(0) = 0$, and $F(y, z)$ has no zeroes in $Y\langle B^{**}\rangle \times \{z\colon |z| \geqq C\}$.

PROOF. Existence of C is obvious and then the existence of B^{**} follows by compactness of $\Gamma\langle C\rangle$. For any $y \in Y\langle B^{**}\rangle$, $f(y, z)$ has exactly d zeroes in $Z\langle C\rangle$.[4] Label these zeroes arbitrarily as $z_1(y), \ldots, z_d(y)$. Let

$$\psi_k(y) = \sum_{\mu=1}^{d} (z_\mu(y))^k \quad \text{and} \quad f_z(y, z) = \frac{\partial f(y, z)}{\partial z}.$$

Taking z for x and $\varphi(z) = z^k$ in (4.2.6) we get

$$\psi_k(y) = \frac{1}{2\pi i} \int_{\Gamma\langle C\rangle} \frac{z^k f_z(y, z)}{f(y, z)} dz \qquad \text{for all} \quad y \in Y\langle B^{**}\rangle.$$

Hence[3] $\psi_k(y)$ is analytic on $Y\langle B^{**}\rangle$. From elementary algrebra we know that the elementary symmetric functions in indeterminates $T_1, \ldots, T_d$ can be expressed as polynomials in

$$\sum_{\mu=1}^{d} T_\mu^k, \qquad (k = 1, \ldots, d),$$

[4] Zeroes counted with their orders. Proof by (4.2.7, 4.1.3).

with integer coefficients. Therefore the elementary symmetric functions $F_1(y),\dots, F_d(y)$ of $z_1(y),\dots, z_d(y)$ are analytic on $Y\langle B^{**}\rangle$.

As a corollary of 1) we get

2) *Assume that* $d = 1$, *i.e.*, $f(0, 0) = 0$ *and* $(\partial f/\partial z)(0, 0) \neq 0$. *Then for all* $y \in Y\langle B^{**}\rangle$, $f(y, z) = 0$ *has a unique (simple) root* $z(y)$ *in* $Z\langle C\rangle$, *and the function* $z(y)$ *is analytic on* $Y\langle B^{**}\rangle$.[5]

REMARK. Clearly F is meant to be the distinguished polynomial associated with f. Thus we want to show that f/F is analytic and nowhere zero on $Y\langle B^{**}\rangle \times Z\langle C\rangle$. If f/F were analytic then by the one variable Cauchy formula (4.2.4) it must be equal to

$$\frac{1}{2\pi i}\int_{\Gamma\langle C\rangle} \frac{f(y, \zeta)}{F(y, \zeta)}\frac{d\zeta}{\zeta - z}.$$

Since $F(y, \zeta)$ is nowhere zero on $Y\langle B^{**}\rangle \times \Gamma\langle C\rangle$, the above integral makes sense. This motivates the following statement and its proof.

3)[6] *Given* $0 < B^* < B^{**}$ *there exists* $C < C^* < \hat{C}$ *such that* $f(b, c) \neq 0$ *whenever* $b \in Y\langle B^*\rangle$ *and* $C \leqq |c| \leqq C^*$. *Let*

$$\delta(y, z) = \frac{1}{2\pi i}\int_{\Gamma\langle C^*\rangle} \frac{f(y, \zeta)}{F(y, \zeta)}\frac{d\zeta}{\zeta - z}.$$

Then δ *is analytic and nowhere zero on* $Y\langle B^*\rangle \times Z\langle C^*\rangle$ *and there we have* $f = \delta F$.

PROOF. Existence of C^* follows by compactness of $\bar{Y}\langle B^*\rangle \times \Gamma\langle C\rangle$. For any $y \in Y\langle B^*\rangle$ let

$$\tilde{\delta}(y, z) = \frac{f(y, z)}{F(y, z)} \quad \text{if} \quad |z| < \hat{C} \quad \text{and} \quad z \neq z_1(y),\dots, z_d(y);$$

and

$$\tilde{\delta}(y, z_\mu((y)) = \lim_{z\to z_\mu(y)} \frac{f(y, z)}{F(y, z)}.$$

Then for each $y \in Y\langle B^*\rangle$, $\tilde{\delta}(y, z)$ is analytic on a neighborhood of $\bar{Z}\langle C^*\rangle$ and hence by the one variable Cauchy formula (4.2.4), $\tilde{\delta} = \delta$ on $Y\langle B^*\rangle \times Z\langle C^*\rangle$. Furthermore, $\tilde{\delta}(y, \zeta)/(\zeta - z)$ is continuous on

[5] For an arbitrary complete nondiscrete valued field K, (13.2.2) was proved in (10.8).
[6] Classically this was called the Weierstrass Preparation Theorem.

$Y\langle B^*\rangle \times Z\langle C^*\rangle \times \Gamma\langle C^*\rangle\{\zeta\}$ and for each $\zeta \in \Gamma\langle C^*\rangle$ it has derivatives $\partial/\partial y_1, \ldots, \partial/\partial y_{n-1}, \partial/\partial z$ everywhere on $Y\langle B^*\rangle \times Z\langle C^*\rangle$. Hence[3] δ is continuous on $Y\langle B^*\rangle \times Z\langle C^*\rangle$ and $\partial\delta/\partial y_1, \ldots, \partial\delta/\partial y_{n-1}, \partial\delta/\partial z$ exist there. Therefore $\tilde{\delta}$ is analytic on $Y\langle B^*\rangle \times Z\langle C^*\rangle$. On $Y\langle B^*\rangle \times Z\langle C^*\rangle$: obviously $\tilde{\delta}$ is nowhere zero and $f = \tilde{\delta}F$. Q.E.D.

(13.3) *Let $f(y, z) \in \mathbf{C}[\langle y, z\rangle]$ be given. Let $d = \mathbf{o}f(0, z)$.*[7] *Assume that $d < \infty$, i.e., $f(0, z) \neq 0$. Given $g(y, z) \in \mathbf{C}[\langle y, z\rangle]$ there exist unique*

$$q(y, z) \in \mathbf{C}[\langle y, z\rangle] \quad \textit{and} \quad r(y, z) = \sum_{0 \leqq \nu < d} r_\nu(y) z^\nu \in \mathbf{C}[\langle y\rangle][z]$$

such that $g = qf + r$. Furthermore we have the following.

1) *Let $\hat{B} \in \mathbf{R}_{++}^{n-1}$, $\hat{C} \in \mathbf{R}_{++}$ be given such that f is convergent in $Y\langle \hat{B}\rangle \times Z\langle \hat{C}\rangle$. Then there exist $0 < B^* < \hat{B}$ and $0 < C < \hat{C}$, depending only on f and not on g, such that for any $0 < B < B^*$ we have* i) *and* ii).

i) *If g is convergent in $Y\langle B\rangle \times Z\langle C\rangle$ then q and r are convergent in $Y\langle B\rangle \times Z\langle C\rangle$.*[8]

ii) *If g is convergent in a neighborhood of $\bar{Y}\langle B\rangle \times \bar{Z}\langle C\rangle$ then q and r are convergent in a neighborhood of $\bar{Y}\langle B\rangle \times \bar{Z}\langle C\rangle$,*[8] *and*

$$\sup|q(\bar{Y}\langle B\rangle \times \bar{Z}\langle C\rangle)| \leqq A \sup|g(\bar{Y}\langle B\rangle \times \bar{Z}\langle C\rangle)|,$$
$$\sup|r(\bar{Y}\langle B\rangle \times \bar{Z}\langle C\rangle)| \leqq A \sup|g(\bar{Y}\langle B\rangle \times \bar{Z}\langle C\rangle)|,$$
$$\sup|r_\nu(\bar{Y}\langle B\rangle)| \leqq A \sup|g(\bar{Y}\langle B\rangle \times \bar{Z}\langle C\rangle)|, \quad 0 \leqq \nu < d,$$

where A is a positive constant depending only on B, C, f and not on g.

2) *Let $Y^{(1)} \supset Y^{(2)} \supset \ldots \supset Y^{(t)} \supset \ldots$ be any given neighborhood basis of the origin in $\mathbf{C}^{n-1}\{y\}$ consisting of finite open polycylinders. Then upon replacing $Y^{(1)}, Y^{(2)}, \ldots$ by a suitable subsequence we can find positive constants $C^{(1)} > C^{(2)} > \ldots$, $A^{(1)}, A^{(2)}, \ldots$ such that upon setting*

$$\bar{Y}^{(t)} = \textit{closure of } Y^{(t)} \text{ in } \mathbf{C}^{n-1},$$
$$X^{(t)} = Y^{(t)} \times Z\langle C^{(t)}\rangle, \qquad \bar{X}^{(t)} = \bar{Y}^{(t)} \times \bar{Z}\langle C^{(t)}\rangle,$$

for any $t > 0$ and for any $g \in \mathbf{C}[\langle y, z\rangle]$ we have i') *and* ii').

i') *If g is convergent in $X^{(t)}$ then q and r are convergent in $X^{(t)}$.*

[7] Obviously $d = \operatorname{wideg} f(y, z)$ in z relative to $\mathbf{C}[\langle y\rangle]$.

[8] We then obviously have $g(a) = q(a)f(a) + r(a)$ for all a in $Y\langle B\rangle \times Z\langle C\rangle$ (resp: for all a in a neighborhood of $\bar{Y}\langle B\rangle \times \bar{Z}\langle C\rangle$).

ii′) *If g is convergent in a neighborhood of $\bar{X}^{(t)}$ then q and r are convergent in a neighborhood of $\bar{X}^{(t)}$ and*

$$\begin{aligned} \sup|q(\bar{X}^{(t)})| &\leqq A^{(t)} \sup|g(\bar{X}^{(t)})|, \\ \sup|r(\bar{X}^{(t)})| &\leqq A^{(t)} \sup|g(\bar{X}^{(t)})|, \\ \sup|r_\nu(\bar{Y}^{(t)})| &\leqq A^{(t)} \sup|g(\bar{X}^{(t)})|, \qquad 0 \leqq \nu < d. \end{aligned}$$

Proof. The proof of uniqueness of q and r given in (10.2.1) being trivial we take it over here; existence will follow from the proof of 1). Also 2) obviously follows from 1). Hence it suffices to prove 1).

By (13.2.3), we can find $0 < B^* < \hat{B}$, $0 < C < C^* < \hat{C}$,

$$F(y, z) = z^d + F_1(y)z^{d-1} + \ldots + F_d(y),$$

and $\delta(y, z)$, such that:

1°) $\delta(y, z)$ is convergent in $Y\langle B^*\rangle \times Z\langle C^*\rangle$ and $\delta(b, c) \neq 0$ whenever $(b, c) \in Y\langle B^*\rangle \times Z\langle C^*\rangle$;
2°) $F_1(y), \ldots, F_d(y)$ are convergent in $Y\langle B^*\rangle$;
3°) $F(b, c) \neq 0$ whenever $(b, c) \in Y\langle B^*\rangle \times \Gamma\langle C\rangle$;
4°) $f(b, c) = \delta(b, c)F(b, c)$ whenever $(b, c) \in Y\langle B^*\rangle \times Z\langle C^*\rangle$.

Let $0 < B < B^*$ be given.

Suppose g is convergent in a neighborhood of $\bar{Y}\langle B\rangle \times \bar{Z}\langle C\rangle$. By uniqueness we must have $q = Q/\delta$ where Q is as in (13.1). By (13.1), Q and r are convergent in a neighborhood of $\bar{Y}\langle B\rangle \times \bar{Z}\langle C\rangle$, and

$$\begin{aligned} \sup|Q(\bar{Y}\langle B\rangle \times \bar{Z}\langle C\rangle)| &\leqq M \sup|g(\bar{Y}\langle B\rangle \times \bar{Z}\langle C\rangle)|, \\ \sup|r(\bar{Y}\langle B\rangle \times \bar{Z}\langle C\rangle)| &\leqq M \sup|g(\bar{Y}\langle B\rangle \times \bar{Z}\langle C\rangle)|, \\ \sup|r_\nu(\bar{Y}\langle B\rangle)| &\leqq M \sup|g(\bar{Y}\langle B\rangle \times \bar{Z}\langle C\rangle)|, \qquad 0 \leqq \nu < d, \end{aligned}$$

where M is a positive constant depending only on B, C, F. Now δ is nowhere zero on the compact set $\bar{Y}\langle B\rangle \times \bar{Z}\langle C\rangle$; hence q is convergent in a neighborhood of $\bar{Y}\langle B\rangle \times \bar{Z}\langle C\rangle$ and we can find a positive constant A depending only on B, C, f such that

$$\begin{aligned} \sup|q(\bar{Y}\langle B\rangle \times \bar{Z}\langle C\rangle)| &\leqq A \sup|g(\bar{Y}\langle B\rangle \times \bar{Z}\langle C\rangle)|, \\ \sup|r(\bar{Y}\langle B\rangle \times \bar{Z}\langle C\rangle)| &\leqq A \sup|g(\bar{Y}\langle B\rangle \times \bar{Z}\langle C\rangle)|, \\ \sup|r_\nu(\bar{Y}\langle B\rangle)| &\leqq A \sup|g(\bar{Y}\langle B\rangle \times \bar{Z}\langle C\rangle)|, \qquad 0 \leqq \nu < d. \end{aligned}$$

Suppose g is convergent in $\underset{\sim}{Y}\langle B\rangle \times Z\langle C\rangle$. By compactness of $\bar{Y}\langle B\rangle \times \Gamma\langle C\rangle$ we can find $0 < \tilde{C}' < C$ such that $F(b, c) \neq 0$ whenever $b \in \bar{Y}\langle B\rangle$ and $\tilde{C}' < |c| < C$. Given $(b, c) \in \underset{\sim}{Y}\langle B\rangle \times \underset{\sim}{Z}\langle C\rangle$ we can find $0 < \tilde{B} < B$, $\tilde{C}' < \tilde{C} < C$, such that $(b, c) \in \underset{\sim}{Y}\langle \tilde{B}\rangle \times \underset{\sim}{Z}\langle \tilde{C}\rangle$. Now F and

g are convergent in a neighborhood of $\bar{Y}\langle B\rangle \times \bar{Z}\langle C\rangle$ and $F(b,c) \neq 0$ whenever $(b, c) \in \bar{Y}\langle \tilde{B}\rangle \times \Gamma\langle \tilde{C}\rangle$. Hence we may take $\tilde{B}$, $\tilde{C}$ for B, C in (13.1); then the Q found in (13.1) is convergent in a neighborhood of $\bar{Y}\langle \tilde{B}\rangle \times \bar{Z}\langle \tilde{C}\rangle$ and hence in particular Q is convergent at (b, c). By uniqueness $q = Q/\delta$. Since $\delta(b, c) \neq 0$ we conclude that q is convergent at (b, c) and hence so is r. Q.E.D.

Thus, for $K = \mathbf{C}$ we have reproved (10.3.1, 10.3.2). At the same time we have obtained explicit information on the domains of convergence of q and r and have obtained bounds for their absolute values.

§14. RIEMANN EXTENSION THEOREM AND CONNECTIVITY OF ALGEBROID HYPERSURFACES

§14A. *Riemann extension theorem*

(14.1) LEMMA. *Let V be an analytic set in a domain X in $\mathbf{C}^n$ such that $V \neq X$. Let $p \in X$ and a neighborhood X^* of p in X be given. Then there exists a coordinate system $(y, z) = (y_1, \ldots, y_{n-1}, z)$ in $\mathbf{C}^n$, which is obtained from the original one by a nonsingular affine transformation, and with respect to which p is at the origin and V has the following description near p. There exist real numbers $B > 0$ and $C' > C > 0$ such that $Y \times Z' \subset X^*$ where*

$$Y = \{b \in \mathbf{C}^{n-1}\{y\}: |b_1| < B, \ldots, |b_{n-1}| < B\},$$

$$Z = \{b \in \mathbf{C}^1\{z\}: |c| < C\}, \qquad Z' = \{c \in \mathbf{C}^1\{z\}: |c| < C'\},$$

$$\Gamma = \textit{circle of radius } C \textit{ around the origin in } \mathbf{C}^1\{\zeta\};$$

and there exists

$$\varphi(y, z) = z^d + \varphi_1(y)z^{d-1} + \ldots + \varphi_d(y), \qquad d \geqq 0,^1$$

where $\varphi_j(y)$ is analytic on Y with $\varphi_j(0) = 0$ for $j = 1, \ldots, d$, such that for each $b \in Y$ all the roots of $\varphi(b, z) = 0$ are in Z and such that

$$V \cap (Y \times Z') \subset \{(b, c) \in Y \times Z: \varphi(b, c) = 0\}.$$

PROOF. Take $q \in X - V$. Join p to q by an arc in X. By compactness of the arc and by the definition of an analytic set, we can find open connected sets $P_1, \ldots, P_h$ in X such that $p \in P_1$, $q \in P_h$, $P_i \cap P_{i+1} \neq \emptyset$ for $i = 1, \ldots, h - 1$, and

$$V \cap P_i = \{r \in P_i : f(r) = 0 \text{ for all } f \in F_i\}$$

for $i = 1, \ldots, h$ where F_i is a finite set of analytic functions on P_i.

Suppose if possible that $f \equiv 0$ on P_1 for all $f \in F_1$. Then $V \cap P_1 = P_1$ and hence $P_1 \cap P_2 \subset V \cap P_2$. Therefore $f \equiv 0$ on the nonempty open

[1] $d = 0 \Leftrightarrow p \notin V$.

subset $P_1 \cap P_2$ of P_2 for all $f \in F_2$ and hence[2] $f \equiv 0$ on P_2 for all $f \in F_2$. Thus $f \equiv 0$ on P_1 for all $f \in F_1$ implies that $f \equiv 0$ on P_2 for all $f \in F_2$ and this in turn implies that $f \equiv 0$ on P_3 for all $f \in F_3$, and so on. In this manner, $f \equiv 0$ on P_1 for all $f \in F_1$ implies that $f \equiv 0$ on P_h for all $f \in F_h$, i.e., $V \cap P_h = P_h$ and in particular $q \in V$ which is a contradiction.

Therefore we can find $f \in F_1$ such that $f \not\equiv 0$ on P_1. Then[2] $f \not\equiv 0$ in the neighborhood of p. Obviously

$$V \cap P_1 \subset \{r \in P_1 : f(r) = 0\}.$$

By a translation bring p to the origin. In view of the Preparation Theorem (10.3.6), by a nonsingular linear transformation we can find a coordinate system $(y, z) = (y_1, \ldots, y_{n-1}, z)$ and a neighborhood $\tilde{X}$ of the origin p in $P_1 \cap X^*$ such that $f = \delta\varphi$ in $\tilde{X}$ where δ and φ are analytic on $\tilde{X}$, δ is nowhere zero in $\tilde{X}$ and

$$\varphi(y, z) = z^d + \varphi_1(y)z^{d-1} + \ldots + \varphi_d(y), \qquad d \geqq 0,$$
$$\varphi_1(0) = \ldots = \varphi_d(0) = 0.$$

By continuity of roots (11.3), we can find $B > 0$, $C' > C > 0$ with the required properties such that $Y \times Z' \subset \tilde{X}$.

(14.2) COROLLARY. *Let V be an analytic set in a domain X in $\mathbf{C}^n$ such that $V \neq X$. Then V is nowhere dense in X.*

Follows from (14.1).

(14.3) RIEMANN EXTENSION THEOREM. *Let V be an analytic set in a domain X in $\mathbf{C}^n$ such that $V \neq X$. Let $f: (X - V) \to \mathbf{C}$ be analytic such that $|f|$ is bounded in the neighborhood of each point of V. Then f has a unique analytic extension to X.*

PROOF. By (14.2), V is nowhere dense in X and hence we get uniqueness. Now suppose that for each point p in X we have found a neighborhood X_p of p in X and an analytic function f_p on X_p such that $f_p|X_p - V = f|X_p - V$. Then

$$\lim_{q \to p \text{ in } X} f(q)$$

is well defined. Set

$$f^*(p) = \lim_{q \to p} f(q)$$

for all $p \in X$. Then $f^*|X_p = f_p$ and hence f^* is an analytic extension of

[2] By Identity Theorem (2.5).

f to X. To prove our supposition for any given p, we use the notation of (14.1). Let

$$g(y, z) = \frac{1}{2\pi i} \int_\Gamma \frac{f(y, \zeta)}{\zeta - z} d\zeta, \qquad (y, z) \in Y \times Z.$$

By continuity and differentiation under integral, g is analytic on $Y \times Z$. Let $b \in Y$ be given. Let $c_1, \ldots, c_e$ be the roots of $\varphi(b, z) = 0$, $(e \leqq d)$. Then $f(b, z)$ is analytic on $Z' - \{c_1, \ldots, c_e\}$ and $|f(b, z)|$ is bounded near $c_1, \ldots, c_e$. Hence by the one variable case (4.11.1), $f(b, z)$ has an analytic extension $h(b, z)$ on Z'; and hence by the one variable Cauchy formula (4.2.4), for all $z \in Z - \{c_1, \ldots, c_e\}$ we get

$$\begin{aligned} f(b, z) = h(b, z) &= \frac{1}{2\pi i} \int_\Gamma \frac{h(b, \zeta)}{\zeta - z} d\zeta \\ &= \frac{1}{2\pi i} \int_\Gamma \frac{f(b, \zeta)}{\zeta - z} d\zeta = g(b, z). \end{aligned}$$

Thus $g(y, z)|(Y \times Z - V) = f(y, z)|(Y \times Z - V)$. Take g for f_p and $Y \times Z$ for X_p.

As another corollary of (14.1), in (14.7) we shall show that "an analytic set in $\mathbf{C}^n$ does not disconnect". First we give a review on connectedness.

§14B. *Review on connectedness*

Let X be a topological space.

(14.4) *Local arcwise connectedness.* For real numbers $a \leqq b$ we write

$$\begin{array}{lll} [a, b] = \{t \in \mathbf{R}: a \leqq t \leqq b\} & & \text{closed interval} \\ ]a, b[= \{t \in \mathbf{R}: a < t < b\} & & \text{open interval} \\ [a, b[= \{t \in \mathbf{R}: a \leqq t < b\} & & \text{half open interval} \\ ]a, b] = \{t \in \mathbf{R}: a < t \leqq b\} & & \text{half open interval.} \end{array}$$

An *arc* $\gamma: I \to X$ in X is a continuous map γ of a real interval I into X. γ is a simple arc if $\gamma(t) \neq \gamma(t')$ for all $t \neq t'$ in I. If I is a closed interval $[a, b]$ then γ is said to *join* $\gamma(a)$ to $\gamma(b)$.

Recall the usual definitions of connected, connected component, arcwise connected, and arcwise connected component. Note that if A is a connected subset of X and $A \subset B \subset \mathrm{cl}_X A$ then B is connected; consequently connected components of X are always closed in X.

X is said to be *locally connected* $\Leftrightarrow$ every point in X has a vicinity basis consisting of connected vicinities. It follows that if X is locally connected then: every open subset Y of X is locally connected and every connected component of Y is open in Y and hence open in X. Consequently: X is locally connected $\Leftrightarrow$ every point in X has a neighborhood basis consisting of connected neighborhoods $\Leftrightarrow$ every connected component of every open subset of X is open in X.

X is said to be *locally arcwise connected* $\Leftrightarrow$ every point in X has a vicinity basis consisting of arcwise connected vicinities. It follows that if X is locally arcwise connected then:

1°) X is locally connected;

2°) every open subset of X is locally arcwise connected;

3°) every arcwise connected component of X is open and hence also closed in X; consequently

4°) X is connected $\Leftrightarrow$ X is arcwise connected; and hence

5°) connected component and arcwise connected component of X are one and the same thing.

From 2°) and 3°) it follows that: X is locally arcwise connected $\Leftrightarrow$ every point in X has a neighborhood basis consisting of arcwise connected neighborhoods $\Leftrightarrow$ every arcwise connected component of every open subset of X is open in X.

(14.5) *Nondisconnecting sets.* DEFINITION. Let $A \subset X$. *A does not disconnect X at $x \in X$* $\Leftrightarrow$ [given a connected neighborhood N of x, there exists a neighborhood M of x such that $M \subset N$ and $M - A$ is connected]. *A disconnects X nowhere* $\Leftrightarrow$ [$x \in X \Rightarrow A$ does not disconnect X at x]. A is (everywhere) *dense* in $X \Leftrightarrow X = \mathrm{cl}_X A$. A is *nowhere dense* in $X \Leftrightarrow$ [given a nonempty open subset N of X, there exists a nonempty open subset M of N such that $M \cap A = \emptyset$]. Obviously, if A is nowhere dense in X then $X - A$ is dense in X. (Converse is false, e.g., X = reals, A = rationals).

1) *Let $x \in X$ and $B \subset A \subset X$. Assume that A is nowhere dense in X and A does not disconnect X at x. Then B does not disconnect X at x.*

Let a connected neighborhood N of x in X be given. Since A does not disconnect X at x we can find a neighborhood M of x in N such that $M - A$ is connected. Now, A is nowhere dense in $X \Rightarrow A \cap M$ is nowhere dense in $M \Rightarrow M - A \subset M - B \subset M = \mathrm{cl}_M(M - A) \Rightarrow M - B$ is connected.

2) *$B \subset A \subset X$, A is nowhere dense in X and disconnects X nowhere $\Rightarrow B$ disconnects X nowhere.*

Follows from 1).

3) *Assume that X is connected. Let A be a nowhere dense subset of X. Assume that A does not disconnect X at any point of A.*[3] *Then $X - A$ is connected.*

PROOF. Let $^-$ stand for closure in X. Suppose if possible that $X - A$ is not connected. Then $X - A = M \cup N$ where M and N are nonempty disjoint open subsets of $X - A$. Since A is nowhere dense in X, we get $X = \overline{X - A} = \bar{M} \cup \bar{N}$. Since X is connected, we must have $\bar{M} \cap \bar{N} \neq \emptyset$. Fix $x \in \bar{M} \cap \bar{N}$. Now, [$M$ and N are disjoint open sets in $X - A$ and $M \cup N = X - A$] $\Rightarrow$ [M and N are closed in $X - A$] $\Rightarrow$ [$\bar{M} \cap (X - A) = M$ and $\bar{N} \cap (X - A) = N$] $\Rightarrow$ [$x \notin X - A$] $\Rightarrow x \in A$. Hence by assumption, A does not disconnect X at x. Since X is connected, we can find a neighborhood P of x in X such that $P - A$ is connected. Let $M' = (P - A) \cap M = P \cap M$ and $N' = (P - A) \cap N = P \cap N$. Since $x \in \bar{M}$ and P is a neighborhood of x in X, we get that $M' = P \cap M \neq \emptyset$. Similarly $N' \neq \emptyset$. Thus M' and N' are nonempty disjoint open subsets of $P - A$ and $M' \cup N' = P - A$. Contradiction to $P - A$ being connected.

4) *Let A be a nowhere dense subset of X. Then the following three conditions are equivalent.*

i) *A disconnects X nowhere.*
ii) *A does not disconnect X at any point of A.*
iii) *For any open connected subset D of X, $D - A$ is connected.*

Obviously iii) $\Rightarrow$ i) $\Rightarrow$ ii). Now assume ii) and let D be any open connected subset of X. Then $D \cap A$ does not disconnect D at any point of $D \cap A$; whence $D - A = D - (D \cap A)$ is connected by 3).

5) *Assume that X is connected and locally arcwise connected. Let A be a closed nowhere dense subset of X such that A does not disconnect X at any point of A.*[3] *Then $X - A$ is arcwise connected and locally arcwise connected.*

Obviously $X - A$ is locally arcwise connected. By 3) it is connected and hence it is arcwise connected.

(14.6) *Coverings.* Let $\varphi: X^* \to X$ be a continuous map of a topological space X^* into X. If $\gamma: I \to X$ and $\gamma^*: I \to X^*$ are arcs where I is a real interval, then γ^* is said to *cover* γ (relative to φ) provided $\varphi(\gamma^*(t)) = \gamma(t)$ for all $t \in I$. φ is said to be a *covering map* provided $X^* \neq \emptyset$, X is connected and locally arcwise connected, and: for each $x \in X$, there is a connected neighborhood N of x in X such that each connected component of $\varphi^{-1}(N)$ is open in X^* and gets mapped homeomorphically onto N by the map

[3] This assumption is satisfied if A disconnects X nowhere.

induced by φ; *X^* is called the covering space; for any $x \in X$, $\varphi^{-1}(x)$ is the fiber above x.*

Now assume that $\varphi: X^* \to X$ is a covering map.

1) Obviously X^* is locally arcwise connected, and the fiber above any point of x is a discrete space.

2) Let $a < b$ be real numbers. Let an arc $\tilde{\gamma}: [a, b] \to X$ and $y \in \varphi^{-1}(\tilde{\gamma}(a))$ be given. By compactness of $[a, b[$ it follows that there exists a unique arc $\tilde{\gamma}^*: [a, b] \to X^*$ covering $\tilde{\gamma}$ such that $\tilde{\gamma}^*(a) = y$. Let an arc $\gamma: [a, b[\to X$ and $y \in \varphi^{-1}(\gamma(a))$ be given. Take $a = a_0 < a_1 < a_2 < \ldots < b$ with $\lim_{p\to\infty} a_p = b$. By the above case there exists an arc $\gamma_p: [a, a_p] \to X^*$ covering $\gamma|[a, a_p]$ such that $\gamma_p(a) = y$. By uniqueness we must have $\gamma_p|[a, a_q] = \gamma_q$ for all $q \leqq p$. Consequently $\gamma^*: [a, b[\to X^*$, $\gamma^*(t) = \gamma_p(t)$ for all $t \in [a, a_p]$ is an arc covering γ such that $\gamma^*(a) = y$. Again applying the uniqueness for the closed arcs to $\gamma^*|[a, a_p]$ for $p = 1, 2, \ldots$ we deduce that γ^* is unique.

3) Let $\gamma: [0, 1] \to X$ be an arc. For any $y \in \varphi^{-1}(\gamma(0))$ let $\gamma_y: [0, 1] \to X^*$ be the unique arc covering γ such that $\gamma_y(0) = y$. Let $f(y) = \gamma_y(1)$. Then f is a mapping of $\varphi^{-1}(\gamma(0))$ into $\varphi^{-1}(\gamma(1))$. Let $\tilde{\gamma}: [0, 1] \to X$ be given by: $\tilde{\gamma}(t) = \gamma(1 - t)$ and let $\tilde{f}: \varphi^{-1}(\gamma(1)) \to \varphi^{-1}(\gamma(0))$ be the corresponding mapping obtained from $\tilde{\gamma}$. Then obviously $\tilde{f}(f(y)) = y$ for all $y \in \varphi^{-1}(\gamma(0))$ and $f(\tilde{f}(y)) = y$ for all $y \in \varphi^{-1}(\gamma(1))$. Therefore f is a one to one map of $\varphi^{-1}(\gamma(0))$ onto $\varphi^{-1}(\gamma(1))$. Since the fibers are discrete, f is actually a homeomorphism.

Since X is arcwise connected, from 3) we get

4) The fibers above any two points of X are homeomorphic and in particular have the same cardinal number. Consequently φ maps X onto X^*.

The cardinal number of any fiber is called the *degree of* φ.

5) Let Y be any connected and locally arcwise connected subspace of X, (for example $Y = X$). Let Y^* be the union of any number (at least one) of connected components of $\varphi^{-1}(Y)$. It is then immediate that the map $Y^* \to Y$ induced by φ is a covering map (and hence $\varphi(Y^*) = Y$ by 4)).

6) Let $\emptyset \neq Z \subset Y \subset X$ be such that Y is connected and locally arcwise connected and $\varphi^{-1}(Z)$ is connected. Then $\varphi^{-1}(Y)$ is connected.

PROOF. Since $\varphi^{-1}(Z)$ is connected, it suffices to show that each connected component Y^* of $\varphi^{-1}(Y)$ has a point in common with $\varphi^{-1}(Z)$. By 5), $\emptyset \neq Z \subset Y = \varphi(Y^*)$ and hence $Y^* \cap \varphi^{-1}(Z) \neq \emptyset$.

§14C. *Connectivity of algebroid hypersurfaces*

(14.7) *Let V be an analytic set in a domain X in $\mathbf{C}^n$ such that $V \neq X$. Then we have the following.*

1) *V is closed and nowhere dense in X.*

2) *Given $p \in X$ and a neighborhood X^* of p in X, there exists a connected neighborhood X' of p in X^* such that: any two points in $X' - V$ can be joined by a simple arc in $X' - V$, and any point a in $X' - V$ can be joined to p by a simple arc in X' meeting V at most in p.*[4]

3) *V disconnects X nowhere.*

4) *If Y is any open connected subset of X then $Y - V$ is connected.*

PROOF. V is obviously closed in X and by (14.2) it is nowhere dense in X. Also 3) $\Rightarrow$ 4) by (14.5.4), and obviously 2) $\Rightarrow$3). Hence it suffices to prove 2). Given p and X^* we use the description found in (14.1). Take $X' = Y \times Z'$. Then X' is connected. Note that for any $b \in Y$, $b \times Z'$ is a disk and $(b \times Z') \cap V$ is a finite set. Also $(Y \times \Gamma) \cap V = \emptyset$. Let points $a' = (b', c')$ and $a'' = (b'', c'')$ in $X' - V$ be given where $b', b'' \in Y$ and $c', c'' \in Z'$. If $b' = b''$ then: a' and a'' can be joined by a simple arc in $(b' \times Z') - V$. If $b' \neq b''$ then: a' can be joined to a point α' in $b' \times \Gamma$ by a simple arc in $(b' \times Z') - V$, α' can be joined to a point α'' in $b'' \times \Gamma$ by a simple arc in $Y \times \Gamma$, and α'' can be joined to a'' by a simple arc in $(b'' \times Z') - V$; this gives a simple arc in $X' - V$ joining a' to a''. Now let $a = (b, c)$ in $X' - V$ be given where $a \in Y$ and $b \in Z'$. Let $o = (0,\ldots, 0)$ be the origin in Y, so that $p = (o, 0)$. If $b = o$ then: a can be joined to p by a simple arc in $o \times Z'$ meeting V at most in p. If $b \neq o$ then: a can be joined to a point α in $b \times \Gamma$ by a simple arc in $(b \times Z) - V$, α can be joined to a point α' in $o \times \Gamma$ by a simple arc in $Y \times \Gamma$, and α' can be joined to p by a simple arc in $o \times Z'$ meeting V at most in p; this gives a simple arc in X' joining a to p and meeting V at most in p.

(14.8) *Let $f(y, z) = z^d + f_1(y)z^{d-1} + \ldots + f_d(y)$, $d > 0$, where $f_1(y),\ldots,f_d(y)$ are analytic on a connected neighborhood Y of the origin in $\mathbf{C}^n\{y\}$. Let $V = \{(b, c) \in Y \times \mathbf{C}^1\{z\} : f(b, c) = 0\}$. Let $\pi: V \to Y$ be given by $(b, c) \to b$. Let $\Delta(y)$ be the z-discriminant of $f(y, z)$. Let W' be any analytic set in Y such that $W' \neq Y$.*[5] *Let $W = W' \cup \{b \in Y: \Delta(b) = 0\}$. Assume that $\Delta(y) \not\equiv 0$ in Y.*[6] *Then the map $\pi^{-1}(Y - W) \to Y - W$ induced be π is*

[4] That is, there exists a simple arc $\gamma: [\lambda, \mu] \to X'$ such that $\gamma(\lambda) = a$, $\gamma(\mu) = p$, and $\gamma(t) \notin V$ whenever $t \neq \mu$; $(\lambda = \mu \Leftrightarrow a = p)$.

[5] For example $W' = \emptyset$.

[6] This assumption is satisfied if $f(y, z)$ is irreducible in $\mathbf{C}[\langle y \rangle][z]$.

a covering map. If furthermore $f(y, z)$ is irreducible in $\mathbf{C}[\langle y\rangle][z]$ *then* $\pi^{-1}(Y - W')$ *as well as* $\pi^{-1}(Y - W)$ *are arcwise connected.*

PROOF. 1°) By (14.2), W is nowhere dense in Y and by (14.7), $Y - W$ is connected and locally arcwise connected. Given $p \in Y - W$, by (12.3) there exist analytic functions $\xi_{p,\lambda}$, $(\lambda = 1,\ldots, d)$, on an open polycylinder Y_p in $Y - W$ around p, and there exists a positive real number A_p such that: for any $b \in Y_p$ the distinct roots of $f(b, z) = 0$ in $\mathbf{C}$ are $\xi_{p,1}(b),\ldots, \xi_{p,d}(b)$; and

$$|\xi_{p,\lambda}(p) - \xi_{p,\lambda'}(p)| > 2A_p \qquad \text{for all} \qquad \lambda \neq \lambda',$$
$$|\xi_{p,\lambda}(b) - \xi_{p,\lambda}(p)| < A \qquad \text{for all} \qquad b \in Y_p, \qquad \lambda = 1,\ldots, d.$$

From this it follows that the map $\pi^{-1}(Y - W) \to Y - W$ induced by π is a covering map of degree d.

2°) Let $V_1,\ldots, V_M$ be the distinct connected components of $\pi^{-1}(Y - W)$. Then the map $V_\mu \to V$ induced by π is a covering map of some degree $N_\mu > 0$, and $N_1 + \ldots + N_M = d$. For $\mu = 1,\ldots, M$, define

$$f^{(\mu)}(y, z) = z^{N_\mu} + f_1^{(\mu)}(y)z^{N_\mu - 1} + \ldots + f_{N_\mu}^{(\mu)}(y)$$

by setting

$$f^{(\mu)}(b, z) = \prod_{a \in V_\mu \cap \pi^{-1}(b)} (z - a) \qquad \text{for all} \qquad b \in Y - W.$$

Then obviously $f(b, z) = f_1(b, z)\ldots f_M(b, z)$ for all $b \in Y - W$. Given $p \in Y - W$ let the notation be as above. Since $V_1,\ldots, V_M$ are connected components, we can label $\xi_{p,1},\ldots, \xi_{p,d}$ as $\xi_{p,\mu,\nu}$, $(\mu = 1,\ldots, M; \nu = 1,\ldots, N_\mu)$ so that for any $\mu \leqq M$ and any $b \in Y_p$, $V_\mu \cap \pi^{-1}(b) = \{(b, \xi_{p,\mu,\nu}(b)): \mu = 1,\ldots, N_\mu\}$. Therefore for all $\mu \leqq M$,

$$f^{(\mu)}(y, z) \equiv \prod_{\nu=1}^{N_\mu} (z - \xi_{p,\mu,\nu}(y)) \qquad \text{on } Y_p;$$

and hence the functions $f_\omega^{(\mu)}(y)$ are analytic on Y_p. Since p was an arbitrary point in $Y - W$, the functions $f_\omega^{(\mu)}(y)$ are analytic on $Y - W$.

3°) Given $\beta \in W$, by (12.3) we can find constants $B > 0$, $C > 0$ such that: for any $b \in Y - W$ with $|b_1 - \beta_1| < B,\ldots, |b_n - \beta_n| < B$, all the roots of $f(b, z) = 0$ in $\mathbf{C}$ have absolute value less than C. For any such b, and any (μ, ω), $f_\omega^{(\mu)}(b)$ is an elementary symmetric function of a certain number of these roots. Consequently, $|f_\omega^{(\mu)}|$ is bounded in the neighborhood of β. Thus all the functions $f_\omega^{(\mu)}$, $(\mu = 1,\ldots, M; \omega = 1,\ldots, N_\mu)$, are analytic on $Y - W$ and their absolute values are bounded in the neighborhood of any point $\beta \in W$. Therefore by Riemann Extension Theorem (14.3), $f_\omega^{(\mu)}$ has a unique analytic extension to Y. Denote this extension again by $f_\omega^{(\mu)}$ and for any $y \in Y$ set

$$f^{(\mu)}(y, z) = z^{N_\mu} + f_1^{(\mu)}(y) z^{N_\mu - 1}(y) + \ldots + f_{N_\mu}^{(\mu)}(y).$$

Since $f(y, z) = f_1(y, z) \ldots f_M(y, z)$ for all $y \in Y - W$ and W is nowhere dense in Y, this is so for all $y \in Y$. Now assume that $f(y, z)$ is irreducible in $\mathbf{C}[\langle y \rangle][z]$. Then we must have $M = 1$ and $N_1 = d$.

4°) Therefore $\pi^{-1}(Y - W)$ is connected and hence arcwise connected.

5°) To prove that $\pi^{-1}(Y - W')$ is arcwise connected it suffices to show that given $\tilde{a} \in \pi^{-1}(W)$, some point in $\pi^{-1}(Y - W)$ can be joined to $\tilde{a}$ by a simple arc in V meeting $\pi^{-1}(W)$ only in $\tilde{a}$. Let $\tilde{a} = (\tilde{b}, \tilde{c})$ with $\tilde{b} \in W$, $\tilde{c} \in \mathbf{C}^1\{z\}$. By (12.3) we can find positive real numbers

$$D_1 > D_2 > \ldots, \quad D_m \to 0; \qquad E_1 > E_2 > \ldots, \quad E_m \to 0;$$

such that:

i) $$\tilde{Y}_1 \subset Y, \qquad \pi[V \cap (\tilde{Y}_1 \times \tilde{Z}_1)] = \tilde{Y}_1;$$

and

ii) $$V \cap (\tilde{Y}_m \times \tilde{Z}_1) = V \cap (\tilde{Y}_m \times \tilde{Z}_m) \qquad \text{for all} \qquad m > 0;$$

where

$$\tilde{Y}_m = \{y \in Y: |y_1 - \tilde{b}_1| < D_m, \ldots, |y_n - \tilde{b}_n| < D_m\},$$
$$\tilde{Z}_m = \{z \in \mathbf{C}^1\{z\}: |z - \tilde{c}| < E_m\}.$$

By (14.7), there is an arc $\gamma: [0, 1] \to \tilde{Y}_2$ such that $\gamma(0) = \hat{b} \in \tilde{Y}_2 - W$, $\gamma(1) = \tilde{b}$, and $\gamma(t) \notin W$ whenever $t \neq 1$. Take $\hat{c} \in \tilde{Z}_2$ such that $\hat{a} = (\hat{b}, \hat{c}) \in V$. Since $\pi^{-1}(Y - W) \to Y - W$ is a covering map, we can find an arc $\Gamma: [0, 1[\to V$ which covers $\gamma|[0, 1[$ such that $\Gamma(0) = \hat{a}$. Since the image of $[0, 1[$ by Γ is connected, by ii) we deduce that this image must be contained in $\tilde{Y}_1 \times \tilde{Z}_1$ Let $\Gamma(1) = \tilde{a}$. Since $D_m \to 0$ and $E_m \to 0$, again by ii) we deduce that $\Gamma: [0, 1] \to V$ is continuous. Thus Γ is a simple arc in V joining $\hat{a}$ to $\tilde{a}$ and meeting $\pi^{-1}(W)$ only in $\tilde{a}$.

(**14.8′**) REMARK. As noted in (4.10), (14.8) can also be proved by using analytic continuation. Although this is parallel to the proof given above, it is a bit cumbersome and goes something like this.

1′) Same as 1°).

2′) For any arc γ in $Y - W$ joining a point p to a point q and for any analytic function η in a neighborhood of p in $Y - W$, by $\eta^{(\gamma)}$ we shall denote the analytic continuation (if it exists) of η along γ; $\eta^{(\gamma)}$ is then an analytic function in a neighborhood of q.

By Identity Theorem (2.5) we deduce that if p' and p'' are points in $Y - W$ such that $Y_{p'} \cap Y_{p''} \neq \emptyset$ then the direct analytic continuations of $\xi_{p',1},\ldots,\xi_{p',d}$ from $Y_{p'}$ to $Y_{p''}$ form a permutation of $\xi_{p'',1},\ldots,\xi_{p'',d}$. From this and from the compactness of a closed arc it follows that if γ is any arc in $Y - W$ joining a point p to a point q then $\xi_{p,1}^{(\gamma)},\ldots,\xi_{p,d}^{(\gamma)}$ exist and they form a permutation of $\xi_{q,1},\ldots,\xi_{q,d}$.

Fix p in $Y - W$. Let $\zeta_{\mu,\nu}$, ($\mu = 1,\ldots,M; \nu = 1,\ldots,N_\mu; N_1 + \ldots + N_M = d$), be a labeling of $\xi_{p,1},\ldots,\xi_{p,d}$ such that $\zeta_{\mu'',\nu''}$ is an analytic continuation of $\zeta_{\mu',\nu'}$ along some arc in $Y - W$ if and only if $\mu' = \mu''$. For each y in $Y - W$ fix an arc γ_y in $Y - W$ joining p to y. For any y in $Y - W$ let

$$\begin{aligned} f^{(\mu)}(y, z) &= \prod_{\nu=1}^{N_\mu} [z - \zeta_{\mu,\nu}^{(\gamma_y)}(y)] \\ &= z^{N_\mu} + f_1^{(\mu)}(y) z^{N_\mu - 1} + \ldots + f_{N_\mu}^{(\mu)}(y); \qquad \mu = 1,\ldots,M. \end{aligned}$$

Then obviously

$$f(y, z) = f^{(1)}(y, z) \ldots f^{(M)}(y, z) \qquad \text{for all } y \text{ in } Y - W.$$

We claim that all the functions $f_\omega^{(\mu)}$ are analytic on $Y - W$. So let q in $Y - W$ be given. Let $\xi_{q,\mu,\nu}$, ($\mu = 1,\ldots, M$; $\nu = 1,\ldots, N_\mu$), be the labeling of $\xi_{q,1},\ldots,\xi_{q,d}$ so that $\zeta_{\mu,\nu}^{(\gamma_q)} = \xi_{q,\mu,\nu}$ for all μ, ν. From the way the functions $\zeta_{\mu,\nu}$ have been labeled it follows that if δ_y is any other arc in $Y - W$ joining p to y then for each μ, $(\zeta_{\mu,1}^{(\delta_y)},\ldots,\zeta_{\mu,N_\mu}^{(\delta_y)})$ is a permutation of $(\zeta_{\mu,1}^{(\gamma_y)},\ldots,\zeta_{\mu,N_\mu}^{(\gamma_y)})$. Consequently, by joining q to any point y in Y_q by an arc in Y_q we deduce that $(\zeta_{\mu,1}^{(\gamma_y)}(y),\ldots,\zeta_{\mu,N_\mu}^{(\gamma_y)}(y))$ is a permutation of $(\xi_{q,\mu,1}(y),\ldots, \xi_{q,\mu,N_\mu}(y))$. Therefore for all $y \in Y_q$ we have

$$f^{(\mu)}(y, z) = \prod_{\nu=1}^{N_\mu} (z - \xi_{q,\mu,\nu}(y)), \qquad (\mu = 1,\ldots, M).$$

Since the functions $\xi_{q,\mu,\nu}$ are analytic on Y_q we conclude that the functions $f_\omega^{(\mu)}$ are all analytic on Y_q.

3′) Same as 3°).

4′) Any point in $\pi^{-1}(Y - W)$ is of the form $(q, \xi_{q,\lambda}(q))$ with $q \in Y - W$ and $\lambda \leqq d$; also $\xi_{q,\lambda}$ is the analytic continuation of $\xi_{p,\lambda'}$ for some λ' along some arc in $Y - W$, and $\xi_{p,\lambda'}$ is the analytic continuation of $\xi_{p,1}$ along some arc in $Y - W$; thus $\xi_{q,\lambda} = \xi_{p,1}^{(\gamma)}$ for some arc γ: $[0, 1] \to Y - W$, $\gamma(0) = p$, $\gamma(1) = q$. For any $t \in [0, 1]$ let $\gamma^{(t)} = \gamma|[0, t]$, and then let

$$\Gamma(t) = (\gamma(t), \xi_{p,1}^{(\gamma^{(t)})}(\gamma(t))).$$

Then Γ: $[0, 1] \to \pi^{-1}(Y - W)$ is an arc in $\pi^{-1}(Y - W)$ joining $(p, \xi_{p,1}(p))$ to $(q, \xi_{q,\lambda}(q))$. This shows that $\pi^{-1}(Y - W)$ is arcwise connected.

5') Same as 5°).

§15. OKA COHERENCE

Notation. Let $\mathfrak{M}$ be a module over a ring R. By $\mathfrak{M}^u$ we may denote the u-fold direct sum of $\mathfrak{M}$; in particular R^u is then an R-module. For any finite number of elements $f_1,\ldots, f_u$ in $\mathfrak{M}$ we set

$$\begin{aligned}&\mathrm{Rel}(f_1,\ldots, f_u)\\ &= \textit{Relation module of the u-tuple } (f_1,\ldots, f_u)\\ &= \{g = (g^{(1)},\ldots, g^{(u)}) \in R^u : g^{(1)}f_1 + \ldots + g^{(u)}f_u = 0\}.\end{aligned}$$

$\mathrm{Rel}(f_1,\ldots, f_u)$ is then a submodule of R^u.

The following lemma is needed in the proof of (15.2).

(15.1) *Let* $R = K[[x_1,\ldots, x_n]]$ *or* $K[\langle x_1,\ldots, x_n\rangle]$. *Let* $S = K[[x_1,\ldots, x_{n-1}]]$ *or* $K[\langle x_1,\ldots, x_{n-1}\rangle]$, *respectively. Let* $f_1,\ldots, f_u \in S[x_n]$ *be given such that* f_i *is either zero or is monic in* x_n. *Let* $d = \max(\deg_{x_n} f_1,\ldots, \deg_{x_n} f_u)$. *Assume that* $d \geqq 0$, *i.e.,* $f_i \neq 0$ *for some* i. *Let* $\mathfrak{M} = \mathrm{Rel}(f_1,\ldots, f_u)$ *and* $A = \{g = (g^{(1)},\ldots, g^{(u)}) \in \mathfrak{M}: \deg_{x_n} g^{(i)} \leqq d$ *for* $i = 1,\ldots, u\}$. *Then* $\mathfrak{M} = AR$.

Proof. We shall write deg for $\deg_{x_n}$. Relabel the elements $f_1,\ldots, f_u$ so that $\deg f_u = d$. Let $g = (g^{(1)},\ldots, g^{(u)}) \in \mathfrak{M}$ be given. We want to show that $g \in AR$. By Preparation Theorem (10.3):

$f_u = \delta f^*$, where f^* is a distinguished polynomial of degree $d^* \leqq d$ in x_n with coefficients in S, and δ is a unit in R with $\deg \delta = d - d^*$;

and

$$g^{(i)} = q_i f_u + r^{(i)}, \quad \text{where} \quad q_i, r^{(i)} \in R \text{ and } \deg r^{(i)} < d^*, \quad \text{for} \quad i = 1,\ldots, u-1.$$

Let $r^{(u)} = g^{(u)} + q_1 f_1 + \ldots + q_{u-1} f_{u-1}$. Then

$$\begin{aligned}&(g^{(1)},\ldots, g^{(u)})\\ &= q_1(f_u, 0,\ldots, 0, -f_1) + q_2(0, f_u, 0,\ldots, 0, -f_2)\\ &\quad + \ldots + q_{u-1}(0,\ldots, 0, f_u, -f_{u-1}) + (r^{(1)},\ldots, r^{(u)});\end{aligned}$$

and

$$(f_u, 0,\ldots, 0, -f_1),\ldots, (0,\ldots, 0, f_u, -f_{u-1}) \in A.$$

Consequently $(r^{(1)},\ldots r^{(u)}) \in \mathfrak{M}$ and it suffices to show that $(r^{(1)},\ldots,r^{(u)}) \in AR$. Since $(r^{(1)},\ldots, r^{(u)}) \in \mathfrak{M}$ we get

$$-r^{(1)}f_1 - \ldots - r^{(u-1)}f_{u-1} = (r^{(u)}\delta)f^*.$$

The left-hand side of this equation is in $S[x_n]$ and f^* is a distinguished polynomial in x_n. Hence by (10.3.3), $r^{(u)}\delta \in S[x_n]$. Let

$$s^{(i)} = r^{(i)}\delta \qquad \text{for} \qquad i = 1,\ldots, u.$$

Then $s^{(1)},\ldots, s^{(u)} \in S[x_n]$. Since δ is a unit in R, we get that $(s^{(1)},\ldots, s^{(u)}) \in \mathfrak{M}$ and *it suffices to show that* $(s^{(1)},\ldots, s^{(u)}) \in A$.

Now

$$\deg s^{(i)} = \deg r^{(i)} + \deg \delta \leqq d^* + (d - d^*) = d$$
$$\text{for} \qquad i = 1,\ldots, u-1;$$

and

$$\deg s^{(i)}f_i = \deg s^{(i)} + \deg f_i \leqq d + d = 2d$$
$$\text{for} \qquad i = 1,\ldots, u-1.$$

Since $(s^{(1)},\ldots, s^{(u)}) \in \mathfrak{M}$ we have

$$s^{(u)}f_u = -s^{(1)}f_i - \ldots - s^{(u-1)}f_{u-1}$$

and hence $\deg s^{(u)}f_u \leqq 2d$. Since $\deg f_u = d$, we get $\deg s^{(u)} \leqq d$. Therefore $(s^{(1)},\ldots, s^{(u)}) \in A$.

(15.2) OKA COHERENCE.[1] *Let* $R = K[\langle x_1,\ldots, x_n\rangle]$. *Then for all* $n > 0$, $v > 0$ *we have*

$\mathfrak{O}(n, v)$: *Given a finite number of elements* $f_1,\ldots, f_u$ *in* R^v *there exists a finite number of elements* $g_\lambda = (g_\lambda^{(1)},\ldots, g_\lambda^{(u)})$, $(\lambda = 1,\ldots, l)$, *in* R^u *and a neighborhood* X *of the origin in* K^n *in which* $g_1,\ldots, g_l$, $f_1,\ldots, f_u$ *are convergent, such that*

$$\{\tau_a g_1,\ldots, \tau_a g_l\}R = \mathrm{Rel}(\tau_a f_1,\ldots, \tau_a f_u) \qquad \textit{for all} \qquad a \in X.$$

We shall prove:

(I) *For* $n > 0$, $v > 1$, $[\mathfrak{O}(n, 1) + \mathfrak{O}(n, v-1)] \Rightarrow \mathfrak{O}(n, v)$.
(II) *For* $n > 1$, $[\mathfrak{O}(n-1, v)$ *for all* $v > 0] \Rightarrow \mathfrak{O}(n, 1)$.

A trivial modification of the proof of (II) will yield $\mathfrak{O}(1, 1)$. Hence, by double induction on (n, v), (15.2) will follow from (I) and (II).

[1] Oka [**7**].

Proof of (I). We can write $f_i = (F_i, \bar{f}_i)$ with $F_i \in R^{v-1}$, $\bar{f}_i \in R$. By $\mathfrak{D}(n, v-1)$ there exists a finite number of elements $G_\Lambda = (G_\Lambda^{(1)}, \ldots, G_\Lambda^{(u)}) \in R^u$, $(\Lambda = 1, \ldots, L)$, and a neighborhood X^* of the origin in K^n in which $f_1, \ldots, f_u$, $G_1, \ldots, G_L$ are convergent, such that

$$\{\boldsymbol{\tau}_a G_1, \ldots, \boldsymbol{\tau}_a G_L\}R = \operatorname{Rel}(\boldsymbol{\tau}_a F_1, \ldots, \boldsymbol{\tau}_a F_u) \qquad \text{for all} \qquad a \in X^*.$$

Let $a \in X^*$. For any $h = (h^{(1)}, \ldots, h^{(L)}) \in R^L$ let

$$\alpha_a h = h^{(1)} \boldsymbol{\tau}_a G_1 + \ldots + h^{(L)} \boldsymbol{\tau}_a G_L \in R^u.$$

Then $\alpha_a \colon R^L \to \operatorname{Rel}(\boldsymbol{\tau}_a F_1, \ldots, \boldsymbol{\tau}_a F_u)$ is an epimorphism. Obviously $\operatorname{Rel}(\boldsymbol{\tau}_a f_1, \ldots, \boldsymbol{\tau}_a f_u)$ is a submodule of $\operatorname{Rel}(\boldsymbol{\tau}_a F_1, \ldots, \boldsymbol{\tau}_a F_u)$. Let $\mathfrak{N}_a = \alpha_a^{-1}(\operatorname{Rel}(\boldsymbol{\tau}_a f_1, \ldots, \boldsymbol{\tau}_a f_u))$. For any $h = (h^{(1)}, \ldots, h^{(L)})$ we have:

$$\begin{aligned} & h \in \mathfrak{N}_a \\ \Leftrightarrow & \sum_{\Lambda=1}^{L} h^{(\Lambda)} \boldsymbol{\tau}_a G_\Lambda \in \operatorname{Rel}(\boldsymbol{\tau}_a \bar{f}_1, \ldots, \boldsymbol{\tau}_a \bar{f}_u) \\ \Leftrightarrow & \sum_{i=1}^{u} \sum_{\Lambda=1}^{L} h^{(\Lambda)} (\boldsymbol{\tau}_a G_\Lambda^{(i)})(\boldsymbol{\tau}_a \bar{f}_i) = 0 \\ \Leftrightarrow & h \in \operatorname{Rel}(\boldsymbol{\tau}_a t_1, \ldots, \boldsymbol{\tau}_a t_L) \end{aligned}$$

where

$$t_\Lambda = \sum_{i=1}^{u} G_\Lambda^{(i)} \bar{f}_i.$$

Hence by $\mathfrak{D}(n, 1)$ there exists a neighborhood X of the origin in X^* and a finite number of elements $h_\lambda = (h_\lambda^{(1)}, \ldots, h_\lambda^{(L)}) \in R^L$, $(\lambda = 1, \ldots, l)$, which are convergent in X, such that

$$\{\boldsymbol{\tau}_a h_1, \ldots, \boldsymbol{\tau}_a h_l\}R = \mathfrak{N}_a \qquad \text{for all} \qquad a \in X.$$

Let $g_\lambda = h_\lambda^{(1)} G_1 + \ldots + h_\lambda^{(L)} G_L$. Then $g_1, \ldots, g_l \in R^u$ are convergent in X and

$$\{\boldsymbol{\tau}_a g_1, \ldots, \boldsymbol{\tau}_a g_l\}R = \operatorname{Rel}(\boldsymbol{\tau}_a f_1, \ldots, \boldsymbol{\tau}_a f_u) \qquad \text{for all} \qquad a \in X.$$

Proof of (II). Let $f_i^* = \delta_i f_i$, where δ_i is a unit in R, $(i = 1, \ldots, u)$. Suppose we have found $g_\lambda^* = (g_\lambda^{*(1)}, \ldots, g_\lambda^{*(u)}) \in R^u$, $(\lambda = 1, \ldots, l)$, and a neighborhood X^* of the origin in K^n in which $f_1^*, \ldots, f_u^*$, $g_1^*, \ldots, g_l^*$ are convergent, such that

$$\{\boldsymbol{\tau}_a g_1^*, \ldots, \boldsymbol{\tau}_a g_l^*\}R = \operatorname{Rel}(\boldsymbol{\tau}_a f_1^*, \ldots, \boldsymbol{\tau}_a f_u^*) \qquad \text{for all} \qquad a \in X^*.$$

For X take a neighborhood of the origin in X^* such that $\delta_1,\ldots,\delta_u, f_1,\ldots,f_u$ are all convergent in X, and $\delta_i(a) \neq 0$, i.e., $\boldsymbol{\tau}_a\delta_i$ is a unit in R for all $a \in X$, for $(i = 1,\ldots, u)$. Let $g_\lambda = (\delta_1 g_\lambda^{*(1)},\ldots, \delta_u g_\lambda^{*(u)})$. Then obviously

$$\{\boldsymbol{\tau}_a g_1,\ldots, \boldsymbol{\tau}_a g_l\}R = \mathrm{Rel}(\boldsymbol{\tau}_a f_1,\ldots, \boldsymbol{\tau}_a f_u) \qquad \text{for all} \qquad a \in X.$$

Consequently, in view of Preparation Theorem (10.3.6), by making a nonsingular K-linear transformation on $x_1,\ldots, x_n$ and then multiplying $f_1,\ldots,f_u$ by suitable units in R, without loss of generality *we may assume that f_i is either zero or is a distinguished polynomial in x_n with coefficients in* $S = K[\langle x_1,\ldots, x_{n-1}\rangle]$. Let us write x for x_n and deg for $\deg_{x_n}$.

Let Y^* be a neighborhood of the origin in $K^{n-1}\{x_1,\ldots, x_{n-1}\}$ in which all the coefficients of $f_1,\ldots,f_u$ are convergent. Let $d = \max(\deg f_1,\ldots, \deg f_u)$. If $f_1 = \ldots = f_u = 0$ then our assertion is trivial. So assume that at least one of the elements $f_1,\ldots,f_u$ is nonzero, i.e., $d \geqq 0$. Write[2]

$$f_i = \sum_{j=0}^{d} f_{i,j}x^j \qquad \text{with} \qquad f_{i,j} \in S.$$

Let $f_{i,j} = 0$ for all $j < 0$ and for all $j > d$. Let

$$F_{i,k}^{(\nu)} = f_{i,\nu-k}, \qquad (i = 1,\ldots, u;\ k = 0, 1,\ldots, d;\ \nu = 0, 1,\ldots, 2d).$$

Then the $u(d + 1)$ elements

$$F_{i,k} = (F_{i,k}^{(0)},\ldots, F_{i,k}^{(2,d)})$$

are in S^{2d+1} and they are convergent in Y^*. By $\mathfrak{D}(n - 1, 2d + 1)$ there exists a neighborhood Y of the origin in Y^* and a finite number of elements

$$G_\lambda = (G_\lambda^{(1,0)}, G_\lambda^{(1,1)},\ldots, G_\lambda^{(1,d)}, G_\lambda^{(2,0)},\ldots, G_\lambda^{(u,d)}) \in S^{u(d+1)}, \qquad (\lambda = 1,\ldots, l),$$

which are convergent in Y, such that

$$1^\circ) \quad \{\boldsymbol{\tau}_b G_1,\ldots, \boldsymbol{\tau}_b G_l\}S = \mathrm{Rel}(\ldots, \boldsymbol{\tau}_b F_{i,k},\ldots) \qquad \text{for all} \qquad b \in Y.$$

Let

$$g_\lambda^{(i)} = \sum_{k=0}^{d} G_\lambda^{(i,k)}x^k \in S[x] \subset R, \qquad \text{and} \qquad g_\lambda = (g_\lambda^{(1)},\ldots, g_\lambda^{(u)}) \in R^u;$$

$$(i = 1,\ldots, u; \quad \lambda = 1,\ldots, l).$$

Then $g_1,\ldots, g_l$ are convergent in $X = Y \times Z$ where $Z = K^1\{x\}$. We shall show that

$$\{\boldsymbol{\tau}_a g_1,\ldots, \boldsymbol{\tau}_a g_l\}R = \mathrm{Rel}(\boldsymbol{\tau}_a f_1,\ldots, \boldsymbol{\tau}_a f_u) \qquad \text{for all} \qquad a \in X$$

and this will complete the proof of (II).

[2] We write $f_{i,j}$ for the usual f_{ij} because otherwise it may cause misunderstanding in this proof.

Let $a = (b, c), b \in Y, c \in Z$, be given. Then $\max(\deg \boldsymbol{\tau}_a f_1, \ldots, \deg \boldsymbol{\tau}_a f_u) = d$, and $\deg \boldsymbol{\tau}_a g_\lambda^{(i)} \leqq d$ for $(i = 1, \ldots, u; \lambda = 1, \ldots, l)$. Hence by (15.1) with $\boldsymbol{\tau}_a f_i$ replacing f_i, *it suffices to show that:*

$$\{g = (g^{(1)}, \ldots, g^{(u)}) \in \operatorname{Rel}(\boldsymbol{\tau}_a f_1, \ldots, \boldsymbol{\tau}_a f_u) : \deg g^{(i)} \leqq d \text{ for } i = 1, \ldots, u\}$$
$$\subset \{\boldsymbol{\tau}_a g_1, \ldots, \boldsymbol{\tau}_a g_l\} R;$$

and

$$\boldsymbol{\tau}_a g_\lambda \in \operatorname{Rel}(\boldsymbol{\tau}_a f_1, \ldots, \boldsymbol{\tau}_a f_u) \qquad \text{for} \qquad \lambda = 1, \ldots, l.$$

So let $g = (g^{(1)}, \ldots, g^{(u)}) \in R^u$ be given with $\deg g^{(i)} \leqq d$ for $i = 1, \ldots, u$. Then there exists a unique element

$$\left.\begin{array}{l} G = (\ldots, G^{(i,k)}, \ldots) \in S^{u(d+1)} \\ \text{such that} \\ g^{(i)} = \displaystyle\sum_{k=0}^{d} G^{(i,k)}(x + c)^k \end{array}\right\} \begin{array}{l} (i = 1, \ldots, u), \\ (k = 0, \ldots, d) \end{array}$$

Now

$$\left.\begin{array}{l} \boldsymbol{\tau}_a f_i = \displaystyle\sum_{j=0}^{d} (\boldsymbol{\tau}_b f_{i,j})(x + c)^j; \\ \boldsymbol{\tau}_b f_{i,j} = 0 \quad \text{for} \quad j < 0 \quad \text{and for} \quad j > d; \\ \boldsymbol{\tau}_b F_{i,k}^{(\nu)} = \boldsymbol{\tau}_b f_{i,\nu-k}; \\ \boldsymbol{\tau}_a g_\lambda^{(i)} = \displaystyle\sum_{k=0}^{d} (\boldsymbol{\tau}_b G_\lambda^{(i,k)})(x + c)^k. \end{array}\right\} \begin{array}{l} (i = 1, \ldots, u), \\ (k = 0, \ldots, d), \\ (\nu = 0, \ldots, 2d), \\ (\lambda = 1, \ldots, l). \end{array}$$

Consequently

$$\begin{aligned} \sum_{i=1}^{u} g^{(i)} \boldsymbol{\tau}_a f_i &= \sum_{i=1}^{u} \left(\left[\sum_{k=0}^{d} G^{(i,k)}(x + c)^k \right] \left[\sum_{j=0}^{d} (\boldsymbol{\tau}_b f_{i,j})(x + c)^j \right] \right) \\ &= \sum_{\nu=0}^{2d} \left(\left[\sum_{i=1}^{u} \sum_{k=0}^{d} G^{(i,k)} \boldsymbol{\tau}_b F_{i,k}^{(\nu)} \right] (x + c)^\nu \right). \end{aligned}$$

Hence

$$\begin{aligned} & g \in \operatorname{Rel}(\boldsymbol{\tau}_a f_1, \ldots, \boldsymbol{\tau}_a f_u) \\ & \Leftrightarrow \sum_{i=1}^{u} \sum_{k=0}^{d} G^{(i,k)} \boldsymbol{\tau}_b F_{i,k}^{(\nu)} = 0 \text{ for } \nu = 0, \ldots, 2d \\ & \Leftrightarrow G \in \operatorname{Rel}(\ldots, \boldsymbol{\tau}_b F_{i,k}, \ldots) \\ & \Leftrightarrow G \in \{\boldsymbol{\tau}_b G_1, \ldots, \boldsymbol{\tau}_b G_l\} S \qquad \text{by } 1^\circ) \\ & \Rightarrow g \in \{\boldsymbol{\tau}_a g_1, \ldots, \boldsymbol{\tau}_a g_l\} R. \end{aligned}$$

Taking $g = \boldsymbol{\tau}_a g_\lambda$, this also yields that

$$\boldsymbol{\tau}_a g_\lambda \in \mathrm{Rel}(\boldsymbol{\tau}_a f_1, \ldots, \boldsymbol{\tau}_a f_u) \qquad \text{for} \qquad \lambda = 1, \ldots, l.$$

The following two corollaries of (15.2) will be needed later in the proof of Cartan-coherence.

(15.3)[3] *Let* $R = K[\langle x_1, \ldots, x_n \rangle]$. *Let* $f_1, \ldots, f_u \in R^v$ *be given. For any* $a \in \mathbf{D}(f_1) \cap \ldots \cap \mathbf{D}(f_u)$ *let* $\mathfrak{F}_a = \{\boldsymbol{\tau}_a f_1, \ldots, \boldsymbol{\tau}_a f_u\}R \subset R^v$. *Let* $g \in R$ *be given. Assume that*:

$$[h \in R^v,\ gh \in \mathfrak{F}_0 \Rightarrow h \in \mathfrak{F}_0].^4$$

Then there exists a neighborhood X *of the origin in* K^n *in which* $g, f_1, \ldots, f_u$ *are convergent, such that for all* $a \in X$ *we have*:

$$[h \in R^v,\ (\boldsymbol{\tau}_a g)h \in \mathfrak{F}_a \Rightarrow h \in \mathfrak{F}_a].$$

PROOF. Let $g_j = (0, \ldots, 0, \underset{\substack{\uparrow \\ j\text{th place}}}{g}, 0, \ldots, 0) \in R^v$, $(j = 1, \ldots, v)$. By (15.2) there exist elements

$$G_\mu = (G_\mu^{(1)}, \ldots, G_\mu^{(v)}, F_\mu^{(1)}, \ldots, F_\mu^{(u)}) \in R^{u+v}, \quad (\mu = 1, \ldots, m),$$

and a neighborhood X^* of the origin in K^n in which $g, f_1, \ldots, f_u, G_1, \ldots, G_m$ are all convergent, such that

$$\{\boldsymbol{\tau}_a G_1, \ldots, \boldsymbol{\tau}_a G_m\}R = \mathrm{Rel}(\boldsymbol{\tau}_a g_1, \ldots, \boldsymbol{\tau}_a g_v, \boldsymbol{\tau}_a f_1, \ldots, \boldsymbol{\tau}_a f_u) \quad \text{for all} \quad a \in X^*.$$

In particular taking $a = 0$,[4] for $\mu = 1, \ldots, m$ we get:

$$\sum_{j=1}^{v} G_\mu^{(j)} g_j + \sum_{i=1}^{u} F_\mu^{(i)} f_i = 0,$$

and hence

$$g(G_\mu^{(1)}, \ldots, G_\mu^{(v)}) = \sum_{j=1}^{v} G_\mu^{(j)} g_j = -\sum_{i=1}^{u} F_\mu^{(i)} f_i \in \mathfrak{F}_0,$$

and hence by assumption

$$(G_\mu^{(1)}, \ldots, G_\mu^{(v)}) \in \mathfrak{F}_0.$$

[3] Cartan [**3**].

[4] 0 = origin in K^n. Thus $\mathfrak{F}_0 = \{f_1, \ldots, f_u\}R$.

Consequently, there exists a neighborhood X of the origin in X^* such that

$$(\boldsymbol{\tau}_a G_\mu^{(1)}, \ldots, \boldsymbol{\tau}_a G_\mu^{(v)}) \in \mathfrak{F}_a \qquad \text{for all} \qquad a \in X, \qquad \text{for} \qquad \mu = 1, \ldots, m.$$

Let $a \in X$ and $h = (h^{(1)}, \ldots, h^{(v)}) \in R^v$ be given such that $(\boldsymbol{\tau}_a g)h \in \mathfrak{F}_a$. Then

$$\sum_{j=1}^{v} h^{(j)} \boldsymbol{\tau}_a g_j = (\boldsymbol{\tau}_a g)h = -\sum_{i=1}^{u} r^{(i)}(\boldsymbol{\tau}_a f_i) \qquad \text{with} \qquad r^{(i)} \in R.$$

Hence

$$(h^{(1)}, \ldots, h^{(v)}, r^{(1)}, \ldots, r^{(u)}) \in \operatorname{Rel}(\boldsymbol{\tau}_a g_1, \ldots, \boldsymbol{\tau}_a g_v, \boldsymbol{\tau}_a f_1, \ldots, \boldsymbol{\tau}_a f_u).$$

Consequently

$$(h^{(1)}, \ldots, h^{(v)}, r^{(1)}, \ldots, r^{(u)}) \in \{\boldsymbol{\tau}_a G_1, \ldots, \boldsymbol{\tau}_a G_m\}R,$$

whence in particular

$$\begin{aligned} h &= (h^{(1)}, \ldots, h^{(v)}) \\ &\in \{(\boldsymbol{\tau}_a G_1^{(1)}, \ldots, \boldsymbol{\tau}_a G_1^{(v)}), \ldots, (\boldsymbol{\tau}_a G_m^{(1)}, \ldots, \boldsymbol{\tau}_a G_m^{(v)})\}R \\ &\subset \mathfrak{F}_a. \end{aligned}$$

(15.4)[5] *Let $R = K[\langle x_1, \ldots, x_n \rangle]$. Let $f_1, \ldots, f_\lambda, g_1, \ldots, g_\mu$ be any given finite number of elements in R^v, $(v > 0)$. Then there exists a finite number of elements $h_1, \ldots, h_\nu$ in R^v and a neighborhood X of the origin in K^n in which all the elements f_i, g_j, h_k are convergent, such that for all $a \in X$ we have*

$$\{\boldsymbol{\tau}_a f_1, \ldots, \boldsymbol{\tau}_a f_\lambda\}R \cap \{\boldsymbol{\tau}_a g_1, \ldots, \boldsymbol{\tau}_a g_\mu\}R = \{\boldsymbol{\tau}_a h_1, \ldots, \boldsymbol{\tau}_a h_\nu\}R.$$

PROOF. By (15.2), there exists a finite number of elements

$$r_k = (r_k^{(1)}, \ldots, r_k^{(\lambda+\mu)}) \in R^{\lambda+\mu}, \qquad (k = 1, \ldots, \nu),$$

and a neighborhood X of the origin in K^n in which all the elements f_i, g_j, r_k are convergent, such that for all $a \in X$ we have

$$\operatorname{Rel}(\boldsymbol{\tau}_a f_1, \ldots, \boldsymbol{\tau}_a f_\lambda, \boldsymbol{\tau}_a g_1, \ldots, \boldsymbol{\tau}_a g_\mu) = \{\boldsymbol{\tau}_a r_1, \ldots, \boldsymbol{\tau}_a r_\nu\}R.$$

Let

$$h_k = \sum_{i=1}^{\lambda} r_k^{(i)} f_i \qquad \text{for} \qquad k = 1, \ldots, \nu.$$

[5] In sheaf theoretic language the purport of (15.4) is that the intersection of two coherent sheaves is coherent. A slightly different proof of this will be given in (42.6).

Then $h_1, \ldots, h_\nu$ are elements in R^v which are convergent in X. Let $a \in X$ be given. Then

$$\boldsymbol{\tau}_a h_k = \sum_{i=1}^{\lambda} (\boldsymbol{\tau}_a r_k^{(i)})(\boldsymbol{\tau}_a f_i) \in \{\boldsymbol{\tau}_a f_1, \ldots, \boldsymbol{\tau}_a f_\lambda\}R.$$

Now

$$\boldsymbol{\tau}_a r_k \in \mathrm{Rel}(\boldsymbol{\tau}_a f_1, \ldots, \boldsymbol{\tau}_a f_\lambda, \boldsymbol{\tau}_a g_1, \ldots, \boldsymbol{\tau}_a g_\mu),$$

i.e.,

$$\sum_{i=1}^{\lambda} (\boldsymbol{\tau}_a r_k^{(i)})(\boldsymbol{\tau}_a f_i) + \sum_{j=1}^{\mu} (\boldsymbol{\tau}_a r_k^{(j)})(\boldsymbol{\tau}_a g_j) = 0,$$

and hence

$$\boldsymbol{\tau}_a h_k = - \sum_{j=1}^{\mu} (\boldsymbol{\tau}_a r_k^{(j)})(\boldsymbol{\tau}_a g_j) \in \{\boldsymbol{\tau}_a g_1, \ldots, \boldsymbol{\tau}_a g_\mu\}R$$

Thus

$$\boldsymbol{\tau}_a h_k \in \{\boldsymbol{\tau}_a f_1, \ldots, \boldsymbol{\tau}_a f_\lambda\}R \cap \{\boldsymbol{\tau}_a g_1, \ldots, \boldsymbol{\tau}_a g_\mu\}R \qquad \text{for} \qquad k = 1, \ldots, \nu;$$

i.e.,

$$\{\boldsymbol{\tau}_a h_1, \ldots, \boldsymbol{\tau}_a h_\nu\}R \subset \{\boldsymbol{\tau}_a f_1, \ldots, \boldsymbol{\tau}_a f_\lambda\}R \cap \{\boldsymbol{\tau}_a g_1, \ldots, \boldsymbol{\tau}_a g_\mu\}R.$$

To prove "$\supset$" let

$$h \in \{\boldsymbol{\tau}_a f_1, \ldots, \boldsymbol{\tau}_a f_\lambda\}R \cap \{\boldsymbol{\tau}_a g_1, \ldots, \boldsymbol{\tau}_a g_\mu\}R$$

be given. Then

$$h = \sum_{i=1}^{\lambda} p_i(\boldsymbol{\tau}_a f_i) = \sum_{j=1}^{\mu} q_j(\boldsymbol{\tau}_a g_j) \qquad \text{with} \qquad p_i, q_j \in R.$$

Now

$$\sum_{i=1}^{\lambda} p_i(\boldsymbol{\tau}_a f_i) + \sum_{j=1}^{\mu} (-q_j)(\boldsymbol{\tau}_a g_j) = 0$$

and hence

$$\begin{aligned} &(p_1, \ldots, p_\lambda, -q_1, \ldots, -q_\mu) \\ &\in \mathrm{Rel}(\boldsymbol{\tau}_a f_1, \ldots, \boldsymbol{\tau}_a f_\lambda, \boldsymbol{\tau}_a g_1, \ldots, \boldsymbol{\tau}_a g_\mu) \\ &\subset \{\boldsymbol{\tau}_a r_1, \ldots, \boldsymbol{\tau}_a r_\nu\}R. \end{aligned}$$

Therefore we can find $s_1,\ldots, s_\nu \in R$ such that

$$p_i = \sum_{k=1}^{\nu} s_k(\boldsymbol{\tau}_a r_k^{(i)}) \quad \text{for} \quad i = 1,\ldots, \lambda.$$

This gives

$$h = \sum_{i=1}^{\lambda} p_i(\boldsymbol{\tau}_a f_i) = \sum_{k=1}^{\nu} \sum_{i=1}^{\lambda} s_k(\boldsymbol{\tau}_a r_k^{(i)})(\boldsymbol{\tau}_a f_i)$$
$$= \sum_{k=1}^{\nu} s_k(\boldsymbol{\tau}_a h_k)$$
$$\in \{\boldsymbol{\tau}_a h_1,\ldots, \boldsymbol{\tau}_a h_\nu\}R.$$

§16. CARTAN MODULE BASES[1]

Assume that K is infinite. Let $\hat{R} = K[[x_1,\ldots, x_n]]$ and let $R = K[\langle x_1,\ldots, x_n\rangle]$.[2]

Given a finite number of elements $f_1,\ldots,f_u$ in $\hat{R}^v$, by a *construction* for $f_1,\ldots,f_u$ we mean a sequence of K-linear maps $\alpha_1,\ldots, \alpha_u$ of $\hat{R}^v$ into $\hat{R}$ such that for any f in $\hat{R}^v$ we have[3]:

$$f \in f_1\hat{R} + \ldots + f_u\hat{R} \Leftrightarrow f = \alpha_1(f)f_1 + \ldots + \alpha_u(f)f_u.$$

More generally, let $f_i^{[\lambda]} \in \hat{R}^{v_\lambda}$ and let $\alpha_i^{[\lambda]}$ be a K-linear map of $\hat{R}^{v_\lambda}$ into $\hat{R}$ for $\lambda = 1,\ldots, \Lambda$ and $i = 1,\ldots, u_\lambda$. We say that

$$1°) \qquad \alpha_1^{[1]},\ldots, \alpha_{u_1}^{[1]}; \alpha_1^{[2]},\ldots, \alpha_{u_2}^{[2]};\ldots; \alpha_1^{[\lambda]},\ldots, \alpha_{u_\lambda}^{[\lambda]};\ldots; \alpha_1^{[\Lambda]},\ldots, \alpha_{u_\Lambda}^{[\Lambda]}$$

is a *construction* for

$$2°) \qquad f_1^{[1]},\ldots, f_{u_1}^{[1]}; f_1^{[2]},\ldots, f_{u_2}^{[2]};\ldots; f_1^{[\lambda]},\ldots, f_{u_\lambda}^{[\lambda]};\ldots; f_1^{[\Lambda]},\ldots, f_{u_\Lambda}^{[\Lambda]}$$

provided $\alpha_1^{[\lambda]},\ldots, \alpha_{u_\lambda}^{[\lambda]}$ is a construction for $f_1^{[\lambda]},\ldots, f_{u_\lambda}^{[\lambda]}$ for $\lambda = 1,\ldots, \Lambda$, i.e., provided

$$3°) \quad \begin{cases} \text{for all } \lambda \leqq \Lambda \text{ and for all } f \in \hat{R}^{v_\lambda} \text{ we have that:} \\ f \in f_1^{[\lambda]}\hat{R} + \ldots + f_{u_\lambda}^{[\lambda]}\hat{R} \Leftrightarrow f = \alpha_1^{[\lambda]}(f)f_1^{[\lambda]} + \ldots + \alpha_{u_\lambda}^{[\lambda]}(f)f_{u_\lambda}^{[\lambda]}. \end{cases}$$

Let $f_i^{[\lambda]} \in R^{v_\lambda}$ and let $\alpha_i^{[\lambda]}$ be a K-linear map of R^{v_λ} into R. We say that 1°) is a *convergent construction* for 2°) provided 3°) holds with R replacing

[1] Cartan [2]; also Cartan [**4**: Exposé XI].

[2] For $n = 0$ we take $\hat{R} = R = K$.

[3] Obviously "$\Leftarrow$" always holds.

$\hat{R}$, and provided to each neighborhood X of the origin in K^n there corresponds a neighborhood X^* of the origin in X such that, for all $\lambda \leqq \Lambda$ and for all $f \in R^{v_\lambda}$ we have:

4°) f is convergent in $X \Rightarrow \alpha_1^{[\lambda]}(f),\ldots, \alpha_{u_\lambda}^{[\lambda]}(f)$ are convergent in X^*.

Let $K = \mathbf{C}$, let $f_i^{[\lambda]} \in R^{v_\lambda}$ and let $\alpha_i^{[\lambda]}$ be a K-linear map of R^{v_λ} into R. We say that 1°) is a *bounded convergent construction* for 2°) provided 3°) holds with R replacing $\hat{R}$, and provided via a nonsingular $\mathbf{C}$-linear transformation we can find a vicinity basis $\mathbf{X}$ of the origin in $\mathbf{C}^n$ such that each $X \in \mathbf{X}$ is a finite closed polycylinder (around the origin) and to it corresponds a positive constant $D(X)$, such that for all $\lambda \leqq \Lambda$, $f \in R^{v_\lambda}$, and $X \in \mathbf{X}$, we have:

5°) $\left\{\begin{array}{l} f \text{ is convergent in a neighborhood of } X \\ \Rightarrow \text{for } i = 1,\ldots, u_\lambda,\ \alpha_i^{[\lambda]}(f) \text{ is convergent} \\ \quad \text{in a neighborhood of } X \text{ and} \\ \qquad \sup|\alpha_i^{[\lambda]}(f)(X)| \leqq D(X)\sup|f(X)|; \end{array}\right.$

where for any

$$f = (f^{(1)},\ldots, f^{(v_\lambda)}) \in R^{v_\lambda}, \qquad f^{(j)} \in R, \qquad a \in \mathbf{D}(f),$$

we are taking

$$|f(a)| = \max(|f^{(1)}(a)|,\ldots, |f^{(v_\lambda)}(a)|).$$

Consider the following statements.

$\mathfrak{C}(n, v)$: *Given* $f_i^{[\lambda]} \in \hat{R}^{v_\lambda}$, $0 < v_\lambda \leqq v$, $(i = 1,\ldots, u_\lambda)$, $(\lambda = 1,\ldots, \Lambda)$, *there exists a construction for* $f_1^{[1]},\ldots, f_{u_1}^{[1]};\ldots; f_1^{[\Lambda]},\ldots, f_{u_\Lambda}^{[\Lambda]}$.

(I) *Given* $n > 0$, $v > 1$: $\mathfrak{C}(n, v - 1) \Rightarrow \mathfrak{C}(n, v)$.
(II) *Given* $n > 0$: $[\mathfrak{C}(n - 1, v)$ *for all* $v > 0] \Rightarrow \mathfrak{C}(n, 1)$.

We want to show that $\mathfrak{C}(n, v)$ holds for all $n \geqq 0$, $v > 0$. Since $\mathfrak{C}(0, v)$ is trivial for all $v > 0$, by double induction on (n, v) it suffices to prove (I) and (II). While proving (I) and (II) we shall also give the supplementary arguments for proving the corresponding statements for convergent constructions and bounded convergent constructions.[4]

Proof of (I). Let $f_i^{[\lambda]} \in \hat{R}^{v_\lambda}$, $v_\lambda \leqq v$, $(i = 1,\ldots, u_\lambda)$, $(\lambda = 1,\ldots, \Lambda)$, be given. Relabel $v_1,\ldots, v_\Lambda$ so that $v_\lambda = v$ for $\lambda \leqq \Lambda^*$ and $v_\lambda < v$ for $\lambda > \Lambda^*$.

[4] Either take the statements corresponding to $\mathfrak{C}(0, v)$ to hold trivially, or note that the statements corresponding to $\mathfrak{C}(1, 1)$ follow by trivial modifications in the proof of (II)

For any $f \in \hat{R}^v$, write $f = (F, \bar{f})$ with $F \in \hat{R}^{v-1}$ and $\bar{f} \in \hat{R}$. Let

$$6°) \qquad \mathfrak{M}^{[\lambda]} = \{f \in f_1^{[\lambda]}\hat{R} + \dots + f_{u_\lambda}^{[\lambda]}\hat{R} : \bar{f} = 0\}; \qquad \lambda \leqq \Lambda^*.$$

Since $\hat{R}$ is noetherian, we can find a finite $\hat{R}$-basis

$$7°) \qquad \{g^{[\lambda]} = (G_\mu^{[\lambda]}, 0); \mu = 1, \dots, m_\lambda\}$$

for the $\hat{R}$-module $\mathfrak{M}^{[\lambda]}$. Then

$$8°) \qquad g_\mu^{[\lambda]} = \sum_{i=1}^{u_\lambda} p_{i\mu}^{[\lambda]} f_i^{[\lambda]} \qquad \text{with} \qquad p_{i\mu}^{[\lambda]} \in \hat{R}, \qquad (\mu = 1, \dots, m_\lambda).$$

By $\mathfrak{C}(n, v - 1)$, we can find a construction

$$9°) \qquad \begin{cases} \bar{\alpha}_1^{[1]}, \dots, \bar{\alpha}_{u_1}^{[1]}; \dots; \bar{\alpha}_1^{[\Lambda^*]}, \dots, \bar{\alpha}_{u_{\Lambda^*}}^{[\Lambda^*]}; \\ \beta_1^{[1]}, \dots, \beta_{m_1}^{[1]}; \dots; \beta_1^{[\Lambda^*]}, \dots, \beta_{m_{\Lambda^*}}^{[\Lambda^*]}; \\ \alpha_1^{[\Lambda^*+1]}, \dots, \alpha_{u_{\Lambda^*+1}}^{[\Lambda^*+1]}; \dots; \alpha_1^{[\Lambda]}, \dots, \alpha_{u_\Lambda}^{[\Lambda]}; \end{cases}$$

for

$$10°) \qquad \begin{cases} \bar{f}_1^{[1]}, \dots, \bar{f}_{u_1}^{[1]}; \dots; \bar{f}_1^{[\Lambda^*]}, \dots, \bar{f}_{u_{\Lambda^*}}^{[\Lambda^*]}; \\ G_1^{[1]}, \dots, G_{m_1}^{[1]}; \dots; G_1^{[\Lambda^*]}, \dots, G_{u_{\Lambda^*}}^{[\Lambda^*]}; \\ f_1^{[\Lambda^*+1]}, \dots, f_{u_{\Lambda^*+1}}^{[\Lambda^*+1]}; \dots; f_1^{[\Lambda]}, \dots, f_{u_\Lambda}^{[\Lambda]}. \end{cases}$$

For any $\lambda \leqq \Lambda^*$ and for any $f \in \hat{R}^v$ let

$$11°) \qquad \alpha_i^{[\lambda]}(f) = \bar{\alpha}_i^{[\lambda]}(\bar{f}) + \sum_{\mu=1}^{m_\lambda} p_{i\mu}^{[\lambda]} \beta_\mu^{[\lambda]}(F - \sum_{i=1}^{u_\lambda} \bar{\alpha}_i^{[\lambda]}(\bar{f}) F_i^{[\lambda]}).$$

Since a composition of K-linear maps is a K-linear map, it follows that $\alpha_i^{[\lambda]}$ is a K-linear map of $\hat{R}^v$ into $\hat{R}$. Now let $\lambda \leqq \Lambda^*$ and $f \in f_1^{[\lambda]}\hat{R} + \dots + f_{u_\lambda}^{[\lambda]}\hat{R}$ be given. Then

$$\bar{f} = \sum_{i=1}^{u_\lambda} \bar{\alpha}_i^{[\lambda]}(\bar{f}) \bar{f}_i^{[\lambda]},$$

and hence setting

$$12°) \qquad h = f - \sum_{i=1}^{u_\lambda} \bar{\alpha}_i^{[\lambda]}(\bar{f}) f_i^{[\lambda]}$$

we have that

$$h \in f_1^{[\lambda]}\hat{R} + \dots + f_{u_\lambda}^{[\lambda]}\hat{R}, \qquad \bar{h} = 0, \qquad \text{and} \qquad h = (H, 0)$$

where

$$H = F - \sum_{i=1}^{u_\lambda} \bar{\alpha}_i^{[\lambda]}(\bar{f})F_i^{[\lambda]} \tag{13°)}$$

Therefore $h \in \mathfrak{M}^{[\lambda]}$, and hence

$$H = \sum_{\mu=1}^{m_\lambda} \beta_\mu^{[\lambda]}(H)G_\mu^{[\lambda]}. \tag{14°)}$$

Now, we have the following computation.

$$\begin{aligned}
&f - \sum_{i=1}^{u_\lambda} \bar{\alpha}_i^{[\lambda]}(\bar{f})f_i^{[\lambda]} \\
&= h && \text{by 12°)} \\
&= (H, 0) \\
&= \left(\sum_{\mu=1}^{m_\lambda} \beta_\mu^{[\lambda]}(H)G_\mu^{[\lambda]}, 0\right) && \text{by 14°)} \\
&= \sum_{\mu=1}^{m_\lambda} \left[\beta_\mu^{[\lambda]}\left(F - \sum_{i=1}^{u_\lambda} \bar{\alpha}_i^{[\lambda]}(\bar{f})F_i^{[\lambda]}\right)\right]\left[\sum_{i=1}^{u_\lambda} p_{i\mu}^{[\lambda]} f_i^{[\lambda]}\right] && \text{by 13°), 7°), 8°)} \\
&= \sum_{i=1}^{u_\lambda} \left[\sum_{\mu=1}^{m_\lambda} p_{i\mu}^{[\lambda]}\beta_\mu^{[\lambda]}\left(F - \sum_{i=1}^{u_\lambda} \bar{\alpha}_i^{[\lambda]}(\bar{f})F_i^{[\lambda]}\right)\right] f_i^{[\lambda]}.
\end{aligned}$$

Therefore by 11°) we get

$$f = \sum_{i=1}^{u_\lambda} \alpha_i^{[\lambda]}(f)f_i^{[\lambda]}.$$

This shows that

$$\alpha_1^{[1]},\ldots, \alpha_{u_1}^{[1]};\ldots; \alpha_1^{[\Lambda]},\ldots, \alpha_{u_\Lambda}^{[\Lambda]}; \tag{15°)}$$

is a construction for

$$f_1^{[1]},\ldots, f_{u_1}^{[1]};\ldots; f_1^{[\Lambda]},\ldots, f_{u_\Lambda}^{[\Lambda]}. \tag{16°)}$$

———×———

In the convergent case, everywhere replace $\hat{R}$ by R and "construction" by "convergent construction". Let a neighborhood X of the origin in K^n be given. Take X' to be a neighborhood of the origin in X such that $F_i^{[\lambda]}$ and $p_{i\mu}^{[\lambda]}$ are convergent in X', $(i = 1,\ldots, u_\lambda;\ \lambda = 1,\ldots, \Lambda^*;\ \mu = 1,\ldots, m_\lambda)$.

Since 9°) is a convergent construction for 10°), we can find a neighborhood X^* of the origin in X' such that

for $\lambda \leqq \Lambda^*: \bar{f} \in R$ is convergent in X'

$$\Rightarrow \bar{\alpha}_1^{[\lambda]}(\bar{f}), \ldots, \bar{\alpha}_{u_\lambda}^{[\lambda]}(\bar{f}) \text{ are convergent in } X^*;$$

for $\lambda \leqq \Lambda^*$: $F \in R^{v-1}$ is convergent in X'

$$\Rightarrow \beta_1^{[\lambda]}(F), \ldots, \beta_{m_\lambda}^{[\lambda]}(F) \text{ are convergent in } X^*;$$

and

for $\lambda > \Lambda^*: f \in R^{v_\lambda}$ is convergent in X'

$$\Rightarrow \alpha_1^{[\lambda]}(f), \ldots, \alpha_{u_\lambda}^{[\lambda]}(f) \text{ are convergent in } X^*.$$

In view of 11°) it then follows that for all $\lambda \leqq \Lambda$, and for all $f \in R^{v_\lambda}$ we have that: f is convergent in $X \Rightarrow \alpha_1^{[\lambda]}(f), \ldots, \alpha_{u_\lambda}^{[\lambda]}(f)$ are convergent in X^*. Therefore 15°) is a convergent construction for 16°).

———×———×———

In the bounded convergent case, ($K = \mathbf{C}$), everywhere replace $\hat{R}$ by R, and "construction" by "bounded convergent construction". Since 9°) is a bounded convergent construction for 10°), via a linear transformation we can find a vicinity basis $\tilde{\mathbf{X}}$ of the origin in $\mathbf{C}^n$ such that each $X \in \tilde{\mathbf{X}}$ is a finite closed polycylinder and to it corresponds a positive constant $A(X)$, such that for any $X \in \tilde{\mathbf{X}}$ we have (17°, 18°, 19°).

17°) For $\lambda \leqq \Lambda^*: \bar{f} \in R$ is convergent in a neighborhood of X

$\Rightarrow$ for $i = 1, \ldots, u_\lambda$, $\bar{\alpha}_i^{[\lambda]}(\bar{f})$ is convergent in a neighborhood of X and

$$\sup|\bar{\alpha}_i^{[\lambda]}(\bar{f})(X)| \leqq A(X) \sup|\bar{f}(X)|.$$

18°) For $\lambda \leqq \Lambda^*$: $F \in R^{v-1}$ is convergent in a neighborhood of X

$\Rightarrow$ for $\mu = 1, \ldots, m_\lambda$, $\beta_\mu^{[\lambda]}(F)$ is convergent in a neighborhood of X and

$$\sup|\beta_\mu^{[\lambda]}(F)(X)| \leqq A(X) \sup|F(X)|.$$

19°) For $\lambda > \Lambda^*: f \in R^{v_\lambda}$ is convergent in a neighborhood of X

$\Rightarrow$ for $i = 1, \ldots, u_\lambda$, $\alpha_i^{[\lambda]}(f)$ is convergent in a neighborhood of X and

$$\sup|\alpha_i^{[\lambda]}(f)(X)| \leqq A(X) \sup|f(X)|.$$

We can find $\tilde{X} \in \tilde{\mathbf{X}}$ such that $F_i^{[\lambda]}$ and $p_{i\mu}^{[\lambda]}$ are convergent in a neighborhood of $\tilde{X}$, $(i = 1,..., u_\lambda; \lambda = 1,..., \Lambda^*; \mu = 1,..., m_\lambda)$. Let $\mathbf{X} = \{X \in \tilde{\mathbf{X}}: X \subset \tilde{X}\}$. Then $\mathbf{X}$ is a vicinity basis of the origin. Take positive constants B and C such that

$$\left.\begin{array}{l} B \geqq \sup|F_i^{[\lambda]}(\tilde{X})| \\ C \geqq \sup|p_{i\mu}^{[\lambda]}(\tilde{X})| \end{array}\right\} \quad \begin{array}{l} \text{for} \quad \lambda = 1,..., \Lambda^*; \\ i = 1,..., u_\lambda; \quad \mu = 1,..., m_\lambda. \end{array}$$

Take positive integers u and m such that

$$\left.\begin{array}{l} u \geqq u_\lambda \\ m \geqq m_\lambda \end{array}\right\} \quad \text{for} \quad \lambda = 1,..., \Lambda^*.$$

Let $X \in \mathbf{X}$ be given. Let $A = A(X)$. Set

$$D(X) = A + mAC + muA^2BC.$$

Let $\lambda \leqq \Lambda$, $i \leqq u_\lambda$, and $f \in R^{v_\lambda}$ be given such that f is convergent in a neighborhood of X. From 11°) it follows that $\alpha_i^{[\lambda]}(f)$ is convergent in a neighborhood of X. Let $E = \sup|f(X)|$. If $\lambda > \Lambda^*$ then

$$\sup|\alpha_i^{[\lambda]}(f)(X)| \leqq AE \leqq D(X)E.$$

Now assume that $\lambda \leqq \Lambda^*$. Then by 17°) we get

20°) $$\sup|\bar{\alpha}_i^{[\lambda]}(\bar{f})(X)| \leqq A \sup|\bar{f}(X)| \leqq AE;$$

and hence

$$\begin{aligned} \sup\left|\left(F - \sum_{i=1}^{u_\lambda} \bar{\alpha}_i^{[\lambda]}(\bar{f})F_i^{[\lambda]}\right)(X)\right| &\leqq E + u_\lambda AEB \\ &\leqq (1 + uAB)E. \end{aligned}$$

Therefore by 18°) we get

21°) $$\sup\left|\left(\beta_\mu^{[\lambda]}\left(F - \sum_{i=1}^{u_\lambda} \bar{\alpha}_i^{[\lambda]}(\bar{f})F_i^{[\lambda]}\right)\right)(X)\right| \leqq A(1 + uAB)E$$
$$\text{for} \quad \mu = 1,..., m_\lambda.$$

Finally, (11°, 20°, 21°) yield that

$$\begin{aligned} \sup|\alpha_i^{[\lambda]}(f)(X)| &\leqq AE + m_\lambda CA(1 + uAB)E \\ &\leqq (A + mAC + muA^2BC)E \\ &= D(X)E. \end{aligned}$$

This shows that 15°) is a bounded convergent construction for 16°).

———×———×———×———

Proof of (II). Let $f_i^{[\lambda]} \in \hat{R}$, $(\lambda = 1,\ldots, \Lambda)$, $(i = 1,\ldots, u_\lambda)$, be given. In view of the Preparation Theorem (10.3.6), suitably relabeling the elements and making a linear transformation we can arrange that

for $\lambda \leqq \Lambda^*$: $f_1^{[\lambda]}$ is $\hat{R}$-associate of a distinguished polynomial of degree $d_\lambda > 0$ in x_n with coefficients in

$$\hat{S} = K[[x_1,\ldots, x_{n-1}]];$$

for $\Lambda^* < \lambda \leqq \Lambda'$: $f_1^{[\lambda]}$ is a unit in $\hat{R}$;

and

for $\Lambda' < \lambda \leqq \Lambda$: $f_1^{[\lambda]} = \ldots = f_{u_\lambda}^{[\lambda]} = 0$.

Let us write deg for degree in x_n relative to $\hat{S}$. By Preparation Theorem (10.3.1), for any $f \in \hat{R}$, we can uniquely write

$$f = \bar{f}^{[\lambda]}f_1^{[\lambda]} + F^{[\lambda]} \text{ with } \bar{f}^{[\lambda]}, F^{[\lambda]} \in \hat{R} \text{ and } \deg F^{[\lambda]} < d_\lambda, \text{ for } \lambda \leqq \Lambda^*;$$

and

$$f = \bar{f}^{[\lambda]}f_1^{[\lambda]} \quad \text{with} \quad \bar{f}^{[\lambda]} \in \hat{R}, \quad \text{for} \quad \Lambda^* < \lambda \leqq \Lambda'.$$

Fix a positive integer d such that $d > d_\lambda$ for all $\lambda \leqq \Lambda^*$.

For any $f \in \hat{R}$ let

$$22°)\quad \begin{cases} \text{for } \Lambda' < \lambda \leqq \Lambda: \alpha_i^{[\lambda]}(f) = 0 \quad \text{for} \quad i \leqq u_\lambda; \\ \text{and} \\ \text{for } \Lambda^* < \lambda \leqq \Lambda': \alpha_1^{[\lambda]}(f) = \bar{f}^{[\lambda]}, \quad \text{and} \\ \qquad \alpha_i^{[\lambda]}(f) = 0 \quad \text{for} \quad 1 < i \leqq u_\lambda; \end{cases}$$

then obviously $\alpha_i^{[\lambda]}$ is K-linear and for any $\lambda > \Lambda^*$:

$$f \in f_1^{[\lambda]}\hat{R} + \ldots + f_{u_\lambda}^{[\lambda]}\hat{R} \Rightarrow f = \alpha_1^{[\lambda]}(f)f_1^{[\lambda]} + \ldots + \alpha_{u_\lambda}^{[\lambda]}(f)f_{u_\lambda}^{[\lambda]}.$$

For $\lambda \leqq \Lambda^*$, in a natural manner

$$\mathfrak{M}^{[\lambda]} = \{G \in f_1^{[\lambda]}\hat{R} + \ldots + f_{u_\lambda}^{[\lambda]}\hat{R}: \deg G < d_\lambda\}$$

can be considered to be an $\hat{S}$-submodule of $\hat{S}^{d_\lambda}$; and since $\hat{S}$ is noetherian, we can find a finite $\hat{S}$-basis

$$23°)\qquad G_\mu^{[\lambda]}, \quad (\mu = 1,\ldots, m_\lambda),$$

for $\mathfrak{M}^{[\lambda]}$. Now

24°) $$G_{\mu}^{[\lambda]} = \sum_{i=1}^{u_\lambda} p_{i\mu}^{[\lambda]} f_i^{[\lambda]} \quad \text{with} \quad p_{i\mu}^{[\lambda]} \in \hat{R}.$$

By $\mathfrak{C}(n-1, d)$ we can find a construction

25°) $$\beta_1^{[1]},\ldots, \beta_{m_1}^{[1]};\ldots; \beta_1^{[\Lambda^*]},\ldots, \beta_{m_{\Lambda^*}}^{[\Lambda^*]};$$

for

26°) $$G_1^{[1]},\ldots, G_{m_1}^{[1]};\ldots; G_1^{[\Lambda^*]},\ldots, G_{m_{\Lambda^*}}^{[\Lambda^*]}.$$

For any $\lambda \leqq \Lambda^*$ and $f \in \hat{R}$ let

27°) $$\begin{cases} \alpha_1^{[\lambda]}(f) = \bar{f}^{[\lambda]} + \sum_{\mu=1}^{m_\lambda} p_{1\mu}^{[\lambda]} \beta_\mu^{[\lambda]}(F^{[\lambda]}) \\ \text{and} \\ \alpha_i^{[\lambda]}(f) = \sum_{\mu=1}^{m_\lambda} p_{i\mu}^{[\lambda]} \beta_\mu^{[\lambda]}(F^{[\lambda]}) \quad \text{for} \quad 1 < i \leqq u_\lambda. \end{cases}$$

Obviously $\alpha_1^{[\lambda]},\ldots, \alpha_{u_\lambda}^{[\lambda]}$ are K-linear. Also

$$\begin{aligned} &\sum_{i=1}^{u_\lambda} \alpha_i^{[\lambda]}(f) f_i^{[\lambda]} \\ &= \bar{f}^{[\lambda]} f_1^{[\lambda]} + \sum_{i=1}^{u_\lambda} \left[\sum_{\mu=1}^{m_\lambda} p_{i\mu}^{[\lambda]} \beta_\mu^{[\lambda]}(F^{[\lambda]}) \right] f_i^{[\lambda]} \\ &= \bar{f}^{[\lambda]} f_1^{[\lambda]} + \sum_{\mu=1}^{m_\lambda} \beta_\mu^{[\lambda]}(F^{[\lambda]}) G_\mu^{[\lambda]}. \end{aligned}$$

Hence

$$\begin{aligned} & f \in f_1^{[\lambda]}\hat{R} + \ldots + f_{u_\lambda}^{[\lambda]}\hat{R} \\ \Rightarrow\ & F^{[\lambda]} \in \mathfrak{M}^{[\lambda]} \\ \Rightarrow\ & F^{[\lambda]} = \sum_{\mu=1}^{m_\lambda} \beta_i^{[\lambda]}(F^{[\lambda]}) G_\mu^{[\lambda]} \\ \Rightarrow\ & f = \sum_{i=1}^{u_\lambda} \alpha_i^{[\lambda]}(f) f_i^{[\lambda]}. \end{aligned}$$

This shows that

$$28°) \qquad \alpha_1^{[1]},\ldots, \alpha_{u_1}^{[\lambda]};\ldots; \alpha_1^{[\Lambda]},\ldots, \alpha_{u_\Lambda}^{[\Lambda]}$$

is a construction for

$$29°) \qquad f_1^{[1]},\ldots, f_{u_1}^{[1]};\ldots; f_1^{[\Lambda]},\ldots, f_{u_\Lambda}^{[\Lambda]}.$$

——×——

In the convergent case, everywhere replace $\hat{R}$ by R, $\hat{S}$ by $S = K[\langle x_1,\ldots, x_{n-1}\rangle]$, and "construction" by "convergent construction". Let a neighborhood X of the origin in K^n be given. Take X' to be a neighborhood of the origin in X such that $f_i^{[\lambda]}$ and $p_{i\mu}^{[\lambda]}$ are convergent in X', ($i = 1,\ldots, u_\lambda$; $\lambda = 1,\ldots, \Lambda^*$; $\mu = 1,\ldots, m_\lambda$). By Preparation Theorem (10.3.1) there exists a neighborhood X'' of the origin in X' such that for any $f \in R$ which is convergent in X' we have that, $\bar{f}^{[\lambda]}$ and $F^{[\lambda]}$ are convergent in X'' for all $\lambda \leqq \Lambda^*$, and $\bar{f}^{[\lambda]}$ is convergent in X'' for all $\Lambda^* < \lambda \leqq \Lambda'$. Since 25°) is a convergent construction for 26°), there exists a neighborhood X^* of the origin in X'' such that for any $\lambda \leqq \Lambda^*$ and $F \in R$ with $\deg F < d_\lambda$ we have:

F is convergent in $X'' \Rightarrow \beta_1^{[\lambda]}(F),\ldots, \beta_{m_\lambda}^{[\lambda]}(F)$ are convergent in X^*.

Now by 22°) and 27°) it follows that for any $\lambda \leqq \Lambda$ and $f \in R$:

f is convergent in $X \Rightarrow \alpha_1^{[\lambda]}(f),\ldots, \alpha_{u_\lambda}^{[\lambda]}(f)$ are convergent in X^*.

Therefore 28°) is a convergent construction for 29°).

——×——×——

In the bounded convergent case, ($K = \mathbf{C}$), everywhere replace $\hat{R}$ by R, $\hat{S}$ by $S = \mathbf{C}[\langle x_1,\ldots, x_{n-1}\rangle]$ and "construction" by "bounded convergent construction". For any $\lambda \leqq \Lambda^*$ and $F^{[\lambda]} \in \mathfrak{M}^{[\lambda]}$ we can uniquely write

$$F^{[\lambda]} = \sum_{j=0}^{d_\lambda - 1} F^{[\lambda,j]} x_n^j \qquad \text{with} \qquad F^{[\lambda,j]} \in S.$$

Now $\mathfrak{M}^{[\lambda]}$ is considered as a submodule of S^{d_λ} and 25°) is a bounded convergent construction for 26°). Therefore, via a nonsingular linear transformation on $x_1,\ldots, x_{n-1}$, we can find a vicinity basis $Y_1 \supset Y_2 \supset \ldots$ of the origin in $\mathbf{C}^{n-1}\{x_1,\ldots, x_{n-1}\}$ such that each Y_t is a finite closed polycylinder and to it corresponds a positive constant E_t, such that for any $\lambda \leqq \Lambda^*$ and $t > 0$ and for any

$$F^{[\lambda]} = \sum_{j=0}^{d_\lambda - 1} F^{[\lambda,j]} x_n^j \qquad \text{with} \qquad F^{[\lambda,j]} \in S$$

we have:

30°) $F^{[\lambda,j]}$ is a convergent in a neighborhood of Y_t for all $j < d_\lambda$

$\Rightarrow$ for all $\mu \leqq m_\lambda$, $\beta_\mu^{[\lambda]}(F^{[\lambda]})$ is convergent in a neighborhood of Y_t and

$$\sup|\beta_\mu^{[\lambda]}(F^{[\lambda]})(Y_t)| \leqq E_t \max_{j<d}(\sup|F^{[\lambda,j]}(Y_t)|).$$

By the complex Weierstrass Preparation Theorem (13.3.2), upon replacing $Y_1 \supset Y_2 \supset \ldots$ by a suitable subsequence, we can find positive constants $C_1 > C_2 > \ldots$ and $A_1, A_2, \ldots$ such that upon setting

$$X_t = Y_t \times \{x_n : |x_n| \leqq C_t\},$$

we have that $f_i^{[\lambda]}$ and $p_{i\mu}^{[\lambda]}$ are convergent in a neighborhood of X_1, $(i = 1, \ldots, \mu_\lambda;\ \lambda = 1, \ldots, \Lambda^*;\ \mu = 1, \ldots, m_\lambda)$, and for any $t > 0$ and $f \in R$ the following holds:

31°) f is convergent in a neighborhood of X_t

$\Rightarrow \bar{f}^{[\lambda]}$ is convergent in a neighborhood of X_t and

$$\sup|\bar{f}^{[\lambda]}(X_t)| \leqq A_t \sup|f(X_t)|, \qquad \text{for} \qquad \lambda \leqq \Lambda';$$

and

$F^{[\lambda,j]}$ is convergent in a neighborhood of Y_t and

$$\sup|F^{[\lambda,j]}(Y_t)| \leqq A_t \sup|f(X_t)|, \qquad \text{for} \qquad \lambda \leqq \Lambda^*, \quad j < d_\lambda.$$

Take a positive constant B and a positive integer m such that:

$$B \leqq \sup|p_{i\mu}^{[\lambda]}(X_1)| \qquad \text{for} \qquad \lambda \leqq \Lambda^*, \qquad i \leqq u_\lambda, \qquad \mu \leqq m_\lambda;$$

$$m \geqq m_\lambda \qquad \text{for} \qquad \lambda \leqq \Lambda^*.$$

For any $t > 0$ let

$$D(X_t) = A_t + mBE_tA_t.$$

Let $\lambda \leqq \Lambda$, $i \leqq u_\lambda$, $t > 0$ and $f \in R$ be given such that f is convergent in a neighborhood of X_t. Then by (22°, 27°, 30°, 31°) it follows that $\alpha_i^{[\lambda]}(f)$

is convergent in a neighborhood of X_t and

$$\sup|\alpha_i^{[\lambda]}(f)(X_t)| \leqq D(X_t) \sup|f(X_t)|.$$

Therefore 28°) is a bounded convergent construction for 29°).

———×———×———×———

Thus we have proved the following

(16.1) THEOREM. *Let* $\hat{R} = K[[x_1,..., x_n]]$ *and* $R = K[\langle x_1,..., x_n\rangle]$.[5] *Given* $f_i^{[\lambda]} \in \hat{R}^{v_\lambda}$, $v_\lambda > 0$, $(\lambda = 1,..., \Lambda;\ i = 1,..., u_\lambda)$, *there exists a construction for*

i) $$f_1^{[1]},..., f_{u_1}^{[1]};...; f_1^{[\lambda]},..., f_{u_\lambda}^{[\lambda]};...; f_1^{[\Lambda]},..., f_{u_\Lambda}^{[\Lambda]}.$$

If $f_i^{[\lambda]} \in R^{v_\lambda}$ *for all* λ, i, *then there exists a convergent construction for* i). *If* $K = \mathbf{C}$, *and* $f_i^{[\lambda]} \in R^{v_\lambda}$ *for all* λ, i, *then there exists a bounded convergent construction for* i).

REMARK. For our purposes, the existence of a convergent construction and the existence of a bounded convergent construction are enough. However, by a slight modification of the preceding proof we can prove the following.

(16.2) *Let* $R = K[\langle x_1,..., x_n\rangle]$. Let $f_j^{[\lambda]} \in R^{v_\lambda}$, $v_\lambda > 0$, $(\lambda = 1,..., \Lambda;$ $i = 1,..., u_\lambda)$ *be given. Then there exists a construction*

ii) $$\alpha_1^{[1]},..., \alpha_{u_1}^{[1]};...; \alpha_1^{[\lambda]},..., \alpha_{u_\lambda}^{[\lambda]};...; \alpha_1^{[\Lambda]},..., \alpha_{u_\Lambda}^{[\Lambda]};$$

for

iii) $$f_1^{[1]},..., f_{u_1}^{[1]};...; f_1^{[\lambda]},..., f_{u_\lambda}^{[\lambda]};...; f_1^{[\Lambda]},..., f_{u_\Lambda}^{[\Lambda]};$$

such that the restrictions of $\alpha_i^{[\lambda]}$ *to* R^{v_λ} *constitute a convergent construction (resp: bounded convergent construction in case of* $K = \mathbf{C}$) *for* iii).

In the proofs of the "construction" parts of (I) and (II) replace "construction" by "construction whose restrictions to R^{v_λ} constitute a convergent construction (resp: bounded convergent construction in case of $K = \mathbf{C}$)", and also make the following changes.

In the proof of (II): In 23°) take $G_1^{[\lambda]},..., G_{m_\lambda}^{[\lambda]}$ to be an S-basis of

$$\mathfrak{N}^{[\lambda]} = \{G \in f_1^{[\lambda]}R + ... + f_{u_\lambda}^{[\lambda]}R \colon \deg G < d_\lambda\}$$

[5] In this section we are taking K to be infinite.

where $S = K[\langle x_1,\ldots, x_{n-1}\rangle]$. It then suffices to show that $G_1^{[\lambda]},\ldots, G_{m_\lambda}^{[\lambda]}$ is an $\hat{S}$-basis of $\mathfrak{M}^{[\lambda]}$. In other words we want to show that $\mathfrak{M}^{[\lambda]} = \mathfrak{N}^{[\lambda]}\hat{S}$.[6] Fixing λ, we may suppress that subscript and superscript. Then $f_1,\ldots, f_u \in R$, f_1 is R-associate of a distinguished polynomial of degree $d > 0$ in x_n with coefficients in S,

$$\mathfrak{M} = \{G \in f_1\hat{R} + \ldots + f_u\hat{R}\colon \deg G < d\}, \qquad \text{and}$$
$$\mathfrak{N} = \{G \in f_1R + \ldots + f_uR\colon \deg G < d\}.$$

We want to show that $\mathfrak{M} = \mathfrak{N}\hat{S}$. Obviously $\mathfrak{M} \supset \mathfrak{N}\hat{S}$. Now let

$$G = f_1s_1 + \ldots + f_us_u \in \mathfrak{M} \qquad \text{with} \qquad s_i \in \hat{R}$$

be given. By Preparation Theorem (10.3.1), we can write

$$s_i = q_if_1 + r_i \text{ with } q_i, r_i \in \hat{R} \text{ and } \deg r_i < d, \text{ for } i = 2,\ldots, u.$$

Let

$$r_1 = s_1 + q_2f_2 + \ldots + q_uf_u.$$

Then

$$G = r_1f_1 + \ldots + r_uf_u$$

where $r_1 \in \hat{R}$ and

$$r_i = \sum_{j=0}^{d-1} r_{ij}x_n^j \qquad \text{with} \qquad r_{ij} \in \hat{S}, \qquad \text{for} \qquad i = 2,\ldots, u.$$

Now $f_i \in R$ and $x_n^j \in R$ and hence by (10.3.1) we have

$$x_n^jf_i = \bar{q}_{ij}f_1 + t_{ij} \qquad \text{with} \qquad \bar{q}_{ij}, t_{ij} \in R \qquad \text{and} \qquad \deg t_{ij} < d,$$
$$(i = 2,\ldots, u; \quad j = 0,\ldots, d-1).$$

Hence $t_{ij} \in \mathfrak{N}$, $(i = 2,\ldots, u; j = 0,\ldots, d-1)$. Let

$$p = \sum_{j=0}^{d-1}\sum_{i=2}^{u} r_{ij}t_{ij} \qquad \text{and} \qquad q = r_1 + \sum_{j=0}^{d-1}\sum_{i=2}^{u} r_{ij}\bar{q}_{ij}.$$

Then $p \in \mathfrak{N}\hat{S}$, $p \in \hat{R}$, $q \in \hat{R}$, $G = qf_1 + p$, $\deg G < d$, and $\deg p < d$. Thus $\deg(G - p) < d$ and $G - p = qf_1$. Therefore by the uniqueness part of (10.3.1) we must have $q = 0$; whence $G = p \in \mathfrak{N}\hat{S}$.

[6] For any subring S of a ring $\hat{S}$, and $v \geqq 0$, we can consider S^v to be a subset of $\hat{S}^v$ and then for any S-submodule $\mathfrak{N}$ of S^v, by $\mathfrak{N}\hat{S}$ we denote the $\hat{S}$-submodule of $\hat{S}^v$ generated by $\mathfrak{N}$.

In the proof of (I): In 7°) take

$$\{g_\mu^{[\lambda]} = (G_\mu^{[\lambda]}, 0), \quad \mu = 1,\ldots, m_\lambda\}$$

to be an R-basis of

$$\mathfrak{N}^{[\lambda]} = \{f \in f_1^{[\lambda]}R + \ldots + f_{u_\lambda}^{[\lambda]}R : \bar{f} = 0\}.$$

It then suffices to show that $\mathfrak{M}^{[\lambda]} = \mathfrak{N}^{[\lambda]}\hat{R}$.[6] In view of the equations

$$\mathfrak{M}^{[\lambda]} = (f_1^{[\lambda]}\hat{R} + \ldots + f_{u_\lambda}^{[\lambda]}\hat{R}) \cap \hat{R}^{v-1},$$
$$\mathfrak{N}^{[\lambda]} = (f_1^{[\lambda]}R + \ldots + f_{u_\lambda}^{[\lambda]}R) \cap R^{v-1},$$

this follows from the following result from local algebra.

1*)[7] *Let R be a local ring and let $\hat{R}$ be its completion. Let $\mathfrak{P}$ and $\mathfrak{Q}$ be R-submodules of R^v. Then $(\mathfrak{P}\hat{R}) \cap (\mathfrak{Q}\hat{R}) = (\mathfrak{P} \cap \mathfrak{Q})\hat{R}$.*

This completes the proof of (16.2).

In the rest of this section we deduce several corollaries of Theorem (16.1). Henceforth in this section we take K to be a complete nondiscrete valued field and $R = K[\langle x_1,\ldots, x_n\rangle]$.

(16.3) *Let X be a neighborhood of the origin in K^n. Let $A \subset R^v$ be such that $X \subset \mathbf{D}(f)$ for all $f \in A$. Then there exists a finite subset A^* of A and a neighborhood X^* of the origin in X such that $\{\boldsymbol{\tau}_a A^*\}R = \{\boldsymbol{\tau}_a A\}R$ for all $a \in X^*$.*

Since R is noetherian, we can find a finite subset $A^* = \{f_1,\ldots, f_u\}$ of A such that $A^*R = AR$. Let $\alpha_1,\ldots, \alpha_u$ be a convergent construction for $f_1,\ldots, f_u$. Then there exists a neighborhood X^* of the origin in X such that: $f \in R^v$ and f convergent in $X \Rightarrow \alpha_1(f),\ldots, \alpha_u(f)$ are convergent in X^*. In particular then for all $f \in A$ we have: $f = \alpha_1(f)f_1 + \ldots + \alpha_u(f)f_u$; and $\alpha_1(f),\ldots, \alpha_u(f)$ are convergent in X^*. Therefore $\{\boldsymbol{\tau}_a A^*\}R = \{\boldsymbol{\tau}_a A\}R$ for all $a \in X^*$.

(16.4) *Let X be a neighborhood of the origin in K^n and let $A, B \subset R^v$ be such that $X \subset \mathbf{D}(f)$ for all $f \in A \cap B$. Assume that $AR = BR$. Then there exists a neighborhood X^* of the origin in X such that $\{\boldsymbol{\tau}_a A\}R = \{\boldsymbol{\tau}_a B\}R$ for all $a \in X^*$.*

By (16.3) we can find a neighborhood X' of the origin in X, a finite subset $A^* = \{f_1,\ldots, f_u\}$ of A, and a finite subset $B^* = \{g_1,\ldots, g_v\}$ of B, such

[7] For a proof see Zariski–Samuel [2: Corollary 2 on p. 266].

that for all $a \in X'$ we have $\{\boldsymbol{\tau}_a A^*\}R = \{\boldsymbol{\tau}_a A\}R$ and $\{\boldsymbol{\tau}_a B^*\}R = \{\boldsymbol{\tau}_a B\}R$. Since $AR = BR$, we can write

$$f_i = \sum_{j=1}^{v} p_{ij} g_j \qquad \text{and} \qquad g_i = \sum_{j=1}^{u} q_{ij} f_j$$

with $p_{ij}, q_{ij} \in R$. It suffices to take X^* to be a neighborhood of the origin in X' such that p_{ij} and q_{ij} are convergent in X^* for all i, j.

(16.5) *Remark on the definition of an analytic set.* Let $b \in K^n$ and let $V^* \subset K^n$. In §2 we made the following definition.

1°) V^* is analytic at $b \Leftrightarrow$ there exists a neighborhood X of b in K^n and a *finite* set Φ of analytic functions on X such that

$$V^* \cap X = \{a \in X : \varphi(a) = 0 \text{ for all } \varphi \in \Phi\}.$$

Taking A^* to be the set of Taylor expansions of members of Φ around b, 1°) is then equivalent to

2°) V^* is analytic at $b \Leftrightarrow$ there exists a *finite* subset A^* of R and a neighborhood X of the origin in K^n in which all the elements of A^* are convergent such that for

$$W^* = \{c \in K^n : (c_1 + b_1, \ldots, c_n + b_n) \in V^*\}$$

we have

$$W^* \cap X = \{a \in X : f(a) = 0 \text{ for all } f \in A^*\}.$$

Now let $A \subset R$, A not necessarily finite, be such that all the elements of A are convergent in X. Let

$$W = \{a \in X : f(a) = 0 \text{ for all } f \in A\}.$$

Since R is noetherian, for A^* we may take a finite subset $\{f_1, \ldots, f_u\}$ of A such that $A^*R = AR$. Then obviously $W \subset W^*$. However, the noetherian character alone does not guarantee that $W \cap X^* = W^* \cap X^*$ for some neighborhood X^* of the origin in X. It is true that because $A^*R = AR$, for each f in A we can, possibly in more than one way, write $f = \alpha_1(f)f_1 + \ldots + \alpha_u(f)f_u$ with $\alpha_i(f) \in R$. Off hand, as f varies in the possibly infinite set A, the elements $\alpha_1(f), \ldots, \alpha_u(f)$ may converge only in smaller and smaller neighborhoods, i.e., there may not exist any neighborhood of the origin in which $\alpha_1(f), \ldots, \alpha_u(f)$ converge for all $f \in A$. Here Theorem (16.1) comes to the rescue. Namely, if we take $\alpha_1, \ldots, \alpha_u$ to be a convergent construction for $f_1, \ldots, f_u$ then we can find a neighborhood X^* of the origin in K^n such that $\alpha_1(f), \ldots, \alpha_u(f)$ converge in X^* for all $f \in A$; whence we can assert that $W \cap X^* \supset W^* \cap X^*$ and hence $W \cap X^* = W^* \cap X^*$. Thus *in definition* 2°) *the word "finite" may be omitted.* Consequently *in case* $K = \mathbf{C}$, *the word "finite" may be omitted also from definition* 1°); because in this case, for any function which is analytic on an open polycylinder, its Taylor expansion is valid on the entire polycylinder.

(16.6) *Let* $K = \mathbf{C}$. *Let* $a \in \mathbf{C}^n$ *and let* X *be a neighborhood of* a *in* $\mathbf{C}^n$. *Let* $G_m = (G_m^{(1)},\ldots, G_m^{(v)})$, $(m = 1, 2,\ldots)$, *where* $G_m^{(i)}$ *are analytic functions on* X. G_m *is then a function*: $X \to \mathbf{C}^v$. *Assume that* $G_m \to G = (G^{(1)},\ldots, G^{(v)})$ *as* $m \to \infty$, *with compact uniform convergence on* X. *By* (4.9.1) *we then know that* $G^{(1)},\ldots, G^{(v)}$ *are analytic on* X. *Let* $g_m^{(i)}$ *and* $g^{(i)}$ *be the Taylor expansions around* a *of* $G_m^{(i)}$ *and* $G^{(i)}$, *respectively. Then* $g_m = (g_m^{(1)},\ldots, g_m^{(v)})$ *and* $g = (g^{(1)},\ldots, g^{(v)})$ *are obviously in* R^v. Let $\mathfrak{M}$ *be a submodule of* R^v. *Assume that* $g_m \in \mathfrak{M}$ *for all* $m > 0$. *Then* $g \in \mathfrak{M}$.

Proof. By a translation we can bring a to the origin. Since R is noetherian we can find a finite R-basis $f_1,\ldots, f_u$ of $\mathfrak{M}$. Let $\alpha_1,\ldots, \alpha_u$ be a bounded convergent construction for $f_1,\ldots, f_u$. Via a linear transformation on $x_1,\ldots, x_n$, we can find a finite closed polycylinder $X^* \subset X$ and a positive constant D such that $f_1,\ldots, f_u$ are convergent in a neighborhood of X^* and such that:

$f \in R^v$ is convergent in a neighborhood of X^*

$\Rightarrow \alpha_i(f)$ is convergent in a neighborhood of X^* and

$$\sup|\alpha_i(f)(X^*)| \leqq D \sup|f(X^*)| \qquad \text{for} \qquad i = 1,\ldots, u.$$ [8]

Since X^* is a compact subset of X, by assumption of compact uniform convergence, upon replacing $g_1, g_2,\ldots$ by a suitable subsequence, we can arrange that

$$\sup|(g_{m+1} - g_m)(X^*)| \leqq 2^{-m} \qquad \text{for all} \qquad m > 0.$$

Now

$$g_{m+1} - g_m \in \mathfrak{M},$$

and hence

$$g_{m+1} - g_m = \sum_{i=1}^{u} p_{im} f_i \qquad \text{for all} \qquad m > 0,$$

[8] Recall that for any $f = (f^{(1)},\ldots, f^{(v)}) \in R^v$ and $b \in \mathbf{D}(f)$ we have set

$$|f(b)| = \max(|f^{(1)}(b)|,\ldots, |f^{(v)}(b)|).$$

where $p_{im} = \alpha_i(g_{m+1} - g_m)$ is convergent in a neighborhood of X^*. *Let* X' be the interior of X^*. Let P_{im} and F_i be the functions associated with p_{im} and f_i, respectively. Then the double series

$$\sum_{m=1}^{\infty} \sum_{i=1}^{u} P_{im} F_i$$

is absolutely uniformly convergent on X', and summing it in two different ways we get

$$G - G_1 = \sum_{m=1}^{\infty} \left[\sum_{i=1}^{u} P_{im} F_i \right] = \sum_{i=1}^{u} \left[\sum_{m=1}^{\infty} P_{im} \right] F_i = \sum_{i=1}^{u} P_i F_i$$

where

$$P_i = \sum_{m=1}^{\infty} P_{im}$$

is analytic on X'. Let p_i be the Taylor expansion of P_i around the origin. Then

$$g = g_1 + \sum_{i=1}^{u} p_i f_i \in \mathfrak{M}.$$

CHAPTER III

Review from Local Algebra

As a rule we shall employ only the elementary aspects of local algebra. In this chapter we review the relevant material. General references are to Northcott [**1**] and Zariski–Samuel [**1**: Chapter IV; **2**: Chapters VII and VIII]. Definitions and proofs of results not readily found in these texts will definitely be given.

§17. DEPTH, HEIGHT, AND DIMENSION. COMPLETIONS. DIRECT SUMS. RESULTANTS AND DISCRIMINANTS

Let R be a ring. For a prime ideal $\mathfrak{p}$ in R, by definition

$\mathrm{dpt}_R\mathfrak{p}$ = max e such that there exist distinct prime ideals $\bar{\mathfrak{p}}_0,\dots,\bar{\mathfrak{p}}_e$ in R for which $\mathfrak{p} \subset \bar{\mathfrak{p}}_0 \subset \bar{\mathfrak{p}}_1 \subset \dots \subset \bar{\mathfrak{p}}_e$;

$\mathrm{hgt}_R\mathfrak{p}$ = max e such that there exist distinct prime ideals $\bar{\mathfrak{p}}_0,\dots,\bar{\mathfrak{p}}_e$ in R for which $\bar{\mathfrak{p}}_0 \subset \bar{\mathfrak{p}}_1 \subset \dots \subset \bar{\mathfrak{p}}_e \subset \bar{\mathfrak{p}}$.[1]

Now assume that R is noetherian. Let $\mathfrak{a}$ be any ideal in R. A normal decomposition of $\mathfrak{a}$ (in R) is an irredundant[2] decomposition $\mathfrak{a} = \mathfrak{q}_1 \cap \dots \cap \mathfrak{q}_u$ where $\mathfrak{q}_1,\dots,\mathfrak{q}_u$ are primary ideals whose associated prime ideals $\mathfrak{p}_1,\dots,\mathfrak{p}_u$ are all distinct.[3] $\mathfrak{p}_1,\dots,\mathfrak{p}_u$ are uniquely determined by $\mathfrak{a}$ and they are called the (associated) prime ideals of $\mathfrak{a}$. Each $\mathfrak{p}_i$ which is not contained in any $\mathfrak{p}_j\,(j \neq i)$ is called an (associated) minimal prime ideal of $\mathfrak{a}$; the others are said to be imbedded. For a minimal $\mathfrak{p}_i$, the corresponding $\mathfrak{q}_i$ is uniquely determined by $\mathfrak{a}$ and is called an isolated primary component of

[1] dpt = depth, hgt = height. These terms are used by Zariski–Samuel [**1**: p. 240]. Krull's original terms are dimension and dimensiondefect, respectively. Some authors, e.g., Northcott [**1**], use the terms dimension and rank, respectively. We shall use the term rank for a concept which is related to the usual notion of Jacobian rank.

[2] That is, from which no $\mathfrak{q}_i$ can be omitted.

[3] $u = 0 \Leftrightarrow \mathfrak{a} = R$; i.e., $u > 0 \Leftrightarrow \mathfrak{a}$ is proper. By convention, intersection or product of an empty family of ideals is the unit ideal R.

$\mathfrak{a}$. $\mathfrak{a}$ is said to be unmixed provided all the prime ideals of $\mathfrak{a}$ have the same height; and then obviously they are all minimal. Clearly rad $\mathfrak{a}$ is the intersection of all minimal prime ideals of $\mathfrak{a}$. If $\mathfrak{a}$ is proper then by definition

$$\mathrm{dpt}_R\mathfrak{a} = \max_{1\leqq i\leqq u} \mathrm{dpt}_R\mathfrak{p}_i \qquad \text{and} \qquad \mathrm{hgt}_R\mathfrak{a} = \min_{1\leqq i\leqq u} \mathrm{hgt}_R\mathfrak{p}_i$$

Note that
$\mathrm{dpt}_R\mathfrak{a}$ = max e such that there exist distinct prime ideals $\bar{\mathfrak{p}}_0, \ldots, \bar{\mathfrak{p}}_e$ in R for which $\mathfrak{a} \subset \bar{\mathfrak{p}}_0 \subset \bar{\mathfrak{p}}_1 \subset \ldots \subset \bar{\mathfrak{p}}_e$.

(**17.1**) (Krull). *Let R be a noetherian ring. Let $\alpha_1, \ldots, \alpha_m \in R$ and $\mathfrak{a} = \{\alpha_1, \ldots, \alpha_m\}R$. Then $\mathrm{hgt}_R\mathfrak{p} \leqq m$ for every minimal prime ideal $\mathfrak{p}$ of $\mathfrak{a}$. Hence if $\mathfrak{a}$ is proper then $\mathrm{hgt}_R\mathfrak{a} \leqq m$.*

For proof see Northcott [**1**: Theorem 7 on p. 60] or Zariski–Samuel [**1**: Theorem 30 on p. 240].

DEFINITION. For a local ring $(R, \mathfrak{m})$, by definition

$$\dim R = \mathrm{hgt}_R\mathfrak{m} = \mathrm{dpt}_R\{0\}.$$

For any proper ideal $\mathfrak{a}$ in R we then have:

$$(R/\mathfrak{a}, \mathfrak{m}/\mathfrak{a}) \text{ is a local ring and } \dim R/\mathfrak{a} = \mathrm{dpt}_R\mathfrak{a}.$$

(**17.2**) (Chevalley). *Let $(R, \mathfrak{m})$ be a local ring. Then $\dim R$ = least number of elements in R which generate an ideal which is primary for $\mathfrak{m}$.*[4]

For proof see Northcott [**1**: Theorem 1 on p. 63] or Zariski–Samuel [**2**: Theorem 20 on p. 288]. If $\dim R = e$, then any set of e elements, which generate an ideal which is primary for $\mathfrak{m}$, is called a *system of parameters for R.*

(**17.3**) (Krull). *For any local ring $(R, \mathfrak{m})$ we have*

$$\bigcap_{i=1}^{\infty} \mathfrak{m}^i = \{0\}.$$

We have already noted this in (1.2), and it yields

(**17.4**) *Let $\mathfrak{a}$ be an ideal in a local ring $(R, \mathfrak{m})$. If $\mathfrak{m} = \mathfrak{a} + \mathfrak{m}^2$ then $\mathfrak{a} = \mathfrak{m}$.*

[4] By convention, the empty set generates the zero ideal. Union or sum of an empty family of ideals is the zero ideal.

By induction: $\mathfrak{m} = \mathfrak{a} + \mathfrak{m}^2 = \mathfrak{a} + \mathfrak{m}^3 = \ldots = \mathfrak{a} + \mathfrak{m}^i$ for all i. Therefore

$$\mathfrak{m} = \bigcap_{i=1}^{\infty} \mathfrak{a} + \mathfrak{m}^i.$$

Now apply (17.3) to $R/\mathfrak{a}$.

(17.5) *Completions.* Referring for details to Northcott [**1**: Chapter V] or Zariski–Samuel [**2**: Chapter VIII] we merely recall the following. Let $(R, \mathfrak{m})$ and $(\hat{R}, \hat{\mathfrak{m}})$ be local rings. $\hat{R}$ is said to be a completion of R provided $\hat{R}$ is complete, R is a subring and a subspace of $\hat{R}$, and R is dense in $\hat{R}$. Up to natural isomorphisms, $\hat{R}$ is uniquely determined by R. Following are some of the relative properties of R and $\hat{R}$.

dim R = dim $\hat{R}$. *For any ideal* $\mathfrak{a}$ *in* R *we have* $(\mathfrak{a}\hat{R}) \cap R = \mathfrak{a}$; *and* $\mathfrak{a}$ *is primary for* $\mathfrak{m} \Leftrightarrow \mathfrak{a}\hat{R}$ *is primary for* $\hat{\mathfrak{m}}$. $\mathfrak{m}^i\hat{R} = \hat{\mathfrak{m}}^i$ *for all* $i > 0$. R *is regular* $\Leftrightarrow \hat{R}$ *is regular.*[5] *For any proper ideal* $\mathfrak{a}$ *in* R, $\hat{R}/\mathfrak{a}\hat{R}$ *is a completion of* $R/\mathfrak{a}$. *An element in* R *which is a nonzerodivisor in* R *remains a nonzerodivisor in* $\hat{R}$; *consequently, the total quotient ring* $\mathfrak{K}$ *of* R *can be considered to be a subring of the total quotient ring of* $\hat{R}$, *and from the property* "$(\mathfrak{a}\hat{R}) \cap R = \mathfrak{a}$" *it then follows that* $\hat{R} \cap \mathfrak{K} = R$.

(17.6) *Direct sum of modules.* Let R be a ring and let $\mathfrak{M}_1, \ldots, \mathfrak{M}_u$ be R-modules. The cartesian product $\mathfrak{M}_1 \times \ldots \times \mathfrak{M}_u$ becomes an R-module by taking $(a'_1, \ldots, a'_u) + (a_1, \ldots, a_u) = (a_1 + a'_1, \ldots, a_u + a'_u)$ and $r(a_1, \ldots, a_u) = (ra_1, \ldots, ra_u)$ for all $a'_i, a_i \in \mathfrak{M}_i$, $r \in R$. This R-module is called the direct sum of $\mathfrak{M}_1, \ldots, \mathfrak{M}_u$ and is denoted by $\mathfrak{M}_1 \oplus \ldots \oplus \mathfrak{M}_u$. The R-epimorphism $p_i: \mathfrak{M}_1 \oplus \ldots \oplus \mathfrak{M}_u \to \mathfrak{M}_i$ given by $p_i(a_1, \ldots, a_u) = a_i$ is called the natural projection, and the R-monomorphism $q_i: \mathfrak{M}_i \to \mathfrak{M}_1 \oplus \ldots \oplus \mathfrak{M}_u$ given by $q_i(a_i) = (0, \ldots, 0, a_i, 0, \ldots, 0)$ is called the natural injection; via q_i we may identify $\mathfrak{M}_i$ with $q_i(\mathfrak{M}_i)$. For any R-submodules $\mathfrak{N}_1, \ldots, \mathfrak{N}_u$ of $\mathfrak{M}_1, \ldots, \mathfrak{M}_u$, respectively, $\mathfrak{N}_1 \oplus \ldots \oplus \mathfrak{N}_u$ is an R-submodule of $\mathfrak{M}_1 \oplus \ldots \oplus \mathfrak{M}_u$. Given R-homomorphisms $\varphi_i: \mathfrak{M} \to \mathfrak{M}_i$ where $\mathfrak{M}$ is another R-module, the R-homomorphism $\mathfrak{M} \to \mathfrak{M}_i \oplus \ldots \oplus \mathfrak{M}_u$ given by $a \to (\varphi_1(a), \ldots, \varphi_u(a))$ is called the direct sum of $\varphi_1, \ldots, \varphi_u$ and is denoted by $\varphi_1 \oplus \ldots \oplus \varphi_u$. Note that Ker $\varphi_1 \oplus \ldots \oplus \varphi_u = (\text{Ker } \varphi_1) \cap \ldots \cap (\text{Ker } \varphi_u)$.[6] If $\mathfrak{M}_1 = \ldots = \mathfrak{M}_u = \mathfrak{M}$ then we may denote $\mathfrak{M}_1 \oplus \ldots \oplus \mathfrak{M}_u$ by $\mathfrak{M}^u$.

Every abelian group can uniquely be considered to be a **Z**-module, and hence the above notions apply to abelian groups.

[5] For definition see §21.

[6] For any homomorphism $\varphi: A \to B$ of abelian groups (or rings or modules), Ker φ denotes the kernel of φ.

(17.7) *Direct sum of algebras.* Let R be a ring. An R-algebra is a ring S together with a ring homomorphism $\varphi: R \to S$ where S is also considered to be an R-module by taking $rs = \varphi(r)s$ for all $r \in R$, $s \in S$; φ is called the underlying homomorphism of the algebra; we may express this by simply saying something like "let $\varphi: R \to$ S be an R-algebra". An R-subalgebra S^* of S is a subring of S which is also an R-submodule of S; note that then automatically $\varphi(R) \subset S^*$. Given another R-algebra $\varphi': R \to S'$, an R-algebra-homomorphism $f: S \to S'$ is a ring homomorphism which is also an R-homomorphism. Any overring R' of R can be considered to be an R-algebra by taking the canonical injection $R \to R'$ as the underlying homomorphism; note that an R-subalgebra of R' is the same thing as a subring of R' containing R. Also note that if $\varphi: R \to S$ is any R-algebra then φ is obviously an R-algebra-homomorphism.

Let $\varphi_1: R \to R_1, \ldots, \varphi_u: R \to R_u$ be R-algebras. By taking $(r_1, \ldots, r_u)(r'_1, \ldots, r'_u) = (r_1 r'_1, \ldots, r_u r'_u)$ for all $r_i, r'_i \in R_i$, $R_1 \oplus \ldots \oplus R_u$ becomes a ring such that $\varphi_1 \oplus \ldots \oplus \varphi_u: R \to R_1 \oplus \ldots \oplus R_u$ is a ring homomorphism; the resulting R-algebra is called the R-algebra-theoretic direct sum of $R_1, \ldots, R_u$. If $e_1, \ldots, e_u$ are the identity elements of the rings $R_1, \ldots, R_u$, respectively, then $(e_1, \ldots, e_u)$ is the identity element of the ring $R_1 \oplus \ldots \oplus R_u$. The natural projection $R_1 \oplus \ldots \oplus R_u \to R_i$ is an R-algebra-homomorphism. However, the natural injection $R_i \to R_1 \oplus \ldots \oplus R_u$ is not a ring homomorphism if $u > 1$ and R_j is nonnull for some $j \neq i$, because then $(0, \ldots, 0, e_i, 0, \ldots, 0)$ is not the identity element of the ring $R_1 \oplus \ldots \oplus R_u$. For any subrings $S_1, \ldots, S_u$ of $R_1, \ldots, R_u$, respectively, $S_1 \oplus \ldots \oplus S_u$ is a subring of $R_1 \oplus \ldots \oplus R_u$; if $S_1, \ldots, S_u$ are R-subalgebras of $R_1, \ldots, R_u$, respectively, then $S_1 \oplus \ldots \oplus S_u$ is an R-subalgebra of $R_1 \oplus \ldots \oplus R_u$. If S is another R-algebra and $\psi_1: S \to R_1, \ldots, \psi_u: R \to R_u$ are R-algebra-homomorphisms, then $\psi_1 \oplus \ldots \oplus \psi_u: S \to R_1 \oplus \ldots \oplus R_u$ is automatically an R-algebra-homomorphism.

Every ring can uniquely be considered to be a **Z**-algebra, and hence for any rings $R_1, \ldots, R_u$ we get the notion of the ring theoretic (i.e., **Z**-algebra-theoretic) direct sum of $R_1, \ldots, R_u$.

When the symbol $\oplus$ is meant to stand for ring theoretic or algebra theoretic direct sum, and not merely module theoretic direct sum, this will be made clear from the context.

(17.8)[7] *Ideals in a direct sum.* Let $\varphi_1: R \to R_1, \ldots, \varphi_u: R \to R_u$ be R-algebras such that $\varphi_1 \oplus \ldots \oplus \varphi_u: R \to R_1 \oplus \ldots \oplus R_u$ is an isomorphism.

For any ideal $\mathfrak{a}$ in R let $\psi_i: \mathfrak{a} \to \mathfrak{a}_i = \varphi_i(\mathfrak{a})$ be induced by φ_i; then $\mathfrak{a}_1, \ldots, \mathfrak{a}_u$ are ideals in $R_1, \ldots, R_u$ and $\psi_1 \oplus \ldots \oplus \psi_u: \mathfrak{a} \to \mathfrak{a}_1 \oplus \ldots \oplus \mathfrak{a}_u$ is an

[7] For proofs see Zariski–Samuel [**1**: §13 of Chapter III].

R-isomorphism. Conversely, for any ideals $\mathfrak{a}_1, \ldots, \mathfrak{a}_u$ in $R_1, \ldots, R_u$, let $\mathfrak{a} = (\varphi_1 \oplus \ldots \oplus \varphi_u)^{-1}(\mathfrak{a}_1 \oplus \ldots \oplus \mathfrak{a}_u)$; then $\mathfrak{a}_1 \oplus \ldots \oplus \mathfrak{a}_u$ is an ideal in $R_1 \oplus \ldots \oplus R_u$, $\mathfrak{a}$ is an ideal in R, $\varphi_i(\mathfrak{a}) = \mathfrak{a}_i$ for $i = 1, \ldots, u$, and $\varphi_1 \oplus \ldots \oplus \varphi_u(\mathfrak{a}) = \mathfrak{a}_1 \oplus \ldots \oplus \mathfrak{a}_u$.

For any ideal $\mathfrak{a}$ in R let $\mathfrak{a}_i = \varphi_i(\mathfrak{a})$. Then $\mathfrak{a}$ is respectively primary or prime or maximal $\Leftrightarrow \mathfrak{a}_i = R_i$ for all except one value of i and for that value of i the ideal $\mathfrak{a}_i$ in R_i is respectively primary or prime or maximal.

(17.9)[7] *Comaximal ideals.* Let R be a ring.

1) Ideals $\mathfrak{a}$ and $\mathfrak{b}$ in R are said to be comaxial $\Leftrightarrow \mathfrak{a} + \mathfrak{b} = R$. The following four conditions are easily seen to be equivalent.

i) $\mathfrak{a}$ and $\mathfrak{b}$ are comaximal.
ii) rad $\mathfrak{a}$ and rad $\mathfrak{b}$ are comaximal.
iii) There does not exist any maximal ideal in R containing $\mathfrak{a}$ and $\mathfrak{b}$.
iv) If $\varphi_1 : R \to R_1$ and $\varphi_2 : R \to R_2$ are ring epimorphisms whose kernels are $\mathfrak{a}$ and $\mathfrak{b}$, respectively, then there exist elements α and β in R such that: $\varphi_1(\alpha)$ is a unit in R_1, $\varphi_2(\alpha) = 0$, $\varphi_2(\beta)$ is a unit in R_2, and $\varphi_1(\beta) = 0$.

2) If $\mathfrak{a}_1, \ldots, \mathfrak{a}_u, \mathfrak{b}_1, \ldots, \mathfrak{b}_v$ are ideals in R such that each $\mathfrak{a}_i$ is comaximal with each $\mathfrak{b}_j$, then $\mathfrak{a}_1 \cap \ldots \cap \mathfrak{a}_u$ and $\mathfrak{b}_1 \cap \ldots \cap \mathfrak{b}_v$ are comaximal. If $\mathfrak{a}_1, \ldots, \mathfrak{a}_u$ are pairwise comaximal ideals in R then $\mathfrak{a}_1 \cap \ldots \cap \mathfrak{a}_u = \mathfrak{a}_1 \ldots \mathfrak{a}_u$.

3) Let $\varphi_1 : R \to R_1, \ldots, \varphi_u : R \to R_u$ be ring epimorphisms. Then $\varphi_1 \oplus \ldots \oplus \varphi_u : R \to R_1 \oplus \ldots \oplus R_u$ is an epimorphism $\Leftrightarrow$ Ker $\varphi_1, \ldots,$ Ker φ_u are pairwise comaximal ideals in R. Consequently, $\varphi_1 \oplus \ldots \oplus \varphi_u$ is an isomorphism $\Leftrightarrow$ Ker $\varphi_1, \ldots,$ Ker φ_u are pairwise comaximal and (Ker $\varphi_1) \cap \ldots \cap$ (Ker $\varphi_u) = \{0\}$. Note that by 1), Ker $\varphi_1, \ldots,$ Ker φ_u are pairwise comaximal $\Leftrightarrow$ for all $i \neq j$ there exists $e_{ij} \in R$ such that $\varphi_i(e_{ij})$ is a unit in R_i and $\varphi_j(e_{ij}) = 0$.

4) From 3) we get the following generalization of 3). Let $\varphi_1 : R \to R_1, \ldots, \varphi_u : R \to R_u$ be ring homomorphisms, let R^* be a subring of R, and let $\psi_i : R^* \to R_i^* = \varphi_i(R^*)$ be induced by φ_i. Then the following four conditions are equivalent.

i) $\varphi_1 \oplus \ldots \oplus \varphi_u(R^*) = R_1^* \oplus \ldots \oplus R_u^*$.
ii) $\psi_1 \oplus \ldots \oplus \psi_u : R^* \to R_1^* \oplus \ldots \oplus R_u^*$ is an epimorphism.
iii) Ker $\psi_1, \ldots,$ Ker ψ_u are pairwise comaximal ideals in R^*.
iv) For all $i \neq j$ there exists $e_{ij} \in R^*$ such that $\varphi_i(e_{ij})$ is a unit in R^* and $\varphi_j(e_{ij}) = 0$.

Note that $\psi_1 \oplus \ldots \oplus \psi_m$ is an isomorphism $\Leftrightarrow$ any one of the above four conditions holds and (Ker $\psi_1) \cap \ldots \cap$ (Ker $\psi_u) = \{0\}$.

(17.10) *Resultants and discriminants.* For any positive integers n and m, take indeterminates $A_0, A_1,\ldots, A_n, B_0, B_1,\ldots, B_m, T$ and let $P(A_0, A_1,\ldots, A_n, B_0, B_1,\ldots, B_m) \in \mathbf{Z}[A_0, A_1,\ldots, A_n, B_0, B_1,\ldots, B_m]$ be the determinant of the $n + m$ by $n + m$ matrix

$$((C_{ij}))_{i,j=0,\ldots,n+m-1}$$

where

$$C_{ij} = \begin{cases} A_{j-i} & \text{if } 0 \leqq i < m \text{ and } i \leqq j \leqq n + i \\ B_{j-i+m} & \text{if } m \leqq i < m + n \text{ and } i - m \leqq j \leqq i \\ 0 & \text{otherwise.} \end{cases}$$

1) *There exist elements*

$U(A_0, A_1,\ldots, A_n, B_0, B_1,\ldots, B_m,T)$ *and*
$V(A_0, A_1,\ldots, A_n, B_0, B_1,\ldots, B_m,T)$ *in*
$\mathbf{Z}[A_0, A_1,\ldots, A_n, B_0, B_1,\ldots, B_m,T]$ *such that*

$$\begin{aligned} &P(A_0, A_1,\ldots, A_n, B_0, B_1,\ldots, B_m) \\ &\quad = U(A_0, A_1,\ldots, A_n, B_0,\ldots, B_m,T)(A_0T^n + A_1T^{n-1} +\ldots+ A_n) \\ &\qquad + V(A_0, A_1,\ldots, A_n, B_0,\ldots, B_m,T)(B_0T^m + B_1T^{m-1} +\ldots+ B_m) \end{aligned}$$

in $\mathbf{Z}[A_0, A_1,\ldots, A_n, B_0, B_1,\ldots, B_m,T]$.

Now let S be an integral domain with quotient field $\mathfrak{K}$. Given elements

$$F(T) = a_0T^n + a_1T^{n-1} +\ldots+ a_n$$
$$G(T) = b_0T^m + b_1T^{m-1} +\ldots+ b_m$$

in $S[T]$ of degrees at most n and m in T with coefficients $a_0, a_1,\ldots, a_n$, $b_0, b_1,\ldots, b_m$ in S, we define the T-resultant of the ordered quadruple $(F(T), G(T), n, m)$ to be the element

$$P(a_0, a_1,\ldots, a_n, b_0, b_1,\ldots, b_m) \in S.$$

If $a_0 = 1 = b_0$ then the integers n and m are the degrees of $F(T)$ and $G(T)$, and in that case the T-resultant of the ordered pair $(F(T), G(T))$ is defined to be the T-resultant of $(F(T), G(T), n, m)$ and it is denoted by $\delta_{F,G}$, i.e.,

$$\delta_{F,G} = P(1, a_1,\ldots, a_n, 1, b_1,\ldots, b_m) \in S.$$

In case $a_0 = 1$, the T-discriminant of $F(T)$ is defined to be the T-resultant of $(F(T), F'(T), n, n - 1)$ and it is denoted by Δ_F, (where $F'(T)$ is the T-derivative of $F(T)$), i.e.,

$$\Delta_F = P(1, a_1,\ldots, a_n, n, (n - 1)a_1,\ldots, a_{n-1}) \in S.$$

2) *Let $F(T)$, $G(T) \in S[T]$ be monic of positive degrees n and m in T. Let $\alpha_1, \ldots, \alpha_n, \beta_1, \ldots, \beta_m$ be elements in an algebraic closure of $\mathfrak{K}$ such that*

$$F(T) = \prod_{i=1}^{n} (T - \alpha_i), \qquad G(T) = \prod_{j=1}^{m} (T - \beta_j).$$

Then

$$\delta_{F,G} = \prod_{i=1}^{n} \prod_{j=1}^{m} (\alpha_i - \beta_j);$$

and

$$\Delta_F = \prod_{i<k} (\alpha_i - \alpha_k)^2, \quad \textit{(product over } n(n-1)/2 \textit{ terms).}$$

3) *Let $F(T)$, $G(T) \in S[T]$ be monic of positive degrees in T. Then there exist $U(T)$, $V(T) \in S[T]$ such that $\delta_{F,G} = U(T)F(T) + V(T)G(T)$. Furthermore, $\delta_{F,G} \neq 0 \Leftrightarrow F(T)$ and $G(T)$ have no common roots in any field extension of $\mathfrak{K}$,* i.e., $\Leftrightarrow$ *$F(T)$ and $G(T)$ are coprime in $\mathfrak{K}[T]$.*

4) *Let $F(T) \in S[T]$ be monic of positive degree in T. Then there exist $U(T)$, $V(T) \in S[T]$ such that $\Delta_F = U(T)F(T) + V(T)F'(T)$ where $F'(T)$ is the T-derivative of $F(T)$. Furthermore $\Delta_F \neq 0 \Leftrightarrow F(T)$ has no multiple roots in any field extension of $\mathfrak{K}$.*

5) *Let $F_1(T), \ldots, F_n(T)$, $G_1(T), \ldots, G_m(T) \in S[T]$ be monic of positive degrees in T, $(n > 0, m > 0)$.*
Then

$$\delta_{F_1 \ldots F_n, G_1 \ldots G_m} = \prod_{i=1}^{n} \prod_{j=1}^{m} \delta_{F_i, G_j};$$

and

$$\Delta_{F_1 \ldots F_n} = \left(\prod_{i=1}^{n} \Delta_{F_i} \right) \left(\prod_{i<k} \delta_{F_i, F_k} \right)^2$$

where the last Π is over $n(n-1)/2$ terms.

6) *Let $F_1(T), \ldots, F_n(T) \in S[T]$ be monic of positive degrees in T, $(n > 0)$. Then there exist $V_1(T), \ldots, V_n(T) \in S[T]$ such that*

$$\prod_{i<k} \delta_{F_i, F_k} = \sum_{i=1}^{n} F_1(T) \ldots F_{i-1}(T) V_i(T) F_{i+1}(T) \ldots F_n(T).$$

where Π is over $n(n-1)/2$ terms.

For proofs of 1) and 2), see van der Waerden [**1**: pp. 84–87]. 3), 4), 5) follow immediately from 1) and 2). Also note that 6) is a refinement of the elementary theorem on partial fraction, (see van der Waerden [**1**: pp. 88–90]); namely; if $S = \mathfrak{K}$ and $F_1(T),\ldots, F_n(T)$ are pairwise coprime then 6) reduces to the said theorem, which can also be obtained as a corollary of (17.9). We prove 6) by induction on n. The assertion is trivial for $n = 1$ because a product over an empty family is one. Take $n > 1$ and assume true for $n - 1$. By 3) there exist $U(T), V(T) \in S[T]$ such that

$$\delta_{F_1,F_2\ldots F_n} = U(T)F_1(T) + V(T)F_2(T)\ldots F_n(T).$$

By induction hypothesis, there exist $W_2(T),\ldots, W_n(T) \in S[T]$ such that

$$\prod_{i=2}^{n}\prod_{k=i+1}^{n} \delta_{F_i,F_k} = \sum_{i=2}^{n} F_2(T)\ldots F_{i-1}(T)W_i(T)F_{i+1}(T)\ldots F_n(T).$$

Multiplying the two equations, by 5) we get

$$\prod_{i=1}^{n}\prod_{k=i+1}^{n} \delta_{F_i,F_k} = \sum_{i=1}^{n} F_1(T)\ldots F_{i-1}(T)V_i(T)F_{i+1}(T)\ldots F_n(T)$$

where

$$V_1(T) = V(T)\sum_{i=2}^{n} F_2(T)\ldots F_{i-1}(T)W_i(T)F_{i+1}(T)\ldots F_n(T)$$

and

$$V_i(T) = U(T)W_i(T) \qquad \text{for} \qquad i = 2,\ldots, n.$$

Finally we note the following.

7) *Assume that S is integrally closed in $\mathfrak{K}$. Let $\mathfrak{K}^*$ be a finite algebraic extension of $\mathfrak{K}$ such that $\mathfrak{K}^* = \mathfrak{K}(\alpha)$ where α is integral over S. Let $F(T)$ be the minimal monic polynomial of α over $\mathfrak{K}$ and let S^* be the integral closure of S in $\mathfrak{K}^*$. Then $\Delta_F S^* \subset S$, i.e., $\Delta_F\, s^* \in S$ for all $s^* \in S^*$.*

For definition of integral dependence see §19. Our assumption implies that $F(T) \in S[T]$ and hence $\Delta_F \in S$. Note that $\Delta_F \neq 0 \Leftrightarrow \mathfrak{K}^*$ is separable over $\mathfrak{K}$. Hence, if $\mathfrak{K}^*$ is inseparable over $\mathfrak{K}$ then we have nothing to show. For a proof when $\mathfrak{K}^*$ is separable over $\mathfrak{K}$, see for instance van der Waerden [**2**: pp. 79–80].

§18. QUOTIENT RINGS

In this section, R will denote a nonnull ring.

(18.1) DEFINITION. A multiplicative set in R is a subset M of R such that $0 \notin M$, $1 \in M$, and the product of any two elements in M is again in M.

Let M be a multiplicative set in R. We set

$$\mathfrak{j}_R[M] = \mathfrak{j}[M] = \textit{the isolated } M\textit{-component of } \{0\} \textit{ in } R.$$
$$= \{r \in R : rm = 0 \text{ for some } m \in M\}.$$

Then $\mathfrak{j}[M]$ is a proper ideal in R and $\mathfrak{j}[M] \cap M = \emptyset$. Let $f: R \to R' = R/\mathfrak{j}[M]$ be the natural epimorphism. Then $f(M)$ is a multiplicative set in R' and $f(M)$ contains no zerodivisors of R'. Hence we can form the ring

$$R_M = \textit{quotient ring of } R \textit{ with respect to } M$$
$$= \{\alpha/\beta \in \text{total quotient ring of } R' : \alpha \in R', \quad \beta \in f(M)\}.$$

The map $f: R \to R_M$, (i.e., the original map $f: R \to R'$ followed by the canonical injection $R' \to R_M$), is called the natural homomorphism. For $A \subset R$ we may write AR_M in place of $f(A)R_M$, and for $B \subset R_M$ we may write $B \cap R$ in place of $f^{-1}(B)$. In particular, an ideal $\mathfrak{a}$ in R gives the extended ideal $\mathfrak{a}R_M$ in R_M, and an ideal $\mathfrak{b}$ in R_M gives the contracted ideal $\mathfrak{b} \cap R$ in R. If

$$\mathfrak{P} = \bigcap_{j=1}^{v} \mathfrak{P}_j$$

where $\mathfrak{P}_1, \ldots, \mathfrak{P}_v$, $(0 < v < \infty)$, are prime ideals in R such that $\mathfrak{P}_j \not\subset \mathfrak{P}_{j'}$ for all $j \neq j'$, then

$$M = R - \bigcup_{j=1}^{v} \mathfrak{P}_j = \text{complement of } \bigcup_{j=1}^{v} \mathfrak{P}_j \text{ in } R$$

is a multiplicative set in R. In this case we may write $\mathfrak{j}_R[\mathfrak{P}] = \mathfrak{j}[\mathfrak{P}]$ in place of $\mathfrak{j}[M]$ and call it the *isolated $\mathfrak{P}$-component of* $\{0\}$ *in* R, and we may write $R_{\mathfrak{P}}$ in place of R_M and call it the *quotient ring of R with respect to* $\mathfrak{P}$. Note that

$$f(M) = f(R) - f\left(\bigcap_{j=1}^{v} \mathfrak{P}_j\right) \quad \text{and} \quad \mathfrak{j}[\mathfrak{P}] \subset \mathfrak{P}.$$

There is no clash between the notations R_M and $R_{\mathfrak{P}}$ since always $0 \in \mathfrak{P}$ and $0 \notin M$.

Let U be the set of all nonzerodivisors in R, and let $\mathfrak{L}$ be the total quotient ring of R. For any multiplicative set V in R with $V \subset U$, we obviously have $\mathfrak{j}_R[V] = \{0\}$ and hence we can consider R_V to be a subring of $\mathfrak{L}$, and then in particular $R_U = \mathfrak{L}$.

(18.2) *Let $\varphi: R \to S$ be a ring homomorphism, let M be a multiplicative set in R such that every element of $\varphi(M)$ is a unit in S, and let $f: R \to R_M$ be the natural homomorphism. Then there exists a unique homomorphism $\psi: R_M \to S$ such that $\varphi = \psi \circ f$.*

Proof. Given $\alpha \in R_M$, write $\alpha = f(r)/f(m)$ with $r \in R$, $m \in M$, and set $\psi(\alpha) = \varphi(r)/\varphi(m) \in S$. If $r' \in R$, $m' \in M$ are any other elements such that $\alpha = f(r')/f(m')$, then $f(r'm - rm') = 0$ and hence $(r'm - rm')m^* = 0$ for some $m^* \in M$; consequently $\varphi(m)$, $\varphi(m')$, $\varphi(m^*)$ are units in S and $\varphi(r')\varphi(m)\varphi(m^*) = \varphi(r)\varphi(m')\varphi(m^*)$; therefore $\varphi(r')/\varphi(m') = \varphi(r)/\varphi(m)$. Thus ψ is well defined. It is now straightforward that ψ is a homomorphism of R_M into S such that $\varphi = \psi \circ f$, and that it is the only such homomorphism.

From (18.2) we can easily deduce the following characteristic property of R_M.

(18.3) *Let M be a multiplicative set in R, let $f: R \to R_M$ be the natural homomorphism, and let $f': R \to R'$ be any ring homomorphism satisfying the following two conditions:*

i) *Every element of $f'(M)$ is a unit in R'.*
ii) *For each ring homomorphism $\varphi: R \to S$ for which every element of $\varphi(M)$ is a unit in S, there exists a unique homomorphism $\psi: R' \to S$ such that $\varphi = \psi \circ f'$.*

Then there exists a unique isomorphism $\sigma: R_M \to R'$ such that $f' = \sigma \circ f$.

(18.4) *Let $\varphi: R \to S$ be a ring homomorphism, let M and N be multiplicative sets in R and S, respectively, such that $\varphi(M) \subset N$, and let $f: R \to R_M$ and $g: S \to S_N$ be the natural homomorphisms. Then there exists a unique homomorphism $\psi: R_M \to S_N$ such that $g \circ \varphi = \psi \circ f$; ($\psi$ is said to be induced by φ). If $\varphi(M) = N$ and φ is an epimorphism then ψ is an epimorphism. If $\varphi(M) = N$ and $\mathfrak{a}$ is the kernel of φ then $\mathfrak{a}R_M$ is the kernel of ψ; whence in particular, if $\varphi(M) = N$ and φ is a monomorphism then ψ is a monomorphism.*

Proof. The existence and uniqueness of ψ follows by applying (18.2) to $g \circ \varphi$. Now suppose $\varphi(M) = N$. If φ is an epimorphism then any element $\beta \in S_N$ can be written as $\beta = g(\varphi(r))/g(\varphi(m))$ with $r \in R$, $m \in M$, and then $\beta = \psi(\alpha)$ where $\alpha = f(r)/f(m) \in R_M$; whence ψ is an epimorphism. If

$r \in \mathfrak{a}$ then $\psi(f(r)) = g(\varphi(r)) = g(0) = 0$ and hence $f(r)$ is in the kernel of ψ. Thus $\mathfrak{a}R_M$ is in the kernel of ψ. Conversely, let $\alpha \in R_M$ be such that $\psi(\alpha) = 0$. Write $\alpha = f(r)/f(m)$ with $r \in R$, $m \in M$. Then $g(\varphi(r)) = \psi(f(r)) = \psi(\alpha)\psi(f(m)) = 0$ and hence $n\varphi(r) = 0$ for some $n \in N$. By assumption $N = \varphi(M)$ and hence $n = \varphi(m')$ for some $m' \in M$. Thus $\varphi(rm') = 0$ and hence $rm' \in \mathfrak{a}$. Therefore $\alpha = f(rm')/f(mm') \in \mathfrak{a}R_M$.

(**18.5**) *Natural maps deduced from* (18.4).

1) *Transitivity*. Let $M \subset N$ be multiplicative sets in R, and let $f: R \to R_M$ and $g: R \to R_N$ be the natural homomorphisms. Then $f(N)$ is a multiplicative set in R_M. Let $h: R_M \to (R_M)_{f(N)}$ be the natural homomorphism. By (18.4), f induces a unique homomorphism $\psi: R_N \to (R_M)_{f(N)}$ such that $h \circ f = \psi \circ g$. It can easily be checked that ψ is actually an isomorphism; ψ and ψ^{-1} will again be called natural isomorphisms. Applying to complements of prime ideals, we see that if $\mathfrak{P} \subset \mathfrak{Q}$ are prime ideals in R then the homomorphism $R_{\mathfrak{P}} \to (R_{\mathfrak{Q}})_{f(\mathfrak{P})}$ induced by $f: R \to R_{\mathfrak{Q}}$ is an isomorphism.

2) *Permutability with epimorphisms*. Let $\varphi: R \to S$ be a ring epimorphism whose kernel is a proper ideal $\mathfrak{a}$ in R. Let M be a multiplicative set in R such that $N = \varphi(M)$ is a multiplicative set in S, (i.e., $M \cap \mathfrak{a} = \emptyset$). Let $f: R \to R_M$ and $g: S \to S_N$ be the natural homomorphisms, let $\psi: R_M \to S_N$ be induced by φ, and let $h: R_M \to R_M/\mathfrak{a}R_M$ be the natural epimorphism. By (18.4), ψ is an epimorphism and the kernel of ψ is $\mathfrak{a}R_M$. Therefore there exists a unique isomorphism $\sigma: R_M/\mathfrak{a}R_M \to S_N$ such that $\sigma \circ h = \psi$. Note that then $\sigma \circ h \circ f = g \circ \varphi$, and $h \circ f = \mu \circ g \circ \varphi$ where $\mu = \sigma^{-1}: S_N \to R_M/\mathfrak{a}R_M$ is the inverse isomorphism; σ and μ are again called natural isomorphisms (or induced by φ). Taking M to be the complement of a prime ideal $\mathfrak{P}$ in R, the condition is $\mathfrak{a} \subset \mathfrak{P}$, and the isomorphisms are $\sigma: R_{\mathfrak{P}}/\mathfrak{a}R_{\mathfrak{P}} \to S_{\varphi(\mathfrak{P})}$ and $\mu: S_{\varphi(\mathfrak{P})} \to R_{\mathfrak{P}}/\mathfrak{a}R_{\mathfrak{P}}$.

3) *Another case of permutability*. Let $\varphi: R \to S$ be a ring epimorphism, and let $\mathfrak{a} \subset \mathfrak{b} \subset \mathfrak{P}$ be ideals in R where $\mathfrak{P}$ is prime and $\mathfrak{a}$ is the kernel of φ. Then

$$S_{\varphi(\mathfrak{P})}/\varphi(\mathfrak{b})S_{\varphi(\mathfrak{P})} \approx (S/\varphi(\mathfrak{b}))_{\varphi(\mathfrak{P})/\varphi(\mathfrak{b})} \approx (R/\mathfrak{b})_{\mathfrak{P}/\mathfrak{b}} \approx R_{\mathfrak{P}}/\mathfrak{b}R_{\mathfrak{P}}$$

where the first and the third $\approx$ are by 2) and the second $\approx$ is obvious.[1]

Thus we get

$$S_{\varphi(\mathfrak{P})}/\varphi(\mathfrak{b})S_{\varphi(\mathfrak{P})} \approx R_{\mathfrak{P}}/\mathfrak{b}R_{\mathfrak{P}}.$$

[1] $\approx$ stands for isomorphism.

4) *Monomorphisms.* Let M be a multiplicative set in R and let S be an overring of R. Then M is a multiplicative set in S and by (18.4), the homomorphism $\psi: R_M \to S_M$ induced by the canonical injection $R \to S$ is actually a monomorphism; ψ is again called natural and via it we may sometimes identify R_M with the subring $\psi(R_M)$ of S_M. Note that $\psi(R_M) = S_M$ $\Leftrightarrow$ for each $s \in S$ there exist $m, m' \in M$ and $r \in R$ such that $mm's = mr$.

In particular, suppose that M is the set of all nonzerodivisors in R and that every element of M is a unit in S. Then $\psi: \mathfrak{L} = R_M \to S_M = S$ is a monomorphism where $\mathfrak{L}$ is the total quotient ring of R. If furthermore, every $s \in S$ can be written as $s = r/m$ with $r \in R$, $m \in M$, then ψ is an epimorphism and hence an isomorphism, and then we may identify $\mathfrak{L}$ with S.

A case of the above is this. Let $R_1, \ldots, R_u$ be nonnull rings, let $\mathfrak{L}_1, \ldots, \mathfrak{L}_u$ be their total quotient rings, and consider $R_1 \oplus \ldots \oplus R_u$ to be a subring of $\mathfrak{L}_1 \oplus \ldots \oplus \mathfrak{L}_u$. For any $r_1 \in R_1, \ldots, r_u \in R_u$, it is obvious that $(r_1, \ldots, r_u)$ is a nonzerodivisor in $R_1 \oplus \ldots \oplus R_u \Leftrightarrow r_i$ is a nonzerodivisor in R_i for $i = 1, \ldots, u$. Consequently, every nonzerodivisor in $R_1 \oplus \ldots \oplus R_u$ is a unit in $\mathfrak{L}_1 \oplus \ldots \oplus \mathfrak{L}_u$, and every element s in $\mathfrak{L}_1 \oplus \ldots \oplus \mathfrak{L}_u$ can be written as $s = r/m$ with r and m in $R_1 \oplus \ldots \oplus R_u$ where m is a nonzerodivisor in $R_1 \oplus \ldots \oplus R_u$. Therefore we can consider $\mathfrak{L}_1 \oplus \ldots \oplus \mathfrak{L}_u$ to be the total quotient ring of $R_1 \oplus \ldots \oplus R_u$.

5) *Total quotient rings.* Let U be the set of all nonzerodivisors in R and let $\mathfrak{L} = R_U$ be the total quotient ring of R. Let S be another nonnull ring, let V be the set of all nonzerodivisors in S, and let $\mathfrak{R} = S_V$ be the total quotient ring of S. Let $\varphi: R \to S$ be a ring homomorphism. We make the following observations.

1°) If $\varphi(U) \subset V$ then by (18.4), φ induces $\psi: \mathfrak{L} \to \mathfrak{R}$, i.e., ψ is the unique ring homomorphism of $\mathfrak{L}$ into $\mathfrak{R}$ such that $\psi(r) = \varphi(r)$ for all $r \in R$; we shall say that ψ is the (natural) extension of φ to $\mathfrak{L}$. Conversely, if such an extension exists then we must have $\varphi(U) \subset V$.

2°) Suppose that i) $\varphi(U) \subset V$, and let $\psi: \mathfrak{L} \to \mathfrak{R}$ be the extension of φ. Then $\operatorname{Ker} \psi = (\operatorname{Ker} \varphi)\mathfrak{L}$, and hence in particular ψ is a monomorphism $\Leftrightarrow$ ii) φ is a monomorphism; furthermore ψ is an isomorphism $\Leftrightarrow$ in addition to ii) we have that iii) each $s \in S$ can be written as $s = \varphi(r)/\varphi(u)$ with $r \in R$, $u \in U$. Note that iii) is equivalent to saying that $S \subset \psi(\mathfrak{L})$, which in turn is equivalent to saying that $S = \psi(R^*)$ for some subring R^* of $\mathfrak{L}$.

3°) Consider S as an R-algebra with underlying homomorphism φ. Suppose that conditions (i, ii, iii) are satisfied, let $\psi: \mathfrak{L} \to \mathfrak{R}$ be the extension of φ, and let $\mu = \psi^{-1}|S$; then $\mu: S \to \mathfrak{L}$ is the unique R-algebra-homomorphism of S into $\mathfrak{L}$. Conversely, if there exists an R-algebra-monomorphism $\sigma: S \to \mathfrak{L}$, then conditions (i, ii, iii) are satisfied and $\sigma = \mu$. In other words, there exists an R-algebra-isomorphism λ of S onto some R-subalgebra R^* of $\mathfrak{L} \Leftrightarrow$ conditions (i, ii, iii) hold; and then R^* and λ are uniquely determined by S, namely $R^* = \psi^{-1}(S)$ and $\lambda(s) = \psi^{-1}(s)$ for all $s \in S$.

6) *Total quotient ring of a quotient ring.* Let M be a multiplicative set in R and let $f: R \to R_M$ be the natural homomorphism. Let r be any element in R such that $f(r)$ is a zerodivisor in R_M. Then $f(r)f(r') = 0$ for some $r' \in R$ with $f(r') \neq 0$, and hence $rr'm = 0$ for some $m \in M$. Now $f(m)$ is a unit in R_M and hence $f(r')f(m) \neq 0$. Therefore $r'm \neq 0$ and hence r is a zerodivisor in R. Consequently by 1°) above, f has a unique extension $\psi: \mathfrak{L} \to \mathfrak{R}$ where $\mathfrak{L}$ and $\mathfrak{R}$ are the total quotient rings of R and R_M, respectively; ψ is again said to be the natural homomorphism of $\mathfrak{L}$ into $\mathfrak{R}$.

7) *Direct sums.* Let $R, R_1, \ldots, R_u$ be nonnull rings, let $V, V_1, \ldots, V_u, V'$ be the sets of all nonzerodivisors in $R, R_1, \ldots, R_u, R_1 \oplus \ldots \oplus R_u$, respectively, let $\mathfrak{L}, \mathfrak{L}_1, \ldots, \mathfrak{L}_u$ be the total quotient rings of $R, R_1, \ldots, R_u$, respectively, and consider $\mathfrak{L}_1 \oplus \ldots \oplus \mathfrak{L}_u$ to be the total quotient ring of $R_1 \oplus \ldots \oplus R_u$. Let $\varphi_1: R \to R_1, \ldots, \varphi_u: R \to R_u$ be ring homomorphisms. Concerning the ring homomorphism $\varphi_1 \oplus \ldots \oplus \varphi_u: R \to R_1 \oplus \ldots \oplus R_u$ we note the following.

1°) $\varphi_1 \oplus \ldots \oplus \varphi_u(V) \subset V' \Leftrightarrow \varphi_i(V) \subset V_i$ for $i = 1, \ldots, u$.

2°) $\varphi_1 \oplus \ldots \oplus \varphi_u$ is a monomorphism $\Leftrightarrow \bigcap_{i=1}^{u} \operatorname{Ker} \varphi_i = \{0\}$.

3°) If $\varphi_i(V) \subset V_i$ and $\psi_i: \mathfrak{L} \to \mathfrak{L}_i$ is the extension of φ_i to $\mathfrak{L}$ for $i = 1, \ldots, u$, then $\psi_1 \oplus \ldots \oplus \psi_u: \mathfrak{L} \to \mathfrak{L}_1 \oplus \ldots \oplus \mathfrak{L}_u$ is the extension of $\varphi_1 \oplus \ldots \oplus \varphi_u$ to $\mathfrak{L}$. If furthermore $\varphi_1 \oplus \ldots \oplus \varphi_u$ is a monomorphism then $\psi_1 \oplus \ldots \oplus \psi_u$ is a monomorphism by 5.1°) above.

4°) Let R^* be a subring of $\mathfrak{L}$ with $R \subset R^*$. Assume that $\varphi_i(V) \subset V_i$ and let $\psi_i: \mathfrak{L} \to \mathfrak{L}_i$ be the extension of φ_i to $\mathfrak{L}$ for $i = 1, \ldots, u$. By (17.9.4) we deduce that $\psi_1 \oplus \ldots \oplus \psi_u(R^*) = R_1 \oplus \ldots \oplus R_u \Leftrightarrow \psi_i(R^*) = R_i$ for $i = 1, \ldots, u$, and for all $i \neq j$ there exists $e_{ij} \in R^*$ such that $\psi_i(e_{ij})$ is a unit in R_i and $\psi_j(e_{ij}) = 0$.

In view of 6), the above observations yield the following.

8) *Direct sums.* Let $R, R_1, \ldots, R_u$ be nonnull rings and let $V, V_1, \ldots, V_u$ and $\mathfrak{L}, \mathfrak{L}_1, \ldots, \mathfrak{L}_u$ be their sets of all nonzerodivisors and total quotient rings, respectively. Let R^* be a subring of $\mathfrak{L}$ with $R \subset R^*$. Let $\varphi_1: R \to R_1, \ldots, \varphi_u: R \to R_u$ be ring homomorphisms and consider $R_1 \oplus \ldots \oplus R_u$ to be an R-algebra with underlying homomorphisms $\varphi_1 \oplus \ldots \oplus \varphi_u$. Then $R_1 \oplus \ldots \oplus R_u$ is R-algebra-isomorphic to $R^* \Leftrightarrow$ the following three conditions are satisfied.

i) $(\mathrm{Ker}\, \varphi_1) \cap \ldots \cap (\mathrm{Ker}\, \varphi_u) = \{0\}$.

ii) For $i = 1, \ldots, u$: $\varphi_i(V) \subset V_i$ and $\psi_i(R^*) = R_i$ where $\psi_i: \mathfrak{L} \to \mathfrak{L}_i$ is the extension of φ_i to $\mathfrak{L}$.

iii) For all $i \neq j$, $(i, j = 1, \ldots, u)$, there exists $e_{ij} \in R^*$ such that $\psi_i(e_{ij})$ is a unit in R_i and $\psi_j(e_{ij}) = 0$.

(18.6) *Remark on zerodivisors.*

1) If $\mathfrak{b}$ is an ideal in R and $\mathfrak{P}_1, \ldots, \mathfrak{P}_v$ are prime ideals in R such that

$$\mathfrak{b} \subset \bigcup_{j=1}^{v} \mathfrak{P}_j,$$

then $\mathfrak{b} \subset \mathfrak{P}_j$ for some j.

2) If R is noetherian, then the set of all zerodivisors in R is the union of all the associated prime ideals of $\{0\}$ in R.

1) and 2) are proved in Zariski–Samuel [**1**: Remark on p. 215 and Corollary 3 on p. 214], and they yield 3).

3) If R is noetherian and $\mathfrak{b}$ is an ideal in R, then $\mathfrak{b}$ consists entirely of zerodivisors $\Leftrightarrow$ $\mathfrak{b}$ is contained in some associated prime ideal of $\{0\}$ in R.

4) Let $\mathfrak{a}$ be an ideal in R. By definition, $\alpha \in R$ is said to be prime to $\mathfrak{a} \Leftrightarrow$ the quotient ideal $(\mathfrak{a} : \alpha R) = \mathfrak{a}$, i.e., $\Leftrightarrow$ the residue class mod $\mathfrak{a}$ of α is not a zerodivisor in $R/\mathfrak{a}$; and $A \subset R$ is said to be prime to $\mathfrak{a} \Leftrightarrow$ every element of A is prime to $\mathfrak{a}$. If R is noetherian and $\mathfrak{a} = \mathfrak{q}_1 \cap \ldots \cap \mathfrak{q}_u$ is a normal decomposition of $\mathfrak{a}$ in R where $\mathfrak{q}_i$ is primary for $\mathfrak{p}_i$, then $A \subset R$ is prime to $\mathfrak{a} \Leftrightarrow A \cap \mathfrak{p}_i = \emptyset$ for $i = 1, \ldots, u$.

(18.7) *Ideal theory in a quotient ring.* Let M be a multiplicative set in R, and let

$$\mathfrak{P} = \bigcap_{j=1}^{v} \mathfrak{P}_j$$

where $\mathfrak{P}_1, \ldots, \mathfrak{P}_v$, $(0 < v < \infty)$, are prime ideals in R such that $\mathfrak{P}_j \not\subset \mathfrak{P}_{j'}$ for all $j \neq j'$. We now describe the relation between ideals in R and ideals in R_M. In particular, this description applies to the case when

$$M = R - \bigcup_{j=1}^{v} \mathfrak{P}_j.$$

1) For any ideal $\mathfrak{a}$ in R we have

$$R \cap \mathfrak{a}R_M = \{r \in R : rm \in \mathfrak{a} \text{ for some } m \in M\}.$$

In case R is noetherian, let $\mathfrak{a} = \mathfrak{q}_1 \cap \ldots \cap \mathfrak{q}_u$ be a normal decomposition of $\mathfrak{a}$ in R labeled so that $\mathfrak{q}_i \cap M = \emptyset$ for $i \leqq k$ and $\mathfrak{q}_i \cap M \neq \emptyset$ for $i > k$.[2] Then $\mathfrak{a}R_M = \mathfrak{q}_i R_M \cap \ldots \cap \mathfrak{q}_k R_M$ is a normal decomposition in R_M, and $R \cap \mathfrak{a}R_M = \mathfrak{q}_1 \cap \ldots \cap \mathfrak{q}_k$ is a normal decomposition in R. In particular, $\mathfrak{a}R_M = R_M \Leftrightarrow \mathfrak{q}_i \cap M \neq \emptyset$ for $i = 1, \ldots, u$.

2) An ideal $\mathfrak{a}$ in R is a contracted ideal $\Leftrightarrow \mathfrak{a} = R \cap \mathfrak{a}R_M \Leftrightarrow M$ is prime to $\mathfrak{a}$.

3) Every ideal in R_M is an extended ideal.

4) The map $\mathfrak{a} \rightarrow \mathfrak{a}R_M$ is a 1–1 mapping of the set of all contracted ideals in R onto the set of all ideals in R_M, and this mapping commutes with the ideal theoretic operations of forming intersections, quotients (i.e., $\mathfrak{a} : \mathfrak{a}'$), and radicals.

5) Let $\mathfrak{a}$ be a contracted ideal in R. Then $\mathfrak{a}$ is prime or the unit ideal $\Leftrightarrow \mathfrak{a}R_M$ is prime or the unit ideal, and $\mathfrak{a}$ is primary $\Leftrightarrow \mathfrak{a}R_M$ is primary.

For proofs of the above statements, see Northcott [**1**: 2.6, 2.7] or Zariski–Samuel [**1**: §10 and §11 of Chapter IV]. We note the following consequences of the above properties.

6) $\mathfrak{P}_1 R_{\mathfrak{P}}, \ldots, \mathfrak{P}_v R_{\mathfrak{P}}$ are exactly all the distinct maximal ideals in $R_{\mathfrak{P}}$ and hence $R_{\mathfrak{P}}$ is quasisemilocal.

7) If R is noetherian, then so is R_M. If R is noetherian and $v = 1$, then $(R_{\mathfrak{P}}, \mathfrak{P}R_{\mathfrak{P}})$ is a local ring and $\dim R_{\mathfrak{P}} = \operatorname{hgt}_R \mathfrak{P}$.

8) Assume that R is noetherian and let $\{0\} = \mathfrak{q}_1 \cap \ldots \cap \mathfrak{q}_u$ be a normal decomposition of $\{0\}$ in R labeled so that $\mathfrak{q}_i \cap M = \emptyset$ for $i \leqq k$ and $\mathfrak{q}_i \cap M \neq \emptyset$ for $i > k$.[3] Taking $\{0\}$ for $\mathfrak{a}$ in 1) we then get $\mathfrak{j}_R[M] = \mathfrak{q}_1 \cap \ldots \cap \mathfrak{q}_k$.

[2] Note that if $\mathfrak{p}_i$ is the associated prime ideal of $\mathfrak{q}_i$ then: $\mathfrak{q}_i \cap M = \emptyset \Leftrightarrow \mathfrak{p}_i \cap M = \emptyset$. By (18.6.1), in case of $M = R - \bigcup_{j=1}^{v} \mathfrak{P}_j$ the labeling of $\mathfrak{q}_1, \ldots, \mathfrak{q}_u$ is to be such that, for $i \leqq k$: $\mathfrak{q}_i \subset \mathfrak{P}_j$ for some j, and for $i > k$: $\mathfrak{q}_i \not\subset \mathfrak{P}_j$ for all j.

[3] By (18.6.1), in case of $M = R - \bigcup_{1=j}^{v} \mathfrak{P}_j$ this means that, for $i \leqq k$: $\mathfrak{q}_i \subset \mathfrak{P}_j$ for some j, and for $i > k$: $\mathfrak{q}_i \not\subset \mathfrak{P}_j$ for all j.

(18.8) *Direct sum of local rings.*

1) Suppose there exist ring homomorphisms $\varphi_1: R \to R_1, \ldots, \varphi_u: R \to R_u$ where $(R_1, \mathfrak{m}_1), \ldots, (R_u, \mathfrak{m}_u)$ are local rings such that $\varphi_1 \oplus \ldots \oplus \varphi_u$: $R \to R_1 \oplus \ldots \oplus R_u$ is an isomorphism. Let $\mathfrak{n}_i = \varphi_i^{-1}(\mathfrak{m}_i)$. Let $\{0\} = \mathfrak{q}_1 \cap \ldots \cap \mathfrak{q}_v$ be a normal decomposition of $\{0\}$ in R, let $J = \{1, \ldots, v\}$, $I_i = \{j \in J: \mathfrak{q}_j \subset \mathfrak{n}_i\}$, and $\mathfrak{A}_i = \bigcap_{j \in I_i} \mathfrak{q}_j$. Then we have (i to vi):

i) Given any prime ideal $\mathfrak{p}$ in R, $\mathfrak{p}$ is contained in exactly one maximal ideal in R.

ii) R is a semilocal ring in which $\mathfrak{n}_1, \ldots, \mathfrak{n}_u$ are exactly all the distinct maximal ideals.

iii) $\{I_1, \ldots, I_u\}$ is a partition of J.[4]

iv) Let $f_i: R \to R_{\mathfrak{n}_i}$ be the natural homomorphism. Then $f_i(R - \mathfrak{n}_i) = R_i - \mathfrak{m}_i$ and $(R_i)_{\mathfrak{m}_i} = R_i$. Hence by (18.4), there exists a unique ring homomorphism $g_i: R_{\mathfrak{n}_i} \to R_i$ such that $\varphi_i = g_i \circ f_i$. Actually g_i is an isomorphism and $\mathfrak{A}_i = \mathfrak{j}_R[\mathfrak{n}_i] = \operatorname{Ker} f_i = \operatorname{Ker} \varphi_i$.

v) $f_1 \oplus \ldots \oplus f_u: R \to R_{\mathfrak{n}_1} \oplus \ldots \oplus R_{\mathfrak{n}_u}$ is an isomorphism of R-algebras where $R_{\mathfrak{n}_i}$ is considered to be an R-algebra with underlying homomorphism f_i.

vi) If R_i is an integral domain, then I_i contains exactly one element j and $\mathfrak{q}_j$ is prime. Consequently, if $R_1, \ldots, R_u$ are all integral domains then: each I_i contains exactly one element; $v = u$; and $\mathfrak{q}_1, \ldots, \mathfrak{q}_u$ are all prime.

2) Conversely, if R is a semilocal ring with distinct maximal ideals $\mathfrak{n}_1, \ldots, \mathfrak{n}_u$ such that condition i) is satisfied, then there exist local rings $R_1, \ldots, R_u$ and ring homomorphisms $\varphi_1: R \to R_1, \ldots, \varphi_u: R \to R_u$ such that $\varphi_1 \oplus \ldots \oplus \varphi_u: R \to R_1 \oplus \ldots \oplus R_u$ is an isomorphism. Furthermore this representation is unique in the sense that if $S_1, \ldots, S_t$ are local rings and $f_1: R \to S_1, \ldots, f_t: R \to S_t$ are ring homomorphisms such that $f_1 \oplus \ldots \oplus f_t: R \to S_1 \oplus \ldots \oplus S_t$ is an isomorphism, then $t = u$ and after suitably relabeling $S_1, \ldots, S_u$ there exist isomorphisms $g_i: S_i \to R_i$ such that $\varphi_i = g_i \circ f_i$ for $i = 1, \ldots, u$, (actually, the said relabeling of $S_1, \ldots, S_u$ as well as the isomorphisms $g_1, \ldots, g_u$ are also unique).

Proof of 1). i) and ii) follow from (17.8), and iii) follows from i). To prove iv), first note that φ_i is an epimorphism and hence g_i is an epimorphism by (18.4). Now let $r \in R$ be given. If $r \in \operatorname{Ker} f_i$ then $rm = 0$ for some $m \in R - \mathfrak{n}_i$; hence $\varphi_i(r)\varphi_i(m) = 0$ and $\varphi_i(m)$ is a unit in R_i; therefore $\varphi_i(r) = 0$. Conversely suppose that $\varphi_i(r) = 0$; let $m = (\varphi_1 \oplus \ldots \oplus \varphi_u)^{-1}(0, \ldots, e_i, 0, \ldots, 0)$ where e_i is the identity element of R_i;

[4] That is, $I_1, \ldots, I_u$ are pairwise disjoint nonempty subsets of J and $I_1 \cup \ldots \cup I_u = J$

then $m \in R - \mathfrak{n}_i$ and $\varphi_1 \oplus \ldots \oplus \varphi_u(rm) = 0$, i.e., $rm = 0$, and hence $r \in \operatorname{Ker} f_i$. This shows that $\operatorname{Ker} \varphi_i = \operatorname{Ker} f_i = \mathfrak{j}_R[\mathfrak{n}_i] = \mathfrak{A}_i$. Therefore g_i is a monomorphism and hence an isomorphism. This proves iv), and then v) and vi) follow immediately.

Proof of 2). Uniqueness follows from iv) and existence is also suggested by that description. Namely, let $\{0\} = \mathfrak{q}_1 \cap \ldots \cap \mathfrak{q}_v$ be a normal decomposition of $\{0\}$ in R, let $J = \{1,\ldots, v\}$, $I_i = \{j \in J: \mathfrak{q}_j \subset \mathfrak{n}_i\}$, $\mathfrak{A}_i = \bigcap_{j \in I_i} \mathfrak{q}_j$, and let $\varphi_i: R \to R_i = R/\mathfrak{A}_i$ be the natural epimorphism. By i) we get that $\{I_1,\ldots, I_u\}$ is a partition of J, and $\mathfrak{q}_j + \mathfrak{q}_{j'} = R$ for all $i \neq i'$, $j \in I_i$, $j' \in I_{i'}$. Hence $\mathfrak{A}_1,\ldots, \mathfrak{A}_u$ are pairwise coprime by (17.9.2). Therefore $\varphi_1 \oplus \ldots \oplus \varphi_u$ is an epimorphism by (17.9.3). Also $\mathfrak{A}_1 \cap \ldots \cap \mathfrak{A}_u = \{0\}$ and hence $\varphi_1 \oplus \ldots \oplus \varphi_u$ is a monomorphism. Now $\mathfrak{A}_i \subset \mathfrak{n}_i$ and $\mathfrak{A}_i \not\subset \mathfrak{n}_j$ for all $j \neq i$. Therefore $\varphi_i(\mathfrak{n}_i)$ is the unique maximal ideal in R_i and hence R_i is a local ring.

(18.9) *Total quotient ring of a noetherian ring*. Assume that R is noetherian and $\operatorname{rad}_R\{0\} = \{0\}$. Let V be the set of all nonzerodivisors in R and let $\mathfrak{L}$ be the total quotient ring of R.

1) Let $\varphi: R \to S$ be a ring epimorphism whose kernel is a prime ideal $\mathfrak{p}$ of $\{0\}$ in R. Let W be the set of all nonzero elements in S and let $\mathfrak{K}$ be the quotient field of S. Then $\varphi(V) = W$, the extension $\psi: \mathfrak{L} \to \mathfrak{K}$ of φ to $\mathfrak{L}$ is an epimorphism, $\operatorname{Ker} \psi = \mathfrak{p}\mathfrak{L}$, $\mathfrak{p} = R \cap \mathfrak{p}\mathfrak{L}$, and $\mathfrak{p}\mathfrak{L}$ is a maximal ideal in $\mathfrak{L}$.

2) Let $\mathfrak{p}_1,\ldots, \mathfrak{p}_u$ be the distinct prime ideals of $\{0\}$ in R and let $\mathfrak{P}_i = \mathfrak{p}_i\mathfrak{L}$. Then $\mathfrak{p}_i = R \cap \mathfrak{P}_i$ for $i = 1,\ldots, u$; $\mathfrak{P}_1,\ldots, \mathfrak{P}_u$ are exactly all the distinct prime ideals in $\mathfrak{L}$ and they are all maximal; and $\{0\} = \mathfrak{P}_1 \cap \ldots \cap \mathfrak{P}_u$ is the unique normal decomposition of $\{0\}$ in $\mathfrak{L}$. Let $\varphi_i: R \to R_i$ be a ring epimorphism such that $\operatorname{Ker} \varphi_i = \mathfrak{p}_i$, let V_i be the set of all nonzerodivisors in R_i and let $\mathfrak{L}_i$ be the quotient field of R_i. Then $\varphi_i(V) = V_i$, the extension $\psi_i: \mathfrak{L} \to \mathfrak{L}_i$ of φ_i to $\mathfrak{L}$ is an epimorphism, and $\operatorname{Ker} \psi_i = \mathfrak{P}_i$ for $i = 1,\ldots, u$. Furthermore $\psi_1 \oplus \ldots \oplus \psi_u: \mathfrak{L} \to \mathfrak{L}_1 \oplus \ldots \oplus \mathfrak{L}_u$ is the extension of $\varphi_1 \oplus \ldots \oplus \varphi_u$ to $\mathfrak{L}$, and $\psi_1 \oplus \ldots \oplus \psi_u$ is actually an isomorphism.

3) Let R' be any noetherian subring of $\mathfrak{L}$ such that $R \subset R'$. Let $\mathfrak{p}_1,\ldots, \mathfrak{p}_u$ be the distinct prime ideals of $\{0\}$ in R, and let $\mathfrak{q}_i = R' \cap \mathfrak{p}_i\mathfrak{L}$. Then $\operatorname{rad}_{R'}\{0\} = \{0\}$; $\mathfrak{q}_1,\ldots, \mathfrak{q}_u$ are exactly all the distinct prime ideals of $\{0\}$ in R'; $\mathfrak{p}_i = R \cap \mathfrak{q}_i$ for all i; and $\mathfrak{p}_j \not\subset \mathfrak{q}_i$ for all $j \neq i$.

Proof of 1). Let $\mathfrak{p}_1 = \mathfrak{p}$ and let $\mathfrak{p}_2,\ldots, \mathfrak{p}_u$ be the remaining prime ideals of $\{0\}$ in R. By (18.6), $V = R - (\mathfrak{p}_1 \cup \ldots \cup \mathfrak{p}_u)$ and hence $\varphi(V) \subset W$. Conversely, let $r \in R$ be such that $\varphi(r) \neq 0$, i.e., $r \notin \mathfrak{p}_1$. Relabel $\mathfrak{p}_2,\ldots, \mathfrak{p}_u$

so that $r \notin \mathfrak{p}_i$ for $i = 2, \ldots, h$, and $r \in \mathfrak{p}_i$ for $i = h+1, \ldots, u$. For any i we have that $\mathfrak{p}_1 \cap \ldots \cap \mathfrak{p}_{i-1} \cap \mathfrak{p}_{i+1} \cap \ldots \cap \mathfrak{p}_u \not\subset \mathfrak{p}_i$ and hence we can take $s_i \in \mathfrak{p}_1 \cap \ldots \cap \mathfrak{p}_{i-1} \cap \mathfrak{p}_{i+1} \cap \ldots \cap \mathfrak{p}_u$ such that $s_i \notin \mathfrak{p}_i$. Let $s = s_{h+1} + \ldots + s_u$. Then $r + s \notin \mathfrak{p}_1 \cup \ldots \cup \mathfrak{p}_u$ and $\varphi(r) = \varphi(r+s)$. Therefore $\varphi(V) = W$. By (18.4), it now follows that ψ is an epimorphism and $\operatorname{Ker} \psi = \mathfrak{p}\mathfrak{L}$. Since φ is induced by ψ we get that $\mathfrak{p} = R \cap \mathfrak{p}\mathfrak{L}$, and since $\mathfrak{K}$ is a field we get that $\mathfrak{p}\mathfrak{L}$ is a maximal ideal in $\mathfrak{L}$.

Proof of 2). Since $V = R - (\mathfrak{p}_1 \cup \ldots \cup \mathfrak{p}_u)$, the assertions in the second sentence follow from (18.7); however we shall reprove them below. By 1), $\varphi_i(V) = V_i$, ψ_i is an epimorphism, $\operatorname{Ker} \psi_i = \mathfrak{P}_i$, $\mathfrak{p}_i = R \cap \mathfrak{P}_i$, and $\mathfrak{P}_i$ is a maximal ideal in $\mathfrak{L}$ for $i = 1, \ldots, u$. Now $(\operatorname{Ker} \varphi_1) \cap \ldots \cap (\operatorname{Ker} \varphi_u) = \{0\}$, and hence by (18.5.7), $\psi_1 \oplus \ldots \oplus \psi_u : \mathfrak{L} \to \mathfrak{L}_1 \oplus \ldots \oplus \mathfrak{L}_u$ is the extension of $\varphi_1 \oplus \ldots \oplus \varphi_u$ to $\mathfrak{L}$ and $\psi_1 \oplus \ldots \oplus \psi_u$ is a monomorphism. Therefore $\mathfrak{P}_1 \cap \ldots \cap \mathfrak{P}_u = \{0\}$. For any $i \neq j$, $\mathfrak{p}_i \not\subset \mathfrak{p}_j$, $\mathfrak{p}_i = R \cap \mathfrak{P}_i$, $\mathfrak{p}_j = R \cap \mathfrak{P}_j$, and hence $\mathfrak{P}_i \not\subset \mathfrak{P}_j$. Therefore $\{0\} = \mathfrak{P}_1 \cap \ldots \cap \mathfrak{P}_u$ is the unique normal decomposition of $\{0\}$ in $\mathfrak{L}$; $\mathfrak{P}_1, \ldots, \mathfrak{P}_u$ are exactly all the distinct prime ideals in $\mathfrak{L}$ and they are pairwise comaximal. By (17.9.3) it follows that $\psi_1 \oplus \ldots \oplus \psi_u$ is an isomorphism.

Proof of 3). $\operatorname{rad}_{\mathfrak{L}}\{0\} = \{0\}$ by 2), and hence $\operatorname{rad}_{R'}\{0\} = \{0\}$. The rest also follows from 2) by noting that $\mathfrak{L}$ is also the total quotient ring of R'.

§19. INTEGRAL DEPENDENCE AND FINITE GENERATION

Let $\varphi: R \to R'$ be an R-algebra. For $A \subset R$ we may write AR' in place of $\varphi(A)R'$, and for $B \subset R'$ we may write $B \cap R$ in place of $\varphi^{-1}(B)$. In particular then an ideal $\mathfrak{a}$ in R gives the extended ideal $\mathfrak{a}R'$ in R' and an ideal $\mathfrak{b}$ in R' gives the contracted ideal $\mathfrak{b} \cap R$ in R. For

$$f(T_1, \ldots, T_m) = \sum f_{i_1 \ldots i_m} T_1^{i_1} \ldots T_m^{i_m} \in R[T_1, \ldots, T_m]$$

and $\alpha_1, \ldots, \alpha_m \in R'$ we may write $f(\alpha_1, \ldots, \alpha_m)$ in place of

$$\sum \varphi(f_{i_1 \ldots i_m}) \alpha_1^{i_1} \ldots \alpha_m^{i_m}.$$

For $\alpha_1, \ldots, \alpha_m \in R'$, the image of $R[T_1, \ldots, T_m]$ under the R-algebra-homomorphism $T_i \to \alpha_i$ is denoted by $R[\alpha_1, \ldots, \alpha_m]$. More generally for any $A \subset R'$, the subring $\varphi(R)[A]$ of R' may be denoted by $R[A]$. R' is said to be a finite R-algebra provided there exists a finite number of elements $\alpha_1, \ldots, \alpha_m$ in R' such that $R' = R[\alpha_1, \ldots, \alpha_m]$. An element $\alpha \in R'$ is said to be *integral over* R provided there exists a monic $f(T) \in R[T]$ such that $f(\alpha) = 0$. $B \subset R'$ is said to be integral over R provided every element of B is integral over R. We have the following.

1′) $\alpha \in R'$ is integral over $R \Leftrightarrow R[\alpha]$ is a finite R-module[1] $\Leftrightarrow R[\alpha]$ is contained in a subring of R' which is a finite R-module.

2′) If R is noetherian then, $\alpha \in R'$ is integral over $R \Leftrightarrow R[\alpha]$ is contained in a finite R-submodule of R'.

3′) R' is a finite R-module $\Leftrightarrow R'$ is integral over R and R' is a finite R-algebra.

4′) The set $\tilde{R}$ of all elements of R' which are integral over R is an R-subalgebra of R' and it is called the *integral closure* of R in R'. R is *integrally closed in* $R' \Leftrightarrow$ (def) $\tilde{R} = \varphi(R)$. R is *normal* $\Leftrightarrow$ (def) R is integrally closed in its total quotient ring.

If φ is a monomorphism then identifying R with $\varphi(R)$, R' becomes an overring of R. In the general case, R' is an overring of $\varphi(R)$. Thus it suffices to consider the case of an overring.

(**19.1**) (Lying over and going up theorem). *Let R be a ring and let R' be an overring of R which is integral over R.*

1) *If $\mathfrak{a}$ is a proper ideal in R then $\mathfrak{a}R'$ is a proper ideal in R'.*

2) *Given a prime ideal $\mathfrak{q}$ in R', $\mathfrak{q}$ is maximal in $R' \Leftrightarrow \mathfrak{q} \cap R$ is maximal in R.*

3) *Given a prime ideal $\mathfrak{p}$ in R there exists a prime ideal $\mathfrak{q}$ in R' such that* $\mathfrak{q} \cap R = \mathfrak{p}$; $\mathfrak{q}$ is said to lie over $\mathfrak{p}$.

4) *Given prime ideals $\mathfrak{p}_1 \subset \mathfrak{p}_2$ in R and a prime ideal $\mathfrak{q}_1$ in R' such that $\mathfrak{q}_1 \cap R = \mathfrak{p}_1$, there exists a prime ideal $\mathfrak{q}_2$ in R' such that $\mathfrak{q}_1 \subset \mathfrak{q}_2$ and $\mathfrak{q}_2 \cap R = \mathfrak{p}_2$.*

5) *If $\mathfrak{q}_1 \subsetneq \mathfrak{q}_2$ are ideals in R' such that $\mathfrak{q}_1$ is prime, then $\mathfrak{q}_1 \cap R \subsetneq \mathfrak{q}_2 \cap R$.*

(**19.2**) (Going down theorem). *Let R be a normal integral domain and let R' be an overring of R such that R' is integral over R and such that every nonzero element in R is a nonzerodivisor in R'. Let $\mathfrak{p}_1 \subset \mathfrak{p}_2$ be prime ideals in R and let $\mathfrak{q}_2$ be a prime ideal in R' such that $\mathfrak{q}_2 \cap R = \mathfrak{p}_2$. Then there exists a prime ideal $\mathfrak{q}_1$ in R' such that $\mathfrak{q}_1 \subset \mathfrak{q}_2$ and $\mathfrak{q}_1 \cap R = \mathfrak{p}_1$.*

For integral domains, (19.1) and (19.2) were proved by Krull [**1**] and the general case was then given by Cohen-Seidenberg [**1**]. The latter's proof can be found in Zariski–Samuel [**1**: §§2, 3 of Chapter V] or Abhyankar [**1**: §3]. Note that (19.1.1, 19.1.2) follow immediately from (19.1.3, 19.1.4, 19.1.5).

[1] An R-module $\mathfrak{A}$ is said to be a finite R-module provided there exists a finite number of elements $\alpha_1,\ldots, \alpha_m$ in $\mathfrak{A}$ such that $\mathfrak{A} = \alpha_1 R + \ldots + \alpha_m R$.

(19.3) *Let R be a ring and let R' be an overring of R which is integral over R.*

1) *For any prime ideal* $\mathfrak{q}$ *in* R' *we have* $\text{dpt}_{R'}\mathfrak{q} = \text{dpt}_R(\mathfrak{q} \cap R)$ *and* $\text{hgt}_{R'}\mathfrak{q} \leqq \text{hgt}_R(\mathfrak{q} \cap R)$.

2) *If furthermore R and R' are noetherian then for any proper ideal* $\mathfrak{a}$ *in R we have* $\text{dpt}_R\mathfrak{a} = \text{dpt}_{R'}\mathfrak{a}R'$.

Proof of 1). Let $\mathfrak{p} = \mathfrak{q} \cap R$. Let $\mathfrak{p}_0, \ldots, \mathfrak{p}_e$ be distinct prime ideals in R such that $\mathfrak{p} \subset \mathfrak{p}_0 \subset \ldots \subset \mathfrak{p}_e$. Repeatedly applying (19.1.4) we find prime ideals $\mathfrak{q}_0, \ldots, \mathfrak{q}_e$ in R' such that $\mathfrak{q}_i \cap R = \mathfrak{p}_i$ for $i = 0, \ldots, e$, and $\mathfrak{q} \subset \mathfrak{q}_0 \subset \ldots \subset \mathfrak{q}_e$. Obviously $\mathfrak{q}_0, \ldots, \mathfrak{q}_e$ are all distinct. Therefore $\text{dpt}_R\mathfrak{p} \leqq \text{dpt}_{R'}\mathfrak{q}$. Let $\mathfrak{q}_0', \ldots, \mathfrak{q}_u'$ be distinct prime ideals in R' such that $\mathfrak{q} \subset \mathfrak{q}_0' \subset \ldots \subset \mathfrak{q}_u'$. Then $\mathfrak{p} \subset (\mathfrak{q}_0' \cap R) \subset \ldots \subset (\mathfrak{q}_u' \cap R)$ and by (19.1.5), $(\mathfrak{q}_0' \cap R), \ldots, (\mathfrak{q}_u' \cap R)$ are distinct prime ideals in R. Therefore $\text{dpt}_R\mathfrak{p} \geqq \text{dpt}_{R'}\mathfrak{q}$. Let $\mathfrak{q}_0^*, \ldots, \mathfrak{q}_v^*$ be distinct prime ideals in R' such that $\mathfrak{q}_0^* \subset \ldots \subset \mathfrak{q}_v^* \subset \mathfrak{q}$. Then $(\mathfrak{q}_0^* \cap R) \subset \ldots \subset (\mathfrak{q}_v^* \cap R) \subset \mathfrak{p}$ and by (19.1.5), $(\mathfrak{q}_0^* \cap R), \ldots, (\mathfrak{q}_v^* \cap R)$ are distinct prime ideals in R. Therefore $\text{hgt}_{R'}\mathfrak{q} \leqq \text{hgt}_R\mathfrak{p}$.

Proof of 2). Take a prime ideal $\mathfrak{q}$ in R' such that $\mathfrak{a}R' \subset \mathfrak{q}$ and $\text{dpt}_{R'}\mathfrak{a}R' = \text{dpt}_{R'}\mathfrak{q}$. Then $\mathfrak{q} \cap R$ is a prime ideal in R and $\mathfrak{a} \subset \mathfrak{q} \cap R$. Hence $\text{dpt}_R\mathfrak{a} \geqq \text{dpt}_R(\mathfrak{q} \cap R)$. By 1), $\text{dpt}_{R'}\mathfrak{q} = \text{dpt}_R(\mathfrak{q} \cap R)$ and hence $\text{dpt}_R\mathfrak{a} \geqq \text{dpt}_{R'}\mathfrak{a}R'$.

Take a prime ideal $\mathfrak{p}$ in R such that $\mathfrak{a} \subset \mathfrak{p}$ and $\text{dpt}_R\mathfrak{a} = \text{dpt}_R\mathfrak{p}$. By (19.1.3) there exists a prime ideal $\mathfrak{q}$ in R' such that $\mathfrak{q} \cap R = \mathfrak{p}$. Obviously $\mathfrak{a}R' \subset \mathfrak{q}$ and hence $\text{dpt}_{R'}\mathfrak{a}R' \geqq \text{dpt}_{R'}\mathfrak{q}$. By 1), $\text{dpt}_{R'}\mathfrak{q} = \text{dpt}_R\mathfrak{p}$ and hence $\text{dpt}_{R'}\mathfrak{a}R' \geqq \text{dpt}_R\mathfrak{a}$.

(19.4) *Let R be a normal integral domain and let R' be an overring of R such that R' is integral over R and every nonzero element in R is a nonzerodivisor in R'.*

1) *For any prime ideal* $\mathfrak{q}$ *in* R' *we have* $\text{hgt}_{R'}\mathfrak{q} = \text{hgt}_R(\mathfrak{q} \cap R)$.

2) *If furthermore R and R' are noetherian then for any proper ideal* $\mathfrak{a}$ *in R we have* $\text{hgt}_R\mathfrak{a} = \text{hgt}_{R'}\mathfrak{a}R'$.

Proof of 1). Let $\mathfrak{p}_0, \ldots, \mathfrak{p}_e$ be distinct prime ideals in R such that $\mathfrak{p}_0 \subset \ldots \subset \mathfrak{p}_e \subset (\mathfrak{q} \cap R)$. Repeatedly applying (19.2) we find prime ideals $\mathfrak{q}_0, \ldots, \mathfrak{q}_e$ in R' such that $\mathfrak{q}_i \cap R = \mathfrak{p}_i$ for $i = 0, \ldots, e$, and $\mathfrak{q}_0 \subset \ldots \subset \mathfrak{q}_e \subset \mathfrak{q}$. Obviously $\mathfrak{q}_0, \ldots, \mathfrak{q}_e$ are all distinct. Therefore $\text{hgt}_{R'}\mathfrak{q} \geqq \text{hgt}_R(\mathfrak{q} \cap R)$. Consequently by (19.3.1) we have equality.

Proof of 2). Take a prime ideal $\mathfrak{q}$ in R' such that $\mathfrak{a}R' \subset \mathfrak{q}$ and $\mathrm{hgt}_{R'}\mathfrak{a}R = \mathrm{hgt}_{R'}\mathfrak{q}$. Then $\mathfrak{q} \cap R$ is a prime ideal in R and $\mathfrak{a} \subset \mathfrak{q} \cap R$. Hence $\mathrm{hgt}_R\mathfrak{a} \leqq \mathrm{hgt}_R(\mathfrak{q} \cap R)$. By 1), $\mathrm{hgt}_{R'}\mathfrak{q} = \mathrm{hgt}_R(\mathfrak{q} \cap R)$ and hence $\mathrm{hgt}_R\mathfrak{a} \leqq \mathrm{hgt}_{R'}\mathfrak{a}R'$.

Take a prime ideal $\mathfrak{p}$ in R such that $\mathfrak{a} \subset \mathfrak{p}$ and $\mathrm{hgt}_R\mathfrak{a} = \mathrm{hgt}_R\mathfrak{p}$. By (19.1.3) there exists a prime ideal $\mathfrak{q}$ in R' such that $\mathfrak{q} \cap R = \mathfrak{p}$. Obviously $\mathfrak{a}R' \subset \mathfrak{q}$ and hence $\mathrm{hgt}_{R'}\mathfrak{a}R' \leqq \mathrm{hgt}_{R'}\mathfrak{q}$. By 1), $\mathrm{hgt}_{R'}\mathfrak{q} = \mathrm{hgt}_R\mathfrak{p}$ and hence $\mathrm{hgt}_{R'}\mathfrak{a}R' \leqq \mathrm{hgt}_R\mathfrak{a}$.

(19.5) *Let R be a ring and let R' be an overring of R such that R' is integral over R and every nonzerodivisor in R is a nonzerodivisor in R'. Assume that R contains a subring S such that S is a normal integral domain, R is integral over S, and every nonzero element in S is a nonzerodivisor in R. Then for any prime ideal $\mathfrak{q}$ in R' we have* $\mathrm{hgt}_{R'}\mathfrak{q} = \mathrm{hgt}_R(\mathfrak{q} \cap R)$.

PROOF. Let $\mathfrak{p} = \mathfrak{q} \cap R$ and $\mathfrak{r} = \mathfrak{p} \cap S$. By (19.4), $\mathrm{hgt}_{R'}\mathfrak{q} = \mathrm{hgt}_S\mathfrak{r} = \mathrm{hgt}_R\mathfrak{p}$.

(19.6) REMARK. Nagata [**3**: (II) on p. 57] has given an example of a local integral domain $\mathfrak{o}$ and a prime ideal $\mathfrak{p}_1$ in the integral closure $\mathfrak{o}'$ of $\mathfrak{o}$ in its quotient field such that $\mathrm{hgt}_{\mathfrak{o}'}\mathfrak{p}_1 < \mathrm{hgt}_{\mathfrak{o}}(\mathfrak{p}_1 \cap \mathfrak{o})$.

(19.7) *Let $(R, \mathfrak{m})$ and $(R', \mathfrak{m}')$ be local rings such that R' is an overring of R and is integral over R. Then we have the following.*

1) $\dim R = \dim R'$.

2) *$\mathfrak{m}'$ is the only prime ideal in R' whose contraction to R is $\mathfrak{m}$.*

3) *Given an ideal $\mathfrak{q}$ in R, $\mathfrak{q}$ is primary for $\mathfrak{m} \Leftrightarrow \mathfrak{q}R'$ is primary for $\mathfrak{m}'$.*

4) *Elements $\alpha_1, \ldots, \alpha_e$ in R form a system of parameters for $R \Leftrightarrow$ they form a system of parameters for R'.*

PROOF. 2) follows from (19.1.2). 1) follows from 2) and (19.3.1) since $\dim R = \mathrm{dpt}_R\mathfrak{m}$ and $\dim R' = \mathrm{dpt}_{R'}\mathfrak{m}'$. By (19.1.1), $\mathfrak{q} = R \Leftrightarrow \mathfrak{q}R' = R'$. Now suppose that $\mathfrak{q} \neq R$ and $\mathfrak{q}$ is not primary for $\mathfrak{m}$. Then $\mathfrak{q} \subset \mathfrak{p} \subsetneq \mathfrak{m}$ where $\mathfrak{p}$ is a prime ideal in R. By (19.1.3) we can find a prime ideal $\mathfrak{p}'$ in R' such that $\mathfrak{p}' \cap R = \mathfrak{p}$. Then $\mathfrak{q}R' \subset \mathfrak{p}' \subsetneq \mathfrak{m}'$ and hence $\mathfrak{q}R'$ is not primary for $\mathfrak{m}'$. Next suppose that $\mathfrak{q}R' \neq R'$ and $\mathfrak{q}R'$ is not primary for $\mathfrak{m}'$. Then $\mathfrak{q}R' \subset \mathfrak{p}^* \subsetneq \mathfrak{m}'$ where $\mathfrak{p}^*$ is a prime ideal in R'. Then $\mathfrak{q} \subset (\mathfrak{p}^* \cap R)$ and by (19.1.5), $\mathfrak{p}^* \cap R$ is a prime ideal in R' with $\mathfrak{p}^* \cap R \subsetneq \mathfrak{m}$. Therefore $\mathfrak{q}$ is not primary for $\mathfrak{m}$. This proves 3). 4) follows from 1) and 3).

(19.8) *Let R be a quasisemilocal ring with maximal ideals $\mathfrak{m}_1, \ldots, \mathfrak{m}_u$. Let R' be an overring of R which is a finite R-module. Then for each $i \leqq u$: $R \cap \mathfrak{m}_i R' = \mathfrak{m}_i$; there are only a finite number of prime ideals $\mathfrak{m}'_{i1}, \ldots, \mathfrak{m}'_{iv_i}$ in R' containing $\mathfrak{m}_i$; $\mathfrak{m}_i R' = \mathfrak{n}'_{i1} \cap \ldots \cap \mathfrak{n}'_{iv_i}$ where $\mathfrak{n}'_{ij}$ is a uniquely determined primary ideal for $\mathfrak{m}'_{ij}$; and $\mathfrak{m}_i R'$ is primary if and only if $v_i = 1$. The $v_1 + \ldots + v_u$ ideals $\mathfrak{m}'_{ij}$ are all distinct and they are exactly all the maximal ideals in R'. In particular R' is a quasisemilocal ring.*

PROOF. By (19.1.2, 19.1.3), $R \cap \mathfrak{m}_i R' = \mathfrak{m}_i$ for $i = 1, \ldots, u$, and every maximal ideal in R' lies over some $\mathfrak{m}_i$. Let $f_i \colon R' \to \bar{R}_i = R'/\mathfrak{m}_i R'$ be the natural epimorphism. Since $R \cap \mathfrak{m}_i R' = \mathfrak{m}_i$, we can identify $R/\mathfrak{m}_i$ with a subfield of $\bar{R}_i$. Since R' is a finite R-module, $\bar{R}_i$ is a finite dimensional vector space over $R/\mathfrak{m}_i$. Hence[2] $\bar{R}_i$ contains only a finite number of prime ideals $\bar{\mathfrak{m}}_{i1}, \ldots, \bar{\mathfrak{m}}_{iv_i}$, ($v_i > 0$), they are all maximal, and in $\bar{R}_i$ we have $\{0\} = \bar{\mathfrak{n}}_{i1} \cap \ldots \cap \bar{\mathfrak{n}}_{iv_i}$ where $\bar{\mathfrak{n}}_{ij}$ is a uniquely determined primary ideal for $\bar{\mathfrak{m}}_{ij}$. Let $\mathfrak{m}'_{ij} = f_i^{-1}(\bar{\mathfrak{m}}_{ij})$ and $\mathfrak{n}'_{ij} = f_i^{-1}(\bar{\mathfrak{n}}_{ij})$.

(19.9) *Let $(R, \mathfrak{m})$ be a normal local ring such that* $\operatorname{rad}\{0\} = \{0\}$. *Then R is an integral domain.*

PROOF. $\operatorname{rad}\{0\} = \{0\}$ implies that $\{0\} = \mathfrak{p}_1 \cap \ldots \cap \mathfrak{p}_u$ where $\mathfrak{p}_1, \ldots, \mathfrak{p}_u$ are all the distinct prime ideals of height zero in R, and hence in particular $\mathfrak{p}_i \not\subset \mathfrak{p}_j$ for all $i \neq j$. Suppose if possible that $u > 1$. We can find $b \in \mathfrak{p}_2 \cap \ldots \cap \mathfrak{p}_u$ such that $b \notin \mathfrak{p}_1$, and by (18.6.1) we can find $a \in \mathfrak{p}_1$ such that $a \notin \mathfrak{p}_i$ for all $i > 1$. Then $ab \in \mathfrak{p}_1 \cap \ldots \cap \mathfrak{p}_u$, i.e., $ab = 0$. Also $a + b \notin \mathfrak{p}_1 \cup \ldots \cup \mathfrak{p}_u$ and hence $a + b$ is not a zerodivisor. Therefore $c = a/(a + b)$ is in the total quotient ring of R. Obviously $c^2 - c = 0$. Since R is normal, $c \in R$. Now

$$a(1 - c) = bc \in \mathfrak{p}_2 \text{ and } a \notin \mathfrak{p}_2 \Rightarrow 1 - c \in \mathfrak{p}_2 \subset \mathfrak{m}.$$

Also

$$bc = a(1 - c) \in \mathfrak{p}_1 \text{ and } b \notin \mathfrak{p}_1 \Rightarrow c \in \mathfrak{p}_1 \subset \mathfrak{m}.$$

Therefore $1 \in \mathfrak{m}$. Contradiction.

(19.10) *Let $(R, \mathfrak{m})$ be a normal local ring. Then either every nonunit in R is a zerodivisor or R is an integral domain.*

PROOF. Suppose R contains a nonunit a which is not a zerodivisor. Let b be any nilpotent in R: $b^n = 0$, $n > 0$. By (19.9) it suffices to show

[2] Say by (19.1). $R/\mathfrak{m}_i$ being a field, obviously $\{0\}$ is the only prime ideal in $R/\mathfrak{m}_i$ and $\bar{R}_i$ is noetherian.

that $b = 0$. For all $p > 0$, b/a^p is in the total quotient ring of R and $(b/a^p)^n = 0$, whence $b/a^p \in R$, i.e.,

$$b \in \bigcap_{p=1}^{\infty} a^p R \subset \bigcap_{p=1}^{\infty} \mathfrak{m}^p = \{0\}.$$

(**19.11**) REMARK. (19.9) is false without the assumption that rad $\{0\} = \{0\}$. If every nonunit in R is a zerodivisor then R is its own total quotient ring and hence R is normal. For instance let R be any zero dimensional local ring which is not an integral domain. To construct a positive dimensional example, let $(S, \mathfrak{n})$ be any e dimensional regular local ring, $e > 1$. Let $\mathfrak{p}$ be a prime ideal in S of height one. Let $\mathfrak{q}$ be an ideal in S having $\mathfrak{p}$ and $\mathfrak{n}$ as its associated prime ideals.[3] Let $R = S/\mathfrak{q}$, $\mathfrak{m} = \mathfrak{n}/\mathfrak{q}$. Then $(R, \mathfrak{m})$ is a local ring of dimension $e - 1$ and $\mathfrak{m}$ is an associated prime ideal of zero.

(**19.12**) *Let M be a multiplicative set in an integral domain R. If R is normal then so is R_M. In particular if $\mathfrak{p}$ is a prime ideal in R and R is normal then so is $R_\mathfrak{p}$.*

Zariski–Samuel [**1**: 2) on p. 261].

(**19.13**) *Let R be a local ring such that* rad$\{0\} = \{0\}$ *in R. Let M be a multiplicative set in R. If R is normal then R_M is a normal integral domain.*

Follows from (19.9, 19.12).

(**19.14**) *Let R be a noetherian ring such that* $\text{rad}_R\{0\} = \{0\}$, *and let* $\mathfrak{a}$ *be any prime ideal in R. Then* $\text{rad}_{R_\mathfrak{p}}\{0\} = \{0\}$. *If $R_\mathfrak{p}$ is normal then $R_\mathfrak{p}$ is an integral domain.*

The first assertion follows from (18.7) and then the second assertion follows from (19.9).

(**19.15**) (Krull's principal ideal theorem). *In a noetherian integral domain R all the minimal prime ideals of any nonzero principal ideal have height one. If R is also normal then every principal ideal in R is unmixed.*

Zariski–Samuel [**1**: Theorem 29 on p. 238 and Theorem 14 on p. 277].

(**19.16**) *Let R be a noetherian integral domain which is not a field. Let Ω be the set of all prime ideals in R of height one. Assume that for every*

[3] Existence of $\mathfrak{q}$ follows from Zariski–Samuel [**1**: Theorem 21 on p. 230].

nonzero principal ideal in R all the associated prime ideals have height one. Then $R = \bigcap_{\mathfrak{p}\in\Omega} R_{\mathfrak{p}}$. Consequently, if $R_{\mathfrak{p}}$ is normal for all $\mathfrak{p} \in \Omega$,[4] *then R is normal.*

PROOF. Let $S = \bigcap_{\mathfrak{p}\in\Omega} R_{\mathfrak{p}}$. It is clear that $R \subset S$. Now let $0 \neq a \in S$. Then $a = b/c$ where b and c are nonzero elements in R. By assumption $cR = \mathfrak{q}_1 \cap ... \cap \mathfrak{q}_u$ where $\mathfrak{q}_1, ..., \mathfrak{q}_u$ are primary ideals whose associated prime ideals $\mathfrak{p}_1, ..., \mathfrak{p}_u$ are all distinct and have height one; and $bR = \mathfrak{q}'_1 \cap ... \cap \mathfrak{q}'_v$ where $\mathfrak{q}'_1, ..., \mathfrak{q}'_v$ are primary ideals whose associated prime ideals $\mathfrak{p}'_1, ..., \mathfrak{p}'_v$ are all distinct and have height one.

Let $i \leqq u$ be given. Then $a \in S \Rightarrow a \in R_{\mathfrak{p}_i} \Rightarrow bR_{\mathfrak{p}_i} \subset cR_{\mathfrak{p}_i}$ and hence $c \in \mathfrak{p}_i \Rightarrow cR_{\mathfrak{p}_i} \neq R_{\mathfrak{p}_i} \Rightarrow bR_{\mathfrak{p}_i} \neq R_{\mathfrak{p}_i}$. If $\mathfrak{p}_i$ were different from $\mathfrak{p}'_j$ for all j then we would get the contradiction that $bR_{\mathfrak{p}_i} = R_{\mathfrak{p}_i}$. Therefore $\mathfrak{p}_i$ equals exactly one of the prime ideals $\mathfrak{p}'_1, ..., \mathfrak{p}'_v$.

Thus we can relabel $\mathfrak{q}'_1, ..., \mathfrak{q}'_v$ so that $\mathfrak{p}'_i = \mathfrak{p}_i$ for $i = 1, ..., u$. Then for all $i \leqq u$: $\mathfrak{q}'_i = R \cap bR_{\mathfrak{p}_i} \subset R \cap cR_{\mathfrak{p}_i} = \mathfrak{q}_i$. Therefore $bR \subset cR$, i.e., $a \in R$. This shows that $R = \bigcap_{\mathfrak{p}\in\Omega} R_{\mathfrak{p}}$.

(**19.17**) *Let R be a normal noetherian integral domain which is not a field. Let Ω be the set of all prime ideals in R of height one. Then $R = \bigcap_{\mathfrak{p}\in\Omega} R_{\mathfrak{p}}$.*

Follows from (19.15, 19.16).

(**19.18**) *Let R be a noetherian integral domain which is not a field and let R' be the integral closure of R in its quotient field. Let Ω be the set of all prime ideals in R of height one. Assume that*

i) *R' is noetherian;*
ii) *$R_{\mathfrak{p}}$ is normal for all $\mathfrak{p} \in \Omega$;*[4] *and*
iii) *R contains a normal subring S over which R is integral.*

Then $R' = \bigcap_{\mathfrak{p}\in\Omega} R_{\mathfrak{p}}$.

PROOF. Let $R^* = \bigcap_{\mathfrak{p}\in\Omega} R_{\mathfrak{p}}$. Then R^* is normal. Since $R \subset R^*$ we get that $R' \subset R^*$. Let Ω' be the set of all prime ideals in R' of height one. By (19.17), $R' = \bigcap_{\mathfrak{q}\in\Omega'} R'_{\mathfrak{q}}$. Given $\mathfrak{q} \in \Omega'$ let $\mathfrak{p} = R \cap \mathfrak{q}$. Then $R'_{\mathfrak{q}} \supset R_{\mathfrak{p}}$. By (19.5), $\text{hgt}_R \mathfrak{p} = \text{hgt}_{R'} \mathfrak{q} = 1$ and hence $\mathfrak{p} \in \Omega$. Therefore $R_{\mathfrak{p}} \supset R^*$. Hence $R'_{\mathfrak{q}} \supset R^*$. This being so for all $\mathfrak{q} \in \Omega'$, we get that $R' = \bigcap_{\mathfrak{q}\in\Omega'} R'_{\mathfrak{q}} \supset R^*$. Therefore $R' = R^*$.

[4] Note that $R_{\mathfrak{p}}$ is a one dimensional local integral domain and hence by (21.4), $R_{\mathfrak{p}}$ is normal if and only if it is regular.

(19.19) *Let* $(R, \mathfrak{m})$ *be a local ring. Let* $\mathfrak{p}_1, \ldots, \mathfrak{p}_u$ *be the prime ideals of* $\{0\}$ *in* R. *Assume that* $u > 1$, *and* $\operatorname{hgt}_R \mathfrak{p}_i = 0$ *for* $i = 1, \ldots, u$. *Then there exists a nonunit nonzerodivisor* α *in* R *such that some prime ideal of* αR *contains* $\mathfrak{p}_i + \mathfrak{p}_j$ *for some* $i \neq j$.

PROOF. Let $\{0\} = \mathfrak{q}_1 \cap \ldots \cap \mathfrak{q}_u$ be the normal decomposition of $\{0\}$ labeled so that $\mathfrak{q}_i$ is primary for $\mathfrak{p}_i$. Take $a_i \in R$ such that $a_i \notin \mathfrak{p}_i$ and $a_i \in \mathfrak{q}_j$ for all $j \neq i$. Let $\alpha = a_1 + \ldots + a_u$. Then $\alpha \notin \mathfrak{p}_1 \cup \ldots \cup \mathfrak{p}_u$ and hence α is a nonzerodivisor. Also $\mathfrak{p}_i \subset \mathfrak{m}$ for all i and hence α is a nonunit. Suppose if possible that $a_1 \in \alpha R$. Then $a_2 + \ldots + a_u = \alpha - a_1 \in \alpha R$. Hence $a_1 = \alpha r$ and $\alpha - a_1 = \alpha s$ with $r, s \in R$. Thus $\alpha = \alpha(r + s)$. Since α is a nonzerodivisor, we get that $r + s = 1$.

Now

$$r \notin \mathfrak{m} \Rightarrow \alpha \in a_1 R \subset \mathfrak{p}_2 \Rightarrow \text{contradiction};$$

and

$$s \notin \mathfrak{m} \Rightarrow \alpha \in \{a_2, \ldots, a_u\}R \subset \mathfrak{p}_1 \Rightarrow \text{contradiction}.$$

Therefore $r \in \mathfrak{m}$ and $s \in \mathfrak{m}$; hence $1 = r + s \in \mathfrak{m}$; contradiction. *Therefore* $a_1 \notin \alpha R$.

Let $\alpha R = \mathfrak{q}_1' \cap \ldots \cap \mathfrak{q}_v'$ be a normal decomposition of αR where $\mathfrak{q}_j'$ is primary for $\mathfrak{p}_j'$. Assume if possible that each prime ideal of αR contains only one of the prime ideals of $\{0\}$. Let $\mathfrak{p}'$ be any maximal prime ideal of αR, i.e., a maximal element of the set $\{\mathfrak{p}_1', \ldots, \mathfrak{p}_v'\}$. Let $\mathfrak{p}_{k_1}', \ldots, \mathfrak{p}_{k_h}'$ be all the prime ideals of αR contained in $\mathfrak{p}'$. Let $\mathfrak{p}_g \subset \mathfrak{p}'$. We can find $t \in R$ such that $t \notin \mathfrak{p}'$ and $t \in \mathfrak{q}_i$ for all $i \neq g$. Then

$$\begin{aligned} \mathfrak{q}_g &= \{0\} : tR \\ &\subset \alpha R : tR \\ &= (\mathfrak{q}_1' : tR) \cap \ldots \cap (\mathfrak{q}_v' : tR) \\ &\subset \mathfrak{q}_{k_1}' \cap \ldots \cap \mathfrak{q}_{k_h}' \end{aligned}$$

Now if $g \neq 1$ then $a_1 \in \mathfrak{q}_g$, and if $g = 1$ then $\alpha - a_1 \in \mathfrak{q}_g$. Hence always $a_1 \in \mathfrak{q}_{k_1}' \cap \ldots \cap \mathfrak{q}_{k_h}'$. Since every prime ideal of αR is contained in some maximal prime ideal of αR, we conclude that $a_1 \in \mathfrak{q}_1' \cap \ldots \cap \mathfrak{q}_v' = \alpha R$. Contradiction. Therefore some prime ideal of αR contains $\mathfrak{p}_i + \mathfrak{p}_j$ for some $i \neq j$.

(**19.20**) *Let R be a local ring such that*

i) $\operatorname{rad}_R\{0\} = \{0\}$;

ii) *for every nonunit nonzerodivisor α in R all the prime ideals of αR have height one; and*

iii) *$R_{\mathfrak{p}}$ is normal for every prime ideal $\mathfrak{p}$ in R of height one.*[5]

Then R is a normal integral domain.

Proof. Let $\mathfrak{p}_1, \ldots, \mathfrak{p}_u$ be the prime ideals of $\{0\}$ in R. If $u > 1$ then by (19.19), we can find a nonunit nonzerodivisor α in R and a prime ideal $\mathfrak{p}$ of αR such that $\mathfrak{p}_i + \mathfrak{p}_j \subset \mathfrak{p}$ for some $i \neq j$. Then $R_{\mathfrak{p}}$ is not an integral domain and hence by iii), $\operatorname{hgt}_R \mathfrak{p} > 1$ which contradicts ii). Therefore $u = 1$, i.e., R is an integral domain. Now the result follows from (19.16).

(**19.21**) *Conductor.* Let R be a nonnull ring and let R' be the integral closure of R in its total quotient ring. Then

$$\{r \in R : rR' \subset R, \text{ i.e., } rr' \in R \text{ for all } r' \in R'\}$$

is an ideal in R; this ideal is called the conductor of R in R' or simply *the conductor of R* and *we shall denote it by $\mathfrak{c}(R)$*. The following basic property of the conductor is proved in Zariski–Samuel [**1**: p. 269].

1) *Let R be an integral domain such that the integral closure of R in its quotient field is a finite R-module. Then for any multiplicative set M in R we have that: R_M is normal $\Leftrightarrow \mathfrak{c}(R) \cap M \neq \emptyset$. In particular, for any prime ideal $\mathfrak{p}$ in R we have that: $R_{\mathfrak{p}}$ is normal $\Leftrightarrow \mathfrak{c}(R) \not\subset \mathfrak{p}$.*

Using the "$\Rightarrow$" part of this we now prove the following.

2) *Let R be a nonnull noetherian ring such that $\operatorname{rad}_R\{0\} = \{0\}$. Let $\mathfrak{p}_1, \ldots, \mathfrak{p}_u$ be the distinct prime ideals of $\{0\}$ in R and assume that the integral closure of $R/\mathfrak{p}_i$ in its quotient field is a finite $(R/\mathfrak{p}_i)$-module for $i = 1, \ldots, u$. Let $\mathfrak{p}$ be any prime ideal in R such that $R_{\mathfrak{p}}$ is normal. Then $\mathfrak{c}(R) \not\subset \mathfrak{p}$.*

Proof. Let $\mathfrak{L}$ be the total quotient ring of R and let R' be the integral closure of R in $\mathfrak{L}$. Let $\varphi_i : R \to R_i = R/\mathfrak{p}_i$ be the natural epimorphism, let $\mathfrak{L}_i$ be the quotient field of R_i and let R_i' be the integral closure of R_i in $\mathfrak{L}_i$. By (18.9.2), φ_i has a unique extension $\psi_i : \mathfrak{L} \to \mathfrak{L}_i$ to $\mathfrak{L}$ for $i = 1, \ldots, u$, and $(\operatorname{Ker} \psi_1) \cap \ldots \cap (\operatorname{Ker} \psi_u) = \{0\}$. Note that obviously $\psi_i(R') \subset R_i'$ for $i = 1, \ldots, u$.

By (19.14), $R_{\mathfrak{p}}$ is an integral domain and hence $j_R[\mathfrak{p}]$ is a prime ideal, i.e., $\mathfrak{p}_i = j_R[\mathfrak{p}] \subset \mathfrak{p}$ for a unique value i and $\mathfrak{p}_j \not\subset \mathfrak{p}$ for all $j \neq i$. Now

[5] In view of i), $R_{\mathfrak{p}}$ is then an integral domain by (19.14). Since $R_{\mathfrak{p}}$ is a one dimensional local ring, by (21.4), $R_{\mathfrak{p}}$ is normal if and only if it is regular.

$\varphi_i(\mathfrak{p})$ is a prime ideal in the integral domain R_i and $R_{\mathfrak{p}} = (R_i)_{\varphi_i(\mathfrak{p})}$. Therefore $\mathfrak{c}(R_i) \not\subset \varphi_i(\mathfrak{p})$ by 1), and hence we can find $r \in R$ such that $r \notin \mathfrak{p}$ and $\varphi_i(r) \in \mathfrak{c}(R_i)$. Now $\mathfrak{p}_j \not\subset \mathfrak{p}$ for all $j \neq i$ and hence we can find $s \in R$ such that $s \notin \mathfrak{p}$ and $s \in \mathfrak{p}_j$ for all $j \neq i$. Let $t = rs$. Then $t \in R$ and $t \notin \mathfrak{p}$. It suffices to show that $t \in \mathfrak{c}(R)$. So let $\alpha \in R'$ be given. Then $\psi_i(\alpha) \in R_i'$ and hence $\psi_i(r\alpha) = \psi_i(r)\psi_i(\alpha) \in R_i$ because $\psi_i(r) \in \mathfrak{c}(R_i)$. Therefore there exists $r' \in R$ such that $\psi_i(r\alpha) = \psi_i(r')$, i.e., $\psi_i(r\alpha - r') = 0$. Let $s' = r's$. Then $s' \in R$ and $\psi_i(t\alpha - s') = \psi_i(r\alpha - r')\psi_i(s) = 0$. Also $\psi_j(t\alpha - s') = 0$ for all $j \neq i$ because then $\psi_j(t\alpha - s') = \psi_j(r\alpha - r')\psi_j(s)$ and $\psi_j(s) = \varphi_j(s) = 0$. Therefore $t\alpha - s' = 0$, i.e., $t\alpha = s' \in R$.

(19.22) *For $i = 1,\ldots, u$, let R_i be a nonnull ring, let $\mathfrak{L}_i$ be the total quotient ring of R_i, and let R_i' be the integral closure of R_i in $\mathfrak{L}_i$. Then $R_1' \oplus\ldots\oplus R_u'$ is the integral closure of $R_1 \oplus\ldots\oplus R_u$ in $\mathfrak{L}_1 \oplus\ldots\oplus \mathfrak{L}_u$; hence in particular $R_1 \oplus\ldots\oplus R_u$ is normal $\Leftrightarrow R_i$ is normal for $i = 1,\ldots, u$.*

PROOF. Let $p_i\colon \mathfrak{L}_1 \oplus\ldots\oplus \mathfrak{L}_u \to \mathfrak{L}_i$ be the natural projection and let $q_i\colon \mathfrak{L}_i \to \mathfrak{L}_1 \oplus\ldots\oplus \mathfrak{L}_u$ be the natural injection. Let $\alpha = (\alpha_1,\ldots, \alpha_u) \in \mathfrak{L}_1 \oplus\ldots\oplus \mathfrak{L}_u$ be given. Now $p_i(R_1 \oplus\ldots\oplus R_u) = R_i$ and hence if α is integral over $R_1 \oplus\ldots\oplus R_u$ then $p_i(\alpha) = \alpha_i$ is integral over R_i, i.e., $\alpha_i \in R_i'$ for $i = 1,\ldots, u$, and hence $\alpha \in R_1' \oplus\ldots\oplus R_u'$. Conversely, if $\alpha_i \in R_i'$ for some i, then there exists an integer n and elements $r_1,\ldots, r_n \in R_i$ such that

$$\alpha_i^n + \sum_{j=1}^{n} r_j \alpha_i^{n-j} = 0;$$

and then

$$(q_i(\alpha_i))^n + \sum_{j=1}^{n} q_i(r_j)(q_i(\alpha_i))^{n-j} = 0, \qquad q_i(r_j) \in R_1 \oplus\ldots\oplus R_u;$$

and hence $q_i(\alpha_i)$ is integral over $R_1 \oplus\ldots\oplus R_u$. Now $\alpha = q_1(\alpha_1) + \ldots + q_u(\alpha_u)$, and consequently, if $\alpha \in R_1' \oplus\ldots\oplus R_u'$ then $q_1(\alpha_1),\ldots, q_u(\alpha_u)$ are all integral over $R_1 \oplus\ldots\oplus R_u$ and hence α is integral over $R_1 \oplus\ldots\oplus R_u$.

(19.23) *Let R be a nonnull noetherian ring such that* $\operatorname{rad}_R\{0\} = \{0\}$. *Let $\mathfrak{p}_1,\ldots, \mathfrak{p}_u$ be the distinct prime ideals of $\{0\}$ in R, let $\mathfrak{L}$ be the total quotient ring of R, and let R' be the integral closure of R in $\mathfrak{L}$. Let $\varphi_i\colon R \to R_i$ be a ring epimorphism whose kernel is $\mathfrak{p}_i$, let $\mathfrak{L}_i$ be the quotient field of R_i, and let R_i' be the integral closure of R_i in $\mathfrak{L}_i$. By* (18.9.2), *φ_i has a unique extension $\psi_i\colon \mathfrak{L} \to \mathfrak{L}_i$ to $\mathfrak{L}$, and $\psi_1 \oplus\ldots\oplus \psi_u\colon \mathfrak{L} \to \mathfrak{L}_1 \oplus\ldots\oplus \mathfrak{L}_u$ is an isomorphism. Let $q_i\colon \mathfrak{L}_i \to \mathfrak{L}_1 \oplus\ldots\oplus \mathfrak{L}_u$ be the natural injection.*

Assume that R_i' is a finite R_i-module for $i = 1,\dots, u$, and take any finite number of elements $\beta_{i1},\dots, \beta_{iv_i}$ in R_i' which generate R_i' as an R_i-module. Let $\alpha_{ik} = (\psi_1 \oplus\dots\oplus \psi_u)^{-1}(q_i(\beta_{ik}))$. Then the $v_1 +\dots+ v_u$ elements α_{ik} generate R' as an R-module and hence R' is a finite R-module. Furthermore $\psi_1 \oplus\dots\oplus \psi_u(R') = R_1' \oplus\dots\oplus R_u'$, i.e., $R' = \bigcap_{i=1}^{u} \psi_i^{-1}(R_i')$, i.e., for any $r \in \mathfrak{L}$ we have that: r is integral over $R \Leftrightarrow \psi_i(r)$ is integral over R_i for $i = 1,\dots, u$.

PROOF. Let $R^* = (\psi_1 \oplus\dots\oplus \psi_u)^{-1}(R_1' \oplus\dots\oplus R_u')$. Obviously $\psi_i(R') \subset R_i'$ for $i = 1,\dots, u$, i.e., $R' \subset R^*$. All the elements α_{ik} are in R^* and $\psi_j(\alpha_{ik}) = 0$ for all $j \neq i$. Given any element α in R^* we can write

$$\psi_i(\alpha) = \sum_{j=1}^{v_i} \beta_{ij}\psi_i(a_{ij}) \qquad \text{with} \qquad a_{ij} \in R, \qquad \text{for} \qquad i = 1,\dots, u,$$

and then setting

$$\alpha' = \sum_{i=1}^{u} \sum_{j=1}^{v_i} \alpha_{ij}a_{ij}$$

we have that $\psi_i(\alpha) = \psi_i(\alpha')$ for $i = 1,\dots, u$, and hence $\alpha = \alpha'$. This shows that the $v_1 +\dots+ v_u$ elements α_{ik} generate R^* as an R-module, and hence R^* is a finite R-module. Therefore R^* is integral over R, i.e., $R^* \subset R'$, and hence $R' = R^*$. The rest is now obvious.

(19.24) *Let R be a nonnull noetherian ring. Let $\mathfrak{p}_1,\dots, \mathfrak{p}_u$ be the prime ideals of $\{0\}$ in R, let $\mathfrak{L}$ be the total quotient ring of R, and let R' be the integral closure of R in $\mathfrak{L}$. Let $\varphi_i\colon R \to R_i = R/\mathfrak{p}_i$ be the natural epimorphism, let $\mathfrak{L}_i$ be the quotient field of R_i, and let R_i' be the integral closure of R_i in $\mathfrak{L}_i$. Let Ω be the set of all prime ideals in R of height one. For any $\mathfrak{p} \in \Omega$ let $f_\mathfrak{p}$ be the natural homomorphism of $\mathfrak{L}$ into the total quotient ring of $R_\mathfrak{p}$. Assume that*

i) $\mathrm{rad}_R\{0\} = \{0\}$;
ii) *R_i' is a finite R_i-module for $i = 1,\dots, u$;*
iii) *$\Omega \neq \emptyset$ and $R_\mathfrak{p}$ is normal for all $\mathfrak{p} \in \Omega$;*[5] *and*
iv) *R contains a subring S such that S is a normal integral domain, R is integral over S, and every nonzero element in S is a nonzerodivisor in R.*[6]

Then $R' = \bigcap_{\mathfrak{p}\in\Omega} f_\mathfrak{p}^{-1}(R_\mathfrak{p})$.

[6] The last assumption is equivalent to saying that $S \cap \mathfrak{p}_i = \{0\}$ for $i = 1,\dots, u$.

PROOF. Let $\Omega_i = \{\mathfrak{p} \in \Omega : \mathfrak{p}_i \subset \mathfrak{p}\}$. Given $\mathfrak{p} \in \Omega$, $R_\mathfrak{p}$ is an integral domain and hence $\mathfrak{p} \in \Omega_i$ for exactly one value of i; i.e., $\Omega = \bigcup_{i=1}^{u} \Omega_i$ and $\Omega_i \cap \Omega_j = \emptyset$ for all $i \neq j$. Relabel $\mathfrak{p}_1, \ldots, \mathfrak{p}_u$ so that $\Omega_i \neq \emptyset$ for $i \leqq v$ and $\Omega_i = \emptyset$ for $i > v$. By assumption $\Omega \neq \emptyset$ and hence $v > 0$. By (19.23), φ_i has a unique extension $\psi_i : \mathfrak{L} \to \mathfrak{L}_i$ to $\mathfrak{L}$, and $R' = \bigcap_{i=1}^{u} \psi_i^{-1}(R_i')$. For $i > v$, $R_i = R_i' = \mathfrak{L}_i$ and hence

$$R' = \bigcap_{i=1}^{v} \psi_i^{-1}(R_i').$$

Also obviously

$$\bigcap_{\mathfrak{p} \in \Omega} f_\mathfrak{p}^{-1}(R_\mathfrak{p}) = \bigcap_{i=1}^{v} \left[\bigcap_{\mathfrak{p} \in \Omega_i} f_\mathfrak{p}^{-1}(R_\mathfrak{p}) \right].$$

Hence it suffices to show that

$$\bigcap_{\mathfrak{p} \in \Omega_i} f_\mathfrak{p}^{-1}(R_\mathfrak{p}) = \psi_i^{-1}(R_i') \qquad \text{for all} \qquad i \leqq v.$$

So let $i \leqq v$ be given. For any $\mathfrak{p} \in \Omega_i$, we have $j_R[\mathfrak{p}] = \mathfrak{p}_i$ and hence $f_\mathfrak{p} = \psi_i$ and $R_\mathfrak{p} = (R_i)_{\varphi_i(\mathfrak{p})}$, and hence

$$f_\mathfrak{p}^{-1}(R_\mathfrak{p}) = \psi_i^{-1}((R_i)_{\varphi_i(\mathfrak{p})}).$$

Now R_i is a noetherian integral domain which is not a field, R_i' is noetherian because it is a finite R_i-module, $\varphi_i(S)$ is a normal subring of R_i over which R_i is integral, and $\{\varphi_i(\mathfrak{p}) : \mathfrak{p} \in \Omega_i\}$ is the set of all prime ideals in R_i of height one. Consequently, applying (19.18) to R_i we get that

$$R_i' = \bigcap_{\mathfrak{p} \in \Omega_i} (R_i)_{\varphi_i(\mathfrak{p})}.$$

Therefore

$$\bigcap_{\mathfrak{p} \in \Omega_i} f_\mathfrak{p}^{-1}(R_\mathfrak{p}) = \psi_i^{-1}(R_i').$$

(19.25) *Let R be a nonnull noetherian ring such that* $\operatorname{rad}_R\{0\} = \{0\}$. *Let $\mathfrak{p}_1, \ldots, \mathfrak{p}_u$ be the distinct prime ideals of $\{0\}$ in R, let $\mathfrak{L}$ be the total quotient ring of R, and let R' be the integral closure of R in $\mathfrak{L}$. Let $\varphi_i : R \to R_i$ be a ring epimorphism whose kernel is $\mathfrak{p}_i$, and let $\mathfrak{L}_i$ be the quotient field of R_i. By* (18.9.2), *φ_i has a unique extension $\psi_i : \mathfrak{L} \to \mathfrak{L}_i$ for $i = 1, \ldots, u$, and $\psi_1 \oplus \ldots \oplus \psi_u : \mathfrak{L} \to \mathfrak{L}_1 \oplus \ldots \oplus \mathfrak{L}_u$ is an isomorphism. Let S be a subring of R such that S is an integral domain and every nonzero element in S is a nonzerodivisor in R.*[6] *Then the quotient field $\mathfrak{K}$ of S can be considered to be* *a subring of* $\mathfrak{L}$. *Let* $\mathfrak{K}_i = \psi_i(\mathfrak{K})$. *Then* $\mathfrak{K}_i$ *is the quotient field of* $\psi_i(S)$, *and* $\mathfrak{K} \cap \operatorname{Ker} \psi_i = \{0\}$, *i.e.,* ψ_i *maps* $\mathfrak{K}$ *isomorphically onto* $\mathfrak{K}_i$. *Now assume that* R *is a finite* S*-module.*[7] *Then we have the following.*

1) $[\mathfrak{L}: \mathfrak{K}] = \sum_{i=1}^{u} [\mathfrak{L}_i: \mathfrak{K}_i] < \infty$.[8]

2) $\mathfrak{L} = \mathfrak{K}[R]$.

3) *Let* $\alpha_1, \ldots, \alpha_\lambda$ *be any finite number of elements in* R. *If* $\alpha_1, \ldots, \alpha_\lambda$ *generate* R *as an* S*-module, then they generate* $\mathfrak{L}$ *as a* $\mathfrak{K}$*-module. If* $\alpha_1, \ldots, \alpha_\lambda$ *are linearly independent over* S,[9] *then they are linearly independent over* $\mathfrak{K}$. *If* $\alpha_1, \ldots, \alpha_\lambda$ *generate* R *as an* S*-module and are linearly independent over* S, *then* $\lambda = \sum_{i=1}^{u} [\mathfrak{L}_i: \mathfrak{K}_i]$.

4) *Suppose that* S *is normal and there exists a finite number of elements* $\zeta_1, \ldots, \zeta_m, \omega$ *in* R *and* $0 \neq s \in S$ *such that* $R = S[\zeta_1, \ldots, \zeta_m]$ *and* $s\zeta_j \in S[\omega]$ *for* $j = 1, \ldots, m$. *Let* $F_i(T)$ *be the (unique) monic element in* $\mathfrak{K}[T]$ *such that applying* ψ_i *to the coefficients of* $F_i(T)$ *we get the minimal monic polynomial of* $\psi_i(\omega)$ *over* $\mathfrak{K}_i$, *and let* Δ *be the* T*-discriminant of* $F_1(T) \ldots F_u(T)$. *Then:* $\mathfrak{L} = \mathfrak{K}[\omega]$; $F_1(T), \ldots, F_u(T)$ *are pairwise coprime in* $\mathfrak{K}[T]$; $F_i(T) \in S[T]$ *for* $i = 1, \ldots, u$ *and hence* $\Delta \in S$; *and for any* $r' \in R'$ *we have* $\Delta r' \in S[\omega]$ *and hence* $\Delta \in \mathfrak{c}(R)$.

Proof of 1). Since R is a finite S-module, R_i is a finite $\psi_i(S)$-module. Hence $[\mathfrak{L}_i: \mathfrak{K}_i] < \infty$. Take a vector space basis $\beta_{i1}, \ldots, \beta_{i\lambda_i}$ of $\mathfrak{L}_i$ over $\mathfrak{K}_i$ where $\lambda_i = [\mathfrak{L}_i: \mathfrak{K}_i]$. Let $q_i: \mathfrak{L}_i \to \mathfrak{L}_1 \oplus \ldots \oplus \mathfrak{L}_u$ be the natural injection, and let $\alpha_{ik} = (\psi_i \oplus \ldots \oplus \psi_u)^{-1}(q_i(\beta_{ik}))$. Then the $\lambda_1 + \ldots + \lambda_u$ elements are in $\mathfrak{L}$ and $\psi_j(\alpha_{ik}) = 0$ for all $j \neq i$. Given any $\alpha \in \mathfrak{L}$ we can write

$$\psi_i(\alpha) = \sum_{k=1}^{\lambda_i} \beta_{ik} \psi_i(a_{ik}) \qquad \text{with} \qquad a_{ik} \in \mathfrak{K}, \qquad \text{for} \qquad i = 1, \ldots, u,$$

and then setting

$$\alpha' = \sum_{i=1}^{u} \sum_{k=1}^{\lambda_i} \alpha_{ik} a_{ik}$$

[7] Equivalently: R is integral over S and there exists a finite number of elements $r_1, \ldots, r_n$ in R such that $R = S[r_1, \ldots, r_n]$.

[8] Here the dots denote vector space dimension.

[9] That is, $a_1\alpha_1 + \ldots + a_\lambda\alpha_\lambda = 0$ with $a_1, \ldots, a_\lambda \in S \Rightarrow a_1 = \ldots = a_\lambda = 0$.

we get that $\psi_i(\alpha) = \psi_i(\alpha')$ for $i = 1,\dots, u$, and hence $\alpha = \alpha'$. Furthermore, if a_{ik} are any elements in $\mathfrak{K}$ such that

$$\sum_{i=1}^{u} \sum_{k=1}^{\lambda_i} \alpha_{ik} a_{ik} = 0$$

then for $i = 1,\dots, u$ we get that

$$\sum_{k=1}^{\lambda} \beta_{ik} \psi_i(a_{ik}) = 0$$

and hence $\psi_i(a_{ik}) = 0$ for all k and hence $a_{ik} = 0$ for all k because $\mathfrak{K} \cap (\operatorname{Ker} \psi_i) = \{0\}$. Thus the $\lambda_1 + \dots + \lambda_u$ elements α_{ik} form a vector space basis of $\mathfrak{L}$ over $\mathfrak{K}$, and hence $[\mathfrak{L} : \mathfrak{K}] = \lambda_1 + \dots + \lambda_u$.

Proof of 2). Let $\alpha \in \mathfrak{L}$ be given. Then $\psi_i(\alpha)$ is algebraic over $\mathfrak{K}_i$. Let $D_i(T) \in \mathfrak{K}[T]$ be such that applying ψ_i to the coefficients of $D_i(T)$ we get the minimal monic polynomial of $\psi_i(\alpha)$ over $\mathfrak{K}_i$. Then $\psi_i(D_i(\alpha)) = 0$. Let

$$D(T) = D_1(T) \dots D_u(T) \in \mathfrak{K}[T].$$

Then $\psi_i(D(\alpha)) = 0$ for $i = 1,\dots, u$, and hence $D(\alpha) = 0$. Assume that α is a nonzerodivisor in $\mathfrak{L}$. Then $\psi_i(\alpha) \neq 0$ and hence $D_i(T)$ and T are coprime in $\mathfrak{K}[T]$ for $i = 1,\dots, u$. Consequently we can write

$$TA(T) + D(T)B(T) = 1 \qquad \text{with} \qquad A(T), B(T) \in \mathfrak{K}[T].$$

Therefore $\alpha A(\alpha) = 1$, i.e., $(1/\alpha) = A(\alpha) \in \mathfrak{K}[\alpha]$. In particular, if $\alpha \in R$ and α is a nonzerodivisor in R, then α is a nonzerodivisor in $\mathfrak{L}$ and hence $(1/\alpha) \in \mathfrak{K}[\alpha]$. Therefore $\mathfrak{L} = \mathfrak{K}[R]$.

Proof of 3). Assume that $\alpha_1,\dots, \alpha_\lambda$ generate R as an S-module, i.e., $R = \alpha_1 S + \dots + \alpha_\lambda S$. Given $\beta \in \mathfrak{L}$, by 2) we can write $\beta = E(\gamma_1,\dots, \gamma_\mu)$ with $E(T_1,\dots, T_\mu) \in \mathfrak{K}[T_1,\dots, T_\mu]$ and $\gamma_1,\dots, \gamma_\mu \in R$. We can take $0 \neq s \in S$ such that

$$sE(T_1,\dots, T_\mu) = E^*(T_1,\dots, T_\mu) \in S[T_1,\dots, T_\mu]$$

and then

$$s\beta = E^*(\gamma_1,\dots, \gamma_\mu) \in S[\gamma_1,\dots, \gamma_\mu] \subset \alpha_1 S + \dots + \alpha_\lambda S.$$

Hence $\beta \in \alpha_1 \mathfrak{K} + \dots + \alpha_\lambda \mathfrak{K}$. This shows that $\alpha_1,\dots, \alpha_\lambda$ generate $\mathfrak{L}$ as a $\mathfrak{K}$-module.

Assume that $\alpha_1,\dots, \alpha_\lambda$ are linearly independent over S. Let $b_1,\dots, b_\lambda \in \mathfrak{K}$ be such that $b_1\alpha_1 + \dots + b_\lambda\alpha_\lambda = 0$. We can write $b_i = a_i/c$ with $0 \neq c \in S$ and $b_1,\dots, b_\lambda \in S$. Then $a_1\alpha_1 + \dots + a_\lambda\alpha_\lambda = 0$ and hence $a_1 = \dots = a_\lambda = 0$, i.e., $b_1 = \dots = b_\lambda = 0$. Therefore $\alpha_1, \dots, \alpha_\lambda$ are linearly independent over $\mathfrak{K}$.

This proves the first two assertions and now the last assertion follows from them by 1).

Proof of 4). Since $R = S[\zeta_1, \dots, \zeta_m]$, by 2) we get that $\mathfrak{L} = \mathfrak{K}[\zeta_1, \dots, \zeta_m]$. Hence, given $\alpha \in \mathfrak{L}$ we can write $\alpha = E(\zeta_1, \dots, \zeta_m)$ where $E(T_1, \dots, T_m)$ is a polynomial of some degree n in $T_1, \dots, T_m$ with coefficients in $\mathfrak{K}$, and then we can find $0 \neq s' \in S$ such that

$$s'E(T_1, \dots, T_m) = E^*(T_1, \dots, T_m) \in S[T_1, \dots, T_m].$$

Now $s\zeta_j \in S[\omega]$ for $j = 1, \dots, m$, and hence

$$s^n s' \alpha = s^n E^*(\zeta_1, \dots, \zeta_m) \in S[\omega].$$

Now $0 \neq s^n s' \in S$, and hence $\alpha \in \mathfrak{K}[\omega]$. This shows that $\mathfrak{L} = \mathfrak{K}[\omega]$.

Let $\lambda_i = [\mathfrak{L}_i : \mathfrak{K}_i]$ and $\lambda = \lambda_1 + \dots + \lambda_u$. Then $\lambda = [\mathfrak{L} : \mathfrak{K}]$ by 1). Let μ_i be the degree of $F_i(T)$ in T. Then $F_i(T)$ is irreducible in $\mathfrak{K}[T]$ and

$$\mu_i = [\mathfrak{K}_i(\psi_i(\omega)) : \mathfrak{K}_i] \leqq \lambda_i.$$

Let $F(T)$ be the product of the distinct elements of the set $\{F_1(T), \dots, F_u(T)\}$. Then $\psi_i(F(\omega)) = 0$ for $i = 1, \dots, u$, and hence $F(\omega) = 0$. Let μ be the degree of $F(T)$ in T. Given $\alpha \in \mathfrak{L} = \mathfrak{K}[\omega]$ we can write $\alpha = D(\omega)$ with $D(T) \in \mathfrak{K}[T]$. By division algorithm, we can write

$$D(T) = A(T)F(T) + B(T) \qquad \text{with} \qquad A(T), B(T) \in \mathfrak{K}[T],$$

where $B(T)$ is the degree $< \mu$ in T, and then $\alpha = B(\omega)$. This shows that $1, \omega, \dots, \omega^{\mu-1}$ generate $\mathfrak{L}$ as a vector space over $\mathfrak{K}$. Therefore we must have $\mu \geqq \lambda$. Consequently: $\mu = \lambda$; $\mu_i = \lambda_i$ and $\mathfrak{K}_i(\psi_i(\omega)) = \mathfrak{L}_i$ for $i = 1, \dots, u$; $F_1(T), \dots, F_u(T)$ are all distinct and hence pairwise coprime in $\mathfrak{K}[T]$; and $F(T) = F_1(T) \dots F_u(T)$.

Now $\omega \in R$ and R is integral over S. Therefore ω is integral over S and hence $\psi_i(\omega)$ is integral over $\psi_i(S)$. Since $\psi_i(S)$ is normal, the minimal monic polynomial of $\psi_i(\omega)$ over $\mathfrak{K}_i$ must have all its coefficients in $\psi_i(S)$. Therefore $F_i(T) \in S[T]$ for $i = 1, \dots, u$. Let

$$\Delta' = \Delta_{F_1} \dots \Delta_{F_u}$$

and

$$\delta = \prod_{i=1}^{u} \prod_{k=i+1}^{u} \delta_{F_i, F_k}.$$

Then Δ' and δ are elements in S and by (17.10.5) we get

1°) $$\Delta = \Delta' \delta^2.$$

By (17.10.6) we can find $V_1(T),\ldots, V_u(T)$ in $S[T]$ such that

$$\delta = \sum_{i=1}^{u} F_1(T)\ldots F_{i-1}(T)V_i(T)F_{i+1}(T)\ldots F_u(T).$$

Let $s_i = V_i(\omega)$. Then $s_1,\ldots, s_u$ are elements in $S[\omega]$ and

$$2^\circ)\qquad \delta = \sum_{i=1}^{u} F_1(\omega)\ldots F_{i-1}(\omega)s_i F_{i+1}(\omega)\ldots F_u(\omega).$$

Let $r' \in R'$ be given. Then r' is integral over S because R is integral over S. Therefore $\psi_i(r')$ is integral over $\psi_i(S)$. Now $\psi_i(\Delta_{F_i})$ is the T-discriminant of the minimal monic polynomial of $\psi_i(\omega)$ over $\mathfrak{R}_i$ and hence $\psi_i(\Delta_{F_i})\psi_i(r') \in \psi_i(S[\omega])$ by (17.10.7). Now Δ_{F_i} divides Δ' in S and hence $\psi_i(\Delta')\psi_i(r') \in \psi_i(S[\omega])$, i.e., there exists $r_i \in S[\omega]$ such that

$$3^\circ)\qquad \psi_i(\Delta' r' - r_i) = 0.$$

Let

$$4^\circ)\qquad r = \sum_{i=1}^{u} F_1(\omega)\ldots F_{i-1}(\omega)s_i r_i F_{i+1}(\omega)\ldots F_u(\omega).$$

Then $r \in S[\omega]$. Now $\psi_i(F_i(\omega)) = 0$ and hence $\psi_i(\Delta'\delta r' - r) = 0$ by (2°, 3°, 4°). This being so for $i = 1,\ldots, u$, we get that $\Delta'\delta r' - r = 0$. Therefore $\Delta'\delta r' = r \in S[\omega]$ and hence $\Delta r' \in S[\omega]$ by 1°).

§20. HENSELIAN RINGS

Let $(R, \mathfrak{m})$ be a quasilocal ring. Let $\varphi: R \to K = R/\mathfrak{m}$ be the natural epimorphism. Let y be an indeterminate. Then φ uniquely extends to an epimorphism $\psi: R[y] \to K[y]$ such that $y \to y$. The definition given in §12A is thus. R is *Henselian* provided the following condition holds.

(I) *If $F(y)$ is a monic polynomial in $R[y]$ and $\psi F(y) = G_1(y)\ldots G_p(y)$ where $G_1(y),\ldots, G_p(y)$ are pairwise coprime monic polynomials in $K[y]$, then $F(y) = F_1(y)\ldots F_p(y)$ where $F_i(y)$ is a monic polynomial in $R[y]$ with $\psi F_i(y) = G_i(y)$ for $i = 1,\ldots, p$.*

Let us say that R is *weakly Henselian* provided the following condition holds.

(II) *If $F(y)$ is a monic polynomial in $R[y]$ and $\psi F(y) = (y + b)y^e$, $0 \neq b \in K$, $e > 0$, then $F(y) = (y + a)F^*(y)$ where $a \in R$ with $\varphi a = b$ and $F^*(y)$ is a monic polynomial in $R[y]$ with $\psi F^*(y) = y^e$.*

It is obvious that if R is a Henselian integral domain then R is weakly Henselian. In §12A, as a direct consequence of the Preparation Theorem we have proved the following: If R is either a complete Hausdorff quasilocal integral domain or $R = K[\langle x,..., x_n \rangle]$, then R is weakly Henselian; if furthermore K is algebraically closed then R is Henselian. In this section, among other things, we shall prove that if R is a normal weakly Henselian quasilocal integral domain then R is Henselian.

(20.1) *Let $\mu: R \to S$ be an epimorphism where S is a nonnull ring. If R is Henselian then so is S.*

PROOF. $\mu(\mathfrak{m})$ is the maximal ideal in S and hence $\varphi = \alpha \circ \mu$ where $\alpha: S \to K$ is the natural epimorphism. μ and α uniquely extend, respectively, to $\nu: R[y] \to S[y]$ and $\beta: S[y] \to K[y]$ so that $y \to y$. Now $\psi = \beta \circ \nu$ and hence our assertion follows trivially.

(20.2) *Assume that R is a Henselian integral domain. Let R' be an overring of R such that R' is an integral domain and R' is integral over R. Then R' is quasilocal.*

PROOF. By (19.1.1), $\mathfrak{m}R' \neq R'$ and hence $\mathrm{rad}_{R'}\mathfrak{m}R' \neq R'$. Hence it suffices to show that every nonunit in R' is contained in $\mathrm{rad}_{R'}\mathfrak{m}R'$. Let b be a nonunit in R'. Let $F(y) = y^d + a_1y^{d-1} + ... + a_d$ be a monic polynomial of least degree $d > 0$ in y with coefficients a_i in R such that $F(b) = 0$. Since $a_d = -b(b^{d-1} + ... + a_{d-1})$ and b is a nonunit in R', we get that a_d is a nonunit in R, i.e., $a_d \in \mathfrak{m}$. Suppose if possible that $a_i \notin \mathfrak{m}$ for some i. Take e maximum such that $a_e \notin \mathfrak{m}$. Then

$$\psi F(y) = y^{d-e}(y^e + \varphi(a_1)y^{e-1} + ... + \varphi(a_e)), \qquad \varphi(a_e) \neq 0,$$

is a factorization of $\psi F(y)$ into two coprime monic factors in $K[y]$. R being Henselian, we can write $F(y) = F_1(y)F_2(y)$ where $F_1(y)$ and $F_2(y)$ are monic polynomials of degrees $d - e$ and e in y with coefficients in R. This gives

$$0 = F(b) = F_1(b)F_2(b).$$

Since R' is an integral domain, we must have either $F_1(b) = 0$ or $F_2(b) = 0$. Now $0 < e < d$ and $0 < d - e < d$. Contradiction to the minimality of d. Therefore $a_i \in \mathfrak{m}$ for all i. Consequently

$$b^d = -(a_1b^{d-1} + ... + a_d) \in \mathfrak{m}R',$$

and hence $b \in \mathrm{rad}_{R'}\mathfrak{m}R'$.

(20.3) *Assume that R is a Henselian local ring. Let $\alpha: R \to R^*$ be an R-algebra such that R^* is a finite R-module, and let $\beta: R^* \to R'$, R' nonnull, be an R^*-algebra such that R' is a finite R^*-module. Then R' is isomorphic to a direct sum of local rings.*

PROOF. Let $\gamma = \beta \circ \alpha$. Then R' is an overring of $\gamma(R)$ and R' is a finite $\gamma(R)$-module. By (20.1), $\gamma(R)$ is a Henselian local ring. Upon replacing R by $\gamma(R)$ we may thus assume that R' is an overring of R and R' is a finite R-module. By (19.8), R' is a semilocal ring. In virtue of (18.8), it suffices to show that any prime ideal in R' is contained in only one maximal ideal in R'. Let, if possible, $\mathfrak{p}'$ be a prime ideal in R' which is contained in more than one maximal ideal in R'. Let $\mathfrak{p} = \mathfrak{p}' \cap R$. Let $\bar{R}' = R'/\mathfrak{p}'$ and $\bar{R} = R/\mathfrak{p}$. Then $\bar{R}'$ is not a quasilocal ring, $\bar{R}'$ is an overring of $\bar{R}$, $\bar{R}'$ is integral over $\bar{R}$, $\bar{R}'$ and $\bar{R}$ are both integral domains, and $\bar{R}$ is Henselian by (20.1). Contradiction to (20.2).

(20.4) *Assume that R is a normal quasilocal integral domain and that R is not Henselian. Then there exists an overring R' of R such that R' is an integral domain, R' is a finite R-module, and R' is not quasilocal. Consequently R' is not isomorphic to a direct sum of local rings.*

PROOF. Let $F(y)$ be a monic polynomial of least positive degree in y with coefficients in R for which condition (I) does not hold. Then $\psi F(y) = G_1(y)G_2(y)$ where $G_1(y)$ and $G_2(y)$ are coprime monic polynomials of positive degrees in y with coefficients in K and

1°) $F(y)$ cannot be written in the form $F(y) = F_1(y)F_2(y)$ with monic $F_1(y)$, $F_2(y)$ in $R[y]$ such that $\psi F_i(y) = G_i(y)$ for $i = 1, 2$.

Suppose if possible that $F(y)$ is reducible in $\mathfrak{K}[y]$ where $\mathfrak{K}$ is the quotient field of R. Since R is normal, we can then write $F(y) = F'(y)F^*(y)$ where $F'(y)$ and $F^*(y)$ are monic polynomials of positive degrees in y with coefficients in R. Then

$$\psi F'(y)\psi F^*(y) = G_1(y)G_2(y).$$

Consequently

$$G_i(y) = G_i'(y)G_i^*(y), \qquad (i = 1, 2),$$

where $G_1'(y)$, $G_1^*(y)$, $G_2'(y)$, $G_2^*(y)$ are monic polynomials in $K[y]$ and

$$\psi F'(y) = G_1'(y)G_2'(y), \qquad \psi F^*(y) = G_1^*(y)G_2^*(y).$$

Now G_1 and G_2 are coprime and hence G_1' and G_2' are coprime and G_1^* and G_2^* are coprime. In view of 1°) it follows that condition (I) fails either for F' or for F^*. Since the degree of F is minimal, we have a contradiction. Therefore $F(y)$ is irreducible in $\mathfrak{K}[y]$.

Let a be a root of $F(y) = 0$ in some algebraic closure of $\mathfrak{K}$. Let $R' = R[a]$. Then R' is a finite R-module. We claim that R' is not quasilocal, i.e., R'

contains more than one maximal ideal. In view of (19.8), this is equivalent to saying that $\mathfrak{m}R'$ is not primary. Consider the diagram

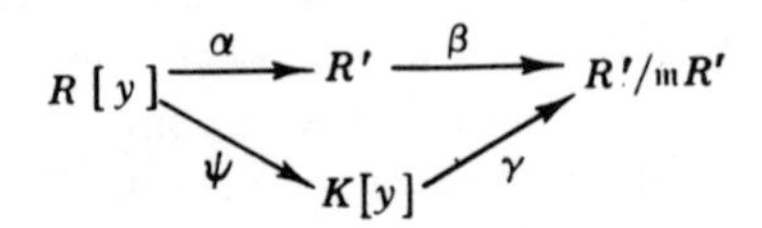

where α is the R-epimorphism which maps y onto a, and β is the natural epimorphism. Obviously $\operatorname{Ker}\alpha = \{F(y)\}R[y]$ and hence $\operatorname{Ker}\beta\circ\alpha = (\{F(y)\} \cup \mathfrak{m})R[y]$. Now $\operatorname{Ker}\psi = \mathfrak{m}R[y]$ and hence there exists a unique epimorphism γ which makes the above diagram commutative, and we have that $\operatorname{Ker}\gamma = \{\psi F(y)\}K[y]$. Now

$$\begin{aligned} &\mathfrak{m}R' \text{ is primary} \\ \Leftrightarrow &\{0\} \text{ is primary in } R'/\mathfrak{m}R' \\ \Leftrightarrow &\operatorname{Ker}\gamma \text{ is primary in } K[y]. \end{aligned}$$

Since $\psi F(y) = G_1(y)G_2(y)$ where $G_1(y)$ and $G_2(y)$ are coprime, we deduce that $\operatorname{Ker}\gamma$ is not primary. Therefore $\mathfrak{m}R'$ is not primary.

Using Galois theory of quasilocal rings[1] we next prove

(20.5) *Let R be a quasilocal integral domain such that R is normal and weakly Henselian. Then R is Henselian.*

PROOF. Suppose that R is not Henselian. Let R' be as in (20.4). Let $\mathfrak{K}$ and $\mathfrak{K}'$ be the quotient fields of R and R', respectively. Let $\mathfrak{K}''$ be a finite normal extension of $\mathfrak{K}$ containing $\mathfrak{K}'$ and let R'' be the integral closure of R in $\mathfrak{K}''$. Then R'' is integral over R'. Since R' contains more than one maximal ideal, so does R''. Let $\mathfrak{K}^*$ be the maximal separable extension of $\mathfrak{K}$ in $\mathfrak{K}''$ and let R^* be the inegral closure of R in $\mathfrak{K}^*$. Since R'' contains more than one maximal ideal, so does R^*. Let $\mathfrak{m}^*$ be a maximal ideal in R^*. Let G be the Galois group of $\mathfrak{K}^*$ over $\mathfrak{K}$. Let H be the splitting group of $\mathfrak{m}^*$ over $\mathfrak{K}$, i.e., $H = \{g \in G : g\mathfrak{m}^* = \mathfrak{m}^*\}$. Let $G = H + Hg_1 + \ldots + Hg_e$ be a right coset representation of G with respect to the subgroup H. Let $\mathfrak{m}_i^* = g_i\mathfrak{m}^*$. Then $\mathfrak{m}^*, \mathfrak{m}_1^*, \ldots, \mathfrak{m}_e^*$, $(e > 0)$, are exactly all the distinct maximal ideals in R^*. Let $\tilde{\mathfrak{K}}$ be the fixed field of H and let $\tilde{R} = R^* \cap \tilde{\mathfrak{K}}$. Let $\tilde{\mathfrak{m}} = \tilde{R} \cap \mathfrak{m}^*$, $\tilde{\mathfrak{m}}_i = \tilde{R} \cap \mathfrak{m}_i^*$. Then $\tilde{\mathfrak{m}}, \tilde{\mathfrak{m}}_1, \ldots, \tilde{\mathfrak{m}}_e$ are exactly all the maximal ideals in $\tilde{R}$ and $\tilde{\mathfrak{m}} \neq \tilde{\mathfrak{m}}_i$ for $i = 1, \ldots, e$.[2] We can find $c \in \tilde{R}$ such that $c \notin \tilde{\mathfrak{m}}$ and $c \in \tilde{\mathfrak{m}}_i$ for $i = 1, \ldots, e$. Let $c_i = g_i c$. Since $c \in \tilde{\mathfrak{K}}$, we know

[1] For results to be used from this theory, see Abhyankar [**1**: §7 and Proposition 1.25 of §3].

[2] $\tilde{\mathfrak{m}}_1, \ldots, \tilde{\mathfrak{m}}_e$ need not all be distinct.

that $c, c_1, \ldots, c_e$ are exactly all the $\mathfrak{K}$-conjugates of c. Given $i \leqq e$ we can find $j \leqq e$ such that $g_j^{-1} \in Hg_i$; and then $g_j^{-1}c = g_ic = c_i$; since $g_j^{-1}\tilde{\mathfrak{m}}_j = \tilde{\mathfrak{m}}$ and $c \in \tilde{\mathfrak{m}}_j$ we get that $c_i \in \tilde{\mathfrak{m}}$. Thus $c_i \in \tilde{\mathfrak{m}}$ and hence $c_i \neq c$ for $i = 1, \ldots, e$. Suppose if possible that $c_i = c_j$ for some $i \neq j$, i.e., $g_ic = g_jc$, i.e., $(g_ig_j^{-1})c = c$; now $g_ig_j^{-1} \in Hg_k$ for some k and hence $c = (g_ig_j^{-1})c = g_kc = c_k$ which contradicts what we have just proved.

Thus $c, c_1, \ldots, c_e$ are all exactly the *distinct* $\mathfrak{K}$-conjugates of c, $c \in \tilde{\mathfrak{K}}$, $c \notin \tilde{\mathfrak{m}}$, and $c_i \in \tilde{\mathfrak{m}}$ for $i = 1, \ldots, e$. Let $F(y) = y^{e+1} + a_1y^e + \ldots + a_e$ be the minimal monic polynomial of c over $\mathfrak{K}$. Then $a_1, \ldots, a_e \in R$; $a_1 \notin \mathfrak{m}$; and $a_i \in \tilde{\mathfrak{m}} \cap R = \mathfrak{m}$ for all $i > 1$. Therefore $\psi F(y) = (y + \varphi(a_1))y^e$, $e > 0$, $0 \neq \varphi(a_1) \in K$. Since $F(y)$ is irreducible in $R[y]$ we have reached a contradiction to the assumption that R is weakly Henselian.

We now summarize the above results in the following proposition.

(20.6) PROPOSITION.

1) *Every (nonnull) homomorphic image of a Henselian ring is Henselian.*

2) *Let R be a Henselian quasilocal integral domain and let R' be an overring of R such that R' is an integral domain and R' is integral over R. Then R' is quasilocal.*

3) *Let R be a Henselian local ring and let R^* be an R-algebra which is a finite R-module (for instance $R^* = R$). Then every nonnull R^*-algebra which is a finite R^*-module is isomorphic to a direct sum of local rings.*

4) *If R is a normal quasilocal integral domain then: R is Henselian $\Leftrightarrow$ every integral domain which is an overring of R and a finite R-module is quasilocal.*

5) HENSEL'S LEMMA. *Let R be either a complete Hausdorff quasilocal normal integral domain (this includes the case of $R = K[[x_1, \ldots, x_n]]$, K arbitrary), or $R = K[\langle x_1, \ldots, x_n \rangle]$, K arbitrary complete nondiscrete valued. Then R is Henselian.*

REMARK. In Zariski-Samuel [**2**: §7 of Chapter VIII] for the case when R is complete, a more general form of Hensel's lemma—known as the Bilinear Lemma—is proved and from it is deduced: i) Hensel's lemma, and the fact that ii) a complete semilocal ring is a direct sum of local rings. In our treatment we have preferred to deduce the analogous statements as corollaries of the Preparation Theorem. This has enabled us to include the case of $K[\langle x_1, \ldots, x_n \rangle]$. Although $K[\langle x_1, \ldots, x_n \rangle]$ is not complete, it does share many properties of complete local rings, exactly because it is Henselian.

§21. ORDER AND RANK IN LOCAL RINGS. REGULAR LOCAL RINGS

(21.1) DEFINITION. Let $(R, \mathfrak{m})$ be a local ring. For any nonempty subset A of R *we define*

$$\operatorname{ord}_R A = \max e \textit{ such that } A \subset \mathfrak{m}^e.$$

Note that:

$$\operatorname{ord}_R A = \operatorname{ord}_R AR; \quad \operatorname{ord}_R A = 0 \Leftrightarrow A \not\subset \mathfrak{m}; \quad \operatorname{ord}_R A = \infty \Leftrightarrow A = \{0\}.$$

In a natural way, $\mathfrak{m}/\mathfrak{m}^2$ can be considered to be a (finite dimensional) vector space over the field $R/\mathfrak{m}$. For $A \subset \mathfrak{m}$, $(AR + \mathfrak{m}^2)/\mathfrak{m}^2$ is a subspace of this vector space, and *we define*

$$\operatorname{rnk}_R A = \textit{vector space dimension of } (AR + \mathfrak{m}^2)/\mathfrak{m}^2 \textit{ over } R/\mathfrak{m}.$$

Note that $\operatorname{rnk}_R A = 0 \Leftrightarrow \operatorname{ord}_R A > 1$. Let $u_1, \ldots, u_p \in A \subset \mathfrak{m}$. In accordance with the usual situation in vector spaces, we shall say: $u_1, \ldots, u_p$ are *linearly independent* $\operatorname{mod} \mathfrak{m}^2 \Leftrightarrow [a_1 u_1 + \ldots + a_p u_p \in \mathfrak{m}^2$ with $a_i \in R \Rightarrow a_i \in \mathfrak{m}$ for $i = 1, \ldots, p]$; $u_1, \ldots, u_p$ *generate* $A \operatorname{mod} \mathfrak{m}^2 \Leftrightarrow [u \in A \Rightarrow$ there exist $a_1, \ldots, a_p \in R$ such that $u - a_1 u_1 - \ldots - a_p u_p \in \mathfrak{m}^2]$; $u_1, \ldots, u_p$ *form a basis of* $A \operatorname{mod} \mathfrak{m}^2 \Leftrightarrow [u_1, \ldots, u_p$ generate $A \operatorname{mod} \mathfrak{m}^2$ and are linearly independent $\operatorname{mod} \mathfrak{m}^2]$.

We define

$$\operatorname{emdim} R = \textit{embedding dimension of } R$$
$$= \operatorname{rnk}_R \mathfrak{m}.$$

By (17.4) it follows that a set of elements in $\mathfrak{m}$ generate $\mathfrak{m}$ as an ideal in R, if and only if, they generate $\mathfrak{m} \operatorname{mod} \mathfrak{m}^2$. Therefore we get the equality in 1) below and the inequality there follows from (17.2).

1) $\operatorname{emdim} R =$ *number of elements in any irredundant set of generators of* $\mathfrak{m}$ $\geqq \dim R$.

2) *For any proper ideal* $\mathfrak{a}$ *in* R *we have*: $\operatorname{rnk}_R \mathfrak{a} = \operatorname{emdim} R - \operatorname{emdim} R/\mathfrak{a}$.

PROOF. Let $\varphi: R \to \bar{R} = R/\mathfrak{a}$ be the natural epimorphism. Take a basis $u_1, \ldots, u_p$ of $\mathfrak{a} \operatorname{mod} \mathfrak{m}^2$. We can find $v_1, \ldots, v_q \in \mathfrak{m}$ such that $u_1, \ldots, u_p, v_1, \ldots, v_q$ is a basis of $\mathfrak{m} \operatorname{mod} \mathfrak{m}^2$. Obviously $\varphi(v_1), \ldots, \varphi(v_q)$ generate $\varphi(\mathfrak{m})$ and hence it suffices to show that they are linearly independent $\operatorname{mod} \varphi(\mathfrak{m})^2$. Let $\bar{b}_i$, $\bar{b}_{i_1 \ldots i_q}$ be any elements in $\bar{R}$ such that

$$\sum_{i=1}^{q} \bar{b}_i \varphi(v_i) = \sum_{i_1 + \ldots + i_q = 2} \bar{b}_{i_1 \ldots i_q} \varphi(v_1)^{i_1} \ldots \varphi(v_q)^{i_q}.$$

Fix elements b_i, $b_{i_1 \dots i_q}$ in R such that $\varphi(b_i) = \bar{b}_i$ and $\varphi(b_{i_1 \dots i_q}) = \bar{b}_{i_1 \dots i_q}$, and let

$$w = \sum_{i=1}^{q} b_i v_i - \sum_{i_1 + \dots + i_q = 2} b_{i_1 \dots i_q} v_1^{i_1} \dots v_q^{i_q}.$$

Then $w \in \mathfrak{a}$. Since $u_1, \dots, u_p$ form a basis of $\mathfrak{a}$ mod $\mathfrak{m}^2$, we can find elements $a_1, \dots, a_p$ in R such that

$$w - a_1 u_1 - \dots - a_p u_p \in \mathfrak{m}^2.$$

Since $u_1, \dots, u_p, v_1, \dots, v_q$ are linearly independent mod $\mathfrak{m}^2$, all the elements a_i, b_j must be in $\mathfrak{m}$; whence in particular $b_1, \dots, b_q \in \mathfrak{m}$. Therefore $\bar{b}_1, \dots, \bar{b}_q \in \varphi(\mathfrak{m})$. Thus $\varphi(v_1), \dots, \varphi(v_q)$ are linearly independent mod $\varphi(\mathfrak{m})^2$.

(21.2) DEFINITION. Let $\mathfrak{p}$ be a prime ideal in a noetherian ring S, let $R = S_{\mathfrak{p}}$ and $\mathfrak{m} = \mathfrak{p}R$. For elements in S, the concepts of ord_R, rnk_R, and generators and basis and linear independence mod $\mathfrak{m}^2$, are to be meant as for the images of these elements under the natural homomorphism $S \to R$. From properties of quotient rings we get the following.

1) *Let $w_1, \dots, w_p$ be a set of generators of $\mathfrak{p}$ and let A be a nonempty subset of S. Then* $\mathrm{ord}_R A = \max e$ *such that: given $u \in A$, there exists $a \in S$, $a \notin \mathfrak{p}$, for which $au \in \mathfrak{p}^e$*, i.e.,

$$au = \sum_{i_1 + \dots + i_p = e} a_{i_1 \dots i_p} w_1^{i_1} \dots w_p^{i_p} \qquad \textit{with} \qquad a_{i_1 \dots i_p} \in S.$$

2) *Elements $u_1, \dots, u_q$ in $\mathfrak{p}$ are linearly independent* mod $\mathfrak{m}^2 \Leftrightarrow [a_1 u_1 + \dots + a_q u_q \in \mathfrak{p}^2$ *with* $a_1, \dots, a_q \in S \Rightarrow a_1, \dots, a_q \in \mathfrak{p}]$.

3) *Let $u_1, \dots, u_q \in A \subset \mathfrak{p}$. Then $u_1, \dots, u_q$ generate A* mod $\mathfrak{m}^2 \Leftrightarrow$ [*given $u \in A$, there exist $a \in S$, $a \notin \mathfrak{p}$, $a_i \in S$, $b \in \mathfrak{p}^2$ such that $au = a_1 u_1 + \dots + a_q u_q + b$*].

(21.3) DEFINITION. A local ring R is said to be *regular* $\Leftrightarrow \mathrm{emdim}\, R = \dim R$.

For any regular local ring $(R, \mathfrak{m})$ we have the following where 1) follows from Zariski–Samuel [**2**: Theorem 21 on p. 292], and 2) and 3) follow from 1).

1) *Let $u_1, \dots, u_n$ be any irredundant set of generators of $\mathfrak{m}$ and let*

$$v = \sum_{i_1 + \dots + i_n = p} a_{i_1 \dots i_n} u_1^{i_1} \dots u_n^{i_n}$$

where $a_{i_1 \dots i_n}$ are elements in R at least one of which is not in $\mathfrak{m}$. Then $\mathrm{ord}_R v = p$.

2) ord_R *is a valuation function, i.e.,* $\operatorname{ord}_R(uv) = (\operatorname{ord}_R u) + (\operatorname{ord}_R v)$ *for all* $u, v \in R$.

3) *For all* $q \geqq 0$, *the dimension of* $\mathfrak{m}^q/\mathfrak{m}^{q+1}$ *as a vector space over* $R/\mathfrak{m}$ *equals* $\binom{n+q+1}{q}$ *where* $n = \dim R$.

(21.4) *Let R be a one dimensional local ring. Then*

$$\begin{aligned} R \text{ is regular} &\Leftrightarrow R \text{ is a normal integral domain} \\ &\Leftrightarrow R \text{ is a real discrete valuation ring} \\ &\Leftrightarrow R \text{ is a principal ideal domain.} \end{aligned}$$

For instance see Northcott [**1**: Theorem 8 on p. 76].

(21.5) *For any regular local ring R we have the following.*

1) (Krull). *R is a normal integral domain.*

2) (Krull). *For any proper ideal* $\mathfrak{a}$ *in R we have* $\operatorname{dpt}_R\mathfrak{a} + \operatorname{hgt}_R\mathfrak{a} = \dim R$.

3) (Cohen–Macaulay). *Let* $\mathfrak{a}$ *be a proper ideal in R such that* $\mathfrak{a}$ *is generated by m elements where* $m = \operatorname{hgt}_R\mathfrak{a}$. *Then* $\operatorname{hgt}_R\mathfrak{p} = m$ *for every associated prime ideal* $\mathfrak{p}$ *of* $\mathfrak{a}$.

For proofs see Zariski–Samuel [**2**: p. 302] for 1) and Zariski-Samuel [**2**: Appendix 6] for 2) and 3).

(21.6) *For any proper ideal* $\mathfrak{a}$ *in a regular local ring* $(R, \mathfrak{m})$ *we have the following.*

1)
$$\begin{aligned} \operatorname{rnk}_R\mathfrak{a} &= \dim R - \operatorname{emdim} R/\mathfrak{a} \\ &\leqq \dim R - \dim R/\mathfrak{a} \\ &= \operatorname{hgt}_R\mathfrak{a}. \end{aligned}$$

2) *The following five conditions are equivalent.*

i) $R/\mathfrak{a}$ *is regular.*
ii) $\operatorname{rnk}_R\mathfrak{a} = \operatorname{hgt}_R\mathfrak{a}$.
iii) $\operatorname{rnk}_R\mathfrak{a} = \dim R - \dim R/\mathfrak{a}$.
iv) $\mathfrak{a}$ *can be generated by elements which are linearly independent* mod $\mathfrak{m}^2$.
v) *There exists an irredundant set* $u_1,\dots, u_n$ *of generators of* $\mathfrak{m}$ *such that* $\{u_1,\dots, u_m\}R = \mathfrak{a}$ *for some m.*

PROOF. 1) follows from (21.1, 21.5.2). By definition, $R/\mathfrak{a}$ is regular if and only if $\operatorname{emdim} R/\mathfrak{a} = \dim R/\mathfrak{a}$, and hence the equivalence of i), ii), and iii) follows from 1). The equivalence of i) and iv) is proved in Zariski–Samuel [**2**: p. 303]. The equivalence of iv) and v) is obvious.

(21.7) *Let $(R, \mathfrak{m})$ be a regular local ring and let $\varphi: R \to S$ be an epimorphism whose kernel is a proper ideal $\mathfrak{a}$ in R such that* $\operatorname{rad} \mathfrak{a} = \mathfrak{a}$ *and $\mathfrak{a}$ is generated by k elements where* $k = \dim R - \dim S$. *Then we have the following.*

i) $\dim S/\mathfrak{p} = \dim S$ *for every prime ideal $\mathfrak{p}$ of $\{0\}$ in S.*

ii) *For every nonunit nonzerodivisor α in S all the prime ideals of αS have height one.*

iii) *If S is not an integral domain then there exist two distinct prime ideals $\bar{\mathfrak{p}}_1$ and $\bar{\mathfrak{p}}_2$ of $\{0\}$ in S such that* $\operatorname{hgt}_S(\bar{\mathfrak{p}}_1 + \bar{\mathfrak{p}}_2) = 1$.

iv) *If $S_{\mathfrak{P}}$ is regular for every prime ideal $\mathfrak{P}$ of height one in S,*[1] *then S is a normal integral domain.*

PROOF. iii) follows from i) and ii) by (19.19). iv) follows from ii) by (19.20). In virtue of (17.1, 21.5.2), the assumptions on $\mathfrak{a}$ imply that $\mathfrak{a} = \mathfrak{p}_1 \cap \ldots \cap \mathfrak{p}_h$ where $\mathfrak{p}_1, \ldots, \mathfrak{p}_h$ are distinct prime ideals in R such that $\operatorname{hgt}_R \mathfrak{p}_i = k$ and $\operatorname{dpt}_R \mathfrak{p}_i = \dim S$ for $i = 1, \ldots, h$. Therefore $\varphi(\mathfrak{p}_1), \ldots, \varphi(\mathfrak{p}_h)$ are exactly all the distinct prime ideals in S having height zero, $\{0\} = \varphi(\mathfrak{p}_1) \cap \ldots \cap \varphi(\mathfrak{p}_h)$ is the unique normal decomposition of $\{0\}$ in S, and $\varphi(\mathfrak{p}_1) \cup \ldots \cup \varphi(\mathfrak{p}_h)$ is the set of all zerodivisors in S. Now $\dim S/\varphi(\mathfrak{p}_i) = \dim R/\mathfrak{p}_i = \dim S$ for $i = 1, \ldots, h$, which proves i). To prove ii), take $\beta \in \varphi^{-1}(\alpha)$ and let $\mathfrak{b} = \mathfrak{a} + \beta R$. Then $\mathfrak{a} \subset \mathfrak{b} \subset \mathfrak{m}$ and $\mathfrak{b} \not\subset \mathfrak{p}_i$ for $i = 1, \ldots, h$. Let $\mathfrak{b} = \mathfrak{q}_1^* \cap \ldots \cap \mathfrak{q}_t^*$ be a normal decomposition of $\mathfrak{b}$ where $\mathfrak{q}_j^*$ is primary for $\mathfrak{p}_j^*$. Since $\mathfrak{a} \subset \mathfrak{b} \not\subset \mathfrak{p}_i$ for $i = 1, \ldots, h$, we get $\operatorname{hgt}_R \mathfrak{p}_j^* \geqq k + 1$ for $j = 1, \ldots, t$, and hence $\operatorname{hgt}_R \mathfrak{b} \geqq k + 1$. Since $\mathfrak{b}$ is generated by $k + 1$ elements, (17.1) yields that $\operatorname{hgt}_R \mathfrak{b} = k + 1$, and then (21.5.3) yields that $\operatorname{hgt}_R \mathfrak{p}_j^* = k + 1$ for $j = 1, \ldots, t$. Therefore $\varphi(\mathfrak{p}_1^*), \ldots, \varphi(\mathfrak{p}_t^*)$ are the prime ideals of αS and $\operatorname{hgt}_S \varphi(\mathfrak{p}_j^*) = 1$ for $j = 1, \ldots, t$.

(21.8) DEFINITION. Let R be a *regular* local ring and let $\mathfrak{L}$ be the quotient field of R. In virtue of (21.3.2), for any $w = u/v \in \mathfrak{L}$ with $u, v \in R$, $v \neq 0$, *we* can unambiguously *set*

$$\operatorname{ord}_R w = \operatorname{ord}_R u - \operatorname{ord}_R v.$$

Then ord_R becomes a real discrete valuation of $\mathfrak{L}$. Obviously *for any $w \in \mathfrak{L}$ we then have*:

1°) $w \in R \Rightarrow \operatorname{ord}_R w \geqq 0$;

2°) if $\dim R = 1$ then, $w \in R \Leftrightarrow \operatorname{ord}_R w \geqq 0$.

More generally let S be a noetherian ring, let $\mathfrak{p}$ be a prime ideal in S, and let $R = S_{\mathfrak{p}}$. Let $\mathfrak{K}$ be the total quotient ring of S. Assume that R

[1] Note that by (19.14, 21.4), $S_{\mathfrak{P}}$ is regular if and only if it is normal.

is *regular*. Let $\mathfrak{L}$ be the quotient field of R and let $f: \mathfrak{K} \to \mathfrak{L}$ be the natural homomorphism. For any $w \in \mathfrak{K}$ *set*

$$\text{ord}_R w = \text{ord}_R f(w).$$

In other words, write $w = u/v$ with $u, v \in S$, v a nonzerodivisor in S; then $f(v) \neq 0$ and

$$\text{ord}_R w = \text{ord}_R f(u) - \text{ord}_R f(v).$$

For any nonempty subset $A \subset \mathfrak{K}$ *we* may then *set*

$$\text{ord}_R A = \min_{w \in A}(\text{ord}_R w).$$

Note that *for any* $w \in \mathfrak{K}$ *we then have*:

3°) $w \in f^{-1}(R) \Rightarrow \text{ord}_R w \geqq 0$;

4°) if $\dim R = 1$ then, $w \in f^{-1}(R) \Leftrightarrow \text{ord}_R w \geqq 0$.

In virtue of 4°), (19.17) and (19.24) can now be restated, respectively, as (21.9) and (21.10).

(21.9) *Let R be a normal noetherian integral domain and let $\mathfrak{L}$ be the quotient field of R. Let Ω be the set of all prime ideals in R having height one. Then for any $\mathfrak{p} \in \Omega$, $R_\mathfrak{p}$ is a one dimensional regular local ring; and for any $w \in \mathfrak{L}$ we have*:

$$w \in R \Leftrightarrow \text{ord}_{R_\mathfrak{p}} w \geqq 0 \textit{ for all } \mathfrak{p} \in \Omega.$$

(21.10) *Let R be a nonnull noetherian ring, let $\mathfrak{L}$ be the total quotient ring of R, and let Ω be the set of all prime ideals in R of height one. Assume that*

i) $\text{rad}_R\{0\} = \{0\}$;

ii) *for every prime ideal $\mathfrak{p}$ of $\{0\}$ in R, the integral closure of $R/\mathfrak{p}$ in the quotient field of $R/\mathfrak{p}$ is a finite $(R/\mathfrak{p})$-module*;[2]

iii) $R_\mathfrak{p}$ *is regular for all* $\mathfrak{p} \in \Omega$;[3] and

iv) *R contains a subring S such that S is a normal integral domain, R is integral over S, and every nonzero element in S is a nonzerodivisor in R.*

Then for any $w \in \mathfrak{L}$ we have:

$$w \textit{ is integral over } R \Leftrightarrow \text{ord}_{R_\mathfrak{p}} w \geqq 0 \textit{ for all } \mathfrak{p} \in \Omega.$$

[2] If R is an integral domain and the integral closure of R in $\mathfrak{L}$ is noetherian, then condition ii) may be omitted; see (19.18).

[3] Note that by (19.14, 21.4), $R_\mathfrak{p}$ is regular if and only if it is normal. Also note that if $\Omega = \emptyset$ then $\mathfrak{L} = R$.

(21.11) JACOBIAN RANK.[4] Let $(R, \mathfrak{m})$ be the n dimensional regular local ring $K[[x_1,\dots, x_n]]$ or $K[\langle x_1,\dots, x_n\rangle]$. For any $u \in R$, $\operatorname{ord}_R u$ is then simply the leading degree $\mathbf{o}u$ of u. Let $\varphi: \mathfrak{m} \to \mathfrak{m}/\mathfrak{m}^2$ be the natural K-epimorphism and let $\bar{x}_j = \varphi(x_j)$. Then $\bar{x}_1,\dots, \bar{x}_n$ is a basis of the K-vector-space $\mathfrak{m}/\mathfrak{m}^2$. For any $f \in \mathfrak{m}$, $(\partial f/\partial x_j)(0)$ is the coefficient of x_j in the expansion of f and hence

$$\varphi(f) = \sum_{j=1}^{n} \left(\frac{\partial f}{\partial x_j}(0)\right)\bar{x}_j.$$

1) Let $\mathfrak{a} = \{g_1,\dots, g_m\}R$ where $g_1,\dots, g_m \in \mathfrak{m}$. From the above observation we get 1°) and from it, in view of (21.6), we get 2°) and 3°).

1°)
$$\operatorname{rnk}_R \mathfrak{a} = \operatorname{rnk} \frac{J(g_1,\dots, g_m)}{J(x_1,\dots, x_n)}(0).$$

2°)
$$\operatorname{rnk} \frac{J(g_1,\dots, g_m)}{J(x_1,\dots, x_n)}(0) \leqq n - \dim R/\mathfrak{a},$$

and equality holds $\Leftrightarrow$ *$R/\mathfrak{a}$ is regular.*

3°) *If*
$$\operatorname{rnk} \frac{J(g_1,\dots, g_m)}{J(x_1,\dots, x_n)}(0) = m$$

then $R/\mathfrak{a}$ is a regular local ring of dimension $n - m$.[5]

To generalize the above results, take $0 < e \leqq n$ and let $\mathfrak{p} = \{x_1,\dots, x_e\}R$, $S = R_\mathfrak{p}$, $\mathfrak{n} = \mathfrak{p}S$, and $\mathfrak{K} = K((x_{e+1},\dots, x_n))$ or $K(\langle x_{e+1},\dots, x_n\rangle)$, respectively. Then $\mathfrak{K} \subset S$, and $\mathfrak{K}$ maps isomorphically onto $S/\mathfrak{n}$ under the natural epimorphism $S \to S/\mathfrak{n}$. Now $\operatorname{rnk}_R\mathfrak{p} = e$ and hence $\dim S = \operatorname{hgt}_R\mathfrak{p} = e$ by (21.6.2). Since $\mathfrak{n}$ is generated by the e elements $x_1,\dots, x_e$, it follows that $(S, \mathfrak{n})$ is an e dimensional regular local ring and $x_1,\dots, x_e$ is a basis of $\mathfrak{n}$ mod $\mathfrak{n}^2$. We can consider S to be a subring of $\mathfrak{K}[[x_1,\dots, x_e]]$ and then for any $u \in S$, $\operatorname{ord}_S u$ is simply the leading degree of u as an element in $\mathfrak{K}[[x_1,\dots, x_e]]$. For any $f \in \mathfrak{m}$ we can uniquely write

$$f = \sum_{i=1}^{e} \bar{f}^{(i)}x_i + \sum_{i_1+\dots+i_e>1} \hat{f}^{(i_1\dots i_e)}x_1^{i_1}\dots x_e^{i_e}$$

with

$$\bar{f}^{(i)},\quad \hat{f}^{(i_1\dots i_e)} \in K[[x_{e+1},\dots, x_n]] \quad \text{or} \quad K[\langle x_{e+1},\dots, x_n\rangle], \text{ respectively,}$$

[4] For definition of Jacobians see (2.6).

[5] In (10.11), we have actually proved that $R/\mathfrak{a}$ is then isomorphic to $K[[x_1,\dots, x_{n-m}]]$ or $K[\langle x_1,\dots, x_{n-m}\rangle]$, respectively.

and then:

$$f \equiv \sum_{i=1}^{e} \bar{f}^{(i)} x_i \mod \mathfrak{n}^2$$

and

$$\frac{\partial f}{\partial x_i}(0,\ldots, 0, x_{e+1},\ldots, x_n) = \bar{f}^{(i)} \qquad \text{for} \qquad i = 1,\ldots, e.$$

2) Let $\mathfrak{b} = \{g_1,\ldots, g_m\}S$ where $g_1,\ldots, g_m \in \mathfrak{m}$. From the above observations we get 1°) and from it, in view of (21.6), we get 2°) and 3°).

1°) $$\operatorname{rnk}_S \mathfrak{b} = \operatorname{rnk} \frac{J(g_1,\ldots, g_m)}{J(x_1,\ldots, x_e)}(0,\ldots, 0, x_{e+1},\ldots, x_n).$$

2°) $$\operatorname{rnk} \frac{J(g_1,\ldots, g_m)}{J(x_1,\ldots, x_e)}(0,\ldots, 0, x_{e+1},\ldots, x_n) \leqq e - \dim S/\mathfrak{b},$$

and equality holds $\Leftrightarrow$ $S/\mathfrak{b}$ *is regular.*

3°) *If* $$\operatorname{rnk} \frac{J(g_1,\ldots, g_m)}{J(x_1,\ldots, x_e)}(0,\ldots, 0, x_{e+1},\ldots, x_n) = m$$

then $S/\mathfrak{b}$ *is a regular local ring of dimension* $e - m$.

§22. ANOTHER PROOF THAT A FORMAL POWER SERIES RING IS NOETHERIAN

We shall now give a proof of the noetherian character of $K[[x_1,\ldots, x_n]]$ without using the Preparation Theorem, where K is an arbitrary field which is not necessarily infinite. Actually we shall prove slightly more.

(22.1) *Let H be a nonnull noetherian ring. Then $R = H[[x_1,\ldots, x_n]]$ is noetherian.*

Proof. Induction on n. For $n = 0$, $R = H$. Now let $n > 0$ and assume that $S = H[[x_1,\ldots, x_{n-1}]]$ is noetherian. Let an ideal $\mathfrak{a}$ in R be given. Let $\mathfrak{b}_i = \{\varphi \in S : \varphi x_n^i + \psi x_n^{i+1} \in \mathfrak{a} \text{ for some } \psi \in R\}$. Then $\mathfrak{b}_i$ is an ideal in S. Also

$$\begin{aligned}\varphi \in \mathfrak{b}_i &\Rightarrow \varphi x_n^i + \psi x_n^{i+1} \in \mathfrak{a} \text{ for some } \psi \in R \\ &\Rightarrow \varphi x_n^{i+1} + \psi x_n^{i+2} \in \mathfrak{a} \\ &\Rightarrow \varphi \in \mathfrak{b}_{i+1}.\end{aligned}$$

Thus $\mathfrak{b}_0 \subset \mathfrak{b}_1 \subset \mathfrak{b}_2 \subset \ldots$. Since S is noetherian, there exists λ such that $\mathfrak{b}_i = \mathfrak{b}_\lambda$ for all $i \geqq \lambda$, and $\mathfrak{b}_i$ has a finite basis $\{\varphi_{ij} : j = 1,\ldots, \mu\}$ for all $i \leqq \lambda$. Now

$$f_{ij} = \varphi_{ij} x_n^i + \psi_{ij} x_n^{i+1} \in \mathfrak{a} \text{ for some } \psi_{ij} \in R.$$

We claim that $\{f_{ij}: i = 0,\ldots, \lambda; j = 1,\ldots, \mu\}$ is a basis of $\mathfrak{a}$. So let $g \in \mathfrak{a}$ be given.

By induction on p we shall show that for all $p \leqq \lambda$ there exists $a_{ij} \in S$, $(i = 0,\ldots, p; j = 1,\ldots, \mu)$, such that

$$g_p = g - \sum_{j=1}^{\mu} \sum_{i=0}^{p} a_{ij} f_{ij} \in \mathfrak{a} \cap x_n^{p+1} R.$$

Take $p = 0$. Since $g \in R$ we can write $g = \varphi + \psi x_n$ with $\varphi \in S$ and $\psi \in R$. Since $g \in \mathfrak{a}$ we then have $\varphi \in \mathfrak{b}_0$ and hence

$$\varphi = \sum_{j=1}^{\mu} a_{0j} \varphi_{0j} \qquad \text{with} \qquad a_{0j} \in S.$$

Now obviously

$$g_0 = g - \sum_{j=1}^{\mu} a_{0j} f_{0j} \in \mathfrak{a} \cap x_n R.$$

Take $p > 0$ and assume true for $p - 1$. Since $g_{p-1} \in x_n^p R$, we can write $g_{p-1} = \varphi' x_n^p + \psi' x_n^{p+1}$ with $\varphi' \in S$ and $\psi' \in R$. Since $g_{p-1} \in \mathfrak{a}$ we then have $\varphi' \in \mathfrak{b}_p$ and hence

$$\varphi' = \sum_{j=1}^{\mu} a_{pj} \varphi_{pj} \qquad \text{with} \qquad a_{pj} \in S.$$

Now obviously

$$g_p = g - \sum_{j=1}^{\mu} \sum_{i=0}^{p} a_{ij} f_{ij} \in \mathfrak{a} \cap x_n^{p+1} R.$$

This completes the induction on p.

By induction on q we shall show that for all $q \geqq 0$ there exists $b_{ij} \in S$, $(i = 0,\ldots, q; j = 1,\ldots, \mu)$, such that

$$h_{\lambda+q} = g_\lambda - \sum_{i=0}^{q} \left(\sum_{j=1}^{\mu} b_{ij} f_{\lambda j} \right) x_n^i \in \mathfrak{a} \cap x_n^{\lambda+q+1} R.$$

For $q = 0$ we can take $b_{01} = \ldots = b_{0\mu} = 0$. Take $q > 0$ and assume true for $q - 1$. Since $h_{\lambda+q-1} \in x_n^{\lambda+q} R$, we can write $h_{\lambda+q-1} = \varphi^* x_n^{\lambda+q} + \psi^* x_n^{\lambda+q+1}$ with $\varphi^* \in S$ and $\psi^* \in R$. Since $h_{\lambda+q-1} \in \mathfrak{a}$ we then have $\varphi^* \in \mathfrak{b}_{\lambda+q} = \mathfrak{b}_\lambda$ and hence

$$\varphi^* = \sum_{j=1}^{\mu} b_{qj} \varphi_{\lambda j} \qquad \text{with} \qquad b_{qj} \in S.$$

Now obviously

$$h_{\lambda+q} = g_\lambda - \sum_{i=0}^{q} \left(\sum_{j=1}^{\mu} b_{ij} f_{\lambda j} \right) x_n^i \in \mathfrak{a} \cap x_n^{\lambda+q+1} R.$$

This completes the induction on q.

Let

$$u_j = \sum_{i=0}^{\infty} b_{ij} x_n^i.$$

Then $u_1, \ldots, u_\mu \in R$ and

$$g - \sum_{j=1}^{\mu} \sum_{i=0}^{\lambda} a_{ij} f_{ij} - \sum_{j=1}^{\mu} u_j f_{\lambda j} \in x_n^{\lambda+q} R \qquad \text{for all} \qquad q \geqq 0.$$

Therefore

$$g = \sum_{j=1}^{\mu} \sum_{i=0}^{\lambda} a_{ij} f_{ij} + \sum_{j=1}^{\mu} u_j f_{\lambda j}.$$

Taking $H = K$ in (22.1) we get

(**22.2**) *Let K be an arbitrary field. Then $K[[x_1, \ldots, x_n]]$ is noetherian.*

By a slight modification in the proof of (22.1) we shall prove (22.5). First we prove two lemmas.

(**22.3**) *Let L be a field, let K be a subfield of L, and let $x_1, \ldots, x_n$ be indeterminates over L. Then any finite number of elements $k_1, \ldots, k_q$ of L which are linearly independent over K are linearly independent over $K((x_1, \ldots, x_n))$.*[1]

PROOF. Let $f^{(1)}, \ldots, f^{(q)} \in K((x_1, \ldots, x_n))$ be such that $k_1 f^{(1)} + \ldots + k_q f^{(q)} = 0$. Multiplying $f^{(1)}, \ldots, f^{(q)}$ by a nonzero element of $K[[x_1, \ldots, x_n]]$ we can assume that $f^{(1)}, \ldots, f^{(q)} \in K[[x_1, \ldots, x_n]]$. Then

$$f^{(i)} = \sum f^{(i)}_{j_1 \ldots j_n} x_1^{j_1} \ldots x_n^{j_n} \qquad \text{with} \qquad f^{(i)}_{j_1 \ldots j_n} \in K.$$

Equating coefficients of $x_1^{j_1} \ldots x_n^{j_n}$ we get

$$\sum_{i=1}^{q} k_i f^{(i)}_{j_1 \ldots j_n} = 0 \qquad \text{and hence} \qquad f^{(i)}_{j_1 \ldots j_n} = 0 \qquad \text{for} \qquad i = 1, \ldots, q.$$

This being so for all $j_1, \ldots, j_n$ we get $f^{(1)} = \ldots = f^{(q)} = 0$.

(**22.4**) *Let K be a field and let K^* be a (not necessarily finite) algebraic extension of K. Let Ω be the set of all finite algebraic extensions of K in K^*. Let $R = \bigcup_{L \in \Omega} L[[x_1, \ldots, x_n]]$.*[2] *For any ideal $\mathfrak{a}$ in $K[[x_1, \ldots, x_n]]$ we then have $K[[x_1, \ldots, x_n]] \cap \mathfrak{a}R = \mathfrak{a}$.*

[1] L and $K((x_1, \ldots, x_n))$ are considered to be subfields of $L((x_1, \ldots, x_n))$.

[2] $L[[x_1, \ldots, x_n]]$ is to be thought of as a subring of $K^*[[x_1, \ldots, x_n]]$. R is then a subring of $K^*[[x_1, \ldots, x_n]]$.

PROOF. Any $f \in \mathfrak{a}R$ can be written as a finite sum

$$f = \sum_{i=1}^{p} a_i f_i \qquad \text{with} \qquad a_i \in \mathfrak{a},\ f_i \in R.$$

Assume that $f \in K[[x_1,\ldots, x_n]]$. Take $L \in \Omega$ such that $f_1,\ldots, f_p \in L[[x_1,\ldots, x_n]]$. Let $k_1,\ldots, k_q$ be a vector space basis of L over K where $k_1 = 1$. We can then write

$$f_i = \sum_{i=1}^{p} k_j g_{ij} \qquad \text{with} \qquad g_{ij} \in K[[x_1,\ldots, x_n]].$$

Let

$$b_j = \sum_{i=1}^{p} a_i g_{ij}.$$

Then $b_1,\ldots, b_q \in \mathfrak{a}$ and

$$f = \sum_{j=1}^{q} k_j b_j.$$

Now $f, b_1,\ldots, b_q \in K((x_1,\ldots, x_n))$; $k_1,\ldots, k_q \in L$; $k_1 = 1$; and by (22.3), $k_1,\ldots, k_q$ are linearly independent over $K((x_1,\ldots, x_n))$. Therefore $f = b_1 \in \mathfrak{a}$.

(22.5) *Let K be a field and let K^* be a (not necessarily finite) algebraic extension of K. Let Ω be the set of all finite algebraic extensions of K in K^*. Let $R^* = K^*[[x_1,\ldots, x_n]]$ and $R = \bigcup_{L\in\Omega} L[[x_1,\ldots, x_n]]$.*[2] *Then R is an n dimensional regular local ring in which the maximal ideal is generated by $x_1,\ldots, x_n$. R is integral over $K[[x_1,\ldots, x_n]]$ and R^* is a completion of R.*

PROOF. By induction on n we shall show that R is noetherian. For $n = 0, R = R^* = K^*$. Now let $n > 0$ and assume that $S = \bigcup_{L\in\Omega} L[[x_1,\ldots, x_{n-1}]]$ is noetherian. Let an ideal $\mathfrak{a}$ in R be given. Let

$$\mathfrak{b}_i = \{\varphi \in S: \varphi x_n^i + \psi x_n^{i+1} \in \mathfrak{a} \text{ for some } \psi \in R\}.$$

Then $\mathfrak{b}_0 \subset \mathfrak{b}_1 \subset \mathfrak{b}_2 \subset \ldots$ are ideals in S. Consequently there exists λ such that $\mathfrak{b}_i = \mathfrak{b}_\lambda$ for all $i \geqq \lambda$, and $\mathfrak{b}_i$ has a finite basis $\{\varphi_{ij}: j = 1,\ldots, \mu\}$ for all $i \leqq \lambda$. Now

$$f_{ij} = \varphi_{ij} x_n^i + \psi_{ij} x_n^{i+1} \in \mathfrak{a} \qquad \text{for some} \qquad \psi_{ij} \in R.$$

We claim that $\{f_{ij}: i = 0,\ldots, \lambda;\ j = 1,\ldots, \mu\}$ is a basis of $\mathfrak{a}$. So let $g \in \mathfrak{a}$ be given. We can find $L \in \Omega$ such that all the elements g and ψ_{ij} are in $\tilde{R}$ and all the elements φ_{ij} are in $\tilde{S}$, where $\tilde{R} = L[[x_1,\ldots, x_n]]$ and $\tilde{S} = L[[x_1,\ldots, x_{n-1}]]$. Let $\tilde{\mathfrak{b}}_i = \mathfrak{b}_i \cap \tilde{S}$. Then $\tilde{\mathfrak{b}}_0 \subset \tilde{\mathfrak{b}}_1 \subset \tilde{\mathfrak{b}}_2 \subset \ldots$ are ideals in $\tilde{S}$, $\tilde{\mathfrak{b}}_i = \tilde{\mathfrak{b}}_\lambda$ for all $i \geqq \lambda$; and by (22.4) we have that $\tilde{\mathfrak{b}}_i = \{\varphi_{i1}, \ldots, \varphi_{i\mu}\}\tilde{S}$ for all $i \leqq \lambda$. Now take over the proof of (22.1) beginning with "By induction on p..." with $\tilde{S}$, $\tilde{R}$, $\tilde{\mathfrak{b}}_i$ replacing S, R, $\mathfrak{b}_i$, respectively. This yields elements $a_{ij} \in \tilde{S}$, $(i = 0, \ldots, \lambda;\ j = 1, \ldots, \mu)$, and elements $u_1, \ldots, u_\mu \in \tilde{R}$ such that

$$g = \sum_{j=1}^{\mu} \sum_{i=0}^{\lambda} a_{ij} f_{ij} + \sum_{j=1}^{\mu} u_j f_{\lambda j}.$$

This completes the induction on n and proves that R is noetherian. It is obvious that $\{x_1, \ldots, x_n\}R$ is the ideal of all nonunits in R. Also obviously $\{0\} \subset \{x_1\}R \subset \ldots \subset \{x_1, \ldots, x_n\}R$ is a chain of distinct prime ideals in R. Therefore R is an n-dimensional regular local ring. Also R^* is clearly a completion of R and R is integral over $K[[x_1, \ldots, x_n]]$.

CHAPTER IV

Parameters in Power Series Rings

To avoid repetition we let $[\{\ \}]$ stand for $[[\ ]]$ or $[\langle\ \rangle]$. Thus $K[\{x_1,\dots,x_n\}]$ stands for $K[[x_1,\dots,x_n]]$ or $K[\langle x_1,\dots,x_n\rangle]$; in the latter case it being understood that K is a complete nondiscrete valued field. In a single context, only one of these meanings of $[\{\ \}]$ is to be taken consistently. Thus for instance, the considerations of §23 hold with $[\{\ \}]$ always standing for $[[\ ]]$, and they also hold with $[\{\ \}]$ always standing for $[\langle\ \rangle]$. Correspondingly, $(\{\ \})$ will stand for $((\ ))$ or $(\langle\ \rangle)$.

§23. PARAMETERS FOR IDEALS

Let $R = K[\{x_1,\dots,x_n\}]$ and $S = K[\{x_1,\dots,x_e\}]$, $e \leqq n$. Let $\mathfrak{m}$ be the maximal ideal in R. Let $\mathfrak{K}$ be the quotient field of S. If for a proper ideal $\mathfrak{a}$ in R we have $\mathfrak{a} \cap S = \{0\}$ then we shall identify S with the corresponding subring of $R/\mathfrak{a}$.

(23.1) DEFINITION. Let $\mathfrak{a}$ be a proper ideal in R. Elements $y_1,\dots,y_p$ in R are said to form a *system of parameters for* R mod $\mathfrak{a} \Leftrightarrow$ their residue classes mod $\mathfrak{a}$ form a system of parameters for $R/\mathfrak{a}$, i.e., $\Leftrightarrow \dim R/\mathfrak{a} = p$ and $\{y_1,\dots,y_p,\mathfrak{a}\}R$ is primary for $\mathfrak{m}$. $\mathfrak{a}$ is said to be *regular relative to* $S \Leftrightarrow \{x_1,\dots,x_e\}$ form a system of parameters for R mod $\mathfrak{a}$.

(23.2) *Let* $\mathfrak{a} \subset \mathfrak{b}$ *be proper ideals in* R *and let* $y_1,\dots,y_p \in R$. *If* $\{y_1,\dots,y_p,\mathfrak{a}\}R$ *is primary for* $\mathfrak{m}$ *then so is* $\{y_1,\dots,y_p,\mathfrak{b}\}R$. *If* $\{y_1,\dots,y_p\}$ *form a system of parameters for* R mod $\mathfrak{a}$ *then*: $\{y_1,\dots,y_p\}$ *form a system of parameters for* R mod $\mathfrak{b} \Leftrightarrow \dim R/\mathfrak{a} = \dim R/\mathfrak{b}$.

Obvious.

(23.3) *Let $\mathfrak{a}$ be a proper ideal in R. For any element or subset r of R let $\bar{r}$ denote the image of r under the natural epimorphism $R \to R/\mathfrak{a}$. Let $R_i = K[\{x_1,\ldots, x_i\}]$.*

1) *Assume that $\{x_1,\ldots, x_e, \mathfrak{a}\}R$ is primary for $\mathfrak{m}$. Then $\dim \bar{R} = \dim \bar{S} \leqq e$, $\bar{R} = \bar{S}[\bar{x}_{e+1},\ldots, \bar{x}_n]$, and $\bar{R}$ is integral over $\bar{S}$. Furthermore $\mathfrak{a}$ has a finite basis consisting of elements in $S[x_{e+1},\ldots, x_n]$, or equivalently $(\mathfrak{a} \cap S[x_{e+1},\ldots, x_n])R = \mathfrak{a}$. Given $w \in R$, there exists a monic polynomial $F(T)$ of positive degree in T with coefficients in S such that $F(w) \in \mathfrak{a}$; if $w \in \mathfrak{m}$ then $F(T)$ may be chosen to be a distinguished polynomial in T with coefficients in S. In particular for all $i > e$, $\mathfrak{a}$ contains a distinguished polynomial $F_i(x_i)$ of positive degree in x_i with coefficients in S.*

2) *$\{x_1,\ldots, x_e, \mathfrak{a}\}R$ is primary for $\mathfrak{m} \Leftrightarrow \bar{R}$ is integral over $\bar{S}$.*

3) *$\{x_1,\ldots, x_e, \mathfrak{a}\}R$ is primary for $\mathfrak{m} \Leftrightarrow$ for all $i > e$, $\mathfrak{a}$ contains a monic polynomial in x_i with coefficients in R_{i-1}.*

4) *$\mathfrak{a}$ is regular relative to S*

$$\Leftrightarrow \{x_1,\ldots, x_e, \mathfrak{a}\}R \text{ is primary for } \mathfrak{m} \text{ and } \dim \bar{R} \geqq e$$

$$\Leftrightarrow \{x_1,\ldots, x_e, \mathfrak{a}\}R \text{ is primary for } \mathfrak{m} \text{ and } S \cap \mathfrak{a} = \{0\}.$$

Proof of 1). Assertion being trivial for $e = n$, suppose that $e < n$. By assumption $\{x_1,\ldots, x_e, \mathfrak{a}\}R$ is primary for $\mathfrak{m}$ and obviously $\{x_1,\ldots, x_{n-1}\}R$ is not primary for $\mathfrak{m}$. Hence $\mathfrak{a} \not\subset \{x_1,\ldots, x_{n-1}\}R$. Take $f(x_1,\ldots, x_n) \in \mathfrak{a}$ such that $f \notin \{x_1,\ldots, x_{n-1}\}R$, i.e., $f(0,\ldots, 0, x_n) \neq 0$. By Preparation Theorem (10.3.1, 10.3.2), upon multiplying f by a unit in R we can arrange that f is a distinguished polynomial in x_n with coefficients in R_{n-1}, and for each $g \in R$ we can write $g = qf + r$, with $q \in R$ and $r \in R_{n-1}[x_n]$. Hence $\bar{R} = \bar{R}_{n-1}[\bar{x}_n]$, and $\bar{x}_n$ is integral over $\bar{R}_{n-1}$, i.e., $\bar{R}$ is integral over $\bar{R}_{n-1}$. Hence by (19.7), $\dim \bar{R} = \dim \bar{R}_{n-1}$, and $\{\bar{x}_1,\ldots, \bar{x}_e\}\bar{R}_{n-1}$ is primary for the maximal ideal in $\bar{R}_{n-1}$, i.e., $\{x_1,\ldots, x_e, R_{n-1} \cap \mathfrak{a}\}R_{n-1}$ is primary for the maximal ideal in R_{n-1}. If $e < n - 1$, then replacing R and $\mathfrak{a}$ by R_{n-1} and $R_{n-1} \cap \mathfrak{a}$ in the above argument, we deduce that $\dim \bar{R}_{n-1} = \dim \bar{R}_{n-2}$, $\{x_1,\ldots, x_e, R_{n-2} \cap \mathfrak{a}\}R_{n-2}$ is primary for the maximal ideal in R_{n-2}, $\bar{R}_{n-2} = \bar{R}_{n-1}[\bar{x}_{n-1}]$, and $\bar{R}_{n-1}$ is integral over $\bar{R}_{n-2}$. If $e < n - 2$ then.... Thus by induction it follows that $\dim \bar{R} = \dim \bar{S}$, $\bar{R} = \bar{S}[\bar{x}_{e+1},\ldots, \bar{x}_n]$, and $\bar{R}$ is integral over $\bar{S}$. Obviously $\dim \bar{S} \leqq \dim S = e$.

Let $w \in R$ be given. Since $\bar{w}$ is integral over $\bar{S}$, we can find a monic polynomial $F(T) \in S[T]$ of positive degree in T such that $F(w) \in \mathfrak{a}$. Suppose that $w \in \mathfrak{m}$. Then $F(0) \in \{w, \mathfrak{a}\}R \subset \mathfrak{m}$ and hence by Preparation Theorem $F(T) = G(T)H(T)$ where $G(T)$ is a distinguished polynomial of positive degree in T with coefficients in S, and $H(T) \in S[T]$ such that $H(0)$ is a unit in S. Since $w \in \mathfrak{m}$, $H(w)$ is a unit in R. Now $G(w)H(w) = F(w) \in \mathfrak{a}$ and hence $G(w) \in \mathfrak{a}$. For $i > e$, x_i is in $\mathfrak{m}$ and hence there exists a distinguished polynomial $F_i(T)$ of positive degree in T with coefficients in S such that $F_i(x_i) \in \mathfrak{a}$; obviously $F_i(x_i)$ is a distinguished polynomial of positive degree in x_i with coefficients in S.

Let u_λ, $(\lambda = 1,\ldots, \Lambda)$, be a basis of $\mathfrak{a}$. By Preparation Theorem we can write $u_\lambda = s_\lambda + t_\lambda F_n(x_n)$ where $t_\lambda \in R$ and

$$s_\lambda = \sum_j s_{\lambda j} x_n^j \in R_{n-1}[x_n] \qquad \text{with} \quad s_{\lambda j} \in R_{n-1}.$$

Again by Preparation Theorem

$$s_{\lambda j} = s'_{\lambda j} + t'_{\lambda j} F_{n-1}(x_{n-1})$$

where $t'_{\lambda j} \in R_{n-1}$ and

$$s'_{\lambda j} = \sum_k s'_{\lambda jk} x_{n-1}^k \in R_{n-2}[x_{n-1}] \qquad \text{with} \quad s'_{\lambda jk} \in R_{n-2}.$$

So on. In this manner we can write

$$u_\lambda = s_\lambda^* + \sum_{\mu=e+1}^{n} t_{\lambda\mu}^* F_\mu(x_\mu)$$

with $s_\lambda^* \in S[x_{e+1},\ldots, x_n]$ and $t_{\lambda\mu}^* \in R$. Consequently

$$\{F_{e+1}(x_{e+1}),\ldots, F_n(x_n), s_1^*,\ldots, s_\Lambda^*\}$$

is a basis of $\mathfrak{a}$ consisting of elements in $S[x_{e+1},\ldots, x_n]$ and hence $\mathfrak{a} = (\mathfrak{a} \cap S[x_{e+1},\ldots, x_n])R$.

Proof of 2). "$\Rightarrow$" is proved in 1). Now $\{\bar{x}_1,\ldots, \bar{x}_e\}\bar{S}$ is primary for the maximal ideal in $\bar{S}$. Hence, if $\bar{R}$ is integral over $\bar{S}$ then by (19.7), $\{\bar{x}_1,\ldots, \bar{x}_e\}\bar{R}$ is primary for the maximal ideal in $\bar{R}$, i.e., $\{x_1,\ldots, x_e, \mathfrak{a}\}R$ is primary for $\mathfrak{m}$.

Proof of 3). "$\Rightarrow$" is proved in 1). "$\Leftarrow$": For $i > e$, $R_i \cap \mathfrak{a}$ contains a monic polynomial f in x_i with coefficients in R_{i-1}; by Preparation Theorem every element g in R_i can be written as $g = qf + r$ with $q \in R_i$ and $r \in R_{i-1}[x_i]$; hence $\bar{R}_i = \bar{R}_{i-1}[\bar{x}_i]$ and $\bar{R}_i$ is integral over $\bar{R}_{i-1}$. Therefore $\bar{R} = \bar{S}[\bar{x}_{e+1},\ldots, \bar{x}_n]$ and $\bar{R}$ is integral over $\bar{S}$. Therefore by 2), $\{x_1,\ldots, x_e, \mathfrak{a}\}R$ is primary for $\mathfrak{m}$.

Proof of 4). Follows from 1) in virtue of the fact that $\dim \bar{S} = \dim S \Leftrightarrow S \cap \mathfrak{a} = \{0\}$.

(23.4) *Let* $\mathfrak{p} \subsetneq \mathfrak{q}$ *be proper ideals in* R *such that* $\mathfrak{p}$ *is prime and* $\mathfrak{p}$ *is regular relative to* S. *Then* $S \cap \mathfrak{q} \neq \{0\}$.

PROOF. Otherwise by (23.3.3, 23.3.4), $\mathfrak{q}$ would be regular relative to S and then we would have $\dim R/\mathfrak{p} = \dim R/\mathfrak{q}$ in contradiction to the assumption that $\mathfrak{p}$ is prime.

(23.5) *Assume that K is infinite and let $\mathfrak{a}_\lambda$, $(\lambda = 1,..., \Lambda)$, be a finite number of proper ideals in R. Via a "generic"*[1] *nonsingular K-linear transformation on $x_1,..., x_n$ it can be arranged that $\mathfrak{a}_\lambda$ is regular relative to $K[\{x_1,..., x_{e_\lambda}\}]$, where $e_\lambda = \dim R/\mathfrak{a}_\lambda$, for $\lambda = 1,..., \Lambda$.*

PROOF. Induction on n. Trivial for $n = 0$. So let $n > 0$ and assume true for $n - 1$. Relabel $\mathfrak{a}_1,..., \mathfrak{a}_\Lambda$ so that $\mathfrak{a}_\lambda \neq \{0\}$ for $\lambda \leqq \Lambda'$ and $\mathfrak{a}_\lambda = \{0\}$ for $\lambda > \Lambda'$. Let

$$0 \neq P(..., A_{ij},...) \in K[..., A_{ij},...]$$

be given where A_{ij}, $(i, j = 1,..., n)$, are indeterminates. Take $0 \neq f_\lambda(x_1,..., x_n) \in \mathfrak{a}_\lambda$ for $\lambda \leqq \Lambda'$. By Preparation Theorem (10.3.6) we can find $a_{ij} \in K$, $(i, j = 1,..., n)$, with $P(..., a_{ij},...) \neq 0$ and $\det((a_{ij})) \neq 0$, such that taking

$$y_i = \sum_{j=1}^{n} a_{ij}x_j, \qquad (i = 1,..., n)$$

and letting

$$g_\lambda(y_1,..., y_n) \in K[\{y_1,..., y_n\}] \qquad \text{with} \qquad g_\lambda(y_1,..., y_n) = f_\lambda(x_1,..., x_n),$$

we have that $g_\lambda = g_\lambda^* G_\lambda^{(n)}$ where g_λ^* is a unit in R and $G_\lambda^{(n)}$ is a distinguished polynomial in y_n with coefficients in $R_{n-1} = K[\{y_1,..., y_{n-1}\}]$, for all $\lambda \leqq \Lambda'$. Let $Q(..., B_{ij},...)$ be the polynomial in indeterminates B_{ij}, $(i, j = 1,..., n - 1)$, with coefficients in K obtained by first substituting

$$\sum_{k=1}^{n} B_{ik}a_{kj} \qquad \text{for } A_{ij}, \ (i, j = 1,..., n),$$

in $P(..., A_{ij},...)$ and then putting

$$\begin{cases} 0 \text{ for } B_{nj} & \text{for all} \quad j \neq n, \\ 0 \text{ for } B_{in} & \text{for all} \quad i \neq n, \\ 1 \text{ for } B_{nn}. \end{cases}$$

Let

$$z_i = \sum_{j=1}^{n} b_{ij}y_j \qquad \text{where} \quad b_{ij} \in K, \qquad (i, j = 1,..., n),$$

[1] See footnote 3 in §10.

are to be chosen so that:

$$1^\circ)\quad \begin{cases} b_{nj} = 0 & \text{for all} \quad j \neq n, \\ b_{in} = 0 & \text{for all} \quad i \neq n, \\ b_{nn} = 1, \\ \det((b_{ij}))_{i,j=1,\dots,n-1} \neq 0, \\ \text{and} \\ Q(\dots, b_{ij}, \dots)_{i,j=1,\dots,n-1} \neq 0. \end{cases}$$

Let

$$c_{ij} = \sum_{k=1}^{n} b_{ik} a_{kj}, \qquad (i, j = 1, \dots, n).$$

Then

$$z_i = \sum_{j=1}^{n} c_{ij} x_j \quad \text{for} \quad i = 1, \dots, n; \qquad z_n = y_n;$$

$$\det((c_{ij}))_{i,j=1,\dots,n} \neq 0;$$

and obviously

$$P(\dots, c_{ij}, \dots)_{i,j=1,\dots,n} = Q(\dots, b_{ij}, \dots)_{i,j=1,\dots,n-1}.$$

Let

$$\delta_{ij} = \begin{cases} 1 & \text{if} \quad i = j \\ 0 & \text{if} \quad i \neq j. \end{cases}$$

Then

$$Q(\dots, \delta_{ij}, \dots)_{i,j=1,\dots,n-1} = P(\dots, a_{ij}, \dots)_{i,j=1,\dots,n} \neq 0.$$

Hence $Q(\dots, B_{ij}, \dots)$ is a nonzero polynomial. By induction hypothesis we can find $b_{ij} \in K$, $(i, j = 1, \dots, n)$, satisfying properties 1°) such that $R_{n-1} \cap \mathfrak{a}_\lambda$ is regular relative to $K[\{z_1, \dots, z_{e_\lambda}\}]$, for some $e_\lambda \leqq n - 1$, for all $\lambda \leqq \Lambda'$. By (23.3.3, 23.3.4), for $\lambda \leqq \Lambda'$ and $e_\lambda < i < n$, $R_{n-1} \cap \mathfrak{a}_\lambda$ contains a monic polynomial $G_\lambda^{(i)}$ in z_i with coefficients in $K[\{z_1, \dots, z_{i-1}\}]$, and $\{0\} = K[\{z_1, \dots, z_{e_\lambda}\}] \cap (R_{n-1} \cap \mathfrak{a}_\lambda) = K[\{z_1, \dots, z_{e_\lambda}\}] \cap \mathfrak{a}_\lambda$. Since $G_\lambda^{(n)} \in \mathfrak{a}_\lambda$, again by (23.3.3, 23.3.4) we conclude that $\mathfrak{a}_\lambda$ is regular relative to $K[\{z_1, \dots, z_{e_\lambda}\}]$ for all $\lambda \leqq \Lambda'$; by definition we must have $e_\lambda = \dim R/\mathfrak{a}_\lambda$. For all $\lambda > \Lambda'$, obviously $\mathfrak{a}_\lambda = \{0\}$ is regular relative to $K[\{z_1, \dots, z_n\}] = R$.

In view of (23.3), (23.5) can be formulated in the following slightly stronger form.

(23.6) *Assume that K is infinite and let $\mathfrak{a}_\lambda$, $(\lambda = 1, \dots, \Lambda)$, be a finite number of proper ideals in R. Let $p \leqq n$ and assume that for all $i > p$ and $\lambda \leqq \Lambda$, $\mathfrak{a}_\lambda$ contains a monic polynomial in x_i with coefficients in $K[\{x_1, \dots, x_{i-1}\}]$.*

Then via a generic nonsingular K-linear transformation on $x_1, \ldots, x_p$ *it can be arranged that* $\mathfrak{a}_\lambda$ *is regular relative to* $K[\{x_1, \ldots, x_{e_\lambda}\}]$ *where* $\dim R/\mathfrak{a}_\lambda = e_\lambda \leqq p$, *for all* $\lambda \leqq \Lambda$.

Apply (23.5) to $K[\{x_1, \ldots, x_p\}] \cap \mathfrak{a}_\lambda$, $(\lambda = 1, \ldots, \Lambda)$, and then invoke (23.3).

(23.7) Definition. Let $\mathfrak{p}$ be a prime ideal in R such that $\mathfrak{p}$ is regular relative to S. Then by (23.3), the quotient field $\mathfrak{L}$ of $R/\mathfrak{p}$ is a finite algebraic extension of the quotient field $\mathfrak{K}$ of S. If furthermore $\mathfrak{L}$ is separable over $\mathfrak{K}$ then we shall say that $\mathfrak{p}$ is *strictly regular relative to* S. In (24.5) we shall show that given a prime ideal $\mathfrak{p}$ in R, via a generic nonsingular K-linear transformation on $x_1, \ldots, x_n$ it can be arranged that $\mathfrak{p}$ is strictly regular relative to $K[\{x_1, \ldots, x_{e'}\}]$, $e' = \dim R/\mathfrak{p}$. For characteristic zero, "strictly regular" and "regular" are of course one and the same thing.

(23.8) *Assume that* K *is infinite. Let* $\mathfrak{p}$ *be a prime ideal in* R *and let* $\bar{R} = R/\mathfrak{p}$.

1) *For any proper ideal* $\bar{\mathfrak{a}}$ *in* $\bar{R}$ *we have*

$$\operatorname{dpt}_{\bar{R}}\bar{\mathfrak{a}} + \operatorname{hgt}_{\bar{R}}\bar{\mathfrak{a}} = \dim \bar{R}.$$

2) *For any prime ideal* $\mathfrak{q}$ *in* R *with* $\mathfrak{p} \subset \mathfrak{q}$ *we have*

$$\operatorname{hgt}_R\mathfrak{q} = \operatorname{hgt}_R\mathfrak{p} + \operatorname{hgt}_{\bar{R}}\mathfrak{q}/\mathfrak{p}.$$

Proof. Let $\bar{\mathfrak{p}}_1, \ldots, \bar{\mathfrak{p}}_u$ be the associated prime ideals of $\bar{\mathfrak{a}}$. By definition,

$$\operatorname{dpt}_{\bar{R}}\bar{\mathfrak{a}} = \max(\operatorname{dpt}_{\bar{R}}\bar{\mathfrak{p}}_1, \ldots, \operatorname{dpt}_{\bar{R}}\bar{\mathfrak{p}}_u);$$

and

$$\operatorname{hgt}_{\bar{R}}\bar{\mathfrak{a}} = \min(\operatorname{hgt}_{\bar{R}}\bar{\mathfrak{p}}_1, \ldots, \operatorname{hgt}_{\bar{R}}\bar{\mathfrak{p}}_u).$$

Hence if

$$\operatorname{dpt}_{\bar{R}}\bar{\mathfrak{p}}_i + \operatorname{hgt}_{\bar{R}}\bar{\mathfrak{p}}_i = \dim \bar{R} \quad \text{for} \quad i = 1, \ldots, u,$$

then

$$\operatorname{dpt}_{\bar{R}}\bar{\mathfrak{a}} + \operatorname{hgt}_{\bar{R}}\bar{\mathfrak{a}} = \dim \bar{R}.$$

Thus it suffices to prove 1) when $\bar{\mathfrak{a}}$ is prime.

Let $\bar{\mathfrak{q}} = \mathfrak{q}/\mathfrak{p}$. R being regular, by (21.5.2) we get

$$\operatorname{hgt}_R\mathfrak{q} = \dim R - \operatorname{dpt}_R\mathfrak{q} \quad \text{and} \quad \operatorname{hgt}_R\mathfrak{p} = \dim R - \operatorname{dpt}_R\mathfrak{p}.$$

Also obviously

$$\operatorname{dpt}_R\mathfrak{q} = \operatorname{dpt}_{\bar{R}}\bar{\mathfrak{q}} \quad \text{and} \quad \operatorname{dpt}_R\mathfrak{p} = \dim \bar{R}.$$

Therefore

$$\mathrm{hgt}_R\mathfrak{q} = \mathrm{hgt}_R\mathfrak{p} + \mathrm{hgt}_{\bar{R}}\bar{\mathfrak{q}} \Leftrightarrow \mathrm{dpt}_{\bar{R}}\bar{\mathfrak{q}} + \mathrm{hgt}_{\bar{R}}\bar{\mathfrak{q}} = \dim \bar{R}.$$

Thus only using the fact that R is regular we have shown that to prove (23.8) it suffices to prove any one of the following two statements.

1′) For any prime ideal $\bar{\mathfrak{q}}$ in $\bar{R}$ we have

$$\mathrm{dpt}_{\bar{R}}\bar{\mathfrak{q}} + \mathrm{hgt}_{\bar{R}}\bar{\mathfrak{q}} = \dim \bar{R}.$$

2′) For any prime ideal $\mathfrak{q}$ in R with $\mathfrak{p} \subset \mathfrak{q}$ we have

$$\mathrm{hgt}_R\mathfrak{q} = \mathrm{hgt}_R\mathfrak{p} + \mathrm{hgt}_{\bar{R}}\mathfrak{q}/\mathfrak{p}.$$

We prove 1′). Let $e' = \dim \bar{R}$. By (23.5) we can arrange that $\mathfrak{p}$ is regular relative to $S' = K[\{x_1, \dots, x_{e'}\}]$. Then S' is a normal integral domain, and by (23.3) $\bar{R}$ is an overring of S' and $\bar{R}$ is integral over S'. Since $\bar{R}$ is an integral domain, by (19.3, 19.4)

$$\mathrm{dpt}_{\bar{R}}\bar{\mathfrak{q}} = \mathrm{dpt}_{S'}(\bar{\mathfrak{q}} \cap S') \qquad \text{and} \qquad \mathrm{hgt}_{\bar{R}}\bar{\mathfrak{q}} = \mathrm{hgt}_{S'}(\bar{\mathfrak{q}} \cap S').$$

Since S' is regular, by (21.5.2)

$$\mathrm{dpt}_{S'}(\bar{\mathfrak{q}} \cap S') + \mathrm{hgt}_{S'}(\bar{\mathfrak{q}} \cap S') = \dim S' = e' = \dim \bar{R}.$$

(**23.9**) REMARK. (23.8) *remains valid for an arbitrary regular local ring R.*

As shown above it suffices to prove 2′). Let $R' = R_{\mathfrak{q}}$. Then

$$\mathrm{hgt}_R\mathfrak{q} = \dim R', \qquad \mathrm{hgt}_R\mathfrak{p} = \mathrm{hgt}_{R'}\mathfrak{p}R', \qquad \text{and} \qquad \mathrm{hgt}_{\bar{R}}\mathfrak{q}/\mathfrak{p} = \mathrm{dpt}_{R'}\mathfrak{p}R'.$$

Now R' is regular (see 25.6 and 25.7. 2°), and hence by (21.5.2) we have

$$\mathrm{dpt}_{R'}\mathfrak{p}R' + \mathrm{hgt}_{R'}\mathfrak{p}R' = \dim R'.$$

(**23.10**) DEFINITION. Let $\mathfrak{a}$ be a proper ideal in R such that $\mathfrak{a} = \mathfrak{p}_1 \cap \dots \cap \mathfrak{p}_u$ where $\mathfrak{p}_1, \dots, \mathfrak{p}_u$ are distinct prime ideals in R and $\dim(R/\mathfrak{p}_i) = \dim(R/\mathfrak{a})$ for $i = 1, \dots, u$; in other words $\mathfrak{a} = \mathrm{rad}\,\mathfrak{a}$ and $\mathfrak{a}$ is unmixed. Let $\varphi : R \to \bar{R} = R/\mathfrak{a}$ be the natural epimorphism. Let $\mathfrak{L}$ be the total quotient ring of $\bar{R}$. Assume that $\mathfrak{a}$ is regular relative to S. Then by (23.2), $\mathfrak{p}_1, \dots, \mathfrak{p}_u$ are all regular relative to S. Now $\varphi(\mathfrak{p}_1) \cup \dots \cup \varphi(\mathfrak{p}_u)$ is the set of all zerodivisors in $\bar{R}$, and $\mathfrak{p}_1 \cap S = \dots = \mathfrak{p}_u \cap S = \{0\}$. Hence a nonzerodivisor in S remains a nonzerodivisor in $\bar{R}$. Therefore the quotient field $\mathfrak{K}$ of S can be considered to be a subring of $\mathfrak{L}$.

Let $z \in R$ be given. Then

$$\{f(T) \in \mathfrak{K}[T] : f(\varphi z) = 0\} = F(T)\mathfrak{K}[T]$$

where $F(T)$ is a uniquely determined monic polynomial of positive degree in T with coefficients in $\mathfrak{K}$. *We set*

$$F(T) = \textit{minimal monic polynomial of } z \bmod \mathfrak{a} \textit{ over } S.$$

Let $F_i(T)$ be the minimal monic polynomial of z mod $\mathfrak{p}_i$ over S. Now S is a unique factorization domain, and $R/\mathfrak{p}_i$ is an integral domain which is integral over S. Therefore $F_i(T) \in S[T]$, $F_i(z) \in \mathfrak{p}_i$, $F_i(T)$ is irreducible in $\mathfrak{K}[T]$ as well as in $S[T]$, and

$$[H_i(T) \in S[T] \text{ with } H_i(z) \in \mathfrak{p}_i \Rightarrow F_i(T) \text{ divides } H_i(T) \text{ in } S[T]].$$

Let $F^*(T)$ be the product of the distinct (and hence coprime) elements of the set $\{F_1(T),\ldots, F_u(T)\}$. Then $F^*(T)$ is a monic polynomial of positive degree in T with coefficients in S, $F^*(z) \in \mathfrak{p}_1 \cap \ldots \cap \mathfrak{p}_u = \mathfrak{a}$, and

$$\begin{aligned}&[H(T) \in S[T] \text{ with } H(z) \in \mathfrak{a}\\ &\Rightarrow H(z) \in \mathfrak{p}_i \text{ for } i = 1,\ldots, u\\ &\Rightarrow F_i(T) \text{ divides } H(T) \text{ in } S[T] \text{ for } i = 1,\ldots, u\\ &\Rightarrow F^*(T) \text{ divides } H(T) \text{ in } S[T]].\end{aligned}$$

Now

$$\begin{aligned}&[G(T) \in \mathfrak{K}[T] \text{ with } G(\varphi z) = 0\\ &\Rightarrow \text{there exists } 0 \neq a \in S \text{ such that } H(T) = aG(T) \in S[T]\\ &\quad\ \text{and then } H(z) \in \mathfrak{a}\\ &\Rightarrow F^*(T) \text{ divides } H(T) \text{ in } S[T]\\ &\Rightarrow F^*(T) \text{ divides } G(T) \text{ in } \mathfrak{K}[T]].\end{aligned}$$

Therefore $F^*(T) = F(T)$. Thus we have proved the following.

1) *The minimal monic polynomial $F(T)$ of z* mod $\mathfrak{a}$ *over S is the unique monic polynomial (of positive degree) in $S[T]$ with the following two properties:*

i) $F(z) \in \mathfrak{a}$.
ii) $H(T) \in S[T]$ *with* $H(z) \in \mathfrak{a} \Leftrightarrow F(T)$ *divides* $H(T)$ *in* $S[T]$.

Equivalently, let $\varphi_i : R \to R/\mathfrak{p}_i$ be the natural epimorphism, and let $F_i(T)$ be the minimal monic polynomial (in the sense of field extensions) of $\varphi_i(z)$ over $\mathfrak{K}$; then $F_i(T) \in S[T]$ for $i = 1,\ldots, u$, and $F(T)$ is product of the distinct (or equivalently, coprime) elements of the set $\{F_1(T),\ldots, F_u(T)\}$.

Note that

2) *If $z \in \mathfrak{m}$ then $F(T)$ is a distinguished polynomial in T with coefficients in S.*

By (23.3) there exists a distinguished polynomial $G(T)$ in T with coefficients in S such that $G(z) \in \mathfrak{a}$. By 1), $F(T)$ divides $G(T)$ in $S[T]$ and hence $F(T)$ is also distinguished.

From 1) we also get

3) *If* $\mathfrak{p}_1,\ldots,\mathfrak{p}_u$ *are strictly regular relative to* S *then* $F(T)$ *is a separable polynomial.*

(23.11) *Let* $\mathfrak{b} = \mathfrak{p}_1 \cap \ldots \cap \mathfrak{p}_u$ *where* $\mathfrak{p}_1,\ldots,\mathfrak{p}_u$, $(u > 0)$, *are distinct prime ideals in* R *of depth* e, *such that* $\mathfrak{b}$ *is regular relative to* S. *Let* $\psi : R \to \bar{R} = R/\mathfrak{b}$ *be the natural epimorphism. Let* $0 \neq s \in S$ *and* $\eta \in R$ *be such that* $\psi(sz_i) \in S[\psi(\eta)]$ *for* $i = 1,\ldots, m$. *Let* $f(T) \in S[T]$ *be monic of positive degree in* T *such that* $f(\eta) \in \mathfrak{b}$, *and let* Δ *be the* T*-discriminant of* $f(T)$. *Then* $\Delta \in \mathfrak{c}(\bar{R})$.

Proof. Let $\zeta_i = \psi(z_i)$ and $\omega = \psi(\eta)$. Then $s\zeta_i \in S[\omega]$ for $i = 1,\ldots, m$. By (23.3), $\bar{R} = S[\zeta_1,\ldots, \zeta_m]$. Let $F(T)$ be the minimal monic polynomial of η mod $\mathfrak{b}$ over S. Then taking $\bar{R}$ for R in (19.25.4) we get that $\Delta_F \in \mathfrak{c}(\bar{R})$. Now $F(T)$ divides $f(T)$ in $S[T]$ and hence Δ_F divides Δ in S by (17.10.5). Therefore $\Delta \in \mathfrak{c}(\bar{R})$.

(23.12) *Let* $\mathfrak{b}$ *be a proper ideal in* R *such that all the isolated primary components of* $\mathfrak{b}$ *are prime ideals and have the same depth. Assume that* $\mathfrak{b}$ *is regular relative to* S. *By* (23.2), *also* rad $\mathfrak{b}$ *is then regular relative to* S. *Let* $\eta \in R$ *be given. Let* $F(T)$ *be the minimal monic polynomial of* η mod rad $\mathfrak{b}$ *over* S. *Let a monic polynomial* $f(T) \in S[T]$ *be given such that* $f(\eta) \in \mathfrak{b}$. *Let* Δ *be the* T*-discriminant of* $f(T)$. *Then there exists a positive integer* N *such that* $\Delta^N F(\eta) \in \mathfrak{b}$.

Proof. $f(\eta) \in \mathfrak{b} \subset \text{rad}\, \mathfrak{b}$ implies that $f(T) = F(T)G(T)$ where $G(T) \in S[T]$ is monic. Hence by (17.10.5, 17.10.6), $\Delta = F(T)F^*(T) + G(T)G^*(T)$ with $F^*(T), G^*(T) \in S[T]$. Let $\mathfrak{b} = \mathfrak{p}_1 \cap \ldots \cap \mathfrak{p}_u \cap \mathfrak{q}_1^* \cap \ldots \cap \mathfrak{q}_v^*$ be a normal decomposition of $\mathfrak{b}$ where $\mathfrak{p}_1,\ldots, \mathfrak{p}_u$ are the minimal prime ideals of $\mathfrak{b}$ and the prime ideals $\mathfrak{p}_1^*,\ldots, \mathfrak{p}_v^*$ of $\mathfrak{q}_1^*,\ldots, \mathfrak{q}_v^*$ are the imbedded prime ideals of $\mathfrak{b}$. Then rad $\mathfrak{b} = \mathfrak{p}_1 \cap \ldots \cap \mathfrak{p}_u$ and hence $F(\eta) \in \mathfrak{p}_1 \cap \ldots \cap \mathfrak{p}_u$.

Given $j \leqq v$, we have that $\mathfrak{p}_i \subset \mathfrak{p}_j^*$ for some i and hence $F(\eta) \in \mathfrak{p}_j^*$; therefore:

$$G(\eta) \in \mathfrak{p}_j^* \Rightarrow \Delta = F(\eta)F^*(\eta) + G(\eta)G^*(\eta) \in \mathfrak{p}_j^*$$
$$\Rightarrow \Delta^{N_j} \in \mathfrak{q}_j^* \text{ for some } N_j > 0;$$

and

$$G(\eta) \notin \mathfrak{p}_j^* \Rightarrow [F(\eta)G(\eta) = f(\eta) \in \mathfrak{b} \subset \mathfrak{q}_j^*, \quad G(\eta) \notin \mathfrak{p}_j^*]$$
$$\Rightarrow F(\eta) \in \mathfrak{q}_j^*;$$

consequently either $\Delta^{N_j} \in \mathfrak{q}_j^*$ or $F(\eta) \in \mathfrak{q}_j^*$.

Let $N = \Sigma N_j$ where the sum is taken over all j, $(1 \leqq j \leqq v)$, for which $F(\eta) \notin \mathfrak{q}_j^*$. Then $\Delta^N F(\eta) \in \mathfrak{p}_1 \cap \ldots \cap \mathfrak{p}_u \cap \mathfrak{q}_1^* \cap \ldots \cap \mathfrak{q}_v^* = \mathfrak{b}$.

§24. PERFECT FIELDS

For an integral domain H of characteristic $p \neq 0$, we set[1]

$$H^p = \{h^p : h \in H\},$$

and

$$H^{1/p} = \{h \in \text{a fixed algebraic closure of the quotient field of } H : h^p \in H\}.$$

H^p and $H^{1/p}$ are then integral domains and $H^p \subset H \subset H^{1/p}$. Note that $h \to h^p$ is an isomorphism of H onto H^p. Also note that obviously $(H^p)^{1/p} = H$. Recall that a field H is said to be perfect if either H is of characteristic zero or H is of characteristic $p \neq 0$ and $H^p = H$.

(24.1) *Let K be a perfect field of characteristic $p \neq 0$. Let $R = K[\{x_1, \ldots, x_n\}]$ and $\mathfrak{M} = K(\{x_1, \ldots, x_n\})$. Then $R = R^p[x_1, \ldots, x_n]$, $\mathfrak{M} = \mathfrak{M}^p[x_1, \ldots, x_n]$, $[\mathfrak{M} : \mathfrak{M}^p] = p^n$, and R is a finite R^p-module.*

PROOF. Each f in $K[[x_1, \ldots, x_n]]$ can uniquely be written as

$$f = \sum_{0 \leqq d_1 < p, \ldots, 0 \leqq d_n < p} f_{d_1 \ldots d_n} x_1^{d_1} \ldots x_n^{d_n}$$

with $f_{d_1 \ldots d_n} \in K[[x_1^p, \ldots, x_n^p]]$, and it is obvious that if f is in $K[\langle x_1, \ldots, x_n \rangle]$ then so are all the elements $f_{d_1 \ldots d_n}$. Since K is perfect, we can write $f_{d_1 \ldots d_n} = (g_{d_1 \ldots d_n})^p$ with $g_{d_1 \ldots d_n} \in K[[x_1, \ldots, x_n]]$. From this it will follow that $R = R^p[x_1, \ldots, x_n]$ provided we show that for any

$$h = \sum_{i_1, \ldots, i_n \geqq 0} h_{i_1 \ldots i_n} x_1^{i_1} \ldots x_n^{i_n} \in K[[x_1, \ldots, x_n]], \qquad h_{i_1 \ldots i_n} \in K,$$

if

$$h^p = \sum (h_{i_1 \ldots i_n})^p x_1^{p i_1} \ldots x_n^{p i_n} \quad \text{is in} \quad K[\langle x_1, \ldots, x_n \rangle]$$

then

$$h \quad \text{is in} \quad K[\langle x_1, \ldots, x_n \rangle].$$

So assume that $h^p \in K[\langle x_1, \ldots, x_n \rangle]$. Then we can find positive real numbers $A_1, \ldots, A_n, B$ such that

$$|(h_{i_1 \ldots i_n})^p| A_1^{p i_1} \ldots A_n^{p i_n} \leqq B \qquad \text{for all} \quad i_1, \ldots, i_n.$$

[1] In this section, H^p will not stand for the p-fold direct sum of H.

Consequently

$$|h_{i_1\dots i_n}|A_1^{i_1}\dots A_n^{i_n} \leqq B^{1/p} \qquad \text{for all} \quad i_1,\dots, i_n.$$

Therefore $h \in K[\langle x_1,\dots, x_n\rangle]$. This shows that $R = R^p[x_1,\dots, x_n]$, and hence $\mathfrak{M} = \mathfrak{M}^p[x_1,\dots, x_n]$. Now $x_{i+1} \notin \mathfrak{M}^p[x_1,\dots, x_i]$ and $x_{i+1}^p \in \mathfrak{M}^p[x_1,\dots, x_i]$ for $i = 0,\dots, n-1$. Consequently

$$\{x_1^{d_1}\dots x_n^{d_n}: 0 \leqq d_1 < p,\dots, 0 \leqq d_n < p\}$$

is a vector space basis of $\mathfrak{M}$ over $\mathfrak{M}^p$ and hence $[\mathfrak{M} : \mathfrak{M}^n] = p^n$. The above is also a module basis of R over R^p and hence R is a finite R^p-module.

(24.2) *Let $R = K[\{x_1,\dots, x_n\}]$ where K is a perfect field of characteristic $p \neq 0$. Then $R^{1/p}$ is a finite R-module.*

Proof. Since R and R^p are isomorphic, it suffices to show that $(R^p)^{1/p}$ is a finite (R^p)-module. However, $(R^p)^{1/p} = R$ and hence we are reduced to (24.1).

(24.3) Let $\sigma : K[\{x_1,\dots, x_n\}] \to R$ be a ring epimorphism whose kernel is a proper ideal $\mathfrak{a}$ in $K[\{x_1,\dots, x_n\}]$. Assume that K is an infinite perfect field and $\mathrm{rad}_R\{0\} = \{0\}$. Let $\mathfrak{L}$ be the total quotient ring of R and let R' be the integral closure of R in $\mathfrak{L}$. Let $\mathfrak{p}_1,\dots, \mathfrak{p}_u$ be the distinct prime ideals of $\{0\}$ in R. Let $\varphi_i : R \to R_i$ be a ring epimorphism whose kernel is $\mathfrak{p}_i$. Let $\mathfrak{L}_i$ be the quotient field of R_i and let R_i' be the integral closure of R_i in $\mathfrak{L}_i$. By (18.9.2), φ_i has a unique extension $\psi_i : \mathfrak{L} \to \mathfrak{L}_i$, for $i = 1,\dots, u$; $\psi_1 \oplus\dots\oplus \psi_u : \mathfrak{L} \to \mathfrak{L}_1 \oplus\dots\oplus \mathfrak{L}_u$ is the unique extension of $\varphi_1 \oplus\dots\oplus \varphi_u$; and $\psi_1 \oplus\dots\oplus \psi_u$ is actually a ring isomorphism.

1) *If R_i^* is any overring of R_i such that R_i^* is an integral domain, R_i^* is integral over R_i and the quotient field of R_i^* is a finite algebraic extension of $\mathfrak{L}_i$, then R_i^* is a local ring and a finite R_i-module. In particular R_i' is a local ring and a finite R_i-module.*

2) *R' is a finite R-module.*

3) *$\psi_i(R') = R_i'$ for $i = 1,\dots, u$; and $\lambda_1 \oplus\dots\oplus \lambda_u : R' \to R_1' \oplus\dots\oplus R_u'$ is a ring isomorphism where $\lambda_i : R' \to R_i'$ is induced by ψ_i. $R_1',\dots, R_u'$ are local rings. Let $\mathfrak{m}_i$ be the maximal ideal in R_i', $\mathfrak{n}_i = \lambda_i^{-1}(\mathfrak{m}_i)$, and $\mathfrak{q}_i = \mathrm{Ker}\,\lambda_i$ for $i = 1,\dots, u$. Then R' is a semilocal ring; $\mathfrak{n}_1,\dots, \mathfrak{n}_u$ are exactly all the distinct maximal ideals in R'; $\mathfrak{q}_1,\dots, \mathfrak{q}_u$ are exactly all the distinct prime ideals of $\{0\}$ in R'; $\{0\} = \mathfrak{q}_1 \cap\dots\cap \mathfrak{q}_u$ is the unique normal decomposition of $\{0\}$ in R'; $\mathfrak{p}_i \subset \mathfrak{q}_i \subset \mathfrak{n}_i$ and $\mathfrak{p}_i = R \cap \mathfrak{q}_i$ for all i; and $\mathfrak{p}_j \not\subset \mathfrak{q}_i$ and $\mathfrak{q}_j \not\subset \mathfrak{n}_i$*

for all $j \neq i$. *If* $\tilde{R}_1,\ldots,\tilde{R}_v$ *are local rings and* $\mu_1 : R' \to \tilde{R}_1,\ldots, \mu_v : R' \to \tilde{R}_v$ *are ring homomorphisms such that* $\mu_1 \oplus\ldots\oplus \mu_v : R' \to \tilde{R}_1 \oplus\ldots\oplus \tilde{R}_v$ *is an isomorphism, then* $v = u$ *and upon relabeling* $\tilde{R}_1,\ldots,\tilde{R}_v$ *there exist ring isomorphisms* $\nu_i : R_i' \to \tilde{R}_i$ *such that* $\mu_i = \nu_i \circ \lambda_i$ *for* $i = 1,\ldots, u$; (*the said relabeling of* $\tilde{R}_1,\ldots,\tilde{R}_u$ *as well as the isomorphisms* $\nu_1,\ldots,\nu_u$ *are unique*).

4) *If* $\mathfrak{p}$ *is any prime ideal in* R *such that* $R_{\mathfrak{p}}$ *is normal, then* $\mathfrak{c}(R) \not\subset \mathfrak{p}$.

5) *Assume that* $\dim R_1 = \ldots = \dim R_u$. *Let* Ω *be the set of all prime ideals in* R *of height one, and assume that* $R_{\mathfrak{p}}$ *is regular for all* $\mathfrak{p} \in \Omega$. *Then for any* $w \in \mathfrak{L}$ *we have that*: $w \in R' \Leftrightarrow \operatorname{ord}_{R_{\mathfrak{p}}} w \geqq 0$ *for all* $\mathfrak{p} \in \Omega$.

Proof of 1). Upon replacing R by R_i, we may assume that $\mathfrak{a}$ is a prime ideal. What we now have to prove is that: if an overring R^* of R is such that R^* is an integral domain, $R^*$is integral over R and the quotient field $\mathfrak{L}^*$ of R^* is a finite algebraic extension of $\mathfrak{L}$, then R^* is a local ring and a finite R-module. By (23.5), upon making a linear transformation on $x_1,\ldots,x_n$ we can arrange that $\mathfrak{a}$ is regular relative to $S = K[\{x_1,\ldots, x_e\}]$ where $e = \dim R$. By (23.3), $S \cap \mathfrak{a} = \{0\}$ and upon identifying $\sigma(S)$ with S, R is integral over S and $\mathfrak{L}$ is a finite algebraic extension of the quotient field $\mathfrak{K}$ of S. Consequently, R^* is integral over S and $\mathfrak{L}^*$ is a finite algebraic extension of $\mathfrak{K}$. Recall the following well known results from algebra[2]: if H is any normal noetherian integral domain such that either H is of characteristic zero or H is of characteristic $p \neq 0$ and $H^{1/p}$ is a finite H-module, and if H^* is any overring of H such that H^* is an integral domain, H^* is integral over H and the quotient field of H^* is a finite algebraic extension of the quotient field of H, then H^* is a finite H-module. In our case S is a normal noetherian integral domain, and if S is of characteristic $p \neq 0$ then $S^{1/p}$ is a finite S-module by (24.2). Therefore R^* is a finite S-module. Consequently R^* is a finite R-module; and by (20.6), R^* is a local ring.

Proof of 2) *and* 3). By 1), R_i' is a finite R_i-module for $i = 1,\ldots, u$. Therefore by (19.23), R' is a finite R-module and $\psi_1 \oplus\ldots\oplus\psi_u(R') = R_1' \oplus\ldots\oplus R_u'$. Consequently $\psi_i(R') = R_i'$ for $i = 1,\ldots, u$, and $\lambda_1 \oplus\ldots\oplus \lambda_u : R' \to R_1' \oplus\ldots\oplus R_u'$ is an isomorphism. By 1), $R_1',\ldots, R_u'$ are local integral domains and hence the rest of 3) now follows from (18.8, 18.9.3).

Proof of 4). By 1), R_i' is a finite R_i-module for $i = 1,\ldots, u$, and hence we are reduced to (19.21.2).

Proof of 5). By (23.5), upon making a linear transformation on $x_1,\ldots, x_n$ we can arrange that $\mathfrak{a}$ is regular relative to $S = K[\{x_1,\ldots, x_e\}]$ where

[2] For instance see van der Waerden [2: pp. 79–81].

$e = \dim R = \dim R_1 = \ldots = \dim R_u$. By (23.3), $S \cap \mathfrak{a} = S \cap \sigma^{-1}(\mathfrak{p}_1) = \ldots = S \cap \sigma^{-1}(\mathfrak{p}_u) = \{0\}$, and R is integral over $\sigma(S)$. Thus $\sigma(S)$ is a subring of R such that $\sigma(S)$ is a normal integral domain, R is integral over $\sigma(S)$, and every nonzero element in $\sigma(S)$ is a nonzerodivisor in R. By 1), R_i' is a finite R_i-module for $i = 1,\ldots, u$. Consequently we are reduced to (21.10).

(24.4) *Let K be an infinite perfect field of characteristic $p \neq 0$. Let $R = K[\{x_1,\ldots, x_n\}]$ and $\mathfrak{M} = K(\{x_1,\ldots, x_n\})$. Let $\mathfrak{p}$ be a prime ideal in R. Let $e = \dim R/\mathfrak{p}$. Let $\varphi : R \to \bar{R} = R/\mathfrak{p}$ be the natural epimorphism. For any element or subset r of R let $\bar{r}$ denote $\varphi(r)$. Let $\mathfrak{L}$ be the quotient field of $\bar{R}$. Then $\mathfrak{L} = \mathfrak{L}^p[\bar{x}_1,\ldots, \bar{x}_n]$ and $[\mathfrak{L} : \mathfrak{L}^p] = p^e$.*

PROOF. By (23.5), via a K-linear transformation on $x_1,\ldots, x_n$, we can arrange that $\mathfrak{p}$ is regular relative to $S = K[\{x_1,\ldots, x_e\}]$. Identify $\mathfrak{K} = K(\{x_1,\ldots, x_e\})$ with a subfield of $\mathfrak{L}$. By (24.1), $R = R^p[x_1,\ldots, x_n]$ and hence $\bar{R} = \bar{R}^p[\bar{x}_1,\ldots, \bar{x}_n]$. Therefore $\mathfrak{L} = \mathfrak{L}^p[\bar{x}_1,\ldots, \bar{x}_n]$. Applying (24.1) to S we get $[\mathfrak{K} : \mathfrak{K}^p] = p^e$. Via the isomorphism $h \to h^p$ we get $[\mathfrak{L} : \mathfrak{K}] = [\mathfrak{L}^p : \mathfrak{K}^p]$. Now $[\mathfrak{L} : \mathfrak{K}][\mathfrak{K} : \mathfrak{K}^p] = [\mathfrak{L} : \mathfrak{K}^p] = [\mathfrak{L} : \mathfrak{L}^p][\mathfrak{L}^p : \mathfrak{K}^p]$ and hence $[\mathfrak{L} : \mathfrak{L}^p] = p^e$.

(24.5) *In the situation of* (24.4), *there exists a generic nonsingular K-linear transformation*

$$y_i = \sum_{j=1}^{n} a_{ij}x_j, \qquad (i = 1,\ldots, n), \qquad a_{ij} \in K,$$

such that $\mathfrak{p}$ is strictly regular relative to $K[\{y_1,\ldots, y_e\}]$.

PROOF. Let $T_1,\ldots, T_e$ be indeterminates. Label the monomials

$$T_1^{d_1}\ldots T_e^{d_e}, \qquad (0 \leqq d_1 < p,\ldots, 0 \leqq d_e < p),$$

as $f_\alpha(T_1,\ldots, T_e)$, $(\alpha = 1,\ldots, p^e)$. In view of (24.4), upon relabeling $x_1,\ldots, x_n$ we can arrange that $\mathfrak{L} = \mathfrak{L}^p[\bar{x}_1,\ldots, \bar{x}_e]$, and then $\{\xi_1,\ldots, \xi_{p^e}\}$ is a vector space basis of $\mathfrak{L}$ over $\mathfrak{L}^p$ where

$$\xi_\alpha = f_\alpha(\bar{x}_1,\ldots, \bar{x}_e).$$

Let $A = (\ldots, A_{ij},\ldots)$, $(i = 1,\ldots, e;\ j = 1,\ldots, n)$, be indeterminates. Let

$$g_i(A) = \sum_{j=1}^{n} A_{ij}\bar{x}_j, \qquad (i = 1,\ldots, e),$$

and

$$\eta_\alpha(A) = \eta_\alpha(..., A_{ij},...)$$
$$= f_\alpha(g_1(A),..., g_e(A)).$$

Then

$$\eta_\alpha(A) = \sum_{\beta=1}^{p^e} h_{\alpha\beta}(A)\xi_\beta, \qquad (\alpha = 1,.., p^e), \qquad \text{with} \qquad h_{\alpha\beta}(A) \in \mathfrak{L}^p[A].$$

Let

$$P(A) = P(..., A_{ij},...)$$
$$= \det((h_{\alpha\beta}(A))), \qquad (\alpha, \beta = 1,..., p^e).$$

Let

$$\delta_{ij} = \begin{cases} 1 & \text{if } i = j \\ 0 & \text{if } i \neq j. \end{cases}$$

Then $\eta_\alpha(..., \delta_{ij},...) = \xi_\alpha$ and hence $P(..., \delta_{ij},...) \neq 0$. Therefore $0 \neq P(..., A_{ij},...) \in \mathfrak{L}^p[A]$. Consequently by (23.5) we can find "generic" $a_{ij} \in K$ such that $P(..., a_{ij},...) \neq 0$, and such that $\{y_1,..., y_e\}$ is a system of parameters for R mod $\mathfrak{p}$ where

$$y_i = \sum_{j=1}^{n} a_{ij}x_j.$$

Let $S = K[\{y_1,..., y_e\}]$ and $\mathfrak{K} = K(\{y_1,..., y_e\})$. Then $\mathfrak{L}$ is a finite algebraic extension of $\mathfrak{K}$. Since $P(..., a_{ij},...) \neq 0$, it follows that

$$\{f_\alpha(y_1,..., y_e): \alpha = 1,..., p^e\}$$

is a vector space basis of $\mathfrak{L}$ over $\mathfrak{L}^p$. Consequently $\mathfrak{L} = \mathfrak{L}^p(\mathfrak{K})$. Therefore $\mathfrak{L}$ is separable over $\mathfrak{K}$.[3]

(24.6) *Weierstrassian rings.*[4]

1) DEFINITION. Let R and R' be integral domains such that R' is an overring of R. R' is said to be an *almost finite integral extension of R* if R' is integral over R and the quotient field of R' is a finite algebraic extension of the quotient field of R. R' is said to be a *finite integral extension of R* if R' is a finite R-module.

[3] Let $\mathfrak{K}$ be any field of characteristic $p \neq 0$ and let $\mathfrak{L}$ be any finite algebraic extension of $\mathfrak{K}$. Then $\mathfrak{L}$ is separable over $\mathfrak{K} \Leftrightarrow \mathfrak{L} = \mathfrak{L}^p(\mathfrak{K})$; Zariski-Samuel [**1**: Theorem 8 on p. 69].

[4] Results of (24.6) will not be used elsewhere. The concept of a Weierstrassian ring and Proposition (24.6.2) are due to Nagata [**2**: §2].

A family $G = \{G_0, G_1, ..., G_n, ...\}$ of sets of rings is called a *Weierstrassian family* provided the following three conditions hold.

i) Every member of G_n is a Henselian regular local ring of dimension n.

ii) Every almost finite integral extension of $R \in G_n$ is a finite R-module.

iii) If $\mathfrak{p}$ is a prime ideal of height one in $R \in G_n$ then $R/\mathfrak{p}$ is isomorphic to a finite integral extension of a member of G_{n-1}.

An n dimensional local ring R is said to be a *Weierstrassian ring* provided there exists a Weierstrassian family $G = \{G_0, G_1, ..., G_n, ...\}$ of rings such that R is isomorphic to a member of G_n.

2) (Nagata). *Let R be a Weierstrassian ring, let $\hat{R}$ be the completion of R, let $\mathfrak{M}$ be the quotient field of R and let $\hat{\mathfrak{M}}$ be the quotient field of $\hat{R}$. Then $\mathfrak{M}$ is relatively algebraically closed in $\hat{\mathfrak{M}}$.*[5] *Let $\mathfrak{p}$ be a prime ideal in R. Then $\mathfrak{p}\hat{R}$ is a prime ideal in $\hat{R}$. Let R' be a finite integral extension of R and let $\hat{R}'$ be the completion of R'. Then $\hat{R}'$ is an integral domain. If furthermore R' is normal and the quotient field of R' is separable over the quotient field of R then $\hat{R}'$ is normal.*

Taking $G_n = K[\{x_1, ..., x_n\}]$ where K is infinite perfect, in virtue of (20.6.5, 24.3.1, 23.5) we see that $K[\{x_1, ..., x_n\}]$ is a Weierstrassian ring. Also by (24.5), if $\mathfrak{p}$ is a prime ideal in $R = K[\{x_1, ..., x_n\}]$ then $R/\mathfrak{p}$ is isomorphic to a finite integral extension $\bar{R}'$ of $K[\{x_1, ..., x_e\}]$, ($e = \dim R/\mathfrak{p}$), such that the quotient field of $\bar{R}'$ is separable over $K(\{x_1, ..., x_e\})$. Noting that $K[\{x_1, ..., x_n\}]$ is a unique factorization domain, 2) yields the following.

3) *Let $R = K[\{x_1, ..., x_n\}]$, $\hat{R} = K[[x_1, ..., x_n]]$, $\mathfrak{M} = K(\{x_1, ..., x_n\})$ $\hat{\mathfrak{M}} = K((x_1, ..., x_n))$, where K is infinite perfect. Then $\mathfrak{M}$ is relatively algebraically closed in $\hat{\mathfrak{M}}$.*[5] *Let $\mathfrak{p}$ be any prime ideal in R, let $\bar{R} = R/\mathfrak{p}$ and $\hat{\bar{R}}$ = completion of $\bar{R}$, ($\hat{\bar{R}} \approx \hat{R}/\mathfrak{p}\hat{R}$). Then $\hat{\bar{R}}$ is an integral domain, i.e., $\mathfrak{p}\hat{R}$ is prime. If furthermore $\bar{R}$ is normal then $\hat{\bar{R}}$ is normal. More generally let $\bar{R}'$ be any finite integral extension of $\bar{R}$ and let $\hat{\bar{R}}'$ be the completion of $\bar{R}'$. Then $\hat{\bar{R}}'$ is an integral domain. If furthermore $\bar{R}'$ is normal and the quotient field of $\bar{R}'$ is separable over the quotient field of $\bar{R}$ then $\hat{\bar{R}}'$ is normal. Taking $\mathfrak{p}$ to be principal, we see that any irreducible nonunit in R remains irreducible in $\hat{R}$.*

[5] That is, every element in $\hat{\mathfrak{M}}$ which is algebraic over $\mathfrak{M}$ is already in $\mathfrak{M}$. Since R is normal, this implies that R is integrally closed in $\hat{\mathfrak{M}}$.

§25. REGULARITY OF QUOTIENT RINGS

(25.1) LEMMA. *Let $\mathfrak{K}^*$ be a field and let $\mathfrak{K}$ be a subfield of $\mathfrak{K}^*$. Let $z = (z_1, \ldots, z_m)$ be indeterminates over $\mathfrak{K}^*$. Then we have the following.*

1) *Any finite number of elements of $\mathfrak{K}^*$ which are linearly independent over $\mathfrak{K}$ are linearly independent over $\mathfrak{K}(z)$.*

2) *For any ideal $\mathfrak{b}$ in $\mathfrak{K}[z]$ we have $\mathfrak{K}[z] \cap \mathfrak{b}\mathfrak{K}^*[z] = \mathfrak{b}$.*

PROOF. 1) is obvious. To prove 2) let $\alpha \in \mathfrak{K}[z] \cap \mathfrak{b}\mathfrak{K}^*[z]$ be given. $\alpha \in \mathfrak{b}\mathfrak{K}^*[z]$ implies that $\alpha = \sum_i a_i b_i$ with $a_i = a_i(z) \in \mathfrak{K}^*[z]$, $b_i \in \mathfrak{b}$. Let W be the set of all the coefficients of all the elements $a_i(z)$. Let $d_1, \ldots, d_e$ be a $\mathfrak{K}$-basis of the $\mathfrak{K}$-vector space spanned by $W \cup \{1\}$, where we take $d_1 = 1$. Then $a_j = \sum_i d_i a^*_{ij}$ with $a^*_{ij} \in \mathfrak{K}[z]$. Let $b^*_i = \sum_j a^*_{ij} b_j$. Then $b^*_i \in \mathfrak{b}$ and $\alpha = \sum_i d_i b^*_i$. By 1), $d_1, \ldots, d_e$ are linearly independent over $\mathfrak{K}(z)$. Since $\alpha, b^*_1, \ldots, b^*_e \in \mathfrak{K}(z)$ and $d_1 = 1$, we get $\alpha = b^*_1 \in \mathfrak{b}$.

(25.2) LEMMA. *Let $\mathfrak{K}$ be a field and let $z = (z_1, \ldots, z_m)$ be indeterminates over $\mathfrak{K}$. Let $g_i(z_i) \in \mathfrak{K}[z_i]$ be monic of positive degree, and let $\mathfrak{b} = \{g_1(z_1), \ldots, g_m(z_m)\}\mathfrak{K}[z]$. Then we have the following.*

1) *$\mathfrak{b} \neq \mathfrak{K}[z]$, and $\mathfrak{b}$ is contained only in a finite number of prime ideals $\mathfrak{p}_1, \ldots, \mathfrak{p}_u$, $(u > 0)$, in $\mathfrak{K}[z]$. Each $\mathfrak{p}_j$ is maximal in $\mathfrak{K}[z]$, and for the natural epimorphism $\psi_j : \mathfrak{K}[z] \to \mathfrak{L}_j = \mathfrak{K}[z]/\mathfrak{p}_j$ we have that: $\mathfrak{L}_j$ is a finite algebraic extension of $\mathfrak{K}$ and $\mathfrak{L}_j = \mathfrak{K}[\psi_j(z_1), \ldots, \psi_j(z_m)]$,* (since $\mathfrak{p}_j \cap \mathfrak{K} = \{0\}$, we identify $\mathfrak{K}$ with $\psi_j(\mathfrak{K})$).

2) *If furthermore the z_i-discriminant of $g_i(z_i)$ is nonzero for $i = 1, \ldots, m$, then* rad $\mathfrak{b} = \mathfrak{b}$.

Proof of 1). Let $\mathfrak{K}^*$ be an algebraic closure of $\mathfrak{K}$. Suppose if possible that $1 = \sum g_i(z_i) f_i(z)$ with $f_i(z) \in \mathfrak{K}[z]$. Let a_i be a root of $g_i(z_i)$ in $\mathfrak{K}^*$. Then $1 = \sum g_i(a_i) f_i(a_1, \ldots, a_m) = 0$ which is a contradiction. Therefore $\mathfrak{b} \neq \mathfrak{K}[z]$. Let $\mathfrak{p}$ be a prime ideal in $\mathfrak{K}[z]$ containing $\mathfrak{b}$ and let $\psi: \mathfrak{K}[z] \to \mathfrak{L} = \mathfrak{K}[z]/\mathfrak{p}$ be the natural epimorphism. Then $\mathfrak{L} = \mathfrak{K}[\psi z_1, \ldots, \psi z_m]$ and ψz_i is algebraic over $\mathfrak{K}$ since $g_i(\psi z_i) = 0$. Therefore $\mathfrak{L}$ is a finite algebraic extension of $\mathfrak{K}$. The rest is now obvious.

Proof of 2). Let $\mathfrak{K}^*$ be an algebraic closure of $\mathfrak{K}$. Note that the discriminant of $g_i(z_i)$ is the same whether $g_i(z_i)$ is considered as an element of $\mathfrak{K}[z]$ or of $\mathfrak{K}^*[z]$. If

$$\text{rad}(\mathfrak{b}\mathfrak{K}^*[z]) = \mathfrak{b}\mathfrak{K}^*[z]$$

then by (25.1.2) we would get that

$$\text{rad}\, \mathfrak{b} \subset [\text{rad}(\mathfrak{b}\mathfrak{K}^*[z])] \cap \mathfrak{K}[z] = (\mathfrak{b}\mathfrak{K}^*[z]) \cap \mathfrak{K}[z] = \mathfrak{b}.$$

Thus it suffices to show that $\text{rad}(\mathfrak{b}\mathfrak{K}^*[z]) = \mathfrak{b}\mathfrak{K}^*[z]$, i.e., *we may assume that* $\mathfrak{K}$ *is algebraically closed*. Then by 1), $\mathfrak{L}_j = \mathfrak{K}$. Let $a_{ij} = \psi_j z_i \in \mathfrak{K}$. Then $z_i - a_{ij} \in \mathfrak{p}_j$. Now

$$\{z_1 - a_{1j},\ldots, z_m - a_{mj}\}\mathfrak{K}[z]$$

is a maximal ideal in $\mathfrak{K}[z]$ contained in $\mathfrak{p}_j$ and hence it equals $\mathfrak{p}_j$. For any $f(z_i) \in \mathfrak{K}[z_i]$ we have $\psi_j f(z_i) = f(a_{ij})$, and hence $f(z_i) \in \mathfrak{p}_j \Leftrightarrow f(a_{ij}) = 0$. Now $g_i(z_i) = (z_i - a_{ij}) f_i(z_i)$ with $f_i(a_{ij}) \neq 0$. Therefore

$$\mathfrak{b}(\mathfrak{K}[z])_{\mathfrak{p}_j} = \mathfrak{p}_j(\mathfrak{K}[z])_{\mathfrak{p}_j} \qquad \text{for} \quad j = 1,\ldots, u.$$

Therefore $\mathfrak{b} = \text{rad}\, \mathfrak{b}$.

(25.3) LEMMA. *Let S be an integral domain and let $z = (z_1,\ldots, z_m)$ be indeterminates. Let $g_i(z_i)$ be a monic polynomial of degree $d_i > 0$ in z_i with coefficients in S. Let $0 \neq f \in S[z]$ be such that* $\deg_{z_i} f < d_i$ *for $i = 1,\ldots, m$. Then*

$$f \notin \{g_1(z_1),\ldots, g_m(z_m)\}S[z].$$

PROOF. Induction on m. Trivial for $m = 1$. So let $m > 1$ and assume true for $m - 1$. Suppose if possible that

$$f \in \{g_1(z_1),\ldots, g_m(z_m)\}S[z].$$

Then

$$f = \sum_{i=1}^{m} f_i g_i(z_i) \qquad \text{with} \quad f_i \in S[z].$$

Since $g_m(z_m)$ is monic, we can write

$$f_i = q_i g_m(z_m) + r_i \qquad \text{for} \quad i = 1,\ldots, m - 1,$$

where $q_i \in S[z]$ and

$$r_i = \sum_{j=0}^{d_m - 1} r_{ij} z_m^j \qquad \text{with} \qquad r_{ij} \in S[z_1,\ldots, z_{m-1}].$$

Then

$$f - \sum_{i=1}^{m-1} r_i g_i(z_i) = [f_m + \sum_{i=1}^{m-1} q_i g_i(z_i)] g_m(z_m).$$

Since the degree of the left hand side in z_m is $< d_m$ and since $S[z_1,\ldots, z_{m-1}]$ is an integral domain, we must have

1°) $$f = \sum_{i=1}^{m-1} r_i g_i(z_i).$$

By assumption

$$f = \sum_{j=0}^{d_m-1} s_j z_m^j \quad \text{with} \quad s_j \in S[z_1,\ldots, z_{m-1}] \quad \text{such that}$$

$$\deg_{z_i} s_j < d_i \quad \text{for} \quad i = 1,\ldots, m-1.$$

Equating coefficients of z_m in 1°) we get

$$s_j = \sum_{i=1}^{m-1} r_{ij} g_i(z_i) \quad \text{for} \quad j = 0,\ldots, d_m - 1,$$

and hence by induction hypothesis $s_j = 0$ for $j = 0,\ldots, d_m - 1$, i.e., $f = 0$.

(25.4) LEMMA. *Let* $y = (y_1,\ldots, y_e)$, $z = (z_1,\ldots, z_m)$, $S = K[\{y\}]$, $R = K[\{y, z\}]$, $R^* = S[z]$. *Let* $g_i(z_i)$ *be a distinguished polynomial of degree* $d_i > 0$ *in* z_i *with coefficients in* S. *Let* $\mathfrak{a}^* = \{g_1(z_1),\ldots, g_m(z_m)\}R^*$. *Then we have the following.*

1) $R^* \cap \mathfrak{a}^*R = \mathfrak{a}^*$.

2) *If* $0 \neq f \in R^*$ *is such that* $\deg_{z_i} f < d_i$ *for* $i = 1,\ldots, m$, *then* $f \notin \mathfrak{a}^*R$.

Proof of 1). Induction on m. Take $m = 1$. Let $a \in \mathfrak{a}^*R$. Then $a = qg_1(z_1)$ with $q \in R$. Assume $a \in R^* = S[z_1]$. Since $g_1(z_1)$ is a distinguished polynomial in z_1, by Preparation Theorem (10.3.3) it follows that $q \in S[z_1]$, i.e., $a \in \mathfrak{a}^*$. Now take $m > 1$ and assume true for $m - 1$. Let $H = K[\{y_1,\ldots, y_e, z_1,\ldots, z_{m-1}\}]$. Let $a \in R^* \cap \mathfrak{a}^*R$ be given. We want to show that $a \in \mathfrak{a}^*$. Since $a \in R^*$ we can write

$$a = \sum_{j=0}^{N} a_j z_m^j \quad \text{where} \quad a_j \in S[z_1,\ldots, z_{m-1}] \text{ and } N \text{ is an integer.}$$

Since $g_m(z_m)$ is monic, we can write

$$z_m^j = \bar{q}_j g_m(z_m) + \bar{r}_j \quad \text{with} \quad \bar{q}_j, \bar{r}_j \in S[z_m], \quad \deg_{z_m} \bar{r}_j < d_m.$$

Let

$$\alpha = \sum_{j=0}^{N} a_j \bar{r}_j.$$

Then

$$\alpha = \sum_{j=0}^{d_m-1} \alpha_j z_m^j \qquad \text{with} \qquad \alpha_j \in S[z_1, \ldots, z_{m-1}].$$

Also

$$a - \alpha = \left(\sum_{j=0}^{N} a_j \bar{q}_j \right) g_m(z_m) \in g_m(z_m) R^* \subset \mathfrak{a}^*.$$

Hence $\alpha \in \mathfrak{a}^* R$ and it suffices to show that $\alpha \in \mathfrak{a}^*$. Since $\alpha \in \mathfrak{a}^* R$ we can write

$$\alpha = \sum_{i=1}^{m} f_i g_i(z_i) \qquad \text{with} \quad f_i \in R.$$

By Preparation Theorem (10.3.1), we can write

$$\left.\begin{aligned} f_i &= q_i g_m(z_m) + r_i \text{ with } \quad q_i \in R \\ \text{and} \quad r_i &= \sum_{j=0}^{d_m-1} r_{ij} z_m^j \qquad \text{with} \quad r_{ij} \in H \end{aligned}\right\} \qquad i = 1, \ldots, m-1.$$

We thus get

$$\alpha - \sum_{i=1}^{m-1} r_i g_i(z_i) = [f_m + \sum_{i=1}^{m-1} q_i g_i(z_i)] g_m(z_m).$$

The left-hand side is a polynomial of degree $< d_m$ in z_m with coefficients in H and $g_m(z_m)$ is distinguished of degree d_m. Therefore by the uniqueness part of (10.3.1) we must have

$$f_m + \sum_{i=1}^{m-1} q_i g_i(z_i) = 0,$$

i.e.,

$$\alpha = \sum_{i=1}^{m-1} r_i g_i(z_i).$$

Equating coefficients of z_m^j in the above equation, we get

$$\alpha_j = \sum_{i=1}^{m-1} r_{ij} g_i(z_i) \qquad \text{for} \quad j = 0, \ldots, d_m - 1.$$

Therefore

$$\alpha_j \in (\{g_1(z_1), \ldots, g_{m-1}(z_{m-1})\} H) \cap S[z_1, \ldots, z_{m-1}]$$

and hence by induction hypothesis we must have

$$\alpha_j \in \{g_1(z_1), \ldots, g_{m-1}(z_{m-1})\} S[z_1, \ldots, z_{m-1}] \qquad \text{for} \quad j = 0, \ldots, d_m - 1.$$

Therefore

$$\alpha = \sum_{j=0}^{d_m-1} \alpha_j z_m^j \in \{g_1(z_1),\dots, g_{m-1}(z_{m-1})\}S[z_1,\dots, z_m] \subset \mathfrak{a}^*.$$

Proof of 2). Follows from 1) and (25.3).

(25.5) PROPOSITION. *Let $y = (y_1,\dots, y_e)$, $z = (z_1,\dots, z_m)$, $S = K[\{y\}]$, $R = K[\{y, z\}]$. Let $g_i(z_i)$ be a distinguished polynomial of positive degree in z_i with coefficients in S. Let $\mathfrak{a} = \{g_1(z_1),\dots, g_m(z_m)\}R$. Then $\mathfrak{a}$ is regular relative to S. Let $\mathfrak{p}$ be a prime ideal in R such that $\mathfrak{p} \supset \mathfrak{a}$ and $\mathfrak{p}$ is regular relative to S. Then $\mathfrak{p}$ is a minimal prime ideal of $\mathfrak{a}$. Let $\mathfrak{q}$ be the corresponding isolated primary component of $\mathfrak{a}$. Assume that the z_i-discriminant of $g_i(z_i)$ is nonzero for $i = 1,\dots, m$. Then $\mathfrak{q} = \mathfrak{p}$, $\mathfrak{a}R_\mathfrak{p} = \mathfrak{p}R_\mathfrak{p}$, and $R_\mathfrak{p}$ is a regular local ring of dimension m.*

PROOF. $\mathfrak{a} \cap S = \{0\}$ by (25.4) and hence $\mathfrak{a}$ is regular relative to S by (23.3.3, 23.3.4).[1] Therefore $\dim R/\mathfrak{p} = \dim R/\mathfrak{a} = e$ and hence $\mathfrak{p}$ is a minimal prime ideal of $\mathfrak{a}$. Let $\mathfrak{a} = \mathfrak{q} \cap \mathfrak{q}_1 \cap\dots\cap \mathfrak{q}_u$ be a normal decomposition of $\mathfrak{a}$ where $\mathfrak{q}$ is primary for $\mathfrak{p}$ and $\mathfrak{q}_j$ is primary for $\mathfrak{p}_j$. Then $\mathfrak{p}_j \not\subset \mathfrak{p}$ for $j = 1,\dots, u$. Now assume that the z_i-discriminant of $g_i(z_i)$ is nonzero for $i = 1,\dots, m$. Let $\mathfrak{K} = K(\{y\})$, $R^* = S[z]$, and $\mathfrak{a}^* = \{g_1(z_1),\dots, g_m(z_m)\}R^*$. Let $\varphi : R \to \bar{R} = R/\mathfrak{a}$ and $\varphi^* : R^* \to \bar{R}^* = R^*/\mathfrak{a}^*$ be the natural epimorphisms. Let $\bar{z}_i = \varphi(z_i)$. Then $\bar{R} = S[\bar{z}_1,\dots,\bar{z}_m] = \varphi R^*$. By (25.4.1), $\mathfrak{a}^* = R^* \cap \mathfrak{a}^*R = R^* \cap \mathfrak{a}$. Hence we may identify $\bar{R}^*$ with φR^*. Let $\mathfrak{p}^* = \varphi^{*-1}\varphi\mathfrak{p}$, $\mathfrak{q}^* = \varphi^{*-1}\varphi\mathfrak{q}$, $\mathfrak{p}_j^* = \varphi^{*-1}\varphi\mathfrak{p}_j$, $\mathfrak{q}_j^* = \varphi^{*-1}\varphi\mathfrak{q}_j$. Then $\mathfrak{a}^* = \mathfrak{q}^* \cap \mathfrak{q}_1^* \cap\dots\cap \mathfrak{q}_u^*$, $\mathfrak{q}^*$ is primary for $\mathfrak{p}^*$, $\mathfrak{q}_j^*$ is primary for $\mathfrak{p}_j^*$, $\mathfrak{p}_j^* \not\subset \mathfrak{p}^*$ for $j = 1,\dots, u$, and $\mathfrak{p}^* \cap S = \{0\}$. Since $\mathfrak{p}_j^* \not\subset \mathfrak{p}^*$ we can find $a_j \in \mathfrak{q}_j^*$ such that $a_j \notin \mathfrak{p}^*$. Let $a = a_1\dots a_u$. Then $a \in \mathfrak{q}_1^* \cap\dots\cap \mathfrak{q}_u^*$ and $a \notin \mathfrak{p}^*$. *Let α be any element in* $\mathfrak{p}^*$. Then $\alpha a \in \operatorname{rad}_{R^*}\mathfrak{a}^*$. Now $\operatorname{rad}_{R^*}\mathfrak{a}^* \subset \operatorname{rad}_{\mathfrak{K}[z]}\mathfrak{a}^*\mathfrak{K}[z]$, and by (25.2.2), $\operatorname{rad}_{\mathfrak{K}[z]}\mathfrak{a}^*\mathfrak{K}[z] = \mathfrak{a}^*\mathfrak{K}[z]$. Therefore $\alpha a \in \mathfrak{a}^*\mathfrak{K}[z]$. Hence we can find $0 \neq b \in S$ such that $\alpha ab \in \mathfrak{a}^* \subset \mathfrak{q}^*$. Since $0 \neq b \in S$ and $S \cap \mathfrak{p}^* = \{0\}$, we get $b \notin \mathfrak{p}^*$. Hence $ab \notin \mathfrak{p}^*$. *Therefore* $\alpha \in \mathfrak{q}^*$. This shows that $\mathfrak{p}^* = \mathfrak{q}^*$ and hence $\mathfrak{p} = \mathfrak{q}$. Consequently $\mathfrak{p}R_\mathfrak{p} = \mathfrak{a}R_\mathfrak{p}$ and hence the maximal ideal $\mathfrak{p}R_\mathfrak{p}$ in the local ring $R_\mathfrak{p}$ is generated by the m elements $g_1(z_1),\dots, g_m(z_m)$. Since R is regular, by (21.5.2) we have $\dim R_\mathfrak{p} = \operatorname{hgt}_R\mathfrak{p} = \dim R - \dim R/\mathfrak{p} = (e + m) - e = m$. Therefore $R_\mathfrak{p}$ is regular.

(25.6) PROPOSITION. *Assume that K is an infinite perfect field.* Let $R = K[\{x_1,\dots, x_n\}]$. *Let $\mathfrak{p}$ be any prime ideal in R. Then $R_\mathfrak{p}$ is a regular local ring and* $\dim R_\mathfrak{p} = n - \dim R/\mathfrak{p}$.

[1] Alternatively: $\operatorname{hgt}_R\mathfrak{a} \leq m$ by (17.1), hence $\dim R/\mathfrak{a} \geq e$ by (21.5.2), therefore $\mathfrak{a}$ is regular relative to S by (23.3.3, 23.3.4).

PROOF. Let dim $R/\mathfrak{p} = e$, $m = n - e$. In virtue of (23.5, 24.5), via a nonsingular K-linear transformation on $x_1,..., x_n$, we can arrange that $\mathfrak{p}$ is strictly regular relative to $S = K[\{x_1,..., x_e\}]$. Let $z_i = x_{e+i}$ for $i = 1,..., m$. Let $g_i(z_i)$ be the minimal monic polynomial of z_i mod $\mathfrak{p}$ over S. Then $g_i(z_i)$ is a distinguished polynomial of positive degree in z_i with coefficients in S and the z_i-discriminant of $g_i(z_i)$ is nonzero for $i = 1,..., m$. Thus we are reduced to (25.5).

(**25.7**) REMARK. 1°) In view of the transitivity of quotient rings (18.5.1), from (25.6) it follows that if $\mathfrak{p} \subset \mathfrak{P}$ are prime ideals in R then $(R_{\mathfrak{P}})_{\mathfrak{p}R_{\mathfrak{P}}}$ is a regular local ring of dimension (n − dim $R/\mathfrak{p}$).

2°) By methods of homological algebra, Auslander, Buchsbaum, and Serre have proved (25.6) for an arbitrary regular ring R; see Auslander–Buchsbaum [**1**: Theorem 1.11 on p. 396].

3°) In the proof of (25.5) and (25.6) we did not use the Cohen-Macauley Theorem (21.5.3).[2] Using (21.5.3) we now get the following.[3]

(**25.8**) PROPOSITION. *Let* $y = (y_1,..., y_e)$, $z = (z_1,..., z_m)$, $S = K[\{y\}]$, $R = K[\{y, z\}]$. *Let* $g_i(z_i)$ *be a monic polynomial of positive degree in* z_i *with coefficients in* S *such that* $g_i(0)$ *is a nonunit in* S. *Let* $\mathfrak{a} = \{g_1(z_1),..., g_m(z_m)\}R$. *Let* d_i *be the Weierstrass degree of* $g_i(z_i)$ *in* z_i *relative to* S. *Then we have the following.*

1) $\mathfrak{a}$ *is regular relative to* S *and* $\mathfrak{a}$ *is unmixed, i.e.,* $\mathfrak{a} \cap S = \{0\}$ *and* $\mathfrak{a} = \mathfrak{q}_1 \cap ... \cap \mathfrak{q}_u$, $(u > 0)$, *where* $\mathfrak{q}_j$ *is primary for* $\mathfrak{p}_j$, *and* $\mathfrak{p}_1,..., \mathfrak{p}_u$ *are distinct prime ideals which are regular relative to* S.

2) *If* $\mathfrak{q}_j = \mathfrak{p}_j$ *for* $j = 1,..., u$, *then*

$$\sum_{j=1}^{u} [\mathfrak{L}_j : \mathfrak{K}] = d_1 ... d_m$$

where $\mathfrak{L}_j$ *is the quotient field of* $R/\mathfrak{p}_j$ *and* $\mathfrak{K}$ *is the quotient field of* S *considered as a subfield of* $\mathfrak{L}_j$.

3)[3] *If* $d_1 = ... = d_m = 1$ *then* $R/\mathfrak{a}$ *is a regular local ring of dimension* e, *and hence in particular* $\mathfrak{a}$ *is prime.*

4) *If the* z_i*-discriminant of* $g_i(z_i)$ *is nonzero for* $i = 1,..., m$, *then for* $i = 1,..., u$: $\mathfrak{q}_j = \mathfrak{p}_j$, $\mathfrak{p}_j$ *is strictly regular relative to* S, $\mathfrak{a}R_{\mathfrak{p}_j} = \mathfrak{p}_j R_{\mathfrak{p}_j}$, *and* $R_{\mathfrak{p}_j}$ *is a regular local ring of dimension* m.

[2] In this connection see Abhyankar [**2**: (13.14)].

[3] The proofs of (25.8.3) and (25.9.5) depend only on (21.6.2) and not on (21.5.3). Actually in (10.13) and (10.14) we have already deduced (25.8.3) and (25.9.5) as consequences of the Preparation Theorem.

PROOF. By Preparation Theorem, $g_i(z_i) = h_i(z_i)g_i^*(z_i)$ where $g_i^*(z_i)$ is a distinguished polynomial of degree $d_i > 0$ in z_i with coefficients in S and $h_i(z_i)$ is a monic polynomial in z_i with coefficients in S such that $h_i(0)$ is a unit in S. Obviously $\mathfrak{a} = \{g_1^*(z_1),\ldots, g_m^*(z_m)\}R$. Also, if the z_i-discriminant of $g_i(z_i)$ is nonzero then the z_i-discriminant of $g_i^*(z_i)$ is nonzero by (17.10.5). Therefore we may assume that $g_i(z_i)$ is already a distinguished polynomial of degree $d_i > 0$ in z_i with coefficients in S.

$\mathfrak{a} \cap S = \{0\}$ by (25.4), and hence $\mathfrak{a}$ is regular relative to S by (23.3.3, 23.3.4).[1] In particular $\dim R/\mathfrak{a} = e$, and hence $\text{hgt}_R\mathfrak{a} = m$ by (21.5.2). Therefore by (21.5.3), $\mathfrak{a}$ is unmixed, i.e., $\mathfrak{a} = \mathfrak{q}_1 \cap\ldots\cap \mathfrak{q}_u$ where $\mathfrak{q}_j$ is primary for $\mathfrak{p}_j$ and $\dim R/\mathfrak{p}_j = e$ for $j = 1,\ldots, u$. By (23.2), $\mathfrak{p}_j$ is regular relative S for $j = 1,\ldots, u$. This proves 1).

To prove 2), assume that $\mathfrak{q}_j = \mathfrak{p}_j$ for $j = 1,\ldots, u$. For any element r of R let $\bar{r}$ denote the image of r under the natural epimorphism $R \to \bar{R} = R/\mathfrak{a}$. Then $\bar{R} = S[\bar{z}_1,\ldots, \bar{z}_m]$ and $g_i(\bar{z}_i) = 0$ for $i = 1,\ldots, m$. Therefore the $d_1\ldots d_m$ elements $\{\bar{z}_1^{k_1}\ldots\bar{z}_m^{k_m} : 0 \leqq k_i < d_i\}$ form an S-module-basis of $\bar{R}$, and by (25.4.2) they are linearly independent over S. Therefore by (19.25.3) we get

$$\sum_{j=1}^{u} [\mathfrak{L}_j : \mathfrak{K}] = d_1\ldots d_m.$$

To prove 3), assume that $d_1 = \ldots = d_m = 1$. Then $g_1(z_1),\ldots, g_m(z_m)$, $y_1,\ldots, y_e$ is an irredundant set of generators of the maximal ideal in R and hence by (21.6.2), $R/\mathfrak{a}$ is a regular local ring.

Finally to prove 4), assume that the z_i-discriminant of $g_i(z_i)$ is nonzero for $i = 1,\ldots, m$. Then by (25.5) it follows that for $j = 1,\ldots, u : \mathfrak{q}_j = \mathfrak{p}_j$, $\mathfrak{a}R_{\mathfrak{p}_j} = \mathfrak{p}_jR_{\mathfrak{p}_j}$, and $R_{\mathfrak{p}_j}$ is a regular local ring of dimension m. Let $\varphi_j : R \to R/\mathfrak{p}_j$ be the natural epimorphism. Then $R/\mathfrak{p}_j = S[\varphi_j z_1,\ldots, \varphi_j z_m]$ and for $i = 1,\ldots, m$ we have that: $g_i(z_i)$ is a separable monic polynomial in the indeterminate z_i with coefficients in S, and $g_i(\varphi_j z_i) = 0$. Therefore $\mathfrak{p}_j$ is strictly regular relative to S.

(25.9) PROPOSITION. *Let K be complete nondiscrete valued. Let $y = (y_1,\ldots,y_e)$, $z = (z_1,\ldots, z_m)$, $S = K[\langle y\rangle]$, $R = K[\langle y, z\rangle]$. Let $g_i(y, z_i)$ be a monic polynomial of positive degree in z_i with coefficients in S. Let $\Delta_i(y)$ be the z_i-discriminant of $g_i(y, z_i)$. Let $a = (b, c) \in K^e \times K^m$ be such that all the coefficients of $g_1(y, z_1),\ldots, g_m(y, z_m)$ are convergent at b, and $g_i(b, c_i) = 0$ for $i = 1,\ldots, m$. Let l_i be the order of zero of $g_i(b, z_i)$ at c_i, i.e.,*

$$g_i(b, z_i) = (z_i - c_i)^{l_i} g_i^*(z_i) \quad \textit{with} \quad g_i^*(z_i) \in K[z_i],\ \ g_i^*(c_i) \neq 0.$$

Let $\mathfrak{b} = \{\tau_a g_1(y, z_1),\ldots, \tau_a g_m(y, z_m)\}R$. Then we have the following.

1) *$\boldsymbol{\tau}_a g_i(y, z_i)$ is a monic polynomial in z_i with coefficients in S and l_i is its Weierstrass degree in z_i relative to S.*

2) *If $\Delta_i(b) \neq 0$ then $l_i = 1$.*

3) *$\mathfrak{b}$ is regular relative to S and $\mathfrak{b}$ is unmixed, i.e., $\mathfrak{b} \cap S = \{0\}$ and $\mathfrak{b} = \mathfrak{q}_1 \cap \ldots \cap \mathfrak{q}_u$, $(u > 0)$, where $\mathfrak{q}_j$ is primary for $\mathfrak{p}_j$, and $\mathfrak{p}_1, \ldots, \mathfrak{p}_u$ are distinct prime ideals which are regular relative to S.*

4) *If $\mathfrak{q}_j = \mathfrak{p}_j$ for $j = 1, \ldots, u$ then*

$$\sum_{j=1}^{u} [\mathfrak{L}_j : \mathfrak{K}] = l_1 \ldots l_m$$

where $\mathfrak{L}_j$ is the quotient field of $R/\mathfrak{p}_j$ and $\mathfrak{K}$ is the quotient field of S considered as a subfield of $\mathfrak{L}_j$.

5)[3] *If $l_1 = \ldots = l_m = 1$ then $R/\mathfrak{b}$ is a regular local ring of dimension e, and hence in particular $\mathfrak{b}$ is prime.*

6) *If $\boldsymbol{\tau}_b \Delta_i \neq 0$ for $i = 1, \ldots, m$ then for $j = 1, \ldots, u$: $\mathfrak{q}_j = \mathfrak{p}_j$, $\mathfrak{p}_j$ is strictly regular relative to S, $\mathfrak{b} R_{\mathfrak{p}_j} = \mathfrak{p}_j R_{\mathfrak{p}_j}$, and $R_{\mathfrak{p}_j}$ is a regular local ring of dimension m.*

PROOF. 1) and 2) are obvious and then the rest follows from (25.8) by taking $\boldsymbol{\tau}_a g_i(y, z_i)$ for $g_i(z_i)$, $\mathfrak{b}$ for $\mathfrak{a}$, and l_i for d_i.

§26. TRANSLATES OF IDEALS

Let $R = K[\langle x_1, \ldots, x_n \rangle]$. Let $\mathfrak{p}$ be a proper ideal in R. Let $u_1, \ldots, u_\nu$ be a basis of $\mathfrak{p}$. Let $\tilde{X}$ be a neighborhood of the origin in $\bigcap_{i=1}^{\nu} \mathbf{D}(u_i)$. For any a in $\tilde{X}$ let

$$\boldsymbol{\tau}_a \mathfrak{p} = \{\boldsymbol{\tau}_a u_1, \ldots, \boldsymbol{\tau}_a u_\nu\} R.$$

Note that if $v_1, \ldots, v_\mu$ is any other basis of $\mathfrak{p}$ then for all a in some neighborhood of the origin we have

$$\boldsymbol{\tau}_a \mathfrak{p} = \{\boldsymbol{\tau}_a v_1, \ldots, \boldsymbol{\tau}_a v_\mu\} R.$$

Let

$$V = \{a \in \tilde{X} : u_1(a) = \ldots = u_\nu(a) = 0\}.$$

(**26.1**) *Let $e \leqq n$. Assume that for all $i > e$, $\mathfrak{p}$ contains a monic polynomial in x_i with coefficients in $K[\langle x_1, \ldots, x_{i-1} \rangle]$. Then there exists a neighborhood X of the origin in $\tilde{X}$ such that for all $a \in V \cap X$ and for all $i > e$, $\boldsymbol{\tau}_a \mathfrak{p}$ contains a distinguished polynomial of positive degree in x_i with coefficients in $K[\langle x_1, \ldots, x_e \rangle]$.*

PROOF. Let $g_i(x_i)$ be a monic polynomial in x_i with coefficients $K[\langle x_1, \ldots, x_{i-1}\rangle]$ such that $g_i(x_i) \in \mathfrak{p}$. There exists a neighborhood X_i of the origin in $\tilde{X}$ such that g_i is convergent in X_i and $\boldsymbol{\tau}_a g_i \in \boldsymbol{\tau}_a \mathfrak{p}$ for all $a \in X_i$. Let $X = \bigcap_{e<i\leqq n} X_i$. For given $a \in X$ let $\tilde{g}_i = \boldsymbol{\tau}_a g_i$. Then $\tilde{g}_i$ is a monic polynomial in x_i with coefficients in $K[\langle x_1, \ldots, x_{i-1}\rangle]$. Now assume that $a \in V \cap X$. Then $\boldsymbol{\tau}_a \mathfrak{p}$ is a proper ideal in R. By (23.6), via a K-linear transformation on $x_1, \ldots, x_e$ it can be arranged that $\boldsymbol{\tau}_a \mathfrak{p}$ is regular relative to $K[\langle x_1, \ldots, x_{e'}\rangle]$, $e' \leqq e$. By (23.3), for all $i > e'$, $\boldsymbol{\tau}_a \mathfrak{p}$ then contains a distinguished polynomial of positive degree in x_i with coefficients in $K[\langle x_1, \ldots, x_{e'}\rangle]$.

(26.2) *There exists a neighborhood X of the origin in $\tilde{X}$ such that* $\dim R/\boldsymbol{\tau}_a \mathfrak{p} \leqq \dim R/\mathfrak{p}$ *for all $a \in V \cap X$.*

PROOF. Let $e = \dim R/\mathfrak{p}$. By (23.5), via a K-linear transformation on $x_1, \ldots, x_n$ we can arrange that $\mathfrak{p}$ is regular relative to $K[\langle x_1, \ldots, x_e\rangle]$. Then by (23.3), for all $i > e$, $\mathfrak{p}$ contains a monic polynomial in x_i with coefficients in $K[\langle x_1, \ldots, x_{i-1}\rangle]$. Let X be as in (26.1). Then by (23.3), $\dim R/\boldsymbol{\tau}_a \mathfrak{p} \leqq e$ for all $a \in V \cap X$.

(26.3) *Assume that $\mathfrak{p}$ is prime and K is perfect. Also assume that there exists a neighborhood X^* of the origin in $\tilde{X}$ such that for any $a \in V \cap X^*$ and for any minimal prime ideal $\bar{\mathfrak{p}}$ of $\boldsymbol{\tau}_a \mathfrak{p}$ we have* $\dim R/\bar{\mathfrak{p}} = \dim R/\mathfrak{p}$. *Then there exists $\Delta \in R$ which is convergent in a neighborhood X of the origin in X^* such that for any $a \in V \cap X$, upon letting $\psi : R \to \bar{R} = R/\operatorname{rad} \boldsymbol{\tau}_a \mathfrak{p}$ to be the natural epimorphism, we have that $\psi(\boldsymbol{\tau}_a \Delta)$ is a nonzerodivisor in $\bar{R}$ and $\psi(\boldsymbol{\tau}_a \Delta) \in \mathfrak{c}(\bar{R})$.*

PROOF. To avoid repetition in the next proof, we divide this proof into four parts. If $\mathfrak{p} = \{0\}$ then we can take $\Delta = 1$. Now assume that $\mathfrak{p} \neq \{0\}$.

(I) Let $\dim R/\mathfrak{p} = e < n$. By (23.5, 24.5) we may assume that $\mathfrak{p}$ is strictly regular relative to $S = K[\langle x_1, \ldots, x_e\rangle]$. Let $y_i = x_i$ for $i = 1, \ldots, e$; $y = (y_1, \ldots, y_e)$; $m = n - e$; $z_i = x_{e+i}$ for $i = 1, \ldots, m$; $z = (z_1, \ldots, z_m)$. Let $\varphi : R \to R/\mathfrak{p}$ be the natural epimorphism. Let $\mathfrak{K}$ be the quotient field of S and $\mathfrak{L}$ be the quotient field of $R/\mathfrak{p}$. Then $\mathfrak{L}$ is a finite separable algebraic extension of $\mathfrak{K}$ and $\mathfrak{L} = \mathfrak{K}(\varphi z_1, \ldots, \varphi z_m)$. Since K is infinite, we can find $\kappa_1, \ldots, \kappa_m \in K$ such that $\mathfrak{L} = \mathfrak{K}(\varphi w)$ where $w = \kappa_1 z_1 + \ldots + \kappa_m z_m$.

Let

$$g_i(T) = \sum_j g_{ij} T^j \in S[T], \qquad g_{ij} \in S,$$

be the minimal monic polynomial of z_i mod $\mathfrak{p}$ over S. Let Δ_i be the T-discriminant of $g_i(T)$. Then $0 \neq \Delta_i \in S$ for $i = 1,\ldots, m$. Let

$$Q(T) = \sum_j Q_j T^j \in S[T], \qquad Q_j \in S,$$

be the minimal monic polynomial of w mod $\mathfrak{p}$ over S. Let Δ be the T-discriminant of $Q(T)$. Then $0 \neq \Delta \in S$. Since φz_i is integral over S, we can find

$$h_i(T) = \sum_j h_{ij} T^j \in S[T], \qquad h_{ij} \in S,$$

such that

$$\Delta z_i \equiv h_i(w) \bmod \mathfrak{p} \qquad \text{for} \quad i = 1,\ldots, m.$$

We can find a neighborhood $X = Y \times Z$ of the origin in $K^e \times K^m$ such that:

$X \subset \tilde{X}$;

all the elements Q_j, g_{ij}, h_{ij} are convergent in Y;

$\boldsymbol{\tau}_b\Delta_1,\ldots, \boldsymbol{\tau}_b\Delta_m, \boldsymbol{\tau}_b\Delta$ are nonzero elements of S for all $b \in Y$;

$\boldsymbol{\tau}_a Q(w) \in \boldsymbol{\tau}_a\mathfrak{p}$ for all $a \in X$;

$\boldsymbol{\tau}_a g_i(z_i) \in \boldsymbol{\tau}_a\mathfrak{p}$ for all $a \in X$ for $i = 1,\ldots, m$;

and

1°) $(\boldsymbol{\tau}_a\Delta)(\boldsymbol{\tau}_a z_i) \equiv \boldsymbol{\tau}_a h_i(w) \bmod \boldsymbol{\tau}_a\mathfrak{p}$ for $i = 1,\ldots, m$.[1]

(II) Let $a = (b, c) \in V \cap (Y \times Z)$ be given. Let $\mathfrak{b} = \operatorname{rad} \boldsymbol{\tau}_a\mathfrak{p}$ and let $\psi : R \to \bar{R} = R/\mathfrak{b}$ be the natural epimorphism. By assumption $\mathfrak{b} = \mathfrak{p}_1 \cap \ldots \cap \mathfrak{p}_\mu$ where $\mathfrak{p}_1,\ldots, \mathfrak{p}_\mu$, $(\mu > 0)$, are distinct prime ideals in R of depth e. Now $\boldsymbol{\tau}_a g_i(z_i)$ is a monic polynomial of positive degree in z_i with coefficients in S and $\boldsymbol{\tau}_a g_i(z_i) \in \boldsymbol{\tau}_a\mathfrak{p} \subset \mathfrak{b}$ for $i = 1,\ldots, m$. Therefore $\mathfrak{b}, \mathfrak{p}_1,\ldots, \mathfrak{p}_\mu$ are regular relative to S by (23.3). In particular $\mathfrak{p}_1 \cap S = \ldots = \mathfrak{p}_\mu \cap S = \{0\}$. Now $0 \neq \boldsymbol{\tau}_a\Delta \in S$ and $\psi(\mathfrak{p}_1) \cup \ldots \cup \psi(\mathfrak{p}_\mu)$ is the set of all zerodivisors in $\bar{R}$. Therefore $\psi(\boldsymbol{\tau}_a\Delta)$ is a nonzerodivisor in $\bar{R}$.

(III) Let $\eta = \boldsymbol{\tau}_a w$. Now

$$\begin{aligned}
&(\boldsymbol{\tau}_a\Delta)z_i \\
&= (\boldsymbol{\tau}_a\Delta)(-c_i + \boldsymbol{\tau}_a z_i) \\
&= -\,c_i(\boldsymbol{\tau}_a\Delta) + (\boldsymbol{\tau}_a\Delta)(\boldsymbol{\tau}_a z_i) \\
&\equiv -\,c_i(\boldsymbol{\tau}_a\Delta) + \boldsymbol{\tau}_a h_i(w) \bmod \boldsymbol{\tau}_a\mathfrak{p} \qquad \text{by } 1°) \\
&= H_i(\eta)
\end{aligned}$$

[1] For $a = (b, c) \in Y \times Z$ and $s \in S$ such that s is convergent at b we have: $\boldsymbol{\tau}_a s = \boldsymbol{\tau}_b s$.

where

$$H_i(T) = -c_i(\boldsymbol{\tau}_b\Delta) + \sum_j (\boldsymbol{\tau}_a h_{ij})T^j \in S[T].$$

Thus

2°) $(\boldsymbol{\tau}_a\Delta)z_i \equiv H_i(\eta) \bmod \boldsymbol{\tau}_a\mathfrak{p}$ with $H_i(T) \in S[T]$, for $i = 1,\ldots, m$.

Let

$$f(T) = \sum_j (\boldsymbol{\tau}_b Q_j)T^j.$$

Then $f(T)$ is a monic polynomial of positive degree in T with coefficients in S, and

$$f(\eta) = f(\boldsymbol{\tau}_a w) = \boldsymbol{\tau}_a Q(w) \in \boldsymbol{\tau}_a\mathfrak{p}.$$

Also $\boldsymbol{\tau}_a\Delta = \boldsymbol{\tau}_b\Delta$ is the T-discriminant of $f(T)$.

(IV) Now $\boldsymbol{\tau}_a\mathfrak{p} \subset \mathfrak{b}$ and hence $f(\eta) \in \mathfrak{b}$. By 2°) we get that $\psi(sz_i) \in S[\psi(\eta)]$ for $i = 1,\ldots, m$, where $0 \neq s = \boldsymbol{\tau}_a\Delta \in S$. Therefore $\psi(\boldsymbol{\tau}_a\Delta) \in \mathfrak{c}(\bar{R})$ by (23.11).

(26.4) *Assume that* $\mathfrak{p}$ *is prime and* K *is perfect. Also assume that there exists a neighborhood* X^* *of the origin in* $\tilde{X}$ *such that for any* $a \in V \cap X^*$ *and any minimal prime ideal* $\bar{\mathfrak{p}}$ *of* $\boldsymbol{\tau}_a\mathfrak{p}$ *we have* $\dim R/\bar{\mathfrak{p}} = \dim R/\mathfrak{p}$. *Then there exists a neighborhood* X *of the origin in* X^* *such that* $\operatorname{rad} \boldsymbol{\tau}_a\mathfrak{p} = \boldsymbol{\tau}_a\mathfrak{p}$ *for all* $a \in X$.

PROOF. Note that for $a \notin V$, $\boldsymbol{\tau}_a\mathfrak{p} = R = \operatorname{rad} \boldsymbol{\tau}_a\mathfrak{p}$. Hence it suffices to consider $a \in V$. Assertion being trivial for $\mathfrak{p} = \{0\}$ we may also assume that $\mathfrak{p} \neq \{0\}$.

Take over Part (I) of the proof of (26.3).

Since $\mathfrak{p}$ is prime and $\Delta \notin \mathfrak{p}$ we have that $[r \in R,\ \Delta r \in \mathfrak{p} \Rightarrow r \in \mathfrak{p}]$. Therefore by (15.3), upon replacing Y and Z by suitably smaller neighborhoods of the origins in K^e and K^m, respectively, we can arrange that:

$$r \in R,\quad (\boldsymbol{\tau}_a\Delta)r \in \boldsymbol{\tau}_a\mathfrak{p} \Rightarrow r \in \boldsymbol{\tau}_a\mathfrak{p}.[1]$$

From this it follows that for all $a \in X$ we have:

3°) $\quad r \in R,\quad (\boldsymbol{\tau}_a\Delta)^M r \in \boldsymbol{\tau}_a\mathfrak{p}$ for some $M > 0 \Rightarrow r \in \boldsymbol{\tau}_a\mathfrak{p}$.

Let $a = (b, c) \in V \cap (Y \times Z)$ be given. Then for $i = 1,\ldots, m$: $\boldsymbol{\tau}_a g_i(z_i)$ is a monic polynomial of positive degree in z_i with coefficients in S, its constant term is a nonunit in S, and its z_i-discriminant equals $\boldsymbol{\tau}_b\Delta_i$. Let

$$\mathfrak{a} = \{\boldsymbol{\tau}_a g_1(z_1),\ldots, \boldsymbol{\tau}_a g_m(z_m)\}R.$$

By (25.8), $\mathfrak{a}$ is an intersection of prime ideals of depth e. Now $\mathfrak{a} \subset \boldsymbol{\tau}_a\mathfrak{p}$

and by assumption $\dim R/\boldsymbol{\tau}_a\mathfrak{p} = e$. Therefore by (23.3), $\boldsymbol{\tau}_a\mathfrak{p}$ is regular relative to S. Let $\bar{\mathfrak{q}}$ be any isolated primary component of $\boldsymbol{\tau}_a\mathfrak{p}$ and let $\bar{\mathfrak{p}}$ be the corresponding prime ideal. Since $\mathfrak{a} \subset \boldsymbol{\tau}_a\mathfrak{p}$, we can find a prime ideal $\mathfrak{n}$ of $\mathfrak{a}$ such that $\mathfrak{n} \subset \bar{\mathfrak{p}}$. Now $\dim R/\mathfrak{n} = e$ and by assumption $\dim R/\bar{\mathfrak{p}} = e$. Therefore $\mathfrak{n} = \bar{\mathfrak{p}}$. Since $\mathfrak{a} \subset \boldsymbol{\tau}_a\mathfrak{p}$ we get

$$\mathfrak{n} = [\mathfrak{a}R_{\mathfrak{n}}] \cap R \subset [(\boldsymbol{\tau}_a\mathfrak{p})R_{\mathfrak{n}}] \cap R = \bar{\mathfrak{q}}.$$

Therefore $\bar{\mathfrak{q}} = \bar{\mathfrak{p}}$.

Thus $\boldsymbol{\tau}_a\mathfrak{p}$ is regular relative to S and all the isolated primary components of $\boldsymbol{\tau}_a\mathfrak{p}$ are prime and have the same depth.

Take over Part (III) of the proof of (26.3).

Let $F(T)$ be the minimal monic polynomial of η mod rad $\boldsymbol{\tau}_a\mathfrak{p}$ over S. Taking $\boldsymbol{\tau}_a\mathfrak{p}$ for $\mathfrak{b}$ in (23.12), we find a positive integer N such that

$$(\boldsymbol{\tau}_a\Delta)^N F(\eta) \in \boldsymbol{\tau}_a\mathfrak{p}.$$

By 3°) we then get

4°) $$F(\eta) \in \boldsymbol{\tau}_a\mathfrak{p}.$$

Let $r \in R$ be given. Since $\boldsymbol{\tau}_a\mathfrak{p}$ is regular relative to S, by (23.3) there exists $r' \in S[z]$ such that $r \equiv r' \bmod \boldsymbol{\tau}_a\mathfrak{p}$. Hence by (26.3.2°), there exists $P(T) \in S[T]$ and a positive integer M such that

5°) $$(\boldsymbol{\tau}_a\Delta)^M r \equiv P(\eta) \bmod \boldsymbol{\tau}_a\mathfrak{p}.$$

Now assume that $r \in \operatorname{rad} \boldsymbol{\tau}_a\mathfrak{p}$. Then $P(\eta) \in \operatorname{rad} \boldsymbol{\tau}_a\mathfrak{p}$. Therefore $F(T)$ divides $P(T)$ in $S[T]$. Consequently $P(\eta) \in \boldsymbol{\tau}_a\mathfrak{p}$ by 4°). Therefore $(\boldsymbol{\tau}_a\Delta)^M r \in \boldsymbol{\tau}_a\mathfrak{p}$ by 5°), and hence $r \in \boldsymbol{\tau}_a\mathfrak{p}$ by 3°). Thus $\operatorname{rad} \boldsymbol{\tau}_a\mathfrak{p} = \boldsymbol{\tau}_a\mathfrak{p}$.

§27. DIMENSION OF AN INTERSECTION

In this section we want to give an elementary proof of (27.8). In (27.1) to (27.5), K is assumed to be infinite and perfect.

(27.1) *Let $x = (x_1,\dots, x_n)$, $\tilde{x} = (\tilde{x}_1,\dots, \tilde{x}_\nu)$, $R = K[\{x\}]$, $\tilde{R} = K[\{\tilde{x}\}]$, $S = K[\{x, \tilde{x}\}]$. Let $\mathfrak{a}$ and $\tilde{\mathfrak{a}}$ be proper ideals in R and $\tilde{R}$ respectively. Then $(\mathfrak{a}S + \tilde{\mathfrak{a}}S) \cap R = \mathfrak{a}$ and $(\mathfrak{a}S + \tilde{\mathfrak{a}}S) \cap \tilde{R} = \tilde{\mathfrak{a}}$.*

For instance we prove $(\mathfrak{a}S + \tilde{\mathfrak{a}}S) \cap R = \mathfrak{a}$. Let

$$f(x) = \sum_i a_i(x)g_i(x, \tilde{x}) + \sum_j \tilde{a}_j(\tilde{x})g'_j(x, \tilde{x}) \in K[\{x\}]$$

with $a_i(x) \in \mathfrak{a}$, $\tilde{a}_j(\tilde{x}) \in \tilde{\mathfrak{a}}$. Since $\tilde{\mathfrak{a}}$ is proper, we must have $\tilde{a}_j(0) = 0$. Substituting $\tilde{x} = 0$ in the equation for $f(x)$ we get

$$f(x) = \sum_i a_i(x)g_i(x, 0) \in \mathfrak{a}.$$

(27.2) *Let* $y = (y_1,..., y_e)$, $z = (z_1,..., z_m)$, $n = e + m$, $x_i = y_i$, $x_{e+i} = z_i$, $x = (x_1,..., x_n)$. *Let* $F(T)$ *be a monic polynomial of positive degree in an indeterminate* T *with coefficients in* $K[\{y\}]$. *If* $F(T)$ *is irreducible in* $K[\{y\}][T]$ *then* $F(T)$ *is irreducible in* $K(\{x\})[T]$.

Write $F(T) = F(y, T)$. Since $F(T)$ is monic and $K[\{x\}]$ is a unique factorization domain, if $F(T)$ were reducible in $K(\{x\})[T]$ then we would have $F(y, T) = G(y, z, T)H(y, z, T)$ where G and H are monic polynomials of positive degrees in T with coefficients in $K[\{y, z\}]$. Putting $z = 0$ this would yield the factorization $F(y, T) = G(y, 0, T)H(y, 0, T)$ in $K[\{y\}][T]$.

(27.3) *Let* $y = (y_1,..., y_e)$, $z = (z_1,..., z_m)$, $n = e + m$, $x_i = y_i$, $x_{e+i} = z_i$, $x = (x_1,..., x_n)$, $R = K[\{x\}]$, *and let* $\mathfrak{p}$ *be a prime ideal in* R *which is strictly regular relative to* $K[\{y\}]$. *Let* $\tilde{y} = (\tilde{y}_1,..., \tilde{y}_\epsilon)$, $\tilde{z} = (\tilde{z}_1,..., \tilde{z}_\mu)$, $\nu = \epsilon + \mu$, $\tilde{x}_i = \tilde{y}_i$, $\tilde{x}_{\epsilon+i} = \tilde{z}_i$, $\tilde{x} = (\tilde{x}_1,..., \tilde{x}_\nu)$, $\tilde{R} = K[\{\tilde{x}\}]$, *and let* $\tilde{\mathfrak{p}}$ *be a prime ideal in* $\tilde{R}$ *which is strictly regular relative to* $K[\{\tilde{y}\}]$. *Let* $S = K[\{x, \tilde{x}\}]$. *Then*:

1) $\mathfrak{p}S$ *and* $\tilde{\mathfrak{p}}S$ *are prime ideals in* S *and they are strictly regular relative to* $K[\{y, \tilde{x}\}]$ *and* $K[\{x, \tilde{y}\}]$, *respectively.*

2) $\mathfrak{p}S + \tilde{\mathfrak{p}}S$ *is regular relative to* $K[\{y, \tilde{y}\}]$, *or equivalently* $(\mathfrak{p}S + \tilde{\mathfrak{p}}S) \cap K[\{y, \tilde{y}\}] = \{0\}$. *In particular*

$$\dim S/(\mathfrak{p}S + \tilde{\mathfrak{p}}S) = e + \epsilon = \dim R/\mathfrak{p} + \dim \tilde{R}/\tilde{\mathfrak{p}}.$$

PROOF. By symmetry it suffices to prove 1) for $\mathfrak{p}$. It is trivial for $\mathfrak{p} = \{0\}$. So assume that $\mathfrak{p} \neq \{0\}$, i.e., $m > 0$. Let

$$u(y, \tilde{x}) = \sum_i p^{(i)}(x)v^{(i)}(x, \tilde{x}) \in K[\{y, \tilde{x}\}], \qquad p^{(i)}(x) \in \mathfrak{p}.$$

Write

$$u(y, \tilde{x}) = \sum_{k_1,...,k_\nu} u_{k_1...k_\nu}(y)\tilde{x}_1^{k_1}...\tilde{x}_\nu^{k_\nu}$$

and

$$v^{(i)}(x, \tilde{x}) = \sum_{k_1,...,k_\nu} v^{(i)}_{k_1...k_\nu}(x)\tilde{x}_1^{k_1}...\tilde{x}_\nu^{k_\nu}.$$

Equating coefficients of $\tilde{x}_1^{k_1}...\tilde{x}_\nu^{k_\nu}$ we get

$$u_{k_1...k_\nu}(y) = \sum_i p^{(i)}(x)v^{(i)}_{k_1...k_\nu}(x).$$

By assumption $\mathfrak{p} \cap K[\{y\}] = \{0\}$. Hence

$$u_{k_1...k_\nu}(y) = 0 \qquad \text{for all } k_1,..., k_\nu, \qquad \text{i.e., } u(y, \tilde{x}) = 0.$$

Thus $\mathfrak{p}S \cap K[\{y, \tilde{x}\}] = \{0\}$. Therefore $\mathfrak{p}S$ is regular relative to $K[\{y, \tilde{x}\}]$.

Let φ: $R \to R/\mathfrak{p}$ be the natural epimorphism. Then $R/\mathfrak{p} = K[\{y\}][\varphi z_1, \ldots, \varphi z_m]$, $R/\mathfrak{p}$ is integral over $K[\{y\}]$, and the quotient field $\mathfrak{L}$ of $R/\mathfrak{p}$ is a finite separable algebraic extension of $K(\{y\})$. Since K is infinite, via a nonsingular K-linear transformation on $z_1, \ldots, z_m$ we can arrange that φz_1 is a primitive element of $\mathfrak{L}$ over $K(\{y\})$. Let $F(T)$ be the minimal monic polynomial of z_1 mod $\mathfrak{p}$ over $K[\{y\}]$. Let d be the degree of $F(T)$ in T. Let Δ be the T-discriminant of $F(T)$. Then $d > 0$ and $0 \neq \Delta \in K[\{y\}]$. Since $R/\mathfrak{p}$ is integral over $K[\{y\}]$, we can find polynomials $a_{i\lambda}(T)$ of degree $<d$ in T with coefficients in $K[\{y\}]$ such that

$$\Delta z_i^\lambda = a_{i\lambda}(z_1) + \text{an element in } \mathfrak{p}, \qquad (i = 1, \ldots, m), \qquad (\lambda \geqslant 0).$$

Let $f \in S$ be given. Since $\mathfrak{p}S$ is regular relative to $K[\{y, \tilde{x}\}]$, we can find

$$f^*(z_1, \ldots, z_m) \in K[\{y, \tilde{x}\}][z_1, \ldots, z_m]$$

such that

$$f \equiv f^*(z_1, \ldots, z_m) \bmod \mathfrak{p}S;$$

whence in view of the above equations for Δz_i^λ we can find $f'(T) \in K[\{y, \tilde{x}\}][T]$ of degree $<d$ in T such that

$$\Delta f \equiv f'(z_1) \bmod \mathfrak{p}S.$$

Now let $f'(T)$ be any nonzero polynomial of degree $<d$ in T with coefficients in $K[\{y, \tilde{x}\}]$. By (27.2), $F(T)$ is irreducible in $K(\{y, \tilde{x}\})[T]$. Hence we can write $w = A(T)F(T) + B(T)f'(T)$ with $A(T)$, $B(T) \in K[\{y, \tilde{x}\}][T]$ and $0 \neq w \in K[\{y, \tilde{x}\}]$. Obviously $w \equiv B(z_1)f'(z_1)$ mod $\mathfrak{p}S$. Since $\mathfrak{p}S \cap K[\{y, \tilde{x}\}] = \{0\}$, we thus get $f'(z_1) \notin \mathfrak{p}S$. Thus we have proved

1°) *Given $f \in S$, there exists $f'(T) \in K[\{y, \tilde{x}\}][T]$ of degree $<d$ in T such that $\Delta f \equiv f'(z_1)$ mod $\mathfrak{p}S$. Furthermore $f'(T)$ is uniquely determined by f. In other words, if $f'(T)$ is any nonzero polynomial of degree $<d$ in T with coefficients in $K[\{y, \tilde{x}\}]$ then $f'(z_1) \notin \mathfrak{p}S$.*

Let $0 \neq r \in K[\{y\}]$ and $f \in S$ be such that $rf \in \mathfrak{p}S$. Then

$$rf = \sum_i p^{(i)}(x)g^{(i)}(x, \tilde{x}), \qquad p^{(i)}(x) \in \mathfrak{p}, \qquad g^{(i)}(x, \tilde{x}) \in S.$$

We can write

$$f = \sum_{k_1, \ldots, k_\nu} f_{k_1 \ldots k_\nu}(x)\tilde{x}_1^{k_1} \ldots \tilde{x}_\nu^{k_\nu}$$

and

$$g^{(i)}(x, \tilde{x}) = \sum_{k_1,\dots,k_\nu} g^{(i)}_{k_1\dots k_\nu}(x)\tilde{x}_1^{k_1}\dots\tilde{x}_\nu^{k_\nu}$$

with

$$f_{k_1\dots k_\nu}(x) \quad \text{and} \quad g^{(i)}_{k_1\dots k_\nu}(x) \quad \text{in} \quad K[\{x\}]$$

Equating coefficients of $\tilde{x}_1^{k_1}\dots\tilde{x}_\nu^{k_\nu}$ we get

$$rf_{k_1\dots k_\nu}(x) = \sum_i p^{(i)}(x)g^{(i)}_{k_1\dots k_\nu}(x) \in \mathfrak{p}.$$

Now $\mathfrak{p}$ is prime and $r \in R$, $r \notin \mathfrak{p}$. Hence $f_{k_1\dots k_\nu}(x) \in \mathfrak{p}$. Therefore $f \in \mathfrak{p}K[[x, \tilde{x}]]$. Now $K[[x, \tilde{x}]]$ being the completion of S we have $(\mathfrak{p}K[[x, \tilde{x}]]) \cap S = \mathfrak{p}S$. Since $f \in S$, we conclude that $f \in \mathfrak{p}S$. Thus we have proved

2°) *Let* $0 \neq r \in K[\{y\}]$ *and* $f \in S$. *Then* $f \in \mathfrak{p}S \Leftrightarrow rf \in \mathfrak{p}S$.

Now let $f, g \in S$; $f, g \notin \mathfrak{p}S$. Then by 2°), $\Delta f \notin \mathfrak{p}S$ and $\Delta g \notin \mathfrak{p}S$. Hence by 1°),

$$\Delta f \equiv f'(z_1) \bmod \mathfrak{p}S \qquad \text{and} \qquad \Delta g \equiv g'(z_1) \bmod \mathfrak{p}S,$$

where $f'(T)$ and $g'(T)$ are nonzero polynomials of degree $< d$ in T with coefficients in $K[\{y, \tilde{x}\}]$. Since $F(T)$ is monic, we can write

$$f'(T)g'(T) = q(T)F(T) + h(T)$$

where $q(T), h(T) \in K[\{y, \tilde{x}\}][T]$ and the degree of $h(T)$ in T is $< d$. Since $F(T)$ is irreducible in $K(\{y, \tilde{x}\})[T]$, $h(T)$ must be a nonzero polynomial. Therefore by 1°), $h(z_1) \notin \mathfrak{p}S$. Since $F(z_1) \in \mathfrak{p}S$, we get

$$\Delta^2 fg \equiv h(z_1) \bmod \mathfrak{p}S$$

and hence $\Delta^2 fg \notin \mathfrak{p}S$. Therefore $fg \notin \mathfrak{p}S$. Thus we have proved

3°) $\mathfrak{p}S$ *is a prime ideal in* S.

Let $G_i(T)$ be the minimal monic polynomial of z_i mod $\mathfrak{p}$ over $K[\{y\}]$. Since $\mathfrak{p}$ is strictly regular relative to $K[\{y\}]$, $G_i(T)$ is a separable polynomial. Now the quotient field of $S/\mathfrak{p}S$ is generated over $K(\{y, \tilde{x}\})$ by the residues mod $\mathfrak{p}S$ of $z_1,\dots, z_m$. Therefore $\mathfrak{p}S$ is strictly regular relative to $K[\{y, \tilde{x}\}]$. *This completes the proof of* 1).

2) is trivial in case $\mathfrak{p} = \{0\}$ and $\tilde{\mathfrak{p}} = \{0\}$. Now assume the contrary. Upon relabeling, we may assume that $\mathfrak{p} \neq \{0\}$. Let $f \in (\mathfrak{p}S + \tilde{\mathfrak{p}}S) \cap K[\{y, \tilde{y}\}]$ be given. Then

$$\Delta f \equiv \sum_j g_j\tilde{p}_j \bmod \mathfrak{p}S \qquad \text{with} \qquad \tilde{p}_j \in \tilde{\mathfrak{p}}, \quad g_j \in \Delta S.$$

By 1°) we can find polynomials $b_j(T)$ of degree $<d$ in T with coefficients in $K[\{y, \tilde{x}\}]$ such that

$$g_j \equiv b_j(z_1) \bmod \mathfrak{p}S.$$

Now $\tilde{p}_j \in K[\{\tilde{x}\}] \subset K[\{y, \tilde{x}\}]$ and hence

$$\sum_j b_j(T)\tilde{p}_j$$

is a polynomial of degree $<d$ in T with coefficients in $K[\{y, \tilde{x}\}]$ and

$$\Delta f \equiv \sum_j b_j(z_1)\tilde{p}_j \bmod \mathfrak{p}S.$$

Since $\Delta f \in K[\{y, \tilde{y}\}] \subset K[\{y, \tilde{x}\}]$, by the uniqueness part of 1°) we get

$$\Delta f = \sum_j b_j(0)\tilde{p}_j.$$

Therefore

$$\Delta f \in (\tilde{\mathfrak{p}}S) \cap K[\{y, \tilde{y}\}] \subset (\tilde{\mathfrak{p}}S) \cap K[\{x, \tilde{y}\}].$$

By 1), $(\tilde{\mathfrak{p}}S) \cap K[\{x, \tilde{y}\}] = \{0\}$ and hence $\Delta f = 0$. Therefore $f = 0$. This shows that $(\mathfrak{p}S + \tilde{\mathfrak{p}}S) \cap K[\{y, \tilde{y}\}] = \{0\}$. Consequently $\mathfrak{p}S + \tilde{\mathfrak{p}}S$ is regular relative to $K[\{y, \tilde{y}\}]$ and the proof of 2) is completed.

In view of (24.5), (27.3) yields

(27.4) *Let* $x = (x_1, \ldots, x_n)$, $\tilde{x} = (\tilde{x}_1, \ldots, \tilde{x}_\nu)$, $R = K[\{x\}]$, $\tilde{R} = K[\{\tilde{x}\}]$, $S = K[\{x, \tilde{x}\}]$. *Let* $\mathfrak{p}$ *and* $\tilde{\mathfrak{p}}$ *be prime ideals in* R *and* $\tilde{R}$, *respectively. Then* $\mathfrak{p}S$ *and* $\tilde{\mathfrak{p}}S$ *are prime ideals in* S, $\mathfrak{p}S + \tilde{\mathfrak{p}}S$ *is a proper ideal in* S *and* $\dim S/(\mathfrak{p}S + \tilde{\mathfrak{p}}S) = \dim R/\mathfrak{p} + \dim \tilde{R}/\tilde{\mathfrak{p}}$.

Now we are ready to prove

(27.5) *Let* $x = (x_1, \ldots, x_n)$, $R = K[\{x\}]$, *and let* $\mathfrak{a}$ *and* $\mathfrak{b}$ *be proper ideals in* R. *Then*

$$\mathrm{hgt}_R(\mathfrak{a} + \mathfrak{b}) \leqq \mathrm{hgt}_R\mathfrak{a} + \mathrm{hgt}_R\mathfrak{b}$$

or equivalently

$$\dim R/(\mathfrak{a} + \mathfrak{b}) \geqq (\dim R/\mathfrak{a}) + (\dim R/\mathfrak{b}) - (\dim R).$$

PROOF. That the two statements are equivalent, follows from (21.5.2). Let $\mathfrak{p}$ and $\mathfrak{q}$ be associated prime ideals of $\mathfrak{a}$ and $\mathfrak{b}$, respectively, such that $\dim R/\mathfrak{a} = \dim R/\mathfrak{p}$ and $\dim R/\mathfrak{b} = \dim R/\mathfrak{q}$. Then $\mathfrak{a} + \mathfrak{b} \subset \mathfrak{p} + \mathfrak{q}$ and hence $\dim R/(\mathfrak{a} + \mathfrak{b}) \geqq \dim R/(\mathfrak{p} + \mathfrak{q})$. Hence it suffices to show that

$$\dim R/(\mathfrak{p} + \mathfrak{q}) \geqq (\dim R/\mathfrak{p}) + (\dim R/\mathfrak{q}) - n.$$

Let $\tilde{x} = (\tilde{x}_1, \ldots, \tilde{x}_n)$, $\tilde{R} = K[\{\tilde{x}\}]$, $S = K[\{x, \tilde{x}\}]$. For any element or subset r of R let $\tilde{r}$ denote the image of r under the isomorphism of R onto $\tilde{R}$ given by $f(x) \to f(\tilde{x})$. Let $y_i = x_i - \tilde{x}_i$ and $y = (y_1, \ldots, y_n)$. Let $\mathfrak{d} = \{y_1, \ldots, y_n\}S$. Let $\varphi : S \to S/\mathfrak{d}$ be the natural epimorphism and let $\psi = \varphi \mid R$. Now $S = K[\{x, y\}]$ and hence by (27.1), $\mathfrak{d} \cap R = \{0\}$. Let $f(x, \tilde{x})$ be any element of S. Now

$$x_1^{k_1} \ldots x_n^{k_n} - \tilde{x}_1^{k_1} \ldots \tilde{x}_n^{k_n} \in \mathfrak{d} \qquad \text{for all} \quad k_1, \ldots, k_n;$$

and hence $f(x, \tilde{x}) - f(x, x) \in \mathfrak{d}K[[x, \tilde{x}]]$. Since $K[[x, \tilde{x}]]$ is the completion of $K[\{x, \tilde{x}\}]$ we get $f(x, \tilde{x}) - f(x, x) \in \mathfrak{d}$.[1] Therefore ψ is an isomorphism of R onto $S/\mathfrak{d}$. Since $f(x, \tilde{x}) - f(x, x) \in \mathfrak{d}$ for all $f(x, \tilde{x}) \in S$, in particular we get that $\tilde{r} - r \in \mathfrak{d}$ for all $r \in R$. Therefore for any element or subset r of R we have $\varphi(r) = \varphi(\tilde{r})$. Consequently $\varphi(\mathfrak{p}S + \tilde{\mathfrak{q}}S) = \psi(\mathfrak{p} + \mathfrak{q})$, and hence the local rings $R/(\mathfrak{p} + \mathfrak{q})$ and $S/(\mathfrak{d} + \mathfrak{p}S + \tilde{\mathfrak{q}}S)$ are isomorphic. We can take a prime ideal $\mathfrak{t}$ in S such that $\mathfrak{p}S + \tilde{\mathfrak{q}}S \subset \mathfrak{t}$ and

$$\dim S/\mathfrak{t} = \dim S/(\mathfrak{p}S + \tilde{\mathfrak{q}}S).$$

Now

$$\dim R/(\mathfrak{p} + \mathfrak{q}) = \dim S/(\mathfrak{d} + \mathfrak{p}S + \tilde{\mathfrak{q}}S) \geqq \dim S/(\mathfrak{d} + \mathfrak{t})$$

and by (27.4) we have

$$\dim S/(\mathfrak{p}S + \tilde{\mathfrak{q}}S) = (\dim R/\mathfrak{p}) + (\dim R/\mathfrak{q}).$$

Therefore

1°) $$\dim R/(\mathfrak{p} + \mathfrak{q}) \geqq \dim S/(\mathfrak{d} + \mathfrak{t})$$

and

2°) $$\dim S/\mathfrak{t} = (\dim R/\mathfrak{p}) + (\dim R/\mathfrak{q}).$$

Let $\alpha : S \to S/\mathfrak{t}$ be the natural epimorphism. Then

$$\dim S/(\mathfrak{d} + \mathfrak{t}) = \dim \alpha(S)/\alpha(\mathfrak{d}) = \operatorname{dpt}_{\alpha(S)}\alpha(\mathfrak{d})$$

and by (23.8.1) we have

$$\operatorname{dpt}_{\alpha(S)}\alpha(\mathfrak{d}) + \operatorname{hgt}_{\alpha(S)}\alpha(\mathfrak{d}) = \dim \alpha(S).$$

Therefore

3°) $$\dim S/(\mathfrak{d} + \mathfrak{t}) = (\dim S/\mathfrak{t}) - \operatorname{hgt}_{\alpha(S)}\alpha(\mathfrak{d}).$$

Since $\alpha(\mathfrak{d})$ is generated by n elements, by (17.1) we get

4°) $$\operatorname{hgt}_{\alpha(S)}\alpha(\mathfrak{d}) \leqq n.$$

[1] It is obvious that if $f(x, \tilde{x})$ is convergent then so is $f(x, x)$.

By (1°, 2°, 3°, 4°) we get

$$\dim R/(\mathfrak{p} + \mathfrak{q}) \geqq (\dim R/\mathfrak{p}) + (\dim R/\mathfrak{q}) - n.$$

(27.6) *Let R, R', $\hat{R}$ be regular local rings such that R' is an overring of R and is integral over R, and $\hat{R}$ is a completion of R. Then we have the following.*

1) *If* (27.5) *holds for R' then it holds for R.*

2) *If* (27.5) *holds for $\hat{R}$ then it holds for R.*

PROOF. Let $\mathfrak{a}$ and $\mathfrak{b}$ be any proper ideals in R. By (19.4), $\operatorname{hgt}_R\mathfrak{a} = \operatorname{hgt}_{R'}\mathfrak{a}R'$, $\operatorname{hgt}_R\mathfrak{b} = \operatorname{hgt}_{R'}\mathfrak{b}R'$, and $\operatorname{hgt}_R(\mathfrak{a} + \mathfrak{b}) = \operatorname{hgt}_{R'}(\mathfrak{a} + \mathfrak{b})R' = \operatorname{hgt}_{R'}(\mathfrak{a}R' + \mathfrak{b}R')$. If (27.5) holds for R' then

$$\operatorname{hgt}_{R'}(\mathfrak{a}R' + \mathfrak{b}R') \leqq \operatorname{hgt}_{R'}\mathfrak{a}R' + \operatorname{hgt}_{R'}\mathfrak{b}R'$$

and hence

$$\operatorname{hgt}_R(\mathfrak{a} + \mathfrak{b}) \leqq \operatorname{hgt}_R\mathfrak{a} + \operatorname{hgt}_R\mathfrak{b}.$$

By (17.5), $\dim R = \dim \hat{R}$, $\dim R/\mathfrak{a} = \dim \hat{R}/\mathfrak{a}\hat{R}$, $\dim R/\mathfrak{b} = \dim \hat{R}/\mathfrak{b}\hat{R}$, and $\dim R/(\mathfrak{a} + \mathfrak{b}) = \dim \hat{R}/(\mathfrak{a} + \mathfrak{b})\hat{R} = \dim \hat{R}/(\mathfrak{a}\hat{R} + \mathfrak{b}\hat{R})$. If (27.5) holds for $\hat{R}$ then

$$\dim \hat{R}/(\mathfrak{a}\hat{R} + \mathfrak{b}\hat{R}) \geqq (\dim \hat{R}/\mathfrak{a}\hat{R}) + (\dim \hat{R}/\mathfrak{b}\hat{R}) - (\dim \hat{R})$$

and hence

$$\dim R/(\mathfrak{a} + \mathfrak{b}) \geqq (\dim R/\mathfrak{a}) + (\dim R/\mathfrak{b}) - (\dim R).$$

(27.7) (27.5) *is valid for an arbitrary regular local ring $(R, \mathfrak{m})$ such that R and $R/\mathfrak{m}$ have the same characteristic.*

PROOF. Let $\hat{R}$ be the completion of R. By Cohen Structure Theorem[2] $\hat{R} = K[[x_1,\ldots, x_n]]$ where $K \approx R/\mathfrak{m}$ and $n = \dim R$. Let K^* be an algebraic closure of K. Let Ω be the set of all finite algebraic extensions of K in K^*. Let $R' = \bigcap_{L\in\Omega} L[[x_1,\ldots, x_n]]$ and $\hat{R}' = K^*[[x_1,\ldots, x_n]]$. By (27.5), (27.5) is valid for $\hat{R}'$. By (22.5), R' is a regular local ring and $\hat{R}'$ is a completion of R'. Therefore by (27.6.2), (27.5) is valid for R'. By (22.5), R' is integral over $\hat{R}$; and hence by (27.6.1), (27.5) is valid for $\hat{R}$. Since $\hat{R}$ is a completion of R, by (27.6.2), (27.5) is valid for R.

[2] Zariski-Samuel [**2**: p. 307].

(27.8) PROPOSITION. *Let $(R, \mathfrak{m})$ be any regular local ring such that R and $R/\mathfrak{m}$ have the same characteristic. Let $\mathfrak{a}$ and $\mathfrak{b}$ be any proper ideals in R. Then we have the following.*

1)
$$\operatorname{hgt}_R(\mathfrak{a} + \mathfrak{b}) \leqq \operatorname{hgt}_R\mathfrak{a} + \operatorname{hgt}_R\mathfrak{b}$$

or equivalently

$$\dim R/(\mathfrak{a} + \mathfrak{b}) \geqq (\dim R/\mathfrak{a}) + (\dim R/\mathfrak{b}) - (\dim R).$$

2) *If $\mathfrak{a}$ and $\mathfrak{b}$ are prime and $\mathfrak{c}$ is any associated minimal prime ideal of $\mathfrak{a} + \mathfrak{b}$, then*

$$\operatorname{hgt}_R\mathfrak{c} \leqq \operatorname{hgt}_R\mathfrak{a} + \operatorname{hgt}_R\mathfrak{b}$$

or equivalently

$$\dim R/\mathfrak{c} \geqq (\dim R/\mathfrak{a}) + (\dim R/\mathfrak{b}) - (\dim R).$$

PROOF. 1) has been proved in (27.7). To prove 2) let $R' = R_\mathfrak{c}$ and $\mathfrak{m}' = \mathfrak{c}R'$. Then $(R', \mathfrak{m}')$ is a regular local ring[3] and R' and $R'/\mathfrak{m}'$ have the same characteristic. Since $\mathfrak{c}$ is a minimal prime ideal of $\mathfrak{a} + \mathfrak{b}$, $(\mathfrak{a} + \mathfrak{b})R' = \mathfrak{a}R' + \mathfrak{b}R'$ is primary for $\mathfrak{m}'$ and hence

$$\operatorname{hgt}_{R'}(\mathfrak{a}R' + \mathfrak{b}R') = \operatorname{hgt}_{R'}\mathfrak{m}'.$$

Applying (27.7) to $\mathfrak{a}R'$, $\mathfrak{b}R'$ we thus get

$$\operatorname{hgt}_{R'}\mathfrak{m}' \leqq \operatorname{hgt}_{R'}\mathfrak{a}R' + \operatorname{hgt}_{R'}\mathfrak{b}R'.$$

Now $\mathfrak{a} \subset \mathfrak{c}$, $\mathfrak{b} \subset \mathfrak{c}$, and $\mathfrak{a}$, $\mathfrak{b}$, $\mathfrak{c}$ are prime; hence $\operatorname{hgt}_R\mathfrak{a} = \operatorname{hgt}_{R'}\mathfrak{a}R'$, $\operatorname{hgt}_R\mathfrak{b} = \operatorname{hgt}_{R'}\mathfrak{b}R'$, $\operatorname{hgt}_R\mathfrak{c} = \operatorname{hgt}_R\mathfrak{m}'$. Therefore

$$\operatorname{hgt}_R\mathfrak{c} \leqq \operatorname{hgt}_R\mathfrak{a} + \operatorname{hgt}_R\mathfrak{b}.$$

(27.9) REMARK. 1°) For the case of $R = K[[x_1,\ldots, x_n]]$, K algebraically closed, (27.8) was first proved by Chevalley [**3**]. His proof is based on the notion of complete tensor products of local rings.

2°) Serre [**3**] has proved (27.8) for arbitrary regular local rings, i.e., without the assumption of equal characteristics. His proof uses homological algebra and the notion of complete tensor products of local rings.

3°) In the situation of (27.4), assume that K is algebraically closed. Chevalley [**2**] has shown that in the formal case, $\mathfrak{p}S + \tilde{\mathfrak{p}}S$ is a prime ideal in S. In view of (24.6.3) and (17.5), this also holds in the convergent case.

[3] For the case of $R = K[\{x_1,\ldots, x_n\}]$ with infinite perfect K, it suffices to invoke (25.6); for the general case see (25.7. 2°).

§28. ALGEBRAIC LEMMAS ON ALGEBROID FUNCTIONS

Let K be complete nondiscrete valued and algebraically closed. Let $y = (y_1,..., y_e)$, and T be indeterminates. Let $S = K[\langle y \rangle]$ and $\mathfrak{K} = K(\langle y \rangle)$. For a polynomial

$$u(y, \Omega_1,..., \Omega_n) = \sum u_{i_1...i_n}(y)\Omega_1^{i_1}...\Omega_n^{i_n} \in S[\Omega_1,..., \Omega_n]$$

in indeterminates $\Omega_1,..., \Omega_n$ with coefficients in S, we shall say that u is convergent at $b \in K^e$ if all the coefficients $u_{i_1...i_n}$ are convergent at b; and then we write

$$u(b, \Omega_1,..., \Omega_n) = \sum u_{i_1...i_n}(b)\Omega_1^{i_1}...\Omega_n^{i_n} \in K[\Omega_1,..., \Omega_n].$$

Let

$$f(y, T) = T^d + f_1(y)T^{d-1} + ... + f_d(y), \qquad f_\nu \in S, \quad d > 0,$$

be irreducible in $\mathfrak{K}[T]$. Let $\Delta^* = \Delta^*(y)$ be the T-discriminant of $f(y, T)$. Let $0 \neq \Delta'' \in S$. Let $\Delta = \Delta^*\Delta''$. Let Y be a neighborhood of the origin in K^e in which $\Delta'', f_1,..., f_d$ are convergent. Let w be a root of $f(y, T) = 0$ in an algebraic closure $\bar{\mathfrak{K}}$ of $\mathfrak{K}$. Let $\mathfrak{L} = \mathfrak{K}(w)$. For any $b \in Y$ let $\omega_\mu[b]$, $(\mu = 1,..., d)$, be the roots of $f(b, T) = 0$ in K, i.e.,

$$f(b, T) = \prod_{\mu=1}^{d} (T - \omega_\mu[b]).$$

Note that if $\Delta(b) \neq 0$ then $\omega_1[b],..., \omega_d[b]$ are distinct. Our aim in this section is to prove lemma (28.3) and its corollaries (28.4, 28.5).

—×—

First we consider the following universal construction for the norm.[1] Let $A_1,..., A_d, B_1,..., B_d, C_0,..., C_p$ be further indeterminates. Polynomials over the ring **Z** of ordinary integers will be denoted by $F, G, P, Q_{\lambda\nu}, Q_\lambda^*$, N, M_ν; equations relating these will be polynomial identities over **Z**. Let **Q** denote the quotient field of **Z**. Let

$$G(A_1,..., A_d, T) = \prod_{\mu=1}^{d} (T - A_\mu)$$

$$= T^d + \sum_{\nu=1}^{d} M_\nu(A_1,..., A_d)T^{d-\nu}.^2$$

[1] For the various standard equivalent definitions of the norm and the field polynomial, see Zariski-Samuel [**1**: Chapter II, §10]. Let $\mathfrak{L}^*$ be a finite algebraic extension of a field $\mathfrak{K}^*$. For $u \in \mathfrak{L}^*$, the norm of u relative to the field extension $\mathfrak{L}^*/\mathfrak{K}^*$ will be denoted by $\mathfrak{N}_{\mathfrak{L}^*/\mathfrak{K}^*}u$.

[2] $M_\nu(A_1,..., A_d) \in \mathbf{Z}[A_1,..., A_d]$ is $(-1)^\nu$ times the elementary symmetric function of degree ν in $A_1,..., A_d$.

Let

$$F(B_1,\ldots, B_d, T) = T^d + B_1T^{d-1} + \ldots + B_d.$$

Then

$$F(M_1(A_1,\ldots, A_d),\ldots, M_d(A_1,\ldots, A_d), T) = G(A_1,\ldots, A_d, T).$$

Let

$$P(C_0,\ldots, C_p, T) = \sum_{j=0}^{p} C_jT^j.$$

Then

$$\begin{aligned} &P(C_0,\ldots, C_p, T)T^\lambda \\ &= \sum_{\nu=0}^{d-1} Q_{\lambda\nu}(B_1,\ldots, B_d, C_0,\ldots, C_p)T^\nu \\ &\quad + Q^*_\lambda(B_1,\ldots, B_d, C_0,\ldots, C_p, T)F(B_1,\ldots, B_d, T) \end{aligned}$$

where $Q_{\lambda\nu}$ and Q^*_λ are uniquely determined polynomials in the exhibited indeterminates with coefficients in $\mathbf{Z}$. Let

$$\begin{aligned} &N(B_1,\ldots, B_d, C_0,\ldots, C_p) \\ 1^\circ)\qquad &= \det((Q_{\lambda\nu}(B_1,\ldots, B_d, C_0,\ldots, C_p)))_{\lambda,\nu=0,\ldots,d-1} \\ &\in \mathbf{Z}[B_1,\ldots, B_d, C_0,\ldots, C_p]. \end{aligned}$$

Let

$$\mathfrak{K}^* = \mathbf{Q}(C_0,\ldots, C_p, M_1(A_1,\ldots, A_d),\ldots, M_d(A_1,\ldots, A_d)),$$

and $\mathfrak{L}^* = \mathfrak{K}^*(A_1)$. Then $G(A_1,\ldots, A_d, T)$ is the minimal monic polynomial of A_1 over $\mathfrak{K}^*$; $A_1,\ldots, A_d$ are its roots; and $1, A_1,\ldots, A_1^{d-1}$ is a vector space basis of $\mathfrak{L}^*$ over $\mathfrak{K}^*$. Taking the definition of the norm $\mathfrak{N}_{\mathfrak{L}^*/\mathfrak{K}^*}$ in terms of linear transformations, we see that

$$\begin{aligned} &\mathfrak{N}_{\mathfrak{L}^*/\mathfrak{K}^*}P(C_0,\ldots, C_p, A_1) \\ &= N(M_1(A_1,\ldots, A_d),\ldots, M_d(A_1,\ldots, A_d), C_0,\ldots, C_p). \end{aligned}$$

Taking the definition of the norm as the product of conjugates we get that

$$\mathfrak{N}_{\mathfrak{L}^*/\mathfrak{K}^*}P(C_0,\ldots, C_p, A_1) = \prod_{\mu=1}^{d} P(C_0,\ldots, C_d, A_\mu).$$

There results the following identity over $\mathbf{Z}$.

$$\begin{aligned} &N(M_1(A_1,\ldots, A_d),\ldots, M_d(A_1,\ldots, A_d), C_0,\ldots, C_p) \\ 2^\circ)\qquad &= \prod_{\mu=1}^{d} P(C_0,\ldots, C_p, A_\mu). \end{aligned}$$

—x—

Now we apply the above construction to the situation we are interested in. Let $w_1 = w$, and let $w_2, \ldots, w_d$ be the other roots of $f(y, T) = 0$ in $\mathfrak{K}$, i.e.,

$$f(y, T) = \prod_{\mu=1}^{d} (T - w_\mu).$$

Let $\Omega_1, \ldots, \Omega_n$ be further indeterminates. Let $\mathfrak{K}' = \mathfrak{K}(\Omega_1, \ldots, \Omega_n)$ and $\mathfrak{L}' = \mathfrak{L}(\Omega_1, \ldots, \Omega_n)$. Then $f(y, T)$ remains irreducible in $\mathfrak{K}'[T]$. Let $u_j(y, \Omega_1, \ldots, \Omega_n) \in S[\Omega_1, \ldots, \Omega_n]$, $(j = 0, \ldots, p)$, be given and let $b \in Y$ at which $u_0, \ldots, u_p$ are convergent. Now $M_\nu(w_1, \ldots, w_d) = f_\nu(y)$ and hence by the definition of the norm in terms of linear transformations, from 1°) we see that

$$\begin{aligned} &\mathfrak{N}_{\mathfrak{L}'/\mathfrak{K}'} P(u_0(y, \Omega_1, \ldots, \Omega_n), \ldots, u_p(y, \Omega_1, \ldots, \Omega_n), w) \\ &= N(f_1(y), \ldots, f_d(y), u_0(y, \Omega_1, \ldots, \Omega_n), \ldots, u_p(y, \Omega_1, \ldots, \Omega_n)) \end{aligned}$$

is a polynomial in $\Omega_1, \ldots, \Omega_n$ with coefficients in S and it is convergent at b. Let this polynomial be denoted by $U(y, \Omega_1, \ldots, \Omega_n)$. Furthermore, $M_\nu(\omega_1[b], \ldots, \omega_d[b]) = f_\nu(b)$ and hence

$$\begin{aligned} &U(b, \Omega_1, \ldots, \Omega_n) \\ &= N(f_1(b), \ldots, f_d(b), u_0(b, \Omega_1, \ldots, \Omega_n), \ldots, u_p(b, \Omega_1, \ldots, \Omega_n)) \\ &= N(M_1(\omega_1[b], \ldots, \omega_d[b]), \ldots, M_d(\omega_1[b], \ldots, \omega_d[b]), \\ &\qquad u_0(b, \Omega_1, \ldots, \Omega_n), \ldots, u_p(b, \Omega_1, \ldots, \Omega_n)). \end{aligned}$$

Substituting in the identity 2°), this last expression equals

$$\prod_{\mu=1}^{d} P(u_0(b, \Omega_1, \ldots, \Omega_n), \ldots, u_p(b, \Omega_1, \ldots, \Omega_n), \omega_\mu[b]).$$

Taking

$$u(y, \Omega_1, \ldots, \Omega_n, T) = P(u_0(y, \Omega_1, \ldots, \Omega_n), \ldots, u_p(y, \Omega_1, \ldots, \Omega_n), T)$$

we have thus proved the following.

(28.1) *Let $\Omega_1, \ldots, \Omega_n$ be indeterminates. Let $u(y, \Omega_1, \ldots, \Omega_n, T) \in S[y, \Omega_1, \ldots, \Omega_n, T]$. Then the norm of $u(y, \Omega_1, \ldots, \Omega_n, w)$ relative to the field extension $\mathfrak{L}(\Omega_1, \ldots, \Omega_n)/\mathfrak{K}(\Omega_1, \ldots, \Omega_n)$ is an element $U(y, \Omega_1, \ldots, \Omega_n)$ in $S[\Omega_1, \ldots, \Omega_n]$. If u is convergent at $b \in Y$ then so is U and we have*

$$U(b, \Omega_1, \ldots, \Omega_n) = \prod_{\mu=1}^{d} u(b, \Omega_1, \ldots, \Omega_n, \omega_\mu[b]).$$

Let $\sigma + \rho = n$, $\chi_i = \Omega_i$ for $i \leqq \sigma$ and $T_i = \Omega_{\sigma+i}$ for $i \leqq \rho$. Let $\Gamma_1,\ldots, \Gamma_\rho$ be further indeterminates. Let

$$v(y, \Gamma_1,\ldots, \Gamma_\rho, \chi_1,\ldots, \chi_\sigma) \in S[\Gamma_1,\ldots, \Gamma_\rho, \chi_1,\ldots, \chi_\sigma]$$

and

$$\alpha_i^{(\nu)}(y) \in S, \qquad (i = 1,\ldots, \rho;\ \nu = 0,\ldots, d-1),$$

be given. Taking

$$v(y, T_1 - \sum_{\nu=0}^{d-1} \alpha_1^{(\nu)}(y)T^\nu,\ldots, T_\rho - \sum_{\nu=0}^{d-1} \alpha_\rho^{(\nu)}(y)T^\nu, \chi_1,\ldots, \chi_\sigma)$$

for

$$u(y, T_1,\ldots, T_\rho, \chi_1,\ldots, \chi_\sigma, T)$$

in (28.1) we get

(28.2) *Let $\Gamma_1,\ldots, \Gamma_\rho$, $T_1,\ldots, T_\rho$, $\chi_1,\ldots, \chi_\sigma$ be indeterminates. Let $v(y, \Gamma_1,\ldots, \Gamma_\rho, \chi_1,\ldots, \chi_\sigma) \in S[\Gamma_1,\ldots, \Gamma_\rho, \chi_1,\ldots, \chi_\sigma]$, and $\alpha_i^{(\nu)}(y) \in S$ for $(i = 1,\ldots, \rho;\ \nu = 0,\ldots, d-1)$ be given. Then the norm of*

$$v(y, T_1 - \sum_{\nu=0}^{d-1} \alpha_1^{(\nu)}(y)w^\nu,\ldots, T_\rho - \sum_{\nu=0}^{d-1} \alpha_\rho^{(\nu)}(y)w^\nu, \chi_1,\ldots, \chi_\sigma)$$

relative to the field extension

$$\mathfrak{L}(T_1,\ldots, T_\rho, \chi_1,\ldots, \chi_\sigma)/\mathfrak{K}(T_1,\ldots, T_\rho, \chi_1,\ldots, \chi_\sigma)$$

is an element

$$U(y, T_1,\ldots, T_\rho, \chi_1,\ldots, \chi_\sigma) \quad \text{in} \quad S[T_1,\ldots, T_\rho, \chi_1,\ldots, \chi_\sigma].$$

Let $b \in Y$ at which v and all the elements $\alpha_i^{(\nu)}$ are convergent. Then U is convergent at b and

$$U(b, T_1,\ldots, T_\rho, \chi_1,\ldots, \chi_\sigma) = \prod_{\mu=1}^{d} v(b, T_1 - \sum_{\nu=0}^{d-1} \alpha_1^{(\nu)}(b)\omega_\mu[b]^\nu,\ldots, T_\rho - \sum_{\nu=0}^{d-1} \alpha_\rho^{(\nu)}(b)\omega_\mu[b]^\nu, \chi_1,\ldots, \chi_\sigma).$$

Now assume that $\Delta^* \neq 0$, i.e., $\mathfrak{L}$ is separable over $\mathfrak{K}$. Let $\alpha_1,\ldots, \alpha_\rho$ be elements in $\mathfrak{L}$ which are integral over S. We can uniquely write

$$\Delta\alpha_i = \sum_{\nu=0}^{d-1} \alpha_i^{(\nu)}(y)w^\nu \quad \text{with} \quad \alpha_i^{(\nu)} \in S.$$

Since S is a unique factorization domain, so is $S[T_1,\ldots, T_\rho, \chi_1,\ldots, \chi_\sigma]$; whence the latter is integrally closed in its quotient field

$$\mathfrak{K}' = \mathfrak{K}(T_1,\ldots, T_\rho, \chi_1,\ldots, \chi_\sigma).$$

Now

$$v(y, T_1 - \alpha_1,\ldots, T_\rho - \alpha_\rho, \chi_1,\ldots, \chi_\sigma)$$

is an element of $\mathfrak{L}' = \mathfrak{L}(T_1,\ldots, T_\rho, \chi_1,\ldots, \chi_\sigma)$ and it is integral over $S[T_1,\ldots, T_\rho, \chi_1,\ldots, \chi_\sigma]$. Therefore all the $\mathfrak{K}'$-conjugates of that element are integral over $S[T_1,\ldots, T_\rho, \chi_1,\ldots, \chi_\sigma]$. Consequently

$$\mathfrak{N}_{\mathfrak{L}'/\mathfrak{K}'}\, v(y, T_1 - \alpha_1,\ldots, T_\rho - \alpha_\rho, \chi_1,\ldots, \chi_\sigma)$$

is an element

$$\Theta(y, T_1,\ldots, T_\rho, \chi_1,\ldots, \chi_\sigma) \qquad \text{in} \qquad S[T_1,\ldots, T_\rho, \chi_1,\ldots, \chi_\sigma].$$

Now assume that $v(y, \Gamma_1,\ldots, \Gamma_\rho, \chi_1,\ldots, \chi_\sigma)$ is homogeneous of some degree q in $\Gamma_1,\ldots, \Gamma_\rho$. Taking the definition of norm as product of conjugates and considering polynomial equations in $T_1,\ldots, T_\rho, \chi_1,\ldots, \chi_\sigma$ over $\mathfrak{K}$ we get the following

$$\begin{aligned}
&\Delta^{qd}\Theta(y, T_1,\ldots, T_\rho, \chi_1,\ldots, \chi_\sigma)\\
&= \Delta^{qd}\mathfrak{N}_{\mathfrak{L}'/\mathfrak{K}'}\, v(y, T_1 - \alpha_1,\ldots, T_\rho - \alpha_\rho, \chi_1,\ldots, \chi_\sigma)\\
&= \Delta^{qd} \prod_{\mu=1}^{d} v(y, T_1 - \Delta(y)^{-1} \sum_{\nu=0}^{d-1} \alpha_1^{(\nu)}(y) w_\mu^\nu,\ldots,\\
&\qquad\qquad T_\rho - \Delta(y)^{-1} \sum_{\nu=0}^{d-1} \alpha_\rho^{(\nu)}(y) w_\mu^\nu, \chi_1,\ldots, \chi_\sigma)\\
&= \prod_{\mu=1}^{d} v(y, \Delta(y)T_1 - \sum_{\nu=0}^{d-1} \alpha_1^{(\nu)}(y) w_\mu^\nu,\ldots, \Delta(y)T_\rho - \sum_{\nu=0}^{d-1} \alpha_\rho^{(\nu)}(y) w_\mu^\nu, \chi_1,\ldots, \chi_\sigma)\\
&= U(y, \Delta(y)T_1,\ldots, \Delta(y)T_\rho, \chi_1,\ldots, \chi_\sigma).
\end{aligned}$$

Let $b \in Y$ be such that Θ, v, and all the elements $\alpha_i^{(\nu)}$ are convergent at b; and $\Delta(b) \neq 0$. Then

$$\begin{aligned}
&\Theta(b, T_1,\ldots, T_\rho, \chi_1,\ldots, \chi_\sigma)\\
&= \Delta(b)^{-qd} U(b, \Delta(b)T_1,\ldots, \Delta(b)T_\rho, \chi_1,\ldots, \chi_\sigma)\\
&\qquad\qquad \text{[by what we just proved above]}\\
&= \Delta(b)^{-qd} \prod_{\mu=1}^{d} v(b, \Delta(b)T_1 - \sum_{\nu=0}^{d-1} \alpha_i^{(\nu)}(b)\omega_\mu[b]^\nu,\ldots,\\
&\qquad\qquad \Delta(b)T_\rho - \sum_{\nu=0}^{d-1} \alpha_\rho^{(\nu)}(b)\omega_\mu[b]^\nu, \chi_1,\ldots, \chi_\sigma) \quad \text{[by (28.2)]}\\
&= \prod_{\mu=1}^{d} v(b, T_1 - \Delta(b)^{-1} \sum_{\nu=0}^{d-1} \alpha_1^{(\nu)}(b)\omega_\mu[b]^\nu,\ldots,\\
&\qquad\qquad T_\rho - \Delta(b)^{-1} \sum_{\nu=0}^{d-1} \alpha_\rho^{(\nu)}(b)\omega_\mu[b]^\nu, \chi_1,\ldots, \chi_\sigma)
\end{aligned}$$

where the last equality is due to the fact that $v(y, \Gamma_1,\dots, \Gamma_\rho, \chi_1,\dots, \chi_\sigma)$ is homogeneous of degree q in $\Gamma_1,\dots, \Gamma_\sigma$. Thus we have proved (28.3) below.

Notation for (28.3, 28.4, 28.5). Assume that $\Delta^* \neq 0$, i.e., $\mathfrak{L}$ is separable over $\mathfrak{K}$. Given $\alpha \in \mathfrak{L}$ such that α is integral over S, we can uniquely write

$$\Delta\alpha = \sum_{\nu=0}^{d-1} \alpha^{(\nu)}(y)w^\nu \qquad \text{with} \quad \alpha^{(\nu)} \in S.$$

For any $b \in Y$ such that $\alpha^{(0)},\dots, \alpha^{(d-1)}$ are convergent at b and $\Delta(b) \neq 0$ let

$$\alpha^{[\mu]}[b] = \Delta(b)^{-1} \sum_{\nu=0}^{d-1} \alpha^{(\nu)}(b)\omega_\mu[b]^\nu, \qquad (\mu = 1,\dots, d).$$

(28.3) *Let $\Gamma_1,\dots, \Gamma_\rho, T_1,\dots, T_\rho, \chi_1,\dots, \chi_\sigma$ be indeterminates. Let $\alpha_1,\dots, \alpha_\rho \in \mathfrak{L}$ be given which are integral over S. Let $v(y, \Gamma_1,\dots, \Gamma_\rho, \chi_1,\dots, \chi_\sigma] \in S[\Gamma_1,\dots, \Gamma_\rho, \chi_1,\dots, \chi_\sigma]$ be homogeneous in $\Gamma_1,\dots, \Gamma_\rho$. Then the norm of $v(y, T_1 - \alpha_1,\dots, T_\rho - \alpha_\rho, \chi_1,\dots, \chi_\sigma)$ relative to the field extension $\mathfrak{L}(T_1,\dots, T_\rho, \chi_1,\dots, \chi_\sigma)/\mathfrak{K}(T_1,\dots, T_\rho, \chi_1,\dots, \chi_\sigma)$ is an element $\Theta(y, T_1,\dots, T_\rho, \chi_1,\dots, \chi_\sigma)$ in $S[T_1,\dots, T_\rho, \chi_1,\dots, \chi_\sigma]$. Let $b \in Y$ be such that all the elements $\alpha_i^{(\nu)}$ and all the coefficients of Θ and v are convergent at b, and $\Delta(b) \neq 0$. Then*

$$\Theta(b, T_1,\dots, T_\rho, \chi_1,\dots, \chi_\sigma)$$
$$= \prod_{\mu=1}^{d} v(b, T_1 - \alpha_1^{[\mu]}[b],\dots, T_\rho - \alpha_\rho^{[\mu]}[b], \chi_1,\dots, \chi_\sigma)$$

(28.4) *Let $\alpha_1,\dots, \alpha_m \in \mathfrak{L}$ be given which are integral over S. Let $z_1,\dots, z_m, \chi_1,\dots, \chi_m$ be indeterminates. Then the norm of $(z_1 - \alpha_1)\chi_1 + \dots + (z_m - \alpha_m)\chi_m$ relative to the field extension $\mathfrak{L}(z_1,\dots, z_m, \chi_1,\dots, \chi_m)/\mathfrak{K}(z_1,\dots, z_m, \chi_1,\dots, \chi_m)$ is an element $\Theta(y, z_1,\dots, z_m, \chi_1,\dots, \chi_m)$ in $S[z_1,\dots, z_m, \chi_1,\dots, \chi_m]$. Let $b \in Y$ be such that all the elements $\alpha_i^{(\nu)}$ and all the coefficients of Θ are convergent at b, and $\Delta(b) \neq 0$. Then*

$$\Theta(b, z_1,\dots, z_m, \chi_1,\dots, \chi_m) = \prod_{\mu=1}^{d} \sum_{i=1}^{m} (z_i - \alpha_i^{[\mu]}[b])\chi_i.$$

PROOF. In (28.3) take $\sigma = \rho = m$ and $v(y, \Gamma_1,\dots, \Gamma_m, \chi_1,\dots, \chi_m) = \Gamma_1\chi_1 + \dots + \Gamma_m\chi_m$, and write z_i for T_i.

(28.5) *Let $\alpha \in \mathfrak{L}$ be integral over S. Then the field polynomial $H(y, T)$ of α relative to the field extension $\mathfrak{L}/\mathfrak{K}$ is a monic polynomial of degree d in T*

with coefficients in S.[3] *Let* $b \in Y$ *be such that* $\alpha^{(0)},\ldots,\alpha^{(d-1)}$ *and all the coefficients of* $H(y, T)$ *are convergent at* b, *and* $\Delta(b) \neq 0$. *Then*

$$H(b, T) = \prod_{\mu=1}^{d} (T - \alpha^{[\mu]}[b]).$$

PROOF. In (28.3), take $\rho = 1$, $\sigma = 0$, $v(y, \Gamma_1) = \Gamma_1$, and write T for T_1.

[3] Let $H^*(y, T)$ be the minimal monic polynomial of α over K. Then $H(y, T) = H^*(y, T)^{d/d'}$ where $d' = [\mathfrak{K}(\alpha) : \mathfrak{K}]$.

CHAPTER V

Analytic Sets

In this chapter, unless otherwise stated, K will denote a complete nondiscrete valued field and from (30.12) onward K will be assumed to be algebraically closed.

§29. THE LANGUAGE OF GERMS

(**29.1**) Let a be a point in a topological space X. Let Φ be a class of which each object is defined on some neighborhood (depending on the object) of a in X. Objects P and Q in Φ which are defined respectively on neighborhoods Y and Z of a in X are said to be *equivalent in X at a* $\Leftrightarrow$ there exists a neighborhood U of a in $Y \cap Z$ such that the restrictions of P and Q to U coincide. A *Φ-germ in X at a* is an equivalence class under this equivalence relation. The Φ-germ in X at a containing P is denoted by $\gamma_{a,X}P$ or $\gamma_a P$, and P is said to be a representative of $\gamma_a P$.

(**29.2**) Let a be a point in a topological space X. Taking Φ to be the set of all subsets of X we get the notion of a set-germ in X at a. In other words, for subsets P and Q of X we have: $\gamma_a P = \gamma_a Q \Leftrightarrow P \cap U = Q \cap U$ for some neighborhood U of a in X. In the set Ψ of all set-germs in X at a, in a unique way we can define the inclusion relations $\subset$, $\supset$ and the lattice operations $\cup$, $\cap$ of finite unions and finite intersections, such that $P \to \gamma_a P$ preserves $\subset$, $\supset$, $\cup$, $\cap$. For an infinite subset Ω of Ψ, $\bigcap_{W \in \Omega} W$ is said to exist $\Leftrightarrow$ there exists $W^* \in \Psi$ such that:

i) $W^* \subset W$ for all $W \in \Omega$; and
ii) $[W' \in \Psi$ with $W' \subset W$ for all $W \in \Omega] \Rightarrow W' \subset W^*$.

If W^* exists then it is unique and we set $W^* = \bigcap_{W \in \Omega} W$. For let $\bar{W}^*$ be any other such. Then $\bar{W}^* \subset W^*$ and $W^* \subset \bar{W}^*$, whence $W^* = \bar{W}^*$.
The germ of the empty set $\emptyset$ is again denoted by $\emptyset$.

(29.3) Let X and X^* be nonempty topological spaces. *The set of all continuous functions from* X *into* X^* *will be denoted by* $\mathfrak{C}(X; X^*)$.[1] $f \in \mathfrak{C}(X; X^*)$ is said to be *constant* $\Leftrightarrow$ $f(X)$ consists of a single point in X^*; the constant elements in $\mathfrak{C}(X; X^*)$ are in one to one correspondence with the points in X^* and hence we may sometimes identify X^* with a subset of $\mathfrak{C}(X; X^*)$; $f \in \mathfrak{C}(X; X^*)$ is said to be *nonconstant* $\Leftrightarrow$ f is not constant. For any $\emptyset \neq X' \subset X$, the map $\mathfrak{C}(X; X^*) \to \mathfrak{C}(X'; X^*)$ given by: $f \to f\,|X'$ is called the restriction map. If X^* is a topological group then $\mathfrak{C}(X; X^*)$ becomes a group, and the constant element in $\mathfrak{C}(X; X^*)$ corresponding to the element 0 in X^* is the zero element of $\mathfrak{C}(X; X^*)$ and it is again denoted by 0. If X^* is a topological ring then $\mathfrak{C}(X; X^*)$ becomes a ring and then similarly we get $1 \in \mathfrak{C}(X; X^*)$. If X^* is a topological group then for any $f \in \mathfrak{C}(X; X^*)$ and $V \subset X$ we write $f(V) = 0$ to mean that $f(b) = 0$ for all $b \in V$.

Let $a \in X$. Taking $\Phi = \bigcup \mathfrak{C}(Y; X^*)$ where the union is taken over the family of all neighborhoods Y of a in X, we get the notion of an X^*-valued continuous function germ in X at a. In other words, for $f \in \mathfrak{C}(Y; X^*)$ and $g \in \mathfrak{C}(Z; X^*)$ where Y and Z are neighborhoods of a in X we have: $\gamma_a f = \gamma_a g \Leftrightarrow f\,|U = g|U$ for some neighborhood U of a in $Y \cap Z$. *The set of all these germs will be denoted by* $\mathfrak{C}(a, X; X^*)$. For any neighborhood Y of a in X and $f \in \mathfrak{C}(Y; X^*)$: i) $f(a)$ is called the value of $\gamma_a f \in \mathfrak{C}(a, X; X^*)$ and is denoted by $(\gamma_a f)(a)$, ii) $\gamma_a f \in \mathfrak{C}(a, X; X^*)$ is said to be *constant* $\Leftrightarrow$ $f\,|U$ is constant for some neighborhood U of a in X; these definitions are obviously independent of the particular representative f of $\gamma_a f$. The constant elements in $\mathfrak{C}(a, X; X^*)$ are in one to one correspondence with the points in X^* and hence we may sometimes identify X^* with a subset of $\mathfrak{C}(a, X; X^*)$. $F \in \mathfrak{C}(a, X; X^*)$ is said to be *nonconstant* $\Leftrightarrow$ F is not constant. If X^* is a topological group then $\mathfrak{C}(a, X; X^*)$ becomes a group so that $f \to \gamma_a f$ preserves finite sums; the constant element in $\mathfrak{C}(a, X; X^*)$ corresponding to the element 0 in X^* is the zero element in $\mathfrak{C}(a, X; X^*)$ and it is again denoted by 0. If X^* is a topological ring then $\mathfrak{C}(a, X; X^*)$ becomes a ring so that $f \to \gamma_a f$ preserves finite sums and products; the constant element in $\mathfrak{C}(a, X; X^*)$ corresponding to the element 1 in X^* is the identity element in $\mathfrak{C}(a, X; X^*)$ and it is again denoted by 1. If X^* is a topological group, Y is a neighborhood of a in X, $f \in \mathfrak{C}(Y; X^*)$ and $P \subset X$, then for the element $\gamma_a f \in \mathfrak{C}(a, X; X^*)$ and the set germ $\gamma_a P$ in X at a we write $(\gamma_a f)(\gamma_a P) = 0$ to mean that $f(P \cap U) = 0$ for some neighborhood U of a in Y; again this definition is obviously independent of the particular representatives

[1] If X^* has trivial topology, i.e., if $\emptyset$ and X^* are the only open subsets of X^*, then $\mathfrak{C}(X; X^*) =$ the set of *all* functions from X into X^*.

f and P of $\gamma_a f$ and $\gamma_a P$. For any $X' \subset X$ with $a \in X'$, we get the *restriction map* $\varphi: \mathfrak{E}(a, X; X^*) \to \mathfrak{E}(a, X'; X^*)$ as follows: for any neighborhood Y of a in X and $f \in \mathfrak{E}(Y; X^*)$ let $\varphi(\gamma_{a,X} f) = \gamma_{a,X'}(f \mid Y \cap X')$. If X^* is a topological group (resp: topological ring) then obviously φ is a group homomorphism (resp: ring homomorphism).

When there is no confusion, *we may write* $\mathfrak{E}(X)$ *and* $\mathfrak{E}(a, X)$ for the rings $\mathfrak{E}(X; K)$ and $\mathfrak{E}(a, X; K)$ where K is the complete nondiscrete valued field which remains fixed most of the time.

(**29.4**) Let X be a nonempty open set in K^n. For $a \in X$ *we set*

$$R(a, X) = \textit{ring of all analytic function germs in } X \textit{ at } a.$$

To review the definition of $R(a, X)$, for any $r \in K[\langle x_1, \ldots, x_n \rangle]$ let $\tilde{\sigma}_a r$ be the germ at a of the K-valued function: $(p_1 + a_1, \ldots, p_n + a_n) \to r(p_1, \ldots, p_n)$ for all $p \in \mathbf{D}(r)$. Then $\tilde{\sigma}_a: K[\langle x_1, \ldots, x_n \rangle] \to \mathfrak{E}(a, X)$ is a homomorphism. The Identity Theorem (10.5.1) says that $\tilde{\sigma}_a$ is actually a monomorphism. By definition, $R(a, X)$ is the image of $K[\langle x_1, \ldots, x_n \rangle]$ under $\tilde{\sigma}_a$. The corresponding isomorphism of $R(a, X)$ onto $K[\langle x_1, \ldots, x_n \rangle]$ will usually be denoted by $\boldsymbol{\sigma}_{a,X}$ or $\boldsymbol{\sigma}_a$ or $\boldsymbol{\sigma}$. For $F \in R(a, X)$, $\boldsymbol{\sigma}_a F$ is simply the Taylor expansion of F (i.e., of any representative of F) around a, and hence $\boldsymbol{\sigma}_a$ may be called the *Taylor isomorphism.*

For $V \subset X$ and $a \in X$ *we set*[2]

$$\begin{aligned} \mathfrak{i}(a, V, X) = \mathfrak{i}(a, \gamma_a V, X) &= \mathfrak{i}(\gamma_a V, X) \\ &= \{F \in R(a, X) : F(\gamma_a V) = 0\}. \end{aligned}$$

Note that $\mathfrak{i}(a, V, X)$ is an ideal in $R(a, X)$ which is its own radical, and we have: $\mathfrak{i}(a, V, X) = R(a, X) \Leftrightarrow a \notin$ (closure of V in X). *If* $a \in V$ *then we set*

$$R(a, V) = \textit{image of } R(a, X) \textit{ under the restriction map } \mathfrak{E}(a, X) \to \mathfrak{E}(a, V).$$

The corresponding epimorphism $R(a, X) \to R(a, V)$ is again called *the restriction map*; note that $\mathfrak{i}(a, V, X)$ is the kernel of this epimorphism. If V is analytic at a then *we define*

$$\begin{aligned} \dim_a V &= \textit{dimension of } V \textit{ at } a \\ &= \dim \gamma_a V = \textit{dimension of } \gamma_a V \\ &= \begin{cases} \dim R(a, V) & \text{if } a \in V \\ -1 & \text{if } a \notin V. \end{cases} \end{aligned}$$

[2] The notations $\mathfrak{i}(\gamma_a V, X)$ and $\mathfrak{i}(\gamma_a W, V)$ are perhaps more logical than the notations $\mathfrak{i}(a, \gamma_a V, X)$ and $\mathfrak{i}(a, \gamma_a W, V)$. However we shall usually use the latter because they are clearer.

If V is analytic in X then *we define*

$$\dim V = \textit{dimension of } V = \begin{cases} \max_{a \in V} \dim_a V & \text{if } V \neq \emptyset \\ -1 & \text{if } V = \emptyset. \end{cases}$$

If V is nonempty and analytic in X then *we set*

$$R(V) = \{f \in \mathfrak{E}(V): \gamma_a f \in R(a, V) \text{ for all } a \in V\}.$$

$R(V)$ is then a subring of $\mathfrak{E}(V)$. Note that obviously $R(X)$ is the ring of all analytic functions on X.

Let V and W be subsets of X which are analytic at $a \in X$ such that $a \in V$ and $W \subset V$. *We set*[2]

$$\mathfrak{i}(a, W, V) = \mathfrak{i}(a, \gamma_a W, V) = \mathfrak{i}(\gamma_a W, V)$$
$$= \{F \in R(a, V): F(\gamma_a W) = 0\}.$$

Then $\mathfrak{i}(a, W, V)$ is an ideal in $R(a, V)$ which is its own radical. Also $\mathfrak{i}(a, W, V)$ is the image of $\mathfrak{i}(a, W, X)$ under the restriction map $R(a, X) \to R(a, V)$. Now assume that $a \in W$. Then $R(a, W)$ is clearly the image of $R(a, V)$ under the restriction map $\mathfrak{E}(a, V) \to \mathfrak{E}(a, W)$; the corresponding epimorphism $R(a, V) \to R(a, W)$ is again called *the restriction map*. Note that $\mathfrak{i}(a, W, V)$ is the kernel of this map $R(a, V) \to R(a, W)$, and that the composition of the restriction maps $R(a, X) \to R(a, V) \to R(a, W)$ is the restriction map $R(a, X) \to R(a, W)$.

A set germ $\tilde{W}$ in K^n at a is said to be *analytic* provided $\tilde{W}$ has a representative which is analytic at a; and then every representative of $\tilde{W}$ is analytic at a.

Let $\tilde{W}$ be an analytic set germ in K^n at a. $\tilde{W}$ is said to be *reducible* $\Leftrightarrow$ $\tilde{W}$ can be written as $\tilde{W} = \tilde{W}_1 \cup \tilde{W}_2$ where $\tilde{W}_1$ and $\tilde{W}_2$ are analytic set germs in K^n at a such that $\tilde{W}_i \neq \tilde{W}$ for $i = 1, 2$. $\tilde{W}$ is said to be *irreducible* $\Leftrightarrow$ $\tilde{W}$ is not reducible.

§30. DECOMPOSITION OF AN ANALYTIC SET GERM

Notation for (30.1) *to* (30.15). Let $a \in K^n$ be given. Let γ denote γ_{a,K^n}. Let

$$\mathbf{V}^* = \text{set of all set germs in } K^n \text{ at } a;$$
$$\mathbf{V} = \text{set of all analytic set germs in } K^n \text{ at } a;$$
$$R = R(a, K^n);$$
$$\mathbf{I}^* = \text{set of all ideals in } R;$$
$$\mathbf{I} = [\mathfrak{a} \in \mathbf{I}^*: \operatorname{rad} \mathfrak{a} = \mathfrak{a}].$$

For any $V \in \mathbf{V}^*$ let

$$\mathfrak{i}(V) = \mathfrak{i}(a, V, K^n).$$

Let $\mathfrak{a} \in \mathbf{I}^*$. Since R is noetherian, there exists a finite number of analytic functions $f_1, \ldots, f_u$ on a neighborhood X of a in K^n such that $\gamma f_1, \ldots, \gamma f_u$ generate $\mathfrak{a}$. *We set*

$$\mathfrak{V}(\mathfrak{a}) = \gamma\{b \in X : f_1(b) = \ldots = f_u(b) = 0\}.$$

Let $g_1, \ldots, g_v$ be analytic functions on a neighborhood X' of a in K^n such that $\gamma g_1, \ldots, \gamma g_v$ generate $\mathfrak{a}$. Then there exist analytic functions p_{ij}, q_{ij} on a neighborhood X'' of a in $X \cap X'$ such that on X'' we have $g_i = \sum_j p_{ij} f_j$ and $f_i = \sum_j q_{ij} g_j$. Consequently

$$\mathfrak{V}(\mathfrak{a}) = \gamma\{b \in X' : g_1(b) = \ldots = g_v(b) = 0\}.$$

Thus, the definition of $\mathfrak{V}(\mathfrak{a})$ is independent of the particular finite basis of $\mathfrak{a}$. For any subset A of R *we set* $\mathfrak{V}(A) = \mathfrak{V}(AR)$. Note that, since R is noetherian, A contains a finite basis of AR.

(**30.1**) *Obviously* $\mathfrak{V}(\mathfrak{a}) = \mathfrak{V}(\text{rad } \mathfrak{a})$ *for all* $\mathfrak{a} \in \mathbf{I}^*$. *Consequently* $\mathbf{V} = \mathfrak{V}(\mathbf{I}^*) = \mathfrak{V}(\mathbf{I})$.

(**30.2**) *For any* $V \in \mathbf{V}^*$ *we have*:

1) $V \subset \mathfrak{V}(\mathfrak{i}(V))$.

2) $V \in \mathbf{V} \Leftrightarrow V = \mathfrak{V}(\mathfrak{i}(V))$.

Proof of 1) Let $f_1, \ldots, f_u$ be analytic functions on a neighborhood X of a in K^n such that $\{\gamma f_1, \ldots, \gamma f_u\}R = \mathfrak{i}(V)$, and let $\bar{V}$ be a representative of V. By definition of $\mathfrak{i}$, there exists a neighborhood X' of a in X such that $f_1(\bar{V} \cap X') = \ldots = f_u(\bar{V} \cap X') = 0$. Hence by definition of $\mathfrak{V}$ we get $V \subset \mathfrak{V}(\mathfrak{i}(V))$.

Proof of 2). "$\Leftarrow$" is obvious. "$\Rightarrow$": There exist analytic functions $f_1, \ldots, f_u$ on a neighborhood X of a in K^n such that

$$V = \gamma\{b \in X : f_1(b) = \ldots = f_u(b) = 0\}.$$

We then have $\gamma f_1, \ldots, \gamma f_u \in \mathfrak{i}(V)$, and hence $V \supset \mathfrak{V}(\mathfrak{i}(V))$. Therefore $V = \mathfrak{V}(\mathfrak{i}(V))$ by 1).

(**30.3**) *For any finite number of elements* $\mathfrak{a}_1, \ldots, \mathfrak{a}_t$ *in* $\mathbf{I}^*$ *we have the following*.

1) $$\mathfrak{a}_1 \supset \mathfrak{a}_2 \Rightarrow \mathfrak{V}(\mathfrak{a}_1) \subset \mathfrak{V}(\mathfrak{a}_2).$$

2) $$\mathfrak{V}\left(\bigcap_{i=1}^{t} \mathfrak{a}_i\right) = \mathfrak{V}\left(\prod_{i=1}^{t} \mathfrak{a}_i\right) = \bigcup_{i=1}^{t} \mathfrak{V}(\mathfrak{a}_i).$$

3) $$\mathfrak{V}\left(\sum_{i=1}^{t} \mathfrak{a}_i\right) = \bigcap_{i=1}^{t} \mathfrak{V}(\mathfrak{a}_i).$$

PROOF. There exist analytic functions $f_{i1},\ldots,f_{iu_i}$ on a neighborhood X_i of a in K^n such that $\gamma f_{i1},\ldots, \gamma f_{iu_i}$ is a basis of $\mathfrak{a}_i$. Let $X = \bigcap_{i=1}^{t} X_i$.

1) $\mathfrak{a}_1 \supset \mathfrak{a}_2 \Rightarrow$ there exist analytic functions $p_{\lambda\mu}$ on a neighborhood X' of a in X such that $f_{2\lambda} = \sum_{\mu} p_{\lambda\mu} f_{1\mu}$ on X'. Therefore $\mathfrak{V}(\mathfrak{a}_1) \subset \mathfrak{V}(\mathfrak{a}_2)$.

2) Let $f_{k_1\ldots k_t} = f_{tk_1}\cdots f_{tk_t}$ on X. Then

$$\mathfrak{V}\left(\prod_{i=1}^{t} \mathfrak{a}_i\right) = \gamma\{b \in X: f_{k_1\ldots k_t}(b) = 0 \text{ for all } k_1,\ldots, k_t\}$$

$$= \bigcup_{i=1}^{t} \mathfrak{V}(\mathfrak{a}_i).$$

Next,

$$\bigcap_{i=1}^{t} \mathfrak{a}_i \supset \prod_{i=1}^{t} \mathfrak{a}_i$$

and hence by 1)

$$\mathfrak{V}\left(\bigcap_{i=1}^{t} \mathfrak{a}_i\right) \subset \mathfrak{V}\left(\prod_{i=1}^{t} \mathfrak{a}_i\right) = \bigcup_{i=1}^{t} \mathfrak{V}(\mathfrak{a}_i).$$

For all j:

$$\mathfrak{a}_j \supset \bigcap_{i=1}^{t} \mathfrak{a}_i$$

and hence

$$\mathfrak{V}(\mathfrak{a}_j) \subset \mathfrak{V}\left(\bigcap_{i=1}^{t} \mathfrak{a}_i\right) \quad \text{by 1).}$$

Therefore

$$\mathfrak{V}\left(\bigcap_{i=1}^{t} \mathfrak{a}_i\right) = \bigcup_{i=1}^{t} \mathfrak{V}(\mathfrak{a}_i) = \mathfrak{V}\left(\prod_{i=1}^{t} \mathfrak{a}_i\right).$$

3)
$$\mathfrak{V}\left(\sum_{i=1}^{t} \mathfrak{a}_i\right) = \gamma\{b \in X: f_{ij}(b) = 0 \text{ for all } i, j\}$$

$$= \bigcap_{i=1}^{t} \mathfrak{V}(a_i).$$

(30.4) **V** *is closed with respect to finite unions and finite intersections.* Follows from (30.1, 30.3).

(30.5) *For any finite number of elements $V_1,\ldots, V_t$ in* **V** *we have the following.*

1) $$V_1 = V_2 \Leftrightarrow \mathfrak{i}(V_1) = \mathfrak{i}(V_2).$$

2) $$V_1 \subset V_2 \Leftrightarrow \mathfrak{i}(V_1) \supset \mathfrak{i}(V_2).$$

3) $$V_1 \underset{\neq}{\subset} V_2 \Leftrightarrow \mathfrak{i}(V_1) \underset{\neq}{\supset} \mathfrak{i}(V_2).$$

4) $$V = \bigcup_{i=1}^{t} V_i \Leftrightarrow \mathfrak{i}(V) = \bigcap_{i=1}^{t} \mathfrak{i}(V_i).$$

PROOF. 1) "$\Rightarrow$" is obvious and "$\Leftarrow$" follows from (30.2). 2) "$\Rightarrow$" is obvious and "$\Leftarrow$" follows from (30.2, 30.3). 3) follows from 1) and 2). 4) "$\Rightarrow$" is obvious and "$\Leftarrow$" follows from (30.2, 30.3).

(30.6) *Let Ω be a nonempty (not necessarily finite) subset of* $\mathbf{I}^*$. *Then there exists a finite nonempty subset Ω^* of Ω such that* $\sum_{\mathfrak{a}\in\Omega} \mathfrak{a} = \sum_{\mathfrak{a}\in\Omega^*} \mathfrak{a}$, *and hence*

$$\bigcap_{\mathfrak{a}\in\Omega} \mathfrak{V}(\mathfrak{a}) = \mathfrak{V}\left(\sum_{\mathfrak{a}\in\Omega} \mathfrak{a}\right) = \mathfrak{V}\left(\sum_{\mathfrak{a}\in\Omega^*} \mathfrak{a}\right) = \bigcap_{\mathfrak{a}\in\Omega^*} \mathfrak{V}(\mathfrak{a}).$$

PROOF. Fix $\mathfrak{a}_1 \in \Omega$. If $\mathfrak{a}_1 \supset \sum_{\mathfrak{a}\in\Omega} \mathfrak{a}$ then we are through. If not, then there exists $\mathfrak{a}_2 \in \Omega$ such that $\mathfrak{a}_1 \not\supset \mathfrak{a}_2$. If $\mathfrak{a}_1 + \mathfrak{a}_2 \supset \sum_{\mathfrak{a}\in\Omega} \mathfrak{a}$ then stop. If not, then there exists $\mathfrak{a}_3 \in \Omega$ such that $\mathfrak{a}_1 + \mathfrak{a}_2 \not\supset \mathfrak{a}_3$; etc. Thus

$$\mathfrak{a}_1 \underset{\neq}{\subset} \mathfrak{a}_1 + \mathfrak{a}_2 \underset{\neq}{\subset} \mathfrak{a}_1 + \mathfrak{a}_2 + \mathfrak{a}_3 \underset{\neq}{\subset} \dots .$$

Since R is noetherian, this must stop after a finite number of steps, say after t steps. Let $\Omega^* = \{\mathfrak{a}_1, \mathfrak{a}_2, \dots, \mathfrak{a}_t\}$. Then $\sum_{\mathfrak{a}\in\Omega} \mathfrak{a} = \sum_{\mathfrak{a}\in\Omega^*} \mathfrak{a}$. Hence by (30.3),

$$\mathfrak{V}\left(\sum_{\mathfrak{a}\in\Omega} \mathfrak{a}\right) = \mathfrak{V}\left(\sum_{\mathfrak{a}\in\Omega^*} \mathfrak{a}\right) = \bigcap_{\mathfrak{a}\in\Omega^*} \mathfrak{V}(\mathfrak{a}).$$

For any $\mathfrak{b} \in \Omega$ we have $\mathfrak{b} \subset \sum_{\mathfrak{a}\in\Omega} \mathfrak{a}$ and hence $\mathfrak{V}(\mathfrak{b}) \supset \mathfrak{V}(\sum_{\mathfrak{a}\in\Omega} \mathfrak{a})$ by (30.3). Also

$$W \in \mathbf{V}^* \text{ with } W \subset \mathfrak{V}(\mathfrak{b}) \text{ for all } \mathfrak{b} \in \Omega$$

$$\Rightarrow W \subset \bigcap_{i=1}^{t} \mathfrak{V}(\mathfrak{a}_i) = \mathfrak{V}\left(\sum_{\mathfrak{a}\in\Omega} \mathfrak{a}\right).$$

Therefore

$$\bigcap_{\mathfrak{a}\in\Omega} \mathfrak{V}(\mathfrak{a}) = \mathfrak{V}\left(\sum_{\mathfrak{a}\in\Omega} \mathfrak{a}\right).$$

(30.7) **1)** *Every strictly descending chain in* $\mathbf{V}$ *is finite.* **2)** $\mathbf{V}$ *is closed with respect to arbitrary (not necessarily finite) intersections.*

Since R is noetherian, 1) follows from (30.5). 2) follows from (30.6).

(**30.8**) *Let $V \in \mathbf{V}$. Then V is irreducible* $\Leftrightarrow$ $\mathfrak{i}(V)$ *is prime or the unit ideal.*

PROOF. "$\Rightarrow$": Otherwise there exist $F_1, F_2 \in R$ such that $F_1, F_2 \notin \mathfrak{i}(V)$ and $F_1F_2 \in \mathfrak{i}(V)$. Let $V_i = \mathfrak{V}(\mathfrak{i}(V) + F_iR)$. By (30.5), $V_i \subsetneq V$ for $i = 1, 2$. By (30.2), (30.3),

$$V_1 \cup V_2 = \mathfrak{V}([\mathfrak{i}(V) + F_1R][\mathfrak{i}(V) + F_2R]) \supset \mathfrak{V}(\mathfrak{i}(V)) = V \supset V_1 \cup V_2.$$

Therefore $V = V_1 \cap V_2$. This contradicts the irreducibility of V.

"$\Leftarrow$": Otherwise there exist $V_1, V_2 \in \mathbf{V}$ such that $V = V_1 \cup V_2$ and $V_i \subsetneq V$ for $i = 1, 2$. By (30.5), $\mathfrak{i}(V) = \mathfrak{i}(V_1) \cap \mathfrak{i}(V_2)$. Since $\mathfrak{i}(V)$ is a prime ideal or the unit ideal, there exists i such that $\mathfrak{i}(V) = \mathfrak{i}(V_i)$ and then $V = V_i$ by (30.5). Contradiction.

(**30.9**) *In* $\mathbf{V}$, *every element can uniquely be expressed as an irredundant finite union of irreducible elements.*[1]

PROOF. Suppose if possible that $V \in \mathbf{V}$ cannot be expressed as a finite union of irreducible elements in $\mathbf{V}$. Then in particular V is not irreducible, i.e., $V = V_1 \cup V'$, $V_1 \neq V$, $V' \neq V$, with $V_1, V' \in \mathbf{V}$. If V_1 and V' were finite unions of irreducible elements in $\mathbf{V}$ then so would be V. Consequently either V_1 or V' is not expressible as a finite union of irreducible elements in $\mathbf{V}$. Say this is so for V_1.

Thus, [$V \in \mathbf{V}$ such that V is not expressible as a finite union of irreducible elements in $\mathbf{V}$] $\Rightarrow$ [there exists $V_1 \in \mathbf{V}$ with $V_1 \subsetneq V$ such that V_1 is not expressible as a finite union of irreducible elements in $\mathbf{V}$] $\Rightarrow$ [there exists $V_2 \in \mathbf{V}$ with $V_2 \subsetneq V_1$ such that V_2 is not expressible as a finite union of irreducible elements in $\mathbf{V}$] $\Rightarrow \ldots$. This yields $V_i \in \mathbf{V}$ with $V \supsetneq V_1 \supsetneq V_2 \supsetneq \ldots$ which contradicts (30.7).

Consequently, given $V \in \mathbf{V}$ we can write $V = V_1 \cup \ldots \cup V_t$ where $V_1, \ldots, V_t$ are a finite number of irreducible elements in $\mathbf{V}$. Throwing away a certain number of V_i we get an expression of V as an irredundant finite union of irreducible elements in $\mathbf{V}$.

To prove uniqueness, for $V \in \mathbf{V}$ let $V = V_1 \cup \ldots \cup V_t$ and $V = W_1 \cup \ldots \cup W_s$ be any two expressions of V as irredundant finite unions of irreducible elements in $\mathbf{V}$. Then for any i we have that

$$V_i = V_i \cap V = V_i \cap (W_1 \cup \ldots \cup W_s) = (V_i \cap W_1) \cup \ldots \cup (V_i \cap W_s).$$

[1] A finite union $V_1 \cup \ldots \cup V_t$ of elements V_i in $\mathbf{V}$ is said to be irredundant if for $i = 1, \ldots, t$ we have that $V_1 \cup \ldots \cup V_t \neq V_1 \cup \ldots \cup V_{i-1} \cup V_{i+1} \cup \ldots \cup V_t$. By convention, the union of an empty family of set germs is the empty set germ $\emptyset$. Therefore, if $V_1 \cup \ldots \cup V_t = \emptyset$, then $V_1 \cup \ldots \cup V_t$ is irredundant if and only if $t = 0$.

Since V_i is irreducible, there exists an integer $p(i)$ such that $V_i = V_i \cap W_{p(i)}$ i.e., $V_i \subset W_{p(i)}$. Similarly for any j there exists an integer $q(j)$ such that $W_j \subset V_{q(j)}$. Then $V_i \subset W_{p(i)} \subset V_{q(p(i))}$ and hence $V_i \subset V_{q(p(i))}$. Since the expression $V = V_1 \cup ... \cup V_t$ is irredundant, we must have $q(p(i)) = i$. This being so for $i = 1,..., t$ we conclude that: $s = t$; $(p(1),..., p(t))$ is a permutation of $(1,..., t)$; and $W_{p(i)} = V_i$ for $i = 1,..., t$.

(**30.10**) Definition. *Let V, $W \in \mathbf{V}$. W is said to be an irreducible component of $V \Leftrightarrow$*

i) $\emptyset \neq W \subset V$, W is irreducible; and
ii) $W \subset W^* \subset V$, $W^* \in \mathbf{V}$, W^* irreducible $\Rightarrow W = W^*$.

From (30.9) we immediately deduce the following. *Let $V \in \mathbf{V}$ be given. Then V has only a finite number of irreducible components $V_1,..., V_t$, $(t = 0 \Leftrightarrow V = \emptyset)$, and $V = V_1 \cup ... \cup V_t$ is the unique expression of V as an irredundant finite union of irreducible elements in* $\mathbf{V}$. This representation will be called the *normal decomposition of V*.

(**30.11**) *Let V be an analytic set in a neighborhood X of a in K^n. Then there exists a neighborhood Y of a in X and analytic sets $V_1,..., V_t$ in Y such that*

i) *$\gamma V_1,..., \gamma V_t$ are irreducible;*
ii) *$V \cap Y = V_1 \cup ... \cup V_t$;*
iii) *for any neighborhood Y' of a in Y and for $i = 1,..., t$ we have* $V_i \cap Y' \not\subset \bigcup_{j \neq i} (V_j \cap Y')$.

Furthermore, if in any other neighborhood Y^* of a in X we have any other such decomposition, then these two decompositions coincide in some neighborhood of a in $Y \cap Y^*$.

Proof. This is merely a reformulation of (30.9) without using the language of germs.

(**30.12**) Rückert Nullstellensatz.[2] *Assume that K is algebraically closed. Then for any ideal $\mathfrak{a}$ in R we have* $\mathfrak{i}(\mathfrak{V}(\mathfrak{a})) = \operatorname{rad} \mathfrak{a}$.

Since $\mathfrak{V}(\operatorname{rad} \mathfrak{a}) = \mathfrak{V}(\mathfrak{a})$ and $\operatorname{rad}(\operatorname{rad} \mathfrak{a}) = \operatorname{rad} \mathfrak{a}$, we may assume that $\operatorname{rad} \mathfrak{a} = \mathfrak{a}$. Then $\mathfrak{a} = \mathfrak{p}_1 \cap ... \cap \mathfrak{p}_t$ where $\mathfrak{p}_1,..., \mathfrak{p}_t$ are prime ideals in R.[3] By (30.3), $\mathfrak{V}(\mathfrak{a}) = \bigcup_{i=1}^{t} \mathfrak{V}(\mathfrak{p}_i)$ and then by (30.5), $\mathfrak{i}(\mathfrak{V}(\mathfrak{a})) = \bigcap_{i=1}^{t} \mathfrak{i}(\mathfrak{V}(\mathfrak{p}_i))$.

[2] By analogy with algebraic geometry, this has sometimes been called Hilbert Nullstellensatz. In view of the fundamental contributions of Rückert [**1**], it seems more appropriate to ascribe it to Rückert.

[3] $t = 0 \Leftrightarrow \mathfrak{a} = R$.

Consequently it suffices to show that $\mathfrak{i}(\mathfrak{V}(\mathfrak{p})) = \mathfrak{p}$ for any prime ideal $\mathfrak{p}$ in R. Let $\mathfrak{m}$ be the maximal ideal in R. Then:

$$\mathfrak{p} = \mathfrak{m} \Rightarrow \mathfrak{V}(\mathfrak{p}) = \gamma\{a\} \Rightarrow \mathfrak{i}(\mathfrak{V}(\mathfrak{p})) = \mathfrak{m};$$

and

$$\mathfrak{p} = \{0\} \Rightarrow \mathfrak{V}(\mathfrak{p}) = \gamma K^n \Rightarrow \mathfrak{i}(\mathfrak{V}(\mathfrak{p})) = \{0\}.$$

Hence we may assume that $\mathfrak{p}$ is a nonzero nonmaximal prime ideal in R. Via Taylor expansions around a, identify R with $K[\langle x_1,..., x_n\rangle]$. Then what we have to prove is this.

1°) *Let $\mathfrak{p}$ be a nonzero nonmaximal prime ideal in $K[\langle x_1,..., x_n\rangle]$. Let $u_1,..., u_\nu$ be a finite basis of $\mathfrak{p}$. Let X be a neighborhood of the origin in K^n in which $u_1,..., u_\nu$ are convergent. Let*

$$V = \{b \in X: u_1(b) = ... = u_\nu(b) = 0\}$$

and

$$\mathfrak{r} = \{v \in K[\langle x_1,..., x_n\rangle]: v \text{ is convergent in a neighborhood } X' \text{ of the origin in } X \text{ and } v(b) = 0 \text{ for all } b \in X' \cap V\}.$$

Then $\mathfrak{r} = \mathfrak{p}$. (Obviously $\mathfrak{r}$ is an ideal in $K[\langle x_1,..., x_n\rangle]$ and $\mathfrak{p} \subset \mathfrak{r}$.)

We shall prove 1°) in (31.9). Let us make the following observations.

2°) *The Nullstellensatz is not valid if K is not algebraically closed.* Take $n = 2$, let a be at the origin, and identify R with $K[\langle x_1, x_2\rangle]$. Let $f(x_1, x_2) = x_2^d F(x_1/x_2)$ where $F(T)$ is a monic irreducible polynomial of degree $d > 1$ in T with coefficients in K. Then $\mathfrak{a} = fR$ is a nonmaximal prime ideal in R. However $\mathfrak{V}(\mathfrak{a}) = \gamma\{(0, 0)\}$ and hence $\mathfrak{i}(\mathfrak{V}(\mathfrak{a}))$ is the maximal ideal in R.

3°) *If $K = \mathbf{R}$ then every element $V \in \mathbf{V}$ is of the form $\mathfrak{V}(\mathfrak{a})$ where $\mathfrak{a}$ is a principal ideal in R.* For let $f_1,..., f_u$ be a finite number of elements in R such that $V = \mathfrak{V}(\{f_1,..., f_u\}R)$ and take $\mathfrak{a} = (f_1^2 + ... + f_u^2)R$.

In the rest of this section, K is assumed to be algebraically closed.

In virtue of the Nullstellensatz, the results of this section imply that the ideal theory in R can effectively be used to study the structure of analytic set germs. For instance, we have the following immediate corollaries (30.13, 30.14, 30.15) of the results proved so far in this section.

(30.13) $\mathfrak{V}$ *maps* $\mathbf{I}$ *in a one to one inclusion reversing manner onto* $\mathbf{V}$; *and* $\mathfrak{i} = \mathfrak{V}^{-1}$.

(30.14) *Let $V_1, \dots, V_t$, $(t > 0)$, be a finite number of analytic set germs in K^n at a. Then:*

1) $\dim \bigcup_{i=1}^{t} V_i = \max_{1 \leq i \leq t} \dim V_i$.

2) $[V_1 \subsetneq V_2$, *V_2 irreducible*$] \Rightarrow \dim V_1 < \dim V_2$.

3) *$V_1 \subset V_2$ and V' is an irreducible component of $V_1 \Rightarrow V'$ is contained in some irreducible component of V_2.*

(30.15) *Let $\mathfrak{a}$ be any ideal in R. Let $\mathfrak{p}_1, \dots, \mathfrak{p}_t$ be the distinct minimal prime ideals of $\mathfrak{a}$. Then $\mathfrak{V}(\mathfrak{p}_1) \cup \dots \cup \mathfrak{V}(\mathfrak{p}_t)$ is the normal decomposition of $\mathfrak{V}(\mathfrak{a})$.*

(30.16) Definition. Let V be an analytic set in an open set X in K^n Let $a \in V$. We introduce the following definitions and terminology.

1) *V is pure e dimensional at a*
$\Leftrightarrow$ *$\gamma_a V$ is pure e dimensional*
$\Leftrightarrow$ every irreducible component of $\gamma_a V$ is e dimensional, i.e.,
$\Leftrightarrow$ $\dim R(a, X)/\mathfrak{p} = e$ for every prime ideal $\mathfrak{p}$ of $\mathfrak{i}(a, V, X)$.

2) *V is pure e dimensional*
$\Leftrightarrow V \neq \emptyset$ and $\dim_b V = e$ for all $b \in V$.
For $Y \subset X$, *V is pure e dimensional in Y*
$\Leftrightarrow V \cap Y \neq \emptyset$ and $\dim_b V = e$ for all $b \in V \cap Y$

3) $W \subset V$ is a *thin subset of* $V \Leftrightarrow$ given $b \in V$ there exists an analytic set W^* in a neighborhood X^* of b in X such that $W \cap X^* \subset W^* \subset V$ and $\dim_\beta W^* < \dim_\beta V$ for all $\beta \in V \cap X^*$.

4) a is a *simple point of* $V \Leftrightarrow V$ is *simple at* $a \Leftrightarrow \gamma_a V$ is *simple* $\Leftrightarrow R(a, V)$ is a regular local ring. a is a *singular point of* $V \Leftrightarrow V$ is *singular at* $a \Leftrightarrow \gamma_a V$ is *singular* $\Leftrightarrow \gamma_a V$ is *singular* $\Leftrightarrow \gamma_a V$ is not simple.

$$\mathbf{S}(V) = \textit{singular locus of } V = \{b \in V: V \text{ is singular at } b\}.$$
$$\mathbf{S}(\gamma_a V) = \textit{singular locus of } \gamma_a V = \gamma_a \mathbf{S}(V).$$

We note the following. Let A be a finite set of analytic functions on X and let $U = \{b \in X: f(b) = 0 \text{ for all } f \in A\}$. For $b \in U$, if $R(b, X)/(\gamma_b A)R(b, X)$ is a regular local ring, then $(\gamma_b A)R(b, X)$ is a prime ideal in $R(b, X)$ and hence by the Nullstellensatz $(\gamma_b A)R(b, X) = \mathfrak{i}(b, U, X)$ and hence b is a simple point of U.

5) a is a *normal point of* $V \Leftrightarrow V$ is *normal at* $a \Leftrightarrow \gamma_a V$ is *normal* $\Leftrightarrow R(a, V)$ is normal.

$$\mathbf{N}(V) = \textit{nonnormal locus of } V = \{b \in V: V \text{ is not normal at } b\}.$$

6) V is *irreducible* (resp: *reducible*) *at* $a \Leftrightarrow \gamma_a V$ is irreducible (resp: reducible).

$$\mathbf{N}^*(V) = \{b \in V: V \text{ is reducible at } b\}.$$

REMARK. By (19.9, 21.5.1) it follows that $\mathbf{N}^*(V) \subset \mathbf{N}(V) \subset \mathbf{S}(V)$. Later on we shall prove that $\mathbf{N}(V)$ and $\mathbf{S}(V)$ are analytic sets in X and $\dim_b \mathbf{S}(V) < \dim_b V$ for all $b \in V$. However, $\mathbf{N}^*(V)$ is in general not analytic as can be seen from the following example. Let $X = K^3\{x, y, z\}$, $V = : z^3 + xyz + x^2 = 0$, $L = : x = z = 0$, $\alpha = (0, 0, 0)$. Then $\mathbf{S}(V) = \mathbf{N}(V) = L$ and $\mathbf{N}^*(V) = L - \{\alpha\}$. Therefore $\mathbf{N}^*(V)$ is not analytic at α.

(**30.17**) *Let V be an analytic set in an open set X in K^n.*

1) *Given $a \in X$ there exists a neighborhood Y of a in X such that* $\dim_b V \leqq \dim_a V$ *for all $b \in Y \cap V$.*

2) *Assume that $V \neq \emptyset$ and let e be a nonnegative integer. Then, V is pure e dimensional $\Leftrightarrow \gamma_a V$ is pure e dimensional for all $a \in V$.*

3) *Let a be a simple point of V. If V_1 is an analytic set germ in X at a such that* $\dim V_1 \geqq \dim \gamma_a V$ *and $V_1 \subset \gamma_a V$, then $V_1 = \gamma_a V$.*

Proof of 1). Follows from (26.2).

Proof of 2). "$\Leftarrow$" is obvious. To prove "$\Rightarrow$" let $a \in V$ be given. Let $V_1, \ldots, V_h$ be analytic sets in a neighborhood X^* of a in X such that $V \cap X^* = V_1 \cup \ldots \cup V_h$ and $\gamma_a V = \gamma_a V_1 \cup \ldots \cup \gamma_a V_h$ is the normal decomposition of $\gamma_a V$. Let X' be a neighborhood of a in X^* such that for all $b \in X'$ we have $\dim_b V_i \leqq \dim_a V_i$ for $i = 1, \ldots, h$. Now $\gamma_a V_1 \not\subset \gamma_a V_2 \cup \ldots \cup \gamma_a V_h$ and hence there exists $b \in X'$ such that $b \in V_1$ and $b \notin V_2 \cup \ldots \cup V_h$. Since $V_2, \ldots, V_h$ are closed in X^*, we can find a neighborhood $\tilde{X}$ of b in X' such that $\tilde{X} \cap (V_2 \cup \ldots \cup V_h) = \emptyset$. Therefore $\tilde{X} \cap V = \tilde{X} \cap V_1$ and hence $\dim_b V = \dim_b V_1$. Consequently $e = \dim_b V = \dim_b V_1 \leqq \dim_a V_1 \leqq \dim_a V = e$ and hence $\dim_a V_1 = e$. Similarly $\dim_a V_i = e$ for $i = 2, \ldots, h$.

Proof of 3). Since $\gamma_a V$ is simple, it is irreducible. Now invoke (30.14.2).

(**30.18**) Intersection Multiplicity. Let $\tilde{Y}$ and $\tilde{Z}$ be open sets in K^e and K^m, respectively. Let $\tilde{X} = \tilde{Y} \times \tilde{Z}$ and let $\pi : \tilde{X} \to \tilde{Y}$ be the natural projection. Let X be an open set in $\tilde{X}$. Let V be an analytic set in X and let $a = (b, c) \in \tilde{X}, b \in \tilde{Y}, c \in \tilde{Z}$. Let $L_b = b \times \tilde{Z}$. Let $n = e + m$. Let $\boldsymbol{\sigma}: R(a, \tilde{X}) \to R = K[\langle x_1, \ldots, x_n \rangle]$ be the Taylor isomorphism. Then $\boldsymbol{\sigma}(\mathfrak{i}(a, L_b, \tilde{X})) = \{x_1, \ldots, x_e\}R$. Let $\mathfrak{a} = \boldsymbol{\sigma}(\mathfrak{i}(a, V, X))$. Then

a is an isolated point of $V \cap L_b$
$\Leftrightarrow \gamma_a(V \cap L_b) = \gamma_a\{a\}$
$\Leftrightarrow \{\mathfrak{a}, x_1, \ldots, x_e\}R$ is primary for the maximal ideal in R
$\Leftrightarrow$ (by 23.3) $\mathfrak{a} \neq R$ and $\mathfrak{a}$ contains a monic polynomial in x_i with coefficients in $K[\langle x_1, \ldots, x_{i-1} \rangle]$ for $i = e + 1, \ldots, n$
$\Rightarrow$ (by 23.3) $\dim R/\mathfrak{a} = \dim_a V \leqq e$.

Now assume that either $a \notin V$ or a is an isolated point of $V \cap L_b$. Let $\mathfrak{P}_1, \ldots, \mathfrak{P}_{k^*}$ be the minimal prime ideals of $\mathfrak{a}$ labeled so that $\dim R/\mathfrak{P}_j = e$ for $j \leqq k$ and $\dim R/\mathfrak{P}_j < e$ for $j > k$. By (23.3), $\mathfrak{P}_1, \ldots, \mathfrak{P}_k$ are regular relative to $S = K[\langle x_1, \ldots, x_e \rangle]$. Let $\mathfrak{K} = K(\langle x_1, \ldots, x_e \rangle)$ and let $\mathfrak{L}_j$ be the quotient field of $R/\mathfrak{P}_j$ considered as an extension of $\mathfrak{K}$. We define

$$\begin{aligned} \mathbf{i}(a, L_b \cdot V) &= \textit{intersection multiplicity of } L_b \textit{ and } V \textit{ at } a \\ = \mathbf{d}(a, \pi, V) &= \textit{degree of } \pi \textit{ on } V \textit{ at } a \\ = \mathbf{d}(a, \pi|V) &= \textit{degree of } \pi|V \textit{ at } a \\ &= \sum_{j=1}^{k} [\mathfrak{L}_j : \mathfrak{K}] \end{aligned}$$

where the sum is taken to be zero if $k = 0$. Note that then $\mathbf{d}(a, \pi, V)$ is a nonnegative integer and it is positive if and only if $\dim_a V = e$. For any $b \in \tilde{Y}$ we also define

$$\mathbf{i}(L_b \cdot V) = \mathbf{d}(b, (V|\pi)^{-1}) = \sum_{a \in V \cap \pi^{-1}(b)} \mathbf{i}(a, L_b \cdot V)$$

provided each term in the sum is defined and the sum is $< \infty$.

(**30.19**) Remark. Consider the situation of §12C. By (25.9.4, 25.9.6) we get this. Let $\Delta_i \in S$ be the z_i-discriminant of $g_i(y, z_i)$. Let $b \in Y$ be such that $\boldsymbol{\tau}_b \Delta_i \neq 0$ for $i = 1, \ldots, m$. Then

$$l(a) = \mathbf{d}(a, \pi, W) \qquad \text{for all} \quad a \in K^m,$$

and hence

$$\mathbf{d}(b, (W|\pi)^{-1}) = d_1 \dots d_m.$$

Alternative proofs of this can be deduced from (35.1) or (35.3).

(**30.20**) REMARK. In the situation of (30.18) assume that V is pure e dimensional at a, or equivalently $\mathfrak{a} = \mathfrak{P}_1 \cap \dots \cap \mathfrak{P}_k$. Let $\bar{R} = R/\mathfrak{a}$ and let $\mathfrak{L}$ be the total quotient ring of $\bar{R}$. Then every nonzero element in S is a nonzerodivisor in $\bar{R}$ and hence $\mathfrak{K}$ can be considered to be a subring of $\mathfrak{L}$. By (19.25.1, 19.25.3) we get

$$\mathbf{d}(a, V, \pi) = [\bar{R}: S] = [\mathfrak{L}: \mathfrak{K}]$$

where : denotes the maximum number of linearly independent elements.

Let[4] $\hat{R} = K[[x_1, \dots, x_n]]$, $\hat{S} = K[[x_1, \dots, x_e]]$, $\hat{\mathfrak{K}} = K((x_1, \dots, x_e))$, $\hat{\bar{R}} = \hat{R}/\mathfrak{a}\hat{R}$. By (17.5, 23.3), $\hat{\bar{R}}$ is a completion of $\bar{R}$, $\mathfrak{a}\hat{R}$ is regular relative to $\hat{S}$ and $\hat{\bar{R}} = \hat{S}[\bar{R}]$. Let $u_1, \dots, u_\lambda \in \bar{R}$ be linearly independent over S where $\lambda = [\bar{R}: S]$. Let $v_1, \dots, v_\mu \in \bar{R}$ be such that $\bar{R} = v_1 S + \dots + v_\mu S$. We can find $0 \neq \delta \in S$ such that $\delta v_i \in u_1 S + \dots + u_\lambda S$ for $i = 1, \dots, \mu$. Since $\hat{\bar{R}} = \hat{S}[\bar{R}]$, we get $\hat{\bar{R}} = v_1 \hat{S} + \dots + v_\mu \hat{S}$ and hence $\delta \hat{\bar{R}} \subset u_1 \hat{S} + \dots + u_\lambda \hat{S}$. Since $u_1, \dots, u_\lambda \in \bar{R}$ are linearly independent over S, by a result from local algebra[5] they are linearly independent over $\hat{S}$. Hence $[\hat{\bar{R}}: \hat{S}] \geqq \lambda$. Let $w_1, \dots, w_\nu$ be any elements in $\hat{\bar{R}}$ with $\nu > \lambda$. Then $\delta w_i = \sum_{j=1}^{\lambda} t_{ij} u_j$ with $t_{ij} \in \hat{S}$. Consider the system

$$\sum_{i=1}^{\nu} T_i t_{ij} = 0, \qquad (j = 1, \dots, \lambda),$$

of homogeneous linear equations in unknowns $T_1, \dots, T_\nu$. Since there are more unknowns than equations,[6] there exist elements $t_1, \dots, t_\nu$ in $\hat{S}$ which are not all zero such that

$$\sum_{i=1}^{\nu} t_i t_{ij} = 0, \quad (j = 1, \dots, \lambda).$$

Now

$$\sum_{i=1}^{\nu} (\delta t_i) w_i = \sum_{j=1}^{\lambda} \left(\sum_{i=1}^{\nu} t_i t_{ij} \right) u_j = 0$$

and hence $w_1, \dots, w_\nu$ are linearly dependent over $\hat{S}$. Hence $[\hat{\bar{R}}: \hat{S}] \leqq \lambda$.

[4] The rest of (30.20) will be not be used elsewhere.

[5] Zariski–Samuel [**2**: Corollary 1 on p. 265].

[6] The usual method of determinants works over any ring.

Consequently

$$[\hat{\bar{R}}: \hat{S}] = [\bar{R}: S] = \mathbf{d}(a, \pi, V),$$

i.e., our definition of intersection multiplicity agrees with the definition given by Chevalley [**1**, **3**] in the formal case. Let $\hat{\mathfrak{P}}_i = \mathfrak{P}_i\hat{R}$. By (24.6.3), $\hat{\mathfrak{P}}_1, \ldots, \hat{\mathfrak{P}}_k$ are prime ideals in $\hat{R}$, and by another result from local algebra[7] $\mathfrak{a}\hat{R} = \hat{\mathfrak{P}}_1 \cap \ldots \cap \hat{\mathfrak{P}}_k$. From what we have proved so far it now follows that $\hat{\mathfrak{P}}_1, \ldots, \hat{\mathfrak{P}}_k$ are regular relative to $\hat{S}$, and letting $\hat{\mathfrak{L}}_j$ and $\hat{\mathfrak{L}}$ to be respectively the quotient field of $\hat{R}/\hat{\mathfrak{P}}_j$ and the total quotient ring of $\hat{R}$ we have:

$$[\hat{\mathfrak{L}}_j: \hat{\mathfrak{K}}] = [\mathfrak{L}_j: \mathfrak{K}] \qquad \text{for} \quad j = 1, \ldots, k,$$

and hence

$$[\hat{\bar{R}}: \hat{S}] = [\hat{\mathfrak{L}}: \hat{\mathfrak{K}}] = \sum_{j=1}^{k} [\hat{\mathfrak{L}}_j: \hat{\mathfrak{K}}] = \sum_{j=1}^{k} [\mathfrak{L}_j: \mathfrak{K}]$$
$$= [\mathfrak{L}: \mathfrak{K}] = [\bar{R}: S] = \mathbf{d}(a, \pi, V).$$

(**30.21**) Let $y = (y_1, \ldots, y_e)$, $z = (z_1, \ldots, z_m)$, $S = K[\langle y \rangle]$, $R = K[\langle y, z \rangle]$. Let $\pi: K^e\{y\} \times K^m\{z\} \to K^e\{y\}$ be the natural projection. For any $D > 0$, $E > 0$, $\beta \in K^e$, $\gamma \in K^m$, let

$$Y\langle D, \beta \rangle = \{b \in K^e: |b_1 - \beta_1| < D, \ldots, |b_e - \beta_e| < D\},$$
$$Z\langle E, \gamma \rangle = \{c \in K^m: |c_1 - \gamma_1| < E, \ldots, |c_m - \gamma_m| < E\}.$$

Write $Y\langle D \rangle$ for $Y\langle D, (0) \rangle$ and $Z\langle E \rangle$ for $Z\langle E, (0) \rangle$. Let $\mathfrak{a}$ be a proper ideal in R. Let $u_1, \ldots, u_\Lambda$ be a finite basis of $\mathfrak{a}$. Let $X' = Y' \times Z'$ be a neighborhood of the origin in $K^e \times K^m$ in which $u_1, \ldots, u_\Lambda$ are convergent. Let $V = \{a \in X': u_1(a) = \ldots = u_\Lambda(a) = 0\}$. *Assume that* $\{y_1, \ldots, y_e, \mathfrak{a}\}R$ *is primary for the maximal ideal in* R, *or equivalently that the origin in* X' *is an isolated point of* $V \cap \{a \in X': \pi a = (0)\}$. Then by (23.3), $\mathfrak{a}$ contains a distinguished polynomial $g_i(y, z_i)$ of degree $d_i > 0$ in z_i with coefficients in S, for $i = 1, \ldots, m$. By continuity of roots (11.3), there exists a neighborhood $X = Y \times Z$ of the origin in $Y' \times Z'$ such that: the coefficients of $g_1(y, z_1), \ldots, g_m(y, z_m)$ are convergent in Y and

$$V \cap X \subset W \cap (Y \times K^m) = W \cap X$$

where $W = \{(b, c) \in Y \times K^m: g_1(b, c_1) = \ldots = g_m(b, c_m) = 0\}$. *Let* $g_1, \ldots, g_m$, W *and* X *be any such. Then we have the following.*

1) *Given* $E' > 0$ *with* $Z\langle E' \rangle \subset Z$, *there exists* $\bar{D}' > 0$ *with* $Y\langle \bar{D}' \rangle \subset Y$ *such that for all* $0 < D' \leqq \bar{D}'$ *we have*: $V \cap (Y\langle D' \rangle \times Z) =$

[7] Zariski–Samuel [**2**: Corollary 2 on p. 266].

$V \cap (Y\langle D'\rangle \times Z\langle E'\rangle)$; *and for any* $m' \leqq m$, *the map* $V \cap (Y\langle D'\rangle \times Z) \to Y\langle D'\rangle \times K^{m'}$ *induced by* π' *is a continuous proper closed map where* $\pi' : K^e\{y\} \times K^m\{z\} \to K^e\{y\} \times K^{m'}\{z_1,..., z_{m'}\}$ *is the natural projection.*[8]

2) *For any* $\beta \in Y$, $V \cap (\beta \times Z)$ *contains at most* $d_1...d_m$ *distinct points. Let these be* $\alpha^{(\theta)} = (\beta, \gamma^{(\theta)})$, $(\theta = 1,..., N)$. *Then there exist* $D > 0$, $E > 0$ *such that:*

$$Y\langle D, \beta\rangle \subset Y; \qquad \bigcup_{\theta=1}^{N} Z\langle E, \gamma^{(\theta)}\rangle \subset Z;$$

$$Z\langle E, \gamma^{(\theta)}\rangle \cap Z\langle E, \gamma^{(\theta')}\rangle = \emptyset \qquad \text{for all} \quad \theta \neq \theta';$$

$$V \cap (Y\langle D, \beta\rangle \times Z) = \bigcup_{\theta=1}^{N} [V \cap (Y\langle D, \beta\rangle \times Z\langle E, \gamma^{(\theta)}\rangle)];$$

and such that: given $0 < E^* \leqq E$ *there exists* $0 < D^* \leqq D$ *for which*

$$V \cap (Y\langle D^*, \beta\rangle \times Z) = \bigcup_{\theta=1}^{N} [V \cap (Y\langle D^*, \beta\rangle \times Z\langle E^*, \gamma^{(\theta)}\rangle)].$$ [9]

Proof of 1). By continuity of roots (11.3) we can find $\bar{D}' > 0$ with $Y\langle \bar{D}'\rangle \subset Y$ such that for all $0 < D' \leqq \bar{D}'$ we have $W \cap (Y\langle D'\rangle \times K^m) = W \cap (Y\langle D'\rangle \times Z\langle E'\rangle)$. Now $V \cap X \subset W$ and hence $V \cap (Y\langle D'\rangle \times Z) = V \cap (Y\langle D'\rangle \times Z\langle E'\rangle)$. Also $V \cap (Y\langle D'\rangle \times Z)$ is closed in $Y\langle D'\rangle \times Z$ and hence $V \cap (Y\langle D'\rangle \times Z)$ is a closed subset of $W \cap (Y\langle D'\rangle \times K^m)$. Therefore by (12.5), the map $V \cap (Y\langle D'\rangle \times Z) \to Y\langle D'\rangle \times K^{m'}$ induced by π' is a proper closed map.

Proof of 2). Let $\alpha^{(\theta)} = (\beta, \gamma^{(\theta)})$, $(\theta = N + 1,..., M)$, be the remaining points in $W \cap \pi^{-1}(\beta)$. Since $V \cap X$ is closed in X we can take $D_1 > 0$, $E_1 > 0$ such that

$$Y\langle D_1, \beta\rangle \subset Y; \qquad \bigcup_{\theta=1}^{M} Z\langle E_1, \gamma^{(\theta)}\rangle \subset Z;$$

$$Z\langle E_1, \gamma^{(\theta)}\rangle \cap Z\langle E_1, \gamma^{(\theta')}\rangle = \emptyset \qquad \text{for all} \quad \theta \neq \theta', \quad (\theta, \theta' = 1,..., M);$$

$$V \cap \left[\bigcup_{\theta=N+1}^{M} Y\langle D_1, \beta\rangle \times Z\langle E_1, \gamma^{(\theta)}\rangle\right] = \emptyset.$$

By (12.4), we can find $0 < D \leqq D_1$, $0 < E \leqq E_1$ such that

$$W \cap (Y\langle D, \beta\rangle \times K^m) = \bigcup_{\theta=1}^{M} [W \cap (Y\langle D, \beta\rangle \times Z\langle E, \gamma^{(\theta)}\rangle)];$$

[8] If $m' = 0$ then $\pi' = \pi$ and $Y\langle D'\rangle \times K^{m'} = Y\langle D'\rangle$.

[9] For $N = 0$ this is to mean: there exists $D > 0$ such that $Y\langle D, \beta\rangle \subset Y$ and $V \cap (Y\langle D, \beta\rangle \times Z) = \emptyset$.

and given $0 < E^* \leqq E$ again by (12.4) we can find $0 < D^* \leqq D$ such that

$$W \cap (Y\langle D^*, \beta\rangle \times K^m) = \bigcup_{\theta=1}^{M} [W \cap (Y\langle D^*, \beta\rangle \times Z\langle E^*, \gamma^{(\theta)}\rangle)].$$

Now it suffices to note that $V \cap X \subset W$.

REMARK. Let $\mathfrak{a}$ be any proper ideal in $K[\langle x_1,\ldots, x_n\rangle]$. Let $e = \dim R/\mathfrak{a}$. By (23.5), upon making a nonsingular K-linear transformation on $x_1,\ldots, x_n$ it can be arranged that $\mathfrak{a}$ is regular relative to $K[\langle x_1,\ldots, x_e\rangle]$. Then (30.21) becomes applicable. In other words, given any analytic set V in an open set in K^n and given any point in V, upon making an affine transformation on the coordinate system in K^n, there is an open polycylinder X around the given point such that (30.21) is applicable to $V \cap X$.

§31. RÜCKERT-WEIERSTRASS PARAMETRIZATION OF AN IRREDUCIBLE ANALYTIC SET GERM[1]

Let $y = (y_1,\ldots, y_e)$, $e > 0$, $z = (z_1,\ldots, z_m)$, $m > 0$, $S = K[\langle y\rangle]$, $\mathfrak{R} = K(\langle y\rangle)$, $R = K[\langle y, z\rangle]$.[2] Let $\pi: K^e\{y\} \times K^m\{z\} \to K^e\{y\}$ be the natural projection. For any $D > 0$, $E > 0$, $\beta \in K^e$, $\gamma \in K^m$, let

$$Y\langle D, \beta\rangle = \{b \in K^e: |b_1 - \beta_1| < D,\ldots, |b_e - \beta_e| < D\},$$
$$Z\langle E, \gamma\rangle = \{c \in K^m: |c_1 - \gamma_1| < E,\ldots, |c_m - \gamma_m| < E\}.$$

Let $\mathfrak{p}$ be a prime ideal in R which is strictly regular relative to S. For any element or subset r of R let $\bar{r}$ denote the image of r under the natural epimorphism $R \to R/\mathfrak{p}$. Identify S and $\bar{S}$. Let $\mathfrak{L}$ be the quotient field of $\bar{R}$. Let

$$g_i(y, z_i) = \sum_{\nu=0}^{d_i} g_{i\nu}(y) z_i^\nu, \qquad g_{i\nu} \in S, \qquad g_{id_i} = 1, \qquad d_i > 0,$$

be the minimal monic polynomial of z_i mod $\mathfrak{p}$ over S. Let $\Delta_i(y)$ be the z_i-discriminant of $g_i(y, z_i)$. Then $g_{i\nu}(0) = 0$ for $\nu = 0,\ldots, d_i - 1$, and $0 \neq \Delta_i(y) \in S$. Since $\mathfrak{L}$ is separable over $\mathfrak{R}$ and K is infinite, we can find $\kappa_1,\ldots, \kappa_m \in K$ such that $\mathfrak{L} = \mathfrak{R}(\bar{w})$ where

$$w = \kappa_1 z_1 + \ldots + \kappa_m z_m.$$

[1] The reader may first refer to §32 where in (32.1) to (32.4) the main results of §31 are summarized.

[2] In the rest of this chapter, unless otherwise stated, K stands for an algebraically closed complete nondiscrete valued field.

Let

$$f(y, T) = \sum_{\nu=0}^{d} f_\nu(y)T^\nu, \qquad f_\nu \in S, \qquad f_d = 1, \qquad d > 0,$$

be the minimal monic polynomial of $w \bmod \mathfrak{p}$ over S. Let $\Delta^*(y)$ be the T-discriminant of $f(y, T)$. Then $f_\nu(0) = 0$ for $\nu = 0,\ldots, d-1$, and $0 \neq \Delta^*(y) \in S$. Let $0 \neq \Delta' \in S$ be arbitrary and let

$$\Delta = \Delta'\Delta^*\Delta_1\ldots\Delta_m.^3$$

For any $b \in K^e$ at which $f_0,\ldots, f_d$ are convergent and $\Delta(b) \neq 0$, let $\omega_\mu[b]$, $(\mu = 1,\ldots, d)$, be the distinct elements in K such that

$$f(b, T) = \prod_{\mu=1}^{d} (T - \omega_\mu[b]).$$

Since $\mathfrak{L}$ is separable over $\mathfrak{R}$ and $\bar{R}$ is integral over S, for any $r \in R$ we can uniquely write

$$\Delta(y)\bar{r} = \sum_{\nu=0}^{d-1} r^{(\nu)}(y)\bar{\omega}^\nu \qquad \text{with} \qquad r^{(\nu)}(y) \in S.$$

For any $b \in K^e$ at which $f_0,\ldots, f_d$, $r^{(0)},\ldots, r^{(d-1)}$ are convergent and $\Delta(b) \neq 0$, let

$$r^{[\mu]}[b] = (1/\Delta(b)) \sum_{\nu=0}^{d-1} r^{(\nu)}(b)\omega_\mu[b]^\nu \qquad \text{for} \quad \mu = 1,\ldots, d.$$

In particular

$$\Delta(y)\bar{z}_i = \sum_{\nu=0}^{d-1} z_i^{(\nu)}(y)\bar{\omega}^\nu \qquad \text{for} \quad i = 1,\ldots, m.$$

For any $b \in K^e$ at which all the elements f_ν, $z_i^{(\nu)}$ are convergent and $\Delta(b) \neq 0$, let us write $\zeta_i^{[\mu]}[b]$ for $z_i^{[\mu]}[b]$ and $\zeta^{[\mu]}[b]$ for $(\zeta_1^{[\mu]}[b],\ldots, \zeta_m^{[\mu]}[b])$ $(\mu = 1,\ldots, d)$.

Let $u_1,\ldots, u_\Lambda$ be a finite basis of $\mathfrak{p}$. Now $g_i(y, z_i) \in \mathfrak{p}$ and hence

$$g_i(y, z_i) = \sum_{\lambda=1}^{\Lambda} v_{i\lambda}u_\lambda \qquad \text{with} \qquad v_{i\lambda} \in R, \qquad (i = 1,\ldots, m).$$

[3] For instance $\Delta' = 1$, i.e., $\Delta = \Delta^*\Delta_1\ldots\Delta_m$. The fact that $\Delta_1\ldots\Delta_m$ divides Δ will not be used until after (31.9), i.e., all the arguments until (31.9) remain valid with $\Delta = \Delta'\Delta^*$ and hence in particular with $\Delta = \Delta^*$.

Let $X = Y \times Z$ be a neighborhood of the origin in $K^e\{y\} \times K^m\{z\}$ such that: f_ν and $z_i^{(\nu)}$ are convergent in Y for all i, ν; u_λ and $v_{i\lambda}$ are convergent in X for all i, λ; and $\boldsymbol{\tau}_b\Delta \neq 0$ for all $b \in Y$. Then in particular, $\{b \in Y: \Delta(b) = 0\}$ is nowhere dense in Y. Let

$$\mathring{Y} = \{b \in Y: \Delta(b) \neq 0\},$$
$$V = \{a \in X: u_\lambda(a) = 0 \text{ for } \lambda = 1,\ldots, \Lambda\},$$
$$W = \{a = (b, c) \in Y \times K^m: g_i(b, c_i) = 0 \text{ for } i = 1,\ldots, m\},$$
$$\mathring{V} = \{(b, \zeta^{[\mu]}[b]): b \in \mathring{Y}, \mu = 1,\ldots, d\},$$
$$\bar{V} = \text{closure of } \mathring{V} \text{ in } Y \times K^m.$$

Then $V \subset W$. By continuity of roots (11.3) we can find positive real numbers $B_0 > B_1 > \ldots, B_q \to 0$; $C_0 > C_1 > \ldots, C_q \to 0$; such that $Y\langle B_0, (0)\rangle \subset Y$, $Z\langle C_0, (0)\rangle \subset Z$, and

$$W \cap \pi^{-1}(Y\langle B_q, (0)\rangle) \subset Y\langle B_q, (0)\rangle \times Z\langle C_q, (0)\rangle \qquad \text{for all} \quad q \geqq 0.$$

For all $q \geqq 0$ let

$$Y_q = Y\langle B_q, (0)\rangle, \qquad Z_q = Z\langle C_q, (0)\rangle, \qquad \mathring{Y}_q = Y_q \cap \mathring{Y},$$
$$X_q = Y_q \times Z_q, \qquad \mathring{X}_q = \mathring{Y}_q \times Z_q.$$

With all this notation in mind we now proceed to prove a string of lemmas.

(31.1) *Let*

$$P(y, \Omega_1,\ldots, \Omega_N) = \sum P_{i_1\ldots i_N}(y)\Omega_1^{i_1}\ldots\Omega_N^{i_N}$$

and

$$Q(y, \Omega_1,\ldots, \Omega_N) = \sum Q_{i_1\ldots i_N}(y)\Omega_1^{i_1}\ldots\Omega_N^{i_N}$$

be polynomials in indeterminates $\Omega_1,\ldots, \Omega_N$ with coefficients $P_{i_1\ldots i_N}$, $Q_{i_1\ldots i_N}$ in S.[4] *Let $r_1,\ldots, r_N \in R$. Let $q \geqq 0$ be such that all the elements $P_{i_1\ldots i_N}$, $Q_{i_1\ldots i_N}$, $r_j^{(\nu)}$ are convergent in Y_q. If*

$$P(y, \bar{r}_1,\ldots, \bar{r}_N) = Q(y, \bar{r}_1,\ldots, \bar{r}_N)$$

then for all $b \in \mathring{Y}_q$ we have

$$P(b, r_1^{[\mu]}[b],\ldots, r_N^{[\mu]}[b]) = Q(b, r_1^{[\mu]}[b],\ldots, r_N^{[\mu]}[b]) \qquad \textit{for} \quad \mu = 1,\ldots, d.$$

[4] Arbitrary nonnegative integer N.

In particular, if

$$P(y, \bar{r}_1, \ldots, \bar{r}_N) = 0$$

then for all $b \in \mathring{Y}_q$ *we have*

$$P(b, r_1^{[\mu]}[b], \ldots, r_N^{[\mu]}[b]) = 0 \qquad \text{for} \quad \mu = 1, \ldots, d.$$

PROOF. The case of $P(y, \bar{r}_1, \ldots, \bar{r}_N) = \underset{\sim}{Q}(y, \bar{r}_1, \ldots, \bar{r}_N)$ follows from the case of $P(y, \bar{r}_1, \ldots, \bar{r}_N) = 0$ by taking $P - \underset{\sim}{Q}$ for P. So we deal with the case of $P(y, \bar{r}_1, \ldots, \bar{r}_N) = 0$. If $P_{i_1 \ldots i_N}(y) = 0$ for all $i_1, \ldots, i_N$ then we have nothing to prove. So assume the contrary. Let M be the degree of P in $\Omega_1, \ldots, \Omega_N$.

Let

$$P^*(y, \Omega_1, \ldots, \Omega_N) = \sum P^*_{i_1 \ldots i_N}(y) \Omega_1^{i_1} \ldots \Omega_N^{i_N}$$

where

$$P^*_{i_1 \ldots i_N}(y) = P_{i_1 \ldots i_N}(y) \Delta(y)^{M - i_1 - \ldots - i_N}.$$

Let

$$H_j(T) = \sum_{\nu=0}^{d-1} r_j^{(\nu)}(y) T^\nu \qquad \text{for} \quad j = 1, \ldots, N,$$

and let

$$\begin{aligned} F(y, T) &= P^*(y, H_1(T), \ldots, H_N(T)) \\ &= \sum_k F_k(y) T^k \in S[T], \qquad F_k(y) \in S.^5 \end{aligned}$$

Then

$$F(y, \bar{w}) = \Delta(y)^M P(y, \bar{r}_1, \ldots, \bar{r}_N) = 0.$$

Therefore

$$F(y, T) = f(y, T) F^*(y, T)$$

with

$$F^*(y, T) = \sum_{k^*} F^*_{k^*}(y) T^{k^*} \in S[T], \qquad F^*_{k^*}(y) \in S.$$

All the coefficients $F_k(y)$ and $f_\nu(y)$ are convergent in Y_q, and $f(y, T)$ is monic in T. Hence by division algorithm we deduce that all the coefficients

[5] Single indeterminate T.

$F^*_{k^*}(y)$ are convergent in Y_q. Therefore we shall be justified in substituting b for y in $F_k(y)$, $F^*_{k^*}(y), f_\nu(y)$. For $\mu = 1,\dots, d,$ we get

$$\begin{aligned}
&\Delta(b)^M P(b, r_1^{[\mu]}[b],\dots, r_N^{[\mu]}[b]) \\
&= \sum_{i_1,\dots,i_N} P^*_{i_1\dots i_N}(b) \prod_{j=1}^{N} \left[\sum_{\nu=0}^{d-1} r_j^{(\nu)}(b)\omega_\mu[b]^\nu \right]^{i_j} \\
&= \sum_k F_k(b)\omega_\mu[b]^k \\
&= \left[\sum_\nu f_\nu(b)\omega_\mu[b]^\nu \right]\left[\sum_{k^*} F_{k^*}(b)\omega_\mu[b]^{k^*} \right].
\end{aligned}$$

By definition of $\omega_\mu[b]$ we have

$$\sum_\nu f_\nu(b)\omega_\mu[b]^\nu = 0.$$

Since $\Delta(b) \neq 0$, we get that

$$P(b, r_1^{[\mu]}[b],\dots, r_N^{[\mu]}[b]) = 0.$$

(31.2) $\mathring{V} \cap \pi^{-1}(Y_q) \subset W \cap \pi^{-1}(Y_q) = W \cap X_q$ *for all* $q \geqq 0$.

Follows from (31.1) in view of the equations $g_i(y, \bar{z}_i) = 0$, $(i = 1,\dots, m)$. Alternatively, we may use (28.5).

(31.3) *Given* $r = r(y, z) \in R$, *there exists* $q(r) \geqq 0$ *such that*: r *is convergent* in $X_{q(r)}$; $r^{(0)},\dots, r^{(d-1)}$ *are convergent in* $Y_{q(r)}$; *and for all* $b \in \mathring{Y}_{q(r)}$ *we have*

$$r(b, \zeta^{[\mu]}[b]) = r^{[\mu]}[b] \qquad \textit{for} \quad \mu = 1,\dots, d.$$

PROOF. We make induction on i where:

$$i = \min j \quad \text{such that} \quad r \in K[\langle y, z_1,\dots, z_j \rangle].$$

Trivial for $i = 0$. So let $i > 0$ and assume true for $i - 1$. By Preparation Theorem (10.3.1), we can find $r^* = r^*(y, z) \in K[\langle y, z_1,\dots, z_i\rangle]$ and $s_\nu = s_\nu(y, z) \in K[\langle y, z_1,\dots, z_{i-1}\rangle]$ such that

$$r(y, z) = g_i(y, z_i)r^*(y, z) + \sum_{\nu=0}^{d_i-1} s_\nu(y, z)z_i^\nu.$$

Take $q(r) \geqq 0$ such that: $q(r) \geqq q(s_\nu)$ for $\nu = 0,\dots, d_i - 1$; r^* is convergent in $X_{q(r)}$; and $r^{(0)},\dots, r^{(d-1)}$ are convergent in $Y_{q(r)}$. Let $b \in \mathring{Y}_{q(r)}$

be given. By (31.2)

$$\sum_{\nu=0}^{d_i} g_{i\nu}(b)(\zeta_i^{[\mu]}[b])^\nu = 0$$

and hence

1°) $$r(b, \zeta^{[\mu]}[b]) = \sum_{\nu=0}^{d_i-1} s_\nu(b, \zeta^{[\mu]}[b])(\zeta_i^{[\mu]}[b])^\nu.$$

Since $g_i(y, \bar{z}_i) = 0$, we get

$$\bar{r} = \sum_{\nu=0}^{d_i-1} \bar{s}_\nu \bar{z}_i^\nu.$$

Hence by (31.1)

2°) $$r^{[\mu]}[b] = \sum_{\nu=0}^{d_i-1} s_\nu^{[\mu]}[b](\zeta_i^{[\mu]}[b])^\nu \qquad \text{for} \quad \mu = 1,\dots, d.$$

By induction hypothesis

3°) $$s_\nu^{[\mu]}[b] = s_\nu(b, \zeta^{[\mu]}[b]) \qquad \text{for} \quad \mu = 1,\dots, d \text{ and } \nu = 0,\dots, d_i - 1.$$

From (1°, 2°, 3°) we get that

$$r(b, \zeta^{[\mu]}[b]) = r^{[\mu]}[b] \qquad \text{for} \quad \mu = 1,\dots, d.$$

(**31.4**) *There exists* $q_0 \geqq 0$ *such that* $\mathring{V} \cap \pi^{-1}(Y_q) = V \cap \mathring{X}_q$ *for all* $q \geqq q_0$.

PROOF. Let

$$\tilde{w} = \tilde{w}(y, z) = f(y, w), \qquad \text{and} \qquad \tilde{z}_i = \tilde{z}_i(y, z) = \Delta(y)z_i - \sum_{\nu=0}^{d-1} z_i^{(\nu)}(y)w^\nu.$$

Then $\tilde{w} \in \mathfrak{p}$ and $\tilde{z}_i \in \mathfrak{p}$. Hence

$$\tilde{w} = \sum_\lambda \tilde{w}_\lambda u_\lambda, \qquad \text{and} \qquad \tilde{z}_i = \sum_\lambda \tilde{z}_{i\lambda} u_\lambda, \qquad (i = 1,\dots, m),$$

with $\tilde{w}_\lambda = \tilde{w}_\lambda(y, z) \in R$ and $\tilde{z}_{i\lambda} = \tilde{z}_{i\lambda}(y, z) \in R$. Take $q_0 \geqq \max(q(u_1),\dots, q(u_\Lambda))$ such that all the elements $\tilde{w}_\lambda$ and $\tilde{z}_{i\lambda}$ are convergent in X_{q_0}. Let $q \geqq q_0$. Then for all $(b, c) \in Y_q \times Z_q$ we have (1° to 4°).

1°) $$\tilde{w}(b, c) = \sum_{\nu=0}^{d} f_\nu(b)w(b, c)^\nu.$$

2°) $$\tilde{w}(b, c) = \sum_\lambda \tilde{w}_\lambda(b, c)u_\lambda(b, c).$$

3°) $\tilde{z}_i(b, c) = \Delta(b)c_i - \sum_{\nu=0}^{d-1} z_i^{(\nu)}(b)w(b, c)^\nu$ for $i = 1,..., m$.

4°) $\tilde{z}_i(b, c) = \sum_\lambda \tilde{z}_{i\lambda}(b, c)u_\lambda(b, c)$ for $i = 1,..., m$.

Since $q \geqq q(u_\lambda)$ and $\bar{u}_\lambda = 0$ for $\lambda = 1,..., \Lambda$, by (31.1, 31.2, 31.3) we get that

$$\mathring{V} \cap \pi^{-1}(Y_q) \subset V \cap \mathring{X}_q.$$

To prove "$\supset$" let $(b, c) \in V$ be given with $b \in \mathring{Y}_q$, $c \in Z_q$. Then by 2°) and 4°) we get 5°) and 6°).

5°) $\tilde{w}(b, c) = 0$.

6°) $\tilde{z}_i(b, c) = 0$ for $i = 1,..., m$.

Since $\Delta(b) \neq 0$, by 1°) and 5°) we get that $w(b, c) = \omega_\mu[b]$ for some μ, and then by 3°) and 6°) we get that $c = \zeta^{[\mu]}[b]$, i.e., $(b, c) = (b, \zeta^{[\mu]}[b]) \in \mathring{V}$.

(31.5)[6] *Let* $q' = \max(q_0, q(w))$. *Then for all* $b \in \mathring{Y}_{q'}$ *we have that:*

$$\omega_\mu[b] = \kappa_1\zeta_1^{[\mu]}[b] + ... + \kappa_m\zeta_m^{[\mu]}[b] \qquad \textit{for} \quad \mu = 1,..., d;$$

and hence $(b, \zeta^{[1]}[b]),..., (b, \zeta^{[d]}[b])$ *are all distinct and they are exactly all the distinct points in* $V \cap \pi^{-1}(b)$.

PROOF. For $\mu = 1,..., d$ we have

$$\begin{aligned} \omega_\mu[b] &= w^{[\mu]}[b] && \text{(by definition)} \\ &= w(b, \zeta^{[\mu]}[b]) && \text{(by 31.3)} \\ &= \kappa_1\zeta_1^{[\mu]}[b] + ... + \kappa_m\zeta_m^{[\mu]}[b] && \text{(obviously).} \end{aligned}$$

Now $\omega_1[b],..., \omega_d[b]$ are all distinct. Hence $(b, \zeta^{[1]}[b]),..., (b, \zeta^{[d]}[b])$ are all distinct and by definition they are exactly all the points in $\mathring{V} \cap \pi^{-1}(b)$. By (31.4), $\mathring{V} \cap \pi^{-1}(b) = V \cap \pi^{-1}(b)$.

(31.6) *Let* $U = \{(b, \tilde{b}) \in \mathring{Y}_{q'} \times K^1 : f(b, \tilde{b}) = 0\}$. *For any* $(b, \tilde{b}) \in U$ *let*

$$\mathfrak{h}(b, \tilde{b}) = (b, c) \in \mathring{Y}_{q'} \times K^m$$

where

$$c_i = (1/\Delta(b)) \sum_{\nu=0}^{d-1} z_i^{(\nu)}(b)\tilde{b}^\nu \qquad \textit{for} \quad i = 1,..., m.$$

[6] The proof of (31.9) can be read after (31.4). (31.5) to (31.8) are not used in the proof of (3.19).

Then we have the following.

1) $\mathfrak{h}(b, \omega_\mu[b]) = (b, \zeta^{[\mu]}[b])$ *for all* $b \in \mathring{Y}_{q'}$ *and* $\mu = 1,\dots, d$.

2) $\mathfrak{h}$ *is a homeomorphism of* U onto $V \cap \mathring{X}_{q'}$.

3) *If* $K = \mathbf{C}$ *and* $\tilde{Y}$ *is any connected neighborhood of the origin in* $Y_{q'}$ *then* $V \cap \pi^{-1}(\tilde{Y} \cap \mathring{Y})$ *is connected.*

PROOF. 1) is obvious. $\mathfrak{h}$ is obviously continuous on U. By 1) and (31.5): $\mathfrak{h}$ maps U onto $V \cap \mathring{X}_{q'}$ in a one to one manner and $\mathfrak{h}^{-1}$ is continuous on $V \cap \mathring{X}_{q'}$. This proves 2). 3) follows from 2) in virtue of (14.8).

(31.7) *For any* $m' \leqq m$ *let* $\pi' : K^e\{y\} \times K^m\{z\} \to K^e\{y\} \times K^{m'}\{z_1,\dots, z_{m'}\}$ *be the natural projection. Then for any* $q \geqq 0$, *the map* $V \cap X_q \to Y_q \times K^{m'}$ *induced by* π' *is a proper closed map and hence in particular* $\pi'(V \cap X_q)$ *is a closed subset of* $Y_q \times K^{m'}$.

PROOF. Now $V \cap X_q \subset W \cap (Y_q \times K^m) = W \cap X_q$ and $V \cap X_q$ is closed in X_q. Therefore $V \cap X_q$ is a closed subset of $W \cap (Y_q \times K^m)$ and hence our assertion follows from (12.5).

(31.8) $\pi(V \cap X_q) = Y_q$ *for all* $q \geqq q_0$.

PROOF. By (31.4), $\mathring{Y}_q \subset \pi(V \cap X_q)$. Now Y_q is the closure of $\mathring{Y}_q$ in Y_q, and by (31.7), $\pi(V \cap X_q)$ is closed in Y_q. Therefore $\pi(V \cap X_q) = Y_q$.

(31.9) *Let* $\mathfrak{r} = \{r \in R$: *for some* $q \geqq 0$, r *is convergent in* X_q *and* $r(a) = 0$ *for all* $a \in V \cap X_q\}$. *Then* $\mathfrak{r} = \mathfrak{p}$.

PROOF. Obviously $\mathfrak{r}$ is a proper ideal in R and $\mathfrak{p} \subset \mathfrak{r}$. Suppose if possible that $\mathfrak{p} \neq \mathfrak{r}$. Then by (23.4) there exists $0 \neq s \in \mathfrak{r} \cap S$. Take $q \geqq q_0$ such that s is convergent in X_q and $s(a) = 0$ for all $a \in V \cap X_q$. Now $0 \neq \Delta s \in S$ and hence we can find $b \in \mathring{Y}_q$ such that $s(b) \neq 0$. Let $a = (b, \zeta^{[1]}[b])$. Then $s(a) = s(b) \neq 0$ and by (31.4), $a \in V \cap X_q$. Contradiction.

REMARK. This completes the proof of (31.9) and hence as noted in (30.12) the proof of the Rückert Nullstellensatz is now completed. Consequently, henceforth we may use the results of §30.

Since $V \subset W$, any $\alpha \in V$ is an isolated point of $V \cap \pi^{-1}(\beta)$ where $\beta = \pi\alpha$ and hence: $\dim_\alpha V \leqq e$; $\mathbf{d}(\alpha, \pi, V)$ is a well defined nonnegative integer; and $\mathbf{d}(\alpha, \pi, V) > 0 \Leftrightarrow \dim_\alpha V = e$. Let $\boldsymbol{\sigma}$: $R(\alpha, X) \to R$ be the Taylor isomorphism. Let $\tilde{\mathfrak{p}}$ be any prime ideal of $\boldsymbol{\sigma}(\mathfrak{i}(\alpha, V, X))$ having depth e. Then $\tilde{\mathfrak{p}}$ is regular relative to S. Hence the quotient field $\tilde{\mathfrak{L}}$ of $R/\tilde{\mathfrak{p}}$ is generated over $\mathfrak{K}$ by the $\tilde{\mathfrak{p}}$-residues of $z_1, \ldots, z_m$. Let $\tilde{g}_i(y, z_i) = \boldsymbol{\tau}_\alpha g_i(y, z_i)$ and $\tilde{\Delta}_i = \boldsymbol{\tau}_\beta \Delta_i$. Then $\tilde{g}_i(y, z_i)$ is a monic polynomial of degree d_i in z_i with coefficients in S; $0 \neq \tilde{\Delta}_i$ is the z_i-discriminant of $\tilde{g}_i(y, z_i)$; and $\tilde{g}_i(y, z_i) \in \boldsymbol{\sigma}(\mathfrak{i}(\alpha, V, X)) \subset \tilde{\mathfrak{p}}$. Therefore $\tilde{\mathfrak{L}}$ is separable over $\mathfrak{K}$, i.e., $\tilde{\mathfrak{p}}$ is strictly regular relative to S. Thus we have proved

(**31.10**) *Let* α *be any point in* V. *Then* $\dim_\alpha V \leqq e$; $\mathbf{d}(\alpha, \pi, V)$ *is a well defined nonnegative integer; and* $\mathbf{d}(\alpha, \pi, V) > 0 \Leftrightarrow \dim_\alpha V = e$. *Furthermore, every prime ideal of* $\boldsymbol{\sigma}(\mathfrak{i}(\alpha, V, X))$ *having depth e is strictly regular relative to S, where* $\boldsymbol{\sigma}\colon R(\alpha, X) \to R$ *is the Taylor isomorphism.*

Next we prove the following.

(**31.11**) *For any* $\alpha = (\beta, \gamma) \in V$ *with* $\beta \in \mathring{Y}_{q'}$ *we have* $\dim_\alpha V = e$. *Furthermore, given* $D^* > 0$, $E^* > 0$, *there exist* $0 < D \leqq D^*$, $0 < E \leqq E^*$, *with* $Y\langle D, \beta\rangle \subset \mathring{Y}_{q'}$, $Z\langle E, \gamma\rangle \subset Z_{q'}$, *such that*

$$\pi[V \cap (Y\langle D, \beta\rangle \times Z\langle E, \gamma\rangle)] = Y\langle D, \beta\rangle.$$

Proof. By (31.5), $V \cap \pi^{-1}(\beta)$ contains exactly d distinct points. Let these be $\alpha^{(\theta)} = (\beta, \gamma^{(\theta)})$, $(\theta = 1, \ldots, d)$. Then $\alpha = \alpha^{(\theta)}$ for some θ. Now $V \subset W$ and $\Delta_i(\beta) \neq 0$ for $i = 1, \ldots, m$. Hence by (12.4), there exist $0 < D' \leqq D^*$, $0 < E' \leqq E^*$ for which we have 1°) and 2°).

1°) $$Y\langle D', \beta\rangle \subset \mathring{Y}_{q'}; \qquad \bigcup_{\theta=1}^{d} Z\langle E', \gamma^{(\theta)}\rangle \subset Z_{q'};$$

$$Z\langle E', \gamma^{(\theta)}\rangle \cap Z\langle E', \gamma^{(\theta')}\rangle = \emptyset \qquad \text{for all} \quad \theta \neq \theta'.$$

2°) For all $\theta \leqq d$ and $b \in Y\langle D', \beta\rangle$,

$$W \cap (b \times Z\langle E', \gamma^{(\theta)}\rangle) \qquad \text{contains exactly one point.}$$

By (30.21), we can find $0 < D \leqq D'$, $0 < E \leqq E'$, such that

3°) $$V \cap (Y\langle D, \beta\rangle \times Z) = \bigcup_{\theta=1}^{d} [V \cap (Y\langle D, \beta\rangle \times Z\langle E, \gamma^{(\theta)}\rangle)].$$

By (31.5), for any $b \in \mathring{Y}_{q'}$, $V \cap (b \times Z)$ contains exactly d points. Hence by (1°, 2°, 3°) we deduce that for $\theta = 1, \ldots, d$ we have

$$\pi[V \cap (Y\langle D, \beta\rangle \times Z\langle E, \gamma^{(\theta)}\rangle)] = Y\langle D, \beta\rangle,$$

and $\boldsymbol{\gamma}_{\alpha^{(\theta)}} V = \boldsymbol{\gamma}_{\alpha^{(\theta)}} W$. By (10.14 or 25.9.5), $\dim_{\alpha^{(\theta)}} W = e$ and hence $\dim_{\alpha^{(\theta)}} V = e$.

(31.12) *Let* $\alpha = (\beta, \gamma) \in V$ *with* $\beta \in Y$, $\gamma \in Z$, *and* $D' > 0$, $E' > 0$ *with* $Y\langle D', \beta\rangle \subset Y$, $Z\langle E', \gamma\rangle \subset Z$ *be given. Let* $M = \mathbf{d}(\alpha, \pi, V)$. *Then there exist* $0 < D \leqq D'$, $0 < E \leqq E'$, *and an analytic function* t *on* $Y\langle D, \beta\rangle$ *with* $\boldsymbol{\gamma}_\beta t \neq 0$ *such that: for any* $b \in Y\langle D, \beta\rangle$ *for which* $t(b) \neq 0$ *we have that* $V \cap (b \times Z\langle E, \gamma\rangle)$ *contains exactly* M *distinct points.*

Proof. By (30.21), we can find $0 < D'' \leqq D'$, $0 < E'' \leqq E'$, such that:

1°) Given $0 < E \leqq E''$ there exists $0 < \varphi(E) \leqq D''$ depending on E for which we have

$$V \cap (Y\langle \varphi(E), \beta\rangle \times Z\langle E'', \gamma\rangle) = V \cap (Y\langle \varphi(E), \beta\rangle \times Z\langle E, \gamma\rangle).$$

We can take $0 < D^* \leqq D''$, $0 < E^* \leqq E''$, and analytic sets $V_1, \dots, V_{k'}$ in $Y\langle D^*, \beta\rangle \times Z\langle E^*, \gamma\rangle$ such that $\boldsymbol{\gamma}_\alpha V_1 \cup \dots \cup \boldsymbol{\gamma}_\alpha V_{k'}$ is the normal decomposition of $\boldsymbol{\gamma}_\alpha V$, and

2°) $$V \cap (Y\langle D^*, \beta\rangle \times Z\langle E^*, \gamma\rangle) = V_1 \cup \dots \cup V_{k'}.$$

Label $V_1, \dots, V_{k'}$ so that $\dim_\alpha V_j = e$ for $j \leqq k$ and $\dim_\alpha V_j < e$ for $j > k$. Let

3°) $$V' = \left[\bigcup_{j=k+1}^{k'} V_j\right] \cup \left[\bigcup_{\substack{j,j' \leqq k \\ j \neq j'}} (V_j \cap V_{j'})\right].$$

Then $\dim_\alpha V' < e$. Hence by (23.3) we can find $0 < D_0 \leqq D^*$, $0 < E_0 \leqq E^*$, and an analytic function t_0 on $Y\langle D_0, \beta\rangle$ with $\boldsymbol{\gamma}_\beta t_0 \neq 0$ such that

4°) $$t_0(b) = 0 \qquad \text{for all} \quad (b, c) \in V' \cap (Y\langle D_0, \beta\rangle \times Z\langle E_0, \gamma\rangle).$$

Let $M_j = \mathbf{d}(\alpha, \pi, V_j)$. Then $M_j = 0 \Leftrightarrow j > k$, and we have $M = M_1 + \dots + M_k$. By (31.10), $\boldsymbol{\sigma}(\mathfrak{i}(\alpha, V_j, X))$ is strictly regular relative to S for $\leqq k$, where $\boldsymbol{\sigma}: R(\alpha, X) \to R$ is the Taylor isomorphism. Hence applying (31.5) to $\boldsymbol{\gamma}_\alpha V_j$ we can find $0 < D_j \leqq D^*$, $0 < E_j \leqq E^*$, and an analytic function t_j on $Y\langle D_j, \beta\rangle$ with $\boldsymbol{\gamma}_\beta t_j \neq 0$ such that:

5°) For any $j \leqq k$ and $b \in Y\langle D_j, \beta\rangle$ for which $t_j(b) \neq 0$, we have that

$$V \cap (b \times Z\langle E_j, \gamma\rangle) \qquad \text{contains exactly } M_j \text{ distinct points.}$$

Now it suffices to take $E = \min(E_0, E_1, \dots, E_k)$, $D = \min(D_0, D_1, \dots, D_k, \varphi(E))$, and $t = \prod_{j=0}^{k} t_j | Y\langle D, \beta\rangle$.

(**31.13**) *Given* $\beta \in Y_{q'}$, *let* $\alpha^{(\theta)} = (\beta, \gamma^{(\theta)})$, $(\theta = 1,\ldots, N)$, *be the distinct points in* $V \cap \pi^{-1}(\beta)$, *and let* $M_\theta = \mathbf{d}(\alpha^{(\theta)}, \pi, V)$. *Then there exist* $D > 0$, $E > 0$ *and an analytic function* t *on* $Y\langle D, \beta\rangle$ *with* $\gamma_\beta t \neq 0$ *having the following properties.*

i) $Y\langle D, \beta\rangle \subset Y_{q'}$; $\quad \bigcup_{\theta=1}^{N} Z\langle E, \gamma^{(\theta)}\rangle \subset Z_{q'}$;

$$Z\langle E, \gamma^{(\theta)}\rangle \cap Z\langle E, \gamma^{(\theta')}\rangle = \emptyset \qquad \textit{for all} \quad \theta \neq \theta'.$$

ii) $V \cap \pi^{-1}(Y\langle D, \beta\rangle) = \bigcup_{\theta=1}^{N} [V \cap (Y\langle D, \beta\rangle \times Z\langle E, \gamma^{(\theta)}\rangle)]$.

iii) $\Omega = \{b \in Y\langle D, \beta\rangle : t(b) = 0\}$ *is nowhere dense in* $Y\langle D, \beta\rangle$.

iv) *For any* $b \in Y\langle D, \beta\rangle - \Omega$ *and any* $\theta \leqq N$ *we have that* $V \cap (b \times Z\langle E, \gamma^{(\theta)}\rangle)$ *contains exactly* M_θ *distinct points.*

v) *Given* $0 < E^* \leqq E$ *there exists* $0 < D^* \leqq D$ *such that*

$$V \cap (Y\langle D^*, \beta\rangle \times Z\langle E, \gamma^{(\theta)}\rangle) = V \cap (Y\langle D^*, \beta\rangle \times Z\langle E^*, \gamma^{(\theta)}\rangle) \quad \textit{for} \quad \theta = 1,\ldots, N.$$

Proof. By (30.21) we can find $D' > 0$, $E' > 0$ for which we have (1°, 2°, 3°).

1°) $\qquad Y\langle D', \beta\rangle \subset Y_{q'}$; $\quad \bigcup_{\theta=1}^{N} Z\langle E', \gamma^{(\theta)}\rangle \subset Z_{q'}$;

$$Z\langle E', \gamma^{(\theta)}\rangle \cap Z\langle E', \gamma^{(\theta')}\rangle \neq \emptyset \qquad \text{for all} \quad \theta \neq \theta'.$$

2°) $V \cap \pi^{-1}(Y\langle D', \beta\rangle) = \bigcup_{\theta=1}^{N} [V \cap (Y\langle D', \beta\rangle \times Z\langle E', \gamma^{(\theta)}\rangle)]$.

3°) Given $0 < E^* \leqq E'$ there exists $0 < \varphi(E^*) \leqq D'$ depending on E^* such that

$$V \cap (Y\langle \varphi(E^*), \beta\rangle \times Z\langle E', \gamma^{(\theta)}\rangle) = V \cap (Y\langle \varphi(E^*), \beta\rangle \times Z\langle E^*, \gamma^{(\theta)}\rangle) \quad \text{for} \quad \theta = 1,\ldots, N.$$

By (31.12) we can find $0 < D_\theta \leqq D'$, $0 < E_\theta \leqq E'$, and an analytic function t_θ on $Y\langle D_\theta, \beta\rangle$ with $\gamma_\beta t_\theta \neq 0$ such that:

4°) For any $b \in Y\langle D_\theta, \beta\rangle$ with $t_\theta(b) \neq 0$, $V \cap (b \times Z\langle E_\theta, \gamma^{(\theta)}\rangle)$ contains exactly M_θ points.

Let $E = \min(E_1,\ldots, E_N)$. Since $\gamma_\beta t_\theta \neq 0$ for $\theta = 1,\ldots, N$, we can take $0 < D \leqq \min(D_1,\ldots, D_N, \varphi(E))$ such that $\Omega = \{b \in Y\langle D, \beta\rangle : t(b) = 0\}$ is nowhere dense in $Y\langle D, \beta\rangle$ where $t = \prod_{\theta=1}^{N} t_\theta | Y\langle D, \beta\rangle$. Given $0 < E^* \leqq E$ take $D^* = \min(D, \varphi(E^*))$.

(31.14) *Let the situation be as in* (31.13). *Label the points* $\alpha^{(\theta)}$ *so that* $M_\theta > 0$ *for* $\theta \leqq N^*$ *and* $M_\theta = 0$ *for* $\theta > N^*$. *For* $\theta \leqq N^*$ *and* $b \in Y\langle D, \beta\rangle$ *with* $t(b) \neq 0$, *label the points in* $V \cap (b \times Z\langle E, \gamma^{(\theta)}\rangle)$ *as* $(b, \zeta^{\{\theta,\lambda\}}[b])$, $(\lambda = 1,\ldots, M_\theta)$. *Then we have the following.*

1) *For any* $\theta \leqq N^*$ *we have*

$$\lim_{\substack{b\to\beta \\ t(b)\neq 0}} \zeta^{\{\theta,\lambda\}}[b] = \gamma^{(\theta)},$$

i.e., *given* $\epsilon > 0$ *there exists* $0 < \delta(\epsilon) < D$ *such that*:

$$b \in Y\langle\delta(\epsilon), \beta\rangle - \Omega \Rightarrow |\zeta_i^{\{\theta,\lambda\}}[b] - \gamma_i^{(\theta)}| < \epsilon$$

for $i = 1,\ldots, m$ *and* $\lambda = 1,\ldots, M_\theta$.

2) $M_1 + \ldots + M_{N^*} = d$.

3) *For any* $b \in Y\langle D, \beta\rangle \cap \mathring{Y}$ *with* $t(b) \neq 0$,

$$\zeta^{\{\theta,\lambda\}}[b], \qquad (\theta = 1,\ldots, N^*; \lambda = 1,\ldots, M_\theta),$$

is a labeling of the points

$$\zeta^{[\mu]}[b], \qquad (\mu = 1,\ldots, d).$$

4) *For any* $\gamma \in K^m$ *we have that*

$$(\beta, \gamma) \in \bar{V} \Leftrightarrow \gamma = \gamma^{(\theta)} \textit{ for some } \theta \leqq N^*.$$

Proof. 1), 2), 3) follow from (31.13, 31.5). Now $V \cap X_{q'}$ is closed in $X_{q'}$ and by (31.4), $\mathring{V} \cap (Y_{q'} \times K^m) \subset V \cap X_{q'}$. Therefore all the points in $\bar{V} \cap \pi^{-1}(\beta)$ are amongst the points $\alpha^{(1)},\ldots, \alpha^{(N)}$.

Let $\theta \leqq N^*$ be given. Now $\mathring{Y}$ is everywhere dense in Y and $\gamma_\beta t \neq 0$. Hence we can find points $b^{(p)} \in Y\langle D, \beta\rangle \cap \mathring{Y}$ such that $\lim_{p\to\infty} b^{(p)} = \beta$ and $t(b^{(p)}) \neq 0$ for all p. By 3), $(b^{(p)}, \zeta^{\{\theta,1\}}[b^{(p)}]) \in \mathring{V}$ and by 1), $\lim_{p\to\infty}(b^{(p)}, \zeta^{\{\theta,1\}}[b^{(p)}]) = \alpha^{(\theta)}$. Therefore $\alpha^{(\theta)} \in \bar{V}$.

Let $\theta \leqq N$ be given such that $\alpha^{(\theta)} \in \bar{V}$. Then there exists $\tilde{\alpha} = (\tilde{\beta}, \tilde{\gamma}) \in \mathring{V}$ with $\tilde{\beta} \in Y\langle D, \beta\rangle \cap \mathring{Y}$ and $\tilde{\gamma} \in Z\langle E, \gamma^{(\theta)}\rangle$. Now $\tilde{\alpha} \in V$ by (31.4), and hence applying (31.11) at $\tilde{\alpha}$ we can find $\tilde{D} > 0$, $\tilde{E} > 0$ such that:

$$Y\langle\tilde{D}, \tilde{\beta}\rangle \subset Y\langle D, \beta\rangle \cap \mathring{Y}, \qquad Z\langle\tilde{E}, \tilde{\gamma}\rangle \subset Z\langle E, \gamma^{(\theta)}\rangle,$$
$$\pi[V \cap (Y\langle\tilde{D}, \tilde{\beta}\rangle \times Z\langle\tilde{E}, \tilde{\gamma}\rangle)] = Y\langle\tilde{D}, \tilde{\beta}\rangle.$$

Now Ω is nowhere dense in $Y\langle D, \beta\rangle$ and hence there exists $a = (b, c) \in V$ with $b \in Y\langle\tilde{D}, \tilde{\beta}\rangle$, $t(b) \neq 0$, and $c \in Z\langle\tilde{E}, \tilde{\gamma}\rangle$. Therefore $M_\theta > 0$, i.e., $\theta \leqq N^*$.

(31.15) *There exists $q^* \geqq q'$ such that $V \cap X_{q^*}$ is pure e dimensional.*

Proof. Let $\chi_1, \ldots, \chi_m$ be indeterminates. By (28.4), there exists $q \geqq q'$ such that the norm of $(z_1 - \bar{z}_1)\chi_1 + \ldots + (z_m - \bar{z}_m)\chi_m$ relative to the field extension $\mathfrak{L}(z_1, \ldots, z_m, \chi_1, \ldots, \chi_m)/\mathfrak{R}(z_1, \ldots, z_m, \chi_1, \ldots, \chi_m)$ is a polynomial

$$\Theta(y, z_1, \ldots, z_m, \chi_1, \ldots, \chi_m) = \sum_{i_1, \ldots, i_m} \Theta_{i_1 \ldots i_m}(y, z_1, \ldots, z_m)\chi_1^{i_1} \ldots \chi_m^{i_m}$$

in $\chi_1, \ldots, \chi_m$ whose coefficients $\Theta_{i_1 \ldots i_m}(y, z_1, \ldots, z_m)$ are polynomials in $z_1, \ldots, z_m$ with coefficients in S which are convergent in Y_q, and for all $b \in \mathring{Y}_q$ we have

$$\Theta(b, z_1, \ldots, z_m, \chi_1, \ldots, \chi_m) = \prod_{\mu=1}^{d} \left(\sum_{i=1}^{m} (z_i - \zeta_i^{[\mu]}[b])\chi_i \right).$$

Given $\beta \in Y_q$ let the notation be as in (31.13, 31.14). Since $\mathring{Y}_q$ is everywhere dense in Y_q and $\boldsymbol{\gamma}_\beta t \neq 0$, we can find $b^{(p)} \in Y\langle D, \beta \rangle \cap \mathring{Y}_q$ with $t(b^{(p)}) \neq 0$ such that $\lim_{p \to \infty} b^{(p)} = \beta$. By (31.14.3) we then get

$$\Theta(b^{(p)}, z_1, \ldots, z_m, \chi_1, \ldots, \chi_m) = \prod_{\theta=1}^{N^*} \prod_{\lambda=1}^{M\theta} \left(\sum_{i=1}^{m} (z_i - \zeta_i^{\{\theta, \lambda\}}[b^{(p)}])\chi_i \right)$$

for all p. In virtue of (31.14.1) taking limits as $p \to \infty$ we get

$$\Theta(\beta, z_1, \ldots, z_m, \chi_1, \ldots, \chi_m) = \prod_{\theta=1}^{N^*} \left(\sum_{i=1}^{m} (z_i - \gamma_i^{(\theta)})\chi_i \right)^{M\theta}.$$

For any $\gamma \in K^m$ we thus have:

$$\begin{aligned}
&\Theta_{i_1 \ldots i_m}(\beta, \gamma_1, \ldots, \gamma_m) = 0 \text{ for all } i_1, \ldots, i_m \\
\Leftrightarrow\ &\Theta(\beta, \gamma_1, \ldots, \gamma_m, \chi_1, \ldots, \chi_m) = 0 \\
\Leftrightarrow\ &\prod_{\theta=1}^{N^*} \left(\sum_{i=1}^{m} (\gamma_i - \gamma_i^{(\theta)})\chi_i \right)^{M_\theta} = 0 \\
\Leftrightarrow\ &\gamma = \gamma^{(\theta)} \text{ for some } \theta \leqq N^* \\
\Leftrightarrow\ &(\beta, \gamma) \in \bar{V}, \qquad \text{(by 31.14.4).}
\end{aligned}$$

This shows that

$$\begin{aligned}
\bar{V} \cap X_q &= \{(\beta, \gamma) \in Y_q \times K^m : \Theta_{i_1 \ldots i_m}(\beta, \gamma_1, \ldots, \gamma_m) = 0 \text{ for all } i_1, \ldots, i_m\} \\
&\subset V \cap X_q.
\end{aligned}$$

Therefore $\bar{V} \cap X_q$ is an analytic set in X_q. By (31.10), $\dim V \cap X_{q_\circ} \leqq e$ and hence $\dim \bar{V} \cap X_q \leqq e$. Now $\bar{V} \cap X_q$ is the closure of $\mathring{V} \cap \mathring{X}_q$ in X_q and by (31.4, 31.11), $\mathring{V} \cap \mathring{X}_q$ is a pure e dimensional analytic set in $\mathring{X}_q$. Therefore $\bar{V} \cap X_q$ is pure e dimensional by (30.17). Noting that

$(0) \in \bar{V} \cap X_q$, (say by 31.4), we thus get: $\gamma_{(0)}\bar{V}$ is a pure e dimensional analytic set germ, $\gamma_{(0)}V$ is an irreducible e dimensional analytic set germ, and $\gamma_{(0)}\bar{V} \subset \gamma_{(0)}V$. Therefore $\gamma_{(0)}\bar{V} = \gamma_{(0)}V$, i.e., $\bar{V} \cap X_{q^*} = V \cap X_{q^*}$ for some $q^* \geqq q$. Consequently V is pure e dimensional in X_{q^*}.

(31.16) *For any* $\beta \in Y_{q^*}$ *let* $\alpha^{(\theta)}$, $(\theta = 1,\ldots, N)$, *be the distinct points in* $V \cap \pi^{-1}(\beta)$. *Then* $\mathbf{d}(\alpha^{(\theta)}, \pi, V) > 0$ *for* $\theta = 1,\ldots, N$, *and we have*

$$\sum_{\theta=1}^{N} \mathbf{d}(\alpha^{(\theta)}, \pi, V) = \mathbf{d}((0), \pi, V) = d.$$

PROOF. In view of (31.15) the first assertion follows from (31.10). The second assertion was already proved in (31.14.2).

(31.17) *For any* $\beta \in Y_{q^*}$ *let* $\alpha^{(\theta)} = (\beta, \gamma^{(\theta)})$, $(\theta = 1,\ldots, N)$, *be the distinct points in* $V \cap \pi^{-1}(\beta)$. *Then there exist* $D > 0$, $E > 0$, *for which we have* (i *to* v).

i) $Y\langle D, \beta\rangle \subset Y_{q^*}$; $\quad \bigcup_{\theta=1}^{N} Z\langle E, \gamma^{(\theta)}\rangle \subset Z_{q^*}$;

$$Z\langle E, \gamma^{(\theta)}\rangle \cap Z\langle E, \gamma^{(\theta')}\rangle = \emptyset \qquad \textit{for all} \quad \theta \neq \theta'.$$

ii) $V \cap \pi^{-1}(Y\langle D, \beta\rangle) = \bigcup_{\theta=1}^{N} [V \cap (Y\langle D, \beta\rangle \times Z\langle E, \gamma^{(\theta)}\rangle)]$.

iii) *For all* $\tilde{\beta} \in Y\langle D, \beta\rangle$ *and* $\theta = 1,\ldots, N$ *we have*

$$\sum_{\tilde{\alpha} \in V \cap (\tilde{\beta} \times Z\langle E, \gamma^{(\theta)}\rangle)} \mathbf{d}(\tilde{\alpha}, \pi, V) = \mathbf{d}(\alpha^{(\theta)}, \pi, V).$$

iv) $\pi[V \cap (Y\langle D, \beta\rangle \times Z\langle E, \gamma^{(\theta)}\rangle)] = Y\langle D, \beta\rangle \qquad$ *for* $\theta = 1,\ldots, N$.

v) *Given* $0 < E^* \leqq E$ *there exists* $0 < D^* \leqq D$ *such that*

$$V \cap (Y\langle D^*, \beta\rangle \times Z\langle E, \gamma^{(\theta)}\rangle) = V \cap (Y\langle D^*, \beta\rangle \times Z\langle E^*, \gamma^{(\theta)}\rangle)$$

for $\theta = 1,\ldots, N$.

PROOF. By (31.13), we can find $D > 0$, $E > 0$, and a nowhere dense subset Ω of $Y\langle D, \beta\rangle$ such that conditions (i, ii, v) are satisfied, and such that for $\theta = 1,\ldots, N$, we have the following.

1°) For any $b \in Y\langle D, \beta\rangle - \Omega$, $V \cap (b \times Z\langle E, \gamma^{(\theta)}\rangle)$ contains exactly $\mathbf{d}(\alpha^{(\theta)}, \pi, V)$ distinct points.

Let $\tilde{\beta} \in Y\langle D, \beta\rangle$ be given. Let $\tilde{\alpha}^{(\theta,\lambda)} = (\tilde{\beta}, \tilde{\gamma}^{(\theta,\lambda)})$, $(\lambda = 1,\ldots, \Lambda_\theta)$, be the distinct points in $V \cap (\tilde{\beta} \times Z\langle E, \gamma^{(\theta)}\rangle)$. Applying (31.13) at $\tilde{\beta}$ we can find $\tilde{D} > 0$, $\tilde{E} > 0$, and a nowhere dense subset $\tilde{\Omega}$ of $Y\langle \tilde{D}, \tilde{\beta}\rangle$ such that for $\theta = 1,\ldots, N$, we have (2°, 3°, 4°).

2°) $Y\langle\tilde{D},\tilde{\beta}\rangle \subset Y\langle D,\beta\rangle$; $\quad \bigcup_{\lambda=1}^{\Lambda_\theta} Z\langle\tilde{E},\tilde{\gamma}^{(\theta,\lambda)}\rangle \subset Z\langle E,\gamma^{(\theta)}\rangle$;

$$Z\langle\tilde{E},\tilde{\gamma}^{(\theta,\lambda)}\rangle \cap Z\langle\tilde{E},\tilde{\gamma}^{(\theta,\lambda')}\rangle = \emptyset \qquad \text{for all} \quad \lambda \neq \lambda'.$$

3°) $V \cap (Y\langle\tilde{D},\tilde{\beta}\rangle \times Z\langle E,\gamma^{(\theta)}\rangle)$

$$= \bigcup_{\lambda=1}^{\Lambda_\theta} [V \cap (Y\langle\tilde{D},\tilde{\beta}\rangle \times Z\langle\tilde{E},\tilde{\gamma}^{(\theta,\lambda)}\rangle)].$$

4°) For any $b \in Y\langle\tilde{D},\tilde{\beta}\rangle - \tilde{\Omega}$, $V \cap (b \times Z\langle\tilde{E},\gamma^{(\theta,\lambda)}\rangle)$ contains exactly $\mathbf{d}(\tilde{\alpha}^{(\theta,\lambda)},\pi,V)$ distinct points for $\lambda = 1,\ldots,\Lambda_\theta$.

Now $\tilde{\Omega}$ is nowhere dense in $Y\langle\tilde{D},\tilde{\beta}\rangle$ and Ω is nowhere dense in $Y\langle D,\beta\rangle$. Hence there exists $b \in Y\langle\tilde{D},\tilde{\beta}\rangle - (\Omega \cup \tilde{\Omega})$, and then for $\theta = 1,\ldots,N$, we get

$$\begin{aligned} &\mathbf{d}(\alpha^{(\theta)},\pi,V) \\ &= \text{number of distinct points in } V \cap (b \times Z\langle E,\gamma^{(\theta)}\rangle) \\ &= \sum_{\lambda=1}^{\Lambda_\theta} \text{number of distinct points in } V \cap (b \times Z\langle\tilde{E},\tilde{\gamma}^{(\theta,\lambda)}\rangle) \\ &= \sum_{\lambda=1}^{\Lambda_\theta} \mathbf{d}(\tilde{\alpha}^{(\theta,\lambda)},\pi,V). \end{aligned}$$

This proves iii). In virtue of (31.16), iv) follows from iii).

(31.18) *For all* $q \geqq q^*$, $\pi(V \cap X_q) = Y_q$ *and the map* $\pi|V \cap X_q$: $V \cap X_q \to K^e$ *is open.*

Follows from (31.17).

(31.19) *Let* $\alpha = (\beta,\gamma) \in V$ *with* $\beta \in Y_{q^*}$ be such that $\Delta_i(\beta) \neq 0$ *for* $i = 1,\ldots,m$. *Then* $\boldsymbol{\gamma}_\alpha W = \boldsymbol{\gamma}_\alpha V$, *α is a simple point of V, and* $\mathbf{d}(\alpha,\pi,V) = 1$. *Furthermore, there exist* $D > 0$, $E > 0$ *with* $Y\langle D,\beta\rangle \subset Y_{q^*}$, $Z\langle E,\gamma\rangle \subset Z_{q^*}$, *and* $\xi = (\xi_1,\ldots,\xi_m)$ *where* $\xi_1,\ldots,\xi_m$ *are analytic functions on* $Y\langle D,\beta\rangle$, *such that*

$$V \cap (Y\langle D,\beta\rangle \times Z\langle E,\gamma\rangle) = \{(b,\xi(b)) : b \in Y\langle D,\beta\rangle\}.$$

PROOF. By (10.14), α is a simple point of W, $\dim_\alpha W = e$, and $\mathbf{d}(\alpha,\pi,W) = 1$. By (31.15), $\dim_\alpha V = e$ and hence $\boldsymbol{\gamma}_\alpha V = \boldsymbol{\gamma}_\alpha W$. Therefore α is a simple point of V and $\mathbf{d}(\alpha,\pi,V) = 1$. Since $\boldsymbol{\gamma}_\alpha V = \boldsymbol{\gamma}_\alpha W$, the last assertion follows from (12.4).

(31.20) *Let* $\mathbf{\Delta}' = \{b \in Y: \Delta'\Delta_1 \ldots \Delta_m(b) = 0\}$. *Let* $\tilde{Y}$ *be any open subset of* Y_{q^*}. *Then* $V \cap \pi^{-1}(\tilde{Y}) =$ *closure of* $V \cap \pi^{-1}(\tilde{Y} - \mathbf{\Delta}')$ *in* $\tilde{Y} \times Z$.

Follows from (31.17) since $\tilde{Y} - \mathbf{\Delta}'$ is everywhere dense in $\tilde{Y}$.

(31.21) *Let* $\mathbf{\Delta}' = \{b \in Y: \Delta'\Delta_1 \ldots \Delta_m(b) = 0\}$. *Assume that* $K = \mathbf{C}$ *and let* Y *be any connected neighborhood of the origin in* Y_{q^*}. *Let* $Y' = \tilde{Y} - \mathbf{\Delta}'$ *and* $V' = V \cap \pi^{-1}(Y')$. *Then* V' *is arcwise connected and the map* $V' \to Y'$ *induced by* π *is a covering map.*

Proof. Now $\mathring{Y} \cap \tilde{Y}$ is an everywhere dense subset of Y', and hence by (31.17)

$$V' = \text{closure of} \quad V \cap \pi^{-1}(\mathring{Y} \cap \tilde{Y}) \quad \text{in} \quad V'.$$

By (31.6.3), $V \cap \pi^{-1}(\mathring{Y} \cap \tilde{Y})$ is connected and hence V' is connected. If we show that $V' \to Y'$ is a covering map, then it will follow that V' is locally arcwise connected and hence arcwise connected.

Let $\beta \in Y'$ be given. By (31.17, 31.19), there are exactly d points $\alpha^{(\theta)} = (\beta, \gamma^{(\theta)})$, $(\theta = 1, \ldots, d)$, in $V \cap \pi^{-1}(\beta)$ and there exist $D > 0, E > 0$, and $\xi^{(\theta)} = (\xi_1^{(\theta)}, \ldots, \xi_m^{(\theta)})$ where $\xi_i^{(\theta)}$ are analytic functions on $Y\langle D, \beta\rangle$, such that we have (1° to 4°).

1°) $Y\langle D, \beta\rangle \subset Y'$; $\quad \bigcup_{\theta=1}^{d} Z\langle E, \gamma^{(\theta)}\rangle \subset Z_{q^*}$.

2°) $Z\langle E, \gamma^{(\theta)}\rangle \cap Z\langle E, \gamma^{(\theta')}\rangle = \emptyset \quad$ for all $\theta \neq \theta'$.

3°) $V \cap \pi^{-1}(Y\langle D, \beta\rangle) = \bigcup_{\theta=1}^{d} [V \cap (Y\langle D, \beta\rangle \times Z\langle E, \gamma^{(\theta)}\rangle)]$.

4°) $V \cap (Y\langle D, \beta\rangle \times Z\langle E, \gamma^{(\theta)}\rangle) = \{(b, \xi^{(\theta)}(b)) : b \in Y\langle D, \beta\rangle\}$

for $\theta = 1, \ldots, d$.

Let $V_\theta = V \cap (Y\langle D, \beta\rangle \times Z\langle E, \gamma^{(\theta)}\rangle)$. Then by 4°), for $\theta = 1, \ldots, d$ we get: V_θ is open in V' and $\pi | V_\theta$ maps V_θ homeomorphically onto $Y\langle D, \beta\rangle$ and hence in particular V_θ is connected. By 2°) and 3°) we deduce that for all $\theta \neq \theta'$, V_θ and $V_{\theta'}$ belong to different connected components of $V \cap \pi^{-1}(Y\langle D, \beta\rangle)$. Thus $V_1, \ldots, V_d$ are exactly all the distinct connected components of $V' \cap \pi^{-1}(Y\langle D, \beta\rangle)$, and for $\theta = 1, \ldots, d$ we have that V_θ is open in V' and $\pi | V_\theta$ maps V_θ homeomorphically onto $Y\langle D, \beta\rangle$. This shows that $V' \to Y'$ is a covering map.

(31.22) *Let the situation be as in* (31.21) *and let* $\alpha \in V \cap \pi^{-1}(\tilde{Y})$ *be given. Then there exists a simple arc* $\Gamma: [0, 1] \to V \cap \pi^{-1}(\tilde{Y})$ *such that* $\Gamma(1) = \alpha$ *and* $\Gamma([0, 1[) \subset V'$. *Hence in particular* $V \cap \pi^{-1}(\tilde{Y})$ *is arcwise connected.*

PROOF. Let $\alpha = \alpha^{(1)} = (\beta, \gamma^{(1)})$ with $\beta \in \tilde{Y}$. Let $\alpha^{(\theta)} = (\beta, \gamma^{(\theta)})$, $(\theta = 2, \ldots, N)$ be the remaining points in $V \cap \pi^{-1}(\beta)$. Let the remaining notation be as in (31.17). By (14.7), there exists a simple arc $\hat{\Gamma}\colon [0, 1] \to Y\langle D, \beta\rangle \cap \tilde{Y}$ such that $\hat{\Gamma}(1) = \beta$, and $\hat{\Gamma}([0, 1[) \subset Y'$. Take

$$\tilde{\alpha} \in V \cap (Y\langle D, \beta\rangle \times Z\langle E, \gamma^{(1)}\rangle)$$

such that $\pi\tilde{a} = \Gamma(0)$. Then $\tilde{a} \in V'$. By (31.21), $V' \to Y'$ is a covering map and hence there exists an arc $\Gamma\colon [0, 1[\to V'$ such that $\Gamma(0) = \tilde{\alpha}$, $\hat{\Gamma}(\lambda) = \pi(\Gamma(\lambda))$ for all $\lambda \in [0, 1[$. Let $\Gamma(1) = \alpha$. Let

$$\Omega_1 = (Y\langle D, \beta\rangle \times Z\langle E, \gamma^{(1)}\rangle) \cap \Gamma([0, 1[),$$

$$\Omega_2 = \left(\bigcup_{\theta=2}^{N} Y\langle D, \beta\rangle \times Z\langle E, \gamma^{(\theta)}\rangle\right) \cap \Gamma([0, 1[).$$

Then Ω_1 and Ω_2 are disjoint open subsets of $\Gamma([0, 1[)$, $\Omega_1 \cup \Omega_2 = \Gamma([0, 1[)$, and $\Omega_1 \cap \Gamma([0, 1[) \neq \emptyset$. Now $\Gamma([0, 1[)$ is connected and hence we must have $\Gamma([0, 1[) = \Omega_1$, i.e.,

$$\Gamma([0, 1[) \subset V \cap (Y\langle D, \beta\rangle \times Z\langle E, \gamma^{(1)}\rangle).$$

By (31.17) it then follows that $\lim_{\lambda \to 1} \Gamma(\lambda) = \alpha$. Therefore Γ is continuous on $[0, 1]$, and hence $\Gamma\colon [0, 1] \to V \cap \pi^{-1}(\tilde{Y})$ is a simple arc such that $\Gamma(1) = \alpha$ and $\Gamma([0, 1[) \subset V'$.

(31.23) *Given $r \in R$ let $H(y, T)$ be the field polynomial of $\bar{r}$ relative to the field extension $\mathfrak{L}/\mathfrak{K}$. Then there exists $q \geqq q^*$ such that all the coefficients of $H(y, T)$ are convergent in Y_q and for all $\beta \in Y_q$ we have*

$$H(\beta, T) = \prod_{\alpha \in V \cap \pi^{-1}(\beta)} (T - r(\alpha))^{\mathbf{d}(\alpha, \pi, V)}.$$

PROOF. By (28.5) there exists $q \geqq \max(q^*, q(r))$, where $q(r)$ is defined in (31.3), such that all the coefficients of $H(y, T)$ are convergent in Y_q and such that for all $b \in \mathring{Y}_q$ we have

$$H(b, T) = \prod_{\mu=1}^{d} (T - r^{[\mu]}[b]).$$

Given $\beta \in Y_q$ let the notation be as in (31.13, 31.14). Since $\mathring{Y}_q$ is everywhere dense in Y_q and $\boldsymbol{\gamma}_\beta t \neq 0$, we can find points $b^{(p)} \in Y\langle D, \beta\rangle \cap \mathring{Y}_q$

with $t(b^{(p)}) \neq 0$ such that $\lim_{p\to\infty} b^{(p)} = \beta$. We then get

$$\begin{aligned} H(b^{(p)}, T) &= \prod_{\mu=1}^{d} (T - r^{[\mu]}[b^{(p)}]) \\ &= \prod_{\mu=1}^{d} (T - r(b^{(p)}, \zeta^{[\mu]}[b^{(p)}])) \qquad \text{(by 31.3)} \\ &= \prod_{\theta=1}^{N^*} \prod_{\lambda=1}^{M_\theta} (T - r(b^{(p)}, \zeta^{\{\theta,\lambda\}}[b^{(p)}])) \qquad \text{(by 31.14.4).} \end{aligned}$$

Taking limits as $p \to \infty$, by (31.14.1) we get

$$\begin{aligned} H(\beta, T) &= \prod_{\theta=1}^{N^*} \prod_{\lambda=1}^{M_\theta} (T - r(\beta, \gamma^{(\theta)})) \\ &= \prod_{\alpha \in V \cap \pi^{-1}(\beta)} (T - r(\alpha))^{\mathbf{d}(\alpha,\pi,V)}. \end{aligned}$$

In (31.15, 31.23) we used the corollaries (28.4, 28.5) of (28.3). Using the full force of (28.3) we get

(**31.24**) *Let* $\Gamma_1,\ldots,\Gamma_\rho$, $T_1,\ldots,T_\rho$, $\chi_1,\ldots,\chi_\sigma$ *be a finite uumber of indeterminates. Let* $r_1,\ldots,r_\rho \in R$ *be given. Let* $v(y, \Gamma_1,\ldots,\Gamma_\rho, \chi_1,\ldots,\chi_\rho) \in S[\Gamma_1,\ldots,\Gamma_\rho, \chi_1,\ldots,\chi_\sigma]$ *be given which is homogeneous in* $\Gamma_1,\ldots,\Gamma_\rho$. *Then the norm of* $v(y, T_1 - \bar{r}_1,\ldots, T_\rho - \bar{r}_\rho, \chi_1,\ldots,\chi_\sigma)$ *relative to the field extension* $\mathfrak{L}(T_1,\ldots,T_\rho, \chi_1,\ldots,\chi_\sigma)/\mathfrak{R}(T_1,\ldots,T_\rho,\chi_1,\ldots,\chi_\sigma)$ *is an element* $\Theta(y, T_1,\ldots,T_\rho, \chi_1,\ldots,\chi_\sigma)$ *in* $S[T_1,\ldots,T_\rho,\chi_1,\ldots,\chi_\sigma]$. *Furthermore there exists* $q \geqq q^*$ *such that*: $r_1,\ldots,r_\rho$ *are convergent in* X_q; *all the coefficients of* v *and* Θ *are convergent in* Y_q; *and for all* $\beta \in Y_q$ *we have*

$$\begin{aligned} &\Theta(\beta, T_1,\ldots,T_\rho, \chi_1,\ldots,\chi_\sigma) \\ &= \prod_{\alpha\in V\cap\pi^{-1}(\beta)} v(\beta, t_1 - r_1(\alpha),\ldots, t_\rho - r_\rho(\alpha), \chi_1,\ldots,\chi_\sigma)^{\mathbf{d}(\alpha,\pi,V)}. \end{aligned}$$

PROOF. By (28.3), there exists $q \geqq \max(q^*, q(r_1),\ldots, q(r_\rho))$ such that all the coefficients of v and Θ are convergent in Y_q and such that for all $b \in \mathring{Y}_q$ we have

$$\begin{aligned} &\Theta(b, T_1,\ldots,T_\rho, \chi_1,\ldots,\chi_\sigma) \\ &= \prod_{\mu=1}^{d} v(b, T_1 - r_1^{[\mu]}[b],\ldots, T_\rho - r_\rho^{[\mu]}[b], \chi_1,\ldots,\chi_\sigma). \end{aligned}$$

For any given $\beta \in Y_q$ argue as in the proof of (31.23).

—×—

Thus having eliminated all reference to the auxiliary element w, in §32 we shall summarize the main results of §31 with slight notational modifications.

§32. RÜCKERT-WEIERSTRASS PARAMETRIZATION OF AN IRREDUCIBLE ANALYTIC SET GERM (SUMMARY)[1]

Let $R = K[\langle x_1,\ldots, x_n\rangle]$.[2] Let $\mathfrak{p}$ be a nonzero nonmaximal prime ideal in R.[3] Let $e = \dim R/\mathfrak{p}$, $(0 < e < n)$. By (23.5, 24.5), upon making a nonsingular K-linear transformation on $x_1,\ldots, x_n$ we can arrange that $\mathfrak{p}$ is strictly regular relative to $K[\langle x_1,\ldots, x_e\rangle]$. Let $y_i = x_i$ for $i = 1,\ldots, e$, $y = (y_1,\ldots, y_e)$, $S = K[\langle y\rangle]$, $\mathfrak{R} = K(\langle y\rangle)$, $m = n - e$, $z_i = x_{e+i}$ for $i = 1,\ldots, m$, $z = (z_1,\ldots, z_m)$. For any element or subset r of R let $\bar{r}$ denote the image of r under the natural epimorphism $R \to R/\mathfrak{p}$. Let $\mathfrak{L}$ be the quotient field of $\bar{R}$. Let $d = [\mathfrak{L}: \mathfrak{R}]$. Let $g_i(y, z_i)$ be the minimal monic polynomial of z_i mod $\mathfrak{p}$ over S. Let $\Delta_i(y)$ be the z_i-discriminant of $g_i(y, z_i)$. Then $g_i(y, z_i)$ is a distinguished polynomial of positive degree in z_i with coefficients in S and $0 \neq \Delta_i(y) \in S$.

For any $D > 0$, $E > 0$, $\beta \in K^e$, $\gamma \in K^m$, let

$$Y\langle D, \beta\rangle = \{b \in K^e: |b_i - \beta_i| < D \text{ for } i = 1,\ldots, e\},$$
$$Z\langle E, \gamma\rangle = \{c \in K^m: |c_i - \gamma_i| < E \text{ for } i = 1,\ldots, m\}.$$

Let $\pi: K^e\{y\} \times K^m\{z\} \to K^e\{y\}$ be the natural projection.

Let $u_1,\ldots, u_\Lambda$ be a finite basis of $\mathfrak{p}$. Let $X = Y \times Z$ be a neighborhood of the origin in $K^e \times K^m$ such that $u_1,\ldots, u_\Lambda$ are convergent in X, and all the coefficients of $g_1(y, z_1),\ldots, g_m(y, z_m)$ are convergent in Y. Let

$$V = \{a \in X: u_1(a) = \ldots = u_\Lambda(a) = 0\},$$
$$W = \{(b, c) \in Y \times K^m: g_1(b, c_1) = \ldots = g_m(b, c_m) = 0\},$$
$$\boldsymbol{\Delta} = \{b \in Y: \Delta_1\ldots\Delta_m(b) = 0\}.$$

By continuity of roots (11.3) we can find positive real numbers

$$B_0 > B_1 > \ldots, B_q \to 0; \qquad C_0 > C_1 > \ldots, C_q \to 0;$$

such that $Y\langle B_0, (0)\rangle \subset Y$, $Z\langle C_0, (0)\rangle \subset Z$, and $W \cap \pi^{-1}(Y\langle B_q, (0)\rangle) \subset Y\langle B_q, (0)\rangle \times Z\langle C_q, (0)\rangle$ for all $q \geqq 0$. Let $Y_q = \langle B_q, (0)\rangle$,

[1] The proof of the Nullstellensatz (30.12) was completed in (31.9). In the rest of the book, the Nullstellensatz and the resulting correspondence between analytic set germs and ideals will tacitly be used without further ado.

[2] In the rest of this chapter, unless otherwise stated K stands for an algebraically closed complete nondiscrete valued field.

[3] For the case when $\mathfrak{p}$ is either the zero ideal or the maximal ideal, all the relevant results in §32 obviously remain true with trivial modification.

$Z_q = Z\langle C_q, (0)\rangle$, $X_q = Y_q \times Z_q$. Then $X_0 \supset X_1 \supset \ldots$ is a neighborhood basis of the origin in $K^e \times K^m$.

(32.1)[4] *There exists $q^* \geqq 0$ such that we have* (1 *to* 4).

1) *$V \cap X_{q^*} \subset W$ and hence $V \cap (Y_q \times Z_{q^*}) = V \cap X_q$ for all $q \geqq q^*$. $\Delta \cap Y_{q^*}$ is nowhere dense in Y_{q^*}. For all $q \geqq q^*$, $\pi(V \cap X_q) = Y_q$ and the map $V \cap X_q \to Y_q$ induced by π is a continuous open proper closed map. For any $m' \leqq m$ and $q \geqq q^*$, the map $V \cap X_q \to Y_q \times K^{m'}$ induced by π' is a proper closed map where $\pi' : K^e\{y\} \times K^m\{z\} \to K^e\{y\} \times K^{m'}\{z_1, \ldots, z_{m'}\}$ is the natural projection, and hence in particular $\pi'(V' \cap X_q)$ is a closed subset of $Y_q \times K^{m'}$.*

2) *Let α be any point in $V \cap X_{q^*}$. Then $\boldsymbol{\gamma}_\alpha V$ is pure e dimensional; $\mathbf{d}(\alpha, \pi, V)$ is defined and $\mathbf{d}(\alpha, \pi, V) > 0$; and every prime ideal of $\boldsymbol{\sigma}(\mathfrak{i}(\alpha, V, X))$ is strictly regular relative to S where $\boldsymbol{\sigma}: R(\alpha, X) \to R$ is the Taylor isomorphism. If $\pi\alpha \notin \Delta$ then α is a simple point of V, $\mathbf{d}(\alpha, \pi, V) = 1$, and $\boldsymbol{\gamma}_\alpha V = \boldsymbol{\gamma}_\alpha W$.*

3) *For any $\beta \in Y_{q^*}$ we have*

$$\sum_{\alpha \in V \cap (\beta \times Z_{q^*})} \mathbf{d}(\alpha, \pi, V) = d = \mathbf{d}((0), \pi, V).$$

4) *For any $\beta \in Y_{q^*}$* let *$\alpha^{(\theta)} = (\beta, \gamma^{(\theta)})$, $(\theta = 1, \ldots, N)$, be the distinct points in $V \cap (\beta \times Z_{q^*})$. Then there exist $D > 0$, $E > 0$, having the following properties* (i *to* vi).

i) $Y\langle D, \beta\rangle \subset Y_{q^*}$; $\quad \bigcup_{\theta=1}^{N} Z\langle E, \gamma^{(\theta)}\rangle \subset Z_{q^*}$;

$$Z\langle E, \gamma^{(\theta)}\rangle \cap Z\langle E, \gamma^{(\theta')}\rangle = \emptyset \quad \textit{for all} \quad \theta \neq \theta'.$$

ii) $V \cap (Y\langle D, \beta\rangle \times Z_{q^*}) = \bigcup_{\theta=1}^{N} [V \cap (Y\langle D, \beta\rangle \times Z\langle E, \gamma^{(\theta)}\rangle)]$.

iii) *For all $\theta \leqq N$ and for all $b \in Y\langle D, \beta\rangle$ we have that*

$$\sum_{a \in V \cap (b \times Z\langle E, \gamma^{(\theta)}\rangle)} \mathbf{d}(a, \pi, V) = \mathbf{d}(\alpha^{(\theta)}, \pi, V).$$

iv) $\pi[V \cap (Y\langle D, \beta\rangle \times Z\langle E, \gamma^{(\theta)}\rangle)] = Y\langle D, \beta\rangle \quad$ *for* $\quad \theta = 1, \ldots, N$.

v) *Given $0 < E^* \leqq E$ there exists $0 < D^* \leqq D$ such that*

$$V \cap (Y\langle D^*, \beta\rangle \times Z\langle E, \gamma^{(\theta)}\rangle) = V \cap (Y\langle D^*, \beta\rangle \times Z\langle E^*, \gamma^{(\theta)}\rangle)$$
$$\textit{for} \quad \theta = 1, \ldots, N.$$

[4] In the rest of §32, q^* will refer to the integer whose existence is asserted in (32.1). However, the meanings of q, q', q'', etc., will depend on the individual Propositions (32.2), (32.3)....

vi) *If* $\beta \notin \mathbf{\Delta}$ *then there exist* $\xi^{(\theta)} = (\xi_1^{(\theta)}, \ldots, \xi_m^{(\theta)})$ *where* $\xi_i^{(\theta)}$ *are analytic functions on* $Y\langle D, \beta\rangle$ *such that*

$$V \cap (Y\langle D, \beta\rangle \times Z\langle E, \gamma^{(\theta)}\rangle) = \{(b, \xi^{(\theta)}(b)) \colon b \in Y\langle D, \beta\rangle\} \quad \text{for} \quad \theta = 1, \ldots, N.$$

(**32.2**) *Given* $0 \neq \Delta' \in S$,[5] *there exists* $q' \geqq q^*$ *such that* Δ' *is convergent in* $Y_{q'}$, $\mathbf{\Delta}' = \{b \in Y_{q'} \colon \Delta'\Delta_1 \ldots \Delta_m(b) = 0\}$ *is nowhere dense in* $Y_{q'}$, *and such that for any* $q \geqq q'$ *we have the following.*

1) *Let* $\tilde{Y}$ *be any open subset of* Y_q.[6] *Then*

$$V \cap (\tilde{Y} \times Z_q) = \text{closure of} \quad V \cap ((\tilde{Y} - \mathbf{\Delta}') \times Z_q) \quad \text{in} \quad X_q.$$

2) *Assume that* $K = \mathbf{C}$ *and let* $\tilde{Y}$ *be any connected neighborhood of the origin in* Y_q.[6] *Let* $Y' = \tilde{Y} - \mathbf{\Delta}'$ *and* $V' = V \cap (Y' \times Z_q)$. *Then* Y' *and* V' *are arcwise connected and locally arcwise connected and the map* $V' \to Y'$ *induced by* π *is a covering map. Given* $\alpha \in V \cap (\tilde{Y} \times Z_q)$ *there exists a simple arc* $\Gamma \colon [0, 1] \to V \cap (\tilde{Y} \times Z_q)$ *such that* $\Gamma(1) = \alpha$ *and* $\Gamma([0, 1[) \subset V'$. *Hence in particular* $V \cap (\tilde{Y} \times Z_q)$ *is arcwise connected.*

(**32.3**) *Given* $r \in R$ *let* $H(y, T)$ *be the field polynomial of* $\bar{r}$ *relative to the field extension* $\mathfrak{L}/\mathfrak{K}$. *Then* $H(y, T)$ *is a monic polynomial of degree d in T with coefficients in S, and there exists* $q \geqq q^*$ *such that: t is convergent in* X_q, *all the coefficients of* $H(y, T)$ *are convergent in* Y_q, *and for all* $b \in Y_q$ *we have*

$$H(b, T) = \prod_{a \in V \cap (b \times Z_q)} (T - r(a))^{\mathrm{d}(a, \pi, V)}.$$

(**32.4**) *Let* $\Gamma_1, \ldots, \Gamma_\rho, T_1, \ldots, T_\rho, \chi_1, \ldots, \chi_\sigma$ *be a finite number of indeterminates. Let* $r_1, \ldots, r_\rho \in R$ *be given. Let* $v(y, \Gamma_1, \ldots, \Gamma_\rho, \chi_1, \ldots, \chi_\sigma) \in S[\Gamma_1, \ldots, \Gamma_\rho, \chi_1, \ldots, \chi_\sigma]$ *be given which is homogeneous in* $\Gamma_1, \ldots, \Gamma_\rho$. *Then the norm of* $v(y, T_1 - \bar{r}_1, \ldots, T_\rho - \bar{r}_\rho, \chi_1, \ldots, \chi_\sigma)$ *relative to the field extension.* $\mathfrak{L}(T_1, \ldots, T_\rho, \chi_1, \ldots, \chi_\sigma)/\mathfrak{K}(T_1, \ldots, T_\rho, \chi_1, \ldots, \chi_\sigma)$ *is an element* $\Theta(y, T_1, \ldots, T_\rho, \chi_1, \ldots, \chi_\sigma)$ *in* $S[T_1, \ldots, T_\rho, \chi_1, \ldots, \chi_\sigma]$, *and there exists* $q \geqq q^*$ *such that:* $r_1, \ldots, r_\rho$ *are convergent in* X_q, *the coefficients of* v *and* Θ *are convergent in* Y_q, *and for all* $b \in Y_q$ *we have*

$$\Theta(b, T_1, \ldots, T_\rho, \chi_1, \ldots, \chi_\sigma) = \prod_{a \in V \cap (b \times Z_q)} v(b, T_1 - r_1(a), \ldots, T_\rho - r_\rho(a), \chi_1, \ldots, \chi_\sigma)^{\mathrm{d}(a, \pi, V)}.$$

[5] For instance $\Delta' = 1$.

[6] For instance $\tilde{Y} = Y_q$.

All this we have proved in §31. Now we proceed to derive a few more corollaries of the above results.

(32.5) *Let $r \in R$ be convergent in $X_{q'}$ for some $q' \geqq q^*$. Let $\alpha \in V \cap X_{q'}$ and let V' be an irreducible component of $\gamma_\alpha V$. Let $\mathfrak{p}' = \boldsymbol{\sigma}(\mathfrak{i}(\alpha, V', X))$ where $\boldsymbol{\sigma}: R(\alpha, X) \to R$ is the Taylor isomorphism. Let $\varphi: R \to R/\mathfrak{p}'$ be the natural epimorphism. Let $\mathfrak{L}'$ be the quotient field of φR.*[7] *Let $H(y, T)$ be the field polynomial of $\varphi(\boldsymbol{\tau}_\alpha r) - r(\alpha)$ relative to the field extension $\mathfrak{L}'/\mathfrak{K}$. Then we have the following.*

1) $\varphi(\boldsymbol{\tau}_\alpha r) \notin K \Leftrightarrow H(y, 0) \neq 0.$

2) *If $H(y, 0) \neq 0$ then the map $a \to r(a)$ of $V \cap X_{q'}$ into K is open at α.*

PROOF. Let us call the statements 1) and 2) for the case when $\alpha = (0)$ = origin in K^n as 1′) and 2′), respectively. In the general case, let $V_1, \ldots, V_\lambda$ be analytic sets in a neighborhood X' of α in $X_{q'}$ such that $\gamma_\alpha V_1 \cup \ldots \cup \gamma_\alpha V_\lambda$ is the normal decomposition of $\gamma_\alpha V$, $\gamma_\alpha V_1 = V'$, and $V \cap X' = V_1 \cup \ldots \cup V_\lambda$. Applying 1′) and 2′) to $\mathfrak{p}'$ we then get 1) and also this: If $H(y, 0) \neq 0$ then the map $a \to (\boldsymbol{\tau}_\alpha r)(a)$ of V_1 into K is open at the origin. The last assertion means that for any neighborhood X^* of α in X', the point $(\boldsymbol{\tau}_\alpha r)(0) = r(\alpha)$ is an interior point of $r(X^* \cap V_1)$; whence *a fortiori* $r(\alpha)$ is an interior point of $r(X^* \cap V)$, which proves 2).

Thus it suffices to prove 1) and 2) for the case when α is at the origin. Obviously: 1°) the map $a \to r(a)$ of $V \cap X_{q'}$ into K is open at the origin $\Leftrightarrow$ the map $a \to r(a) - r(0)$ of $V \cap X_{q'}$ into K is open at the origin; and 2°) $\bar{r} \in K \Leftrightarrow \bar{r} - r(0) \in K$. Therefore we may also assume that $r(0) = 0$. Then

$$\bar{r} \in K \Leftrightarrow \bar{r} = 0;$$

and the field polynomial $H(y, T)$ of $\bar{r}$ relative to the field extension $\mathfrak{L}/\mathfrak{K}$ is a distinguished polynomial of degree d in T with coefficients in S. Now $H(y, T)$ is a power of the minimal monic polynomial $h(y, T)$ of $\bar{r}$ over $\mathfrak{K}$, and $h(y, T)$ is irreducible in $\mathfrak{K}[T]$. Therefore

$$\bar{r} = 0 \Leftrightarrow h(y, 0) = 0 \Leftrightarrow H(y, 0) = 0.$$

This proves 1). Now assume that $H(y, 0) \neq 0$. By (32.3) there exists $q'' \geqq q'$ such that the coefficients of $H(y, T)$ are convergent in $Y_{q''}$ and

$$H(b, T) = \prod_{a \in V \cap (b \times Z_{q''})} (T - r(a))^{\mathrm{d}(a, \pi, V)} \qquad \text{for all} \quad b \in Y_{q''}.$$

[7] We know that $\mathfrak{p}'$ is strictly regular relative to S.

Therefore for all $q \geqq q''$ we have

$$\{r(a): a \in V \cap X_q\} = \Omega_q$$

where

$$\Omega_q = \{k \in K: H(b, k) = 0 \text{ for some } b \in Y_q\}.$$

Now $H(y, T)$ is a distinguished polynomial of positive degree in T with coefficients in S and $H(y, 0) \neq 0$. Therefore by (11.4.1) we know that $r(0) = 0$ is an interior point of Ω_q for all $q \geqq q''$. This proves 2).

(**32.6**) Open Map Theorem. *Let $r \in R$ be convergent in $X_{q'}$ for some $q' \geqq q^*$. Assume that $\bar{r} \notin K$. Then there exists $q \geqq q'$ such that the following holds.*

1) *$a \to r(a)$ is an open map of $V \cap X_q$ into K.*

2) *For any $\alpha \in V \cap X_q$ and for any prime ideal $\mathfrak{p}'$ of $\boldsymbol{\sigma}(\mathfrak{i}(\alpha, V, X))$ we have that $\varphi(\boldsymbol{\tau}_\alpha r) \notin K$, where $\boldsymbol{\sigma}: R(\alpha, X) \to R$ is the Taylor isomorphism and $\varphi: R \to R/\mathfrak{p}'$ is the natural epimorphism.*

Proof. In view of (32.5) it suffices to prove 2). Also note that for any $\alpha \in V \cap X_{q'}$ and any prime ideal $\mathfrak{p}'$ of $\boldsymbol{\sigma}(\mathfrak{j}(\alpha, V, X))$, where $\boldsymbol{\sigma}: R(\alpha, X) \to R$ is the Taylor isomorphism, upon letting $\varphi: R \to R/\mathfrak{p}'$ to be the natural epimorphism we obviously have:

$$\varphi(\boldsymbol{\tau}_\alpha(r - r(0))) \in K \Leftrightarrow \varphi(\boldsymbol{\tau}_\alpha r) \in K.$$

Therefore, upon replacing r by $r - r(0)$ we may assume that $r(0) = 0$. Let

$$H(y, T) = \sum_{\nu=0}^{d} H_\nu(y) T^\nu$$

be the field polynomial of $\bar{r}$ relative to the field extension $\mathfrak{L}/\mathfrak{K}$. Then $H(y, T)$ is a distinguished polynomial of degree d in T with coefficients in S. Since $\bar{r} \notin K$, by (32.5.1), $H(y, 0) \neq 0$. Now $H(y, r) \in \mathfrak{p}$ and hence we can find $q \geqq q'$ such that $H_0(y), \dots, H_d(y)$ are convergent in Y_q, and

$$\boldsymbol{\tau}_\alpha H(y, r) \in \{\boldsymbol{\tau}_\alpha u_1, \dots, \boldsymbol{\tau}_\alpha u_\Lambda\} R \qquad \text{for all} \quad \alpha \in V \cap X_q.$$

Now let $\alpha = (\beta, \gamma) \in V \cap (Y_q \times Z_q)$ be given and let $\mathfrak{p}'$ be any prime ideal of $\boldsymbol{\sigma}(\mathfrak{i}(\alpha, V, X))$ where $\boldsymbol{\sigma}: R(\alpha, X) \to R$ is the Taylor isomorphism. Let $\varphi: R \to R/\mathfrak{p}'$ be the natural epimorphism and let $\mathfrak{L}'$ be the quotient field of φR. Let $H'(y, T)$ be the field polynomial of $\varphi[(\boldsymbol{\tau}_\alpha r) - r(\alpha)]$ relative to the field extension $\mathfrak{L}'/\mathfrak{K}$ and let $h'(y, T)$ be the minimal monic polynomial of $\varphi[(\boldsymbol{\tau}_\alpha r) - r(\alpha)]$ over $\mathfrak{K}$. Then $H'(y, T)$ and $h'(y, T)$ are distinguished polynomials in T with coefficients in S and H' is a power of h'. Let

$$H^*(y, T) = \boldsymbol{\tau}_{(\beta, r(\alpha))} H(y, T)$$
$$= \sum_{\nu=0}^{d} [\boldsymbol{\tau}_\beta H_\nu(y)][T + r(\alpha)]^\nu.$$

Then

$$\boldsymbol{\tau}_\alpha H(y, r) = \sum_{\nu=0}^{d} [\boldsymbol{\tau}_\beta H_\nu(y)](\boldsymbol{\tau}_\alpha r)^\nu$$
$$= H^*(y, (\boldsymbol{\tau}_\alpha r) - r(\alpha)).$$

Now

$$\boldsymbol{\tau}_\alpha H(y, r) \in \{\boldsymbol{\tau}_\alpha u_1, \ldots, \boldsymbol{\tau}_\alpha u_\Lambda\} R \subset \mathfrak{p}'$$

and hence

$$H^*(y, \varphi[(\boldsymbol{\tau}_\alpha r) - r(\alpha)]) = 0.$$

Therefore $h'(y, T)$ divides $H^*(y, T)$ in $S[T]$.

Thus $H(y, T)$ is a distinguished polynomial in T with coefficients S which are convergent at β, $H(y, 0) \neq 0$, and $h'(y, T)$ divides $\boldsymbol{\tau}_{(\beta, r(\alpha))} H(y, T)$ in $S[T]$. Therefore by (10.7.7) we conclude that $h'(y, 0) \neq 0$. Since $H'(y, T)$ is a power of $h'(y, T)$ we thus get that $H'(y, 0) \neq 0$. Therefore $\varphi(\boldsymbol{\tau}_\alpha r) \notin K$ by (32.5.1).

(32.7) *Given $m' \leqq m$, let $R' = K[\langle y, z_1, \ldots, z_{m'} \rangle]$ and let $\mathfrak{p}' = \mathfrak{p} \cap R'$. Then $\mathfrak{p}'$ is a prime ideal in R' which is strictly regular relative to S. Let π': $K^e\{y\} \times K^m\{z\} \to K^e\{y\} \times K^{m'}\{z_1, \ldots, z_{m'}\}$ and $\pi^*: K^m\{z\} \to K^{m'}\{z_1, \ldots, z_{m'}\}$ be the natural projections. For any $q \geqq 0$ let $Z'_q = \pi^*(Z_q)$ and $X'_q = \pi'(X_q) = Y_q \times Z'_q$. Let $u'_1, \ldots, u'_{\Lambda'}$ be any finite basis of $\mathfrak{p}'$. Take $q_1 \geqq 0$ such that $u'_1, \ldots, u'_{\Lambda'}$ are convergent in X'_{q_1} and let*

$$V' = \{a' \in X'_{q_1} : u'_1(a') = \ldots = u'_{\Lambda'}(a') = 0\}.$$

Then there exists $q_2 \geqq q_1$ such that $V' \cap X'_{q_2}$ is a pure e dimensional analytic set in X'_{q_2} and such that for all $q \geqq q_2$ we have: $V \cap (Y_q \times Z_{q_2}) = V \cap X_q$, $V' \cap (Y_q \times Z'_{q_2}) = V' \cap X'_q$, and $\pi'(V \cap X_q) = V' \cap X'_q$.

Let $\chi_1, \ldots, \chi_{m'}$ be indeterminates. Then the norm of $(z_1 - \bar{z}_1)\chi_1 + \ldots + (z_{m'} - \bar{z}_{m'})\chi_{m'}$ relative to the field extension

$\mathfrak{L}(z_1,\ldots, z_{m'}, \chi_1,\ldots, \chi_{m'})/\mathfrak{R}(z_1,\ldots, z_{m'}, \chi_1,\ldots, \chi_{m'})$ *is a polynomial*

$$\Theta(y, z_1,\ldots, z_{m'}, \chi_1,\ldots, \chi_{m'}) = \sum_{i_1,\ldots,i_{m'}} \Theta_{i_1\ldots i_{m'}}(y, z_1,\ldots, z_{m'})\chi_1^{i_1}\ldots\chi_{m'}^{i_{m'}}$$

in $\chi_1,\ldots, \chi_{m'}$ *whose coefficients* $\Theta_{i_1\ldots i_{m'}}(y, z_1,\ldots, z_{m'})$ *are polynomials in* $z_1,\ldots, z_{m'}$ *with coefficients in* S, *and there exists* $q_3 \geqq q_2$ *such that all the coefficients of the polynomials* $\Theta_{i_1\ldots i_{m'}}(y, z_1,\ldots, z_{m'})$ *are convergent in* Y_{q_3} *and such that for all* $q \geqq q_3$ *we have*

$$V' \cap X'_q$$
$$= \{(b, c') \in Y_q \times K^{m'}: \Theta_{i_1\ldots i_{m'}}(b, c'_1,\ldots, c'_{m'}) = 0 \text{ for all } i_1,\ldots, i_{m'}\}$$

Proof. Now V' is an analytic set in X'_{q_1}. Obviously $\mathfrak{p}'$ is a prime ideal in R' and hence $\gamma_{(0)}V'$ is irreducible. By (23.3) it follows that $\mathfrak{p}'$ is strictly regular relative to S and hence in particular $\dim_{(0)}V' = \dim R'/\mathfrak{p}' = e$. Now $u'_1,\ldots, u'_{\Lambda'} \in \mathfrak{p}' \subset \mathfrak{p}$ and hence there exists $q' \geqq q_1$ such that $\pi'(V \cap X_{q'}) \subset V' \cap X'_{q'}$.

Upon taking $\rho = \sigma = m'$, $r_i = z_i$, $v(y, \Gamma_1,\ldots, \Gamma_{m'}, \chi_1,\ldots, \chi_{m'}) = \Gamma_1\chi_1 + \ldots + \Gamma_{m'}\chi_{m'}$, and writing z_i for T_i in (32.4), we find $q'' \geqq \max(q', q^*)$ such that: the coefficients of the polynomials $\Theta_{i_1\ldots i_{m'}}(y, z_1,\ldots, z_{m'})$ are convergent in $Y_{q''}$ and for all $b \in Y_{q''}$ we have

$$\Theta(b, z_1,\ldots, z_{m'}, \chi_1,\ldots, \chi_{m'}) = \prod_{a=(b,c)\in V\cap(b\times Z_{q''})} \left(\sum_{i=1}^{m'} (z_i - c_i)\chi_i\right)^{\mathbf{d}(a,\pi,V)}$$

For any $(b, c') \in Y_{q''} \times K^{m'}$ we thus get:

$$\begin{aligned}&\Theta_{i_1\ldots i_{m'}}(b, c'_1,\ldots, c'_{m'}) = 0 \text{ for all } i_1,\ldots, i_{m'}\\ \Leftrightarrow\ &\Theta(b, c'_1,\ldots, c'_{m'}, \chi_1,\ldots, \chi_{m'}) = 0\\ \Leftrightarrow\ &\prod_{a=(b,c)\in V\cap(b\times Z_{q''})} \left(\sum_{i=1}^{m'} (c'_i - c_i)\chi_i\right)^{\mathbf{d}(a,\pi,V)} = 0\\ \Leftrightarrow\ &(b, c') = \pi'(b, c) \text{ for some } (b, c) \in V \cap (b \times Z_{q''}).\end{aligned}$$

Therefore for all $q \geqq q''$ we have:

$$\pi'(V \cap X_q)$$
$$= \{(b, c') \in Y_q \times K^{m'}: \Theta_{i_1\ldots i_{m'}}(b, c'_1,\ldots, c'_{m'}) = 0 \text{ for all } i_1,\ldots, i_{m'}\},$$

and hence in particular $\pi'(V \cap X_{q''})$ is an analytic set in $X'_{q''}$. Let $\tilde{\pi}: K^e\{y\} \times K^{m'}\{z_1,\ldots, z_{m'}\} \to K^e\{y\}$ be the natural projection. Then by (32.1), for any $a' \in \pi'(V \cap X_{q''})$ we have that: a' is an isolated point of $\pi'(V \cap X_{q''}) \cap \tilde{\pi}^{-1}(\tilde{\pi}a')$, and the map $\tilde{\pi}|\pi'(V \cap X_{q''})$ of $\pi'(V \cap X_{q''})$

into $K^e\{y\}$ is open at a'; whence $\dim_{a'}\pi'(V \cap X_{q''}) = e$ by (23.3). Thus $\pi'(V \cap X_{q''})$ is a pure e dimensional analytic set in $X'_{q''}$. Hence in particular $\gamma_{(0)}\pi'(V \cap X_{q''})$ is pure e dimensional. Now $\gamma_{(0)}\pi'(V \cap X_{q''}) \subset \gamma_{(0)}V'$ and $\gamma_{(0)}V'$ is an irreducible e dimensional analytic set germ. Therefore we must have $\gamma_{(0)}\pi'(V \cap X_{q''}) = \gamma_{(0)}V'$, i.e., there exists $q_2 = q_3 \geqq q''$ such that $\pi'(V \cap X_{q''}) \cap X'_{q_2} = V' \cap X'_{q_2}$. Now $q_2 \geqq q'' \geqq q^*$ and hence by (32.1.1) for all $q \geqq q_2$ we have:

$$V \cap (Y_q \times Z_{q''}) = V \cap (Y_q \times Z_{q_2}) = V \cap X_q$$

and hence

$$\pi'(V \cap X_q) = V' \cap X'_q = V' \cap (Y_q \times Z'_{q_2}).$$

REMARK. (32.7) could have already been proved at the time when we proved (31.15). To indicate this let the notation be as in §31. Let $\bar{V}'$ be the closure of $\pi'(\mathring{V})$ in $Y \times K^{m'}$. By (31.4, 31.7), for all $q \geqq q_0$ we get:

$$\bar{V}' \cap (Y_q \times K^{m'}) = \bar{V}' \cap \pi'(X_q) = \pi'(\bar{V} \cap X_q) \subset \pi'(V \cap X_q).$$

Consequently by (31.14.4) we get the following modification of (31.14.4): for any $\gamma' \in K^{m'}$ we have that $(\beta, \gamma') \in \bar{V}' \Leftrightarrow \gamma' = (\gamma_1^{(\theta)}, \ldots, \gamma_{m'}^{(\theta)})$ for some $\theta \leqq N^*$. Upon replacing m by m' in the proof of (31.15) and using the above modification instead of (31.14.4), we can find $q'' \geqq q'$ such that for all $q \geqq q''$ we have:

$$\bar{V}' \cap X'_q$$
$$= \{(b, c') \in Y_q \times K^{m'} : \Theta_{i_1 \ldots i_{m'}}(b, c'_1, \ldots, c'_{m'}) = 0 \text{ for all } i_1, \ldots, i_{m'}\}.$$

Therefore $\bar{V}' \cap X'_{q''}$ is analytic in $X'_{q''}$. Let $\tilde{\pi}: K^e\{y\} \times K^{m'}\{z_1, \ldots, z_{m'}\} \to K^e\{y\}$ be the natural projection. By (31.4, 31.11), for any $a' \in \bar{V}' \cap (\mathring{Y}_{q''} \times Z'_{q''})$ we get: a' is an isolated point of $\bar{V}' \cap \tilde{\pi}^{-1}(\tilde{\pi}a')$, and the map $\tilde{\pi}|\bar{V}'$ of $\bar{V}'$ into $K^e\{y\}$ is open at a'; whence $\dim_{a'}\bar{V}' = e$ by (23.3). Therefore $\bar{V}' \cap X'_{q''}$ is pure e dimensional by (30.17). Now $\gamma_{(0)}\bar{V}' \subset \gamma_{(0)}\pi'(V) \subset \gamma_{(0)}V'$, and $\gamma_{(0)}V'$ is an irreducible e dimensional analytic set germ. Therefore $\gamma_{(0)}\bar{V}' = \gamma_{(0)}\pi'(V) = \gamma_{(0)}V'$.

§33. LOCAL PROPERTIES OF ANALYTIC SETS

§33A. *General properties*

Let V be an analytic set in an open set X in K^n. Let $a \in V$.

(33.1) 1) $\dim_a V = \min e$ *such that there exist e analytic functions* $F_1, \ldots, F_e$ *on a neighborhood* X^* *of a in X for which a is an isolated point of*

$$V \cap \{b \in X^*: F_1(b) = \ldots = F_e(b) = 0\};$$

or equivalently, $\dim_a V = \min e$ *such that there exist e elements* $f_1, \ldots, f_e$ *in* $R(a, X)$ *for which* $\{f_1, \ldots, f_e, \mathfrak{i}(a, V, X)\}R(a, X)$ *is primary for the maximal ideal in* $R(a, X)$.

2) $\dim_a V = \min e$ *such that there exists an* $n - e$ *dimensional linear subspace L of* K^n *for which a is an isolated point of* $V \cap L$.

3) $\gamma_a V$ *is pure* $n - 1$ *dimensional* $\Leftrightarrow \mathfrak{i}(a, V, X)$ *is a nonzero principal ideal in* $R(a, X) \Leftrightarrow$ *there exists an analytic function F on a neighborhood* X^* *of a in X such that* $\gamma_a F \neq 0$ *and* $V \cap X^* = \{b \in X^*: F(b) = 0\}$.

1) and 2) follow from (17.2) and (23.5). Since $R(a, X)$ is a unique factorization domain, 3) follows from (21.5.2).

(33.2) *There exists a neighborhood* X^* *of a in X such that* $\dim_b V \leqq \dim_a V$ *for all* $b \in V \cap X^*$.

Follows from (26.2).

(33.3) *If V is pure e dimensional at a then V is pure e dimensional in some neighborhood* X^* *of a in X.*

Remark. Recall the following. V is pure e dimensional at $a \Leftrightarrow$ (def) $\gamma_a V$ is pure e dimensional $\Leftrightarrow$ (def) every irreducible component of $\gamma_a V$ is e dimensional. V is pure e dimensional in $X^* \Leftrightarrow$ (def) $\dim_b V = e$ for all $b \in V \cap X^* \Leftrightarrow$ (by 30.17) $\gamma_b V$ is pure e dimensional for all $b \in V \cap X^*$.

Proof. Take analytic sets $V_1, \ldots, V_\lambda$ in a neighborhood X' of a in X such that $\gamma_a V_1 \cup \ldots \cup \gamma_a V_\lambda$ is the normal decomposition of $\gamma_a V$ and $V \cap X' = V_1 \cup \ldots \cup V_\lambda$. Applying (32.1) to $\gamma_a V_i$ we can find a neighborhood X_i of a in X' such that $\dim_b V_i = e$ for all $b \in V_i \cap X_i$. Take $X^* = X_1 \cap \ldots \cap X_\lambda$.

(33.4) *Suppose* $\gamma_a V$ *has an irreducible component* V' *of dimension e. Then given any neighborhood* X' *of a in X there exists a nonempty open subset* X^* *of* X' *such that* $V \cap X^*$ *is pure e dimensional, (whence in particular* $V \cap X^* \neq \emptyset$).

Proof. Let V'' be the union of all the irreducible components of V different from V'. Take analytic sets V_1' and V_1'' in a neighborhood X_1 of a in X' such that $V \cap X_1 = V_1' \cup V_1''$, $\gamma_a V_1' = V'$, $\gamma_a V_1'' = V''$. By (33.3) we can find a neighborhood X_2 of a in X_1 such that V_1' is pure e dimensional in X_2. Now $\gamma_a(V_1' \cap V_1'') \underset{\neq}{\subset} \gamma_a(V_1')$ and hence there exists $b \in V_1' \cap X_2$ such that $\gamma_b V_1' = \gamma_b V$. Take X^* to be a neighborhood of b in X_2 such that $V_1' \cap X^* = V \cap X^*$.

(**33.5**) *Let $V_1, \ldots, V_\lambda$ be any finite number of analytic sets in X such that $V = V_1 \cup \ldots \cup V_\lambda$. Let $b \in X$ and let V^* be an irreducible component of $\gamma_b V$. Then V^* is an irreducible component of $\gamma_b V_i$ for some i.*
Obvious.

(**33.6**) *Assume that $\gamma_a V$ is irreducible and let W be any analytic set in X. Then we have the following.*

1) $\gamma_a V \subset \gamma_a W \Leftrightarrow \gamma_a V \subset W'$ *for some irreducible component W' of $\gamma_a W$.*

2) *If $\gamma_a W \underset{\neq}{\subset} \gamma_a V$, then there exists a neighborhood X^* of a in X such that $W \cap X^* \subset V \cap X^*$ and such that for each $b \in X^*$ and for each irreducible component V^* of $\gamma_b V$ we have $V^* \not\subset \gamma_b W$.*

3) *If $\gamma_a V \not\subset \gamma_a W$, then there exists a neighborhood X^* of a in X such that for each $b \in X^*$ and for each irreducible component V^* of $\gamma_b V$ we have $V^* \not\subset \gamma_b W$.*

4) *If $\gamma_a W$ is pure $n - 1$ dimensional and $\gamma_a V \not\subset \gamma_a W$ then $\gamma_a(V \cap W)$ is pure $e - 1$ dimensional where $e = \dim_a V$.*
1) is obvious.

Proof of 2). Assertion being trivial if $a \notin W$, assume that $a \in W$. Then $\dim_a W < \dim_a V$. By (33.2, 33.3) we can find a neighborhood X^* of a in X such that $\dim(W \cap X^*) \leqq \dim_a W$ and $V \cap X^*$ is pure e dimensional where $e = \dim_a V$.

Proof of 3). Now $\gamma_a(W \cap V) \underset{\neq}{\subset} \gamma_a V$ and hence by 2) we can find a neighborhood X^* of a in X such that for each $b \in X^*$ and for each irreducible component V^* of $\gamma_b V$ we have $V^* \not\subset \gamma_b(W \cap V)$; and then obviously $V^* \not\subset \gamma_b W$.

Proof of 4). Follows from (19.15, 23.8, 33.1.3).

(**33.7**) *Let W be any analytic set in X. Assume that for each irreducible component V' of $\gamma_a V$ and for each irreducible component W' of $\gamma_a W$ we have $V' \not\subset W'$.*[1] *Then there exists a neighborhood X^* of a in X such that for any $b \in X^*$ and for any irreducible component V^* of $\gamma_b V$ we have $V^* \not\subset \gamma_b W$ and hence a fortiori $V^* \not\subset W^*$ for each irreducible component W^* of $\gamma_b W$.*

Proof. Take analytic sets $V_1, \ldots, V_\lambda$ in a neighborhood X' of a in X such that $\gamma_a V_1 \cup \ldots \cup \gamma_a V_\lambda$ is the normal decomposition of $\gamma_a V$ and

[1] By (33.6.1) this is equivalent to assuming that $V' \not\subset \gamma_a W$ for each irreducible component V' of $\gamma_a V$.

$V \cap X' = V_1 \cup \ldots \cup V_\lambda$. By (33.6.3) we can find a neighborhood X_i of a in X' such that for each $b \in X_i$ and for each irreducible component V^* of $\gamma_b V_i$ we have $V^* \not\subset \gamma_b W$. Take $X^* = X_1 \cap \ldots \cap X_\lambda$ and invoke (33.5).

(33.8) *For any analytic set W in X the following five conditions are equivalent.*

i) $\dim_b(W \cap V) < \dim_b V$ *for all* $b \in V$.
ii) *For each* $b \in X$ *and for each irreducible component* V^* *of* $\gamma_b V$ *we have* $V^* \not\subset \gamma_b W$.
iii) $W \cap V$ *is nowhere dense in* V.
iv) $W \cap V$ *is a thin subset of* V.[2]
v) $V - W$ *is everywhere dense in* V.

Furthermore, if V is pure e dimensional and W is pure $n - 1$ dimensional, then any one of the above conditions implies that $W \cap V$ is either empty or pure $e - 1$ dimensional.

Proof of v) $\Rightarrow$ ii). Let if possible $b \in V$ and an irreducible component V^* of $\gamma_b V$ be such that $V^* \subset \gamma_b W$. Let V' be the union of the remaining irreducible components of $\gamma_b V$. We can find a neighborhood X^* of b in X and analytic sets $\tilde{V}^*$ and $\tilde{V}'$ in X^* such that $V \cap X^* = \tilde{V}^* \cup \tilde{V}'$, $\gamma_b \tilde{V}^* = V^*$, $\gamma_b \tilde{V}' = V'$, and $\tilde{V}^* \subset W \cap X^*$. Now $V^* \not\subset V'$ and hence there exists $\beta \in \tilde{V}^*$ such that $\beta \notin \tilde{V}'$, i.e., $\gamma_\beta \tilde{V}^* = \gamma_\beta V$, and hence $\gamma_\beta V \subset \gamma_\beta W$. Consequently there exists a neighborhood X' of β in X such that $V \cap X' \subset W \cap X'$. Now $(V - W) \cap X' = \emptyset$ and hence $\beta \notin \mathrm{cl}_V(V - W)$. Contradiction.

Proof of ii) $\Rightarrow$ i). Let if possible $b \in V$ be such that $\dim_b(W \cap V) = \dim_b V$. Then there exists an irreducible component V^* of $\gamma_b V$ and an irreducible component U^* of $W \cap V$ such that $V^* = U^*$. Consequently $V^* \subset \gamma_b W$. Contradiction.

Proof of i) $\Rightarrow$ iii). Let X^* be any open subset of X such that $V \cap X^* \neq \emptyset$. Take $b \in V \cap X^*$. By assumption $\dim_b(W \cap V) < \dim_b V$ and hence $\gamma_b(W \cap V) \underset{\neq}{\subset} \gamma_b V$. Therefore there exists $\beta \in V \cap X^*$ such that $\beta \notin W$. Since W is closed in X, there exists a neighborhood X' of β in X^* such that $X' \cap W = \emptyset$.

i) $\Leftrightarrow$ iv) and iii) $\Rightarrow$ v) are obvious. The final assertion in (33.8) follows from (33.6.4) by using condition ii).

[2] For the definition of a thin subset see (30.16.3).

(**33.9**) *Let W be any analytic set in X such that $W \cap V$ is nowhere dense in V. Let any $b \in V$, any irreducible component V^* of $\gamma_b V$, and any neighborhood X^* of b in X be given. Then there exists $\beta \in V \cap X^*$ such that $\beta \notin W$ and* $\dim_\beta V = \dim V^*$.

Follows from (33.4).

(**33.10**) *Let W be any thin subset of V. Then W is nowhere dense in V. Let any $b \in V$, any irreducible component V^* of $\gamma_b V$, and any neighborhood X^* of b in X be given; then there exists $\beta \in V \cap X^*$ such that $\beta \notin W$ and* $\dim_\beta V = \dim V^*$.

Follows from (33.8, 33.9).

(**33.11**) *Let $V_1, \ldots, V_\lambda$ be analytic sets in X such that $\gamma_a V_1 \cup \ldots \cup \gamma_a V_\lambda$ is the normal decomposition of $\gamma_a V$. Then there exists a neighborhood X^* of a in X such that for all $b \in V \cap X^*$ we have the following.*

i) *Let $V^*_{i1} \cup \ldots \cup V^*_{ip_i}$ be the normal decomposition of $\gamma_b V_i$ for $i = 1, \ldots, \lambda$. Then*

$$V^*_{11} \cup \ldots \cup V^*_{1p_1} \cup V^*_{21} \cup \ldots \cup V^*_{2p_2} \cup \ldots \cup V^*_{\lambda p_\lambda}$$

is the normal decomposition of $\gamma_b V$.

ii) *For all i, ν we have $V^*_{i\nu} \not\subset \gamma_b[\bigcup_{j \neq j'} (V_j \cap V_{j'})]$; and hence in particular* $\dim_b[\bigcup_{j \neq j'} (V_j \cap V_{j'})] < \dim_b V$.

Proof. Follows from (33.5, 33.7) in view of the fact that $\gamma_a V_i \not\subset \gamma_a V_{i'}$ for all $i \neq i'$, and $\gamma_a V_i \not\subset \gamma_a[\bigcup_{j \neq j'} (V_j \cap V_{j'})]$ for all i.

(**33.12**)[3] *Let W be any analytic set in X such that $V \subset W$. Let $V'_1, \ldots, V'_\lambda$ be the irreducible components of $\gamma_a V$. Let $W'_1, \ldots, W'_\mu$ be the irreducible components of $\gamma_a W$ labeled so that for $j \leq k$: $V'_i \subset W'_j$ for some i (depending on j), and for $j > k$: $V'_i \not\subset W'_j$ for $i = 1, \ldots, \lambda$. Let $W' = W'_1 \cup \ldots \cup W'_k$ and $W'' = W'_{k+1} \cup \ldots \cup W'_\mu$. Then we have the following.*

1)
$$\mathfrak{j}_{R(a,W)}[\mathfrak{i}(a, V, W)] = \bigcap_{i=1}^{\lambda} \mathfrak{j}_{R(a,W)}[\mathfrak{i}(a, V'_i, W)] = \mathfrak{i}(a, W', W).$$

[3] For the definitions of $\mathfrak{i}(a, V, X)$, $R(a, V, X)$, $\mathfrak{C}(a, V)$, etc., see (29.3, 29.4).

2) *Let* $f \in R(W)$ *be such that* $\gamma_a f \in \mathfrak{j}_{R(a,W)}[\mathfrak{i}(a, V, W)]$. *Then there exists a neighborhood* X^* *of* a *in* X *such that for all* $b \in V \cap X^*$ *we have*: $\gamma_b f \in \mathfrak{j}_{R(b,W)}[\mathfrak{i}(b, V, W)]$ *or equivalently* $\gamma_b f \in \mathfrak{j}_{R(b,W)}[\mathfrak{i}(b, V^*, W)]$ *for each irreducible component* V^* *of* $\gamma_b V$.

Proof of 1). Now

$$\{0\} = \bigcap_{j=1}^{\mu} \mathfrak{i}(a, W'_j, W) \qquad \text{and} \qquad \mathfrak{i}(a, V, W) = \bigcap_{i=1}^{\lambda} \mathfrak{i}(a, V'_i, W)$$

are normal decompositions in $R(a, W)$; $\mathfrak{i}(a, V'_1, W), \ldots, \mathfrak{i}(a, V'_\lambda, W)$ are prime ideals in $R(a, W)$; for $j \leqq k$: $\mathfrak{i}(a, W'_j, W) \subset \mathfrak{i}(a, V'_i, W)$ for some i; and for $j > k$: $\mathfrak{i}(a, W'_j, W) \not\subset \mathfrak{i}(a, V'_i, W)$ for $i = 1, \ldots, \lambda$. Therefore from the definition[4] of $\mathfrak{j}$ we get that

$$\begin{aligned} \mathfrak{j}_{R(a,W)}[\mathfrak{i}(a, V, W)] &= \bigcap_{i=1}^{\lambda} \mathfrak{j}_{R(a,W)}[\mathfrak{i}(a, V'_i, W)] \\ &= \bigcap_{j=1}^{k} \mathfrak{i}(a, W'_j, W) \\ &= \mathfrak{i}(a, W', W). \end{aligned}$$

Proof of 2). Take analytic sets $\tilde{W}'$ and $\tilde{W}''$ in a neighborhood $\tilde{X}$ of a in X such that $W \cap \tilde{X} = \tilde{W}' \cup \tilde{W}''$, $\gamma_a \tilde{W}' = W'$, $\gamma_a \tilde{W}'' = W''$. By 1), $\gamma_a f \in \mathfrak{i}(a, \tilde{W}', W)$ and hence $\gamma_b f \in \mathfrak{i}(b, \tilde{W}', W)$ for all $b \in W \cap \hat{X}$ where $\hat{X}$ is some neighborhood of a in $\tilde{X}$. Now $V'_i \not\subset W'_j$ for all $i \leqq \lambda$ and $j > k$, and hence by (33.7) there exists a neighborhood X^* of a in $\hat{X}$ such that for each $b \in V \cap X^*$ and each irreducible component V^* of $\gamma_b V$ we have $V^* \not\subset \gamma_b \tilde{W}''$. Now $\gamma_b W = \gamma_b \tilde{W}' \cup \gamma_b \tilde{W}''$, and hence if $V^* \subset W^*$ for some irreducible component W^* of $\gamma_b W$ then W^* must be an irreducible component of $\gamma_b \tilde{W}'$. Therefore by 1) we get that

$$\mathfrak{i}(b, \tilde{W}', W) \subset \mathfrak{j}_{R(b,W)}[\mathfrak{i}(b, V^*, W)]$$

and hence

$$\gamma_b f \in \mathfrak{j}_{R(b,W)}[\mathfrak{i}(b, V^*, W)].$$

This being so for each irreducible component V^* of $\gamma_b V$, by 1) we also get that

$$\gamma_b f \in \mathfrak{j}_{R(b,W)}[\mathfrak{i}(b, V, W)].$$

[4] See (18.7.8).

(33.13)[3] *For* $f \in R(V)$ *let* $W = \{b \in V : f(b) = 0\}$. *Then we have the following.*

1) *The following four conditions are equivalent.*

i) $\gamma_a f$ *is a nonzerodivisor in* $R(a, V)$.
ii) $\gamma_a f \notin \mathfrak{i}(a, V', V)$ *for each irreducible component* V' *of* $\gamma_a V$.
iii) $V' \not\subset \gamma_a W$ *for each irreducible component* V' *of* $\gamma_a V$.
iv) *There exists a neighborhood* V^* *of* a *in* V *such that* $W \cap V^*$ *is nowhere dense in* V^*.

2) *If* $\gamma_a f$ *is a nonzerodivisor in* $R(a, V)$ *then* $\gamma_b f$ *is a nonzerodivisor in* $R(b, V)$ *for all* b *in some neighborhood of* a *in* V.

PROOF. i) $\Leftrightarrow$ ii) $\Leftrightarrow$ iii) is obvious. iii) $\Leftrightarrow$ iv) follows from (33.7, 33.8). 2) follows from 1).

(33.14)[3] *Any element in* $R(a, V)$ *which is a nonzerodivisor in* $R(a, V)$ *remains a nonzerodivisor in* $\mathfrak{C}(a, V)$ *and hence the total quotient ring of* $R(a, V)$ *can be considered to be a subring of the total quotient ring of* $\mathfrak{C}(a, V)$.

PROOF. Let $f \in R(V_1)$ be given such that $\gamma_a f$ is a nonzerodivisor in $R(a, V)$ where V_1 is a neighborhood of a in V. Let $W = \{b \in V_1 : f(b) = 0\}$. By (33.13) there exists a neighborhood V_2 of a in V_1 such that $W \cap V_2$ is nowhere dense in V_2. Let V_3 be any neighborhood of a in V_2 and $g \in \mathfrak{C}(V_3)$ be such that $f(b)g(b) = 0$ for all $b \in V_3$. Then $g(b) = 0$ for all $b \in V_3 - W$ and hence $g(b) = 0$ for all $b \in V_3$. Therefore $\gamma_a g = 0$.

(33.15)[3] OPEN MAP THEOREM. *For any* $f \in R(V)$ *we have the following.*

1) $\gamma_a f$ *is nonconstant*[5] $\Leftrightarrow \gamma_a(f - f(a)) \neq 0 \Leftrightarrow$ *the map* $f: V \to K$ *is open at* a.

2) $(\gamma_a f)|V'$ *is nonconstant*[6] *for each irreducible component* V' *of* $\gamma_a V \Leftrightarrow$ $\gamma_a(f - f(a))$ *is a nonzerodivisor in* $R(a, V)$.

3) $\gamma_b(f - f(b))$ *is a nonzerodivisor in* $R(b, V)$ *for all* $b \in V \Leftrightarrow$ *the map* $f: V \to K$ *is open.*

4) $\gamma_a(f - f(a))$ *is a nonzerodivisor in* $R(a, V) \Leftrightarrow$ *the map* $f|V^*: V^* \to K$ *is open for some neighborhood* V^* *of* a *in* V.

[5] That is, in every neighborhood of a in V, f takes at least two distinct values.
[6] That is, if $\tilde{V}$ is a representative of V' then $\gamma_a(f|\tilde{V})$ is nonconstant.

Take analytic sets $V_1, \ldots, V_\lambda$ in a neighborhood X' of a in X such that $\gamma_a V_1 \cup \ldots \cup \gamma_a V_\lambda$ is the normal decomposition of $\gamma_a V$ and $V \cap X' = V_1 \cup \ldots \cup V_\lambda$.

Proof of 1). Obviously, $\gamma_a f$ is nonconstant $\Leftrightarrow \gamma_a(f - f(a)) \neq 0$; and if f is open at a then it is nonconstant in the neighborhood of a.[7] Now suppose that $\gamma_a(f - f(a)) \neq 0$. Then $\gamma_a(f - f(a)) \notin \mathfrak{i}(a, V_i, V)$ for some i. By (32.6), $f | V_i \colon V_i \to K$ is open at a, i.e., for every neighborhood X^* of a in X', $f(a)$ is an interior point of $f(V_i \cap X^*)$; whence *a fortiori* $f(a)$ is an interior point of $f(V \cap X^*)$. Therefore f is open at a.

Proof of 2). Follows from 1) and (33.13.1).

Proof of 3). "$\Rightarrow$" follows from 1). To prove "$\Leftarrow$" let $b \in V$ be given. Take analytic sets $\tilde{V}_1, \ldots, \tilde{V}_\mu$ in a neighborhood $\tilde{X}$ of b in X such that $\gamma_b \tilde{V}_1 \cup \ldots \cup \gamma_b \tilde{V}_\mu$ is the normal decomposition of $\gamma_b V$ and $V \cap \tilde{X} = \tilde{V}_1 \cup \ldots \cup \tilde{V}_\mu$. Suppose if possible that $\gamma_b(f - f(b))$ is a zerodivisor in $R(b, V)$. Then by 2), $\gamma_b(f | \tilde{V}_i)$ is constant for some i, i.e., there exists a neighborhood $\hat{X}$ of b in $\tilde{X}$ such that $f | (\tilde{V}_i \cap \hat{X}) = f(b)$. Now $\gamma_b \tilde{V}_i \not\subset \bigcup_{j \neq i} \gamma_b \tilde{V}_j$ and hence there exists $\beta \in \tilde{V}_i \cap \hat{X}$ such that $\beta \notin \bigcup_{j \neq i} \tilde{V}_j$, and then $f \equiv f(b)$ in some neighborhood of β in V. Contradiction to f being open at β.

Proof of 4). "$\Leftarrow$" follows from 3). Now assume that $\gamma_a(f - f(a))$ is a nonzerodivisor in $R(a, V)$. Then by 1) and 2), we have $\gamma_a(f - f(a)) \notin \mathfrak{i}(a, V_i, V)$ for $i = 1, \ldots, \lambda$. Applying (32.6) to $\gamma_a V_i$ we can find a neighborhood X_i of a in X' such that $f | (V_i \cap X_i) \colon V_i \cap X_i \to K$ is open. Take $V^* = V \cap X_1 \cap \ldots \cap X_\lambda$.

§33B. *The singular locus*[8]

Let V be an analytic set in an open set X in $K^n\{x_1, \ldots, x_n\}$.

(33.16) *Let $a \in V$ and let $V_1, \ldots, V_\lambda$ be analytic sets in X such that $\gamma_a V_1 \cup \ldots \cup \gamma_a V_\lambda$ is the normal decomposition of $\gamma_a V$ and $V = V_1 \cup \ldots \cup V_\lambda$. Then*

$$\mathbf{S}(\gamma_a V) = \left[\bigcup_{i=1,\ldots,\lambda} \mathbf{S}(\gamma_a V_i)\right] \cup \left[\bigcup_{\substack{j,j'=1,\ldots,\lambda \\ j \neq j'}} (\gamma_a V_j \cap \gamma_a V_{j'})\right]$$

[7] Because K is nondiscrete.

[8] For the definitions of $\mathbf{S}(V)$ and $\mathbf{S}(\gamma_a V)$ see (30.16.4). For the definitions and basic properties of derivatives, Jacobians, and bianalytic maps see §2C, (10.9 to 10.14) and (21.11).

or equivalently, there exists a neighborhood X^* of a in X such that

$$\mathbf{S}(V \cap X^*) = \left[\bigcup_{i=1,\dots,\lambda} \mathbf{S}(V_i \cap X^*)\right] \cup \left[\bigcup_{\substack{j,j'=1,\dots,\lambda \\ j\neq j'}} (V_j \cap V_{j'} \cap X^*)\right].$$

PROOF. Take X^* to be a neighborhood of a in X such that (33.11.i) holds for all $b \in X^*$. Then for any $b \in \bigcup_{j\neq j'}(V_j \cap V_{j'} \cap X^*)$, $\gamma_b V$ is reducible and hence $b \in \mathbf{S}(V)$. For any $b \in (V \cap X^*) - \bigcup_{j\neq j'}(V_j \cap V_{j'} \cap X^*)$, $\gamma_b V = \gamma_b V_i$ for a unique value of i and then $b \in \mathbf{S}(V) \Leftrightarrow b \in \mathbf{S}(V_i)$.

(**33.17**) *Let $a \in X$ and let $g_1,\dots, g_m$ be analytic functions on a neighborhood X' of a in X such that $g_1(a) = \dots = g_m(a) = 0$. Let $W = \{b \in X' : g_1(b) = \dots = g_m(b) = 0\}$, and let $\mathfrak{a} = \{\gamma_a g_1,\dots, \gamma_a g_m\}R(a, X)$. Then we have the following.*

1)
$$\operatorname{rnk} \frac{J(g_1,\dots, g_m)}{J(x_1,\dots, x_n)}(a) = \operatorname{rnk}_{R(a,X)} \mathfrak{a}$$
$$\leqq n - \dim_a W$$

and equality holds if and only if $R/\mathfrak{a}$ is regular.

2) *If*
$$\operatorname{rnk} \frac{J(g_1,\dots, g_m)}{J(x_1,\dots, x_n)}(a) = m$$

then we have the following: $m = n - \dim_a W$; $\mathfrak{a} = \mathfrak{i}(a, W, X)$; $R(a, W)$ is regular and is isomorphic to the convergent power series ring in $n - m$ variables over K; and there exists a bianalytic map h of a neighborhood $\tilde{X}$ of a in X' onto a neighborhood $\tilde{Y}$ of the origin in $K^n\{y_1,\dots, y_n\}$ such that $h(a)$ is at the origin in $\tilde{Y}$ and

$$h(W \cap \tilde{X}) = \{(\beta_1,\dots, \beta_n) \in \tilde{Y} : \beta_1 = \dots = \beta_m = 0\}.$$

PROOF. By the Nullstellensatz we know that $\dim R/\mathfrak{a} = \dim_a W$ and that, if $R/\mathfrak{a}$ is regular then $\mathfrak{a} = \mathfrak{i}(a, W, X)$. Upon replacing $g_1,\dots, g_m$ by their Taylor expansions around a, everything else follows from (10.11, 10.12, 21.11).

(**33.18**) *For $a \in V$ let $e = \dim_a V$ and $m = n - e$. Then the following five conditions are equivalent.*

i) *a is a simple point of V, i.e., $R(a, V)$ is regular.*
ii) $\operatorname{rnk}_{R(a,X)} \mathfrak{i}(a, V, X) = m$.

iii) *There exist m analytic functions* $g_1, \ldots, g_m$ *on a neighborhood of a in X such that* $\gamma_a g_1, \ldots, \gamma_a g_m \in \mathfrak{i}(a, V, X)$ *and*

$$\operatorname{rnk} \frac{J(g_1, \ldots, g_m)}{J(x_1, \ldots, x_n)}(a) = m;$$

[and then we automatically have that $\{\gamma_a g_1, \ldots, \gamma_a g_m\} R(a, X) = \mathfrak{i}(a, V, X)$].[9]

iv) $R(a, V)$ *is isomorphic to the convergent power series ring in e variables over K.*

v) *There exists a bianalytic map h of a neighborhood* $\tilde{X}$ *of a in X onto a neighborhood* $\tilde{Y}$ *of the origin in* $K^n\{y_1, \ldots, y_n\}$ *such that* $h(a)$ *is at the origin in* $\tilde{Y}$ *and*

$$h(V \cap \tilde{X}) = \{(\beta_1, \ldots, \beta_n) \in \tilde{Y} : \beta_1 = \ldots = \beta_m = 0\}.$$

PROOF. By (33.17.1) it follows that i) $\Leftrightarrow$ ii) and iii) $\Rightarrow$ ii). Obviously v) $\Rightarrow$ iv) and iv) $\Rightarrow$ i). Thus it remains to show that ii) implies iii) and v). So assume ii). Take analytic functions $g_1, \ldots, g_q$ on a neighborhood of a in X such that $\{\gamma_a g_1, \ldots, \gamma_a g_q\} R(a, X) = \mathfrak{i}(a, V, X)$. By (33.17.1),

$$\operatorname{rnk} \frac{J(g_1, \ldots, g_q)}{J(x_1, \ldots, x_n)}(a) = \operatorname{rnk}_{R(a,X)} \mathfrak{i}(a, V, X) = m.$$

Upon relabeling $g_1, \ldots, g_q$ we can arrange that

$$\operatorname{rnk} \frac{J(g_1, \ldots, g_m)}{J(x_1, \ldots, x_n)}(a) = m.$$

Let $\mathfrak{a} = \{\gamma_a g_1, \ldots, \gamma_a g_m\} R(a, X)$. Then by (33.17.2), $\mathfrak{a}$ is a prime ideal in $R(a, X)$ and $\dim R(a, X)/\mathfrak{a} = e$. Now $\mathfrak{a} \subset \mathfrak{i}(a, V, X)$, $\dim R(a, X)/\mathfrak{i}(a, V, X) = e$, and $\mathfrak{i}(a, V, X)$ is an intersection of prime ideals. Therefore we must have $\mathfrak{a} = \mathfrak{i}(a, V, X)$. By (33.17.2) it now follows that v) holds.

(**33.19**) *For* $a \in V$ *let* $e = \dim_a V$. *Assume that* $\gamma_a V$ *is pure e dimensional. Also assume that there exists a finite number of analytic functions* $g_1, \ldots, g_q$ *on a neighborhood* X' *of a in X such that* $\mathfrak{i}(b, V, X) = \{\gamma_b g_1, \ldots, \gamma_b g_q\} R(b, X)$ *for all* $b \in X'$. *Then there exists a neighborhood* X^* *of a in* X' *such that*

$$\mathbf{S}(V) \cap X^* = \left\{ b \in V \cap X^* : \operatorname{rnk} \frac{J(g_1, \ldots, g_q)}{J(x_1, \ldots, x_n)}(b) < n - e \right\}$$

and hence $\mathbf{S}(V) \cap X^*$ *is analytic in* X^*.

[9] In asserting the equivalence of the five conditions, statement [ ] is not regarded as part of condition iii).

PROOF. By (33.3) we can find a neighborhood X^* of a in X' such that V is pure e dimensional in X^*. For any $b \in V \cap X^*$, by (33.17.1) we have

$$\operatorname{rnk} \frac{J(g_1, \ldots, g_q)}{J(x_1, \ldots, x_n)}(b) \leqq n - e$$

and by (33.18), equality holds if and only if $b \notin \mathbf{S}(V)$.

(33.20) $\mathbf{S}(V)$ *is a thin closed nowhere dense subset of* V. *Let any* $a \in V$, *any irreducible component* V' *of* $\gamma_a V$, *and any neighborhood* $\tilde{X}$ *of* a *in* X *be given; then there exists* $b \in \tilde{X} \cap V$ *such that* $b \notin \mathbf{S}(V)$ *and* $\dim_b V = \dim V'$.

PROOF. If we show that $\mathbf{S}(V)$ is a thin closed subset of V then the rest will follow from (33.10). To prove that $\mathbf{S}(V)$ is thin, let $a \in V$ be given. By (33.11, 33.16) we can take analytic sets $V_1, \ldots, V_\lambda$ in a neighborhood X' of a in X such that:

$$\gamma_a V_1 \cup \ldots \cup \gamma_a V_\lambda \quad \text{is the normal decomposition of} \quad \gamma_a V;$$

$$V \cap X' = V_1 \cup \ldots \cup V_\lambda;$$

$$\mathbf{S}(V) \cap X' = \left[\bigcup_{i=1}^{\lambda} (\mathbf{S}(V_i) \cap X')\right] \cup \left[\bigcup_{j \neq j'} (V_j \cap V_{j'} \cap X')\right];$$

and

$$\dim_b \left[\bigcup_{j \neq j'} (V_j \cap V_{j'})\right] < \dim_b V \qquad \text{for all} \quad b \in V \cap X'.$$

Applying (32.1) to $\gamma_a V_i$ we can find an analytic set W_i in a neighborhood X_i of a in X' such that:

$$\mathbf{S}(V_i \cap X_i) \subset W_i \subset V_i \qquad \text{and} \qquad \dim_b W_i < \dim_b V_i \quad \text{for all} \quad b \in V_i \cap X_i.$$

Let $X^* = X_1 \cap \ldots \cap X_\lambda$ and let

$$W^* = \left[\bigcup_{i=1}^{\lambda} (W_i \cap X^*)\right] \cup \left[\bigcup_{j \neq j'} (V_j \cap V_{j'} \cap X^*)\right].$$

Then W^* is an analytic set in X^*, $\mathbf{S}(V) \cap X^* \subset W^* \subset V$, and $\dim_b W^* < \dim_b V$ for all $b \in V \cap X^*$. This shows that $\mathbf{S}(V)$ is a thin subset of V.

To show that $\mathbf{S}(V)$ is closed in V, let $a \in V - \mathbf{S}(V)$ be given. By (33.18) we can find analytic functions $g_1, \ldots, g_m$ on a neighborhood $\tilde{X}$ of a in X such that

$$V \cap X = \{b \in \tilde{X} : g_1(b) = \ldots = g_m(b) = 0\}$$

and

$$\operatorname{rnk} \frac{J(g_1, \ldots, g_m)}{J(x_1, \ldots, x_n)}(a) = m.$$

By continuity, upon replacing $\tilde{X}$ by a smaller neighborhood of a in X we can arrange that

$$\operatorname{rnk} \frac{J(g_1, \ldots, g_m)}{J(x_1, \ldots, x_n)}(b) = m \qquad \text{for all} \quad b \in \tilde{X}.$$

For any $b \in V \cap \tilde{X}$, by (33.17.2) we deduce that $b \notin \mathbf{S}(V)$. This shows that $V - \mathbf{S}(V)$ is open in V, i.e., $\mathbf{S}(V)$ is closed in V.

REMARK. In §33C we shall show that $\mathbf{S}(V)$ is actually an analytic set in X. However, for many applications (33.20) is adequate. As an example we prove the following.

(33.21) HARTOGS EXTENSION THEOREM. *Assume that* $K = \mathbf{C}$ *and* $\dim V \leqq n - 2$. *Let f be any analytic function on* $X - V$. *Then f has a unique analytic extension to* X.[10]

PROOF. Uniqueness is obvious since V is nowhere dense in X. To prove existence it suffices to show that for any given $p \in V$ there exists a neighborhood X^* of p in X such that $f \mid (X^* - V)$ has an analytic extension to X^*.[11] Let $e = \dim_a V$ and $m = n - e$. First suppose that $a \notin \mathbf{S}(V)$. Then by (33.18) we can find an analytic coordinate system $y_1, \ldots, y_n$ in a neighborhood X^* of a in X such that in X^*, V is given by the equations: $y_1 = \ldots = y_m = 0$. By assumption $2 \leqq m \leqq n$ and hence by (6.6), $f \mid (X^* - V)$ has an analytic extension to X^*.

In the general case we make induction on e. If $e = 0$ then obviously $a \notin \mathbf{S}(V)$. Now let $e > 0$ and assume true for $e - 1$. By (33.2, 33.20), there exists an analytic set W^* in a neighborhood X^* of a in X such that $\mathbf{S}(V) \cap X^* \subset W^* \subset V$ and $\dim W^* \leqq e - 1$. By what we have already

[10] Recall that in Riemann Extension Theorem (14.3), about V it was only required that $\dim V \leqq n - 1$, whereas about f it was furthermore required that $|f|$ be bounded in the neighborhood of each point of V.

[11] See the beginning part of the proof of (14.3).

proved, $f|X^* - V$ has an analytic extension f^* to $X^* - W^*$. By induction hypothesis, f^* has an analytic extension to X^*.

§33C. *Cartan coherence and analyticity of the singular locus*[12]

Consider the following statements.

(33.22) CARTAN COHERENCE. *Let* $R = K[\langle x_1,\ldots, x_n\rangle]$. *Let* $\mathfrak{p}$ *be any ideal in* R *such that* $\operatorname{rad}\mathfrak{p} = \mathfrak{p}$. *Let* $u_1,\ldots, u_t$ *be any finite basis of* $\mathfrak{p}$ *and let* X *be a neighborhood of the origin in* K^n *in which* $u_1,\ldots, u_t$ *are convergent. For any* $b \in X$ *let* $\boldsymbol{\tau}_b\mathfrak{p} = \{\boldsymbol{\tau}_b u_1,\ldots, \boldsymbol{\tau}_b u_t\}R$. *Then there exists a neighborhood* X^* *of the origin in* X *such that* $\operatorname{rad}\boldsymbol{\tau}_b\mathfrak{p} = \boldsymbol{\tau}_b\mathfrak{p}$ *for all* $b \in X^*$.

(33.22′) (33.22) holds under the additional assumption that $\mathfrak{p}$ is prime.

(33.23) CARTAN COHERENCE. *Let* V *be an analytic set in an open set* X *in* K^n. *Let* $a \in X$ *and let* $u_1,\ldots, u_t$ *be any finite number of analytic functions on* X *such that*

$$\{\boldsymbol{\gamma}_a u_1,\ldots, \boldsymbol{\gamma}_a u_t\}R(a, X) = \mathfrak{i}(a, V, X).$$

Then there exists a neighborhood X^* *of* a *in* X *such that*

$$\{\boldsymbol{\gamma}_b u_1,\ldots, \boldsymbol{\gamma}_b u_t\}R(b, X) = \mathfrak{i}(b, V, X) \qquad \text{for all} \quad b \in X^*.$$

(33.23′) (33.23) holds under the additional assumption that $a \in V$ and $\boldsymbol{\gamma}_a V$ is irreducible.

In view of the Nullstellensatz, it is obvious that (33.22) and (33.23) are equivalent, and (33.22′) and (33.23′) are equivalent. In the situation of (33.22) assume that $\mathfrak{p}$ is prime. Then again in view of the Nullstellensatz, by (33.3) we can find a neighborhood X' of the origin in X such that for any $b \in X'$ for which $u_1(b) = \ldots = u_t(b) = 0$ we have: $\dim R/\boldsymbol{\tau}_b\mathfrak{p} = \dim R/\mathfrak{p}$ and $\operatorname{rad}\boldsymbol{\tau}_b\mathfrak{p}$ is unmixed. Consequently by (26.4) there exists a neighborhood X^* of the origin in X' such that $\operatorname{rad}\boldsymbol{\tau}_b\mathfrak{p} = \boldsymbol{\tau}_b\mathfrak{p}$ for all $b \in X^*$. Thus we have proved (33.22′) and hence also (33.23′). Using (33.22′) and (15.4) we shall prove (33.22). Before doing so, first we give the following consequence of (33.23′).

(33.24) *Let* V *be an analytic set in an open set* X *in* $K^n\{x_1,\ldots, x_n\}$. *Then* $\mathbf{S}(V)$ *is an analytic set in* X.

PROOF. Since V is closed in X, it suffices to show that $\mathbf{S}(V)$ is analytic at any given point $a \in V$. Take analytic sets $V_1,\ldots, V_\lambda$ in a neighborhood

[12] §33C will not be used elsewhere in this chapter. In the complex case, (33.23) was proved by Cartan in Cartan [3].

$\tilde{X}$ of a in X such that $\gamma_a V_1 \cup \ldots \cup \gamma_a V_\lambda$ is the normal decomposition of $\gamma_a V$ and $V \cap \tilde{X} = V_1 \cup \ldots \cup V_\lambda$. Then by (33.16),

$$\gamma_a \mathbf{S}(V) = \left[\bigcup_{i=1}^{\lambda} \gamma_a \mathbf{S}(V_i)\right] \cup \left[\bigcup_{j \neq j'} \gamma_a(V_j \cup V_{j'})\right].$$

Consequently it suffices to show that $\mathbf{S}(V_i)$ is analytic at a for any given i. So let i be given. Take analytic functions $g_1, \ldots, g_q$ on a neighborhood X' of a in $\tilde{X}$ such that $\{\gamma_a g_1, \ldots, \gamma_a g_q\}R(a, X) = \mathfrak{i}(a, V_i, X)$. By (33.23′) there exists a neighborhood X^* of a in X' such that $\{\gamma_b g_1, \ldots, \gamma_b g_q\}R(b, X) = \mathfrak{i}(b, V_i, X)$ for all $b \in X^*$. Hence by (33.19), $\mathbf{S}(V_i)$ is analytic at a.

Proof of (33.22). We make induction on the number λ of the distinct prime ideals of $\mathfrak{p}$. If $\lambda = 0$ then $\mathfrak{p} = R$ and our assertion is trivial. So let $\lambda > 0$ and assume true for $\lambda - 1$. Let $\mathfrak{a}$ be a prime ideal of $\mathfrak{p}$ and let $\mathfrak{b}$ be the intersection of the remaining prime ideals of $\mathfrak{p}$. Let $f_1, \ldots, f_p$ and $g_1, \ldots, g_q$ be finite bases of $\mathfrak{a}$ and $\mathfrak{b}$, respectively. Respectively by (33.22′) and the induction hypothesis we can find a neighborhood X' of the origin in X in which all the elements f_i, g_j are convergent, such that for all $b \in X'$ we have:

$$\operatorname{rad}\{\tau_b f_1, \ldots, \tau_b f_p\}R = \{\tau_b f_1, \ldots, \tau_b f_p\}R$$

and

$$\operatorname{rad}\{\tau_b g_1, \ldots, \tau_b g_q\}R = \{\tau_b g_1, \ldots, \tau_b g_q\}R.$$

By (15.4) we can find a finite number of elements $h_1, \ldots, h_r$ in R which are convergent in a neighborhood X'' of the origin in X' such that for all $b \in X''$ we have:

$$\{\tau_b h_1, \ldots, \tau_b h_r\}R = \{\tau_b f_1, \ldots, \tau_b f_p\}R \cap \{\tau_b g_1, \ldots, \tau_b g_q\}R.$$

Then in particular $\{h_1, \ldots, h_r\}R = \mathfrak{p}$, and hence there exists a neighborhood X^* of the origin in X'' such that for all $b \in X^*$ we have:

$$\tau_b \mathfrak{p} = \{\tau_b h_1, \ldots, \tau_b h_r\}R.$$

For any $b \in X^*$ we thus get:

$$\begin{aligned} \tau_b \mathfrak{p} &= \{\tau_b h_1, \ldots, \tau_b h_r\}R \\ &= \{\tau_b f_1, \ldots, \tau_b f_p\}R \cap \{\tau_b g_1, \ldots, \tau_b g_q\}R \\ &= \operatorname{rad}\{\tau_b f_1, \ldots, \tau_b f_p\}R \cap \operatorname{rad}\{\tau_b g_1, \ldots, \tau_b g_q\}R, \end{aligned}$$

and hence

$$\tau_b \mathfrak{p} = \operatorname{rad} \tau_b \mathfrak{p}.$$

§33D. *Projections*

Let $y = (y_1, \ldots, y_e)$, $z = (z_1, \ldots, z_m)$, $S = K[\langle y \rangle]$, $R = K[\langle y, z \rangle]$. Let $\pi \colon K^e\{y\} \times K^m\{z\} \to K^e\{y\}$ be the natural projection. Let $\mathfrak{a}$ be a proper ideal in R. Let $\mathfrak{b} = \mathfrak{a} \cap S$. Let $v_1, \ldots, v_\mu$ and $w_1, \ldots, w_\nu$ be any finite bases of $\mathfrak{a}$ and $\mathfrak{b}$, respectively. Let $\tilde{X} = \tilde{Y} \times \tilde{Z}$ be a neighborhood of the origin in $K^e \times K^m$ such that $v_1, \ldots, v_\mu$ are convergent in $\tilde{X}$ and $w_1, \ldots, w_\nu$ are convergent in $\tilde{Y}$. Let

$$V = \{a \in \tilde{X} : v_1(a) = \ldots = v_\mu(a) = 0\},$$
$$W = \{b \in \tilde{Y} : w_1(b) = \ldots = w_\nu(b) = 0\}.$$

We want to prove the following.

(33.25)[13] *Assume that* $\{y_1, \ldots, y_e, \mathfrak{a}\}R$ *is primary for the maximal ideal in* R,[14] *and let* $Y' \times Z'$ *be any given neighborhood of the origin in* $\tilde{Y} \times \tilde{Z}$. *Then there exists a neighborhood* $Y^* \times Z^*$ *of the origin in* $Y' \times Z'$ *such that: given any neighborhood* Z *of the origin in* Z^* *there exists a neighborhood* $\hat{Y}$ *of the origin in* Y^* *depending on* Z *such that for any neighborhood* Y *of the origin in* $\hat{Y}$ *we have*

$$\pi[V \cap (Y \times Z)] = W \cap Y.$$

Also consider the following slightly weaker statement.

(33.25′) *Assume that* $\{y_1, \ldots, y_e, \mathfrak{a}\}R$ *is primary for the maximal ideal in* R, *and let* $Y' \times Z'$ *be any given neighborhood of the origin in* $\tilde{Y} \times \tilde{Z}$. *Then there exists a neighborhood* $Y \times Z$ *of the origin in* $Y' \times Z'$ *such that*

$$\pi[V \cap (Y \times Z)] = W \cap Y.$$

Proof of (33.25) is in several steps.

1°) *If* (33.25′) *holds for* $\mathfrak{a}$ *then so does* (33.25).

Follows from (30.21).

[13] In the complex case, by using analytic continuation and Riemann Extension Theorem (14.3), several properties of analytic sets given in §33 (excluding §33C) and §34 were proved by Remmert–Stein **[1]**. In their set up, the proposition corresponding to (33.25) was proved first and the others were made to depend on it. In our set up, (33.25) is nowhere used in this chapter and its proof depends only on (32.7). We have not used analytic continuation anywhere, except in (14.8′) to give an *alternative* proof of (14.8). Riemann Extension Theorem was used in (14.8) and after that it is not used until §36 except to make incidental observations in (35.11, 36.13, 35.14, 35.15). Until §36 the only places where (14.8) is used either directly or indirectly are: (31.6.3, 31.21, 31.22, 32.2.2, §34, 35.17).

[14] Equivalently: the origin in $\tilde{X}$ is an isolated point of $V \cap \{a \in \tilde{X} : \pi a = (0)\}$.

2°) (33.25) *holds for* $\mathfrak{a}$ *under the further assumption that*: $\mathfrak{a}$ *is prime and the quotient field of* $R/\mathfrak{a}$ *is separable over the quotient field of* $S/\mathfrak{b}$.

PROOF. In view of 1°) it suffices to show that (33.25′) holds for $\mathfrak{a}$. Let $e' = \dim S/\mathfrak{b}$. By (24.5), via a K-linear transformation on $y_1, \ldots, y_e$ we can arrange that $\mathfrak{b}$ is strictly regular relative to $K[\langle y_1, \ldots, y_{e'} \rangle]$.[15] By (23.3), $\mathfrak{a}$ is then strictly regular relative to $K[\langle y_1, \ldots, y_{e'} \rangle]$. Hence by (32.7) we can find a neighborhood $Y \times Z$ of the origin in $Y' \times Z'$ such that $\pi[V \cap (Y \times Z)] = W \cap Y$.

3°)[16] (33.25) *holds for* $\mathfrak{a}$ *under the further assumption that*: *for every prime ideal* $\mathfrak{p}$ *of* $\mathfrak{a}$, *the quotient field of* $R/\mathfrak{p}$ *is separable over the quotient field of* $S/\mathfrak{p} \cap S$.

PROOF. By 1°) it suffices to show that (33.25′) holds for $\mathfrak{a}$. Let $\mathfrak{p}_1, \ldots, \mathfrak{p}_\lambda$ be the prime ideals of $\mathfrak{a}$. Let $v_{i1}, \ldots, v_{i\mu_i}$ be a finite basis of $\mathfrak{p}_i$ and let $w_{i1}, \ldots, w_{i\nu_i}$ be a finite basis of $\mathfrak{p}_i \cap S$. Let $\hat{Y} \times \hat{Z}$ be a neighborhood of the origin in $Y' \times Z'$ such that the elements v_{ij} are convergent in $\hat{Y} \times \hat{Z}$ and the elements w_{ij} are convergent in $\hat{Y}$. Let

$$V_i = \{a \in \hat{Y} \times \hat{Z}: v_{i1}(a) = \ldots = v_{i\mu_i}(a) = 0\},$$
$$W_i = \{b \in \hat{Y}: w_{i1}(b) = \ldots = w_{i\nu_i}(b) = 0\}.$$

Obviously

$$\mathfrak{p}_1 \cap \ldots \cap \mathfrak{p}_\lambda = \mathrm{rad}_R \mathfrak{a}$$

and

$$\mathrm{rad}_S((\mathfrak{p}_1 \cap S) \cap \ldots \cap (\mathfrak{p}_\lambda \cap S)) = \mathrm{rad}_S \mathfrak{b}.$$

Hence upon replacing $\hat{Y} \times \hat{Z}$ by a smaller neighborhood of the origin in $\hat{Y} \times \hat{Z}$ we can arrange that

$$V \cap (\hat{Y} \times \hat{Z}) = V_1 \cup \ldots \cup V_\lambda, \qquad \text{and} \qquad W \cap \hat{Y} = W_1 \cup \ldots \cup W_\lambda.$$

By 2°) we can find a neighborhood $Y_i^* \times Z_i^*$ of the origin in $\hat{Y} \times \hat{Z}$ such that: given any neighborhood Z of the origin in Z_i^* there exists a neighborhood $\delta_i(Z)$ of the origin in Y_i^* depending on Z such that for any neighborhood Y of the origin in $\delta_i(Z)$ we have

$$\pi[V_i \cap (Y \times Z)] = W_i \cap Y.$$

Take $Z = Z_1^* \cap \ldots \cap Z_\lambda^*$ and $Y = \delta_1(Z) \cap \ldots \cap \delta_\lambda(Z)$. Then

$$\pi[V \cap (Y \times Z)] = W \cap Y.$$

[15] In case K is of characteristic zero, it suffices to invoke (23.5) instead of (24.5).
[16] In case K is of characteristic zero, 3°) completes the proof (33.25).

4°) LEMMA. *Let $\mathfrak{L}$ be any field of characteristic $p \neq 0$. Let $q = p^M$ where M is a positive integer. Let ζ be an element in some algebraic extension of $\mathfrak{L}$ such that $[\mathfrak{L}^q(\zeta): \mathfrak{L}^q] \leqq q$. Then ζ is separable over $\mathfrak{L}$.*

PROOF. Let $f(T)$ be the minimal monic polynomial of ζ over $\mathfrak{L}^q$. Let N be the largest integer such that $f(T) \in \mathfrak{L}^q[T^{p^N}]$, let $q' = p^N$, and let

$$n = (\text{degree of } f(T) \text{ in } T)/q'.$$

Then $[\mathfrak{L}^q(\zeta): \mathfrak{L}^q]_s = n$.[17] By assumption $q' \leqq q$ and hence we can write $f(T) = g(T)^{q'}$ with $g(T) \in \mathfrak{L}[T]$. Then $g(\zeta) = 0$. Let $\mathfrak{L}^*$ be the field generated over $\mathfrak{L}^q$ by the coefficients of $g(T)$. Then $\mathfrak{L}^*$ is a purely inseparable finite algebraic extension of $\mathfrak{L}^q$. Hence

$$\begin{aligned} n &\geqq [\mathfrak{L}^*(\zeta): \mathfrak{L}^*] \\ &\geqq [\mathfrak{L}^*(\zeta): \mathfrak{L}^*]_s \\ &= [\mathfrak{L}^*(\zeta): \mathfrak{L}^*]_s[\mathfrak{L}^*: \mathfrak{L}^q]_s \\ &= [\mathfrak{L}^*(\zeta): \mathfrak{L}^q(\zeta)]_s[\mathfrak{L}^q(\zeta): \mathfrak{L}^q]_s \\ &\geqq n.\end{aligned}$$[18]

Therefore $[\mathfrak{L}^*(\zeta): \mathfrak{L}^*] = [\mathfrak{L}^*(\zeta): \mathfrak{L}^*]_s$, i.e., ζ is separable over $\mathfrak{L}^*$ and hence *a fortiori* ζ is separable over $\mathfrak{L}$.

Proof of the general case of (33.25). By 1°) it suffices to show that (33.25′) holds for $\mathfrak{a}$. By 3°) we are done if K is of characteristic zero. Now assume that K is of characteristic $p \neq 0$. By (23.3), $\mathfrak{a}$ contains a monic polynomial $g_i(y, z_i)$ of degree $d_i > 0$ in z_i with coefficients in S, for $i = 1,\ldots, m$. Let M be any positive integer such that $q \geqq d_i$ for $i = 1,\ldots, m$, where $q = p^M$. Take indeterminates $\tilde{y} = (\tilde{y}_1,\ldots, \tilde{y}_e)$. Let $\tilde{S} = K[\langle \tilde{y} \rangle]$ and $\tilde{R} = K[\langle \tilde{y}, z \rangle]$. Let $\psi: K^e\{\tilde{y}\} \to K^e\{y\}$ and $\varphi: K^e\{\tilde{y}\} \times K^m\{z\} \to K^e\{y\} \times K^m\{z\}$ be given by: $\psi(b_1,\ldots, b_e) = (b_1^q,\ldots, b_e^q)$, and $\varphi(b, c) = (\psi(b), c)$. Let $\tilde{\pi}: K^e\{\tilde{y}\} \times K^m\{z\} \to K^e\{\tilde{y}\}$ be the natural projection. Then $\pi \circ \varphi = \psi \circ \tilde{\pi}$. Identify R with the subring $K[\langle \tilde{y}_1,\ldots, \tilde{y}_e, z \rangle] \cap K[[\tilde{y}_1^q,\ldots, \tilde{y}_e^q, z]]$ of $\tilde{R}$ via the monomorphism: $f(y_1,\ldots, y_e, z) \to f(\tilde{y}_1^q,\ldots, \tilde{y}_e^q, z)$.[19] In other words we set $y_i = \tilde{y}_i^q$ for $i = 1,\ldots, e$. Then S gets identified with the subring $K[\langle \tilde{y}_1,\ldots, \tilde{y}_e \rangle] \cap K[[\tilde{y}_1^q,\ldots, \tilde{y}_e^q]]$ of $\tilde{S}$. Let $\tilde{\mathfrak{a}} = \mathfrak{a}\tilde{R}$ and $\tilde{\mathfrak{b}} = \mathfrak{b}\tilde{S}$. Then obviously $\{\tilde{y}_1,\ldots, \tilde{y}_e, \tilde{\mathfrak{a}}\}\tilde{R}$ is primary for the maximal ideal in $\tilde{R}$.

[17] Zariski–Samuel [**1**: Last paragraph on p. 71]. $[\ ]_s$ denotes the degree of separability.

[18] The last equality follows from Zariski–Samuel [**1**: Corollary 1 on p. 115].

[19] Obviously $f(y_1,\ldots, y_e, z)$ is convergent at $a \Leftrightarrow f(\tilde{y}_1^q,\ldots, \tilde{y}_e^q, z)$ is convergent at $\varphi^{-1}(a)$. In particular, if $f(y_1,\ldots, y_e, z)$ is convergent then $f(\tilde{y}_1^q,\ldots, \tilde{y}_e^q, z)$ is convergent as a power series in $\tilde{y}_1,\ldots, \tilde{y}_e, z$ and conversely.

We claim that $\tilde{\mathfrak{b}} = \tilde{\mathfrak{a}} \cap \tilde{S}$. Obviously $\tilde{\mathfrak{b}} \subset \tilde{\mathfrak{a}} \cap \tilde{S}$. To prove "$\supset$" let $f \in \tilde{\mathfrak{a}} \cap \tilde{S}$ be given. Since $f \in \tilde{\mathfrak{a}} = \mathfrak{a}\tilde{R}$ we can write f as a finite sum:

$$f = \sum_i r_i s_i \qquad \text{with} \qquad r_i \in \mathfrak{a} \quad \text{and} \quad s_i \in \tilde{R}.$$

Label the monomials

$$\{\tilde{y}_1^{i_1} \ldots \tilde{y}_e^{i_e} : 0 \leqq i_1 < q, \ldots, 0 \leqq i_e < q\}$$

as $\xi_1, \ldots, \xi_E$, $(E = q^e)$. Then we can write

$$s_i = \sum_{j=1}^{E} s_{ij} \xi_j \qquad \text{with} \quad s_{ij} \in R.$$

Then

$$f = \sum_{j=1}^{E} t_j \xi_j \qquad \text{where} \qquad t_j = \sum_i r_i s_{ij} \in \mathfrak{a}.$$

Now $f \in K[[\tilde{y}_1, \ldots, \tilde{y}_e]]$ and $t_j \in K[[\tilde{y}_1^q, \ldots, \tilde{y}_e^q, z]]$. Considering $f, t_1, \ldots, t_E$ as elements in $K[[\tilde{y}_1, \ldots, \tilde{y}_e, z]]$, and equating coefficients we deduce that $t_1, \ldots, t_E$ are in S. Therefore $t_1, \ldots, t_E \in \mathfrak{a} \cap S = \mathfrak{b}$ and hence $f \in \tilde{\mathfrak{b}}$.

Let $\tilde{v}_i(\tilde{y}_1, \ldots, \tilde{y}_e, z) = v_i(\tilde{y}_1^q, \ldots, \tilde{y}_e^q, z)$ and $\tilde{w}_i(\tilde{y}_1, \ldots, \tilde{y}_e) = w_i(\tilde{y}_1^q, \ldots, \tilde{y}_e^q)$. Then $\tilde{v}_1, \ldots, \tilde{v}_\mu$ form a basis of $\tilde{\mathfrak{a}}$ and they are convergent in $\varphi^{-1}(Y' \times Z') = \psi^{-1}(Y') \times Z'$; and $\tilde{w}_1, \ldots, \tilde{w}_\nu$ form a basis of $\tilde{\mathfrak{b}}$ and they are convergent in $\psi^{-1}(Y')$. Let

$$\tilde{V} = \{a \in \psi^{-1}(Y') \times Z' : \tilde{v}_1(a) = \ldots = \tilde{v}_\mu(a) = 0\},$$
$$\tilde{W} = \{b \in \psi^{-1}(Y') : \tilde{w}_1(b) = \ldots = \tilde{w}_\nu(b) = 0\}.$$

Suppose we have shown that

5°) *For any prime ideal $\tilde{\mathfrak{p}}$ of $\tilde{\mathfrak{a}}$ in $\tilde{R}$ the quotient field of $\tilde{R}/\tilde{\mathfrak{p}}$ is separable over the quotient field of $\tilde{S}/\tilde{\mathfrak{p}} \cap \tilde{S}$.*

Then by 3°) we can find a neighborhood $\hat{Y} \times Z$ of the origin in $\psi^{-1}(Y') \times Z'$ such that

$$\tilde{\pi}[\tilde{V} \cap (\hat{Y} \times Z)] = \tilde{W} \cap \hat{Y}.$$

Let $Y = \psi(\hat{Y})$. Then $Y \times Z$ is a neighborhood of the origin in $Y' \times Z'$ and

$$\begin{aligned} \pi[V \cap (Y \times Z)] &= \pi \circ \varphi[\tilde{V} \cap (\hat{Y} \times Z)] \\ &= \psi \circ \tilde{\pi}[\tilde{V} \cap (\hat{Y} \times Z)] \\ &= \psi(\tilde{W} \cap \hat{Y}) \\ &= W \cap Y. \end{aligned}$$

To prove 5°) let $\tilde{\mathfrak{p}}$ be any prime ideal of $\tilde{\mathfrak{a}}$ in $\tilde{R}$. Let ζ_i be the image of z_i under the natural epimorphism $\tilde{R} \to \tilde{R}/\tilde{\mathfrak{p}}$. Let $\mathfrak{K}$ be the quotient field of $\tilde{R}/\tilde{\mathfrak{p}}$ and let $\mathfrak{L}$ be the quotient field of $\tilde{S}/\tilde{\mathfrak{p}} \cap \tilde{S}$ considered as a subfield of $\mathfrak{K}$. By (23.3) we have $\mathfrak{K} = \mathfrak{L}(\zeta_1,\ldots, \zeta_m)$ and hence it suffices to show that for any $i \leqq m$ we have that ζ_i is separable over $\mathfrak{L}$. Let $\mathfrak{L}'$ be the quotient field $S/\tilde{\mathfrak{p}} \cap S$ considered as a subfield of $\mathfrak{L}$. Since K is perfect, as in the proof of (24.1) it follows that $\tilde{S}^q = S$. Therefore $\mathfrak{L}^q = \mathfrak{L}'$. Hence by 4°), ζ_i is separable over $\mathfrak{L}$.

§34. CONNECTIVITY PROPERTIES OF COMPLEX ANALYTIC SETS

§34A. *Local connectivity*

(**34.1**) *Let $\mathfrak{a}$ be a proper ideal in $\mathbf{C}[\langle x_1,\ldots, x_n\rangle]$. Let $\mathfrak{p}_1,\ldots, \mathfrak{p}_\lambda$ be the minimal prime ideals of $\mathfrak{a}$. Let $u_{i1},\ldots, u_{i\lambda_i}$ be a finite basis of $\mathfrak{p}_i$. Let $\tilde{X}$ be a neighborhood of the origin in $\mathbf{C}^n$ in which all the elements u_{ij} are convergent. Let*

$$V_i = \{a \in \tilde{X}: u_{i1}(a) = \ldots = u_{i\lambda_i}(a) = 0\}, \qquad \text{and} \qquad V = V_1 \cup \ldots \cup V_\lambda.$$

Let $e_i = \dim R/\mathfrak{p}_i$ and $e = \min(e_1,\ldots, e_\lambda)$. Let W be any analytic set in $\tilde{X}$ such that $\gamma_{(0)}V_i \not\subset \gamma_{(0)}W$ for $i = 1,\ldots, \lambda$.[1] *For any $E_1,\ldots, E_n > 0$ let*

$$X\langle E_1,\ldots, E_n\rangle = \{a \in \mathbf{C}^n: |a_1| < E_1,\ldots, |a_n| < E_n\}.$$

Assume that $\mathfrak{p}_i$ is regular relative to $\mathbf{C}[\langle x_1,\ldots, x_{e_i}\rangle]$ for $i = 1,\ldots, \lambda$; and let $D_1^* > 0,\ldots, D_n^* > 0$ be given such that $X\langle D_1^*,\ldots, D_n^*\rangle \subset \tilde{X}$. Then there exist

$$0 < D_1' \leqq D_1^*,\ldots, 0 < D_e' \leqq D_e^*, 0 < D_{e+1}^* \leqq D_{e+1}^*,\ldots, 0 < D_n \leqq D_n^*,$$

such that for any $0 < D_1 \leqq D_1',\ldots, 0 < D_e \leqq D_e'$ letting $X = X\langle D_1,\ldots, D_n\rangle$ we have i) *and we have* ii), iii), iv) *for $i = 1,\ldots, \lambda$.*[2]

i) $(V_1 \cap X) - \mathbf{S}(V) - W,\ldots, (V_\lambda \cap X) - \mathbf{S}(V) - W$ *are exactly all the distinct connected components of* $(V \cap X) - \mathbf{S}(V) - W$.

ii) $\mathbf{S}(V_i) \cap X \subset \mathbf{S}(V)$.

iii) $V_i \cap X = \mathrm{cl}_X[(V_i \cap X) - \mathbf{S}(V) - W]$.

iv) *Any point $\alpha \in V_i \cap X$ can be joined to a point in $(V_i \cap X) - \mathbf{S}(V) - W$ by a simple arc in $V_i \cap X$ meeting $\mathbf{S}(V) \cup W$ at most in α.*

Proof. By (33.16) there exists a neighborhood $\hat{X}$ of the origin in $\tilde{X}$ such that for any neighborhood X of the origin in $\hat{X}$ we have

$$\mathbf{S}(V) \cap X = \left[\bigcup_{i=1,\ldots,\lambda} (\mathbf{S}(V_i) \cap X)\right] \cup \left[\bigcup_{\substack{j,j'=1,\ldots,\lambda\\ j\neq j'}} (V_j \cap V_{j'} \cap X)\right].$$

[1] For instance $W = \emptyset$.

[2] For $e = 0$ this means: there exist $0 < D_1 \leqq D_1^*,\ldots, 0 < D_n \leqq D_n^*$ such that letting $X = X\langle D_1,\ldots, D_n\rangle$ we have....

Now $(V_1 \cap X) - \mathbf{S}(V) - W, \dots, (V_\lambda \cap X) - \mathbf{S}(V) - W$ are a finite number of pairwise disjoint closed subsets of $(V \cap X) - \mathbf{S}(V) - W$, and

$$(V \cap X) - \mathbf{S}(V) - W = \bigcup_{i=1}^{\lambda} [(V_i \cap X) - \mathbf{S}(V) - W].$$

Therefore for any $j \neq j'$, $(V_j \cap X) - \mathbf{S}(V) - W$ and $(V_{j'} \cap X) - \mathbf{S}(V) - W$ cannot be contained in the same connected component of $(V \cap X) - \mathbf{S}(V) - W$. Consequently it suffices to prove the following.[3]

(I) Let $D_1^* > 0, \dots, D_n^* > 0$ be given such that $X\langle D_1^*, \dots, D_n^*\rangle \subset \tilde{X}$. Then there exist

$$0 < D_1' \leqq D_1^*, \dots, 0 < D_e' \leqq D_e^*, \quad 0 < D_{e+1} \leqq D_{e+1}^*, \dots, 0 < D_n \leqq D_n^*,$$

such that for any $0 < D_1 < D_1', \dots, 0 < D_e < D_e'$ we have (1°, 2°, 3°) for $i = 1, \dots, \lambda$.

1°) $V_i \cap X\langle D_1, \dots, D_n\rangle$ = closure of $(V_i \cap X\langle D_1, \dots, D_n\rangle) - \mathbf{S}(V) - W$ in $X\langle D_1, \dots, D_n\rangle$.

2°) $(V_i \cap X\langle D_1, \dots, D_n\rangle) - \mathbf{S}(V) - W$ is connected.

3°) Any point $\alpha \in V_i \cap X\langle D_1, \dots, D_n\rangle$ can be joined to a point in $(V_i \cap X\langle D_1, \dots, D_n\rangle) - \mathbf{S}(V) - W$ by a simple arc in $V_i \cap X\langle D_1, \dots, D_n\rangle$ meeting $\mathbf{S}(V) \cup W$ at most in α.

Let $m = n - e$. We prove (I) by induction on m. If $m = 0$ then $\Upsilon_{(0)}V = \Upsilon_{(0)}\mathbf{C}^n$ and our assertion follows from (14.7). Now let $m > 0$ and assume true for $m - 1$. Relabel $\mathfrak{p}_1, \dots, \mathfrak{p}_\lambda$ so that $\dim R/\mathfrak{p}_i = e$ for $i \leqq \mu$ and $\dim R/\mathfrak{p}_i > e$ for $i > \mu$. Let $V' = V_1 \cup \dots \cup V_\mu$. By (30.21) we can find

$$0 < A_1^* \leqq D_1^*, \dots, 0 < A_n^* \leqq D_n^*$$

such that: for any

$$0 < A_{e+1} \leqq A_{e+1}^*, \dots, 0 < A_n \leqq A_n^*$$

there exist

$$0 < \varphi_1(A_{e+1}, \dots, A_n) \leqq A_1^*, \dots, 0 < \varphi_e(A_{e+1}, \dots, A_n) \leqq A_e^*,$$

depending on $A_{e+1}, \dots, A_n$ such that

4°)
$$\begin{aligned} &V' \cap X\langle \varphi_1(A_{e+1}, \dots, A_n), \dots, \varphi_e(A_{e+1}, \dots, A_n), A_{e+1}^*, \dots, A_n^*\rangle \\ &= V' \cap X\langle \varphi_1(A_{e+1}, \dots, A_n), \dots, \varphi_e(A_{e+1}, \dots, A_n), A_{e+1}, \dots, A_n\rangle. \end{aligned}$$

[3] We may suppose that $e > 0$. The case $e = 0$ follows by a slight modification of the argument which follows. Or note that indeed if $e = 0$ then $\Upsilon_{(0)}V = \Upsilon_{(0)}\{(0)\}$ and our assertion is trivial.

By (33.8, 33.20) we can find $W^* \subset \tilde{X}$ such that:

5°) W^* is analytic at the origin; $\gamma_{(0)}(\mathbf{S}(V) \cap W) \subset \gamma_{(0)} W^*$, and $\gamma_{(0)} V_i \not\subset \gamma_{(0)} W^*$ for $i = 1,\ldots, \lambda$.

Consider $i \leqq \mu$. In virtue of 5°), by (23.4) there exist

$$0 < B_1^{(i)} \leqq A_1^*,\ldots, 0 < B_n^{(i)} \leqq A_n^*$$

and $0 \neq \Delta_i' \in \mathbf{C}[\langle x_1,\ldots, x_e \rangle]$ which is convergent in

$$\{b \in \mathbf{C}^e \colon |b_1| < B_1^{(i)},\ldots, |b_e| < B_e^{(i)}\}$$

such that

$$\Delta_i'(a_1,\ldots, a_e) = 0 \qquad \text{for all} \quad a \in V_i \cap X\langle B_1^{(i)},\ldots, B_n^{(i)} \rangle \cap (\mathbf{S}(V) \cup W).$$

Applying (32.2) to V_i and Δ_i' we can find

$$0 < \tilde{C}_1^{(i)} \leqq B_1^{(i)},\ldots, 0 < \tilde{C}_e^{(i)} \leqq B_e^{(i)}, \;\; 0 < C_{e+1}^{(i)} \leqq B_{e+1}^{(i)},\ldots, 0 < C_n^{(i)} \leqq B_n^{(i)},$$

such that for all

$$0 < C_1^{(i)} \leqq \tilde{C}_1^{(i)},\ldots, 0 < C_e^{(i)} \leqq \tilde{C}_e^{(i)}$$

we have (6°, 7°, 8°).

6°) $V_i \cap X\langle C_1^{(i)},\ldots, C_n^{(i)} \rangle$
$= \text{closure of } \; (V_i \cap X\langle C_1^{(i)},\ldots, C_n^{(i)} \rangle) - \mathbf{S}(V) - W$
in $X\langle C_1^{(i)},\ldots, C_n^{(i)} \rangle$.

7°) $(V_i \cap X\langle C_1^{(i)},\ldots, C_n^{(i)} \rangle) - \mathbf{S}(V) - W$ is connected.

8°) Any point $\alpha \in V_i \cap X\langle C_1^{(i)},\ldots, C_n^{(i)} \rangle$ can be joined to a point in $(V_i \cap X\langle C_1^{(i)},\ldots, C_n^{(i)} \rangle) - \mathbf{S}(V) - W$ by a simple arc in $V_i \cap X\langle C_1^{(i)},\ldots, C_n^{(i)} \rangle$ meeting $\mathbf{S}(V) \cup W$ at most in α.

Take

$$\hat{C}_j = \min(C_j^{(1)},\ldots, C_j^{(\mu)}) \qquad \text{for} \quad j = e+1,\ldots, n;$$

and then take

$$\hat{C}_j = \min(\tilde{C}_j^{(1)},\ldots, \tilde{C}_j^{(\mu)}, \varphi_j(\hat{C}_{e+1},\ldots, \hat{C}_n)) \qquad \text{for} \quad j = 1,\ldots, e.$$

If $\lambda = \mu$ then taking

$$D_j' = \hat{C}_j \quad \text{for} \quad j = 1,\ldots, e, \qquad \text{and} \qquad D_j = \hat{C}_j \quad \text{for} \quad j = e+1,\ldots, n,$$

from (4°, 6°, 7°, 8°) we deduce that for any

$$0 < D_1 \leqq D_1',\ldots, 0 < D_e \leqq D_e',$$

(1°, 2°, 3°) hold for all $i \leqq \lambda$. Now suppose that $\lambda > \mu$. Then in virtue of 5°), by induction hypothesis we deduce that there exist

$$0 < D_1'' \leqq \hat{C}_1, \ldots, 0 < D_e'' \leqq \hat{C}_e, \quad 0 < D_{e+1} \leqq \hat{C}_{e+1}, \ldots, 0 < D_n \leqq \hat{C}_n,$$

such that for all

$$0 < D_1 \leqq D_1'', \ldots, 0 < D_e \leqq D_e'',$$

(1°, 2°, 3°) hold for all $i > \mu$. Take

$$D_j' = \min(D_j'', \varphi_j(D_{e+1}, \ldots, D_n)) \qquad \text{for} \quad j = 1, \ldots, e.$$

Then by (4°, 6°, 7°, 8°) it follows that for any

$$0 < D_1 \leqq D_1', \ldots, 0 < D_e \leqq D_e',$$

(1°, 2°, 3°) hold for all $i \leqq \mu$ as well.

In virtue of (23.5), (34.1) yields

(34.2) *Let V be an analytic set in an open set X in $\mathbf{C}^n$ and let $a \in V$. Take analytic sets $V_1, \ldots, V_\lambda$ in a neighborhood $\tilde{X}$ of a in X such that $\gamma_a V_1 \cup \ldots \cup \gamma_a V_\lambda$ is the normal decomposition of $\gamma_a V$, and $V \cap \tilde{X} = V_1 \cup \ldots \cup V_\lambda$. Let W be any subset of X such that W is analytic at a and $\gamma_a V_i \not\subset \gamma_a W$* for $i = 1, \ldots, \lambda$.[4] *Then there exists a neighborhood basis $\mathbf{X}'$ of a in $\tilde{X}$ such that upon making an affine transformation on the original coordinate system every member X' of $\mathbf{X}'$ becomes an open polycylinder around a and such that for every $X' \in \mathbf{X}'$ we have* i) *to* vi).

i) $(V_1 \cap X') - \mathbf{S}(V) - W, \ldots, (V_\lambda \cap X') - \mathbf{S}(V) - W$ *are exactly all the distinct connected components of* $(V \cap X') - \mathbf{S}(V) - W$.

ii) $\mathbf{S}(V_i) \cap X' \subset \mathbf{S}(V)$ *for* $i = 1, \ldots, \lambda$.

iii) $V_i \cap X' = \mathrm{cl}_{X'}[(V_i \cap X') - \mathbf{S}(V) - W]$ *for* $i = 1, \ldots, \lambda$.

iv) *For any $i \leqq \lambda$, any point $\alpha \in V_i \cap X'$ can be joined to a point in $(V_i \cap X') - \mathbf{S}(V) - W$ by a simple arc in $V_i \cap X'$ meeting $\mathbf{S}(V) \cup W$ at most in α.*

Since $a \in \bigcap_{i=1}^{\lambda} V_i$, from i), ii), and iv) we get

v) *$V \cap X'$ is arcwise connected; and $V_i \cap X'$, $(V_i \cap X') - \mathbf{S}(V_i)$, $(V_i \cap X') - \mathbf{S}(V)$, and $(V_i \cap X') - \mathbf{S}(V) - W$ are arcwise connected for $i = 1, \ldots, \lambda$.*

From v) we get

vi) *If $\gamma_a V$ is irreducible then $V \cap X'$, $(V \cap X') - \mathbf{S}(V)$, and $(V \cap X') - \mathbf{S}(V) - W$ are arcwise connected.*

[4] For instance $W = \emptyset$.

By (33.20), $\mathbf{S}(V)$ is a thin subset of V. Hence (34.2) yields

(**34.3**) *Let V be an analytic set in an open set in $\mathbf{C}^n$. For any $a \in V$, the following four conditions are equivalent.*

i) *$\gamma_a V$ is irreducible.*
ii) *$\mathbf{S}(V)$ does not disconnect V at a.*
iii) *$[W \subset V,\ W$ analytic at $a,\ \gamma_a W \neq \gamma_a V] \Rightarrow W$ does not disconnect V at a.*
iv) *$[W' \subset W \subset V,\ W$ analytic at $a,\ \gamma_a W \neq \gamma_a V] \Rightarrow W'$ does not disconnect V at a.*

§34B. Global decomposition

Let V be a nonempty analytic set in an open set X in $\mathbf{C}^n$. Let $(V_i)_{i \in I}$ be the distinct connected components of $V - \mathbf{S}(V)$. For any $i \in I$, let $\bar{V}_i = \mathrm{cl}_V V_i = \mathrm{cl}_X V_i$.

(**34.4**) Definition. V is said to be *irreducible* $\Leftrightarrow$ $[V = V' \cup V'',\ V'$ and V'' analytic sets in $X \Rightarrow V = V'$ or $V = V'']$. V is said to be *reducible* $\Leftrightarrow$ V is not irreducible. $W \subset X$ is said to be an *irreducible component* of $V \Leftrightarrow W$ is a nonempty irreducible analytic set in X, $W \subset V$, and $[W \subset W' \subset V,\ W'$ irreducible analytic set in $X \Rightarrow W = W']$.

(**34.5**) *Given $a \in V$ take analytic sets $V'_1, \ldots, V'_\lambda$ in a neighborhood $\tilde{X}$ of a in X such that $\gamma_a V'_1 \cup \ldots \cup \gamma_a V'_\lambda$ is the normal decomposition of $\gamma_a V$; and $V \cap \tilde{X} = V'_1 \cup \ldots \cup V'_\lambda$. Let X'' be any given neighborhood of a in $\tilde{X}$. Then there exists a neighborhood X' of a in X'' such that letting*

$$J_i = \{j \leqq \lambda : V'_j \cap X' \cap V_i \neq \emptyset\} \qquad \textit{and} \qquad I' = \{i \in I : J_i \neq \emptyset\}$$

we have i) *and* ii).

i) *$J_i \cap J_{i'} = \emptyset$ for all $i \neq i'$ in I.*
ii) *For any $i \in I$ we have:*

$$\begin{aligned} i \in I' &\Leftrightarrow V_i \cap X' \neq \emptyset \\ &\Leftrightarrow \bar{V}_i \cap X' \neq \emptyset \\ &\Rightarrow \bar{V}_i \cap X' = \bigcup_{j \in J_i} (V'_j \cap X'). \end{aligned}$$

Proof. By (34.2) we can find a neighborhood X' of a in X'' such that: $(V'_1 \cap X') - \mathbf{S}(V), \ldots, (V'_\lambda \cap X') - \mathbf{S}(V)$ are exactly all the distinct connected components of $(V \cap X') - \mathbf{S}(V)$; and $V'_j \cap X' = \mathrm{cl}_{X'}((V'_j \cap X') - \mathbf{S}(V))$ for $j = 1, \ldots, \lambda$. Now i) follows from the fact that $(V' \cap X') - \mathbf{S}(V)$ is connected for $j = 1, \ldots, \lambda$; and then ii) follows immediately.

(34.6) *$\bar{V}_i$ is analytic in X for all $i \in I$, and we have $V = \bigcup_{i \in I} \bar{V}_i$ and $\dim V = \max_{i \in I} \dim \bar{V}_i$. More generally for any $I^* \subset I$: $\bigcup_{i \in I^*} \bar{V}_i$ is analytic in X', $\dim \bigcup_{i \in I^*} \bar{V}_i = \max_{i \in I^*} \dim \bar{V}_i$, and $\bigcup_{i \in I^*} \bar{V}_i = \mathrm{cl}_V\left(\bigcup_{i \in I^*} V_i\right)$.*

Follows from (34.5).

$$\text{(34.7)} \qquad \mathbf{S}(V) = \left[\bigcup_{i \in I} \mathbf{S}(\bar{V}_i)\right] \cup \left[\bigcup_{\substack{i,i' \in I \\ i \neq i'}} (\bar{V}_i \cap \bar{V}_{i'})\right].$$

Proof. Given $a \in V$ let the notation be as in (34.5). By (33.16) we get

$$\gamma_a \mathbf{S}(V) = \left[\bigcup_{j=1}^{\lambda} \gamma_a \mathbf{S}(V_j')\right] \cup \left[\bigcup_{\substack{j,j' \leqq \lambda \\ j \neq j'}} \gamma_a (V_j' \cap V_{j'}')\right]$$

and for all $i \in I$,

$$\gamma_a \mathbf{S}(\bar{V}_i) = \left[\bigcup_{j \in J_i} \gamma_a \mathbf{S}(V_j')\right] \cup \left[\bigcup_{\substack{j,j' \in J_i \\ j \neq j'}} \gamma_a (V_j' \cap V_{j'}')\right].$$

Therefore

$$\gamma_a \mathbf{S}(V) = \left[\bigcup_{i \in I} \gamma_a \mathbf{S}(\bar{V}_i)\right] \cup \left[\bigcup_{\substack{i,i' \in I \\ i \neq i'}} \gamma_a (\bar{V}_i \cap \bar{V}_{i'})\right].$$

(34.8) *For any $i \neq i'$ in I we have that $\bar{V}_{i'} \cap V_i = \emptyset$.*

Follows from (34.7). Alternatively, by (34.2), V is locally arcwise connected. Therefore V_i is open in $V - \mathbf{S}(V)$ and hence V_i is open in V for all $i \in I$. Now $V_{i'} \cap V_i = \emptyset$ and $\bar{V}_{i'} = \mathrm{cl}_V V_{i'}$. Therefore $\bar{V}_{i'} \cap V_i = \emptyset$.

(34.9) *For any $W \subset X$ we have the following.*

1) *If W is analytic in X, then $W \cap V$ is nowhere dense in $V \Leftrightarrow W \cap \bar{V}_i$ is nowhere dense in $\bar{V}_i$ for all $i \in I$.*[5]

[5] Recall that by (33.8): [$W \cap V$ is nowhere dense in V] $\Leftrightarrow$ [$\dim_a(W \cap V) < \dim_a V$ for all $a \in V$] $\Leftrightarrow$ [for each $a \in X$ and for each irreducible component V^* of $\gamma_a V$ we have $V^* \not\subset \gamma_a W$]. If V is pure e dimensional, W is pure $n-1$ dimensional, and $W \cap V$ is nowhere dense in V, then $W \cap V$ is either empty or is pure $e-1$ dimensional.

2) *$W \cap V$ is a thin subset of $V \Leftrightarrow W \cap \bar{V}_i$ is a thin subset of $\bar{V}_i$ for all $i \in I$.*

Follows from (34.5) in virtue of (33.8).

(**34.10**) *The following five conditions are equivalent.*[6]

i) *V is irreducible.*

ii) *$V - \mathbf{S}(V)$ is connected.*

iii) *If W is any analytic set in X with $V \not\subset W$, then $V \cap W$ is nowhere dense in V.*[5]

iv) *If W is any analytic set in X with $V \not\subset W$, then $V - W$ is connected.*[7]

v) *If W is any thin subset of V, then $V - W$ is connected.*[8]

Proof of i) $\Rightarrow$ ii). Otherwise I contains more than one element. Take $i \in I$, and let

$$V' = \bar{V}_i \qquad \text{and} \qquad V'' = \bigcup_{\substack{i^* \in I \\ i^* \neq i}} \bar{V}_{i^*}.$$

By (34.6), V' and V'' are analytic sets in X and $V = V' \cup V''$. By (34.8), $V' \not\subset V''$ and $V'' \not\subset V'$. Contradiction to V being irreducible.

Proof of ii) $\Rightarrow$ iii). Let $U = \{a \in V - \mathbf{S}(V) : \gamma_a V \subset \gamma_a W\}$. Obviously U is open in $V - \mathbf{S}(V)$. Also V is irreducible at each point in $V - \mathbf{S}(V)$, and hence U is closed in $V - \mathbf{S}(V)$ by (33.7). Now V is the closure of $V - \mathbf{S}(V)$ in X, W is closed in X, and by assumption $V \not\subset W$. Therefore $V - \mathbf{S}(V) \not\subset W$ and hence $U \neq V - \mathbf{S}(V)$. Since $V - \mathbf{S}(V)$ is connected, we must have $U = \emptyset$. Therefore $(V - \mathbf{S}(V)) \cap W$ is nowhere dense in $V - \mathbf{S}(V)$ by (33.8). Since $\mathbf{S}(V)$ is nowhere dense in V, we conclude that $V \cap W$ is nowhere dense in V.

Proof of iii) $\Rightarrow$ i). Let V' and V'' be any analytic sets in X such that $V = V' \cup V''$ and $V \neq V''$. Then there exists $a \in V$ with $a \notin V''$. Since V'' is closed in X, we must have $\gamma_a V = \gamma_a V'$. Hence V' is not nowhere dense in V. Therefore $V = V'$ by iii). This shows that V is irreducible.

Proof of ii) $\Rightarrow$ v). V is irreducible at every point in $V - \mathbf{S}(V)$. Hence by (34.3), $W \cap (V - \mathbf{S}(V))$ disconnects $V - \mathbf{S}(V)$ nowhere. By assumption $V - \mathbf{S}(V)$ is connected and hence by (14.5.4), $V - \mathbf{S}(V) - W$ is connected. Now $\mathbf{S}(V)$ is a thin subset of V and by assumption so is W.

[6] In view of i) $\Leftrightarrow$ ii), in the situation of (34.2.vi) we can say that: if $\gamma_a V$ is irreducible then $V \cap X'$ is irreducible.

[7] $V - W$ is then automatically arcwise connected and locally arcwise connected.

[8] If W is also closed in V then automatically $V - W$ is arcwise connected and locally arcwise connected.

Therefore $W \cup \mathbf{S}(V)$ is a thin subset of V. Consequently $V - W =$ closure of $V - \mathbf{S}(V) - W$ in $V - W$. Therefore $V - W$ is connected.

Proof of v) $\Rightarrow$ ii). Take $W = \mathbf{S}(V)$.

Proof of ii) $\Rightarrow$ iv). In virtue of (33.8), this follows from "ii) $\Rightarrow$ iii)" and "ii) $\Rightarrow$ v)".

Proof of iv) $\Rightarrow$ ii). Follows by taking $W = \mathbf{S}(V)$ and using the fact proved in (33.24) that $\mathbf{S}(V)$ is analytic. If we do not want to use (33.24) then we can proceed as follows. Supposing that I contains more than one element, we want to exhibit an analytic set W in X such that $V \not\subset W$ and $V - W$ is disconnected. Take $i \in I$, and let

$$V' = \bar{V}_i, \qquad V'' = \bigcup_{\substack{i^* \in I \\ i^* \neq i}} \bar{V}_{i^*}, \qquad \text{and} \qquad W = V' \cap V''.$$

Then by (34.6, 34.8): W is an analytic set in X; $V \not\subset W$; $V' - W$ and $V'' - W$ are nonempty disjoint closed subsets of $V - W$; and $V - W = (V' - W) \cup (V'' - W)$.

(**34.11**) *If V is irreducible then V is pure dimensional.*

Proof. For any $\mu \leqq n$ let $V^{(\mu)} = \{a \in V - \mathbf{S}(V) \colon \dim_a V = \mu\}$. Since V is irreducible at each point in $V - \mathbf{S}(V)$, by (33.3) we deduce that $V^{(\mu)}$ is an open subset of $V - \mathbf{S}(V)$. Thus $V - \mathbf{S}(V)$ is the union of the finite number of pairwise disjoint open subsets $V^{(0)}, \ldots, V^{(n)}$. By (34.10), $V - \mathbf{S}(V)$ is connected and hence we must have $V = V^{(e)}$ for some $e \leqq n$, i.e., V is pure dimensional in $V - \mathbf{S}(V)$. Therefore V is pure dimensional by (33.20).

(**34.12**) *If V is connected and $\gamma_a V$ is irreducible for all $a \in V$, then V is irreducible.*

Proof. By (34.3), $\mathbf{S}(V)$ disconnects V nowhere and hence by (14.5.4), $V - \mathbf{S}(V)$ is connected. Therefore V is irreducible by (34.10).

(**34.13**) *For all $i \in I$, $\bar{V}_i$ is an irreducible analytic set in X.*

Proof. By (34.7), $\bar{V}_i - \mathbf{S}(\bar{V}_i) =$ closure of V_i in $\bar{V}_i - \mathbf{S}(\bar{V}_i)$. Therefore $\bar{V}_i - \mathbf{S}(\bar{V}_i)$ is connected. Hence $\bar{V}_i$ is irreducible by (34.10).

(**34.14**) Identity Theorem for Analytic Sets. *For any nonempty irreducible analytic set W in X we have the following.*

1) *The following three conditions are equivalent.*

i) $W \subset V$.
ii) $W \subset \bar{V}_i$ *for some* $i \in I$.
iii) *There exist* $a \in W$ *and an irreducible component* W^* *of* $\gamma_a W$ *such that* $W^* \subset \gamma_a V$.

2) *The following three conditions are equivalent.*

i′) $W = \bar{V}_i$ *for some* $i \in I$.
ii′) *There exist* $a \in W$, *an irreducible component* W^* *of* $\gamma_a W$ *and an irreducible component* V^* *of* $\gamma_a V$ *such that* $W^* = V^*$.
iii′) *Given any* $a \in W$ *and any irreducible component* W^* *of* $\gamma_a W$, *there exists an irreducible component* V^* *of* $\gamma_a V$ *such that* $W^* = V^*$.

It is obvious that ii) ⇒ i) ⇒ iii) and iii′) ⇒ ii′); also i′) ⇒ iii′) by (34.5). Hence it suffices to show that iii) ⇒ ii) and ii′) ⇒ i′).

Proof of iii) ⇒ ii). By (34.5), $W^* \subset \gamma_a \bar{V}_i$ for some $i \in I$. Hence by (33.8), $W \cap \bar{V}_i$ is not nowhere dense in W. Since W is irreducible, upon taking $(W, \bar{V}_i)$ for (V, W) in (34.10.iii) we get that $W \subset \bar{V}_i$.

Proof of ii′) ⇒ i′). By (34.5), V^* is an irreducible component of $\gamma_a \bar{V}_i$ for some $i \in I$. Now $W^* = V^* \subset \gamma_a \bar{V}_i$ and W is irreducible; hence $W \subset \bar{V}_i$ by 1). Again $V^* = W^* \subset \gamma_a W$ and by (34.13), $\bar{V}_i$ is irreducible; hence $\bar{V}_i \subset W$ by 1). Therefore $W = \bar{V}_i$.

(**34.15**) $W \subset X$ *is an irreducible component of* $V \Leftrightarrow W = \bar{V}_i$ *for some* $i \in I$. *Hence* V *is the irredundant union of its irreducible components.*

Proof. Let $i \in I$ be given. By (34.13), $\bar{V}_i$ is an irreducible analytic set in X. Let $\bar{V}_i \subset V' \subset V$ where V' is any irreducible analytic set in X. By (34.14.1), $V' \subset \bar{V}_{i'}$ for some $i' \in I$. Hence $\bar{V}_i = V' = \bar{V}_{i'}$ by (34.8). Conversely let W be any irreducible component of V. By (34.14.1), $W \subset \bar{V}_i$ for some $i \in I$. By (34.13), $\bar{V}_i$ is irreducible and hence $W = \bar{V}_i$. The last assertion now follows from (34.6, 34.8).

(**34.16**) *Assume that* V *is pure* e *dimensional. Then* $\bar{V}_i$ *is pure* e *dimensional for all* $i \in I$. *Let* W *be any pure* e *dimensional analytic set in* X *such that* $W \subset V$. *Then there exists* $I^* \subset I$ *such that* $(\bar{V}_i)_{i \in I^*}$ *are exactly all the distinct irreducible components of* W *and* $W = \bigcup_{i \in I^*} \bar{V}_i$.

The first assertion follows from (34.5), and then the second assertion follows by first applying (34.15) to W and then applying (34.14.2) to each irreducible component of W.

(**34.17**) *Let W be any thin subset of V. Then $\bar{V}_i - W$ is connected and $\bar{V}_i = \mathrm{cl}_X(\bar{V}_i - W)$ for all $i \in I$. If furthermore $W \supset \mathbf{S}(V)$ then $(\bar{V}_i - W)_{i \in I}$ are exactly all the distinct connected components of $V - W$.*

Follows from (34.9.2, 34.10, 34.13).

(**34.18**) *For any $\emptyset \neq I^* \subset I$ let $\tilde{V} = \bigcup_{i \in I^*} \bar{V}_i$. Then $(\bar{V}_i)_{i \in I^*}$ are exactly all the distinct irreducible components of $\tilde{V}$.*

Now $(V_i)_{i \in I}$ are the distinct connected components of $V - \mathbf{S}(V)$ and hence obviously $(V_i)_{i \in I^*}$ are the distinct connected components of $\tilde{V} - \mathbf{S}(V)$. By (33.8, 33.16, 34.5), $\mathbf{S}(\tilde{V}) \subset \mathbf{S}(V)$ and $\mathbf{S}(V) \cap \tilde{V}$ is a thin subset of $\tilde{V}$. Now apply (34.15) and (34.17) to $\tilde{V}$ by taking $\mathbf{S}(V)$ for W.

(**34.19**) *For any analytic set W in X we have: $W \cap V$ is nowhere dense in $V \Leftrightarrow \bar{V}_i \not\subset W$ for all $i \in I$.*[5]

Follows from (34.9.1, 34.10, 34.13).

(**34.20**) REMARK. So far we have not used the fact that $\mathbf{C}^n$ and hence V has a countable[9] basis of open sets. Using this fact we can show that V has only a countable number of irreducible components. Namely: Since V is locally arcwise connected, for any $i \in I$, V_i is open in $V - \mathbf{S}(V)$ and hence it is open in V. Thus $(V_i)_{i \in I}$ are pairwise disjoint nonempty open subsets of V. Since V has a countable basis of open sets, I must be countable. Alternatively: Take $a_i \in V_i$ and let

$$\tilde{V}_i = \bigcup_{\substack{i^* \in I \\ i^* \neq i}} \bar{V}_{i^*}.$$

Then by (34.6, 34.8), $a_i \notin \tilde{V}_i$ and $\tilde{V}_i$ is closed in V. Hence there is a neighborhood Y_i of a_i in V such that $Y_i \cap \tilde{V}_i = \emptyset$. Now $(Y_i)_{i \in I}$ are pairwise disjoint nonempty open subsets of V.

As an application of global decomposition we prove the following.

(**34.21**) *Assume that* $\dim V \leqq e < n$ *and $X = X^* - L$ where X^* is an open set in $\mathbf{C}^n$ and L is an affine subspace of $\mathbf{C}^n$ such that* $\dim L = e$.[10] *Let $p \in X^* \cap L$. Then for any i with $0 \leqq i \leqq e$ there exists an affine subspace M of $\mathbf{C}^n$ such that $p \in M$, $\dim M = n - e + i$, $\dim(L \cap M) = i$, and $\dim(V \cap M) \leqq i$.*

[9] A set is countable if it can be put in a one-to-one correspondence with a subset of the set of positive integers.

[10] Let L be any affine subspace of $\mathbf{C}^n$ and let h be the dimension of L in the sense of affine spaces. Then obviously L is an irreducible pure h dimensional analytic set in $\mathbf{C}^n$ and $\mathbf{S}(L) = \emptyset$.

PROOF. Induction on n. Assertion being trivial for $n = 1$, take $n > 1$ and assume true for $n - 1$. If $i = e$, take $M = \mathbf{C}^n$. Now suppose that $0 \leqq i < e$. Take $p' \in L$ such that $p' \neq p$. Take $p_i \in \bar{V}_i$. Now I is countable by (34.20). Since $\mathbf{C}$ is uncountable, and I is countable, we can find a hyperplane $\mathbf{C}^{n-1}$ in $\mathbf{C}^n$ such that $p \in \mathbf{C}^{n-1}$, $p' \notin \mathbf{C}^{n-1}$, and $p_i \notin \mathbf{C}^{n-1}$ for all $i \in I$. Let $\tilde{L} = L \cap \mathbf{C}^{n-1}$, $\tilde{X}^* = X^* \cap \mathbf{C}^{n-1}$, $\tilde{X} = \tilde{X}^* - \tilde{L}$, and $\tilde{V} = V \cap \mathbf{C}^{n-1}$. Then $\tilde{L}$ is an affine subspace of $\mathbf{C}^{n-1}$ of dimension $e - 1$, $\tilde{X}^*$ and $\tilde{X}$ are open sets in $\mathbf{C}^{n-1}$, and $\tilde{V}$ is an analytic set in $\tilde{X}$. By (34.19), $\dim \tilde{V} \leqq (\dim V) - 1 \leqq e - 1$. Now $n - e + i = (n - 1) - (e - 1) + i$ and $i \leqq e - 1$, and hence by induction hypothesis there exists an affine subspace M of $\mathbf{C}^{n-1}$ such that $p \in M$, $\dim M = n - e + i$, $\dim(\tilde{L} \cap M) = i$, and $\dim(\tilde{V} \cap M) \leqq i$. Obviously $\tilde{L} \cap M = L \cap M$ and $\tilde{V} \cap M = V \cap M$.

§34C. *Maximum Principle*

Let V be a nonempty analytic set in an open set X in $\mathbf{C}^n$.

(**34.22**) *For any $f \in R(V)$ and $a \in V$ we have the following.*

1) OPEN MAP THEOREM. *The following eight conditions are equivalent.*

α) (resp: $\alpha_1, \alpha_2, \alpha_3$). $\gamma_a f$ (resp: $\gamma_a |f|$, $\gamma_a \mathbf{Re}\, f$, $\gamma_a \mathbf{Im}\, f$) *is nonconstant.*
β) (resp: $\beta_1, \beta_2, \beta_3$). *The map* f (resp: $|f|$, $\mathbf{Re}\, f$, $\mathbf{Im}\, f$) *of* V *into* $\mathbf{C}$ (resp: $\mathbf{R}_+$, $\mathbf{R}$, $\mathbf{R}$) *is open at* a.

2) MAXIMUM PRINCIPLE. *If any one of the following five conditions is satisfied then* $\gamma_a f$, $\gamma_a |f|$, $\gamma_a \mathbf{Re}\, f$, *and* $\gamma_a \mathbf{Im}\, f$ *are constant.*

i) $|f(a)| = \sup |f(V)|$.

ii) $\mathbf{Re}\, f(a) = \sup \mathbf{Re}\, f(V)$. iii) $\mathbf{Re}\, f(a) = \inf \mathbf{Re}\, f(V)$.

ii′) $\mathbf{Im}\, f(a) = \sup \mathbf{Im}\, f(V)$. iii′) $\mathbf{Im}\, f(a) = \inf \mathbf{Im}\, f(V)$.

PROOF. $\alpha \Leftrightarrow \beta$ is proved in (33.15). $\beta \Rightarrow \beta_1$, $\beta \Rightarrow \beta_2$, $\beta \Rightarrow \beta_3$ because $t \to |t|$, $t \to \mathbf{Re}\, t$, $t \to \mathbf{Im}\, t$ are open maps of $\mathbf{C}$ onto $\mathbf{R}_+$, $\mathbf{R}$, $\mathbf{R}$, respectively. Obviously $\beta_j \Rightarrow \alpha_j \Rightarrow \alpha$ for $j = 1, 2, 3$. This proves 1). 2) follows from 1).

(**34.23**) *If V is irreducible then we have the following.*

1) IDENTITY THEOREM. *For any $f \neq g$ in $R(V)$ let $W = \{a \in V : f(a) = g(a)\}$. Then $W = \emptyset$ or W is a pure $e - 1$ dimensional analytic set in X where $e = \dim V$; in either case W is nowhere dense in V.*

2) Open Map Theorem. *For any* $f \in R(V)$ *the following twelve conditions are equivalent.*

α) (resp: α_1, α_2, α_3). $\gamma_a f$ (resp: $\gamma_a|f|$, $\gamma_a \mathbf{Re}\, f$, $\gamma_a \mathbf{Im}\, f$) *is nonconstant for some* $a \in V$.
β) (resp: β_1, β_2, β_3). f (resp: $|f|$, $\mathbf{Re}\, f$, $\mathbf{Im}\, f$) *is nonconstant.*
γ) (resp: γ_1, γ_2, γ_3). f (resp: $|f|$, $\mathbf{Re}\, f$, $\mathbf{Im}\, f$) *is an open map of* V *into* $\mathbf{C}$ (resp: $\mathbf{R}_+$, $\mathbf{R}$, $\mathbf{R}$).

3) Maximum Principle. *For any* $f \in R(V)$ *the following ten conditions are equivalent, and if any one of them is satisfied then* f, $|f|$, $\mathbf{Re}\, f$, *and* $\mathbf{Im}\, f$ *are constant.*

i) $|f(a)| = \sup|f(V)|$ *for some* $a \in V$.
ii) $|f(a)| = \sup|f(V^*)|$ *for some neighborhood* V^* *of some point* $a \in V$.
iii) $\mathbf{Re}\, f(a) = \sup \mathbf{Re}\, f(V)$ *for some* $a \in V$.
iv) $\mathbf{Re}\, f(a) = \sup \mathbf{Re}\, f(V^*)$ *for some neighborhood* V^* *of some point* $a \in V$.
v) $\mathbf{Re}\, f(a) = \inf \mathbf{Re}\, f(V)$ *for some* $a \in V$.
vi) $\mathbf{Re}\, f(a) = \inf \mathbf{Re}\, f(V^*)$ *for some neighborhood* V^* *of some point* $a \in V$.
iii′, iv′, v′, vi′). *Same as* iii, iv, v, vi) *with* **Im** *replacing* **Re**.

Proof. 1) follows from (34.10, 34.11, 33.1.3, 33.8). From 1) we get that: f is constant $\Leftrightarrow$ $\gamma_a f$ is constant for some $a \in V$. In view of this, 2) and 3) follow from (34.22).

§34D. *Consequences of the Maximum Principle*

Let $y = (y_1, \ldots, y_e)$, $z = (z_1, \ldots, z_m)$. Let $\pi: \mathbf{C}^e\{y\} \times \mathbf{C}^m\{z\} \to \mathbf{C}^e\{y\}$ be the natural projection. For any $\beta \in \mathbf{C}^e\{y\}$ and positive real number D let

$$Y\langle D, \beta\rangle = \{b \in \mathbf{C}^e: |b_i - \beta_i| < D \text{ for } i = 1, \ldots, e\},$$

$$\bar{Y}\langle D, \beta\rangle = \{b \in \mathbf{C}^e: |b_i - \beta_i| \leqq D \text{ for } i = 1, \ldots, e\},$$

$$\mathring{Y}\langle D, \beta\rangle = \{b \in \mathbf{C}^e: |b_i - \beta_i| = D \text{ for } i = 1, \ldots, e\}.$$

Let Y and Z be nonempty open sets in $\mathbf{C}^e\{y\}$ and $\mathbf{C}^m\{z\}$ respectively. Let $\mathring{Z}$ be the boundary of Z in $\mathbf{C}^m\{z\}$.

(**34.24**) *Let* W *be any analytic set in* Z.

1) *If* W *is compact then* $\dim W = 0$ *and* W *consists of a finite number of points.*

2) *If* Z *is bounded and* $\mathring{Z} \cap$ *(closure of* W *in* $\mathbf{C}^m$) $= \emptyset$ *then* W *is compact.*

PROOF. 2) is obvious. To prove 1) let W' be any irreducible component of W. Then W' is closed in W and hence W' is compact. Therefore $|z_i(c^{(i)})| = \sup|z_i(W')|$ for some $c^{(i)} \in W'$. Hence by (34.23.3), $z_i|W'$ is constant for $i = 1,\ldots, m$; i.e., W' is a point. Therefore by (34.6), $\dim W = 0$, i.e., W consists of isolated points. Since W is compact, it must be finite.

(**34.25**) *Assume that Z is bounded and contains the origin* (0). *Let W be any analytic set in $Z - \{(0)\}$ such that $\mathring{Z} \cap$ (closure of W in $\mathbf{C}^m$) $= \emptyset$. Then* $\dim W = 0$, *i.e., W consists of isolated points.*

PROOF. In virtue of (34.6) it suffices to show that any irreducible component W' of W consists of a single point. Let $\bar{W}'$ be the closure of W' in $\mathbf{C}^m$. Then $\bar{W}'$ is bounded and hence compact. Consequently $|z_i(c^{(i)})| = \sup|z_i(\bar{W}')|$ for some $c^{(i)} \in \bar{W}'$. Now W' is closed in $Z - \{(0)\}$ and hence $\bar{W}' = W'$ or $\bar{W}' = W' \cup \{(0)\}$. If $|z_i(c^{(i)})| = 0$ then $z_i|W' \equiv 0$. If $|z_i(c^{(i)})| \neq 0$ then $c^{(i)} \in W'$ and $|z_i(c^{(i)})| = \sup|z_i(W')|$, whence $z_i|W'$ is constant by (34.23.3). Thus $z_1|W',\ldots, z_m|W'$ are constant, i.e., W' is a point.

(**34.26**) LEMMA. *Let V be an analytic set in $Y \times Z$. Let $\beta \in Y$ and $\gamma \in Z$ be such that $\alpha = (\beta, \gamma) \in V$.*

1) *Assume that $\dim_\alpha V = e$, and α is an isolated point of $V \cap (\beta \times Z)$. Then $\pi|V: V \to \mathbf{C}^e$ is open at α; and hence $y_i|V: V \to \mathbf{C}$ is open at α for $i = 1,\ldots, e$.*

2) *Assume that V is pure e dimensional at α, and α is an isolated point of $V \cap (\beta \times Z)$. Let L be any h dimensional affine subspace of $\mathbf{C}^e\{y\}$ passing through β, $(h \leqq e)$. Then $V \cap (L \times Z)$ is pure h dimensional at α.*

PROOF. In virtue of (23.3), 1) and 2) follow from (32.1.1) and (33.3, 33.7, 33.8), respectively.

(**34.27**) *Let V be a pure e dimensional analytic set in $Y \times Z$.*[11] *Let $\bar{V}$ be the closure of V in $\mathbf{C}^e\{y\} \times \mathbf{C}^m\{z\}$. Assume that Y is connected, Z is bounded, and $(Y \times \mathring{Z}) \cap \bar{V} = \emptyset$. Then for any $\beta \in Y$, $V \cap (\beta \times Z)$ is a nonempty finite set.*

PROOF.

1°) *For any $\beta \in Y$, $V \cap (\beta \times Z)$ is finite.* Follows by (34.24).

[11] By definition V is then nonempty.

2°) $\pi|V: V \to \mathbf{C}^e$ *is open, and hence* $\pi(V)$ *is a nonempty open subset of* Y. Follows by 1°) and (34.26.1).

Since Y is connected, it now remains to show that $\pi(V)$ is closed in Y. So let $\beta \in$ (closure of $\pi(V)$ in Y) be given. We want to show that $\beta \in \pi(V)$. Take $D > 0$ such that $\bar{Y}\langle D, \beta\rangle \subset Y$. Then $Y\langle D, \beta\rangle \cap \pi(V) \neq \emptyset$. Let $\tilde{V} = V \cap (\bar{Y}\langle D, \beta\rangle \times Z)$. Then $\tilde{V}$ is a closed subset of the compact set $\bar{Y}\langle D, \beta\rangle \times (Z \cup \mathring{Z})$. Hence $\tilde{V}$ is a nonempty compact set.

3°) $\beta \in \pi(V)$ *in case* $e = 1$. Suppose not. Let f and g be the restrictions to V of the functions $y - \beta$ and $1/(y - \beta)$. Then $\inf|f(\tilde{V})| = E > 0$ and $|f(\alpha)| = E$ for some $\alpha \in \tilde{V}$. Obviously $\inf|f(\tilde{V})| = \inf|f(V)|$. Therefore $|f(\alpha)| = E = \inf|f(V)|$. Hence $|g(\alpha)| = 1/E = \sup|g(V)|$. Therefore by (34.22), $\gamma_\alpha g$ is constant and hence so is $\gamma_\alpha f$. Thus $\pi|V: V \to \mathbf{C}^e$ is not open at $\alpha \in V$, in contradiction to 2°).[12]

4°) $\beta \in \pi(V)$ *in the general case*. By induction on k we shall show that for any k with $0 \leqq k \leqq e$ there exists $\tilde{\beta} \in Y\langle D, \beta\rangle \cap \pi(V)$ such that $\tilde{\beta}_i = \beta_i$ for all $i \leqq k$. Now $Y\langle D, \beta\rangle \cap \pi(V) \neq \emptyset$ and hence for $k = 0$ we can take $\tilde{\beta}$ to be any point in $Y\langle D, \beta\rangle \cap \pi(V)$. Now let $0 < k \leqq e$ and assume that we have found $\beta' \in Y\langle D, \beta\rangle \cap \pi(V)$ such that $\beta'_i = \beta_i$ for all $i \leqq k - 1$. Let

$$L = \{b \in Y\langle D, \beta\rangle : b_i = \beta'_i \text{ for } i = 1,\ldots, k-1, k+1,\ldots, e\}.$$

Then $V \cap (L \times Z) \neq \emptyset$;

$$(L \times \mathring{Z}) \cap (\text{closure of } V \cap (L \times Z) \text{ in } L \times \mathbf{C}^m\{z\}) = \emptyset;$$

and by 1°) and (34.26.2) it follows that $V \cap (L \times Z)$ is a pure one dimensional analytic set in $L \times Z$. Now L can be considered to be a domain in $\mathbf{C}^1\{y_k\}$ and hence by the $e = 1$ case, there exists $\tilde{\gamma} \in Z$ such that $(\beta_1,\ldots, \beta_k, \beta'_{k+1},\ldots, \beta'_e, \tilde{\gamma}) \in V \cap (L \times Z)$. Let $\tilde{\beta} = (\beta_1,\ldots, \beta_k, \beta'_{k+1},\ldots, \beta'_e)$. Then $\tilde{\beta} \in Y\langle D, \beta\rangle \cap \pi(V)$ and $\tilde{\beta}_i = \beta_i$ for all $i \leqq k$.

(34.28) *Assume that Z contains the origin* (0) *of* $\mathbf{C}^m\{z\}$. *Let V be a pure e dimensional analytic set in $Y \times (Z - \{(0)\})$.*[11] *Let $\bar{V}$ be the closure of V in $\mathbf{C}^e\{y\} \times \mathbf{C}^m\{z\}$. Let U be the closure of $\pi(V)$ in Y. Assume that Y is connected, Z is bounded, and $(Y \times \mathring{Z}) \cap \bar{V} = \emptyset$. Then $U = Y$.*

Also consider the following weaker statement.

(34.28′) *Assume that Z contains the origin* (0) *of* $\mathbf{C}^m\{z\}$. *Let V be a pure e dimensional analytic set in $Y \times (Z - \{(0)\})$.*[11] *Let $\bar{V}$ be the closure of V*

[12] This completes the proof of (34.27) in case $e = 1$.

n $\mathbf{C}^e\{y\} \times \mathbf{C}^m\{z\}$. *Let* U *be the closure of* $\pi(V)$ *in* Y. *Assume that* $Y = Y\langle D, \beta\rangle$ *for some* $\beta \in \mathbf{C}^e\{y\}$ *and* $D > 0$, Z *is bounded and* $(Y \times \mathring{Z}) \cap \bar{V} = \emptyset$. *Then* $\beta \in U$.

Proof of (34.28) is in three steps.

1°) *For given* e: *if* (34.28′) *holds then* (34.28) *holds.*

PROOF. Fix $\tilde{\beta} \in \pi(V)$. Let β' be any point in Y. Join β' to $\tilde{\beta}$ by an arc in Y. By compactness of an arc we can find a finite number of points $\beta^{(1)},\ldots, \beta^{(p+1)}$ in Y and positive real numbers $D_1,\ldots, D_{p+1}$ such that: $\beta^{(1)} = \beta'$, $\beta^{(p+1)} = \tilde{\beta}$; $Y\langle D_q, \beta^{(q)}\rangle \subset Y$ for $q = 1,\ldots, p+1$; and $\beta^{(q+1)} \in Y\langle D, \beta^{(q)}\rangle$ for $q = 1,\ldots, p$. Suppose $\beta^{(q)} \notin U$ for some $q \leqq p$; then applying (34.28′) to $V \cap (Y\langle D_q, \beta^{(q)}\rangle \times Z)$ we deduce that $Y\langle D_q, \beta^{(q)}\rangle \cap \pi(V) = \emptyset$; since $Y\langle D_q, \beta^{(q)}\rangle$ is a neighborhood of $\beta^{(q+1)}$ we must have $\beta^{(q+1)} \notin U$. Thus for any $q \leqq p$: $\beta^{(q)} \notin U \Rightarrow {}^{(}\beta^{q+1)} \notin U$. Now $\tilde{\beta} = \beta^{(p+1)} \in \pi(V) \subset U$ and hence we must have $\beta' = \beta^{(1)} \in U$.

2°) (34.28) *holds in case* $e = 1$.

PROOF. By 1°) it suffices to show that (34.28′) holds in case $e = 1$. Upon replacing V by an irreducible component of V we may assume that V is irreducible. Suppose if possible that $\beta \notin U$. Then there exists $0 < A < 1$ such that

1′) $$Y\langle AD, \beta\rangle \cap U = \emptyset.$$

Take $\tilde{\beta} \in Y\langle D, \beta\rangle$, $\tilde{\gamma} \in Z - \{(0)\}$ such that $(\tilde{\beta}, \tilde{\gamma}) \in V$. Relabeling $z_1,\ldots, z_m$ we can arrange that $\tilde{\gamma}_1 \neq 0$. Since Z is bounded, there exists $E > 0$ such that $|c_1| \leqq E$ for all $c \in Z$. Now $|(\tilde{\beta} - \beta)/D| < 1$ and hence there exists a positive integer q such that

2′) $$E|(\tilde{\beta} - \beta)/D|^q < |\tilde{\gamma}_1|.$$

Let f be the restriction to $\bar{V}$ of the function $(D^q/E)z_1/(y - \beta)^q$. Then f is continuous on the compact set $\bar{V}$ and hence

$|f(\tilde{b}, \tilde{c})| = N = \sup |f(\bar{V})|$ for some $(\tilde{b}, \tilde{c}) \in \bar{V}$, $\tilde{b} \in \bar{Y}\langle D, \beta\rangle$, $\tilde{c} \in Z \cup \mathring{Z}$. Now $|f(\tilde{\beta}, \tilde{\gamma})| > 1$ and hence $N > 1$. Next,

$$\bar{V} - V \subset [\mathring{Y}\langle D, \beta\rangle \times (Z \cup \mathring{Z})] \cup [\bar{Y}\langle D, \beta\rangle \times \{(0)\}]$$

and hence $|f(b, c)| \leqq 1$ for all $(b, c) \in \bar{V} - V$. Therefore $(\tilde{b}, \tilde{c}) \in V$. Consequently $f \equiv f(\tilde{b}, \tilde{c})$ on V by (34.23.3). Let $M = f(\tilde{b}, \tilde{c})E/D^q$. Then $M \neq 0$ is a complex constant and

3′) $$z_1 \equiv M(y - \beta)^q \quad \text{on} \quad V.$$

Now there are two methods for completing the proof of 2°).

First method. Let V^* be the closure of V in $Y \times Z$. By 1′) and 3′),

$$|c_1| \geqq |M|(AD)^q > 0 \qquad \text{for all} \quad (b, c) \in V^*.$$

Therefore $V^* \cap (Y \times \{(0)\}) = \emptyset$. Now V is closed in $Y \times (Z - \{(0)\})$ and hence $V^* - V \subset Y \times \{(0)\}$. Therefore $V = V^*$ and V is closed in $Y \times Z$, i.e., V is an analytic set in $Y \times Z$. Therefore by (34.27), $\pi(V) = Y$ and hence in particular $\beta \in U$ in contradiction to our supposition.

Second method. Let q' be any positive integer such that $q' > q$. Then by 2′)

$$E|(\tilde{\beta} - \beta)/\mathrm{D}|^{q'} < |\tilde{\gamma}_1|.$$

Hence by the argument which led from 2′) to 3′) we conclude that

4′) $z_1 \equiv M'(y - \beta)^{q'}$ on V, where $M' \neq 0$ is a complex constant.

Let

$$g(y) = (y - \beta)^q(M'(y - \beta)^{q'-q} - M).$$

By 3′) and 4′), $g \equiv 0$ on $\pi(V)$ and hence $\pi(V)$ consists of a finite number of points. However by (34.25, 34.26.1), $\pi|V: V \to Y$ is open. Contradiction.

3°) (34.28) *holds in the general case.*

Proof. By 1°) it suffices to prove (34.28′). We want to show that $\beta \in U$, i.e., we want to show that $Y\langle B, \beta\rangle \cap \pi(V) \neq \emptyset$ for any B with $0 < B \leqq D$. By induction on k we shall show that for any k with $0 \leqq k \leqq e$ there exists $\tilde{\beta} \in \pi(V)$ such that $|\tilde{\beta}_i - \beta_i| < B$ for all $i \leqq k$. For $k = 0$ we can take $\tilde{\beta}$ to be any point in $\pi(V)$. So let $0 < k \leqq e$ and suppose that we have found $\beta' \in \pi(V)$ such that $|\tilde{\beta}_i - \beta_i| < B$ for all $i \leqq k - 1$. Let

$$L = \{b \in Y\langle D, \beta\rangle : b_i = \beta'_i \text{ for } i = 1,\ldots, k - 1, k + 1,\ldots, e\}.$$

Then $V \cap (L \times Z) \neq \emptyset$;

$$(L \times \mathring{Z}) \cap (\text{closure of } V \cap (L \times Z) \text{ in } L \times \mathbf{C}^m\{z\}) = \emptyset;$$

and by (34.25, 34.26.2), $V \cap (L \times (Z - \{(0)\}))$ is a pure one dimensional analytic set in $L \times (Z - \{(0)\})$. Now L can be considered to be a domain in $\mathbf{C}^1\{y_k\}$ and hence by 2°) there exists $\beta^*_k \in \mathbf{C}$ and $\gamma^* \in Z - \{(0)\}$ such that $|\beta^*_k - \beta_k| < B$ and $(\beta'_1,\ldots, \beta'_{k-1}, \beta^*_k, \beta'_{k+1},\ldots, \beta'_e, \gamma^*) \in V$. Let $\tilde{\beta} = (\beta'_1,\ldots, \beta'_{k+1}, \beta^*_k, \beta'_{k+1},\ldots, \beta'_e)$. Then $\tilde{\beta} \in \pi(V)$ and $|\tilde{\beta}_i - \beta_i| < B$ for all $i \leqq k$.

§35. PARAMETRIZATION OF A PURE DIMENSIONAL ANALYTIC SET

Let $y = (y_1,\dots, y_e)$, $z = (z_1,\dots, z_m)$, $S = K[\langle y\rangle]$, $R = K[\langle y, z\rangle]$. Let $\pi: K^e\{y\} \times K^m\{z\} \to K^e\{y\}$ be the natural projection. For any $D > 0$, $E > 0$, $\beta \in K^e$, $\gamma \in K^m$, let

$$Y\langle D, \beta\rangle = \{b \in K^e: |b_i - \beta_i| < D \text{ for } i = 1,\dots, e\},$$
$$Z\langle E, \gamma\rangle = \{c \in K^m: |c_i - \gamma_i| < E \text{ for } i = 1,\dots, m\}.$$

We write $Y\langle D\rangle$ for $Y\langle D, (0)\rangle$ and $Z\langle E\rangle$ for $Z\langle E, (0)\rangle$.

§35A. *Local parametrization*

(35.1) Let $\mathfrak{a}$ be a proper ideal in R. Assume that all the minimal prime ideals $\mathfrak{p}_1,\dots, \mathfrak{p}_\mu$ of $\mathfrak{a}$ are strictly regular relative to S.[1] Let $g_i(y, z_i)$ be the minimal monic polynomial of z_i mod $\mathfrak{p}_1 \cap\dots\cap \mathfrak{p}_\mu$ over S. Let $\varphi_j: R \to R/\mathfrak{p}_j$ be the natural epimorphism. Let $\mathfrak{L}_j$ be the quotient field of $R/\mathfrak{p}_j$ considered as an extension of $\mathfrak{K} = K(\langle y\rangle)$. Let $u_1,\dots, u_\Lambda$ be a finite basis of $\mathfrak{a}$, and let $u_{j1},\dots, u_{j\Lambda_j}$ be a finite basis of $\mathfrak{p}_j$. We can then find a neighborhood $X' = Y' \times Z'$ of the origin in $K^e \times K^m$ such that: the coefficients of $g_1(y, z_1),\dots, g_m(y, z_m)$ are convergent in Y'; all the elements u_k, u_{jk} are convergent in X'; and $V = V_1 \cup\dots\cup V_\mu$ where

$$V = \{a \in X': u_1(a) = \dots = u_\Lambda(a) = 0\},$$
$$V_j = \{a \in X': u_{j1}(a) = \dots = u_{j\Lambda_j}(a) = 0\}.$$

Let $\Delta_i(y)$ be the z_i-discriminant of g_i, and let

$$W = \{(b, c) \in Y' \times K^m: g_1(b, c_1) = \dots = g_m(b, c_m) = 0\},$$
$$\boldsymbol{\Delta} = \{b \in Y': \Delta_1\dots\Delta_m(b) = 0\}.$$

Then there exists a neighborhood $X = Y \times Z$ of the origin in $Y' \times Z'$ for which we have (1 *to* 6).

1) $V \cap X \subset W \cap (Y \times K^m) = W \cap X$.

2) *For any $\alpha \in X$ let $\mathfrak{P}_{j1},\dots, \mathfrak{P}_{jt_j}$ be the distinct prime ideals of $\boldsymbol{\sigma}(\mathfrak{i}(\alpha, V_j, X))$ where $\boldsymbol{\sigma}: R(\alpha, X) \to R$ is the Taylor isomorphism. Then $\mathfrak{P}_{jk}$ is strictly regular relative to S for all j, k; and $\mathfrak{P}_{11},\dots, \mathfrak{P}_{1t_1}, \mathfrak{P}_{21},\dots, \mathfrak{P}_{2t_2},\dots, \mathfrak{P}_{\mu t_\mu}$ are exactly all the distinct prime ideals of $\boldsymbol{\sigma}(\mathfrak{i}(\alpha, V, X))$. In particular, $V_1,\dots, V_\mu$, V are pure e dimensional in X.*

3) *For any $\alpha \in V \cap X$, $\mathbf{d}(\alpha, \pi, V_1),\dots, \mathbf{d}(\alpha, \pi, V_\mu)$, $\mathbf{d}(\alpha, \pi, V)$ are defined and*

$$\mathbf{d}(\alpha, \pi, V) = \sum_{j=1}^{\mu} \mathbf{d}(\alpha, \pi, V_j).$$

[1] By (23.3) it then follows that rad $\mathfrak{a} = \mathfrak{p}_1 \cap\dots\cap \mathfrak{p}_\mu$ is regular relative to S.

4) $\Delta \cap Y$ *is nowhere dense in* Y. *For any* $\alpha \in V \cap X$ *with* $\pi\alpha \notin \Delta$ *we have that*: α *is a simple point of* V, $\mathbf{d}(\alpha, \pi, V) = 1$, *and* $\boldsymbol{\gamma}_\alpha V = \boldsymbol{\gamma}_\alpha W$.

5) *For any* $\beta \in Y$ *we have*

$$\sum_{\alpha \in V_j \cap (\beta \times Z)} \mathbf{d}(\alpha, \pi, V_j) = \mathbf{d}((0), \pi, V_j) = [\mathfrak{L}_j : \mathfrak{K}] \qquad \text{for} \quad j = 1,\ldots, \mu,$$

and hence

$$\sum_{\alpha \in V \cap (\beta \times Z)} \mathbf{d}(\alpha, \pi, V) = \mathbf{d}((0), \pi, V) = \sum_{j=1}^{\mu} [\mathfrak{L}_j : \mathfrak{K}].$$

6) *Given* $\beta \in Y$ *let* $\alpha^{(\theta)} = (\beta, \gamma^{(\theta)})$, $(\theta = 1,\ldots, N)$, *be all the distinct points in* $V \cap (\beta \times Z)$. *Then there exist* $D > 0$, $E > 0$ *for which we have* (i *to* vi).

i) $$Y\langle D, \beta\rangle \subset Y; \qquad \bigcup_{\theta=1}^{N} Z\langle E, \gamma^{(\theta)}\rangle \subset Z;$$

$$Z\langle E, \gamma^{(\theta)}\rangle \cap Z\langle E, \gamma^{(\theta')}\rangle = \emptyset \qquad \text{for all} \quad \theta \neq \theta'.$$

ii) $$V \cap (Y\langle D, \beta\rangle \times Z) = \bigcup_{\theta=1}^{N} [V \cap (Y\langle D, \beta\rangle \times Z\langle E, \gamma^{(\theta)}\rangle)].$$

iii) *For any* $b \in Y\langle D, \beta\rangle$ *and* $\theta \leqq N$ we *have*

$$\sum_{a \in V_j \cap (b \times Z\langle E, \gamma^{(\theta)}\rangle)} \mathbf{d}(a, \pi, V_j) = \mathbf{d}(\alpha^{(\theta)}, \pi, V_j) \qquad \text{for} \quad j = 1,\ldots, \mu,$$

and hence

$$\sum_{a \in V \cap (b \times Z\langle E, \gamma^{(\theta)}\rangle)} \mathbf{d}(a, \pi, V) = \mathbf{d}(\alpha^{(\theta)}, \pi, V).$$

iv) $\pi[V \cap (Y\langle D, \beta\rangle \times Z\langle E, \gamma^{(\theta)}\rangle)] = Y\langle D, \beta\rangle \qquad$ *for* $\theta = 1,\ldots, N$.

v) *Given* $0 < E^* \leqq E$ *there exists* $0 < D^* \leqq D$ *such that*

$$V \cap (Y\langle D^*, \beta\rangle \times Z\langle E, \gamma^{(\theta)}\rangle) = V \cap (Y\langle D^*, \beta\rangle \times Z\langle E^*, \gamma^{(\theta)}\rangle)$$

for $\theta = 1,\ldots, N$.

vi) *If* $\beta \notin \Delta$ *then there exist* $\xi^{(\theta)} = (\xi_1^{(\theta)},\ldots, \xi_m^{(\theta)}) \in S^m$ *which are convergent in* $Y\langle D\rangle$ *such that*

$$V \cap (Y\langle D, \beta\rangle \times Z\langle E, \gamma^{(\theta)}\rangle)$$
$$= \{(b, \xi^{(\theta)}(b_1 - \beta_1,\ldots, b_e - \beta_e)) : b \in Y\langle D, \beta\rangle\} \qquad \text{for} \quad \theta = 1,\ldots, N.$$

Proof. Now $0 \neq \Delta_1 \ldots \Delta_m \in S$ and hence upon replacing Y' by a smaller neighborhood of the origin we can arrange that

1°) $\Delta \cap Y'$ is nowhere dense in Y'.

Since $g_i(y, z_i) \in \mathfrak{p}_1 \cap \ldots \cap \mathfrak{p}_\mu$ for $i = 1, \ldots, m$, by continuity of roots (11.3), we can find $D' > 0$, $E' > 0$ such that 2°) and 3°) hold.

2°) $Y\langle D' \rangle \subset Y'$, $Z\langle E' \rangle \subset Z'$, and

$$V \cap (Y\langle D' \rangle \times Z\langle E' \rangle) \subset W \cap (Y\langle D' \rangle \times K^m) = W \cap (Y\langle D' \rangle \times Z\langle E' \rangle).$$

3°) Given $0 < E^* \leqq E'$ there exists $0 < \psi(E^*) \leqq D'$ depending on E^* such that $W \cap (Y\langle \psi(E^*) \rangle \times K^m) = W \cap (Y\langle \psi(E^*) \rangle \times Z\langle E^* \rangle)$.

By (25.9) we get the following:

4°) Let α be any point in $W \cap (Y\langle D' \rangle \times Z\langle E' \rangle)$ and let $\boldsymbol{\sigma}: R(\alpha, X) \to R$ be the Taylor isomorphism. Then every prime ideal of $\boldsymbol{\sigma}(\mathfrak{i}(\alpha, W, X))$ is strictly regular relative to S. If $\pi\alpha \notin \boldsymbol{\Delta}$ then α is a simple point of W and $\mathbf{d}(\alpha, \pi, W) = 1$.

By (33.3, 33.11) we can find a neighborhood $X'' = Y'' \times Z''$ of the origin in $Y\langle D' \rangle \times Z\langle E' \rangle$ for which we have the following:

5°) For any $\alpha \in V \cap X''$, $\boldsymbol{\gamma}_\alpha V$ is pure e dimensional and letting $V_{j1} \cup \ldots \cup V_{jt_j}$ to be the normal decomposition of $\boldsymbol{\gamma}_\alpha V_j$ for $j = 1, \ldots, \mu$ we have that $V_{11} \cup \ldots \cup V_{1t_1} \cup V_{21} \cup \ldots \cup V_{2t_2} \cup \ldots \cup V_{\mu t_\mu}$ is the normal decomposition of $\boldsymbol{\gamma}_\alpha V$.

Applying (32.1.3) to $\boldsymbol{\gamma}_{(0)} V_j$ we can find a neighborhood $X_j = Y_j \times Z_j$ of the origin in $Y'' \times Z''$ such that:

6°) For any $\beta \in Y_j$ we have

$$\sum_{\alpha \in V_j \cap (\beta \times Z_j)} \mathbf{d}(\alpha, \pi, V_j) = \mathbf{d}((0), \pi, V_j).$$

Take $0 < \bar{E} \leqq E'$ such that $Z\langle \bar{E} \rangle \subset Z_j$ for $j = 1, \ldots, \mu$. Take $0 < \bar{D} \leqq \psi(\bar{E})$ such that $Y\langle \bar{D} \rangle \subset Y_j$ for $j = 1, \ldots, \mu$. Let $Y = Y\langle \bar{D} \rangle$, $Z = Z\langle \bar{E} \rangle$, $X = Y \times Z$. From (1° to 6°) we at once deduce that X satisfies the requirements (1 to 5). To prove that X also satisfies 6), let $\beta \in Y$ be given, and let $\alpha^{(\theta)} = (\beta, \gamma^{(\theta)})$, $(\theta = 1, \ldots, N)$, be all the distinct points in $V \cap (\beta \times Z)$. Now $V \cap X$ is closed in X and hence in virtue of 1) and 4), by (12.4) we can find $\hat{D} > 0$, $\hat{E} > 0$ such that we have (7° to 10°).

7°)
$$Y\langle \hat{D} \rangle \subset Y; \qquad \bigcup_{\theta=1}^{N} Z\langle \hat{E}, \gamma^{(\theta)} \rangle \subset Z;$$
$$Z\langle \hat{E}, \gamma^{(\theta)} \rangle \cap Z\langle \hat{E}, \gamma^{(\theta')} \rangle = \emptyset \qquad \text{for all} \quad \theta \neq \theta'.$$

8°)
$$V \cap (Y\langle \hat{D} \rangle \times Z) = \bigcup_{\theta=1}^{N} [V \cap (Y\langle \hat{D} \rangle \times Z\langle \hat{E}, \gamma^{(\theta)} \rangle)].$$

9°) Given $0 < E^* \leqq \hat{E}$ there exists $0 < \psi'(E^*) \leqq \hat{D}$ depending on E^* such that

$$V \cap (Y\langle \psi'(E^*), \beta\rangle \times Z\langle \hat{E}, \gamma^{(\theta)}\rangle) = V \cap (Y\langle \psi'(E^*), \beta\rangle \times Z\langle E^*, \gamma^{(\theta)}\rangle) \quad \text{for} \quad \theta = 1,\dots, N.$$

10°) If $\beta \notin \mathbf{\Delta}$ then there exist $\xi^{(\theta)} = (\xi_1^{(\theta)},\dots, \xi_m^{(\theta)}) \in S^m$ convergent in $Y\langle \hat{D}\rangle$ such that

$$V \cap (Y\langle \hat{D}, \beta\rangle \times Z\langle \hat{E}, \gamma^{(\theta)}\rangle) = \{(b, \xi^{(\theta)}(b_1 - \beta_1,\dots, b_e - \beta_e)) : b \in Y\langle \hat{D}, \beta\rangle\} \quad \text{for} \quad \theta = 1,\dots, N.$$

In virtue of 2), applying 5) to $\boldsymbol{\gamma}_{\alpha^{(\theta)}} V_j$ we can find $0 < D_{j\theta} \leqq \hat{D}$, $0 < E_{j\theta} \leqq \hat{E}$ such that:

11°) For any $b \in Y\langle D_{\theta j}, \beta\rangle$ we have

$$\sum_{a \in V_j \cap (b \times Z\langle E_{j\theta}, \gamma^{(\theta)}\rangle)} \mathbf{d}(a, \pi, V_j) = \mathbf{d}(\alpha^{(\theta)}, \pi, V_j).$$

Take $E > 0$ such that $E \leqq E_{j\theta}$ for $j = 1,\dots, \mu$ and $\theta = 1,\dots, N$. Take $D > 0$ such that $D \leqq \psi'(E)$ and $D \leqq D_{j\theta}$ for $j = 1,\dots, \mu$ and $\theta = 1,\dots, N$. In virtue of 3), by (7° to 11°) it follows that D and E satisfy conditions (i to vi).

(35.2) *Let the situation be as in* (35.1). *Let $\Gamma_1,\dots, \Gamma_\rho, T_1,\dots, T_\rho, \chi_1,\dots, \chi_\sigma$ be a finite number of indeterminates. Let $r_1,\dots, r_\rho \in R$. Let $v(y, \Gamma_1,\dots, \Gamma_\rho, \chi_1,\dots, \chi_\sigma) \in S[\Gamma_1,\dots, \Gamma_\rho, \chi_1,\dots, \chi_\sigma]$ be homogeneous in $\Gamma_1,\dots, \Gamma_\rho$. Let $\Theta = \Theta_1 \dots \Theta_\mu$ where Θ_j is the norm of $v(y, T_1 - \varphi_j(r_1),\dots, T_\rho - \varphi_j(r_\rho), \chi_1,\dots, \chi_\sigma)$ relative to the field extension $\mathfrak{L}_j(T_1,\dots, T_\rho, \chi_1,\dots, \chi_\sigma)/\mathfrak{K}(T_1,\dots, T_\sigma, \chi_1,\dots, \chi_\sigma)$. Then $\Theta = \Theta(y, T_1,\dots, T_\rho, \chi,\dots, \chi_\sigma) \in S[T_1,\dots, T_\rho, \chi_1,\dots, \chi_\sigma]$. Furthermore, there exists a neighborhood $X^* = Y^* \times Z^*$ of the origin in $Y \times Z$, where $Y \times Z$ is as in* (35.1), *such that: $r_1,\dots, r_\rho$ are convergent in X^*; the coefficients of v and Θ are convergent in Y^*; $V \cap (Y^* \times Z) = V \cap (Y^* \times Z^*)$; and such that for all $b \in Y^*$ we have*

$$\Theta(b, T_1,\dots, T_\rho, \chi_1,\dots, \chi_\sigma) = \prod_{a \in V \cap (b \times Z^*)} v(b, T_1 - r_1(a),\dots, T_\rho - r_\rho(a), \chi_1,\dots, \chi_\sigma)^{\mathbf{d}(a, \pi, V)}.$$

Proof. By (32.4), $\Theta_j = \Theta_j(y, T_1,\dots, T_\rho, \chi_1,\dots, \chi_\sigma) \in S[T_1,\dots, T_\rho, \chi_1,\dots, \chi_\sigma]$ and there exists a neighborhood $X_j = Y_j \times Z_j$ of the origin in $Y \times Z$ such that: $r_1,\dots, r_\rho$ are convergent in X_j; the coefficients of v and Θ_j are convergent in Y_j; and such that for all $b \in Y_j$ we have:

$$\Theta_j(b, T_1,\dots, T_\rho, \chi_1,\dots, \chi_\sigma) = \prod_{a \in V_j \cap (b \times Z_j)} v(b, T_1 - r_1(a),\dots, T_\rho - r_\rho(a), \chi_1,\dots, \chi_\sigma)^{\mathbf{d}(a, \pi, V_j)}.$$

Let $Z^* = \bigcap_{j=1}^{\mu} Z_j$. By (35.1.1), $V \cap X \subset W$ and hence by continuity of roots (11.3) we can find a neighborhood Y^* of the origin in $\bigcap_{j=1}^{\mu} Y_j$ such that $V \cap (Y^* \times Z) = V \cap (Y^* \times Z^*)$. Now it suffices to note that by (35.1.3) we have

$$\mathbf{d}(a, \pi, V) = \sum_{j=1}^{\mu} \mathbf{d}(a, \pi, V_j) \qquad \text{for all} \quad a \in V \cap X.$$

(35.3) Let $\mathfrak{a}$ be a proper ideal in R. Let $u_1, \ldots, u_\Lambda$ be a finite basis of $\mathfrak{a}$. Let $X' = Y' \times Z'$ be any neighborhood of the origin in $K^e\{y\} \times K^m\{z\}$ such that $u_1, \ldots, u_\Lambda$ are convergent in X'. Let

$$V = \{a \in X' : u_1(a) = \ldots = u_\Lambda(a) = 0\}.$$

Assume that $\{y_1, \ldots, y_e, \mathfrak{a}\}R$ is primary for the maximal ideal in R, or equivalently that the origin in X' is an isolated point of $V \cap \{a \in X' : \pi a = (0)\}$. Also assume that every prime ideal of $\mathfrak{a}$ having depth e is strictly regular relative to S. *Then there exists a neighborhood $X = Y \times Z$ of the origin in $Y' \times Z'$, $0 \neq \Delta \in S$ which is convergent Y, and a positive integer d, such that we have* (1 *to* 4).

1) *$\{b \in Y : \Delta(b) = 0\}$ is nowhere dense in Y. The origin in X is the only point in $V \cap ((0) \times Z)$. Given $E' > 0$ with $Z\langle E' \rangle \subset Z$, there exists $D' > 0$ with $Y\langle D' \rangle \subset Y$ such that $V \cap (Y\langle D' \rangle \times Z) = V \cap (Y\langle D' \rangle \times Z\langle E' \rangle)$.*

2) *For* any *$\alpha \in V \cap X$ we have: $\dim_\alpha V \leqq e$; every prime ideal of $\boldsymbol{\sigma}(\mathfrak{i}(\alpha, V, X))$ having depth e is strictly regular relative to S where $\boldsymbol{\sigma}: R(\alpha, X) \to R$ is the Taylor isomorphism; $\mathbf{d}(\alpha, \pi, V)$ is defined; $\mathbf{d}(\alpha, \pi, V) > 0 \Leftrightarrow \dim_\alpha V = e$; if $\Delta(\pi\alpha) \neq 0$ then α is a simple point of V and $\mathbf{d}(\alpha, \pi, V) = 1$.*

3) *For any $\beta \in Y$, $V \cap (\beta \times Z)$ contains at most d points and we have*

$$\sum_{\alpha \in V \cap (\beta \times Z)} \mathbf{d}(\alpha, \pi, V) = \mathbf{d}((0), \pi, V).$$

4) *Given $\beta \in Y$, let $\alpha^{(\theta)} = (\beta, \gamma^{(\theta)})$, $(\theta = 1, \ldots, N)$, be the distinct points in $V \cap (\beta \times Z)$. Then there exist $D > 0$, $E > 0$ for which we have* (i *to* v).[2]

i) $$Y\langle D, \beta \rangle \subset Y; \qquad \bigcup_{\theta=1}^{N} Z\langle E, \gamma^{(\theta)} \rangle \subset Z;$$

$$Z\langle E, \gamma^{(\theta)} \rangle \cap Z\langle E, \gamma^{(\theta')} \rangle \neq 0 \qquad \textit{for all} \quad \theta \neq \theta'.$$

[2] For $N = 0$ this is to mean: there exists $D > 0$ such that $Y\langle D, \beta \rangle \subset Y$ and $V \cap (Y\langle D, \beta \rangle \times Z) = \emptyset$.

ii) $$V \cap (Y\langle D, \beta\rangle \times Z) = \bigcup_{\theta=1}^{N} [V \cap (Y\langle D, \beta\rangle \times Z\langle E, \gamma^{(\theta)}\rangle)].$$

iii) *For any* $b \in Y\langle D, \beta\rangle$ *and for* $\theta = 1,\ldots, N$ *we have*

$$\sum_{a\in V\cap(b\times Z\langle E,\gamma^{(\theta)}\rangle)} \mathbf{d}(a, \pi, V) = \mathbf{d}(\alpha^{(\theta)}, \pi, V).$$

iv) *Given* $0 < E^* \leqq E$ *there exists* $0 < D^* \leqq D$ *such that for* $\theta = 1,\ldots, N$ *we have*

$$V \cap (Y\langle D^*, \beta\rangle \times Z\langle E, \gamma^{(\theta)}\rangle) = V \cap (Y\langle D^*, \beta\rangle \times Z\langle E^*, \gamma^{(\theta)}\rangle).$$

v) *If* $\Delta(\beta) \neq 0$ *then for* $\theta = 1,\ldots, N$, *there exists* $\xi^{(\theta)} \in S^m$ *which is convergent in* $Y\langle D\rangle$ *such that*

$$V \cap (Y\langle D, \beta\rangle \times Z\langle E, \gamma^{(\theta)}\rangle) = \{(b, \xi^{(\theta)}(b_1 - \beta_1,\ldots, b_e - \beta_e)): b \in Y\langle D, \beta\rangle\}.$$

PROOF. Follows from (30.21, 35.1) in virtue of (23.3, 33.2).

REMARK. Assume that K is of characteristic zero. Let $\mathfrak{a}$ be any proper ideal in R and let $e = \dim R/\mathfrak{a}$. By (23.5) upon making a nonsingular K-linear transformation on $x_1,\ldots, x_n$ it can be arranged that $\mathfrak{a}$ is regular relative to $S = K[\langle x_1,\ldots, x_e\rangle]$. Then (35.3) becomes applicable. If furthermore rad $\mathfrak{a}$ is unmixed then (35.1, 35.2) are applicable. In other words, given any analytic set V in an open set in K^n and given any point of V, upon making an affine transformation on the coordinate system in K^n, there is an open polycylinder X around the given point such that: (35.3) is applicable to $V \cap X$; and if V is pure dimensional at the given point then (35.1, 35.2) are applicable to $V \cap X$.

(35.4) *Let* $X = Y \times Z$ *be an open set in* $K^e \times K^m$. *Let* V *be an analytic set in* X. *Let* $\alpha^{(\lambda)} = (\beta, \gamma^{(\lambda)})$, $(\lambda = 1,\ldots, N; N > 0)$, *be a finite number of distinct points in* V *with* $\beta \in Y$, *such that for each* λ, *every prime ideal of* $\boldsymbol{\sigma}(\mathfrak{i}(\alpha^{(\lambda)}, V, X))$ *is strictly regular relative to* S *where* $\boldsymbol{\sigma}: R(\alpha^{(\lambda)}, X) \to R$ *is the Taylor isomorphism. Then there exist* $D > 0$, $E > 0$, *for which we have* (i *to* iv).

i) $$Y\langle D, \beta\rangle \subset Y; \qquad \bigcup_{\lambda=1}^{N} Z\langle E, \gamma^{(\lambda)}\rangle \subset Z;$$

$$Z\langle E, \gamma^{(\lambda)}\rangle \cap Z\langle E, \gamma^{(\lambda')}\rangle = \emptyset \qquad \textit{for all} \quad \lambda \neq \lambda'.$$

ii) *For any* $a \in V \cap (Y\langle D, \beta\rangle \times \bigcup_{\lambda=1}^{N} Z\langle E, \gamma^{(\lambda)}\rangle)$, *every prime ideal of* $\boldsymbol{\sigma}(\mathfrak{i}(a, V, X))$ *is strictly regular relative to* S *where* $\boldsymbol{\sigma}: R(a, X) \to R$ *is the Taylor isomorphism.*

iii) *For any* $b \in Y\langle D, \beta\rangle$ *and* $\lambda = 1,\ldots, N$ *we have*

$$\sum_{a \in V \cap (b \times Z\langle E, \gamma^{(\lambda)}\rangle)} \mathbf{d}(a, \pi, V) = \mathbf{d}(\alpha^{(\lambda)}, \pi, V).$$

iv) *Given* $0 < E^* \leqq E$ *there exists* $0 < D^* \leqq D$ *such that for* $\lambda = 1,\ldots, N$ *we have*

$$V \cap (Y\langle D^*, \beta\rangle \times Z\langle E, \gamma^{(\lambda)}\rangle) = V \cap (Y\langle D^*, \beta\rangle \times Z\langle E^*, \gamma^{(\lambda)}\rangle).$$

(**35.5**) *In the situation of* (35.4), $D > 0$ *and* $E > 0$ *can be chosen so that in addition to the properties in* (35.4), *there exists a nowhere dense analytic set* $\mathbf{\Delta}$ *in* $Y\langle D, \beta\rangle$ *such that for any* λ *and any* $\tilde{\alpha} = (\tilde{\beta}, \tilde{\gamma}) \in V$ *with* $\tilde{\beta} \in Y\langle D, \beta\rangle - \mathbf{\Delta}$ *and* $\tilde{\gamma} \in Z\langle E, \gamma^{(\lambda)}\rangle$ *we have the following*: $\tilde{\alpha}$ *is a simple point of* V; $\mathbf{d}(\tilde{\alpha}, \pi, V) = 1$; *and there exist* $\tilde{D} > 0$, $\tilde{E} > 0$ *with* $Y\langle \tilde{D}, \tilde{\beta}\rangle \subset Y\langle D, \beta\rangle - \mathbf{\Delta}$, $Z\langle \tilde{E}, \tilde{\gamma}\rangle \subset Z\langle E, \gamma^{(\lambda)}\rangle$, *and* $\xi = (\xi_1,\ldots, \xi_m)$ *where* $\xi_1,\ldots, \xi_m$ *are analytic functions on* $Y\langle \tilde{D}, \tilde{\beta}\rangle$ *such that*

$$V \cap (Y\langle \tilde{D}, \tilde{\beta}\rangle \times Z\langle \tilde{E}, \tilde{\gamma}\rangle) = \{(b, \xi(b)) : b \in Y\langle \tilde{D}, \tilde{\beta}\rangle\}.$$

Proof of (35.4) *and* (35.5). Take $\hat{D} > 0$, $\hat{E} > 0$ such that

$$Y\langle \hat{D}, \beta\rangle \subset Y; \qquad \bigcup_{\lambda=1}^{N} Z\langle \hat{E}, \gamma^{(\lambda)}\rangle \subset Z; \qquad \text{and}$$

$$Z\langle \hat{E}, \gamma^{(\lambda)}\rangle \cap Z\langle \hat{E}, \gamma^{(\lambda')}\rangle = \emptyset \qquad \text{for all} \quad \lambda \neq \lambda'.$$

Applying (35.1) to $\boldsymbol{\gamma}_{\alpha^{(\lambda)}}V$ we can find $0 < D_\lambda \leqq D$, $0 < E_\lambda \leqq E$, and a nowhere dense analytic set $\mathbf{\Delta}_\lambda$ in $Y\langle D_\lambda, \beta\rangle$ for which we have (1° to 4°).

1°) For any $a \in V \cap (Y\langle D_\lambda, \beta\rangle \times Z\langle E_\lambda, \gamma^{(\lambda)}\rangle$, every prime ideal of $\boldsymbol{\sigma}(\mathfrak{i}(a, V, X))$ is strictly regular relative to S where $\boldsymbol{\sigma}: R(a, X) \to R$ is the Taylor isomorphism.

2°)
$$\sum_{a \in V \cap (b \times Z\langle E_\lambda, \gamma^{(\lambda)}\rangle} \mathbf{d}(a, \pi, V) = \mathbf{d}(\alpha^{(\lambda)}, \pi, V) \quad \text{for all} \quad b \in Y\langle D_\lambda, \beta\rangle.$$

3°) Given $0 < E^* \leqq E_\lambda$ there exists $0 < \psi_\lambda(E^*) \leqq D_\lambda$ depending on E^* such that

$$V \cap (Y\langle \psi_\lambda(E^*), \beta\rangle \times Z\langle E_\lambda, \gamma^{(\lambda)}\rangle) \subset Y\langle \psi_\lambda(E^*), \beta\rangle \times Z\langle E^*, \gamma^{(\lambda)}\rangle.$$

4°) For any $\tilde{\alpha} = (\tilde{\beta}, \tilde{\gamma}) \in V$ with $\tilde{\beta} \in Y\langle D_\lambda, \beta\rangle - \mathbf{\Delta}_\lambda$ and $\tilde{\gamma} \in Z\langle E_\lambda, \gamma^{(\lambda)}\rangle$ we have the following: $\tilde{\alpha}$ is a simple point of V; $\mathbf{d}(\tilde{\alpha}, \pi, V) = 1$; and there exist $\tilde{D} > 0$, $\tilde{E} > 0$ with $Y\langle \tilde{D}, \tilde{\beta}\rangle \subset Y\langle D_\lambda, \beta\rangle - \mathbf{\Delta}_\lambda$, $Z\langle \tilde{E}, \tilde{\gamma}\rangle \subset Z\langle E_\lambda, \gamma^{(\lambda)}\rangle$, and $\xi = (\xi_1,\ldots, \xi_m)$ where $\xi_1,\ldots, \xi_m$ are analytic functions on $Y\langle \tilde{D}, \tilde{\beta}\rangle$ such that

$$V \cap (Y\langle \tilde{D}, \tilde{\beta}\rangle \times Z\langle \tilde{E}, \tilde{\gamma}\rangle) = \{(b, \xi(b)) : b \in Y\langle \tilde{D}, \tilde{\beta}\rangle\}.$$

Take $E = \min(E_1, \ldots, E_N)$, and $D = \min(\psi_1(E), \ldots, \psi_N(E))$. Given $0 < E^* \leqq E$ take $D^* = \min(D, \psi_1(E^*), \ldots, \psi_N(E^*))$. Take

$$\Delta = \bigcup_{\lambda=1}^{N} (\Delta_\lambda \cap Y\langle D, \beta\rangle).$$

§35B. *Global parametrization*

Let Y and Z be open sets in $K^e\{y\}$ and $K^m\{z\}$, respectively, and let $\mathring{Z}$ be the boundary of Z in $K^m\{z\}$. Let V be a nonempty analytic set in $X = Y \times Z$ and let $\bar{V}$ be the closure of V in $K^e\{y\} \times K^m\{z\}$. Make the following three assumptions.

(I) V is pure e dimensional.

(II) There exists a positive integer d such that for all $b \in Y$, $V \cap \pi^{-1}(b)$ is a finite set and

$$\mathbf{d}(b, (\pi|V)^{-1}) = d, \qquad \text{i.e.,} \qquad \sum_{a \in V \cap \pi^{-1}(b)} \mathbf{d}(a, \pi, V) = d.$$

[Definition. Under assumptions (I) and (II) we define: $\mathbf{d}(\pi|V) = d$].

(III) For any $a \in V$, every prime ideal of $\boldsymbol{\sigma}(\mathfrak{i}(a, V, X))$ is strictly regular relative to S where $\boldsymbol{\sigma} : R(a, X) \to R$ is the Taylor isomorphism.[3]

Let $\tilde{\mathfrak{S}}$ be the ring of all K-valued functions on Y and let $\mathfrak{S} = R(Y)$; then $\mathfrak{S}$ is a subring of $\tilde{\mathfrak{S}}$. Let $\tilde{\mathfrak{R}}$ be the ring of all K-valued functions on V and let $\mathfrak{R} = R(V)$; then $\mathfrak{R}$ is a subring of $\tilde{\mathfrak{R}}$.

A polynomial in indeterminates $\Omega_1, \ldots, \Omega_M$ with coefficients in $\tilde{\mathfrak{S}}$ is denoted by writing something like $v(y, \Omega_1, \ldots, \Omega_M) \in \tilde{\mathfrak{S}}[\Omega_1, \ldots, \Omega_M]$; for any $b \in Y$, $v(b, \Omega_1, \ldots, \Omega_M)$ is then in $K[\Omega_1, \ldots, \Omega_M]$; $v(y, \Omega_1, \ldots, \Omega_M) \in \tilde{\mathfrak{S}}[\Omega_1, \ldots, \Omega_M]$ is completely determined by giving $v(b, \Omega_1, \ldots, \Omega_M)$ for all $b \in Y$; $v(y, \Omega_1, \ldots, \Omega_M) \in \mathfrak{S}[\Omega_1, \ldots, \Omega_M]$ means that all the coefficients of $v(y, \Omega_1, \ldots, \Omega_M)$ are actually analytic on Y. For

$$H(y, T) = \sum H_i(y) T^i \in \tilde{\mathfrak{S}}[T]$$

the derivative of $H(y, T)$ with respect to T is denoted by $H'(y, T)$:

$$H'(y, T) = \sum i H_i(y) T^{i-1} \in \tilde{\mathfrak{S}}[T].$$

Obviously for any $b \in Y$, $H'(b, T)$ is the T-derivative of $H(b, T) \in K[T]$. If $H(y, T) \in \mathfrak{S}[T]$ then $H'(y, T) \in \mathfrak{S}[T]$.

[3] (I) together with the part of (II) which says that $V \cap \pi^{-1}(b)$ is a discrete set for any $b \in Y$, imply that $\mathbf{d}(a, \pi, V)$ is defined and is a positive integer for any $a \in V$. If K is of characteristic zero then (III) is a consequence of (I) and the said part of (II).

Let $\Gamma_1,\ldots,\Gamma_\rho, T, T_1,\ldots, T_\rho, \chi_1,\ldots,\chi_\sigma$ be a finite number of indeterminates. Let

$$v(y, \Gamma_1,\ldots,\Gamma_\rho, \chi_1,\ldots,\chi_\sigma) \in \tilde{\mathfrak{S}}[\Gamma_1,\ldots,\Gamma_\rho, \chi_1,\ldots,\chi_\sigma]$$

and $r_1,\ldots, r_\rho \in \tilde{\mathfrak{R}}$ be given.

$$v(y, T_1 - r_1,\ldots, T_\rho - r_\rho, \chi_1,\ldots,\chi_\sigma)$$

is then a polynomial in indeterminates $T_1,\ldots, T_\rho, \chi_1,\ldots,\chi_\sigma$ with coefficients in $\tilde{\mathfrak{R}}$:

$$v(\pi a, T_1 - r_1(a),\ldots, T_\rho - r_\rho(a), \chi_1,\ldots,\chi_\sigma) \in K[T_1,\ldots, T_\rho, \chi_1,\ldots,\chi_\sigma]$$

for all $a \in V$. Or more generally we may think of

$$v(y, T_1 - r_1,\ldots, T_\rho - r_\rho, \chi_1,\ldots,\chi_\sigma)$$

as a polynomial in $T_1,\ldots, T_\rho, \chi_1,\ldots,\chi_\sigma$ with coefficients in the ring of all K-valued functions on $Y \times V$:

$$v(b, T_1 - r_1(a),\ldots, T_\rho - r_\rho(a), \chi_1,\ldots,\chi_\sigma) \in K[T_1,\ldots, T_\rho, \chi_1,\ldots,\chi_\sigma]$$

for all $(b, a) \in Y \times V$.

Let

$$v(y, \Gamma_1,\ldots,\Gamma_\rho, \chi_1,\ldots,\chi_\sigma) \in \tilde{\mathfrak{S}}[\Gamma_1,\ldots,\Gamma_\rho, \chi_1,\ldots,\chi_\sigma]$$

be homogeneous in $\Gamma_1,\ldots,\Gamma_\rho$ and let $r_1,\ldots, r_\rho \in \tilde{\mathfrak{R}}$. By analogy with (32.4) we define *the norm of* $v(y, T_1 - r_1,\ldots, T_\rho - r_\rho, \chi_1,\ldots,\chi_\sigma)$ *relative to* $\pi|V$ to be the element

$$\Theta(y, T_1,\ldots, T_\rho, \chi_1,\ldots,\chi_\sigma) \in \tilde{\mathfrak{S}}[T_1,\ldots, T_\rho, \chi_1,\ldots,\chi_\sigma]$$

given by taking

$$\begin{aligned}&\Theta(b, T_1,\ldots, T_\rho, \chi_1,\ldots,\chi_\sigma)\\ &= \prod_{a\in V\cap\pi^{-1}(b)} v(b, T_1 - r_1(a),\ldots, T_\rho - r_\rho(a), \chi_1,\ldots,\chi_\sigma)^{\mathbf{d}(a,\pi,V)}\\ &\in K[T_1,\ldots, T_\rho, \chi_1,\ldots,\chi_\sigma] \qquad \text{for all} \quad b \in Y.\end{aligned}$$

Again by analogy with (32.3), for any $r \in \tilde{\mathfrak{R}}$ we define the *field polynomial of r relative to $\pi|V$* to be the norm $H(y, T) \in \tilde{\mathfrak{S}}[T]$ of $T - r$ relative to $\pi|V$; $H(y, T)$ is then a monic polynomial of degree d in T with coefficients in $\tilde{\mathfrak{S}}$ and for all $b \in Y$ we have

$$H(b, T) = \prod_{a\in V\cap\pi^{-1}(b)} (T - r(a))^{\mathbf{d}(a,\pi,V)} \in K[T].$$

We shall show that if $r \in \mathfrak{R}$ then $H(y, T) \in \mathfrak{S}[T]$; and more generally if $v(y, \Gamma_1,\ldots,\Gamma_\rho, \chi_1,\ldots,\chi_\sigma) \in \mathfrak{S}[\Gamma_1,\ldots,\Gamma_\rho, \chi_1,\ldots,\chi_\sigma]$ and $r_1,\ldots, r_\rho \in \mathfrak{R}$ then $\Theta(y, T_1,\ldots, T_\rho, \chi_1,\ldots,\chi_\sigma) \in \mathfrak{S}[T_1,\ldots, T_\rho, \chi_1,\ldots,\chi_\sigma]$.

Since forming derivatives and discriminants are purely formal operations we get the following.

(35.6) For any $r \in \mathfrak{R}$ let $H(y, T)$ be the field polynomial of r relative to $\pi|V$ and let $\Delta(y) \in \tilde{\mathfrak{S}}$ be the T-discriminant of $H(y, T)$.[4] Then for any $b \in Y$, $H'(b, T) \in K[T]$ is the T-derivative of $H(b, T) \in K[T]$ and $\Delta(b) \in K$ is the T-discriminant of $H(b, T) \in K[T]$. Consequently for any $a \in V$ we have:

$$\begin{aligned} & H'(\pi a, r(a)) \neq 0 \\ \Leftrightarrow\ & r(a) \text{ is a simple root of } H(\pi a, T) \\ \Leftrightarrow\ & \mathbf{d}(a, \pi, V) = 1 \text{ and } r(a) \neq r(a') \text{ for each } a' \in V \cap \pi^{-1}(\pi a) \\ & \text{with } a \neq a'; \end{aligned}$$

and for any $b \in Y$ we have:

$$\begin{aligned} & \Delta(b) \neq 0 \\ \Leftrightarrow\ & H(\pi a, T) \text{ has no multiple roots} \\ \Leftrightarrow\ & V \cap \pi^{-1}(b) \text{ contains } d \text{ distinct points } a^{(1)},\dots, a^{(d)} \text{ and} \\ & r(a^{(i)}) \neq r(a^{(j)}) \text{ for all } i \neq j. \end{aligned}$$

(35.7) THE OSGOODIAN. Let r and ζ be any two elements in $\tilde{\mathfrak{R}}$. Let $-s_i(y)$ be the coefficients of T^{d-1} in the field polynomial of $r\zeta^i$ relative to $\pi|V$,[5] and let $\eta_i(y)$ be the coefficient of T^{d-i} in the field polynomial $Q(y, T)$ of ζ relative to $\pi|V$. We define the *Osgoodian of* $r\|\zeta$ *relative to* $\pi|V$ to be the element $P(y, T) \in \tilde{\mathfrak{S}}[T]$ of degree $\leqq d - 1$ in T given by:[6]

$$P(y, T) = \sum_{i=0}^{d-1} \left[\sum_{j=0}^{i} \eta_j(y) s_{i-j}(y) \right] T^{d-1-i}.$$

The significance of the Osgoodian $P(y, T)$ is due to

OSGOOD'S LEMMA: *$P(\pi a, \zeta(a)) = r(a)Q'(\pi a, \zeta(a))$ for all $a \in V$.*

Proof is purely formal. Let $b = \pi a$. Let $a^{(1)},\dots, a^{(d)}$ be the points in $V \cap \pi^{-1}(b)$ where each $a^{(\theta)}$ is repeated $\mathbf{d}(a^{(\theta)}, \pi, V)$ times, and $a = a^{(1)}$. Let $\bar{\zeta}_\theta = \zeta(a^{(\theta)})$, $\bar{r}_\theta = r(a^{(\theta)})$, $\eta_i = \bar{\eta}_i(b)$, $\bar{s}_i = s_i(b)$. Then

$$Q(b, T) = \prod_{\theta=1}^{d} (T - \bar{\zeta}_\theta) = \sum_{\mu=0}^{d} \bar{\eta}_{d-\mu} T^\mu,$$

$$Q'(b, \bar{\zeta}_1) = \prod_{\theta=2}^{d} (\bar{\zeta}_1 - \bar{\zeta}_\theta),$$

[4] Note that if $H(y, T) \in \mathfrak{S}[T]$ the $\Delta(y) \in \mathfrak{S}$.

[5] By analogy with field extensions, $s_i(y)$ may be called the trace of ζ^i relative to $\pi|V$.

[6] The term Osgoodian seems appropriate in virtue of Osgood [**1**: pp. 116–117]. We are writing $r\|\zeta$ to avoid saying "Osgoodian of r relative to ζ relative to $|\pi$".

and

1°) $$\bar{s}_i = \sum_{\theta=1}^{d} \bar{r}_\theta \bar{\zeta}_\theta^i.$$

Let

2°) $$\Phi(T) = \sum_{\mu=0}^{d-1} \left[\sum_{\nu=0}^{d-1-\mu} \bar{\eta}_\nu \bar{\zeta}_1^{d-1-\mu-\nu} \right] T^\mu \in K[T].$$

Then

$$\begin{aligned}(T - \bar{\zeta}_1)\Phi(T) &= -\sum_{\nu=0}^{d-1} \bar{\eta}_\nu \bar{\zeta}_1^{d-\nu} + \sum_{\mu=1}^{d-1} \bar{\eta}_{d-\mu} T^\mu + \bar{\eta}_0 T^d \\ &= -\sum_{\nu=0}^{d} \bar{\eta}_\nu \bar{\zeta}_1^{d-\nu} + \sum_{\mu=0}^{d} \bar{\eta}_{d-\mu} T^\mu \\ &= -Q(b, \bar{\zeta}_1) + Q(b, T) \\ &= Q(b, T) \\ &= (T - \bar{\zeta}_1) \prod_{\theta=2}^{d} (T - \bar{\zeta}_\theta).\end{aligned}$$

Therefore

$$\Phi(T) = \prod_{\theta=2}^{d} (T - \bar{\zeta}_\theta),$$

and hence

3°) $$\Phi(\bar{\zeta}_1) = Q'(b, \bar{\zeta}_1), \quad \text{and} \quad \Phi(\bar{\zeta}_\theta) = 0 \quad \text{for all} \quad \theta > 1.$$

Now

$$\begin{aligned}P(\pi a, \zeta(a)) &= P(b, \bar{\zeta}_1) \\ &= \sum_{i=0}^{d-1} \left[\sum_{j=0}^{i} \bar{\eta}_j \bar{s}_{i-j} \right] \bar{\zeta}_1^{d-1-i} && \text{by definition of } P \\ &= \sum_{i=0}^{d-1} \left[\sum_{j=0}^{i} \left(\bar{\eta}_j \sum_{\theta=1}^{d} \bar{r}_\theta \bar{\zeta}_\theta^{i-j} \right) \right] \bar{\zeta}_1^{d-1-i} && \text{by 1°)} \\ &= \sum_{\theta=1}^{d} \left[\sum_{i=0}^{d-1} \left(\sum_{j=0}^{i} \bar{\eta}_j \bar{\zeta}_\theta^{i-j} \right) \bar{\zeta}_1^{d-1-i} \right] \bar{r}_\theta && \text{by rearrangement} \\ &= \sum_{\theta=1}^{d} \left[\sum_{\mu=0}^{d-1} \left(\sum_{\nu=0}^{d-1-\mu} \bar{\eta}_\nu \bar{\zeta}_1^{d-1-\mu-\nu} \right) \bar{\zeta}_\theta^\mu \right] \bar{r}_\theta && \text{by rearrangement} \\ &= \sum_{\theta=1}^{d} \Phi(\bar{\zeta}_\theta) \bar{r}_\theta && \text{by 2°)} \\ &= \bar{r}_1 Q'(b, \bar{\zeta}_1) && \text{by 3°)} \\ &= r(a) Q'(\pi a, \zeta(a)).\end{aligned}$$

After these formalities we proceed to prove some slightly less formal propositions.

(35.8) *For any* $\beta \in Y$ *let* $\alpha^{(\lambda)} = (\beta, \gamma^{(\lambda)})$, $(\lambda = 1,\ldots, N)$, *be the distinct points in* $V \cap \pi^{-1}(\beta)$. *Then there exist* $D > 0, E > 0$ *for which we have* (i *to* iv).

i)
$$Y\langle D, \beta\rangle \subset Y; \qquad \bigcup_{\lambda=1}^{N} Z\langle E, \gamma^{(\lambda)}\rangle \subset Z;$$
$$Z\langle E, \gamma^{(\lambda)}\rangle \cap Z\langle E, \gamma^{(\lambda')}\rangle = \emptyset \qquad \textit{for all} \quad \lambda \neq \lambda'.$$

ii) $$V \cap (Y\langle D, \beta\rangle \times Z) = \bigcup_{\lambda=1}^{N} [V \cap (Y\langle D, \beta\rangle \times Z\langle E, \gamma^{(\lambda)}\rangle)].$$

iii) *For any* $b \in Y\langle D, \beta\rangle$ *and any* $\lambda \leqq N$ *we have*
$$\sum_{a \in V \cap (b \times Z\langle E, \gamma^{(\lambda)}\rangle)} \mathbf{d}(a, \pi, V) = \mathbf{d}(\alpha^{(\lambda)}, \pi, V).$$

iv) *Given* $0 < E^* \leqq E$ *there exists* $0 < D^* \leqq D$ *such that*
$$V \cap (Y\langle D^*, \beta\rangle \times Z\langle E, \gamma^{(\lambda)}\rangle) = V \cap (Y\langle D^*, \beta\rangle \times Z\langle E^*, \gamma^{(\lambda)}\rangle)$$
for $\lambda = 1,\ldots, N$.

By (35.4) we can find $D > 0$, $E > 0$ satisfying i), iii), iv), and then ii) follows from assumption (II).

(35.9) *There exists a closed thin subset* $\mathbf{\Delta}$ *of* Y *such that for any* $\beta \in Y - \mathbf{\Delta}$ *we have the following.* $V \cap \pi^{-1}(\beta)$ *contains* d *distinct points* $\alpha^{(\lambda)} = (\beta, \gamma^{(\lambda)})$, $(\lambda = 1,\ldots, d)$. $\mathbf{d}(\alpha^{(\lambda)}, \pi, V) = 1$ *and* $\alpha^{(\lambda)}$ *is a simple point of* V *for* $\lambda = 1,\ldots, d$. *There exist* $D > 0, E > 0,$ *and* $\xi^{(\lambda)} = (\xi_1^{(\lambda)},\ldots, \xi_m^{(\lambda)})$ *where* $\xi_i^{(\lambda)}$ *are analytic functions on* $Y\langle D, \beta\rangle$, *such that* D *and* E *satisfy conditions* (i *to* iv) *of* (35.8), *and*
$$V \cap (Y\langle D, \beta\rangle \times Z\langle E, \gamma^{(\lambda)}\rangle) = \{(b, \xi^{(\lambda)}(b)) : b \in Y\langle D, \beta\rangle\}$$
for $\lambda = 1,\ldots, d$.

Follows from (35.8) and (35.5).

(35.10)

1) *Let* $(a^{(p)})$ *be any sequence in* V *such that the sequence* $(\pi a^{(p)})$ *contains a subsequence converging to a point in* Y. *Then the sequence* $(a^{(p)})$ *contains a subsequence converging to a point in* V.

2) $\bar{V} \cap (Y \times \mathring{Z}) = \emptyset.$

3) *For any* $m' \leqq m$ *let* $\pi' : K^e\{y\} \times K^m\{z\} \to K^e\{y\} \times K^{m'}\{z_1,\dots, z_{m'}\}$ *be the natural projection. Then the map* $V \to Y \times K^{m'}$ *induced by* π' *is a proper closed map.*

As in the proof of (12.5.1), 1) follows from (35.8), and then as in the proof of (12.5.2), 3) follows from 1). 2) follows immediately from 1).

(35.11) *Let* $v(y, \Gamma_1,\dots, \Gamma_\rho, \chi_1,\dots, \chi_\sigma) \in \tilde{\mathfrak{S}}[\Gamma_1,\dots, \Gamma_\rho, \chi_1,\dots, \chi_\sigma]$ *be homogeneous in* $\Gamma_1,\dots, \Gamma_\rho$, *and let* $r_1,\dots, r_\rho \in \tilde{\mathfrak{R}}$. *Then the norm of*

$$v(y, T_1 - r_1,\dots, T_\rho - r_\rho, \chi_1,\dots, \chi_\sigma)$$

relative to $\pi|V$ *is an element* $\Theta(y, T_1,\dots, T_\rho, \chi_1,\dots, \chi_\sigma) \in \tilde{\mathfrak{S}}[T_1,\dots, T_\rho, \chi_1,\dots, \chi_\sigma]$, *and for any* $b \in Y$ *we have*

$$\Theta(b, T_1,\dots, T_\rho, \chi_1,\dots, \chi_\sigma) = \prod_{a\in V\cap\pi^{-1}(b)} v(b, T_1 - r_1(a),\dots, T_\rho - r_\rho(a), \chi_1,\dots, \chi_\sigma)^{\mathrm{d}(a,\pi,V)}.$$

For $\beta \in Y$, *if the coefficients of* $v(y, \Gamma_1,\dots, \Gamma_\rho, \chi_1,\dots, \chi_\sigma)$ *are continuous at* β *(resp: analytic at* β*), and if* $r_1,\dots, r_\rho$ *are continuous at* α *(resp:* $\gamma_\alpha r_1,\dots, \gamma_\alpha r_\rho$ *are in* $R(\alpha, V)$*)) for all* $\alpha \in V \cap \pi^{-1}(\beta)$, *then the coefficients of* $\Theta(y, T_1,\dots, T_\rho, \chi_1,\dots, \chi_\sigma)$ *are continuous (resp: analytic) at* β. *Hence in particular if* $v(y, \Gamma_1,\dots, \Gamma_\rho, \chi_1,\dots, \chi_\sigma) \in \mathfrak{S}[\Gamma_1,\dots, \Gamma_\rho, \chi_1,\dots, \chi_\sigma]$ *and* $r_1,\dots, r_\rho \in \mathfrak{R}$, *then* $\Theta(y, T_1,\dots, T_\rho, \chi_1,\dots, \chi_\sigma] \in \mathfrak{S}[T_1,\dots, T_\rho, \chi_1,\dots, \chi_\sigma]$. *In case of* $K = \mathbf{C}$, *if the coefficients of* $v(y, \Gamma_1,\dots, \Gamma_\rho, \chi_1,\dots, \chi_\sigma)$ *are continuous on* Y *and analytic at each* $\beta \in Y - Y'$ *where* Y' *is a thin subset of* Y, *and if* $r_1,\dots, r_\rho$ *are continuous on* V *and* $\gamma_\alpha r_1,\dots, \gamma_\alpha r_\rho \in R(\alpha, V)$ *for all* $\alpha \in V - V'$ *where* V' *is a thin subset of* V, *then* $\Theta(y, T_1,\dots, T_\rho, \chi_1,\dots, \chi_\sigma) \in \mathfrak{S}[T_1,\dots, T_\rho, \chi_1,\dots, \chi_\sigma]$.

PROOF. The first assertion is simply the definition of the norm. Given $\beta \in Y$ let the situation be as in (35.8). From the expression of Θ it follows that if the coefficients of $v(y, \Gamma_1,\dots, \Gamma_\rho, \chi_1,\dots, \chi_\sigma)$ are continuous at β and if r_μ is continuous at $\alpha^{(\lambda)}$ for all μ, λ then the coefficients of $\Theta(y, T_1,\dots, T_\rho, \chi_1,\dots, \chi_\sigma)$ are continuous at β. Now suppose that the coefficients of $v(y, \Gamma_1,\dots, \Gamma_\rho, \chi_1,\dots, \chi_\sigma)$ are analytic at β and $\gamma_{\alpha^{(\lambda)}} r_\mu \in R(\alpha^{(\lambda)}, V)$ for all μ, λ. Let $\Theta_\lambda(y, T_1,\dots, T_\rho, \chi_1,\dots, \chi_\sigma)$ be the norm of

$$v(y, T_1 - (r_1|V \cap Y\langle D, \beta\rangle \times Z(E, \gamma^{(\lambda)}\rangle),\dots, T_\rho - (r_\rho|V \cap Y\langle D, \beta\rangle \times Z\langle E, \gamma^{(\lambda)}\rangle), \chi_1,\dots, \chi_\sigma)$$

relative to $\pi|V \cap Y\langle D, \beta\rangle \times Z\langle E, \gamma^{(\lambda)}\rangle$. Applying (35.2) to $\gamma_{\alpha^{(\lambda)}} V$ we deduce that the coefficients of Θ_λ are analytic at β. From the definition of the norm, obviously for all $b \in Y\langle D, \beta\rangle$ we have

$$\Theta(b, T_1,\dots, T_\rho, \chi_1,\dots, \chi_\sigma) = \prod_{\lambda=1}^{N} \Theta_\lambda(b, T_1,\dots, T_\rho, \chi_1,\dots, \chi_\sigma).$$

Therefore the coefficients of Θ are analytic at β. The last assertion now follows by applying the Riemann Extension Theorem (14.3) to the coefficients of Θ after noticing that by (23.3), $\pi V'$ is a thin subset of Y and hence also $Y' \cup \pi V'$ is a thin subset of Y.

(35.12) *For any m' with $1 \leqq m' \leqq m$ let $\pi' : K^e\{y\} \times K^m\{z\} \to K^e\{y\} \times K^{m'}\{z_1, \ldots, z_{m'}\}$ be the natural projection. Then we have the following.*

1) *The norm of*

$$\sum_{j=1}^{m'} (z_j - (z_j | V))\chi_j$$

relative to $\pi | V$ is a homogeneous polynomial

$$\Theta(y, z_1, \ldots z_{m'}, \chi_1, \ldots, \chi_{m'}) = \sum_{i_1, \ldots, i_{m'}} \Theta_{i_1 \ldots i_{m'}}(y, z_1, \ldots, z_{m'})\chi_1^{i_1} \ldots \chi_{m'}^{i_{m'}}$$

of degree d in $\chi_1, \ldots, \chi_{m'}$ with coefficients

$$\Theta_{i_1 \ldots i_{m'}}(y, z_1, \ldots, z_{m'})$$

which are polynomials of degree d in $z_1, \ldots, z_{m'}$ with coefficients in $\mathfrak{S}$; and for all $b \in Y$ we have

$$\Theta(b, z_1, \ldots, z_{m'}, \chi_1, \ldots, \chi_{m'}) = \prod_{a = (b, c) \in V \cap \pi^{-1}(b)} \left[\sum_{j=1}^{m'} (z_j - c_j)\chi_j \right]^{\mathbf{d}(a, \pi, V)}.$$

2) *$\pi'(V) = \{a' \in \pi'(X) : \Theta_{i_1 \ldots i_{m'}}(a') = 0$ for all $i_1, \ldots, i_{m'}\}$.*

3) *$\pi'(V)$ is a pure e dimensional analytic set in $\pi'(X)$.*

PROOF. 1) follows from (35.11) by taking $\rho = \sigma = m'$, $T_j = z_j$, $v(y, \Gamma_1, \ldots, \Gamma_{m'}, \chi_1, \ldots, \chi_{m'}) = \Gamma_1\chi_1 + \ldots + \Gamma_{m'}\chi_{m'}$, and $r_j = z_j | V$. 2) follows from 1), and in turn 2) implies that $\pi'(V)$ is a nonempty analytic set in $\pi'(X)$. To prove that $\pi'(V)$ is pure e dimensional, let $\alpha' \in \pi'(V)$ be given. Then $\alpha' = \pi'\alpha$ for some $\alpha = (\beta, \gamma) \in V$, $\beta \in Y$. Obviously α' is an isolated point of $\pi'(V) \cap \{a' \in \pi'(X) \colon a_1' = \beta_1, \ldots, a_e' = \beta_e\}$ and hence $\{\mathfrak{p}', y_1, \ldots, y_e\}R'$ is primary for the maximal ideal in R' where $R' = K[\langle y_1, \ldots, y_e, z_1, \ldots, z_{m'} \rangle]$ and $\mathfrak{p}'$ is the image of $\mathfrak{i}(\alpha', \pi'(V), \pi'(X))$ under the Taylor isomorphism $R(\alpha', \pi'(X)) \to R'$. By (35.8), we deduce that $\mathfrak{p}' \cap S = \{0\}$. Therefore $\mathfrak{p}'$ is regular relative to S by (23.3). Hence $\dim_{\alpha'} \pi'(V) = e$.

(35.13) Taking $T_1 = T$, $r_1 = r$, $\rho = 1$, $\sigma = 0$, and $v(y, \Gamma_1) = \Gamma_1$ in (35.11) we get the following.

1) *For any $r \in \tilde{\mathfrak{R}}$, the field polynomial of r relative to $\pi|V$ is a monic polynomial $H(y, T)$ of degree d in T with coefficients in $\tilde{\mathfrak{S}}$, and for all $b \in Y$ we have*

$$H(b, T) = \prod_{a \in V \cap \pi^{-1}(b)} (T - r(a))^{\mathbf{d}(a, \pi, V)}$$

For $\beta \in Y$, if r is continuous at α (resp: $\gamma_\alpha r \in R(\alpha, V)$) for all $\alpha \in V \cap \pi^{-1}(\beta)$, then the coefficients of $H(y, T)$ are continuous (resp: analytic) at β. If $r \in \mathfrak{R}$ then $H(y, T) \in \mathfrak{S}[T]$. In case of $K = \mathbf{C}$, if r is continuous on V, and if $\gamma_\alpha r \in R(\alpha, V)$ for all $\alpha \in V - V'$ where V' is a thin subset of V, then $H(y, T) \in \mathfrak{S}[T]$.

Since $\pi(V) = Y$, we get a monomorphism φ of $\tilde{\mathfrak{S}}$ into $\tilde{\mathfrak{R}}$ by taking $(\varphi s)(a) = s(\pi a)$ for all $s \in \tilde{\mathfrak{S}}$, $a \in V$. Now $H^*(r) = 0$ where $H^*(T) \in (\varphi\tilde{\mathfrak{S}})[T]$ is obtained by applying φ to the coefficients of $H(y, T)$. Thus as a consequence of 1) we get

2) *$\tilde{\mathfrak{R}}$ is integral over $\varphi\tilde{\mathfrak{S}}$, and $\mathfrak{R}$ is integral over $\varphi\mathfrak{S}$. In case of $K = \mathbf{C}$, if $r : V \to \mathbf{C}$ is continuous and if $\gamma_\alpha r \in R(\alpha, V)$ for all $\alpha \in V - V'$ where V' is a thin subset of V, then r is integral over $\varphi\mathfrak{S}$ and hence in particular r is integral over $\mathfrak{R}$.*

(35.14) *For r and ζ in $\tilde{\mathfrak{R}}$, let $Q(y, T)$ be the field polynomial of ζ relative to $\pi|V$, and let $P(y, T)$ be the Osgoodian of $r\|\zeta$ relative $\pi|V$. Then $Q'(y, T)$ and $P(y, T)$ are in $\tilde{\mathfrak{S}}[T]$ and for all $a \in V$ we have: $P(\pi a, \zeta(a)) = r(a)Q'(\pi a, \zeta(a))$. Let $\Delta(y)$ be the T-discriminant of $Q(y, T)$ and let $\boldsymbol{\Delta} = \{b \in Y : \Delta(b) = 0\}$. Then for all $a \in V - \pi^{-1}(\boldsymbol{\Delta})$ we have: $Q'(\pi a, \zeta(a)) \neq 0$ and hence $r(a) = P(\pi a, \zeta(a))/Q'(\pi a, \zeta(a))$. For $\beta \in Y$, if r and ζ are continuous at α (resp: $\gamma_\alpha r$ and $\gamma_\alpha \zeta$ are in $R(\alpha, V)$) for all $\alpha \in V \cap \pi^{-1}(\beta)$, then the coefficients of $Q'(y, T)$ and $P(y, T)$ are continuous (resp: analytic) at β. If r and ζ are in $\mathfrak{R}$ then $Q'(y, T)$ and $P(y, T)$ are in $\mathfrak{S}[T]$ and Δ is in $\mathfrak{S}$. In case of $K = \mathbf{C}$, if r and ζ are continuous on V and if $\gamma_\alpha r$ and $\gamma_\alpha \zeta$ are in $R(\alpha, V)$ for all $\alpha \in V - V'$ where V' is a thin subset of V, then $Q'(y, T)$ and $P(y, T)$ are in $\mathfrak{S}[T]$ and Δ is in $\mathfrak{S}$.*

Follows from (35.6, 35.7, 35.13).

(35.15) Let $x = (y_1, \ldots, y_e, z_1, \ldots, z_m)$. Let $\tilde{\mathfrak{R}}^*$ be the ring of all K-valued functions on X, and let $\mathfrak{R}^* = R(X)$. As a special case of (35.14) we get

1) *For $r \in \tilde{\mathfrak{R}}$ and $\zeta = \zeta(x) \in \mathfrak{R}^*$, let $Q(y, T)$ be the field polynomial of $\zeta|V$ relative to $\pi|V$ and let $P(y, T)$ be the Osgoodian of $r\|(\zeta|V)$ relative to $\pi|V$. Let $\Delta(y)$ be the T-discriminant of $Q(y, T)$ and let $\boldsymbol{\Delta} = \{b \in Y : \Delta(b) = 0\}$. Let $q(x) = Q'(y, \zeta(x))$, and $p(x) = P(y, \zeta(x))$. Then $q(x) \in \mathfrak{R}^*$, $\Delta(y) \in \mathfrak{S}$, $p(x) \in \tilde{\mathfrak{R}}^*$; for all $a \in V$ we have $p(a) = r(a)q(a)$; and for all $a \in V - \pi^{-1}(\boldsymbol{\Delta})$*

we have $q(a) \neq 0$ *and hence* $r(a) = p(a)/q(a)$. *If* $r \in \mathfrak{R}$ *then* $p(x) \in \mathfrak{R}^*$. *In case of* $K = \mathbf{C}$, *if* r *is continuous on* V *and if* $\gamma_\alpha r \in R(\alpha, V)$ *for all* $\alpha \in V - V'$ *where* V' *is a thin subset of* V, *then* $p(x) \in \mathfrak{R}^*$.

Next we prove

2) *Assume that* $K = \mathbf{C}$ *and that* Y *is connected. Then there exist* $\kappa_1, \ldots, \kappa_m \in K$ *such that for* $\zeta(x) = \kappa_1 z_1 + \ldots + \kappa_m z_m$, *letting* $Q(y, T) =$ *field polynomial of* $\zeta|V$ *relative to* $\pi|V$, $\Delta(y) = T$*-discriminant of* $Q(y, T)$ *and* $\mathbf{\Delta} = \{b \in Y : \Delta(b) = 0\}$, *we have the following:* $\mathbf{\Delta}$ *is either empty or is a pure* $e - 1$ *dimensional analytic set in* Y; $V \cap \pi^{-1}(\mathbf{\Delta})$ *is either empty or is a pure* $e - 1$ *dimensional analytic set in* X; $V \cap \pi^{-1}(\mathbf{\Delta})$ *is a closed thin subset of* V.

By (35.9) we can find $\beta \in Y$ such that $V \cap \pi^{-1}(\beta)$ contains d distinct points $\alpha^{(\lambda)} = (\beta, \gamma^{(\lambda)})$, $(\lambda = 1, \ldots, d)$. Let

$$L_{\lambda,\lambda'} = \{k \in K^m : k_1\gamma_1^{(\lambda)} + \ldots + k_m\gamma_m^{(\lambda)} = k_1\gamma_1^{(\lambda')} + \ldots + k_m\gamma_m^{(\lambda')}\}.$$

For any $\lambda \neq \lambda'$, $\gamma^{(\lambda)} \neq \gamma^{(\lambda')}$ and hence $L_{\lambda,\lambda'}$ is a hyperplane in K^m. Therefore there exists $\kappa = (\kappa_1, \ldots, \kappa_m) \in K^m$ such that $\kappa \notin L_{\lambda,\lambda'}$ for all $\lambda \neq \lambda'$. Now $\zeta(\alpha^{(1)}), \ldots, \zeta(\alpha^{(d)})$ are all distinct and hence by (35.6), $\Delta(\beta) \neq 0$. Since Y is connected, by Identity Theorem (2.5), $\Delta \not\equiv 0$ in the neighbourhood of each point in Y. Our assertion now follows from (23.3, 33.1.3, 33.8). As a consequence of 1) and 2) we get the following.

3) *Assume that* $K = \mathbf{C}$ *and that* Y *is connected. Let* $r : V \to \mathbf{C}$ *be continuous such that* $\gamma_\alpha r \in R(\alpha, V)$ *for all* $\alpha \in V - V'$ *where* V' *is a thin subset of* V. *Then there exist* $q(x)$ *and* $p(x)$ *in* $\mathfrak{R}^*$ *such that* $p(a) = r(a)q(a)$ *for all* $a \in V$, *and there exists an analytic set* V^* *in* X *such that* V^* *is a thin subset of* V *and such that for all* $a \in V - V^*$ *we have* $q(a) \neq 0$ *and hence* $r(a) = p(a)/q(a)$.

(35.16) *The field polynomial* $g_i(y, T)$ *of* $z_i|V$ *relative to* $\pi|V$ *is a monic polynomial of degree* d *in* T *with coefficients in* $\mathfrak{S}$, *and*

$$V \subset W' = \{(b, c) \in Y \times K^m : g_1(b, c_1) = \ldots = g_m(b, c_m) = 0\}.^7$$

If $m = 1$ *then:* $V = W'$, *the* T*-discriminant* $\Delta_1(y)$ *of* $g_1(y, T)$ *is a nonzero element in* $\mathfrak{S}$, *and there does not exist any monic polynomial* $h(y, T)$ *of degree* $< d$ *in* T *with coefficients in* $\mathfrak{S}$ *such that* $h(b, c) = 0$ *for all* $(b, c) \in V$.

Proof. The first assertion follows from (35.13.1). Now suppose that $m = 1$. Then $V = W'$ by (35.13.1). By (35.9), there exists $\beta \in Y$ such

[7] By (25.9), W' is a pure e dimensional analytic set in $Y \times K^m\{z\}$.

that $V \cap \pi^{-1}(\beta)$ contains d distinct points and then $\Delta_1(\beta) \neq 0$ by (35.6). The last assertion also follows from the fact that $V \cap \pi^{-1}(\beta)$ contains d distinct points.

(35.17) *Remarks on the complex case.* Let $K = \mathbf{C}$. Assume that Y is connected and Z is bounded. Keep assumption (I) but disregard assumptions (II) and (III).[3] Consider the following condition:

(II′) $$\bar{V} \cap (Y \times \mathring{Z}) = \emptyset.$$

1) *Conditions* (II) *and* (II′) *are equivalent.*

PROOF. By (35.10.2), (II) $\Rightarrow$ (II′) without assuming that Y is connected and Z is bounded. Now assume (II′). Then by (34.24) it follows that for any $b \in Y$, $V \cap \pi^{-1}(b)$ is a finite set. Since Y is arcwise connected and a closed arc is compact, it now suffices to show that: given $\beta \in Y$ there exists $D > 0$ with $Y\langle D, \beta\rangle \subset Y$ such that $\mathbf{d}(b, (\pi|V)^{-1}) = \mathbf{d}(\beta, (\pi|V)^{-1})$ for all $b \in Y\langle D, \beta\rangle$. Now $V \neq \emptyset$ and hence $V \cap \pi^{-1}(\beta) \neq \emptyset$ by (34.27). Let $\alpha^{(\lambda)} = (\beta, \gamma^{(\lambda)})$, $(\lambda = 1,\ldots, N)$, be the distinct points in $V \cap \pi^{-1}(\beta)$. By (35.4) we can find $D > 0$ and $E'' > E > E' > 0$ for which we have (1°, 2°, 3°).

1°) $$Y\langle D, \beta\rangle \subset Y; \quad \bigcup_{\lambda=1}^{N} Z\langle E'', \gamma^{(\lambda)}\rangle \subset Z;$$
$$Z\langle E'', \gamma^{(\lambda)}\rangle \cap Z\langle E'', \gamma^{(\lambda')}\rangle = \emptyset \quad \text{for all} \quad \lambda \neq \lambda'.$$

2°) For all $b \in Y\langle D, \beta\rangle$ and $\lambda = 1,\ldots, N$ we have
$$\sum_{a \in V \cap (b \times Z\langle E'', \gamma^{(\lambda)}\rangle)} \mathbf{d}(a, \pi, V) = \mathbf{d}(\alpha^{(\lambda)}, \pi, V).$$

3°) $$V \cap \left[Y\langle D, \beta\rangle \times \bigcup_{\lambda=1}^{N} (Z\langle E'', \gamma^{(\lambda)}\rangle - Z\langle E', \gamma^{(\lambda)}\rangle)\right] = \emptyset.$$

Let
$$Z' = \bigcup_{\lambda=1}^{N} Z\langle E, \gamma^{(\lambda)}\rangle, \qquad Z^* = Z - Z',$$
$$\mathring{Z}^* = \text{boundary of } Z^* \text{ in } \mathbf{C}^m\{z\},$$
$$\mathring{Z}\langle E, \gamma^{(\lambda)}\rangle = \{c \in K^m : |c_i - \gamma_i^{(\lambda)}| = E \text{ for } i = 1,\ldots, m\}.$$

Then
$$\mathring{Z}^* = \mathring{Z} \cup \left[\bigcup_{\lambda=1}^{N} \mathring{Z}\langle E, \gamma^{(\lambda)}\rangle\right].$$

By 3°) we get

$$\bar{V} \cap [Y\langle D, \beta\rangle \times \bigcup_{\lambda=1}^{N} \mathring{Z}\langle E, \gamma^{(\lambda)}\rangle] = \emptyset$$

and hence $\bar{V} \cap (Y\langle D, \beta\rangle \times \mathring{Z}^*) = \emptyset$. Now $V \cap (\beta \times Z^*) = \mathring{\emptyset}$ and hence $V \cap (Y\langle D, \beta\rangle \times Z^*) = \emptyset$ by (34.27). Therefore by 1°) and 2°) we get that $\mathbf{d}(b, (\pi|V)^{-1}) = \mathbf{d}(\beta, (\pi|V)^{-1})$ for all $b \in Y\langle D, \beta\rangle$.

In Grauert-Remmert [**2**: p. 255] the following slightly stronger version of (35.16) is stated.

2) *Assume* (II′). *Then for* $i = 1,..., m$, *there exists a monic polynomial* $G_i(y, z_i)$ *of degree* $d_i \leqq d$ *in* z_i *with coefficients in* $\mathfrak{S}$ *such that letting* $\Delta_i(y) =$ *the* z_i*-discriminant of* $G_i(y, z_i)$ *and* $W = \{(b, c) \in Y \times K^m : G_i(b, c_i) = 0$ *for* $i = 1,..., m\}$ *we have the following. For* $i = 1,..., m$, $\Delta_i(y)$ *is a nonzero element in* $\mathfrak{S}$.[8] *V is the union of a certain number of irreducible components of* $W \cap X$.[9] *For any* $i \leqq m$, *there does not exist a monic polynomial* $h_i(y, z_i)$ *of degree* $< d_i$ *in* z_i *with coefficients in* $\mathfrak{S}$ *such that* $h_i(b, c_i) = 0$ *for all* $(b, c) \in V$. *If V is irreducible then* $G_i(y, z_i)$ *is irreducible in* $\mathfrak{S}[z_i]$ *for* $i = 1,..., m$.

Remark. In applications, when use of 2) is indicated, usually (35.12) can be used more simply and effectively. Still, it may be of interest to give a proof of 2) in our set up.

Proof. For any $i \leqq m$ let $\pi_i^* : K^m\{z\} \to K^1\{z_i\}$, $\pi_i' : K^e\{y\} \times K^m\{z\} \to K^e\{y\} \times K^1\{z_i\}$, $\pi_i'' : K^e\{y\} \times K^1\{z_i\} \to K^e\{y\}$ be the natural projections. Let $V_i = \pi_i'(V)$, $\bar{V}_i =$ closure of V_i in $K^e\{y\} \times K^1\{z_i\}$, $Z_i = \pi_i^*(Z)$, and $\mathring{Z}_i =$ boundary of Z_i in $K^1\{z_i\}$. By 1), condition (II) is satisfied; whence in virtue of (35.10.1), (II′) yields that $\bar{V}_i \cap (Y \times \mathring{Z}_i) = \emptyset$. By (35.12), V_i is a pure e dimensional analytic set in $\pi'(Y \times Z) = Y \times Z_i$. Obviously Z_i is bounded. Thus by 1), $\pi_i''|V_i$ satisfies conditions (I) and (II). Let $G_i(y, z_i)$ be the field polynomial of $z_i|V_i$ relative to $\pi_i''|V_i$.[10] Applying (35.16) to $\pi_i''|V_i$ we deduce that $G_i(y, z_i)$ is a monic polynomial of some degree $d_i > 0$ in z_i with coefficients in $\mathfrak{S}$ and $\Delta_i(y)$ is a nonzero element in $\mathfrak{S}$. Clearly $V \subset W \cap X$ and hence by (34.16), V is the union of a certain number of irreducible components of $W \cap X$.[9] For any $b \in Y$,

[8] Hence in particular $G_i(y, z_i)$ does not have any multiple factors in $\mathfrak{S}[z_i]$. For any $\beta \in Y$, by Identity Theorem (2.5), $\gamma_\beta \Delta_i \neq 0$ and hence the polynomial obtained by replacing the coefficients of $G_i(y, z_i)$ by their Taylor expansions around β is free from multiple factors in $S[z_i]$.

[9] By (25.9), W is a pure e dimensional analytic set in $Y \times K^m\{z\}$.

[10] By analogy with field theory, $G_i(y, z_i)$ may be called the minimal monic polynomial of $z_i|V$ relative to $\pi|V$.

$V_i \cap \pi_i''^{-1}(b)$ contains at most d points and hence applying (35.9) to V_i we deduce that $d_i \leqq d$. Let $h_i(y, z_i)$ be a monic polynomial of some degree d_i^* in z_i with coefficients in $\mathfrak{S}$ such that $h_i(b, c_i) = 0$ for all $(b, c) \in V$. Then $h_i(b, c_i) = 0$ for all $(b, c_i) \in V_i$ and hence $d_i^* \geqq d_i$ by (35.16). Finally assume that V is irreducible. Let if possible $G_i(y, z_i) = G_i'(y, z_i)G_i''(y, z_i)$ where $G_i'(y, z_i)$ and $G_i''(y, z_i)$ are monic polynomials of positive degrees d_i' and d_i'' in z_i with coefficients in $\mathfrak{S}$. Then by (34.10), either $G_i'(b, c_i) = 0$ for all $(b, c) \in V$ or $G_i''(b, c_i) = 0$ for all $(b, c) \in V$. This is a contradiction since $d_i' < d_i$ and $d_i'' < d_i$. Therefore $G_i(y, z_i)$ is irreducible in $\mathfrak{S}[z_i]$.

§36. NORMAL POINTS OF COMPLEX ANALYTIC SETS. REMARKS ON ALGEBRAIC VARIETIES

(36.1) *Let V be an analytic set in an open set X in $\mathbf{C}^n$ and let a be any simple point of V. Then $R(a, V)$ is integrally closed in $\mathfrak{C}(a, V)$.*

PROOF. Let $e = \dim_a V$. In virtue of (33.18), upon replacing V by a suitable neighborhood of a in V we may assume that V is an open set in $\mathbf{C}^e\{y\}$, $y = (y_1, \ldots, y_e)$. For any $\beta \in \mathbf{C}^e$, $\gamma \in \mathbf{C}$, $D > 0$, $E > 0$, let

$$Y\langle D, \beta\rangle = \{b \in \mathbf{C}^e : |b_1 - \beta_1| < D, \ldots, |b_e - \beta_e| < D\},$$
$$Z\langle E, \gamma\rangle = \{c \in \mathbf{C} : |\gamma - c| < E\}.$$

Let $r \in \mathfrak{C}(a, V)$ be given which is integral over $R(a, V)$. Then there exists a monic polynomial $G(T) \in R(a, V)[T]$ such that $G(r) = 0$. We can write

$$G(T) = G_1(T)^{m_1} \ldots G_\lambda(T)^{m_\lambda}, \qquad (m_1 > 0, \ldots, m_\lambda > 0),$$

where $G_1(T), \ldots, G_\lambda(T)$ are distinct irreducible monic polynomials of positive degrees in T with coefficients in the quotient field of $R(a, V)$. Since $R(a, V)$ is a unique factorization domain, the coefficients of $G_1(T), \ldots, G_\lambda(T)$ are in $R(a, V)$, i.e.,

$$G_i(T) = \sum_{j=0}^{d_i} G_{ij} T^j, \qquad d_i > 0, \qquad G_{ij} \in R(a, V), \qquad G_{id_i} = 1.$$

Upon replacing V by a suitable connected neighborhood of a in V, we can find $\tilde{r}(y) \in \mathfrak{C}(V)$ and $\tilde{G}_{ij}(y) \in R(V)$ such that: $\gamma_a \tilde{r} = r$, $\gamma_a \tilde{G}_{ij} = G_{ij}$ for all i, j, and

$$\prod_{i=1}^{\lambda} \left(\sum_{j=0}^{d_i} \tilde{G}_{ij}(b) \tilde{r}(b)^j \right)^{m_i} = 0 \quad \text{for all} \quad b \in V.$$

Then

1°) $$g(b, \tilde{r}(b)) = 0 \quad \text{for all} \quad b \in V,$$

where

$$g(y, T) = \prod_{i=1}^{\lambda} \left(\sum_{j=0}^{d_i} \tilde{G}_{ij}(y) T^j \right).$$

Let $\Delta(y)$ be the T-discriminant of $g(y, T)$. Let

$$W = \{(b, c) \in V \times \mathbf{C}^1 : g(b, c) = 0\}, \qquad \mathbf{\Delta} = \{b \in V : \Delta(b) = 0\}.$$

Now $\gamma_a \Delta$ is the T-discriminant of $G_1(T) ... G_\lambda(T)$ and hence $\gamma_a \Delta \neq 0$. Since V is connected, by Identity Theorem (2.5), $\mathbf{\Delta}$ is a thin subset of V. Hence by Riemann Extension Theorem (14.3), it suffices to show that $\tilde{r}(y)$ is analytic at each point in $V - \mathbf{\Delta}$. Given $\beta \in V - \mathbf{\Delta}$, let $\gamma = \tilde{r}(\beta)$. Then $\Delta(\beta) \neq 0$ and by 1°), $(\beta, \gamma) \in W$. Hence by (12.3), we can find $D > 0$, $E > 0$, and an analytic function $\xi(y)$ on $Y\langle D, \beta\rangle$ such that $Y\langle D, \beta\rangle \subset V$ and $W \cap (Y\langle D, \beta\rangle \times Z\langle E, \gamma\rangle) = \{(b, \xi(b)) : b \in Y\langle D, \beta\rangle\}$. Since $\tilde{r}$ is continuous on V, in virtue of 1°) there exists $0 < D_1 \leqq D$ such that $\tilde{r}(b) = \xi(b)$ for all $b \in Y\langle D_1, \beta\rangle$. Therefore $\tilde{r}$ is analytic at β.

(36.2) *Let V be an analytic set in an open set X in $\mathbf{C}^n$. If $r \in \mathfrak{E}(V)$ is integral over $R(V)$ then $\gamma_a r \in R(a, V)$ for all $a \in V - \mathbf{S}(V)$.*

Follows from (36.1).

(36.3) *Let V be a pure e dimensional analytic set in $Y \times Z$ where Y and Z are open sets in $\mathbf{C}^e\{y\}$ and $\mathbf{C}^m\{z\}$, respectively. Assume that there exists a positive integer d such that for all $b \in Y$, $V \cap \pi^{-1}(b)$ is a finite set and*

$$\sum_{a \in V \cap \pi^{-1}(b)} \mathbf{d}(a, \pi, V) = d$$

where $\pi : \mathbf{C}^e\{y\} \times \mathbf{C}^m\{z\} \to \mathbf{C}^e\{y\}$ is the natural projection. Let $\varphi : R(Y) \to \mathfrak{E}(V)$ be the monomorphism given by: $(\varphi r)(a) = r(\pi a)$ for all $r \in R(Y)$, $a \in V$. Then we have the following.

1) *Integral closure of $\varphi R(Y)$ in $\mathfrak{E}(V)$*
$=$ *integral closure of $R(V)$ in $\mathfrak{E}(V)$*
$= \{r \in \mathfrak{E}(V) : \gamma_\alpha r \in R(\alpha, V)$ for all $\alpha \in V - V'$ where V' is a closed thin subset of $V\}$
$= \{r \in \mathfrak{E}(V) : \gamma_\alpha r \in R(\alpha, V)$ for all $\alpha \in V - \mathbf{S}(V)\}$.

2) *Assume that Y is connected and let $r \in \mathfrak{E}(V)$ be integral over $R(V)$. Then there exist $q, p \in R(X)$ such that for all $a \in V$ we have: $p(a) = r(a)q(a)$; and there exists an analytic set V' in X such that V' is a thin subset of V and such that for all $a \in V - V'$ we have: $q(a) \neq 0$ and hence $r(a) = p(a)/q(a)$.*

3) *Assume that* $\gamma_a V$ *is irreducible for all* $a \in V$. *Let* V' *be a closed thin subset of* V *and let* $r \in R(V - V')$ *be such that* $|r|$ *is bounded in the neighborhood of each point of* V'. *Then there exists a unique* $r^* \in \mathfrak{E}(V)$ *such that* $r^*|V - V' = r$.

In virtue of (36.2), 1) follows from (35.13). 2) follows from 1) and (35.15). To prove 3) we need a topological lemma.

(36.4) *Lemmas from topology*. First we give a review on filters.

Let A be a set and let $\mathfrak{F}$ be a set of subsets of A. By $\langle\mathfrak{F}\rangle_A$ denote the set of subsets of A given by: $G \in \langle\mathfrak{F}\rangle_A \Leftrightarrow F \subset G$ for some $F \in \mathfrak{F}$. For any subset A^* of A, by $\mathfrak{F}|A^*$ denote the set of subsets of A^* given by: $F^* \in \mathfrak{F}|A^* \Leftrightarrow F^* = F \cap A^*$ for some $F \in \mathfrak{F}$; note that $\langle\mathfrak{F}\rangle_A|A^* = \langle\mathfrak{F}|A^*\rangle_{A^*}$. For any map $f: A \to B$ of A into a set B, by $f(\mathfrak{F})$ denote the set of subsets of B given by: $G \in f(\mathfrak{F}) \Leftrightarrow G = f(F)$ for some $F \in \mathfrak{F}$; note that $\langle f(\mathfrak{F})\rangle_B = \langle f(\langle\mathfrak{F}\rangle_A)\rangle_B$. $\mathfrak{F}$ is a filter on A means:

i) if $F \in \mathfrak{F}$ and $F \subset G \subset A$ then $G \in \mathfrak{F}$;
ii) intersection of any finite number of elements in $\mathfrak{F}$ is again in $\mathfrak{F}$;
iii) $\emptyset \notin \mathfrak{F}$.

$\mathfrak{F}$ is a filter base on A means that $\langle\mathfrak{F}\rangle_A$ is a filter on A; this is so $\Leftrightarrow$

i′) intersection of any two elements in $\mathfrak{F}$ contains an element of $\mathfrak{F}$,
ii′) $\mathfrak{F} \neq \emptyset$ and $\emptyset \notin \mathfrak{F}$.

If $\mathfrak{F}$ is a filter base on A and A^* is a subset of A, then $\mathfrak{F}|A^*$ is a filter base on $A^* \Leftrightarrow F \cap A^* \neq \emptyset$ for all $F \in \mathfrak{F}$. If A is a topological space, then for any $\alpha \in A$ the set of all vicinities of α in A is a filter on A and we denote it by $\mathfrak{W}_A(\alpha)$; for any subspace A^* of A, $\mathfrak{W}_A(\alpha)|A^*$ is a filter on $A^* \Leftrightarrow \alpha \in \mathrm{cl}_A A^*$.

Let A be a topological space and let $\mathfrak{F}$ be a filter base on A. $\alpha \in A$ is a limit point of $\mathfrak{F}$ in A means that $\mathfrak{W}_A(\alpha) \subset \langle\mathfrak{F}\rangle_A$. The closure of $\mathfrak{F}$ in A is defined by: $\mathrm{cl}_A\mathfrak{F} = \bigcap_{F \in \mathfrak{F}} \mathrm{cl}_A F$; we then have: $\mathrm{cl}_A\langle\mathfrak{F}\rangle_A = \mathrm{cl}_A\mathfrak{F}$. If α is a limit point of $\mathfrak{F}$ in A then $\alpha \in \mathrm{cl}_A\mathfrak{F}$. If A is Hausdorff, then a filter on A can have at most one limit point. If A is Hausdorff, then A is compact $\Leftrightarrow \mathrm{cl}_A\mathfrak{F} \neq \emptyset$ for every filter $\mathfrak{F}$ on A.

In a Hausdorff space A the following two conditions are equivalent.

i*) Given any $\alpha \in A$ and any closed subset A' of A with $\alpha \notin A'$, there exist open subsets A_1 and A_2 of A such that $\alpha \in A_1$, $A' \subset A_2$, $A_1 \cap A_2 = \emptyset$.

ii*) Given $\alpha \in A$ and a vicinity M of α in A, there exists a vicinity N of α in A such that N is closed in A and $N \subset M$.

A regular (topological) space is a Hausdorff space A satisfying one and hence both of the above conditions. Any subspace of a regular space is regular. Any metric space is regular.

1) *Let A^* be an everywhere dense subset of a topological space A. Let $f : A^* \to B$ be continuous where B is a regular space. Then f has a (unique) continuous extension to A, (i.e., a continuous map $A \to B$ whose restriction to A^* is f), if and only if: for all $\alpha \in A$, the filter base $f(\mathfrak{W}_A(\alpha)|A^*)$ has a limit point in B.*

The definitions and results summarized above can be found for instance in Bourbaki [**1**: §§6–8]. From 1) we now deduce the following lemma given by Grauert-Remmert [**2**: Theorem 1 on p. 249].

2) *Let A be a locally connected topological space and let $A^* = A - A'$ where A' is a nowhere dense subset of A which disconnects A nowhere. Let $f : A^* \to B$ be continuous where B is a regular space. Then f has a (unique) continuous extension to A in case the following two conditions are satisfied.*

1°) *For each $\alpha \in A$, $\mathrm{cl}_B f(\mathfrak{W}_A(\alpha)|A^*)$ is a finite set.*
2°) *If for $\alpha \in A$ and $B_1 \subset B$, $f(\mathfrak{W}_A(\alpha)|A^*)|B_1$ is a filter base on B, then $\mathrm{cl}_B[f(\mathfrak{W}_A(\alpha)|A^*)|B_1] \neq \emptyset$.*

Remark. In a compact space, the closure of any filter base is nonempty and hence condition 2°) is satisfied if the following condition is satisfied.

2′) *Given $\alpha \in A$, there exists a vicinity M of α in A and a compact subset N of B such that $f(M \cap A^*) \subset N$.*

Proof of 2). Given $\alpha \in A$ we want to show that $f(\mathfrak{W}_A(\alpha)|A^*)$ has a limit point in B. By 1°) and 2°), $\mathrm{cl}_B f(\mathfrak{W}_A(\alpha)|A^*)$ is a nonempty finite set; let $\beta_1,\ldots, \beta_m$ be the distinct points in it. Since B is Hausdorff, we can take pairwise disjoint neighborhoods $N_1,\ldots, N_m$ of $\beta_1,\ldots, \beta_m$ in B. Let $B_1 = B - \bigcup_{i=1}^{m} N_i$. Suppose if possible that for each $M \in \mathfrak{W}_A(\alpha)$, $f(M \cap A^*) \not\subset \bigcup_{i=1}^{m} N_i$. Then $f(\mathfrak{W}_A(\alpha)|A^*)|B_1$ is a filter base on B_1, and hence by 2°) there exists $\beta^* \in \mathrm{cl}_B[f(\mathfrak{W}_A(\alpha)|A^*)|B_1]$. Now B_1 is closed in B and hence $\beta^* \in B_1$. Obviously $\mathrm{cl}_B[f(\mathfrak{W}_A(\alpha)|A^*)|B_1] \subset \mathrm{cl}_B f(\mathfrak{W}_A(\alpha)|A^*)$ and hence $\beta^* = \beta_i$ for some i, which is a contradiction. Therefore there exists $M \in \mathfrak{W}_A(\alpha)$ such that $f(M \cap A^*) \subset \bigcap_{i=1}^{m} N_i$. Since A' disconnects A nowhere, we may choose M so that $M \cap A^*$ is connected. Then $f(M \cap A^*)$ is connected and hence $f(M \cap A^*) \subset N_j$ for some j; say $f(M \cap A^*) \subset N_1$.

For any $i > 1$, $f(M \cap A^*) \cap N_i$ is then empty and hence $\beta_i \notin \mathrm{cl}_B f(\mathfrak{W}_A(\alpha)|A^*)$. So we must have $\mathrm{cl}_B f(\mathfrak{W}_A(\alpha)|A^*) = \{\beta_1\}$. Given any neighborhood N of β_1 in B, as above we can find $M' \in \mathfrak{W}_A(\alpha)$ such that $f(M' \cap A^*) \subset N$. Therefore β_1 is a limit point of $f(\mathfrak{W}_A(\alpha)|A^*)$.

REMARK. 2) continues to hold if condition 1°) is replaced by the following condition.

1′). *For each* $\alpha \in A$, $\mathrm{cl}_B f(\mathfrak{W}_A(\alpha)|A^*)$ *is a countable discrete set.*

We used 1°) only to find pairwise disjoint neighborhoods of the points in $\mathrm{cl}_B(\mathfrak{W}_A(\alpha)|A^*)$. Hence it suffices to show that, given distinct points β_1, $\beta_2,\dots$ in B where $\{\beta_1, \beta_2,\dots\}$ is a discrete subset of B, there exist pairwise disjoint neighborhoods $N_1, N_2,\dots$ of $\beta_1, \beta_2,\dots$ in B. B being regular, there exists a closed vicinity M_1 of β_1 in B such that $\beta_i \notin M_1$ for all $i > 1$. Now $B - M_1$ is a neighborhood of β_2 in B and hence there exists a closed vicinity M_2 of β_2 in B such that $M_2 \subset B - M_1$ and $\beta_i \notin M_2$ for all $i > 2$. Now $B - M_1 - M_2$ is a neighborhood of β_3 in B and hence there exists a closed vicinity M_3 of β_3 in B such that $M_3 \subset B - M_1 - M_2$ and $\beta_i \notin M_3$ for all $i > 3$. In this manner, using the fact that a finite union of closed sets is closed, we find pairwise disjoint closed vicinities $M_1, M_2,\dots$ of $\beta_1, \beta_2,\dots$ in B. Take $N_i = \mathrm{int}_B M_i$ for $i = 1, 2,\dots$.

Proof of (36.3.3). Let $Y' = \mathrm{cl}_Y \pi(V')$. Then Y' is a closed thin subset of Y and $V \cap \pi^{-1}(Y')$ is a closed thin subset of V containing V'. Hence upon replacing V' by $V \cap \pi^{-1}(Y')$ we may assume that $V' = V \cap \pi^{-1}(Y')$. Let $Y^* = Y - Y'$ and $V^* = V - V'$. For any $\beta \in Y$, $u \in \mathbf{C}$, $D > 0$, $E > 0$, let

$$Y\langle D, \beta\rangle = \{b \in \mathbf{C}^e : |b_1 - \beta_1| < D,\dots, |b_e - \beta_e| < D\},$$

$$\Omega\langle E, u\rangle = \{v \in \mathbf{C} : |v - u| < E\}.$$

By (34.3), V' disconnects V nowhere. Given $\alpha \in V$ let $\beta = \pi\alpha$. By assumption $|r|$ is bounded in the neighborhood of each point of V' and hence by (35.8) we can find $D_1 > 0$ and $\Lambda > 0$ such that: $Y\langle D_1, \beta\rangle \subset Y$, and $|r(a)| \leqq \Lambda$ for all $a \in V^* \cap \pi^{-1}(Y\langle D_1, \beta\rangle)$. Now $r(V^* \cap \pi^{-1}(Y\langle D_1, \beta\rangle))$ is contained in the compact subset $\{v \in \mathbf{C} : |v| \leqq \Lambda\}$ of $\mathbf{C}$. Hence by (36.4.2) it suffices to show that $\mathrm{cl}_{\mathbf{C}} r(\mathfrak{W}|V^*)$ is a finite set, where $\mathfrak{W}$ is the set of all vicinities of α in V. Upon replacing Y and V by $Y\langle D_1, \beta\rangle$ and $V \cap \pi^{-1}(Y\langle D_1, \beta\rangle)$ we may assume that $|f(a)| \leqq \Lambda$ for all $a \in V^*$. By (35.13.1), the field polynomial $H(y, T)$ of r relative to $\pi|V^*$ is a monic polynomial of degree d in T with coefficients which are analytic on Y^* and for all $b \in Y^*$ we have

$$H(b, T) = \prod_{a \in V \cap \pi^{-1}(b)} (T - r(a))^{\mathrm{d}(a, \pi, V)}.$$

Now $|r(a)| \leq \Lambda$ for all $a \in V^*$ and hence the coefficients of $H(y, T)$ are bounded in the neighborhood of each point in Y'. Therefore by Riemann Extension Theorem (14.3), these coefficients have unique analytic extensions to Y; let the resulting polynomial be again denoted by $H(y, T)$, i.e., $H(y, T)$ is now a monic polynomial of degree d in T with coefficients which are analytic on Y and

$$1°)\quad H(b, T) = \prod_{a \in V \cap \pi^{-1}(b)} (T - r(a))^{\mathrm{d}(a, \pi, V)} \qquad \text{for all} \quad b \in Y^*.$$

Let $u_1, \ldots, u_\mu$ be the distinct roots of $H(\beta, T) = 0$ in $\mathbf{C}$. Let $u \in \mathbf{C}$ be given such that $u \neq u_i$ for $i = 1, \ldots, \mu$. Take $E > 0$ such that

$$\Omega\langle E, u\rangle \cap \left[\bigcup_{i=1}^{\mu} \Omega\langle E, u_i\rangle\right] = \emptyset.$$

By (12.3), there exists $D > 0$ with $Y\langle D, \beta\rangle \subset Y$ such that for any $b \in Y\langle D, \beta\rangle$, all the roots of $H(b, T) = 0$ are in $\bigcap_{i=1}^{\mu} \Omega\langle E, u_i\rangle$. By 1°) we get that

$$r((Y\langle D, \beta\rangle \times Z) \cap V^*) \subset \bigcup_{i=1}^{\mu} \Omega\langle E, u_i\rangle.$$

Now $(Y\langle D, \beta\rangle \times Z) \cap V$ is a neighborhood of α in V, $\Omega\langle E, u\rangle$ is a neighborhood of u in $\mathbf{C}$, and $r((Y\langle D, \beta\rangle \times Z) \cap V^*) \cap \Omega\langle E, u\rangle = \emptyset$. Therefore $u \notin \mathrm{cl}_{\mathbf{C}} r(\mathfrak{W}|V^*)$. Consequently the points in $\mathrm{cl}_{\mathbf{C}} r(\mathfrak{W}|V^*)$ are amongst $u_1, \ldots, u_\mu$, and hence $\mathrm{cl}_{\mathbf{C}} r(\mathfrak{W}|V^*)$ is a finite set.

(36.5) *Let V be a nonempty analytic set in an open set X in $\mathbf{C}^n$. Assume that $\gamma_a V$ is irreducible for all $a \in V$. Let V' be a closed thin subset of V and let $r \in R(V - V')$ be such that $|r|$ is bounded in the neighborhood of each point of V'. Then there exists a unique $r^* \in \mathfrak{E}(V)$ such that $r^*|V - V' = r$.*

PROOF. It suffices to show that, given $\alpha \in V$ there exists a neighborhood X_1 of α in X such that $r|(V - V') \cap X_1$ has a unique continuous extension to $V \cap X_1$. In virtue of (35.1, 23.5), this follows from (36.3.3).

(36.6) *Let V be an analytic set in an open set X in $\mathbf{C}^n$. For $a \in V$ consider the following rings.*

$\mathfrak{R}(a, V)$ = total quotient ring of $R(a, V)$.
$R'(a, V)$ = integral closure of $R(a, V)$ in $\mathfrak{R}(a, V)$.
$R''(a, V)$ = integral closure of $R(a, V)$ in $\mathfrak{E}(a, V)$.

$R_1''(a, V) = \{r \in \mathfrak{E}(a, V)$: there exists a closed thin subset V' in a neighborhood V_1 of a in V and $\tilde{r} \in \mathfrak{E}(V_1)$ such that $\gamma_\alpha \tilde{r} \in R(\alpha, V)$ for all $\alpha \in V_1 - V'$ and $\gamma_a \tilde{r} = r\}$.

$R_2''(a, V) = \{r \in \mathfrak{E}(a, V)$: there exists a neighborhood V_1 of a in V and $\tilde{r} \in \mathfrak{E}(V_1)$ such that $\gamma_\alpha \tilde{r} \in R(\alpha, V)$ for all $\alpha \in V_1 - \mathbf{S}(V)$ and $\gamma_a \tilde{r} = r\}$.

Also consider the following conditions

(I_1) [$\tilde{r} \in \mathfrak{E}(V_1)$ such that $\gamma_\alpha \tilde{r} \in R(\alpha, V)$ for all $\alpha \in V_1 - V'$ where V' is a closed thin subset in a neighborhood V_1 of a in V] $\Rightarrow \gamma_a \tilde{r} \in R(a, V)$.

(I_2) Same as (I_1) with $\mathbf{S}(V)$ replacing V'.

(II_1) [$\tilde{r} \in R(V_1 - V')$ such that $|\tilde{r}|$ is bounded on $V_1 - V'$ where V' is a closed thin subset in a neighborhood V_1 of a in V] $\Rightarrow$ there exists $\tilde{r}^* \in \mathfrak{E}(V_2)$ where V_2 is a neighborhood of a in V_1, such that $\tilde{r}^*|V_2 - V' = \tilde{r}|V_2 - V'$ and $\gamma_a \tilde{r}^* \in R(a, V)$.

(II_2) Same as (II_1) with $\mathbf{S}(V)$ replacing V'.

(N) $\gamma_\alpha V$ is irreducible for all α in some neighborhood of a in V.

Then we have the following.

1) *If* $\gamma_a V$ *is pure dimensional then* $R_1''(a, V) = R_2''(a, V) = R''(a, V) \subset R'(a, V)$.[1]

2) *If* (N) *holds then* $R''(a, V) = R'(a, V)$.

3) *If* (N) *holds, then a is a normal point of* $V \Leftrightarrow (I_1) \Leftrightarrow (I_2)$.[2]

4) *If* (N) *holds and a is a normal point of V then* (II_1) *and* (II_2) *hold.*

5) $(II_2) \Leftrightarrow (II_1) \Rightarrow$ *a is a normal point* V.[3]

Proof of 1). In virtue of (35.1, 23.5), from (36.3.1) we deduce that $R_1''(a, V) = R_2''(a, V) = R''(a, V)$ and in virtue of (33.13), from (36.3.2) we deduce that $R''(a, V) \subset R'(a, V)$.

Before proving the remaining assertions we give the following lemma.

1°) LEMMA.[4] Given $u \in \mathfrak{R}(a, V)$ we can write $u = v/w$ where v and w are in $R(a, V)$ and w is a nonzerodivisor in $R(a, V)$. Assume that $u \in R'(a, V)$.

[1] By (33.14) we can consider $\mathfrak{R}(a, V)$ to be a subring of the total quotient ring of $\mathfrak{E}(a, V)$.

[2] Without the assumption (N) it is not true that $(I_1) \Rightarrow a$ is a normal point of V. For example let V be given by the equation $xy = 0$ in $\mathbf{C}^2\{x, y\}$ and let a be the origin. It is easily checked that (I_1) holds. However a is not a normal point of V since V is reducible at a.

[3] Later on we shall show that if a is a normal point of V then (N) holds. By 4) and 5) it will then follow that: a is a normal point of $V \Leftrightarrow (II_1) \Leftrightarrow (II_2)$.

[4] In this Lemma, $\mathbf{C}$ may be replaced by an arbitrary algebraically closed complete nondiscrete valued field K.

Then there exist $f_1, \ldots, f_\lambda \in R(a, V)$ such that

$$u^\lambda + f_1 u^{\lambda-1} + \ldots + f_\lambda = 0,$$

and hence

$$v^\lambda + f_1 v^{\lambda-1} w + \ldots + f_\lambda w^\lambda = 0.$$

We can find a neighborhood V_1 of a in V and $\tilde{v}, \tilde{w}, \tilde{f}_1, \ldots, \tilde{f}_\lambda \in R(V_1)$ such that $\gamma_a \tilde{v} = v$, $\gamma_a \tilde{w} = w$, $\gamma_a \tilde{f}_1 = f_1, \ldots, \gamma_a \tilde{f}_\lambda = f_\lambda$, and

$$\tilde{v}(\alpha)^\lambda + \tilde{f}_1(\alpha)\tilde{v}(\alpha)^{\lambda-1}\tilde{w}(\alpha) + \ldots + \tilde{f}_\lambda(\alpha)\tilde{w}(\alpha)^\lambda = 0 \qquad \text{for all} \quad \alpha \in V_1.$$

Let $V' = \{\alpha \in V_1 : \tilde{w}(\alpha) = 0\}$. By (33.13) we may assume that V' is a closed thin subset of V_1. Let $\tilde{r}(\alpha) = \tilde{v}(\alpha)/\tilde{w}(\alpha)$ for all $\alpha \in V_1 - V'$. Then $\tilde{r} \in R(V_1 - V')$ and

$$\tilde{r}(\alpha)^\lambda + \tilde{f}_1(\alpha)\tilde{r}(\alpha)^{\lambda-1} + \ldots + \tilde{f}_\lambda(\alpha) = 0 \qquad \text{for all} \quad \alpha \in V_1 - V'.$$

Now $\tilde{f}_1, \ldots, \tilde{f}_\lambda$ are continuous at a and hence by (11.2), upon replacing V_1 by a smaller neighborhood of a in V we get that $|\tilde{r}|$ is bounded on $V_1 - V'$.

Proof of 2). By 1), it suffices to show that $R'(a, V) \subset R''(a, V)$. Given $u \in R'(a, V)$ let the notation be as in the Lemma. In virtue of (35.1, 23.5), by (36.3.3) we can find a neighborhood V_2 of a in V_1 and $\tilde{r}^* \in \mathfrak{E}(V_2)$ such that $\tilde{r}^*|V_2 - V' = \tilde{r}|V_2 - V'$. Now $\tilde{r}^*(\alpha)\tilde{w}(\alpha) = \tilde{v}(\alpha)$ for all $\alpha \in V_2 - V'$ and hence $\tilde{r}^*(\alpha)\tilde{w}(\alpha) = \tilde{v}(\alpha)$ for all $\alpha \in V_2$. Therefore $(\gamma_a \tilde{r}^*)w = v$, i.e., $u = v/w = \gamma_a \tilde{r}^* \in \mathfrak{E}(a, V)$. Hence $u \in R''(a, V)$.

Proof of 3). By definition, a is a normal point of V means that $R(a, V) = R'(a, V)$ and hence our assertion follows from 1) and 2).

Proof of 4). In virtue of (35.1, 23.5), by (36.3.3) we are reduced to the "$\Rightarrow$" part of 3).

Proof of 5). Obviously $(\mathrm{II}_1) \Rightarrow (\mathrm{II}_2)$. If a' is any simple point of V then a' is a normal point of V and $\gamma_\alpha V$ is irreducible for all α in some neighborhood of a' in V; therefore by 4), $(\mathrm{II}_2) \Rightarrow (\mathrm{II}_1)$. Now assume (II_1). Given $u \in R'(a, V)$ let the notation be as in the Lemma. By (II_1) there exists a neighborhood V_2 of a in V_1 and $\tilde{r}^* \in \mathfrak{E}(V_2)$ such that $\tilde{r}^*|V_2 - V' = \tilde{r}|V_2 - V'$ and $\gamma_a \tilde{r}^* \in R(a, V)$. Now $\tilde{r}^*(\alpha)\tilde{w}(\alpha) = \tilde{v}(\alpha)$ for all $\alpha \in V_2 - V'$ and hence $\tilde{r}^*(\alpha)\tilde{w}(\alpha) = \tilde{v}(\alpha)$ for all $\alpha \in V_2$. Therefore $u = v/w = \gamma_a \tilde{r}^* \in R(a, V)$. Thus $R'(a, V) = R(a, V)$ and hence a is a normal point of V.

(36.7) *Remarks on affine algebraic varieties.*[5] Let $x = (x_1, \ldots, x_n)$ be indeterminates over an algebraically closed field K. For any $a \in K^n$ set

$$\mathfrak{J}(a, K^n) = \{f \in K[x] : f(a) = 0\}.$$

[5] We are only giving a brief review. For details see Zariski–Samuel [**2**: §§3 to 6 of Chapter VII].

For any $V \subset K^n$ set

$$\mathfrak{J}(V, K^n) = \{f \in K[x] : f(a) = 0 \text{ for all } a \in V\}$$

and

$$K[V] = (\text{affine coordinate ring of } V) = K[x]/\mathfrak{J}(V, K^n).$$

$V \subset K^n$ is said to be an algebraic set in K^n (or an affine algebraic variety) provided there exists a finite set $\Gamma \subset K[x]$ such that

$$V = \{a \in K^n : f(a) = 0 \text{ for all } f \in \Gamma\}.$$

A nonempty algebraic set V in K^n is said to be algebraically irreducible $\Leftrightarrow [V = V' \cup V''$, V' and V'' algebraic sets in $K^n \Rightarrow V = V'$ or $V = V'']$.

Let $V \subset K^n$ be algebraic and let $a \in V$. We set

$$\begin{aligned} \mathfrak{J}(a, V) &= \text{image of } \mathfrak{J}(a, K^n) \text{ under the map } K[x] \to K[V]; \\ \mathfrak{o}(a, V) &= (\text{algebraic local ring of } a \text{ in } V) = K[V]_{\mathfrak{J}(a, V)}; \\ \hat{\mathfrak{o}}(a, V) &= \text{completion of } \mathfrak{o}(a, V). \end{aligned}$$

a is said to be an algebraically normal (resp: algebraically simple) point of $V \Leftrightarrow \mathfrak{o}(a, V)$ is normal (resp: regular). Let $\rho : K[x] \to K[[x]]$ be the monomorphism given by: $f(x_1, \ldots, x_n) \to f(x_1 + a_1, \ldots, x_n + a_n)$. Then $\rho K[x] = K[x]$ and $\rho\mathfrak{J}(a, K^n) = \mathfrak{m}$ where $\mathfrak{m}$ is the maximal ideal $\{x_1, \ldots, x_n\}K[x]$ in $K[x]$. Hence ρ can be uniquely extended to a monomorphism of $\mathfrak{o}(a, K^n) = K[x]_{\mathfrak{J}(a, K^n)}$ into $K[[x]]$ which we again denote by ρ. Then $\rho\mathfrak{o}(a, K^n) = \mathfrak{o}'$ where $\mathfrak{o}' = K[x]_{\mathfrak{m}}$, and $K[[x]]$ is a completion of $\mathfrak{o}'$. Let $\mathfrak{J}' = (\rho\mathfrak{J}(V, K^n))\mathfrak{o}'$. Then $\mathfrak{o}(a, V) \approx \mathfrak{o}'/\mathfrak{J}'$ and hence by (17.5) we get

1) $\hat{\mathfrak{o}}(a, V) \approx K[[x]]/\mathfrak{J}'K[[x]]$.

The following two results are due, respectively, to Chevalley and Zariski.[6]

2) $\hat{\mathfrak{o}}(a, V)$ *has no nonzero nilpotents.*

3) *If* $\mathfrak{o}(a, V)$ *is normal then* $\hat{\mathfrak{o}}(a, V)$ *is a normal integral domain.*

Now assume that K is complete nondiscrete valued. Then obviously V is an analytic set in K^n. Let $\sigma : R(a, K^n) \to K[\langle x \rangle]$ be the Taylor isomorphism where $K[\langle x \rangle]$ is considered as a subring of $K[[x]]$. Let $\mathfrak{i}' = \sigma\mathfrak{i}(a, V, K^n)$. Then $R(a, V) \approx K[\langle x \rangle]/\mathfrak{i}'$. By Rückert Nullstellensatz, $\text{rad}_{K[\langle x \rangle]}\mathfrak{J}'K[\langle x \rangle] = \mathfrak{i}'$. By (17.5), $K[\langle x \rangle] \cap (\mathfrak{J}'K[[x]]) = \mathfrak{J}'K[\langle x \rangle]$ and hence by 1) and 2), $K[\langle x \rangle]/\mathfrak{J}'K[\langle x \rangle]$ has no nonzero nilpotents. Therefore

4) $\quad \mathfrak{i}' = \mathfrak{J}'K[\langle x \rangle] \quad$ *and* $\quad R(a, V) \approx K[\langle x \rangle]/\mathfrak{i}'$.

[6] Zariski–Samuel [2: Theorems 31 and 32 on p. 320].

In virtue of (17.5), (1,3,4) yield

5) $\mathfrak{o}(a, V) \approx$ *completion of* $R(a, V)$. $\dim_a V = \dim \mathfrak{o}(a, V)$. *a is an algebraically normal* (resp: *algebraically simple*) *point of* $V \Leftrightarrow$ *a is an* (*analytically*) *normal* (resp: *simple*) *point of* $V \Rightarrow V$ *is* (*analytically*) *irreducible at a.*

(36.8) *Remarks on algebraic sets and analytic sets in a projective space.*[5] Let $x = (x_0, \ldots, x_n)$ be indeterminates over an algebraically closed field K. The projective n space $\mathbf{P}^n$ over K is defined to be the quotient space of $\mathring{K}^{n+1} = K^{n+1}\{x\} - \{(0)\}$ by the equivalence relation: $(a_0, \ldots, a_n) \sim (b_0, \ldots, b_n) \Leftrightarrow$ there exists $0 \neq t \in K$ such that $a_j = tb_j$ for $j = 0, \ldots, n$.[7] Let $\mu : \mathring{K}^{n+1} \to \mathbf{P}^n$ be the corresponding map. Let $L_j = \{a \in \mathring{K}^{n+1} : a_j \neq 0\}$. Let $\mu_j : L_j \to K^n$ be given by: $(a_0, \ldots, a_n) \to (a_0/a_j, \ldots, a_{j-1}/a_j, a_{j+1}/a_j, \ldots, a_n/a_j)$. Let $M_j = \mu(L_j)$. Then $\mathbf{P}^n = \bigcup_{j=0}^{n} M_j$. Let $\lambda_j : M_j \to K^n$ be given by: $\mu_j = \lambda_j \circ (\mu | L_j)$. Then λ_j is a one to one map of M_j onto K^n.[8]

$V \subset \mathbf{P}^n$ is said to be an algebraic set in $\mathbf{P}^n$ (or a projective algebraic variety) provided there exists a finite set Ω of homogeneous elements in $K[x]$ such that

$$\{(0)\} \cup \mu^{-1}(V) = \{a \in K^{n+1} : f(a) = 0 \text{ for all } f \in \Omega\}.$$

A nonempty algebraic set V in $\mathbf{P}^n$ is said to be algebraically irreducible $\Leftrightarrow [V = V' \cup V''$, V' and V'' algebraic sets in $\mathbf{P}^n \Rightarrow V = V'$ or $V = V'']$. The following statement gives a relationship between affine and projective varieties.

1) *For any algebraic set* W *in* K^n *let* $\bar{W}$ *be the smallest algebraic set in* $\mathbf{P}^n$ *such that* $\bar{W} \supset \lambda_0^{-1}(W)$; *then* $\lambda_0(\bar{W} \cap M_0) = W$; *if* W *is algebraically irreducible then so is* $\bar{W}$. *If* V *is any algebraic set in* $\mathbf{P}^n$ *such that* $V \not\subset \mathbf{P}^n - M_0$, *then* $\lambda_0(V \cap M_0)$ *is an algebraic set in* K^n; *if furthermore* V *is algebraically irreducible then so is* $\lambda_0(V \cap M_0)$.

Now assume that K is complete nondiscrete valued.

Let $f : X \to K$ where X is an open set in $\mathbf{P}^n$. f is said to be analytic at $\alpha \in X$ provided there exists j with $\alpha \in M_j$ such that

$$f \circ (\lambda_j^{-1} | (\lambda_j(X \cap M_j))) : \lambda_j(X \cap M_j) \to K$$

[7] If K is valued, then $\mathbf{P}^n$ is to be given the quotient topology. In the notation $\mathbf{P}^n$ no reference is made to K because we are mostly interested in the case of $K = \mathbf{C}$.

[8] If K is valued, then M_j is an open subset of $\mathbf{P}^n$ and λ_j is a homeomorphism of M_j onto K^n.

is analytic at $\lambda_j(\alpha)$, and then it follows that

$$f \circ (\lambda_i^{-1} | (\lambda_i(X \cap M_i))) : \lambda_i(X \cap M_i) \to K$$

is analytic at $\lambda_i(\alpha)$ for each i for which $\alpha \in M_i$. f is said to be analytic on X provided f is analytic at each point of X. For any $\alpha \in X$ we set

$$R(\alpha, X) = \text{ring of analytic function germs on } X \text{ at } a.$$

$V \subset \mathbf{P}^n$ is said to be analytic at $\alpha \in \mathbf{P}^n$ provided there exists a finite set Γ of analytic functions on a neighborhood X of α in $\mathbf{P}^n$ such that

$$V \cap X = \{\beta \in X : f(\beta) = 0 \text{ for all } f \in \Gamma\};$$

it is clear that if $\alpha \in M_j$ then V is analytic at $\alpha \Leftrightarrow \lambda_j(V \cap M_j)$ is analytic at $\lambda_j(\alpha)$. Also the following can easily be verified.

2) *Let $V \subset \mathbf{P}^n$ and $\alpha \in \mathbf{P}^n$. Then V is analytic at $\alpha \Leftrightarrow \mu^{-1}(V)$ is analytic at a for some $a \in \mu^{-1}(\alpha) \Leftrightarrow \mu^{-1}(V)$ is analytic at each $a \in \mu^{-1}(\alpha)$.*

Suppose that $V \subset \mathbf{P}^n$ is analytic at α in $\mathbf{P}^n$. Then V is said to be irreducible at α (or that $\gamma_\alpha V$ is irreducible) $\Leftrightarrow [\gamma_\alpha V = V' \cup V''$, V' and V'' analytic set germs in $\mathbf{P}^n$ at $\alpha \Rightarrow \gamma_\alpha V = V'$ or $\gamma_\alpha V = V'']$; it is clear that if $\alpha \in M_j$ then V is irreducible at $\alpha \Leftrightarrow \lambda_j(V \cap M_j)$ is irreducible at $\lambda_j(\alpha)$. We set

$$R(\alpha, V) = \text{the image of } R(\alpha, \mathbf{P}^n) \text{ under the restriction map } \mathfrak{E}(\alpha, \mathbf{P}^n) \to \mathfrak{E}(\alpha, V).$$

α is said to be a normal (resp: simple) point of $V \Leftrightarrow R(\alpha, V)$ is normal (resp: regular). It is clear that if $\alpha \in M_j$ then $R(\alpha, V) \approx R(\lambda_j(\alpha), \lambda_j(V \cap M_j))$, and hence α is a normal (resp: simple) point of $V \Leftrightarrow \lambda_j(\alpha)$ is a normal (resp: simple) point of $\lambda_j(V \cap M_j)$.

$V \subset \mathbf{P}^n$ is said to be analytic in $\mathbf{P}^n$ provided V is analytic at each point in $\mathbf{P}^n$ and then we set $\mathbf{S}(V) = \{\alpha \in V : \alpha \text{ is not a simple point of } V\}$. A nonempty analytic set $V \subset \mathbf{P}^n$ is said to be irreducible $\Leftrightarrow [V = V' \cup V''$, V' and V'' analytic sets in $\mathbf{P}^n \Rightarrow V = V'$ or $V = V'']$.

§37. REMMERT-STEIN-THULLEN THEOREM[1] ON ESSENTIAL SINGULARITIES OF COMPLEX ANALYTIC SETS. THEOREM OF CHOW[2]

Let X be a nonempty open set in $\mathbf{C}^n$. Let W be an analytic set in X. Let V be an analytic set in $X - W$. Let $\bar{V}$ be the closure of V in X.

[1] This refers to statements (37.1, 37.2, 37.3) which were proved by Remmert–Stein [**1**]. Originally (37.3) was proved by Thullen [**1**] for the case of $e = n - 1$.

[2] This refers to (37.5.1). Following Cartan we shall deduce (37.5.1) from (37.1). The original proof of (37.5.1) given by Chow [**1**] is rather different. For a sheaf theoretic proof see Serre [**2**].

A point $p \in X$ is said to be *ordinary relative to* V if $\bar{V}$ is analytic at p; otherwise p is said to be an *essential singularity of* V. Note the following:

i) The set of points of W which are ordinary relative to V is an open subset of W.
ii) If p is an essential singularity of V then $p \in \bar{V} - V =$ (boundary of V in $\bar{V}$) $\subset W$.
iii) $\bar{V}$ is analytic in $X \Leftrightarrow$ every point of W is ordinary relative to V.
iv) If V is pure e dimensional and if $\bar{V}$ is analytic at $p \in \bar{V}$ then by (33.2, 33.4) it follows that $\gamma_p \bar{V}$ is pure e dimensional.

(37.1) *If* $\dim W < \dim_q V$ *for all* $q \in V$ *then* $\bar{V}$ *is analytic in* X.

(37.2) *Assume that* V *is pure* e *dimensional and let* W_1 *be an* e *dimensional irreducible component of* W. *If* $\bar{V}$ *is analytic at some point of* W_1 *then* $\bar{V}$ *is analytic at every point of* W_1 *which is not in any other irreducible component of* W.

(37.3) *Assume that* $\dim W \leqq \dim V$, *and* V *is pure* e *dimensional. Then we have the following.*

1) *Let* M *be the set of all the essential singularities of* V *in* X. *Then* M *is either empty or* M *is a pure* e *dimensional analytic set in* X, *and* M *is the union of a certain number of irreducible components of* W.

2) *If every irreducible component of* W *contains an essential singularity of* V *which is not in any other irreducible component of* W, *then every point of* W *is an essential singularity of* V, *and* W *is either empty or pure* e *dimensional.*

3) *If every* e *dimensional irreducible component of* W *contains a point which is ordinary relative to* V, *then* $\bar{V}$ *is a pure* e *dimensional analytic set in* X.

Also consider the following weaker statements.

(37.1′) *If* $\dim W < \dim V$, *and* V *is pure* e *dimensional, then* $\bar{V}$ *is analytic in* X.

(37.1″) *If* $\dim W < \dim V$, $\mathbf{S}(W) = \emptyset$, *and* V *is pure* e *dimensional, then* $\bar{V}$ *is analytic in* X.

(37.2′) *Assume that* $\dim W = \dim V$, V *is pure* e *dimensional,* $\mathbf{S}(W) = \emptyset$, W *is connected, and* W *contains a point which is ordinary relative to* V. *Then every point of* W *is ordinary relative to* V.

We shall show that: (37.2′) $\Rightarrow$ (37.1″) $\Rightarrow$ (37.1′) $\Rightarrow$ (37.1), (37.2′) + (37.1′) $\Rightarrow$ (37.2), and (37.2) + (37.1′) $\Rightarrow$ (37.3). It will then only remain to prove (37.2′).

Proof that (37.2′) $\Rightarrow$ (37.1″). Given $p \in W$ we have to show that $\bar{V}$ is analytic at p. By (33.18) we can find an analytic coordinate system $x_1, \ldots, x_n$ in a neighborhood X' of p in X such that: p is at the origin, X' is a polycylinder around p, and $X' \cap W = \{x \in X' : x_{k+1} = \ldots = x_n = 0\}$ where $k = \dim_p W < e$. If $X' \cap V = \emptyset$ then $X' \cap \bar{V} = \emptyset$ is analytic at p. Now assume that $X' \cap V \neq \emptyset$. Then $X' \cap V$ is a pure e dimensional analytic set in $X' - W$. Let $W' = \{x \in X' : x_{e+1} = \ldots = x_n = 0\}$. Then $W' - W$ is an e dimensional irreducible analytic set in $X' - W$. If $X' \cap V \subset W'$ then $X' \cap V = W' - W$ by (34.16), and then $X' \cap \bar{V} = W'$ which is analytic at p. Now assume that $X' \cap V \not\subset W'$. Let V^* be the union of all those irreducible components of $X' \cap V$ which do not contain $W' - W$; and let $\bar{V}^*$ be the closure of V^* in X'. By (34.6, 34.15, 34.16, 34.18), V^* is a pure e dimensional analytic set in $X' - W$; and $X' \cap V = V^*$ or $X' \cap V = V^* \cup (W' - W)$ according as $W' - W \not\subset V$ or $W' - W \subset V$. Consequently $X' \cap \bar{V} = \bar{V}^*$ or $X' \cap \bar{V} = \bar{V}^* \cup W'$. Since W' is analytic in X', it suffices to show that $\bar{V}^*$ is analytic in X'. Since $k < e$, there exists $q \in W' - W$ and then $\bar{V}^*$ is analytic at q. Let $V' = V^* - W'$ and $\bar{V}' =$ closure of V' in X'. By (34.19), V^* is the closure of V' in $X' - W$, and hence $\bar{V}^* = \bar{V}'$. Now $\mathbf{S}(W') = \emptyset$, W' is connected, $\dim W' = e$, and V' is a pure e dimensional analytic set in $X' - W'$. Therefore $\bar{V}'$ is analytic in X' by (37.2′).

Proof that (37.1″) $\Rightarrow$ (37.1′). Induction on $k = \dim W$. Trivial for $k = -1$. So let $k \geqq 0$ and assume (37.1′) for all smaller values of k. Given $p \in W$ we have to show that $\bar{V}$ is analytic at p. By (33.20) we can find an analytic set W' in a neighborhood X' of p in X such that $\mathbf{S}(W) \cap X' \subset W' \subset W$ and $\dim W' < \dim W$. By (37.1″), $\bar{V} \cap (X' - W')$ is analytic in $X' - W'$ and hence by induction hypothesis $\bar{V} \cap X'$ is analytic in X'.

Proof that (37.1′) $\Rightarrow$ (37.1). Let $\dim W = k$. For any e let V_e be the union of all the e dimensional irreducible components of V. Then $V = V_{k+1} \cup \ldots \cup V_n$; and for any $e > k$, V_e is either empty or is a pure e dimensional analytic set in $X - W$. Hence by (37.1′), the closure $\bar{V}_e$ of V_e in X is analytic in X. Now $\bar{V} = \bar{V}_{k+1} \cup \ldots \cup \bar{V}_n$ and hence $\bar{V}$ is analytic in X.

Proof that (37.2′) + (37.1′) $\Rightarrow$ (37.2). Let W_2 be the union of all the irreducible components of W other than W_1. Let $X' = X - (\mathbf{S}(W_1) \cup W_2)$

and $W' = X' \cap W_1$. Then $X' \cap \bar{V}$ = closure of V in X'. By (34.19, 33.20), $\mathbf{S}(W_1) \cup (W_1 \cap W_2)$ is a closed thin subset of W_1, and hence W' is connected by (34.17). By assumption $\bar{V}$ is analytic at some point of W_1 and hence $\bar{V}$ is analytic at some point of W'. Whence by (37.2′), $X' \cap \bar{V}$ is a pure e dimensional analytic set in X'. Let $p \in \mathbf{S}(W_1) - W_2$ be given. By (33.20) we can find an analytic set W^* in a neighborhood X^* of p in $X - W_2$ such that $\mathbf{S}(W_1) \cap X^* \subset W^* \subset W_1$ and $\dim W^* < e$. Obviously $X^* \cap \bar{V}$ = closure of $(X^* - W^*) \cap \bar{V}$ in X^*. Now $(X^* - W^*) \cap \bar{V}$ is either empty or is a pure e dimensional analytic set in $X^* - W^*$. Therefore $X^* \cap \bar{V}$ is analytic in X^* by (37.1′). This shows that $\bar{V}$ is analytic at every point in $W_1 - W_2$.

Proof that (37.2) + (37.1′) $\Rightarrow$ (37.3). (37.3.2) and (37.3.3) follow immediately from (37.3.1). To prove (37.3.1), let W^* be the union of all the irreducible components of W having dimension $< e$, let $\tilde{W}$ be the union of those e dimensional irreducible components of W which are contained in M, and let $(W_i)_{i \in I}$ be the remaining e dimensional irreducible components of W. Let

$$W' = \left[\left\{ \bigcup_{\substack{i, j \in I \\ i \neq j}} (W_i \cap W_j) \right\} \cup W^* \right] - \tilde{W}, \qquad \text{and} \quad X' = X - \tilde{W}.$$

By (34.5, 34.6, 34.15, 34.19), $W = W^* \cup \tilde{W} \cup [\bigcup_{i \in I} W_i]$, $\tilde{W}$ is either empty or is a pure e dimensional analytic set in X, and W' is an analytic set in X' with $\dim W' < e$. Let $V' = (X' - W') \cap \bar{V}$. Then V' = closure of V in $X' - W'$, and $X' \cap \bar{V}$ = closure of V' in X'. By (37.2), $M \subset \tilde{W} \cup W'$ and hence V' is a pure e dimensional analytic set in $X' - W'$. Therefore by (37.1′), $X' \cap \bar{V}$ is analytic in X', i.e., $M \subset \tilde{W}$. Therefore $M = \tilde{W}$.

Proof of (37.2′). The assertion is trivial if $e < 1$ or $e = n$. So assume that $1 \leqq e < n$ and let $m = n - e$. Let Ω be the set of all points of W which are ordinary relative to V and let $\bar{\Omega}$ be the closure of Ω in W. Now Ω is a nonempty open subset of W and W is connected. Hence it suffices to show that Ω is closed in W, i.e., given $o \in \bar{\Omega}$ we want to show that $\bar{V}$ is analytic at o. By (33.18, 34.21) we can find an analytic coordinate system $(y, z) = (y_1, \ldots, y_e, z_1, \ldots, z_m)$ in a neighborhood X_1 of o in X such that: o is at the origin; X_1 is a polycylinder around o; $X_1 \cap W = \{(y, z) \in X_1 : z_1 = \ldots z_m = 0\}$; and $V \cap \{(y, z) \in X_1 : y_1 = \ldots = y_e = 0\}$ is a discrete set. Let $p = (0, \ldots, 0)$ be the origin in $\mathbf{C}^e\{y\}$ and let $q = (0, \ldots, 0)$ be the origin in $\mathbf{C}^m\{z\}$, i.e., $o = (p, q)$. Let $\pi : \mathbf{C}^e\{y\} \times \mathbf{C}^m\{z\} \to \mathbf{C}^e\{y\}$ be the natural projection. For any $D > 0$, $E > 0$, $\beta \in \mathbf{C}^e$, $\gamma \in \mathbf{C}^m$, let

$$Y\langle D, \beta\rangle = \{b \in \mathbf{C}^e : |b_i - \beta_i| < D \text{ for } i = 1,\dots, e\},$$
$$Z\langle E, \gamma\rangle = \{c \in \mathbf{C}^m : |c_i - \gamma_i| < E \text{ for } i = 1,\dots, m\},$$
$$\bar{Z}\langle E, \gamma\rangle = \{c \in \mathbf{C}^m : |c_i - \gamma_i| \leqq E \text{ for } i = 1,\dots, m\},$$
$$\mathring{Z}\langle E, \gamma\rangle = \{c \in \mathbf{C}^m : |c_i - \gamma_i| = E \text{ for } i = 1,\dots, m\}.$$

Since $V \cap X_1 \cap \pi^{-1}(p)$ is a discrete set, we can find $C > 0$ such that $p \times \bar{Z}\langle C, q\rangle \subset X_1$ and $V \cap (p \times \mathring{Z}\langle C, q\rangle) = \emptyset$. Now $V \cap X_1$ is a closed subset of $X_1 - W$ and $p \times \mathring{Z}\langle C, q\rangle$ is a compact subset of $X_1 - W$. Hence we can find $B > 0$ such that $Y\langle B, p\rangle \times q \subset X_1$ and $V \cap (Y\langle B, p\rangle \times \mathring{Z}\langle C, q\rangle) = \emptyset$. Let $Y = Y\langle B, p\rangle$, $Z = Z\langle C, q\rangle$, $\mathring{Z} = \mathring{Z}\langle C, q\rangle$, and $V_1 = V \cap (Y \times Z)$. Then

$$(\text{closure of } V_1 \text{ in } \mathbf{C}^e\{y\} \times \mathbf{C}^m\{z\}) \cap (Y \times \mathring{Z}) = \emptyset.$$

Let $\bar{V}_1$ = closure of V_1 in $Y \times Z$, and $\Gamma = \{b \in Y : \bar{V}_1$ is analytic at $(b, q)\}$. Then $\Gamma \times q = \Omega \cap (Y \times q)$. Hence Γ is an open subset of Y. Since $o = (p, q) \in \bar{\Omega}$, we must have $\Gamma \neq \emptyset$. We want to show that $o \in \Omega$, i.e., $p \in \Gamma$. We shall actually show that $\Gamma = Y$. This is trivial if $V_1 = \emptyset$. Now assume that $V_1 \neq \emptyset$.

Upon replacing X by $Y \times Z$ and V by V_1 we thus have the following situation: $Y = Y\langle B, p\rangle$ where $p = (0,\dots, 0)$ is the origin in $\mathbf{C}^e\{y\}$, $Z = Z\langle C, q\rangle$ where $q = (0,\dots, 0)$ is the origin in $\mathbf{C}^m\{z\}$, $\mathring{Z} = \mathring{Z}\langle C, q\rangle$ = boundary of Z in $\mathbf{C}^m\{z\}$, $X = Y \times Z$, V = a pure e dimensional analytic set in $Y \times (Z - \{q\})$, $\bar{V}$ = closure of V in X, and $\Gamma = \{b \in Y : \bar{V}$ is analytic at $(b, q)\}$ = an open subset of Y; we are told that $\Gamma \neq \emptyset$, and

1°) (closure of V in $\mathbf{C}^e\{y\} \times \mathbf{C}^m\{z\}) \cap (Y \times \mathring{Z}) = \emptyset$;

and we want to show that $\Gamma = Y$. In view of 1°), by (34.25) we get

2°) For any $\beta \in Y$, $V \cap \pi^{-1}(\beta)$ is a discrete set; hence for any $\alpha \in V$, $\mathbf{d}(\alpha, \pi, V) = \mathbf{d}(\alpha, \pi, \bar{V})$ is a well defined positive integer.

Let Y' be any connected component of Γ. Then Y' is a nonempty open connected subset of Y. Since $V \neq \emptyset$, by (34.28) we deduce that $V \cap (Y' \times Z) \neq \emptyset$. Let $V' = \bar{V} \cap (Y' \times Z)$. Then V' is a pure e dimensional analytic set in $Y' \times Z$ and by 1°) we get that

$$(\text{closure of } V' \text{ in } \mathbf{C}^e\{y\} \times \mathbf{C}^m\{z\}) \cap (Y' \times \mathring{Z}) = \emptyset.$$

Therefore by (35.17.1), $\mathbf{d}(\pi|V')$ is a well defined positive integer. Let $d = \mathbf{d}(\pi|V')$. Let $\chi_1,\dots, \chi_m$ be indeterminates. By (35.12), the norm of

$\sum_{j=1}^{m}(z_j - (z_j|V'))\chi_j$ relative to $\pi|V'$ is a homogeneous polynomial

$$\Theta(y, z, \chi_1, \ldots, \chi_m) = \sum_{i_1, \ldots, i_m} \Theta_{i_1 \ldots i_m}(y, z)\chi_1^{i_1} \ldots \chi_m^{i_m}$$

of degree d in $\chi_1, \ldots, \chi_m$ where for all $i_1, \ldots, i_m$:

$$\Theta_{i_1 \ldots i_m}(y, z) = \sum_{j_1, \ldots, j_m} \Theta_{i_1 \ldots i_m;\, j_1 \ldots j_m}(y) z_1^{j_1} \ldots z_m^{j_m}$$

is a polynomial of degree d in $z_1, \ldots, z_m$ whose coefficients $\Theta_{i_1 \ldots i_m; j_1 \ldots j_m}(y)$ are analytic functions on Y'; and we have

3°) $\Theta(b, z, \chi_1, \ldots, \chi_m)$

$$= \prod_{a=(b,c) \in \bar{V} \cap \pi^{-1}(b)} \left(\sum_{j=1}^{m} (z_j - c_j)\chi_j \right)^{\mathbf{d}(a, \pi, \bar{V})} \qquad \text{for all} \quad b \in Y'.$$

Now $\bar{V} \subset Y \times Z = Y\langle B, p\rangle \times Z\langle C, q\rangle$. Hence 3°) yields

4°) There exists a positive constant A such that $|\Theta_{i_1 \ldots i_m; j_1 \ldots j_m}(b)| \leqq A$ for all $b \in Y'$, for all $i_1, \ldots, i_m, j_1, \ldots, j_m$.

Suppose if possible that $\Theta_{i_1 \ldots i_m; 0 \ldots 0}(y) \equiv 0$ on Y' for all $i_1, \ldots, i_m$. Then by 3°), $Y' \times q \subset \bar{V}$. By (35.9) there exists $\tilde{\beta} \in Y'$, $\tilde{B} > 0$, $\tilde{C} > 0$ such that: $(\tilde{\beta}, q) \in \bar{V}$, $\mathbf{d}((\tilde{\beta}, q), \pi, \bar{V}) = 1$; $Y\langle \tilde{B}, \tilde{\beta}\rangle \subset Y'$, $Z\langle \tilde{C}, q\rangle \subset Z$; and such that for any $b \in Y\langle \tilde{B}, \beta\rangle$, $\bar{V} \cap (b \times Z\langle \tilde{C}, q\rangle)$ contains exactly one point. Since $Y' \times q \subset \bar{V}$ we must then have $\bar{V} \cap (Y\langle \tilde{B}, \tilde{\beta}\rangle \times Z\langle \tilde{C}, q\rangle) = Y\langle \tilde{B}, \tilde{\beta}\rangle \times q$. Now $V \cap (Y\langle \tilde{B}, \tilde{\beta}\rangle \times q) = \emptyset$ and hence $V \cap (Y\langle \tilde{B}, \tilde{\beta}\rangle \times Z\langle \tilde{C}, q\rangle) = \emptyset$. Therefore

$$\begin{aligned} &\bar{V} \cap (Y\langle \tilde{B}, \tilde{\beta}\rangle \times Z\langle \tilde{C}, q\rangle) \\ &= \text{closure of } V \cap (Y\langle \tilde{B}, \tilde{\beta}\rangle \times Z\langle \tilde{C}, q\rangle) \text{ in } Y\langle \tilde{B}, \tilde{\beta}\rangle \times Z\langle \tilde{C}, q\rangle \\ &= \emptyset. \end{aligned}$$

Contradiction. Thus we have proved

5°) $\Theta_{i_1 \ldots i_m; 0 \ldots 0}(y) \not\equiv 0$ on Y' for some $i_1, \ldots, i_m$.

Let $\mathring{Y}'$ be the boundary of Y' in Y. Let $\beta \in \mathring{Y}'$ be given. Then $\beta \notin \Gamma$ and hence $\alpha^{(0)} = (\beta, \gamma^{(0)}) \in \bar{V}$ where $\gamma^{(0)} = q = (0, \ldots, 0)$. Let $\alpha^{(\lambda)} = (\beta, \gamma^{(\lambda)})$, $(\lambda = 1, \ldots, N)$, be any finite number of distinct points in $V \cap \pi^{-1}(\beta)$. Then $\alpha^{(\lambda)} \neq \alpha^{(0)}$ for $\lambda = 1, \ldots, N$. By (35.4) we can find $D' > 0$, $E' > 0$, for which we have (6°, 7°, 8°).

6°) $$Y\langle D', \beta\rangle \subset Y; \qquad \bigcup_{\lambda=0}^{N} Z\langle E', \gamma^{(\lambda)}\rangle \subset Z;$$

$$Z\langle E', \gamma^{(\lambda)}\rangle \cap Z\langle E', \gamma^{(\lambda')}\rangle = \emptyset \qquad \text{for all} \quad \lambda \neq \lambda', \quad (\lambda, \lambda' = 0, \ldots, N).$$

7°) For any $\lambda > 0$ and $b \in Y\langle D', \beta\rangle$ we have

$$\sum_{a\in\bar{V}\cap(b\times Z\langle E',\gamma^{(\lambda)}\rangle)} \mathbf{d}(a, \pi, \bar{V}) = \mathbf{d}(\alpha^{(\lambda)}, \pi, \bar{V}).$$

8°) Given $0 < E \leqq E'$ there exists $0 < \varphi(E) \leqq D'$ depending on E such that for all $\lambda > 0$ we have

$$\bar{V} \cap (Y\langle\varphi(E), \beta\rangle \times Z\langle E', \gamma^{(\lambda)}\rangle) \subset Y\langle\varphi(E), \beta\rangle \times Z\langle E, \gamma^{(\lambda)}\rangle.$$

Since $\beta \in \mathring{Y}'$, there exists $b \in Y' \cap Y\langle D', \beta\rangle$; and for any such b we have

$$\sum_{a\in\bar{V}\cap\pi^{-1}(b)} \mathbf{d}(a, \pi, \bar{V}) = d.$$

Consequently (6°, 7°, 8°) imply this: $V \cap \pi^{-1}(\beta)$ contains at most a finite number of points; let these again be $\alpha^{(\lambda)} = (\beta, \gamma^{(\lambda)})$, $(\lambda = 1,\dots, N)$; then $\alpha^{(0)},\dots, \alpha^{(N)}$ are exactly all the distinct points in $\bar{V} \cap \pi^{-1}(\beta)$; and $\delta(\beta) \geqq 0$, where

$$\delta(\beta) = d - \sum_{\lambda=1}^{N} \mathbf{d}(\alpha^{(\lambda)}, \pi, \bar{V}).$$

We shall show that actually $\delta(\beta) > 0$.

Take $0 < E^* < E'$. Then $\bar{V} \cap (\beta \times \mathring{Z}\langle E^*, q\rangle) = \emptyset$. By compactness of $\mathring{Z}\langle E^*, q\rangle$ we can find $0 < D^* \leqq \varphi(E^*)$ such that $\bar{V} \cap (Y\langle D^*, \beta\rangle \times \mathring{Z}\langle E^*, q\rangle) = \emptyset$. Let $V_0 = \bar{V} \cap (Y\langle D^*, \beta\rangle \times Z\langle E^*, q\rangle)$. Since $\alpha^{(0)} = (\beta, \gamma^{(0)}) \in \bar{V}$ we must have $V_0 \neq \emptyset$. Therefore V_0 is a pure e dimensional analytic set in $Y\langle D^*, \beta\rangle \times (Z\langle E^*, q\rangle - \{q\})$ and

$$(\text{closure of } V_0 \text{ in } \mathbf{C}^e\{y\} \times \mathbf{C}^m\{z\}) \cap (Y\langle D^*, \beta\rangle \times \mathring{Z}\langle E^*, \beta\rangle) = \emptyset.$$

Now $Y' \cap Y\langle D^*, \beta\rangle$ is a nonempty open subset of $Y\langle D^*, \beta\rangle$ and hence by (34.28) we deduce that $V \cap (b \times Z\langle E^*, q\rangle) \neq \emptyset$ for some $b \in Y' \cap Y\langle D^*, \beta\rangle$. Therefore we must have $\delta(\beta) > 0$. Let

$$Z^* = Z - \bigcup_{\lambda=0}^{N} \bar{Z}\langle E^*, \gamma^{(\lambda)}\rangle, \quad \mathring{Z}^* = \mathring{Z} \cup \left[\bigcup_{\lambda=0}^{N} \mathring{Z}\langle E^*, \gamma^{(\lambda)}\rangle\right],$$

and

$$V^* = V \cap (Y\langle D^*, \beta) \times Z^*).$$

Then V^* is either empty or a pure e dimensional analytic set in $Y\langle D^*, \beta\rangle \times Z^*$ and $\mathring{Z}^* =$ boundary of Z^* in $\mathbf{C}^m\{z\}$. Since $E^* < E'$ and $D^* \leqq \varphi(E^*)$, by 8°) we get that

$$(\text{closure of } V^* \text{ in } \mathbf{C}^e\{y\} \times \mathbf{C}^m\{z\}) \cap (Y\langle D^*, \beta\rangle \times \mathring{Z}^*) = \emptyset.$$

Now $V^* \cap \pi^{-1}(\beta) = \emptyset$ and hence by (34.27) we must have $V^* = \emptyset$ and hence $\bar{V} \cap (Y\langle D^*, \beta\rangle \times Z^*) = \emptyset$. Therefore by (6°, 7°, 8°) we must have:

$$\sum_{a \in \bar{V} \cap (b \times Z\langle E^*, \gamma^{(0)}\rangle)} \mathbf{d}(a, \pi, \bar{V}) = \delta(\beta) \qquad \text{for all} \quad b \in Y' \cap Y\langle D^*, \beta\rangle.$$

Let again $0 < E \leqq E^*$ be given. Then $\bar{V} \cap (\beta \times \mathring{Z}\langle E, q\rangle) = \emptyset$. By compactness of $\mathring{Z}\langle E, q\rangle$ we can find $0 < \psi(E) \leqq \min(D^*, \varphi(E))$ such that $\bar{V} \cap (Y\langle\psi(E), \beta\rangle \times \mathring{Z}\langle E, q\rangle) = \emptyset$. Let

$$Z^{**} = Z - \bigcup_{\lambda=0}^{N} \bar{Z}\langle E, \gamma^{(\lambda)}\rangle.$$

Then as above, in virtue of (6°, 7°, 8°), by (34.27) we deduce that $V \cap (Y\langle\psi(E), \beta\rangle \times Z^{**}) = \emptyset$ and hence $\bar{V} \cap (Y\langle\psi(E), \beta\rangle \times Z^{**}) = \emptyset$. Consequently we must have

$$\bar{V} \cap (Y\langle\psi(E), \beta\rangle \times Z\langle E^*, \gamma^{(0)}\rangle) \subset Y\langle\psi(E), \beta\rangle \times Z\langle E, \gamma^{(0)}\rangle.$$

Thus we have proved the following.

(I) *Given* $\beta \in \mathring{Y}'$, $V \cap \pi^{-1}(\beta)$ *contains at most a finite number of distinct points* $\alpha^{(\lambda)} = (\beta, \gamma^{(\lambda)})$, $(\lambda = 1, \ldots, N)$. *Let* $\alpha^{(0)} = (\beta, \gamma^{(0)})$ *where* $\gamma^{(0)} = q = (0, \ldots, 0)$. *Then* $\alpha^{(0)}, \ldots, \alpha^{(N)}$ *are exactly all the distinct points in* $\bar{V} \cap \pi^{-1}(\beta)$. *Let*

$$\delta(\beta) = d - \sum_{\lambda=1}^{N} \mathbf{d}(\alpha^{(\lambda)}, \pi, \bar{V}).$$

Then $\delta(\beta) > 0$. *There exist* $D^* > 0$, $E^* > 0$ *for which we have* (9°, 10°, 11°).

9°) $$Y\langle D^*, \beta\rangle \subset Y, \qquad \bigcup_{\lambda=0}^{N} Z\langle E^*, \gamma^{(\lambda)}\rangle \subset Z;$$

$$Z\langle E^*, \gamma^{(\lambda)}\rangle \cap Z\langle E^*, \gamma^{(\lambda')}\rangle = \emptyset \qquad \textit{for all} \quad \lambda \neq \lambda', \quad (\lambda, \lambda' = 0, \ldots, N).$$

10°) *For any* $b \in Y' \cap Y\langle D^*, \beta\rangle$ *we have*

$$\sum_{a \in \bar{V} \cap b \times Z\langle E^*, \gamma^{(\lambda)}\rangle)} \mathbf{d}(a, \pi, \bar{V}) = \begin{cases} \mathbf{d}(\alpha^{(\lambda)}, \pi, \bar{V}) & \textit{for} \quad \lambda > 0 \\ \delta(\beta) & \textit{for} \quad \lambda = 0; \end{cases}$$

and hence

$$\bar{V} \cap \pi^{-1}(Y' \cap Y\langle D^*, \beta\rangle) \subset (Y' \cap Y\langle D^*, \beta\rangle) \times \bigcup_{\lambda=0}^{N} Z\langle E^*, \gamma^{(\lambda)}\rangle.$$

11°) *Given* $0 < E \leqq E^*$ *there exists* $0 < \psi(E) \leqq D^*$ *depending on* E *such that for* $\lambda = 0,\dots, N$ *we have*

$$\bar{V} \cap (Y\langle\psi(E), \beta\rangle \times Z\langle E^*, \gamma^{(\lambda)}\rangle) \subset Y\langle\psi(E), \beta\rangle \times Z\langle E, \gamma^{(\lambda)}\rangle.$$

Since $\delta(\beta) > 0$ and $\bar{V} \subset Y\langle B, p\rangle \times Z\langle C, q\rangle$, from (I) and 3°) we deduce that for all $i_1,\dots, i_m$:

$$\lim_{\substack{y\to\beta \\ y\in Y'}} \Theta_{i_1,\dots i_m;0\dots0}(y) = 0 \qquad \text{for all} \qquad \beta \in \mathring{Y}'.$$

Consequently

$$g_{i_1\dots i_m}(y) = \begin{cases} \Theta_{i_1\dots i_m;0\dots0}(y) & \text{for } \ y \in Y' \\ 0 & \text{for } \ y \in Y - Y' \end{cases}$$

is continuous on Y and analytic when it is not zero. Therefore by Radó's Theorem (8.2), $g_{i_1\dots i_m}(y)$ is analytic on Y for all $i_1,\dots, i_m$. Thus

$$U = \{b \in Y : g_{i_1\dots i_m}(b) = 0 \text{ for all } i_1,\dots, i_m\}$$

is an analytic set in Y and $Y - Y' \subset U$. By 5°), U is nowhere dense in Y and hence $Y - Y' = \mathring{Y}'$. By 4°), $|\Theta_{i_1\dots i_m;j_1\cdots j_m}(y)|$ is bounded in the neighborhood of any point of U and hence by Riemann Extension Theorem (14.3), $\Theta_{i_1\cdots i_m;j_1\cdots j_m}(y)$ has a unique analytic extension on Y; let us denote this extension again by $\Theta_{i_1\cdots i_m;j_1\cdots j_m}(y)$ and for any $i_1,\dots, i_m$ let

$$\Theta_{i_1\dots i_m}(y, z) = \sum_{j_1\dots j_m} \Theta_{i_1\dots i_m;j_1\dots j_m}(y) z_1^{j_1}\dots z_m^{j_m} \qquad \text{for all} \quad y \in Y.$$

Let

$$\tilde{V} = \{(b, c) \in Y \times Z : \Theta_{i_1\dots i_m}(b, c) = 0 \text{ for all } i_1,\dots, i_m\}.$$

Then $\tilde{V}$ is an analytic set in $Y \times Z$.

Let $\beta \in Y$ be given. If $\beta \in Y'$ then by 3°) it follows that $\tilde{V} \cap \pi^{-1}(\beta) = \bar{V} \cap \pi^{-1}(\beta)$.

Now suppose that $\beta \in Y - Y' = \mathring{Y}'$ and let the notation be as in (I). Take $b^{(\nu)} \in Y'$ such that $\lim_{\nu\to\infty} b^{(\nu)} = \beta$. By 3°) we get

$$\sum_{i_1,\dots, i_m} \Theta_{i_1\dots i_m}(b^{(\nu)}, z)\chi_1^{i_1}\dots\chi_m^{i_m}$$

$$= \prod_{a=(b^{(\nu)},c)\in\bar{V}\cap\pi^{-1}(b^{(\nu)})} \left(\sum_{j=1}^{m} (z_j - c_j)\chi_j\right)^{\mathrm{d}(a,\,\pi,\,\bar{V})}$$

for all ν. In virtue of (I), taking limits as $\nu \to \infty$ we get

$$\sum_{i_1,\ldots,i_m} \Theta_{i_1\ldots i_m}(\beta, z)\chi_1^{i_1}\ldots\chi_m^{i_m}$$

$$= \left(\sum_{j=1}^{m}(z_j - \gamma_j^{(0)})\chi_j\right)^{\delta(\beta)} \prod_{\lambda=1}^{N}\left(\sum_{j=1}^{m}(z_j - \gamma_j^{(\lambda)})\chi_j\right)^{\mathbf{d}(\alpha^{(\lambda)}, \pi, \overline{V})}.$$

Therefore $\tilde{V} \cap \pi^{-1}(\beta) = \overline{V} \cap \pi^{-1}(\beta)$. Thus $\overline{V} = \tilde{V}$ and $\overline{V}$ is analytic in $Y \times Z$.

This completes the proof of (37.2′) and hence also of (37.1, 37.2, 37.3).

(37.4) *Analytic cones.* $V \subset K^n$, where K is any field, is said to be a cone (with vertex at the origin) provided: $a \in V$, $t \in K \Rightarrow ta = (ta_1,\ldots, ta_n) \in V$. If K is complete nondiscrete valued then $V \subset K^n$ is said to be an analytic cone provided V is a cone and V is analytic in K^n.

1) *Let* $V \subset K^n\{x_1,\ldots, x_n\}$ *where* K *is any complete nondiscrete valued field. Then* V *is an analytic cone, if and only if, there exists a finite set* Ω *of homogeneous polynomials in* $x_1,\ldots, x_n$ *with coefficients in* K *such that* $V = \{a \in K^n : \varphi(a) = 0$ *for all* $\varphi \in \Omega\}$.

PROOF.[3] The "if" part is obvious. Now assume that V is an analytic cone. Let

$$\mathfrak{a} = \{f(x_1,\ldots, x_n) \in K[\langle x_1,\ldots, x_n\rangle] : f(a) = 0 \text{ for all } a \in V \cap X \text{ for some neighborhood } X \text{ of the origin in } \mathbf{D}(f)\}.$$

Any element $f(x_1,\ldots, x_n)$ in $K[[x_1,\ldots, x_n]]$ can uniquely be written as $f(x_1,\ldots, x_n) = \sum_{p\geq 0} f_p(x_1,\ldots, x_n)$ where $f_p(x_1,\ldots, x_n)$ is either zero or is a homogeneous polynomial of degree p in $x_1,\ldots, x_n$ with coefficients in K; $f_p(x_1,\ldots, x_n)$ is called the pth homogeneous component of $f(x_1,\ldots, x_n)$. Now suppose that $f(x_1,\ldots, x_n) \in \mathfrak{a}$ and let X be as above. If V contains no point different from the origin then our assertion is trivial. Now assume the contrary. Then there exists $a \in V \cap X$, $a \neq (0)$. Let $g(y) = f(a_1y,\ldots,a_ny) \in K[[y]]$ where y is an indeterminate. Then $g(y) \in K[\langle y\rangle]$ and $g(y) = \sum_{p\geq 0} f_p(a)y^p$. Since V is a cone, we have $g(b) = 0$ for all b in some neighborhood of 0 in $\mathbf{D}(g)$. Since an analytic function of one variable can have only isolated zeroes, we must have $g(y) = 0$, i.e., $f_p(a) = 0$ for all p. Since V is a cone it now follows that $V = \{a \in K^n : \varphi(a) = 0$ for all $\varphi \in \Omega^*\}$ where Ω^* is the set of all the homogeneous components of all the

[3] For a generalization and a more algebraic proof of (37.4.1) see (37.6).

elements in $\mathfrak{a}$. Now $K[x_1,\ldots, x_n]$ being noetherian, $\Omega^*K[x_1,\ldots, x_n] = \Omega K[x_1,\ldots, x_n]$ for some finite subset Ω of Ω^*, and then $V = \{a \in K^n : \varphi(a) = 0 \text{ for all } \varphi \in \Omega\}$.

2) *Let $V \subset \mathbf{C}^n$ be a cone. If V is analytic at every point in $\mathbf{C}^n - \{(0)\}$ then V is analytic in $\mathbf{C}^n$.*

PROOF. Obviously $\dim_a V > 0$ for any $a \in V$ with $a \neq (0)$. Therefore V is analytic at (0) by (37.1).

(37.5) *Algebraic sets and analytic sets in* $\mathbf{P}^n$.[4] Let $\mathbf{P}^n$ be the complex projective n space. In virtue of (36.8.2), (37.4.1, 37.4.2) at once yield

1) THEOREM OF CHOW. *$V \subset \mathbf{P}^n$ is analytic, if and only if, it is algebraic.*

From (34.2) we get

2) *Any algebraic set in $\mathbf{P}^n$ or $\mathbf{C}^n$ is locally arcwise connected.*

From 1) it follows that an algebraic set in $\mathbf{P}^n$ is algebraically irreducible if and only if it is analytically irreducible. Since the considerations of §34B were based only on the local proposition (34.2), they apply to analytic sets in $\mathbf{P}^n$. In particular (34.10) remains valid for any analytic set V in $\mathbf{P}^n$. Consequently we get

3) *For any nonempty algebraic set V in $\mathbf{P}^n$ the following five conditions are equivalent.*

i) *V is algebraically irreducible.*
ii) *V is analytically irreducible.*
iii) *$V - \mathbf{S}(V)$ is connected.*
iv) *If W is any analytic set in $\mathbf{P}^n$ such that $W \subsetneq V$ then $V - W$ is connected.*
v) *If W is any analytic set in $\mathbf{P}^n$ such that $W \subsetneq V$ then $V - \mathbf{S}(V) - W$ is connected.*

Finally, in virtue of (34.10) and (36.8.1), from 3) we get

4) 3) *remains valid with $\mathbf{C}^n$ replacing $\mathbf{P}^n$.*

(37.6) *Homogeneous ideals.* We shall now generalize (37.4.1). Let $x = (x_1,\ldots, x_n)$. Let $R = K[[x]]$ where K is any infinite field, or $R = K[\langle x\rangle]$ where K is any complete nondiscrete valued field. Let $\mathfrak{m}$ be the maximal ideal in R. Any element $f(x)$ in $K[[x]]$ can uniquely be written as

[4] For definitions see (36.7, 36.8).

$f(x) = \sum_{p \geqq 0} f_p(x)$ where $f_p(x)$ is either zero or is a homogeneous polynomial of degree p (in $x_1, \ldots, x_n$ with coefficients in K); $f_p(x)$ is called the pth homogeneous component of $f(x)$. For any $f(x) \in K[[x]]$ and $t \in K$, $f(tx) = f(tx_1, \ldots, tx_n)$ is an element in $K[[x]]$; note that if $f(x) \in K[\langle x \rangle]$ then $f(tx) \in K[\langle x \rangle]$. Also note that if $f \in \mathfrak{m}^k$ then $f(tx) \in \mathfrak{m}^k$ for all $t \in K$. An ideal $\mathfrak{a}$ in R is said to be *homogeneous* provided: $f(x) \in \mathfrak{a}$, $t \in K \Rightarrow f(tx) \in \mathfrak{a}$.

1) *Let $\mathfrak{a}$ be a homogeneous ideal in R. Let $F(x) \in \mathfrak{a} + \mathfrak{m}^{p+1}$ where $F(x)$ is either zero or is a homogeneous polynomial of degree p. Then $F(x) \in \mathfrak{a}$.*

2) *Let $\mathfrak{a}$ be a homogeneous ideal in R. Then for any $f(x) \in \mathfrak{a}$, all the homogeneous components of $f(x)$ are in $\mathfrak{a}$.*

3) *Let $\mathfrak{a}$ be any ideal in R. Then $\mathfrak{a}$ is a homogeneous principal ideal $\Leftrightarrow$ $\mathfrak{a}$ is generated by a homogeneous polynomial.*

4) *For any ideal $\mathfrak{a}$ in R the following three conditions are equivalent.*

i) *$\mathfrak{a}$ is homogeneous.*
ii) *For any $f(x) \in \mathfrak{a}$ all the homogeneous components of $f(x)$ are in $\mathfrak{a}$.*
iii) *$\mathfrak{a}$ has a finite basis consisting of homogeneous polynomials.*

REMARKS. 4) generalizes to power series rings the usual equivalence of the three ways of defining homogeneous ideals in a polynomial ring over an infinite field. Let $\mathfrak{a}$ be as in the proof of (37.4.1); V being a cone, $\mathfrak{a}$ is homogeneous and hence (37.4.1) follows from 4). For $R = \mathbf{C}[\langle x \rangle]$, 4) was proved by Cartan; his proof is given in Remmert–Stein [**1**]; it uses Cartan module bases (§15) and also a lemma on integration and Riemannian sums. Again for $R = \mathbf{C}[\langle x \rangle]$, a different proof of 3) is given in Remmert–Stein [**1**].

Proof of 1). Now

$$\mathfrak{a} = \bigcap_{q=1}^{\infty} (\mathfrak{a} + \mathfrak{m}^{p+q})$$

and hence it suffices to show that $F(x) \in \mathfrak{a} + \mathfrak{m}^{p+q}$ for all $q \geqq 1$. We do this by induction on q. This being given for $q = 1$, let $q \geqq 1$ and assume that $F(x) \in \mathfrak{a} + \mathfrak{m}^{p+q}$. Then

$$F(x) + G(x) \equiv H(x) \bmod \mathfrak{m}^{p+q+1}$$

where $H(x) \in \mathfrak{a}$ and $G(x)$ is either zero or is a homogeneous polynomial of degree $p + q$. For any $t \in K$ we get

$$t^p F(x) + t^{p+q} G(x) \equiv H(tx) \bmod \mathfrak{m}^{p+q+1}.$$

Eliminating $G(x)$ between the two equations we get

$$(t^{p+q} - t^p)F(x) \equiv t^{p+q}H(x) - H(tx) \bmod \mathfrak{m}^{p+q+1}.$$

Since $\mathfrak{a}$ is homogeneous we have $H(tx) \in \mathfrak{a}$, and hence $(t^{p+q} - t^p)F(x) \in \mathfrak{a} + \mathfrak{m}^{p+q+1}$. Since K is infinite, we can take $t \in K$ such that $t^{p+q} - t^p \neq 0$; whence $F(x) \in \mathfrak{a} + \mathfrak{m}^{p+q+1}$.

Proof of 2). Let $f_j(x)$ be the jth homogeneous component of $f(x)$. By induction on p we shall show that $f_j(x) \in \mathfrak{a}$ for all $j \leqq p$. For $p = -1$ this is trivial. Now let $p \geqq 0$ and assume that $f_j(x) \in \mathfrak{a}$ for all $j < p$. Then $f_p(x) \in \mathfrak{a} + \mathfrak{m}^{p+1}$ and hence $f_p(x) \in \mathfrak{a}$ by 1).

Proof of 3). "$\Leftarrow$" is obvious. Now let $f(x) \in R$ be such that $\mathfrak{a} = f(x)R$. If $f(x) = 0$ then we have nothing to show. Now assume that $f(x) \neq 0$ and let $F(x)$ be the leading form of $f(x)$. Then $F(x) \in \mathfrak{a}$ by 2), and hence $F(x) = f(x)g(x)$ for some $g(x) \in R$. Since $\mathbf{o}F(x) = \mathbf{o}f(x)$, $g(x)$ must be a unit in R. Hence $\mathfrak{a} = F(x)R$.

Proof of 4). i) $\Rightarrow$ ii) is proved in 2). iii) $\Rightarrow$ i) is obvious. Now assume ii) and let Ω^* be the set of all the homogeneous components of all the elements in $\mathfrak{a}$. Now $\bigcap_{p=1}^{\infty} (\Omega^*R + \mathfrak{m}^p) = \Omega^*R$ and obviously $\mathfrak{a} \subset \Omega^*R + \mathfrak{m}^p$ for all p. By assumption $\Omega^* \subset \mathfrak{a}$ and hence $\mathfrak{a} = \Omega^*R$. Since R is noetherian, $\Omega^*R = \Omega R$ for some finite subset Ω of Ω^*.

REMARK. Actually 4) can be somewhat further generalized as follows. Let $(R, \mathfrak{m})$ be any regular local ring such that $R/\mathfrak{m}$ is infinite and has the same characteristic as R. Assume that R contains a field K which maps isomorphically onto $R/\mathfrak{m}$ under the restriction of the natural map $R \to R/\mathfrak{m}$. Let $x_1, \ldots, x_n$ be a minimal basis of $\mathfrak{m}$. Then $\hat{R} = K[[x_1, \ldots, x_n]]$ can be considered to be the completion of R. Since $R \subset \hat{R}$ we can write elements of R as $f(x)$ and can talk about the homogeneous components of $f(x)$, (relative to K and $x_1, \ldots, x_n$), which are then obviously in R. However note that for $f(x) \in R$ and $t \in K$, the element $f(tx) \in \hat{R}$ in general may not be in R. The said generalization of 4) is as follows.

4′) *For any ideal $\mathfrak{a}$ in R the following three conditions are equivalent.*

i′) *For any $f(x) \in \mathfrak{a}$ and $t \in K$, $f(tx)$ is in $\mathfrak{a}\hat{R}$; (or equivalently: $\mathfrak{a}\hat{R}$ is homogeneous).*

ii′) *For any $f(x) \in \mathfrak{a}$, all the homogeneous components of $f(x)$ are in $\mathfrak{a}$.*

iii′) *$\mathfrak{a}$ has a finite basis consisting of homogeneous polynomials (in $K[x_1, \ldots, x_n]$).*

PROOF. ii') $\Rightarrow$ iii') $\Rightarrow$ i') as in 4), and i') $\Rightarrow$ ii') follows from 4) because $(\mathfrak{b}\hat{R}) \cap R = \mathfrak{b}$ for any ideal $\mathfrak{b}$ in R.

§38. TOPOLOGICAL DIMENSION

We want to prove the following proposition.

(38.1) *Let V be a nonempty analytic set in an open set X in $\mathbf{C}^n$. Then* $\operatorname{topdim} V = 2 \dim V$, *and* $\operatorname{topdim}_a V = 2 \dim_a V$ *for all* $a \in V$.

First we give a review on topological dimension theory based on Hurewicz–Wallman [**1**]. This theory is valid in any metrizable topological space having a countable basis of open sets. Let us call such a space an MC-space. Note that any subspace of an MC-space is an MC-space, and in particular every subset of $\mathbf{R}^m$ is an MC-space.

(38.2) DEFINITION. For any MC-space A, by $\operatorname{topdim} A$ we denote the *topological dimension of A*; and for any $p \in A$, by $\operatorname{topdim}_p A$ we denote the *topological dimension of A at p*. The definitions are by induction on $m = 0, 1, 2,\ldots$ and are thus; see Hurewicz–Wallman [**1**: Definition III.1 on p. 24].

$\operatorname{topdim} A = -1 \Leftrightarrow A = \emptyset$.

$\operatorname{topdim}_p A \leqq m \Leftrightarrow$ there exists a basis $\mathfrak{N}$ of neighborhoods of p in A such that for all $N \in \mathfrak{N}$ we have $\operatorname{topdim}(\operatorname{bd}_A N) \leqq m - 1$.

$\operatorname{topdim}_p A = m \Leftrightarrow \operatorname{topdim}_p A \leqq m$ and it is false that $\operatorname{topdim}_p A \leqq m - 1$.

$\operatorname{topdim} A \leqq m \Leftrightarrow \operatorname{topdim}_p A \leqq m$ for all $p \in A$.

$\operatorname{topdim} A = m \Leftrightarrow \operatorname{topdim} A \leqq m$ and it is false that $\operatorname{topdim} A \leqq m - 1$.

$\operatorname{topdim}_p A = \infty \Leftrightarrow$ for each nonnegative integer m it is false that $\operatorname{topdim}_p A \leqq m$.

$\operatorname{topdim} A = \infty \Leftrightarrow$ for each nonnegative integer m it is false that $\operatorname{topdim} A \leqq m$.

Note the following immediate consequences of the above definitions.

1) $\operatorname{topdim}_p A > m \Leftrightarrow$ there exists a neighborhood N' of p in A such that for each neighborhood N of p in N' we have $\operatorname{topdim}(\operatorname{bd}_A N) \geqq m$.

2) $\operatorname{topdim} A = \max_{p \in A} \operatorname{topdim}_p A$, $(A \neq \emptyset)$.

3) For any neighborhood N of p in A we have $\operatorname{topdim}_p N = \operatorname{topdim}_p A$.

We shall need the following results from topological dimension theory.

(38.3) *Let B be a subspace of an MC-space A. If* topdim $A \leqq m$ *then* topdim $B \leqq m$. *For $p \in B$, if* $\text{topdim}_p A \leqq m$ *then* $\text{topdim}_p B \leqq m$.

In Hurewicz–Wallmann [**1**: Theorem III.1 on p. 26] only the first assertion is stated, but the second assertion also follows from the proof given there.

(38.4) *An MC-space which is the countable union of closed subsets of* topdim $\leqq m$ *has* topdim $\leqq m$.

Hurewicz–Wallman [**1**: Theorem III.2 on p. 30].

(38.5) *The union of two subspaces each of which has* topdim $\leqq m$ *and one of which is closed has* topdim $\leqq m$.

Hurewicz–Wallman [**1**: Corollary 1 on p. 32].

(38.6) topdim $\mathbf{R}^m = m$.

Hurewicz–Wallman [**1**: Theorem IV.1 on p. 41]. Now every nonempty open set in $\mathbf{R}^m$ contains an open subset which is homeomorphic to $\mathbf{R}^m$. Also any two points in $\mathbf{R}^m$ can be permuted by a homeomorphism of $\mathbf{R}^m$ onto itself. Therefore by (38.2.2, 38.2.3), (38.6) yields

(38.7) *For any nonempty open subset A of $\mathbf{R}^m$ we have* topdim $A = m$ *and* $\text{topdim}_p A = m$ *for all $p \in A$.*

(38.8) *Let $f : A \to B$ be a continuous closed map of an MC-space A into an MC-space B such that* topdim $f^{-1}(q) \leqq t$ *for all $q \in B$, (t not depending on q). Then* topdim $A \leqq t +$ topdim B.

Hurewicz–Wallman [**1**: Proof of Theorem VI.7 on p. 91]. Since the topdim of any finite set is $\leqq 0$, from (38.8) we get

(38.9) *Let $f : A \to B$ be a continuous closed map of an MC-space A into an MC-space B such that $f^{-1}(q)$ is a finite set for all $q \in B$. Then* topdim $A \leqq$ topdim B.

Proof of (38.1). Given $a \in V$, by (30.21) there exists a continuous closed map of a neighborhood V_1 of a in V into an open set in $\mathbf{C}^e$ where $e = \dim_a V$; hence $\text{topdim}_a V = \text{topdim}_a V_1 \leqq \text{topdim}\, V_1 \leqq 2e$ by (38.2, 38.7, 38.9). This being so for every $a \in V$, we get that topdim $V \leqq 2 \dim V$. By (33.18, 33.20), there exists a nonempty open subset V_1 of V such that V_1 is homeomorphic to a nonempty open set in $\mathbf{C}^e$ where $e = \dim V$; hence topdim $V \geqq$ topdim $V_1 = 2e$ by (38.3, 38.7). Therefore topdim $V = 2 \dim V$. It only remains to show that $\text{topdim}_a V \geqq 2 \dim_a V$ for all $a \in V$. This is obvious if $\dim_a V = 0$. Suppose if possible that V contains a point a such that $\operatorname{topdim}_a V \leqq 2e - 1$ where $0 < e = \dim_a V$. We can find an analytic set V' in a neighborhood X' of a in X such that $V' \subset V$, $\dim_a V' = e$, and $\gamma_a V'$ is irreducible. By (38.3), $\operatorname{topdim}_a V' \leqq \operatorname{topdim}_a V \leqq 2e - 1$. Hence upon replacing X by X' and V by V' we may suppose that $\gamma_a V$ is irreducible. In virtue of (23.5), by (32.1) we can find a continuous proper open map f of a neighborhood V^* of a in V onto an open set Y in $\mathbf{C}^e$ and an $(e - 1)$-dimensional analytic set Δ in Y such that we have the following:

1°) Given $\beta \in Y - \Delta$ there exists a neighborhood Y' of β in $Y - \Delta$ such that: $f^{-1}(Y')$ equals a finite union $\bigcup_{i=1}^{d} N_i$ such that $f|N_i$ is a homeomorphism of N_i onto Y' for $i = 1,\ldots, d$.

Now $\operatorname{topdim}_a V^* = \operatorname{topdim}_a V$ and hence we may assume that $V = V^*$. By assumption $\operatorname{topdim}_a V \leqq 2e - 1$ and hence by definition there exists a basis $\mathfrak{N}$ of neighborhoods of a in V such that $\operatorname{topdim}(\operatorname{bd}_V N) \leqq 2e - 2$ for all $N \in \mathfrak{N}$. Since f is a continuous open map of V onto Y, $\{f(N) : N \in \mathfrak{N}\}$ is a basis of neighborhoods of $f(a)$ in Y. Hence by (38.6, 38.2.1) we can choose $N \in \mathfrak{N}$ such that $\operatorname{topdim}(\operatorname{bd}_Y M) \geqq 2e - 1$ where $M = f(N)$. Since $\dim \Delta = e - 1$, by what we have already proved we get that $\operatorname{topdim} \Delta \leqq 2e - 2$. Hence $\operatorname{topdim}(\Delta \cap (\operatorname{bd}_Y M)) \leqq 2e - 2$ by (38.3). Now $\Delta \cap (\operatorname{bd}_Y M)$ is closed in $\operatorname{bd}_Y M$ and hence $\operatorname{topdim}((\operatorname{bd}_Y M) - \Delta) \geqq 2e - 1$ by (38.5). Hence there exists $\beta \in (\operatorname{bd}_Y M) - \Delta$ such that $\operatorname{topdim}_\beta((\operatorname{bd}_Y M) - \Delta) \geqq 2e - 1$. Let Y' be a neighborhood of β in $Y - \Delta$ as in 1°) and let $M' = Y' \cap \operatorname{bd}_Y M$. Then

$$\operatorname{topdim} M' \geqq \operatorname{topdim}_\beta M' = \operatorname{topdim}_\beta((\operatorname{bd}_Y M) - \Delta)$$

by (38.2.2, 38.2.3). Hence

2°) $$\operatorname{topdim} M' \geqq 2e - 1.$$

Let $N_i' = N_i \cap f^{-1}(M')$. Suppose we have shown that

3°) $$(\operatorname{bd}_V N) \cap f^{-1}(\beta') \neq \emptyset \quad \text{for all} \quad \beta' \in \operatorname{bd}_Y M.$$

Then

4°) $$M' = \bigcup_{i=1}^{d} f(N_i' \cap \operatorname{bd}_V N).$$

Since $f|N_i$ is a homeomorphism of N_i onto Y', $(N_i' \cap \operatorname{bd}_V N)$ and $f(N_i' \cap \operatorname{bd}_V N)$ are homeomorphic. Therefore $\operatorname{topdim} f(N_i' \cap \operatorname{bd}_V N) = \operatorname{topdim}(N_i' \cap \operatorname{bd}_V N)$. Now $\operatorname{topdim}(\operatorname{bd}_V N) \leqq 2e - 2$ and by (38.3), $\operatorname{topdim}(N_i' \cap \operatorname{bd}_V N) \leqq \operatorname{topdim}(\operatorname{bd}_V N)$. Therefore

5°) $$\operatorname{topdim} f(N_i' \cap \operatorname{bd}_V N) \leqq 2e - 2 \qquad \text{for} \quad i = 1,\ldots, d.$$

Since $f|N_i$ is a homeomorphism of N_i onto Y', $f|N_i'$ is a homeomorphism of N_i' onto $f(N_i') = M'$. Now $N_i' \cap \mathrm{bd}_V N$ is closed in N_i' and hence we get that

6°) $\quad f(N_i' \cap \mathrm{bd}_V N)$ is closed in M' for $i = 1,\dots, d$.

In virtue of (38.4), by (4°, 5°, 6°) we get that topdim $M' \leqq 2e - 2$ which contradicts 2°). It now only remains to prove 3°). So let $\beta' \in \mathrm{bd}_Y M$ be given. Then $\beta' \notin M$ and there exist $b^{(\lambda)} \in M$ such that $\lim_{\lambda\to\infty} b^{(\lambda)} = \beta'$. Since $f(N) = M$, we can find $a^{(\lambda)} \in N$ such that $f(a^{(\lambda)}) = b^{(\lambda)}$ for all λ. Now $\{b^{(1)}, b^{(2)},\dots\} \cup \{\beta'\}$ is a compact subset of Y and f is a proper map of V onto Y. Therefore $Z = f^{-1}(\{b^{(1)}, b^{(2)},\dots\} \cup \{\beta'\})$ is compact. Now $a^{(\lambda)} \in Z$ for all λ and hence upon replacing $(b^{(\lambda)})$ by a suitable subsequence we get that $\lim_{\lambda\to\infty} a^{(\lambda)} = \alpha \in V$ and hence $\beta' = \lim_{\lambda\to\infty} f(a^{(\lambda)}) = f(\alpha)$. Now $f(N) = M$ and $\beta' \notin M$. Therefore $\alpha \notin N$ and hence $\alpha \in \mathrm{bd}_V N$. Therefore $(\mathrm{bd}_V N) \cap f^{-1}(\beta') \neq \emptyset$.

§39. REMARKS ON THE FUNDAMENTAL GROUP[1]

We want to prove (39.7) which can be considered to be "a Bertini theorem" or "a Lefschetz theorem". First we give some elementary lemmas. The closed unit interval $[0, 1]$ will be denoted by I.

DEFINITION Let $\beta: A \to B$ be a continuous map of a topological space A onto a topological space B, let $C \subset A$, and let d be a positive integer. We shall say that C is a d-fold cross-section relative to β provided: for each $b \in B$ there is a neighborhood N of b in B and continuous maps $\lambda_j : N \to A$, $j = 1,\dots, d$, such that:

i) $\beta \circ \lambda_j =$ identity on N for all j;
ii) $\lambda_1(N) \cup \dots \cup \lambda_d(N) = C \cap \beta^{-1}(N)$;
iii) $\lambda_j(N) \cap \lambda_{j'}(N) = \emptyset$ for all $j \neq j'$.

(39.1) *Let $f(y, z) = z^d + f_1(y)z^{d-1} + \dots + f_d(y)$, $d > 0$, where $f_1(y),\dots, f_d(y)$ are analytic on an open set Y in $\mathbf{C}^{n-1}\{y\}$. Let $\Delta(y)$ be the z-discriminant*

[1] This section is based on Abhyankar [2] which in turn is based on Grauert–Remmert [**1**: Hilfssatz 3]. For the notions of fundamental group and universal covering space see for instance Steenrod [**1**: §14]. The fundamental group of a connected and locally arcwise connected topological space A with base point a is denoted by $\pi_1(A, a)$ or simply by $\pi_1(A)$. For any connected and locally arcwise connected subspace B of A there is a natural homomorphism $\pi_1(B) \to \pi_1(A)$ where the base point is taken in B. A is simply connected means that $\pi_1(A)$ is the identity group. A is locally simply connected means that every point in A has a neighborhood which is connected and simply connected.

of $f(y, z)$. Let $V = \{(b, c) \in Y \times \mathbf{C}^1\{z\} : f(b, c) = 0\}$, and $\boldsymbol{\Delta} = \{b \in Y : \Delta(b) = 0\}$. Let Z be an open set in $\mathbf{C}^1\{z\}$ such that $V \subset Y \times Z$. Let $X = Y \times Z$. Let $\mu : X \times I \to X, \nu : X \times I \to I, \rho : X \to Y, \sigma : X \to Z$, $\beta : Z \times I \to I$, be the natural projections. Given an arc $\gamma : I \to Y - \boldsymbol{\Delta}$ let $M' = \{w \in X \times I : \gamma \circ \nu(w) = \rho \circ \mu(w)\}$, $M = M' \cap ((X - V) \times I)$; $M'_t = M' \cap \nu^{-1}(t)$ and $M_t = M \cap \nu^{-1}(t)$ for all $t \in I$. Denoting by $\delta : M' \to Z \times I$ the map given by: $\delta(w) = (\sigma \circ \mu(w)) \times \nu(w)$ we have the following.

i) *δ is a homeomorphism of M' onto $Z \times I$.*
ii) *$\delta^{-1}(Z \times t) = M'_t$ for all $t \in I$.*
iii) *$(Z \times I) - \delta(M)$ is a d-fold cross-section relative to β.*

PROOF. i) and ii) are obvious, and iii) follows from (12.3).

(**39.2**) *Let $\alpha : Z \times I \to Z$ and $\beta : Z \times I \to I$ be the natural projections where Z is an open polycylinder around some point in $\mathbf{C}^1\{z\}$, let $J \subset Z \times I$ be a d-fold cross-section relative to β, and let $v_1,\ldots, v_d$ be the distinct points in $\alpha(J \cap (Z \times 0))$. Then there exists a homeomorphism τ of $Z \times I$ onto itself such that $\beta = \beta \circ \tau$, $\tau(v \times 0) = v \times 0$ for all $v \in Z$, and $\tau(J) = (v_1 \times I) \cup \ldots \cup (v_d \times I)$.*

Since Z is homeomorphic to $\mathbf{C}^1\{z\}$ we may assume that $Z = \mathbf{C}^1\{z\}$. For any $v \in Z$ and $\epsilon > 0$ let $Z\langle\epsilon, v\rangle = \{c \in Z : |c - v| < \epsilon\}$, $\bar{Z}\langle\epsilon, v\rangle = \{c \in Z : |c - v| \leqq \epsilon\}$, $\mathring{Z}\langle\epsilon, v\rangle = \{c \in Z : |c - v| = \epsilon\}$. We first prove (39.2) under additional assumptions.

(**39.2′**) *The assertion of* (39.2) *holds if there exist $\epsilon > 0$ and continuous maps $\lambda_j : I \to Z \times I, j = 1,\ldots, d$, such that:*

i) *$\beta \circ \lambda_j$ = identity on I for all j;*
ii) *$\lambda_1(I) \cup \ldots \cup \lambda_d(I) = J$;*
iii) *$\alpha \circ \lambda_j(I) \subset Z\langle\epsilon, v_j\rangle$ for all j;*
iv) *$\bar{Z}\langle\epsilon, v_j\rangle \cap \bar{Z}\langle\epsilon, v_{j'}\rangle = \emptyset$ for all $j \neq j'$.*

Proof of (39.2′). For any $v \times t \in Z \times I$ we have the following three mutually exclusive possibilities.

1°) $v \notin \bar{Z}\langle\epsilon, v_1\rangle \cup \ldots \cup \bar{Z}\langle\epsilon, v_d\rangle$.
2°) $v \times t \in J$. Then we have $v = \alpha \circ \lambda_j(t)$ for a unique j.
3°) $v \times t \notin J$ but $v \in \bar{Z}\langle\epsilon, v_1\rangle \cup \ldots \cup \bar{Z}\langle\epsilon, v_d\rangle$. Then we have $v \in \bar{Z}\langle\epsilon, v_j\rangle$ for a unique j and it follows that $v \neq \alpha \circ \lambda_j(t)$, whence there exists a unique positive real number $e(v \times t)$ such that $|\omega(v \times t)| = \epsilon$

where $\omega(v \times t) = e(v \times t)(v - \alpha \circ \lambda_j(t)) + \alpha \circ \lambda_j(t) - v_j$. It suffices to take $\tau : Z \times I \to Z \times I$ defined thus:

$$\tau(v \times t) = \begin{cases} v \times t & \text{in Case 1°)} \\ v_j \times t & \text{in Case 2°)} \\ (v_j + (\omega(v \times t)/e(v \times t))) \times t & \text{in Case 3°).} \end{cases}$$

Proof of (39.2). Since I is compact, by continuity we can find: a positive real number ϵ, closed subintervals $I_k = [t_{k-1}, t_k]$, $0 = t_0 < \ldots < t_m = 1$, of I and for each k continuous maps $\lambda_{kj} : I_k \to Z \times I$, $j = 1,\ldots, d$, with the following four properties.

1′) $\beta \circ \lambda_{kj} =$ identity on I_k for all k, j.
2′) $\lambda_{k1}(I_k) \cup \ldots \cup \lambda_{kd}(I_k) = J \cap \beta^{-1}(I_k)$ for all k.
3′) $\alpha \circ \lambda_{kj}(I_k) \subset Z\langle \epsilon, \alpha \circ \lambda_{kj}(t_{k-1})\rangle$ for all k, j.
4′) $\bar{Z}\langle \epsilon, \alpha \circ \lambda_{kj}(t_{k-1})\rangle \cap \bar{Z}\langle \epsilon, \alpha \circ \lambda_{kj'}(t_{k-1})\rangle = \emptyset$ whenever $j \neq j'$.

By 2′) in particular we get: $\bigcup_{j=1}^{d} \{v_j\} = \bigcup_{j=1}^{d} \{\alpha \circ \lambda_{1j}(0)\}$. Upon applying (39.2′) to $J \cap (Z \times I_k) \subset Z \times I_k$ we can find a homeomorphism τ_k of $Z \times I_k$ onto itself such that $\beta \circ \tau_k = \beta$ on $Z \times I_k$, $\tau_k(v \times t_{k-1}) = v \times t_{k-1}$ for all $v \in Z$, and

$$\tau_k(J \cap (Z \times I_k)) = \bigcup_{j=1}^{d} ((\alpha \circ \lambda_{kj}(t_{k-1})) \times I_k) \qquad \text{for} \quad k = 1,\ldots, m.$$

We set $H_k = I_1 \cup \ldots \cup I_k$ and by induction on k, for $k = 1,\ldots, m$ we show the existence of a homeomorphism ζ_k of $Z \times H_k$ onto itself such that $\beta \circ \zeta_k = \beta$ on $Z \times H_k$ and $\zeta_k(J \cap (Z \times H_k)) = (v_1 \times H_k) \cup \ldots \cup (v_k \times H_k)$. For $k = 1$ we can take $\zeta_k = \tau_1$. Now let $k > 1$ and suppose the map ζ_{k-1} has been constructed. For any $v \in Z$ let $\xi(v) = \alpha \circ \zeta_{k-1}(v \times t_{k-1})$. Then ξ is a homeomorphism of Z onto itself. For any $v \times t \in Z \times I_k$ let $\zeta(v \times t) = (\xi \circ \alpha \circ \tau_k(v \times t)) \times t$. Then ζ is a homeomorphism of $Z \times I_k$ onto itself and $\zeta | Z \times t_{k-1} = \zeta_{k-1} | Z \times t_{k-1}$. Define ζ_k by setting: $\zeta_k | Z \times H_{k-1} = \zeta_{k-1}$ and $\zeta_k | I_k = \zeta$. Then ζ_k has the required properties. This completes the induction and now it suffices to take $\tau = \zeta_m$.

(39.3) *For a subspace B of a topological space A, where both A and B are connected, locally arcwise connected and locally simply connected, the following three conditions are equivalent.*

i) *The natural map $\pi_1(B, a) \to \pi_1(A, a)$ is an epimorphism, $(a \in B)$.*
ii) *If $\eta : A^* \to A$ is any connected covering, then $\eta^{-1}(B)$ is connected.*
iii) *If $\eta : A^* \to A$ is the universal covering, then $\eta^{-1}(B)$ is connected.*

Proof is trivial. Note that condition i) is equivalent to the following: any arc $\gamma : I \to A$ with $\gamma(0) = \gamma(1) = a$ can be deformed to an arc $\gamma' : I \to B$ leaving a fixed, i.e., there exists a continuous map $\Gamma : I \times I \to A$ such that for all $t \in I$ we have: $\Gamma(0 \times t) = \Gamma(1 \times t) = a$, $\Gamma(t \times 0) = \gamma(t)$, $\Gamma(t \times 1) = \gamma'(t)$.

(39.4) *Let A be a connected and locally arcwise connected topological space, and let B be a closed nowhere dense nowhere disconnecting subset of A. If $\eta : A^* \to A$ is any connected covering, then $\eta^{-1}(A - B)$ is connected and the map $\eta^{-1}(A - B) \to A - B$ induced by η is a covering map.*

PROOF. Since η is a covering map, obviously $\eta^{-1}(B)$ is a closed nowhere dense nowhere disconnecting subset of A^*. Therefore our assertion follows from (14.5.5, 14.6.5).

(39.5) *Let A be a connected, locally arcwise connected and locally simply connected topological space and let $\eta : B \to A \times I$ be a connected covering. Then $\eta^{-1}(A \times t)$ is connected for all $t \in I$.*

PROOF. Let $\zeta : A^* \to A$ be a universal covering. For any $u \times t \in A^* \times I$ let $\xi(u \times t) = \zeta(u) \times t$. Then $\xi : A^* \times I \to A \times I$ is a universal covering because $A^* \times I$ is connected and simply connected. The assertion now follows from (39.3).

(39.6) *Let $f(y, z) = z^d + f_1(y)z^{d-1} + \dots + f_d(y)$, $d > 0$, where $f_1(y), \dots, f_d(y)$ are analytic on an open set Y in $\mathbf{C}^{n-1}\{y\}$. Let $\Delta(y)$ be the z-discriminant of $f(y, z)$. Let $V = \{(b, c) \in Y \times \mathbf{C}^1\{z\} : f(b, c) = 0\}$ and $\mathbf{\Delta} = \{b \in Y : \Delta(b) = 0\}$. Let Z be an open polycylinder around some point in $\mathbf{C}^1\{z\}$ such that $V \subset Y \times Z$. Let $X = (Y \times Z) - V$. Let $\mu : X \times I \to X$, $\nu : X \times I \to I$ be the natural projections, and let $\rho : X \to Y$ be the restriction to X of the natural projection $Y \times Z \to Y$. Given an arc $\gamma : I \to Y - \mathbf{\Delta}$, let $M = \{w \in X \times I : \gamma \circ \nu(w) = \rho \circ \mu(w)\}$, and $M_t = M \cap \nu^{-1}(t)$ for all $t \in I$. If $\eta : M^* \to M$ is a connected covering then $\eta^{-1}(M_t)$ is connected for all $t \in I$.*

PROOF. Follows from (39.1, 39.2, 39.5).

(39.7) *Let $f(y, z) = z^d + f_1(y)z^{d-1} + \dots + f_d(y)$, $d > 0$, where $f_1(y), \dots, f_d(y)$ are analytic on an open polycylinder Y around some point in $\mathbf{C}^{n-1}\{y\}$.*[2] *Let $\Delta(y)$ be the z-discriminant of $f(y, z)$. Assume that $\Delta \not\equiv 0$ on Y.*[3] *Let*

[2] For instance $Y = \mathbf{C}^{n-1}\{y\}$.

[3] This assumption is satisfied if for some $b \in Y$, $z^d + \tilde{f}_1(y)z^{d-1} + \dots + \tilde{f}_d(y)$ is irreducible in $\mathbf{C}[\langle y \rangle][z]$ where $\tilde{f}_j(y)$ is the Taylor expansion of $f_j(y)$ around b.

$V = \{(b, c) \in Y \times \mathbf{C}^1\{z\} : f(b, c) = 0\}$, and $\mathbf{\Delta} = \{b \in Y : \Delta(b) = 0\}$. Let Z be an open polycylinder around some point in $\mathbf{C}^1\{z\}$ such that $V \subset Y \times Z$.[4] *Let W be an analytic set in $Y \times Z$ such that $W \subset V$.*[5] *Let $L = p \times Z$ with $p \in Y - \mathbf{\Delta}$, and let d' be the number of distinct points in $W \cap L$.*[6] *If $\varphi_1 : X_1^* \to ((Y \times Z) - W)$ is any connected covering, then $\varphi_1^{-1}(L - W)$ is connected. Furthermore, the natural map $\pi_1(L - W) \to \pi_1((Y \times Z) - W)$ is an epimorphism, and hence the group $\pi_1((Y \times Z) - W)$ has a system of d' generators.*[7]

PROOF. Let $X_1 = (Y \times Z) - W$, $X = (Y \times Z) - V$, $X^* = \varphi_1^{-1}(X)$, and let $\varphi : X^* \to X$ be induced by φ_1. By (14.7), $X_1 \cap V$ is a closed nowhere dense nowhere disconnecting subset of X_1, and hence $\varphi : X^* \to X$ is a connected covering by (39.4). Let $\mu : X \times I \to X$, $\nu : X \times I \to I$, $\mu^* : X^* \times I \to X^*$ be the natural projections. For any $v^* \times t \in X^* \times I$ let $\psi(v^* \times t) = \varphi(v^*) \times t$. Then $\psi : X^* \times I \to X \times I$ is a connected covering. Let $\rho : X \to Y$ be the restriction to X of the natural projection $Y \times Z \to Y$. Then $\rho(X) = Y$.

Suppose if possible that $\varphi^{-1}(L - V)$ is not connected. Take two distinct connected components L_0^* and L_1^* of $\varphi^{-1}(L - V)$ and take $r_i \in L_i^*$ for $i = 0, 1$. By (14.7), $(\mathbf{\Delta} \times Z) - V$ is a closed nowhere dense nowhere disconnecting subset of X, and hence $\varphi^{-1}(X - (\mathbf{\Delta} \times Z))$ is arcwise connected by (39.4). Now $\varphi^{-1}(L - V) \subset \varphi^{-1}(X - (\mathbf{\Delta} \times Z))$ and hence we can find an arc $\gamma^* : I \to \varphi^{-1}(X - (\mathbf{\Delta} \times Z))$ with $\gamma^*(i) = r_i$ for $i = 0, 1$. Let $\gamma = \rho \circ \varphi \circ \gamma^*$. Then $\gamma : I \to Y - \mathbf{\Delta}$ is an arc such that $\gamma(i) = p$ for $i = 0, 1$. Let $M = \{w \in X \times I : \gamma \circ \nu(w) = \rho \circ \mu(w)\}$, and $M_t = M \cap \nu^{-1}(t)$ for all $t \in I$. Let $\delta : I \to X^* \times I$ be the arc given by: $\delta(t) = \gamma^*(t) \times t$ for all $t \in I$. Then $\delta(I) \subset \psi^{-1}(M)$. Let M^* be the connected component of $\psi^{-1}(M)$ containing the connected set $\delta(I)$, let $\eta : M^* \to M$ be induced by ψ, and let $M_t^* = \eta^{-1}(M_t)$ for all $t \in I$. Then $\eta : M^* \to M$ is a connected covering by (14.6.5), and hence by (39.6), M_t^* is connected for all $t \in I$. Therefore $\mu^*(M_t^*)$ is connected for all $t \in I$. Obviously

$$\gamma^*(t) \in \mu^*(M_t^*) \subset \varphi^{-1}(\rho^{-1}(\gamma(t))) \qquad \text{for all} \quad t \in I.$$

Now $r_0 = \gamma^*(0) \in L_0^*$ and $\rho^{-1}(\gamma(0)) = L - V$, and hence

$$r_0 \in L_0^* \cap \mu^*(M_0^*) \qquad \text{and} \qquad \mu^*(M_0^*) \subset \varphi^{-1}(L - V).$$

[4] For instance $Z = \mathbf{C}^1\{z\}$.

[5] For instance $W = V$.

[6] Obviously $d' \leqq d$, and if $W = V$ then $d' = d$.

[7] A group G has a system of m generators means there exists an epimorphism $F_m \to G$ where F_m is a free group on d generators; (F_0 = the identity group).

Since L_0^* is a connected component of $\varphi^{-1}(L - V)$ and $\mu^*(M_0^*)$ is connected, it follows that $\mu^*(M_0^*) \subset L_0^*$. Replacing 0 by 1 we similarly get $\mu^*(M_1^*) \subset L_1^*$. Thus we have proved

1°) $$\mu^*(M_i^*) \subset L_i^* \qquad \text{for} \quad i = 0, 1.$$

Now $\gamma(I)$ is a compact subset of Y and by assumption Y is an open polycylinder around some point b' in $\mathbf{C}^{n-1}\{y\}$. Therefore we can find a compact polycylinder $\tilde{Y}$ around b' such that $\gamma(I) \subset \tilde{Y} \subset Y$. By (12.5), the restriction to V of the natural projection $Y \times Z \to Y$ is a proper map of V onto Y. Therefore $V \cap (\tilde{Y} \times Z)$ is a compact subset of $Y \times Z$. By assumption Z is an open polycylinder around some point in $\mathbf{C}^1\{z\}$. Consequently we can find $c \in Z$ such that $(\tilde{Y} \times c) \cap V = \emptyset$. Let $\tilde{X} = \tilde{Y} \times c$. Then $\tilde{X} \subset X$; and $\tilde{X}$ is connected, locally arcwise connected and simply connected. Therefore for any connected component $\tilde{X}^*$ of $\varphi^{-1}(\tilde{X})$, $\varphi|\tilde{X}^*$ is a homeomorphism of $\tilde{X}^*$ onto $\tilde{X}$. Consequently, any such $\tilde{X}^*$ contains exactly one point in $\varphi^{-1}(p \times c)$. Setting $D_i = L_i^* \cap \varphi^{-1}(p \times c)$ we get $D_0 \cap D_1 = \emptyset$. Let furthermore E_i be the union of all those connected components of $\varphi^{-1}(\tilde{X})$ which have a nonempty intersection with D_i. Then we have 2°) and 3°).

2°) $$E_0 \cap E_1 = \emptyset.$$

3°) $$L_i^* \cap \varphi^{-1}(\tilde{X}) \subset E_i \qquad \text{for} \quad i = 0, 1.$$

Let $\tilde{M} = M \cap \mu^{-1}(\tilde{X})$. Then $\tilde{M} = \{u \times c \times t : \gamma(t) = u; \quad t \in I\}$. Therefore $\nu|\tilde{M}$ is a homeomorphism of $\tilde{M}$ onto I; and for any $t \in I$, $M_t \cap \tilde{M}$ contains exactly one point. Let $\tilde{M}^*$ be a connected component of $\eta^{-1}(\tilde{M})$. Then $\eta|\tilde{M}^*$ is a homeomorphism of $\tilde{M}^*$ onto $\tilde{M}$, because $\tilde{M}$ is homeomorphic to I. Therefore for any $t \in I$, $M_t^* \cap \tilde{M}^*$ contains exactly one point $\tilde{r}_t$ and we have

4°) $$\mu^*(\tilde{r}_t) \in \mu^*(M_t^*) \qquad \text{for all} \quad t \in I.$$

From the connectedness of $\tilde{M}^*$ it follows that

5°) $$\mu^*(\tilde{M}^*) \quad \text{is connected.}$$

As $\mu(\tilde{M}) \subset \tilde{X}$ we further get

6°) $$\mu^*(\tilde{r}_t) \in \mu^*(\tilde{M}^*) \subset \varphi^{-1}(\tilde{X}) \qquad \text{for all} \quad t \in I.$$

Now 1°) and 4°) imply

7°) $$\mu^*(\tilde{r}_i) \in L_i^* \qquad \text{for} \quad i = 0, 1.$$

By 3°), 6°), and 7°) we get

8°) $$\mu^*(\tilde{r}_i) \in E_i \qquad \text{for} \quad i = 0, 1.$$

By 6°) and 8°), $E_i \cap \mu^*(\tilde{M}^*) \neq \emptyset$ for $i = 0, 1$; and by 5°) and 6°), $\mu^*(\tilde{M}^*)$ is connected and is contained in $\varphi^{-1}(\tilde{X})$. Since E_i is the union of a certain number of connected components of $\varphi^{-1}(\tilde{X})$, it follows that $\mu^*(\tilde{M}^*) \subset E_i$ for $i = 0, 1$. This however implies that $E_0 \cap E_1 \neq \emptyset$ which contradicts 2°). Therefore $\varphi^{-1}(L - V)$ must be connected. Consequently $\varphi_1^{-1}(L - W)$ is connected by (14.6.6). The remaining assertions now follow from (39.3) because $\pi_1(L - W)$ is a free group on d' generators.

Now we give some corollaries of (39.7).

(39.8)[8] *Let W be an analytic set in an open set X' in $\mathbf{C}^n$ and let $a \in X'$ with $\dim_a W \leqq n - 2$. Then there exists a neighborhood basis $\mathbf{X}$ of a in X' such that: $X - W$ is connected and simply connected for each $X \in \mathbf{X}$; and upon making an affine transformation each $X \in \mathbf{X}$ becomes an open polycylinder around a.*

PROOF. We have nothing to show if $a \notin W$; so assume that $a \in W$. By (23.5) and (23.3), upon making an affine transformation, we can find: a coordinate system $(y, z) = (y_1, \ldots, y_{n-1}, z)$ in $\mathbf{C}^n$ with respect to which a is at the origin, a neighborhood $Y_2 \times Z_1$ of the origin in X', a distinguished polynomial $g(y, z)$ of positive degree in z with coefficients in $\mathbf{C}[\langle y \rangle]$ which are convergent in Y_2, and $0 \neq h(y) \in \mathbf{C}[\langle y \rangle]$ which is convergent in Y_2, such that: $g(b, c) = 0 = h(b)$ for all $(b, c) \in (Y_2 \times Z_1) \cap W$. Let Y_1 be a neighborhood of the origin in Y_2 in which all the coefficients of all the irreducible monic factors of $g(y, z)$ in $\mathbf{C}[\langle y \rangle][z]$ are convergent. Let $f(y, z)$ be the product of the distinct irreducible monic factors of $g(y, z)$ in $\mathbf{C}[\langle y \rangle][z]$, and let $\Delta(y)$ be the z-discriminant of $f(y, z)$. Then $0 \neq \Delta(y) \in \mathbf{C}[\langle y \rangle]$, and $f(b, c) = 0 = h(b)$ for all $(b, c) \in (Y_1 \times Z_1) \cap W$. By continuity of roots (11.3), we can find a neighborhood basis $\mathbf{X}$ of the origin in $Y_1 \times Z_1$ consisting of open polycylinders $X = Y \times Z$ around the origin such that $c \in Z$ for any $(b, c) \in Y \times \mathbf{C}^1\{z\}$ with $f(b, c) = 0$. Given $X = Y \times Z$ in $\mathbf{X}$ we can take $L = p \times Z$ with $\Delta(p) \neq 0 \neq h(p)$; then $L \cap W = \emptyset$ and hence $X - W$ is simply connected by (39.7).

(39.9) *Let V be an algebraic hypersurface of order d in $\mathbf{C}^n$, and let L be a line in $\mathbf{C}^n$ which meets V in exactly d distinct points. If $\varphi : X^* \to \mathbf{C}^n - V$ is any connected covering then $\varphi^{-1}(L - V)$ is connected. The natural map $\pi_1(L - V) \to \pi_1(\mathbf{C}^n - V)$ is an epimorphism, and hence $\pi_1(\mathbf{C}^n - V)$ has a system of d generators.*

[8] This expresses the "purity of branch locus" at a simple point for finite as well as infinite "analytic coverings". The corresponding theorem for algebro-geometric regular local rings is due to Zariski [5] and the general case of arbitrary regular local rings is due to Nagata [4].

PROOF. Take affine coordinates $(y, z) = (y_1, \ldots, y_{n-1}, z)$ in $\mathbf{C}^n$ such that: $V = \{(b, c) \in Y \times Z : f(b, c) = 0\}$ where $Y = \mathbf{C}^{n-1}\{y\}$, $Z = \mathbf{C}^1\{z\}$, and $f(y, z)$ is a monic polynomial of degree d in z with coefficients in $\mathbf{C}[y]$; and $L = \{(b, c) \in Y \times Z : b = (0)\}$. Now apply (39.7) to $W = V$.

(39.10)[9] *Let V be an algebraic hypersurface of order d in the complex projective space $\mathbf{P}^n$ and let L be a projective line in $\mathbf{P}^n$ which meets V in exactly d distinct points. If $\varphi : X^* \to \mathbf{P}^n - V$ is any connected covering then $\varphi^{-1}(L - V)$ is connected. The natural map $\pi_1(L - V) \to \pi_1(\mathbf{P}^n - V)$ is an epimorphism; and hence $\pi_1(\mathbf{P}^n - V)$ has a system of $d - 1$ generators.*

PROOF. Let H be a hyperplane in $\mathbf{P}^n$ such that $L \cap V \cap H = \emptyset$. By (14.7), $H - V$ is a closed nowhere dense nowhere disconnecting subset of $\mathbf{P}^n - V$; and hence $\varphi^{-1}(\mathbf{P}^n - H - V) \to \mathbf{P}^n - H - V$ is a connected covering by (39.4). Therefore $\varphi^{-1}(L - H - V)$ is connected by (39.9), and hence $\varphi^{-1}(L - V)$ is connected by (14.6.6). The remaining assertions now follow from (39.3) because $\pi_1(L - V)$ is a free group on $d - 1$ generators.

[9] This is contained in Zariski [**1**] where the possibility of triangulating $\mathbf{P}^n$ so that V becomes a subcomplex is used.

CHAPTER VI

Language of Sheaves

In this chapter we give a review of elementary sheaf theory. Basic references are to Eilenberg-Steenrod [**1**: Chapter VIII and §§9–10 of Chapter V], Godement [**1**], Grothendieck [**1** and **2**], and above all to Serre [**1**]. We include a brief treatment of tensor products although they will not be used in Chapter VII. To introduce the reader to the current language of categories and functors we shall use these terms a few times but only in such a manner that nothing is lost by not knowing their formal meaning.

In this chapter K will denote a ring. We are mainly interested in the case when K is a complete nondiscrete valued field.

§40. INDUCTIVE SYSTEMS AND PRESHEAVES

(40.1) *Exact sequence.* For a homomorphism $\varphi : M \to N$ of abelian groups we set: $\operatorname{Ker} \varphi$ = kernel of φ, $\operatorname{Im} \varphi$ = image of φ, $\operatorname{Coker} \varphi = N/\operatorname{Im} \varphi$, $\operatorname{Coim} \varphi = M/\operatorname{Ker} \varphi$. Recall that φ is said to be a monomorphism (resp: epimorphism) $\Leftrightarrow \operatorname{Ker} \varphi = 0$ (resp: $\operatorname{Im} \varphi = N$, i.e., $\operatorname{Coker} \varphi = 0$), and φ is said to be an isomorphism (notation: $\approx$) $\Leftrightarrow \varphi$ is a monomorphism as well as an epimorphism. A sequence

$$\ldots \to M_{p-1} \overset{\varphi_p}{\to} M_p \overset{\varphi_{p+1}}{\to} M_{p+1} \to \ldots$$

of homomorphisms of abelian groups is exact means: $\operatorname{Im} \varphi_p = \operatorname{Ker} \varphi_{p+1}$ for all p. For instance for any homomorphism $\varphi : M \to N$ of abelian groups we have the following exact sequences:

$$\begin{aligned}
&0 \to \operatorname{Ker} \varphi \to M \to N \to \operatorname{Coker} \varphi \to 0,\\
&0 \to \operatorname{Ker} \varphi \to M \to \operatorname{Im} \varphi \to 0,\\
&0 \to \operatorname{Im} \varphi \to N \to \operatorname{Coker} \varphi \to 0,\\
&0 \to \operatorname{Coim} \varphi \to \operatorname{Im} \varphi \to 0.
\end{aligned}$$

(**40.2**) *Homomorphism.* Let $\sigma : A \to B$ be a ring homomorphism. Let N be a B-module. N becomes an A-module by taking $an = \sigma(a)n$ for all $a \in A$, $n \in N$; we denote this A-module by $N_{[\sigma]}$ or simply by N. Let M be an A-module. By a σ-homomorphism $\varphi : M \to N$ we mean an A-homomorphism of M into $N_{[\sigma]}$; in other words, φ is a homomorphism of abelian groups and $\varphi(am) = \sigma(a)\varphi(m)$. For any A-homomorphism $\varphi : M \to N$ of A-modules M and N, Ker φ, Im φ, Coker φ, and Coim φ are all A-modules; more generally this is so for any σ-homomorphism $\varphi : M \to N$. In particular, via σ, $B = B_{[\sigma]}$ becomes an A-module (it is the A-module associated with the A-algebra B with underlying homomorphism σ), and then σ is a σ-homomorphism; Ker σ is an A-submodule of A and Im σ is an A-subalgebra of B.

Any abelian group can uniquely be considered to be a **Z**-module, and then any homomorphism of abelian groups is a σ-homomorphism where σ is the identity map of **Z**. If K is a field and $\alpha : K \to A$ is a K-algebra then A is a nonnull ring $\Leftrightarrow$ α is a monomorphism; and then K may be identified with Im α.

(**40.3**) *Module of homomorphisms.* Let A be a ring. For any A-modules M and N, the set of all A-homomorphisms of M into N is again an A-module; it is denoted by $\mathrm{Hom}_A(M, N)$ or simply by $\mathrm{Hom}(M, N)$. Given any A-homomorphisms $\varphi : M' \to M$ and $\psi : N \to N'$, they induce the A-homomorphism $\mathrm{Hom}(\varphi, \psi) : \mathrm{Hom}(M, N) \to \mathrm{Hom}(M', N')$ defined by $\mathrm{Hom}(\varphi, \psi)f = \psi \circ f \circ \varphi$ for all $f \in \mathrm{Hom}(M, N)$. If $\varphi' : M'' \to M'$ and $\psi' : N' \to N''$ are any other A-homomorphisms, then $\mathrm{Hom}(\varphi \circ \varphi', \psi' \circ \psi) = \mathrm{Hom}(\varphi', \psi') \circ \mathrm{Hom}(\varphi, \psi)$. If i_M and i_N are the identity maps of M and N, respectively, then $\mathrm{Hom}(i_M, i_N)$ is the identity map of $\mathrm{Hom}(M, N)$; the maps $\mathrm{Hom}(\varphi, i_N) : \mathrm{Hom}(M, N) \to \mathrm{Hom}(M', N)$ and $\mathrm{Hom}(i_M, \psi) : \mathrm{Hom}(M, N) \to \mathrm{Hom}(M, N')$ are said to be induced by φ and ψ, respectively. All this is expressed by saying that Hom is a functor of two variables from the category of A-modules into the category of A-modules; it is contravariant in the first variable and covariant in the second. Note that $\mathrm{Hom}(M, N) = 0$ if either $M = 0$ or $N = 0$. If

$$M'' \to M' \to M \to 0, \qquad 0 \to N \to N' \to N''$$

are exact sequences of A-homomorphisms, then the induced sequences

$$0 \to \mathrm{Hom}(M, N) \to \mathrm{Hom}(M', N) \to \mathrm{Hom}(M'', N),$$
$$0 \to \mathrm{Hom}(M, N) \to \mathrm{Hom}(M, N') \to \mathrm{Hom}(M, N'')$$

are exact; this is expressed by saying that the functor Hom is left exact (in both the variables). For any A-modules M, M', N, N' there are natural A-isomorphisms

$$\operatorname{Hom}(M \oplus M', N) \approx \operatorname{Hom}(M, N) \oplus \operatorname{Hom}(M', N),$$
$$\operatorname{Hom}(M, N \oplus N') \approx \operatorname{Hom}(M, N) \oplus \operatorname{Hom}(M, N').$$

For any A-module M we define

$$\begin{aligned}\operatorname{Anh}_A M = \operatorname{Anh} M &= \textit{annihilator of } M \text{ (relative to } A)\\ &= \{a \in A : am = 0 \text{ for all } m \in M\}.\end{aligned}$$

Note that $\operatorname{Anh} M = \operatorname{Ker} \alpha$ where $\alpha : A \to \operatorname{Hom}(M, M)$ is the natural A-homomorphism given by taking $\alpha(a)m = am$ for all $m \in M$. For any A-submodules P and Q of M we define

$$\begin{aligned}P :_A Q = P : Q &= \textit{transporter of } Q \textit{ in } P \text{ (relative to } A)\\ &= \{a \in A : aq \in P \text{ for all } q \in Q\}.\end{aligned}$$

Note that

$$P : Q = 0 : ((P + Q)/P) = \operatorname{Anh}((P + Q)/P).$$

If $M = A$ then $P : Q$ coincides with its usual ideal theoretic meaning. Note that if A' is the integral closure of A in its total quotient ring then regarding A' as an A-module we have that

$$\mathfrak{c}(A) = A : A' = 0 : (A'/A) = \operatorname{Anh}(A'/A).$$

(40.4) *Tensor product.* Let A be a ring. For A-modules L, M, N, a map $\varphi : M \times N \to L$ is A-bilinear means: for each $m \in M, n \to \varphi(m, n)$ is an A-homomorphism of N into L, and for each $n \in N, m \to \varphi(m, n)$ is an A-homomorphism of M into L. The tensor product (over A) of A-modules M and N is an A-module $M \otimes_A N$ (or simply $M \otimes N$) together with an A-bilinear map $\mu : M \times N \to M \otimes_A N$ with the following two properties:

i) As an A-module, $M \otimes_A N$ is generated by elements of the form $m \otimes n$ with $m \in M, n \in N$ where $m \otimes n = \mu(m, n)$.

ii) Given any A-module L and any A-bilinear map $\varphi : M \times N \to L$, there exists a unique A-homomorphism $\psi : M \otimes_A N \to L$ such that $\varphi = \psi \circ \mu$.

Let $A \xrightarrow{\sigma} B \xrightarrow{\sigma'} B'$ be ring homomorphisms. Given σ-homomorphisms $\varphi : M \to M'$ and $\psi : N \to N'$, there exists a unique σ-homomorphism $\varphi \otimes \psi : M \otimes_A N \to M' \otimes_B N'$ such that $(\varphi \otimes \psi)(m \otimes n) = \varphi(m) \otimes \psi(n)$ for all $m \in M$, $n \in N$; $\varphi \otimes \psi$ is said to be induced by the pair (φ, ψ). If

$\varphi' : M' \to M''$ and $\psi' : N' \to N''$ are σ'-homomorphisms then $\varphi' \circ \varphi$ and $\psi' \circ \psi$ are $(\sigma' \circ \sigma)$-homomorphisms and we have $(\varphi' \otimes \psi') \circ (\varphi \otimes \psi) = (\varphi' \circ \varphi) \otimes (\psi' \circ \psi)$.

In particular, for A-homomorphisms $\varphi : M \to M'$ and $\psi : N \to N'$, $\varphi \otimes \psi : M \otimes_A N \to M' \otimes_A N'$ is an A-homomorphism. If i_M and i_N denote the identity maps of M and N, respectively, then $i_M \otimes i_N$ is the identity map of $M \otimes_A N$; the maps $\varphi \otimes i_N : M \otimes_A N \to M' \otimes_A N$ and $i_M \otimes \psi : M \otimes_A N \to M \otimes_A N'$ are said to be induced by φ and ψ, respectively. Thus $\otimes_A$ is a functor of two variables, covariant in both of them, from the category of A-modules into the category of A-modules. Note that if either $M = 0$ or $N = 0$ then $M \otimes_A N = 0$. If

$$M \to M' \to M'' \to 0, \qquad N \to N' \to N'' \to 0$$

are exact sequences of A-homomorphisms, then the induced sequences

$$M \otimes_A N \to M' \otimes_A N \to M'' \otimes_A N \to 0,$$
$$M \otimes_A N \to M \otimes_A N' \to M \otimes_A N'' \to 0$$

are exact; i.e., the functor $\otimes_A$ is right exact. For any A-modules M, M', N, N' there are natural A-isomorphisms

$$(M \oplus M') \otimes_A N \approx (M \otimes_A N) \oplus (M' \otimes_A N),$$
$$M \otimes_A (N \oplus N') \approx (M \otimes_A N) \oplus (M \otimes_A N').$$

For any A-module M, $A \otimes_A M$ (resp: $M \otimes_A A$) can be identified with M via the A-isomorphism $1 \otimes m \to m$ (resp: $m \otimes 1 \to m$). For any A-module M, $M \otimes_A B (\approx B \otimes_A M)$ can be made into a B-module by taking $(m \otimes b)b' = m \otimes (bb')$ for all $m \in M$ and $b, b' \in B$. For abelian groups M and N, $M \otimes N$ can be defined to be $M \otimes_{\mathbf{Z}} N$.

(40.5) *Preordered set.* A preordered set I is a set with a binary relation $i \leqq j$ which holds between certain pairs of elements in I and which is transitive: $i \leqq j$ and $j \leqq k \Rightarrow i \leqq k$, and reflexive : $i \leqq i$ for all i in I. A preordered set I is said to be ordered provided: $i \leqq j$ and $j \leqq i \Rightarrow i = j$. A preordered set I is said to be decreasing (resp: increasing) filtered provided: given i and j in I there exists k in I such that $k \leqq i$ and $k \leqq j$ (resp: $i \leqq k$ and $j \leqq k$). A subset I' of a preordered set I is said to be coinitial (resp: cofinal) with I provided: given i in I there exists i' in I' such that $i' \leqq i$ (resp: $i \leqq i'$).

(40.6) *Inductive system.* Let I be a preordered set. An inductive system $M = [M_i, \mu_i^j]$ of abelian groups (resp: rings, K-modules, K-algebras) *over* I consists of an abelian group (resp: ring, K-module, K-algebra) M_i

for each i in I, and a group (resp: ring, K-module, K-algebra) homomorphism $\mu_i^j : M_j \to M_i$ for all $i \leqq j$ in I, such that $\mu_i^j \circ \mu_j^k = \mu_i^k$ for all $i \leqq j \leqq k$ in I and μ_i^i = identity map of M_i for all i in I. Given another inductive system $N = [N_i, \nu_i^j]$ of abelian groups (resp: rings, K-modules, K-algebras) over I, a homomorphism $\varphi : M \to N$ consists of a group (resp: ring, K-module, K-algebra) homomorphism $\varphi_i : M_i \to N_i$ for each i in I, such that $\nu_i^j \circ \varphi_j = \varphi_i \circ \mu_i^j$ for all $i \leqq j$ in I; φ is said to be an inductive isomorphism provided φ_i is an isomorphism for all i in I. For homomorphisms $\varphi : M \to N$ and $\psi : N \to N'$ of inductive systems of abelian groups (resp: rings, K-modules, K-algebras) over I, the homomorphism $\psi \circ \varphi : M \to N'$ is defined by taking $(\psi \circ \varphi)_i = \psi_i \circ \varphi_i$ for all i in I. An inductive system $P = [P_i, \pi_i^j]$ of abelian groups (resp: rings, K-modules, K-algebras) over I is said to be a subsystem of M provided P_i is a subgroup (resp: subring, K-submodule, K-subalgebra) of M_i for all i in I, and $\pi_i^j(u) = \mu_i^j(u)$ for all $i \leqq j$ in I and $u \in P_j$ (thus we require that $\mu_i^j(P_j) \subset P_i$).

Let $A = [A_i, \alpha_i^j]$ be an inductive system of rings over I. An inductive A-module is an inductive system $M = [M_i, \mu_i^j]$ of abelian groups over I such that M_i is an A_i-module for all i in I and μ_i^j is an α_i^j-homomorphism for all $i \leqq j$ in I. An inductive system P of abelian groups over I which is a subsystem of M is said to be an inductive A-submodule of M provided P_i is an A_i-submodule of M_i for all i in I.

Let $\sigma : A \to B$ be a homomorphism of inductive systems of rings over I. For inductive A-module M and inductive B-module N, by an inductive σ-homomorphism $\varphi : M \to N$ we mean a homomorphism $\varphi : M \to N$ of inductive systems of abelian groups such that φ_i is a σ_i-homomorphism for all i in I; in particular, taking $A = B$ and σ = identity map of A (i.e., σ_i = identity map of A_i for all i in I) we get the notion of an inductive A-homomorphism $\varphi : M \to N$ of inductive A-modules M and N. Alternatively: an inductive A-homomorphism $\varphi : M \to N$ of inductive A-modules M and N is a homomorphism of inductive systems of abelian groups such that φ_i is an A_i-homomorphism for all i in I; given any inductive B-module $N = [N_i, \nu_i^j]$, $N_{[\sigma]} = [N_{i[\sigma_i]}, \nu_i^j]$ is an inductive A-module (when there is no confusion, we may write N instead of $N_{[\sigma]}$); for inductive A-module M and inductive B-module N, an inductive σ-homomorphism $\varphi : M \to N$ is an inductive A-homomorphism $\varphi : M \to N_{[\sigma]}$. In particular $B = B_{[\sigma]}$ can be considered to be an inductive A-module and then σ is an inductive σ-homomorphism.

For inductive systems $M = [M_i, \mu_i^j]$ and $N = [N_i, \nu_i^j]$ of abelian groups (resp: K-modules) over I we set $M \oplus N = [M_i \oplus N_i, *]$ where the maps $*$ are induced by μ_i^j and ν_i^j; $M \oplus N$ is then an inductive system of abelian groups (resp: K-modules) over I; in particular $M^p = M \oplus \ldots \oplus M$ is an inductive system of abelian groups (resp: K-modules) over I. For subsystems P and Q of M we set $P \mathring{+} Q = [P_i + Q_i, *]$ and $P \mathring{\cap} Q = [P_i \cap Q_i, *]$ where the maps $*$ are induced by μ_i^j; these are again subsystems of M. If A is an inductive system of rings over I and M and N are inductive A-modules then $M \oplus N$ (in particular M^p) becomes an inductive A-module; if P and Q are inductive A-submodules of M then $P \mathring{+} Q$ and $P \mathring{\cap} Q$ are inductive A-submodules of M.

Let $M = [M_i, \mu_i^j]$ be an inductive system of abelian groups (resp: K-modules) over I and let P be a subsystem of M. For each i in I let $\tau_i : M_i \to M_i/P_i$ be the natural epimorphism, and for each $i \leqq j$ in I let $\lambda_i^j : M_j/P_j \to M_i/P_i$ be the unique homomorphism such that $\lambda_i^j \circ \tau_j = \tau_i \circ \mu_i^j$. Then $[M_i/P_i, \lambda_i^j]$ is an inductive system of abelian groups (resp: K-modules) over I and $\tau : M \to [M_i/P_i, \lambda_i^j]$ is a homomorphism. The inductive system $[M_i/P_i, \lambda_i^j]$ is denoted by $M \mathring{/} P$ and $\tau : M \to M \mathring{/} P$ is called the natural homomorphism. If A is an inductive system of rings over I, M is an inductive A-module and P is an inductive A-submodule of M, then $M \mathring{/} P$ uniquely becomes an inductive A-module such that $\tau : M \to M \mathring{/} P$ is an inductive A-homomorphism. If furthermore $M = A$, then $M \mathring{/} P$ uniquely becomes an inductive system of rings over I such that τ is a homomorphism of inductive systems of rings.

For any homomorphism $\varphi : M \to N$ of inductive systems $M = [M_i, \mu_i^j]$ and $N = [N_i, \nu_i^j]$ of abelian groups (resp: K-modules) over I, we set $\mathring{\text{K}}\text{er}\ \varphi = [\text{Ker}\ \varphi_i, *]$, $\mathring{\text{I}}\text{m}\ \varphi = [\text{Im}\ \varphi_i, *]$, $\mathring{\text{C}}\text{oker}\ \varphi = [\text{Coker}\ \varphi_i, *]$, $\mathring{\text{C}}\text{oim}\ \varphi = [\text{Coim}\ \varphi_i, *]$ where the maps $*$ are induced by φ_i, μ_i^j, ν_i^j; all these are inductive systems of abelian groups (resp: K-modules) over I, in particular $\mathring{\text{K}}\text{er}\ \varphi$ and $\mathring{\text{I}}\text{m}\ \varphi$ are subsystems of M and N, respectively. A sequence $M \xrightarrow{\varphi} N \xrightarrow{\psi} N'$ of homomorphisms of inductive systems of abelian groups over I is said to be inductively exact provided $\mathring{\text{I}}\text{m}\ \varphi = \mathring{\text{K}}\text{er}\ \psi$; similarly for longer sequences. For instance for $\varphi : M \to N$ we have the exact sequence[1]

$$0 \to \mathring{\text{K}}\text{er}\ \varphi \to M \to N \to \mathring{\text{C}}\text{oker}\ \varphi \to 0.$$

If A is an inductive system of rings over I and $\varphi : M \to N$ is an inductive A-homomorphism, then $\mathring{\text{K}}\text{er}\ \varphi$, $\mathring{\text{I}}\text{m}\ \varphi$, $\mathring{\text{C}}\text{oker}\ \varphi$, $\mathring{\text{C}}\text{oim}\ \varphi$ are all inductive A-modules; in particular $\mathring{\text{K}}\text{er}\ \varphi$ and $\mathring{\text{I}}\text{m}\ \varphi$ are inductive A-submodules of M and N, respectively.

Let $A \xrightarrow{\sigma} B \xrightarrow{\sigma'} B'$ be homomorphisms of inductive systems of rings over I. The inductive tensor product $M \mathring{\otimes}_A N$ of inductive A-modules

[1] The inductive system $L = [L_i = 0$ for all i in I, $*]$ is denoted by 0.

$M = [M_i, \mu_i^j]$ and $N = [N_i, \nu_i^j]$ is defined to be the inductive A-module $[M_i \otimes_{A_i} N_i, \mu_i^j \otimes \nu_i^j]$. Given inductive σ-homomorphisms $\varphi : M \to M'$ and $\psi : N \to N'$ they induce the inductive σ-homomorphism $\varphi \mathring{\otimes} \psi : M \mathring{\otimes}_A N \to M' \mathring{\otimes}_B N'$ where $(\varphi \mathring{\otimes} \psi)_i = \varphi_i \otimes \psi_i$. If $\varphi' : M' \to M''$ and $\psi' : N' \to N''$ are inductive σ'-homomorphisms then $\varphi' \circ \varphi$ and $\psi' \circ \psi$ are inductive $(\sigma' \circ \sigma)$-homomorphisms and $(\varphi' \circ \varphi) \mathring{\otimes} (\psi' \circ \psi) = (\varphi' \mathring{\otimes} \psi') \circ (\varphi \mathring{\otimes} \psi)$.

(**40.7**) *Inductive limit.* Let I be a preordered decreasing filtered set. Let $M = [M_i, \mu_i^j]$ be an inductive system of abelian groups (resp: rings, K-modules, K-algebras) over I. Let $\tilde{M}$ be the disjoint union of the sets M_i as i ranges over I. Let M_∞ be the set of equivalence classes of $\tilde{M}$ under the equivalence relation: $u \in M_i$ and $v \in M_j$ are equivalent $\Leftrightarrow$ there exists k in I with $k \leqq i$ and $k \leqq j$ such that $\mu_k^i(u) = \mu_k^j(v)$. For any i in I define $\mu_i : M_i \to M_\infty$ by taking $\mu_i(u)$ = equivalence class containing u. Then

$$M_\infty = \bigcup_{i \in I} \mu_i(M_i) \quad \text{and} \quad \mu_i \circ \mu_i^j = \mu_j \quad \text{for all} \quad i \leqq j.$$

In a unique manner M_∞ becomes an abelian group (resp: ring, K-module, K-algebra) such that $\mu_i : M_i \to M_\infty$ is a homomorphism of groups (resp: rings, K-modules, K-algebras) for all i in I. M_∞ is called the inductive (or direct) limit of M over I and is variously denoted by:

$$\operatorname*{lim\,ind}_{i \in I} M_i, \qquad \operatorname{lim\,ind} M_i, \qquad \varinjlim_{i \in I} M_i, \qquad \varinjlim M_i.$$

If I' is any coinitial subset of I then

$$\operatorname*{lim\,ind}_{i \in I} M_i$$

can be identified with

$$\operatorname*{lim\,ind}_{i \in I'} M_i.$$

Note that if all the M_i are nonnull rings then so is M_∞.

A homomorphism $\varphi : M \to N$ of inductive systems $M = [M_i, \mu_i^j]$ and $N = [N_i, \nu_i^j]$ of abelian groups (resp: rings, K-modules, K-algebras) over I induces a unique homomorphism $\varphi_\infty : M_\infty \to N_\infty$ of groups (resp: rings, K-modules, K-algebras) such that $\varphi_\infty \circ \mu_i = \nu_i \circ \varphi_i$ for all i in I; φ_∞ is called the inductive limit of φ over I. If γ is the identity map of M then obviously γ_∞ is the identity map of M_∞. If $N \xrightarrow{\psi} L$ is another homomorphism of inductive systems of abelian groups (resp: rings, K-modules, K-algebras) over I then $(\psi \circ \varphi)_\infty = \psi_\infty \circ \varphi_\infty$. Thus lim ind is a covariant functor of one variable from the category of inductive systems of abelian groups (resp: rings, K-modules, K-algebras) over I into the category of abelian groups (resp: rings, K-modules, K-algebras). Furthermore, if $\mathring{\mathrm{I}}\mathrm{m}\,\varphi = \mathring{\mathrm{K}}\mathrm{er}\,\psi$ then $\mathrm{Im}\,\varphi_\infty = \mathrm{Ker}\,\psi_\infty$; this is expressed by saying that the functor lim ind is exact. For any inductive systems M and N of abelian groups over I, $(M \oplus N)_\infty$ can be identified with $M_\infty \oplus N_\infty$.

If A is an inductive system of rings over I and M is an inductive A-module then M_∞ becomes an A_∞-module. If $\varphi : M \to N$ is an inductive A-homomorphism then $\varphi_\infty : M_\infty \to N_\infty$ is an A_∞-homomorphism. More generally, if $\sigma : A \to B$ is a homomorphism of inductive systems of rings over I and $\varphi : M \to N$ is an inductive σ-homomorphism, then $(N_{[\sigma]})_\infty = (N_\infty)_{[\sigma_\infty]}$ is an A_∞-module and $\varphi_\infty : M_\infty \to N_\infty$ is a σ_∞-homomorphism.

Let $A \overset{\sigma}{\to} B$ be a homomorphism of inductive systems of rings over I and let $M = [M_i, \mu_i^j]$ and $N = [N_i, \nu_i^j]$ be inductive A-modules. Let $M \mathring{\otimes}_A N = L = [L_i = M_i \otimes_{A_i} N_i, \lambda_i^j = \mu_i^j \otimes \nu_i^j,]$. Let $\mu_i : M_i \to M_\infty$, $\nu_i : N_i \to N_\infty$, $\lambda_i : L_i \to L_\infty$ be the natural maps. Then there exists a unique A_∞-homomorphism $\tau : L_\infty \to M_\infty \otimes_{A_\infty} N_\infty$ such that $\tau(\lambda_i(m_i \otimes n_i)) = (\mu_i m_i) \otimes (\nu_i n_i)$ for all $i \in I$, $m_i \in M_i$, $n_i \in N_i$. Actually τ is an isomorphism and hence we can identify L_∞ with $M_\infty \otimes_{A_\infty} N_\infty$. If $\varphi : M \to M'$ and $\psi : N \to N'$ are inductive σ-homomorphisms then under this identification we have $(\varphi \mathring{\otimes} \psi)_\infty = \varphi_\infty \otimes \psi_\infty$.

Example. Let a be a point in a topological space X, let I be the set of all neighborhoods of a in X ordered by taking $\subset$ for $\leqq$, let $A_i = \mathfrak{E}(i; K)$ where K is assumed to be a complete nondiscrete valued field, and let $\alpha_i^j : \mathfrak{E}(j; K) \to \mathfrak{E}(i; K)$ be the restriction maps.[2] Then $A_\infty = \mathfrak{E}(a, X; K)$ and $\alpha_i = \Upsilon_a | A_i$. Identifying constant functions with elements of K, each A_i and hence A_∞ become K-algebras. If X is an analytic set in an open set in K^n then $R(a, X)$ is a K-subalgebra of A_∞.

(40.8) *Presheaf.* Let X be a topological space and let I be the set of all open subsets of X ordered by taking $\subset$ for $\leqq$.

A presheaf of abelian groups (resp: rings, K-modules, K-algebras) on X is an inductive system $\mathscr{M} = [\mathscr{M}(U), \mu_U^V]$, ($U$ and $U \subset V$ ranging over I), of abelian groups (resp: rings, K-modules, K-algebras) over I such that $\mathscr{M}(\emptyset) = 0$.[3]

[2] For notation see (29.3, 29.4).

[3] Because of the conditions $\mathscr{M}(\emptyset) = 0$, in giving a presheaf $\mathscr{M}$ it suffices to prescribe $\mathscr{M}(U)$ and μ_U^V only for nonempty open subsets U, V of X. Some authors do not require a presheaf to satisfy this condition. Another alternative is not to define $\mathscr{M}(\emptyset)$ at all, i.e., to consider a presheaf to be an inductive system over the set of all nonempty open subsets of X. Taking $\mathscr{M}(U) = 0$ for all U in I we get a presheaf on X; this presheaf is called the zero presheaf and is denoted by 0.

The maps $\mu_U^V : \mathscr{M}(V) \to \mathscr{M}(U)$ are called the restriction maps belonging to $\mathscr{M}$. Elements in $\mathscr{M}(U)$ are called sections of $\mathscr{M}$ on U. Elements in $\mathscr{M}(X)$ are called global sections of $\mathscr{M}$. For $U \subset V$ in I and $F \subset \mathscr{M}(V)$ we may write $F|U$ instead of $\mu_U^V F$. For U, V, W in I with $U \subset V \cap W$ and $F \subset \mathscr{M}(V)$, $G \subset \mathscr{M}(W)$, we may write "$F = G$ on U" to mean "$F|U = G|U$". For U, $V_1, \ldots, V_m$, $W_1, \ldots, W_n$ in I with $U \subset V_i$, $U \subset W_j$ for all i, j, and $f_i \in \mathscr{M}(V_i)$, $g_j \in \mathscr{M}(W_j)$, we may denote $f_1|U + \ldots + f_m|U$ by writing something like "$f_1 + \ldots + f_m \in \mathscr{M}(U)$", and we may write "$f_1 + \ldots + f_m = g_1 + \ldots + g_n$ on U" to mean "$(f_1|U) + \ldots + (f_m|U) = (g_1|U) + \ldots + (g_n|U)$"; similarly for sums of products in case $\mathscr{M}$ is a presheaf of rings. For any $a \in X$ we set

$$\mathscr{M}_a = \textit{stalk of } \mathscr{M} \textit{ at } a = \operatorname*{lim\,ind}_{a \in U} \mathscr{M}(U)$$

where the inductive limit is taken over the set of all neighborhoods U of a in X. For each neighborhood U of a in X we then have a group (resp: ring, K-module, K-algebra) homomorphism $\mu_{a,U} : \mathscr{M}(U) \to \mathscr{M}_a$, ($\mu_{a,U}$ is again said to belong to $\mathscr{M}$), such that $\mu_{a,U} \circ \mu_U^V = \mu_{a,V}$ for any neighborhoods $U \subset V$ of $a \in X$. For a neighborhood U of a in X and $f \in \mathscr{M}(U)$, the element $\mu_{a,U} f$ in $\mathscr{M}_a$ (i.e., the germ $\gamma_a f$ of f in X at a) will usually be denoted by f_a; similarly for $F \subset \mathscr{M}(U)$, the subset $\mu_{a,U} F$ of $\mathscr{M}_a$ will usually be denoted by F_a. For neighborhoods U, V of a in X and $F \subset \mathscr{M}(U)$, $G \subset \mathscr{M}(V)$, we may write "$F = G$ about a" to mean "$F_a = G_a$". For neighborhoods $V_1, \ldots, V_m$, $W_1, \ldots, W_n$ of a in X and $f_i \in \mathscr{M}(V_i)$, $g_j \in \mathscr{M}(W_j)$ we may write "$f_1 + \ldots + f_m = g_1 + \ldots + g_n$ about a" to mean "$(f_1)_a + \ldots + (f_m)_a = (g_1)_a + \ldots + (g_n)_a$"; similarly for sums of products in case $\mathscr{M}$ is a presheaf of rings. A presheaf $\mathscr{P}$ of abelian groups (resp: rings, K-modules, K-algebras) on X is said to be a subpresheaf of $\mathscr{M}$ provided $\mathscr{P}$ is a subsystem of the inductive system $\mathscr{M}$ over I.

A homomorphism $\varphi : \mathscr{M} \to \mathscr{N}$ of presheaves $\mathscr{M}$ and $\mathscr{N}$ of abelian groups (resp: rings, K-modules, K-algebras) on X is by definition a homomorphism of inductive systems over I. For any U in I the corresponding homomorphism $\mathscr{M}(U) \to \mathscr{N}(U)$ is denoted by $\varphi(U)$; for $F \subset \mathscr{M}(U)$ we may write $\varphi(F)$ instead of $\varphi(U)F$. For any $a \in X$ the homomorphism $\mathscr{M}_a \to \mathscr{N}_a$ induced by φ is denoted by φ_a. $\varphi : \mathscr{M} \to \mathscr{N}$ is a presheaf-isomorphism means that $\varphi(U) : \mathscr{M}(U) \to \mathscr{N}(U)$ is an isomorphism for all U in I. For any subpresheaf $\mathscr{P}$ of $\mathscr{M}$, the canonical injection of $\mathscr{P}$ into $\mathscr{M}$ is the homomorphism $i : \mathscr{P} \to \mathscr{M}$ defined by taking $i(U)$ to be the canonical injection of $\mathscr{P}(U)$ into $\mathscr{M}(U)$ for all U in I. In particular, the canonical injection of $\mathscr{M}$ into $\mathscr{M}$ is called the identity map of $\mathscr{M}$.

Let $\mathscr{A}$ be a presheaf of rings on X. A presheaf $\mathscr{M}$ of abelian groups on X is said to be an $\mathscr{A}$-presheaf-module provided $\mathscr{M}$ is an inductive

$\mathscr{A}$-module; then $\mathscr{M}_a$ is an $\mathscr{A}_a$-module for any $a \in X$. For U, V_i, V'_i, W_j, W'_j in I with $U \subset V_i$, $U \subset V'_i$, $U \subset W_j$, $U \subset W'_j$, and $f_i \in \mathscr{M}(V_i)$, $g_j \in \mathscr{M}(W_j)$, $r_i \in \mathscr{A}(V'_i)$, $s_j \in \mathscr{A}(W'_j)$, $(i = 1,..., m; j = 1,..., n)$, we may denote $(r_1|U)(f_1|U) + ... + (r_m|U)(f_m|U)$ by writing something like "$r_1 f_1 + ... + r_m f_m \in \mathscr{M}(U)$", and we may write "$r_1 f_1 + ... + r_m f_m = s_1 g_1 + ... + s_n g_n$ on U" to mean "$(r_1|U)(f_1|U) + ... + (r_m|U)(f_m|U) = (s_1|U)(g_1|U) + ... + (s_n|U)(g_n|U)$"; also for $a \in U$ we may write "$r_1 f_1 + ... + r_m f_m = s_1 g_1 + ... + s_n g_n$ about a" to mean "$(r_1)_a(f_1)_a + ... + (r_m)_a(f_m)_a = (s_1)_a(g_1)_a + ... + (s_n)_a(g_n)_a$". A subpresheaf $\mathscr{P}$ of $\mathscr{M}$ is said to be an $\mathscr{A}$-presheaf-submodule of $\mathscr{M}$ provided $\mathscr{P}$ is an inductive $\mathscr{A}$-submodule of $\mathscr{M}$.

Let $\sigma : \mathscr{A} \to \mathscr{B}$ be a homomorphism of presheaves of rings on X. A σ-presheaf-homomorphism $\varphi : \mathscr{M} \to \mathscr{N}$ of an $\mathscr{A}$-presheaf-module $\mathscr{M}$ into a $\mathscr{B}$-presheaf-module $\mathscr{N}$ is by definition simply an inductive σ-homomorphism; then $\varphi_a : \mathscr{M}_a \to \mathscr{N}_a$ is a σ_a-homomorphism for any $a \in X$. Taking $\sigma =$ identity map of $\mathscr{A}$, we get the notion of an $\mathscr{A}$-presheaf-homomorphism $\varphi : \mathscr{M} \to \mathscr{N}$ of an $\mathscr{A}$-presheaf-module $\mathscr{M}$ into an $\mathscr{A}$-presheaf-module $\mathscr{N}$; then $\varphi_a : \mathscr{M}_a \to \mathscr{N}_a$ is an $\mathscr{A}_a$-homomorphism for any $a \in X$. Alternatively: for $\mathscr{A}$-presheaf-modules $\mathscr{M}$ and $\mathscr{N}$, an $\mathscr{A}$-presheaf-homomorphism $\varphi : \mathscr{M} \to \mathscr{N}$ is defined to be an inductive $\mathscr{A}$-homomorphism; given any $\mathscr{B}$-presheaf-module $\mathscr{N}$, $\mathscr{N}_{[\sigma]} = \mathscr{N}$ is an $\mathscr{A}$-presheaf-module and for any $\mathscr{A}$-presheaf-module $\mathscr{M}$ a σ-presheaf-homomorphism $\varphi : \mathscr{M} \to \mathscr{N}$ is simply an $\mathscr{A}$-presheaf-homomorphism $\varphi : \mathscr{M} \to \mathscr{N}_{[\sigma]}$; note that then $\mathscr{N}_a = (\mathscr{N}_a)_{[\sigma_a]} = (\mathscr{N}_{[\sigma]})_a$ is an $\mathscr{A}_a$-module for any $a \in X$. The presheaf of rings $\mathscr{B}$ when considered also as an $\mathscr{A}$-presheaf-module (i.e., $\mathscr{B}_{[\sigma]}$) is called an $\mathscr{A}$-presheaf-algebra. Given another $\mathscr{A}$-presheaf-algebra $\sigma' : \mathscr{A} \to \mathscr{B}'$, an $\mathscr{A}$-presheaf-algebra-homomorphism $\mathscr{B} \to \mathscr{B}'$ is by definition a homomorphism of presheaves of rings which is also an $\mathscr{A}$-presheaf-homomorphism.

Let $\mathscr{A} \xrightarrow{\sigma} \mathscr{B} \xrightarrow{\sigma'} \mathscr{B}'$ be homomorphisms of presheaves of rings on X. For any $\mathscr{A}$-presheaf-modules $\mathscr{M}$ and $\mathscr{N}$, $\mathscr{M} \mathring{\otimes}_{\mathscr{A}} \mathscr{N}$ (or simply $\mathscr{M} \mathring{\otimes} \mathscr{N}$) is again an $\mathscr{A}$-presheaf-module, and for any $a \in X$ we identify $(\mathscr{M} \mathring{\otimes}_{\mathscr{A}} \mathscr{N})_a$ with $\mathscr{M}_a \otimes_{\mathscr{A}_a} \mathscr{N}_a$; note that under this identification, for any neighborhood U of a in X and $f, g \in \mathscr{M}(U)$, $r, s \in \mathscr{A}(U)$ we have $(rf \otimes sg)_a = r_a f_a \otimes s_a g_a$. For any σ-presheaf-homomorphisms $\varphi : \mathscr{M} \to \mathscr{M}'$ and $\psi : \mathscr{N} \to \mathscr{N}'$, $\varphi \mathring{\otimes} \psi : \mathscr{M} \mathring{\otimes}_{\mathscr{A}} \mathscr{N} \to \mathscr{M}' \mathring{\otimes}_{\mathscr{B}} \mathscr{N}'$ is again a σ-presheaf-homomorphism, and $(\varphi \mathring{\otimes} \psi)_a = \varphi_a \otimes \psi_a$ for all $a \in X$. If $\varphi' : \mathscr{M}' \to \mathscr{M}''$ and $\psi' : \mathscr{N}' \to \mathscr{N}''$ are σ'-presheaf-homomorphisms then $\varphi' \circ \varphi$ and $\psi' \circ \psi$ are $(\sigma' \circ \sigma)$-presheaf-homomorphisms and $(\varphi' \circ \varphi) \mathring{\otimes} (\psi' \circ \psi) = (\varphi' \mathring{\otimes} \psi') \circ (\varphi \mathring{\otimes} \psi)$. If $i_{\mathscr{M}}$ and $i_{\mathscr{N}}$ are the identity maps of $\mathscr{A}$-presheaf-modules $\mathscr{M}$ and $\mathscr{N}$, respectively, then $i_{\mathscr{M}} \mathring{\otimes} i_{\mathscr{N}}$ is the identity map of $\mathscr{M} \mathring{\otimes}_{\mathscr{A}} \mathscr{N}$. Thus $\mathring{\otimes}_{\mathscr{A}}$ is a covariant functor of two variables from the category of $\mathscr{A}$-presheaf-modules into the category of $\mathscr{A}$-presheaf-modules. For any $\mathscr{A}$-presheaf-module $\mathscr{M}$ and for any U in I, $(\mathscr{M} \mathring{\otimes}_{\mathscr{A}} \mathscr{B})(U) = \mathscr{M}(U) \otimes_{\mathscr{A}(U)} \mathscr{B}(U)$ can be regarded as a $\mathscr{B}(U)$-module, and hence $\mathscr{M} \mathring{\otimes}_{\mathscr{A}} \mathscr{B}$ can be regarded as a $\mathscr{B}$-presheaf-module.

(40.9) *Presheaf-exact sequence.* Let $\mathscr{A}$ be a presheaf of rings on a topological space X. For presheaves $\mathscr{M}$ and $\mathscr{N}$ of abelian groups (resp: K-modules) on X, $\mathscr{M} \oplus \mathscr{N}$ and $\mathscr{M}^p$ (for any positive integer p) are again presheaves of abelian groups (resp: K-modules) on X, and for any $a \in X$ we identify $(\mathscr{M} \oplus \mathscr{N})_a$ and $(\mathscr{M}^p)_a$ with $\mathscr{M}_a \oplus \mathscr{N}_a$ and $(\mathscr{M}_a)^p$, respectively; if $\mathscr{M}$ and $\mathscr{N}$ are $\mathscr{A}$-presheaf-modules then so are $\mathscr{M} \oplus \mathscr{N}$ and $\mathscr{M}^p$ (and hence in particular $\mathscr{A}^p$). If $\mathscr{M}$ is a presheaf of abelian groups (resp: K-modules) on X and $\mathscr{P}$ and $\mathscr{Q}$ are subpresheaves of $\mathscr{M}$ then $\mathscr{P} \mathring{+} \mathscr{Q}$ and $\mathscr{P} \mathring{\cap} \mathscr{Q}$ are subpresheaves of $\mathscr{M}$; if $\mathscr{M}$ is an $\mathscr{A}$-presheaf-module and $\mathscr{P}$ and $\mathscr{Q}$ are $\mathscr{A}$-presheaf-submodules of $\mathscr{M}$ then so are $\mathscr{P} \mathring{+} \mathscr{Q}$ and $\mathscr{P} \mathring{\cap} \mathscr{Q}$. For any subpresheaf $\mathscr{P}$ of a presheaf $\mathscr{M}$ of abelian groups (resp: K-modules) on X, $\mathscr{M} \mathring{/} \mathscr{P}$ is a presheaf of abelian groups (resp: K-modules) on X and the natural homomorphism $\tau : \mathscr{M} \to \mathscr{M} \mathring{/} \mathscr{P}$ of presheaves is defined to be the natural homomorphism of inductive systems; if $\mathscr{M}$ is an $\mathscr{A}$-presheaf-module and $\mathscr{P}$ is an $\mathscr{A}$-presheaf submodule of $\mathscr{M}$ then $\mathscr{M} \mathring{/} \mathscr{P}$ is an $\mathscr{A}$-presheaf-module and τ is an $\mathscr{A}$-presheaf-homomorphism, in particular if $\mathscr{M} = \mathscr{A}$ then $\mathscr{M} \mathring{/} \mathscr{P}$ is also a presheaf of rings on X and τ is a homomorphism of presheaves of rings on X. For any homomorphism $\varphi : \mathscr{M} \to \mathscr{N}$ of presheaves of abelian groups (resp: K-modules) on X, $\mathring{\text{Ker}}\, \varphi$, $\mathring{\text{Im}}\, \varphi$, $\mathring{\text{Coker}}\, \varphi$, $\mathring{\text{Coim}}\, \varphi$ are again presheaves of abelian groups (resp: K-modules) on X, in particular $\mathring{\text{Ker}}\, \varphi$ and $\mathring{\text{Im}}\, \varphi$ are subpresheaves of $\mathscr{M}$ and $\mathscr{N}$, respectively; if $\mathscr{M}$ and $\mathscr{N}$ are $\mathscr{A}$-presheaf-modules and φ is an $\mathscr{A}$-presheaf-homomorphism then $\mathring{\text{Ker}}\, \varphi$, $\mathring{\text{Im}}\, \varphi$, $\mathring{\text{Coker}}\, \varphi$, $\mathring{\text{Coim}}\, \varphi$, are $\mathscr{A}$-presheaf-modules, and in particular $\mathring{\text{Ker}}\, \varphi$ and $\mathring{\text{Im}}\, \varphi$ are $\mathscr{A}$-presheaf-submodules of $\mathscr{M}$ and $\mathscr{N}$, respectively. It is obvious that a homomorphism $\varphi : \mathscr{M} \to \mathscr{N}$ of presheaves is a presheaf-isomorphism $\Leftrightarrow$ $\mathring{\text{Im}}\, \varphi = \mathscr{N}$ and $\mathring{\text{Ker}}\, \varphi = 0$.

A sequence $\mathscr{M} \xrightarrow{\varphi} \mathscr{N} \xrightarrow{\psi} \mathscr{L}$ of homomorphisms of presheaves of abelian groups on X is said to be presheaf-exact provided $\mathring{\text{Im}}\, \varphi = \mathring{\text{Ker}}\, \varphi$, i.e., provided it is inductively exact; note that the induced sequence $\mathscr{M}_a \to \mathscr{N}_a \to \mathscr{L}_a$ is then exact for all $a \in X$ (but not conversely); similarly for longer sequences. In particular if $\mathring{\text{Ker}}\, \varphi = 0$ (resp: $\mathring{\text{Im}}\, \varphi = \mathscr{N}$) then $\text{Ker}\, \varphi_a = 0$ (resp: $\text{Im}\, \varphi_a = \mathscr{N}_a$) for all $a \in X$.

Let $\mathscr{P}$ be a subpresheaf of a presheaf $\mathscr{M}$ of abelian groups (resp: rings, K-modules, K-algebras) on X. Then

$$0 \to \mathscr{P} \xrightarrow{i} \mathscr{M} \xrightarrow{\tau} \mathscr{M} \mathring{/} \mathscr{P} \to 0$$

is presheaf-exact, where i is the canonical injection and τ is the natural homomorphism. Therefore, for any $a \in X$ the induced sequence

$$0 \to \mathscr{P}_a \to \mathscr{M}_a \to (\mathscr{M} \mathring{/} \mathscr{P})_a \to 0$$

is exact. Consequently we may identify $\mathscr{P}_a$ with the subgroup (resp: subring, K-submodule, K-subalgebra) $i_a(\mathscr{P}_a)$ of $\mathscr{M}_a$, and then we may identify $(\mathscr{M} \mathring{/} \mathscr{P})_a$ with $\mathscr{M}_a/\mathscr{P}_a$. As a rule we shall tacitly make the first identification; note that then $\mathscr{P}_a$ is the union of $\mu_{a,U}(\mathscr{P}(U))$ taken over all neighborhoods U of a in X where $\mu_{a,U} : \mathscr{M}(U) \to \mathscr{M}_a$ is the homomorphism belonging to $\mathscr{M}$. Furthermore, by this identification, for any homomorphism $\varphi : \mathscr{M} \to \mathscr{N}$ of presheaves of abelian groups on X we have $(\mathring{\mathrm{K}}\mathrm{er}\,\varphi)_a = \mathrm{Ker}\,\varphi_a$ and $(\mathring{\mathrm{I}}\mathrm{m}\,\varphi)_a = \mathrm{Im}\,\varphi_a$ for all $a \in X$, and for any subpresheaves $\mathscr{P}$ and $\mathscr{Q}$ of $\mathscr{M}$ we have $(\mathscr{P} \mathring{+} \mathscr{Q})_a = \mathscr{P}_a + \mathscr{Q}_a$ and $(\mathscr{P} \mathring{\cap} \mathscr{Q})_a = \mathscr{P}_a \cap \mathscr{Q}_a$ for all $a \in X$.

(40.10) *Restriction to an open set.* Let U be an open set in a topological space X. Given any presheaf $\mathscr{M}$ on X we get a presheaf $\mathscr{M}'$ on U by taking $\mathscr{M}'(U') = \mathscr{M}(U')$ for any open set U' in U and by taking the restriction map $\mathscr{M}'(V') \to \mathscr{M}'(U')$ belonging to $\mathscr{M}'$ to be the restriction map $\mathscr{M}(V') \to \mathscr{M}(U')$ belonging to $\mathscr{M}$ for all open sets $U' \subset V'$ in U; $\mathscr{M}'$ is called the restriction of $\mathscr{M}$ to U and is denoted by $\mathscr{M}|U$. Given any homomorphism $\varphi : \mathscr{M} \to \mathscr{N}$ of presheaves on X, we get a homomorphism $\varphi' : \mathscr{M}|U \to \mathscr{N}|U$ of presheaves on U by taking $\varphi'(U') = \varphi(U')$ for each open set U' in U; φ' is called the restriction of φ to U and is denoted by $\varphi|U$; note if V is any open set in X with $U \subset V$ then $(\mathscr{M}|V)|U = \mathscr{M}|U$ and $(\varphi|V)|U = \varphi|U$. Given any homomorphism $\varphi : \mathscr{M} \to \mathscr{N}$ of presheaves on X and given any subpresheaf $\mathscr{P}$ of $\mathscr{M}|U$, we get a homomorphism $\psi : \mathscr{P} \to \mathscr{N}|U$ of presheaves on U by taking $\psi(U') = \varphi(U')|\mathscr{P}(U') : \mathscr{P}(U') \to \mathscr{N}(U')$ for each open set U' in U; ψ' is called the restriction of φ to $\mathscr{P}$ and is denoted by $\varphi|\mathscr{P}$; note that $\varphi|(\mathscr{M}|U) = \varphi|U$. If $\sigma : \mathscr{A} \to \mathscr{B}$ is a homomorphism of presheaves of rings on X and $\varphi : \mathscr{M} \to \mathscr{N}$ is a σ-presheaf-homomorphism then $\mathscr{M}|U$ is an $\mathscr{A}|U$-presheaf-module, $\mathscr{N}|U$ is a $\mathscr{B}|U$-presheaf-module, and $\varphi|U : \mathscr{M}|U \to \mathscr{N}|U$ is a $\sigma|U$-presheaf-module; etc. If $i : \mathscr{M} \to \mathscr{M}$ is the identity map of a presheaf $\mathscr{M}$ on X and $\mathscr{P}$ is any subpresheaf of $\mathscr{M}$ then $i|\mathscr{P} : \mathscr{P} \to \mathscr{M}$ is obviously the canonical injection of $\mathscr{P}$ into $\mathscr{M}$.

(40.11) *Support.* The support of any presheaf $\mathscr{M}$ of abelian groups on a topological space X is defined by

$$\mathrm{Supp}\,\mathscr{M} = \{a \in X : \mathscr{M}_a \neq 0\}.$$

More generally, for any open set U in X and any $F \subset \mathscr{M}(U)$, the support of F is defined by

$$\operatorname{Supp} F = \{a \in U : F_a \neq 0, \text{ i.e., } f_a \neq 0 \text{ for some } f \in F\}.$$

For $f \in \mathscr{M}(U)$ and $a \in U$, if $f_a = 0$ then obviously $f_b = 0$ for all b in some neighborhood of a in U; thus $U - \operatorname{Supp} f$ is open in U, i.e., $\operatorname{Supp} f$ is closed in U. Also obviously $\operatorname{Supp} F = \bigcup_{f \in F} \operatorname{Supp} \{f\}$, and hence we get the following.

1) Let $\mathscr{M}$ be a presheaf of abelian groups on X, let U be an open set in X and let $F \subset \mathscr{M}(U)$. If F is a finite set then $\operatorname{Supp} F$ is a closed subset of U.

Let $\mathscr{A}$ be a presheaf of rings on X, let $\mathscr{M}$ be an $\mathscr{A}$-presheaf-module and let F be a set of sections of $\mathscr{M}$ on an open set U in X such that $\mathscr{M}_b = F_b\mathscr{A}_b$ for all $b \in U$. Then obviously $\operatorname{Supp} F = \operatorname{Supp} (\mathscr{M}|U) = U \cap \operatorname{Supp} \mathscr{M}$. Hence by 1) we get

2) Let $\mathscr{A}$ be a presheaf of rings on X and let $\mathscr{M}$ be an $\mathscr{A}$-presheaf-module. Assume that for each $a \in X$ there exists a finite set F of sections of $\mathscr{M}$ on a neighborhood U of a in X such that $\mathscr{M}_b = F_b\mathscr{A}_b$ for all $b \in U$. Then $\operatorname{Supp} \mathscr{M}$ is a closed subset of X.

§41. SHEAVES

Let X be a topological space.

(41.1) *Sheaf.* A presheaf $\mathscr{M}$ (of abelian groups or rings or K-modules or K-algebras) on X is said to be a sheaf provided $\mathscr{M}$ satisfies the following two conditions for each open set U in X.

(S_1) If $(U_j)_{j \in J}$ is any open covering of U and f and g are any two elements in $\mathscr{M}(U)$ such that $f = g$ on U_j for all $j \in J$, then $f = g$ (on U).[1]

(S_2) Given any open covering $(U_j)_{j \in J}$ of U and given any $f_j \in \mathscr{M}(U_j)$ for each $j \in J$ such that $f_j = f_k$ on $U_j \cap U_k$ for all $j, k \in J$, there exists $f \in \mathscr{M}(U)$ such that $f = f_j$ on U_j for all j in J.

Note that condition S_1 is equivalent to each of the following two conditions.

[1] $(U_j)_{j \in J}$ is an open covering of U means that each U_j is an open subset of U and $\bigcup_{j \in J} U_j = U$.

(S_1') For any $f, g \in \mathcal{M}(U)$ we have: $f = g \Leftrightarrow f_a = g_a$ for all $a \in U$.
(S_1'') For any $f \in \mathcal{M}(U)$ we have: $f = 0 \Leftrightarrow f_a = 0$ for all $a \in U$.[2]

For any sheaf $\mathcal{M}$ on X and any open set U in X, $\mathcal{M}(U)$ is sometimes denoted by $\Gamma(U, \mathcal{M})$. For any sheaf $\mathcal{M}$ on X and any open set U in X, $\mathcal{M}|U$ is obviously a sheaf on U. A subpresheaf $\mathcal{P}$ of a sheaf $\mathcal{M}$ on X is said to be a subsheaf of $\mathcal{M}$ provided $\mathcal{P}$ is also a sheaf. Note that for a subpresheaf $\mathcal{P}$ of a sheaf $\mathcal{M}$ on X the following four conditions are equivalent.

i) $\mathcal{P}$ is a sheaf.
ii) $\mathcal{P}$ satisfies condition S_2 for each open set U in X.
iii) For each open covering $(U_j)_{j \in J}$ of each open set U in X we have

$$\mathcal{P}(U) = \{f \in \mathcal{M}(U) : f|U_j \in \mathcal{P}(U_j) \text{ for all } j \in J\}.$$

iv) For each open set U in X we have

$$\mathcal{P}(U) = \{f \in \mathcal{M}(U) : f_a \in \mathcal{P}_a \text{ for all } a \in U\}.$$

Also note that if $\mathcal{P}$ and $\mathcal{Q}$ are any subsheaves of a sheaf $\mathcal{M}$ on X then: $\mathcal{P} = \mathcal{Q} \Leftrightarrow \mathcal{P}_a = \mathcal{Q}_a$ for all $a \in X$. For any sheaves $\mathcal{M}$ and $\mathcal{N}$ (of abelian groups or rings or K-modules or K-algebras) on X, by definition a homomorphism $\varphi : \mathcal{M} \to \mathcal{N}$ is simply a homomorphism of presheaves.

Let $\sigma : \mathcal{A} \to \mathcal{B}$ be a homomorphism of sheaves of rings on X. An $\mathcal{A}$-presheaf-module $\mathcal{M}$ is called an $\mathcal{A}$-module provided $\mathcal{M}$ is a sheaf, and then an $\mathcal{A}$-presheaf-submodule $\mathcal{P}$ of $\mathcal{M}$ is called an $\mathcal{A}$-submodule of $\mathcal{M}$ provided $\mathcal{P}$ is also a sheaf. For $\mathcal{A}$-modules $\mathcal{M}$ and $\mathcal{N}$, an $\mathcal{A}$-homomorphism $\mathcal{M} \to \mathcal{N}$ is by definition simply an $\mathcal{A}$-presheaf-homomorphism. An $\mathcal{A}$-submodule of $\mathcal{A}$ is called an $\mathcal{A}$-ideal or an ideal in $\mathcal{A}$. For any $\mathcal{B}$-module $\mathcal{N}$, $\mathcal{N}_{[\sigma]} = \mathcal{N}$ is an $\mathcal{A}$-module. For an $\mathcal{A}$-module $\mathcal{M}$ and a $\mathcal{B}$-module $\mathcal{N}$, a σ-homomorphism $\mathcal{M} \to \mathcal{N}$ is by definition simply a σ-presheaf-homomorphism, i.e., an $\mathcal{A}$-homomorphism $\mathcal{M} \to \mathcal{N}_{[\sigma]}$. The sheaf of rings $\mathcal{B}$ when regarded also as an $\mathcal{A}$-module (i.e., $\mathcal{B}_{[\sigma]}$) is called an $\mathcal{A}$-algebra; σ is called the underlying homomorphism of the algebra; we may express this by saying something like "let $\sigma : \mathcal{A} \to \mathcal{B}$ be an $\mathcal{A}$-algebra". An $\mathcal{A}$-subalgebra of $\mathcal{B}$ is by definition a subsheaf of $\mathcal{B}$ (as a sheaf of rings) which is also an $\mathcal{A}$-submodule of $\mathcal{B}$.

[2] The said equivalence holds without assuming the condition $\mathcal{M}(\emptyset) = 0$ which we have required of every presheaf. This condition actually follows from S_1'' for $U = \emptyset$. Because of this condition, in S_2 it suffices to require $f_j = f_k$ on $U_j \cap U_k$ only for those $j, k \in J$ for which $U_j \cap U_k \neq \emptyset$. Note that if S_1'' is satisfied for each open set U in X, then $\mathcal{M} = 0 \Leftrightarrow \mathcal{M}_a = 0$ for all $a \in X$. Also note that the zero presheaf is obviously a sheaf.

Given another $\mathscr{A}$-algebra $\sigma' : \mathscr{A} \to \mathscr{B}'$, an $\mathscr{A}$-algebra-homomorphism $\mathscr{B} \to \mathscr{B}'$ is by definition a homomorphism of sheaves of rings which is also an $\mathscr{A}$-homomorphism. Given any sheaf $\mathscr{A}'$ of rings on X such that $\mathscr{A}$ is a subsheaf (as a sheaf of rings) of $\mathscr{A}'$, $\mathscr{A}'$ is to be regarded as an $\mathscr{A}$-algebra with the canonical injection $\mathscr{A} \to \mathscr{A}'$ as the underlying homomorphism. For any sheaves $\mathscr{M}$ and $\mathscr{N}$ of abelian groups (resp: K-modules) on X, the presheaves $\mathscr{M} \oplus \mathscr{N}$ and $\mathscr{M}^p$ are again sheaves; if $\mathscr{M}$ and $\mathscr{N}$ are $\mathscr{A}$-modules then $\mathscr{M} \oplus \mathscr{N}$ and $\mathscr{M}^p$ (in particular $\mathscr{A}^p$) are $\mathscr{A}$-modules.

Let $\mathscr{A}$ be a sheaf of rings on X and let $\mathscr{M}$ be an $\mathscr{A}$-module. For any open sets $U \subset V$ in X and any $F \subset \mathscr{M}(V)$ we get an $\mathscr{A}|U$-submodule $\mathscr{P}$ of $\mathscr{M}|U$ by taking

$$\mathscr{P}(U') = \{f \in \mathscr{M}(U') : f_a \in F_a\mathscr{A}_a \text{ for all } a \in U'\}$$

for each open set U' in U; $\mathscr{P}$ is called the $\mathscr{A}|U$-submodule of $\mathscr{M}|U$ generated by F and is denoted by $(F|U)(\mathscr{A}|U)$ or $F(\mathscr{A}|U)$ or $(F|U)\mathscr{A}$; note that for any $a \in U$ we have $((F|U)\mathscr{A})_a = F_a\mathscr{A}_a$ and for any open set U^* in U we have $((F|U)\mathscr{A})|U^* = (F|U^*)\mathscr{A}$. Given any open sets U, V, W in X with $U \subset V \cap W$, $F \subset \mathscr{M}(V)$, and an $\mathscr{A}|W$-submodule $\mathscr{P}$ of $\mathscr{M}|W$, we shall say that "F generates $\mathscr{P}$ on U" to mean "$\mathscr{P}|U = (F|U)\mathscr{A}$", i.e., to mean "$\mathscr{P}_a = F_a\mathscr{A}_a$ for all $a \in U$"; also for $a \in U$, we shall say that "F generates $\mathscr{P}$ at a" or "F generates $\mathscr{P}_a$" to mean "$\mathscr{P}_a = F_a\mathscr{A}_a$".

Let $\mathscr{A}$ be a sheaf of rings on X, let $\sigma : \mathscr{A} \to \mathscr{B}$ be an $\mathscr{A}$-algebra, let $U \subset V$ be open sets in X, and let $F \subset \mathscr{B}(V)$. Then we get an $\mathscr{A}|U$-subalgebra $\mathscr{P}$ of $\mathscr{B}|U$ by taking

$$\mathscr{P}(U') = \{f \in \mathscr{B}(U') : f_a \in \mathscr{A}_a[F_a] \text{ for all } a \in U'\}$$

for each open set U' in U; we shall denote $\mathscr{P}$ by $(\mathscr{A}|U)[F|U]$ or $(\mathscr{A}|U)[F]$ or $\mathscr{A}[F|U]$. Note that for any $a \in U$ we have $(\mathscr{A}[F|U])_a = \mathscr{A}_a[F_a]$ and for any open set U^* in U we have $(\mathscr{A}[F|U])|U^* = \mathscr{A}[F|U^*]$.

(41.2) *Sheaf of germs.*[3] Let X^* be any topological group (resp: topological ring). We get a sheaf $\mathscr{E}_{X;X^*}$ of abelian groups (resp: rings) on X by taking $\mathscr{E}_{X;X^*}(U) = \mathfrak{E}(U; X^*)$ for each nonempty open set U in X and by taking the ordinary restriction maps as the restriction maps belonging to $\mathscr{E}_{X;X^*}$;[4] this sheaf is called the sheaf of germs of continuous X^*-valued functions on X and it will always be denoted by $\mathscr{E}_{X;X^*}$; note that for any $a \in X$ we have $(\mathscr{E}_{X;X^*})_a = \mathfrak{E}(a, X; X^*)$. Now suppose that

[3] For notation see (29.3, 29.4).

[4] By general convention, $\mathscr{E}_{X;X^*}(\emptyset) = 0$.

$X^* = K$ where K is assumed to be a complete nondiscrete valued field. Identifying constant functions with elements of K, $\mathscr{E}_{X;K}$ becomes a sheaf of K-algebras on X and it will always be regarded as such; since K will remain fixed most of the time, we may write $\mathscr{E}_X$ instead of $\mathscr{E}_{X;K}$. Now suppose that X is an analytic set in an open set in K^n. Then we get a subsheaf $\mathscr{R}_{X;K}$ of $\mathscr{E}_{X;K}$ by taking $\mathscr{R}_{X;K}(U) = R(U)$ for each nonempty open set U in X where the restriction maps belonging to $\mathscr{R}_{X;K}$ are again the ordinary restriction maps. This subsheaf of $\mathscr{E}_{X;K}$ is called the sheaf of (K-valued) analytic function germs on X and it will always be denoted by $\mathscr{R}_{X;K}$ or simply $\mathscr{R}_X$. Note that for any $a \in X$ we have $(\mathscr{R}_X)_a = R(a, X)$. For any $Y \subset X$ we get an ideal $\mathscr{I}(Y, X)$ in $\mathscr{R}_X$ by taking

$$\mathscr{I}(Y, X)(U) = \{f \in R(U) : f(Y \cap U) = 0\}$$

for each nonempty open set U in X. Again, this ideal will always be denoted by $\mathscr{I}(Y, X)$. Note that for any $a \in X$ we have $(\mathscr{I}(Y, X))_a = \mathfrak{i}(a, Y, X)$.

(41.3) *Sheaf associated with a presheaf.* Let $\mathscr{M} = [\mathscr{M}(U), \mu_U^V]$ be any presheaf of abelian groups (resp: rings, K-modules, K-algebras) on X. For any nonempty open set U in X let $\langle\mathscr{M}\rangle(U)$ be the set of all functions f on U which to each a in U assign an element $f_{(a)}$ in $\mathscr{M}_a$ such that: given $a' \in U$ there exists a neighborhood U' of a' in U and $f' \in \mathscr{M}(U')$ such that $f_{(a)} = f'_a$ for all $a \in U'$. For any $f, g \in \langle\mathscr{M}\rangle(U)$ define $f + g \in \langle\mathscr{M}\rangle(U)$ by taking $(f + g)_{(a)} = f_{(a)} + g_{(a)}$ for all $a \in U$; if $\mathscr{M}$ is a presheaf of rings then define $fg \in \langle\mathscr{M}\rangle(U)$ by taking $(fg)_{(a)} = f_{(a)}g_{(a)}$ for all $a \in U$; and if $\mathscr{M}$ is a presheaf of K-modules then for any $k \in K$ define $kf \in \langle\mathscr{M}\rangle(U)$ by taking $(kf)_{(a)} = kf_{(a)}$ for all $a \in U$. Thus $\langle\mathscr{M}\rangle(U)$ is an abelian group (resp: ring, K-module, K-algebra). For any nonempty open sets $U \subset V$ in X and $f \in \langle\mathscr{M}\rangle(V)$, let $\langle\mu_U^V\rangle f = f|U \in \langle\mathscr{M}\rangle(U)$. For any nonempty open set U in X and $f \in \mathscr{M}(U)$, let $\theta(U)f \in \langle\mathscr{M}\rangle(U)$ be defined by taking $(\theta(U)f)_{(a)} = f_a$ for all $a \in U$. Then $\langle\mathscr{M}\rangle$ is a presheaf of abelian groups (resp: rings, K-modules, K-algebras) on X and $\theta : \mathscr{M} \to \langle\mathscr{M}\rangle$ is a homomorphism of presheaves.[5] For any $a \in X$, the induced homomorphism $\mathscr{M}_a \to \langle\mathscr{M}\rangle_a$ is an isomorphism and hence $\langle\mathscr{M}\rangle_a$ may be identified with $\mathscr{M}_a$, (for any nonempty open set U in X and any $f \in \langle\mathscr{M}\rangle(U)$ we then have $f_{(a)} = f_a$ for all $a \in U$). Actually $\langle\mathscr{M}\rangle$ is a sheaf on X and is called the sheaf associated with the presheaf $\mathscr{M}$. The following two statements can easily be proved.

1) Let U be any open set in X. Then $\mathscr{M}(U) \to \langle\mathscr{M}\rangle(U)$ is a monomorphism $\Leftrightarrow$ condition S_1 holds.

[5] $\langle\mathscr{M}\rangle(\emptyset) = 0$.

2) Let U be any open set in X such that $\mathcal{M}(U') \to \langle\mathcal{M}\rangle(U')$ is a monomorphism for each open subset U' of U. Then $\mathcal{M}(U) \to \langle\mathcal{M}\rangle(U)$ is an epimorphism $\Leftrightarrow$ condition S_2 holds.

From 1) and 2) we get

3) $\mathcal{M} \to \langle\mathcal{M}\rangle$ is a presheaf-isomorphism $\Leftrightarrow$ $\mathcal{M}$ is a sheaf.

Consequently if $\mathcal{M}$ satisfies condition S_1 for each open set U in X then we may identify $\mathcal{M}$ with a subpresheaf of $\langle\mathcal{M}\rangle$; and if $\mathcal{M}$ is a sheaf then we may identify $\langle\mathcal{M}\rangle$ with $\mathcal{M}$.

Let $\varphi : \mathcal{M} \to \mathcal{N}$ be a homomorphism of presheaves on X. To φ we associate the homomorphism $\langle\varphi\rangle : \langle\mathcal{M}\rangle \to \langle\mathcal{N}\rangle$ where for any nonempty open set U in X and any $f \in \langle\mathcal{M}\rangle(U)$ we define $\langle\varphi\rangle(U)(f) \in \langle\mathcal{N}\rangle(U)$ by taking $(\langle\varphi\rangle(U)f)_{(a)} = \varphi_a f_{(a)}$ for all $a \in U$. It is immediately seen that if $\mathring{\text{K}}\text{er}\ \varphi = 0$ then $\mathring{\text{K}}\text{er}\ \langle\varphi\rangle = 0$. Consequently if $\mathcal{P}$ is a subpresheaf of $\mathcal{M}$ then $\langle\mathcal{P}\rangle$ can be identified with a subsheaf of $\langle\mathcal{M}\rangle$. In particular, if $\mathcal{M}$ is a sheaf and $\mathcal{P}$ is a subpresheaf of $\mathcal{M}$ then taking $\langle\mathcal{M}\rangle = \mathcal{M}$, for any open set U in X we have

$$\langle\mathcal{P}\rangle(U) = \{f \in \mathcal{M}(U) : f_a \in \mathcal{P}_a \text{ for all } a \in U\}.$$

If $\mathcal{A}$ is a presheaf of rings on X and $\mathcal{M}$ is an $\mathcal{A}$-presheaf-module, then $\langle\mathcal{M}\rangle$ becomes an $\langle\mathcal{A}\rangle$-module and the map $\mathcal{M} \to \langle\mathcal{M}\rangle$ is an $(\mathcal{A} \to \langle\mathcal{A}\rangle)$-presheaf-homomorphism. If $\sigma : \mathcal{A} \to \mathcal{B}$ is a homomorphism of presheaves of rings on X and $\varphi : \mathcal{M} \to \mathcal{N}$ is a σ-presheaf-homomorphism, then $\langle\varphi\rangle : \langle\mathcal{M}\rangle \to \langle\mathcal{N}\rangle$ is a $\langle\sigma\rangle$-homomorphism; in particular, if $\varphi : \mathcal{M} \to \mathcal{N}$ is an $\mathcal{A}$-presheaf-homomorphism then $\langle\varphi\rangle : \langle\mathcal{M}\rangle \to \langle\mathcal{N}\rangle$ is an $\langle\mathcal{A}\rangle$-homomorphism; and so on.

For any subsheaves $\mathcal{P}$ and $\mathcal{Q}$ of a sheaf $\mathcal{M}$ of abelian groups (resp: K-modules) on X, we set $\mathcal{P} + \mathcal{Q} = \langle\mathcal{P} \mathbin{\mathring{+}} \mathcal{Q}\rangle$ and $\mathcal{P} \cap \mathcal{Q} = \langle\mathcal{P} \mathbin{\mathring{\cap}} \mathcal{Q}\rangle$; these are then subsheaves of $\mathcal{M}$ and for any open set U in X we have

$$(\mathcal{P} + \mathcal{Q})(U) = \{f \in \mathcal{M}(U) : f_a \in \mathcal{P}_a + \mathcal{Q}_a \text{ for all } a \in U\},$$
$$(\mathcal{P} \cap \mathcal{Q})(U) = \{f \in \mathcal{M}(U) : f_a \in \mathcal{P}_a \cap \mathcal{Q}_a \text{ for all } a \in U\}.$$

If $\mathcal{A}$ is a sheaf of rings on X, $\mathcal{M}$ is an $\mathcal{A}$-module, and $\mathcal{P}$ and $\mathcal{Q}$ are $\mathcal{A}$-submodules of $\mathcal{M}$, then $\mathcal{P} + \mathcal{Q}$ and $\mathcal{P} \cap \mathcal{Q}$ are $\mathcal{A}$-submodules of $\mathcal{M}$; in particular this applies to ideals in $\mathcal{A}$.

(41.4) *Exact sequence.* For any subsheaf $\mathcal{P}$ of a sheaf $\mathcal{M}$ of abelian groups (resp: K-modules) on X we set $\mathcal{M}/\mathcal{P} = \langle\mathcal{M} \mathbin{\mathring{/}} \mathcal{P}\rangle$ which is then a sheaf of abelian groups (resp: K-modules) on X. It is easily seen that $\mathcal{M} \mathbin{\mathring{/}} \mathcal{P}$ satisfies condition S_1 (but not necessarily S_2) for each open set U

in X, and hence $\mathscr{M}\mathring{|}\mathscr{P}$ can be considered to be a subpresheaf of $\mathscr{M}|\mathscr{P}$. The natural homomorphism $\mathscr{M} \to \mathscr{M}\mathring{|}\mathscr{P}$ followed by the canonical injection $\mathscr{M}\mathring{|}\mathscr{P} \to \mathscr{M}|\mathscr{P}$ gives a homomorphism $\lambda : \mathscr{M} \to \mathscr{M}|\mathscr{P}$ which is again called natural; note that for any $a \in X$ we have $\operatorname{Im} \lambda_a = (\mathscr{M}|\mathscr{P})_a = (\mathscr{M}\mathring{|}\mathscr{P})_a \approx \mathscr{M}_a|\mathscr{P}_a$. If $\mathscr{A}$ is a sheaf of rings on X, $\mathscr{M}$ is an $\mathscr{A}$-module and $\mathscr{P}$ is an $\mathscr{A}$-submodule of $\mathscr{M}$, then $\mathscr{M}|\mathscr{P}$ is an $\mathscr{A}$-module and λ is an $\mathscr{A}$-homomorphism; if furthermore $\mathscr{M} = \mathscr{A}$, then $\mathscr{A}|\mathscr{P}$ is a sheaf of rings on X and λ is a homomorphism of sheaves of rings.

For any homomorphism $\varphi : \mathscr{M} \to \mathscr{N}$ of sheaves of abelian groups (resp: K-modules) on X we set $\operatorname{Ker} \varphi = \langle \mathring{\operatorname{Ker}}\, \varphi \rangle$ and $\operatorname{Im} \varphi = \langle \mathring{\operatorname{Im}}\, \varphi \rangle$; these are then subsheaves of $\mathscr{M}$ and $\mathscr{N}$, respectively, and for any open set U in X we have

$$(\operatorname{Ker} \varphi)(U) = \{f \in \mathscr{M}(U) : f_a \in \operatorname{Ker} \varphi_a \text{ for all } a \in U\},$$

and

$$\begin{aligned}(\operatorname{Im} \varphi)(U) &= \{g \in \mathscr{N}(U) : g_a \in \operatorname{Im} \varphi_a \text{ for all } a \in U\} \\ &= \{g \in \mathscr{N}(U) : \text{there exists an open covering} \\ &\quad (U_j)_{j \in J} \text{ of } U \text{ and } f_j \in \mathscr{M}(U_j) \text{ such that} \\ &\quad \varphi(U_j)f_j = g|U_j \text{ for all } j \in J\}.\end{aligned}$$

Note that actually $\operatorname{Ker} \varphi = \mathring{\operatorname{Ker}}\, \varphi$, whereas in general $\mathring{\operatorname{Im}}\, \varphi$ is only a subpresheaf of $\operatorname{Im} \varphi$. We also set $\operatorname{Coker} \varphi = \mathscr{N}/\operatorname{Im} \varphi$ and $\operatorname{Coim} \varphi = \mathscr{M}/\operatorname{Ker} \varphi$ which are then sheaves of abelian groups (resp: K-modules). For any open sets $Y \subset Z$ in X and any subsheaf $\mathscr{M}'$ of $\mathscr{M}|Z$, the subsheaf $\operatorname{Im}(\varphi|(\mathscr{M}'|Y))$ of $\mathscr{N}|Y$ may be denoted by $\varphi(\mathscr{M}'|Y)$; in particular then $\varphi(\mathscr{M}) = \operatorname{Im} \varphi$. Let $i : \mathscr{M}' \to \mathscr{M}$ and $j : \mathscr{N}' \to \mathscr{N}$ be the canonical injections of subsheaves $\mathscr{M}'$ and $\mathscr{N}'$ of $\mathscr{M}$ and $\mathscr{N}$, respectively; then there exists a homomorphism $\varphi' : \mathscr{M}' \to \mathscr{N}'$ such that $\varphi \circ i = j \circ \varphi' \Leftrightarrow \varphi(\mathscr{M}') \subset \mathscr{N}'$ (i.e., $\varphi(\mathscr{M}')$ is a subsheaf of $\mathscr{N}'$); if φ' exists then it is unique and is said to be induced by φ. If $\mathscr{A}$ is a sheaf of rings on X and φ is an $\mathscr{A}$-homomorphism then $\operatorname{Coker} \varphi$ and $\operatorname{Coim} \varphi$ are $\mathscr{A}$-modules, and $\operatorname{Ker} \varphi$ and $\operatorname{Im} \varphi$ are $\mathscr{A}$-submodules of $\mathscr{M}$ and $\mathscr{N}$, respectively; furthermore, if $\mathscr{M}'$ and $\mathscr{N}'$ are $\mathscr{A}$-submodules of $\mathscr{M}$ and $\mathscr{N}$, respectively, such that $\varphi(\mathscr{M}') \subset \mathscr{N}'$ then the map $\mathscr{M}' \to \mathscr{N}'$ induced by φ is an $\mathscr{A}$-homomorphism.

A sequence $\mathscr{M} \xrightarrow{\varphi} \mathscr{N} \xrightarrow{\psi} \mathscr{L}$ of homomorphisms of sheaves of abelian groups on X is said to be exact $\Leftrightarrow \operatorname{Im} \varphi = \operatorname{Ker} \psi$; note that this is so $\Leftrightarrow$ the induced sequence $\mathscr{M}_a \to \mathscr{N}_a \to \mathscr{L}_a$ is exact for all $a \in X$; similarly for longer sequences. Furthermore, φ is said to be a monomorphism (resp: epimorphism) $\Leftrightarrow \operatorname{Ker} \varphi = 0$ (resp: $\operatorname{Im} \varphi = \mathscr{N}$); and φ is said to be an isomorphism $\Leftrightarrow \varphi$ is a monomorphism as well as an epimorphism.

From the above definitions it follows that for any homomorphisms $\mathscr{M} \xrightarrow{\varphi} \mathscr{N} \xrightarrow{\psi} \mathscr{L}$ of sheaves of abelian groups on X we have the following (1 to 7).

1) $\operatorname{Ker} \varphi = 0 \Leftrightarrow \mathring{\operatorname{Ker}}\, \varphi = 0 \Leftrightarrow \operatorname{Ker} \varphi_a = 0$ for all a in $X \Leftrightarrow 0 \to \mathscr{M} \to \mathscr{N}$ is exact $\Leftrightarrow 0 \to \mathscr{M} \to \mathscr{N}$ is presheaf-exact.

2) $\operatorname{Im} \varphi = \mathscr{N} \Leftrightarrow \operatorname{Im} \varphi_a = \mathscr{N}_a$ for all $a \in X \Leftrightarrow \operatorname{Coker} \varphi = 0 \Leftrightarrow \mathscr{M} \to \mathscr{N} \to 0$ is exact. Furthermore $\mathring{\operatorname{Im}}\, \varphi = \mathscr{N} \Rightarrow \operatorname{Im} \varphi = \mathscr{N}$ (but not conversely).

3) $\operatorname{Im} \varphi = 0 \Leftrightarrow \mathring{\operatorname{Im}}\, \varphi = 0 \Leftrightarrow \operatorname{Im} \varphi_a = 0$ for all $a \in X$. The condition $\operatorname{Im} \varphi = 0$ may be expressed by writing $\varphi = 0$.

4) φ is an isomorphism $\Leftrightarrow 0 \to \mathscr{M} \to \mathscr{N} \to 0$ is exact $\Leftrightarrow 0 \to \mathscr{M} \to \mathscr{N} \to 0$ is presheaf-exact $\Leftrightarrow \varphi$ is a presheaf-isomorphism.

5) $\mathscr{M} \to \mathscr{N} \to \mathscr{L}$ is presheaf-exact $\Rightarrow \mathscr{M} \to \mathscr{N} \to \mathscr{L}$ is exact.

6) $0 \to \mathscr{M} \to \mathscr{N} \to \mathscr{L}$ is exact $\Rightarrow 0 \to \mathscr{M} \to \mathscr{N} \to \mathscr{L}$ is presheaf-exact. In other words, the identity functor from the category of sheaves of abelian groups on X into the category of presheaves of abelian groups on X is left exact.

7) The following sequences of natural homomorphisms are exact.[6]

$$0 \to \operatorname{Ker} \varphi \to \mathscr{M} \to \mathscr{N} \to \operatorname{Coker} \varphi \to 0,$$
$$0 \to \operatorname{Ker} \varphi \to \mathscr{M} \to \operatorname{Im} \varphi \to 0,$$
$$0 \to \operatorname{Im} \varphi \to \mathscr{N} \to \operatorname{Coker} \varphi \to 0,$$
$$0 \to \operatorname{Coim} \varphi \to \operatorname{Im} \varphi \to 0.$$

Now let $\mathscr{P}$ be a subsheaf of a sheaf $\mathscr{M}$ of abelian groups on X, let $i : \mathscr{P} \to \mathscr{M}$ and $j : \mathscr{M}\mathring{/}\mathscr{P} \to \mathscr{M}/\mathscr{P}$ be the canonical injections, and let $\tau : \mathscr{M} \to \mathscr{M}\mathring{/}\mathscr{P}$ be the natural homomorphism. Then $\lambda = j \circ \tau : \mathscr{M} \to \mathscr{M}/\mathscr{P}$ is the natural homomorphism. Obviously $\mathring{\operatorname{Im}}\, \lambda = \mathring{\operatorname{Im}}\, \tau = \mathscr{M}\mathring{/}\mathscr{P}$ and $\operatorname{Im} \lambda = \mathscr{M}/\mathscr{P}$. Consequently $0 \to \mathscr{P} \to \mathscr{M} \to \mathscr{M}\mathring{/}\mathscr{P} \to 0$ is presheaf-exact, and $0 \to \mathscr{P} \to \mathscr{M} \to \mathscr{M}/\mathscr{P} \to 0$ is exact but in general not presheaf-exact. Furthermore, for any homomorphism $\varphi : \mathscr{M} \to \mathscr{N}$ of sheaves of abelian groups on X we have the following where 8) is obvious and 9) follows from it.

8) There exists a homomorphism $\alpha : \mathscr{M}\mathring{/}\mathscr{P} \to \mathscr{N}$ such that $\varphi = \alpha \circ \tau \Leftrightarrow \mathscr{P} \subset \operatorname{Ker} \varphi$; and if α exists then it is unique.

[6] The explanation of the last sequence will follow from 9).

9) There exists a homomorphism $\beta : \mathscr{M}/\mathscr{P} \to \mathscr{N}$ such that $\varphi = \beta \circ \lambda \Leftrightarrow \mathscr{P} \subset \operatorname{Ker} \varphi$; and if β exists then it is unique and $\alpha = \beta \circ j$. Furthermore β is a monomorphism (resp: epimorphism) $\Leftrightarrow \mathscr{P} = \operatorname{Ker} \varphi$ (resp: $\operatorname{Im} \varphi = \mathscr{N}$). If $\mathscr{A}$ is a sheaf of rings on X, φ is an $\mathscr{A}$-homomorphism, and $\mathscr{P}$ is an $\mathscr{A}$-submodule of $\mathscr{M}$, then β is an $\mathscr{A}$-homomorphism; if furthermore $\mathscr{M} = \mathscr{A}$ and φ is a homomorphism of sheaves of rings then so is β.

The maps α and β are said to be induced by φ.

(41.5) *Constant presheaf and simple sheaf.* For any abelian group (resp: ring, K-module, K-algebra) P we get a presheaf $\mathring{P}\{X\}$ of abelian groups (resp: rings, K-modules, K-algebras) on X by taking $\mathring{P}\{X\}(U) = P$ for each nonempty open set U in X and taking the restriction map $\mathring{P}\{X\}(V) \to \mathring{P}\{X\}(U)$ belonging to $\mathring{P}\{X\}$ to be the identity map of P for any nonempty open sets $U \subset V$ in X.[7] For any $a \in X$, $(\mathring{P}\{X\})_a$ may be identified with P. $\mathring{P}\{X\}$ obviously satisfies condition S_1 for each open set in X (but in general not S_2, i.e., $\mathring{P}\{X\}$ may not be a sheaf) and hence $\mathring{P}\{X\}$ can be considered to be a subpresheaf of the sheaf $P\{X\} = \langle \mathring{P}\{X\} \rangle$.

A presheaf $\mathscr{M}$ of abelian groups (resp: rings, K-modules, K-algebras) on X is said to be a constant presheaf $\Leftrightarrow \mathscr{M}$ is presheaf-isomorphic to $\mathring{P}\{X\}$ for some abelian group (resp: ring, K-module, K-algebra) P. Note that $\mathscr{M} \approx \mathring{P}\{X\} \Leftrightarrow \mathscr{M}(X) \approx P$ and the restriction map $\mathscr{M}(X) \to \mathscr{M}(U)$ belonging to $\mathscr{M}$ is an isomorphism for each nonempty open set U in X; and then actually the restriction map $\mathscr{M}(V) \to \mathscr{M}(U)$ belonging to $\mathscr{M}$ is an isomorphism for all nonempty open sets $U \subset V$ in X.

A sheaf $\mathscr{M}$ of abelian groups (resp: rings, K-modules, K-algebras) on X is said to be a simple sheaf $\Leftrightarrow \mathscr{M} \approx P\{X\}$ for some abelian group (resp: ring, K-module, K-algebra) P.

A presheaf of abelian groups (resp: rings, K-modules, K-algebras) on X is essentially the smae thing as a $\mathring{\mathbf{Z}}\{X\}$-presheaf-module (resp: $\mathring{\mathbf{Z}}\{X\}$-presheaf-algebra, $\mathring{K}\{X\}$-presheaf-module, $\mathring{K}\{X\}$-presheaf-algebra), and a homomorphism of presheaves of abelian groups (resp: rings, K-modules, K-algebras) on X is simply a $\mathring{\mathbf{Z}}\{X\}$-presheaf-homomorphism (resp: $\mathring{\mathbf{Z}}\{X\}$-presheaf-algebra-homomorphism, $\mathring{K}\{X\}$-presheaf-homomorphism, $\mathring{K}\{X\}$-presheaf-algebra-homomorphism). Again, a sheaf of abelian groups (resp: rings, K-modules, K-algebras) on X can naturally be regarded as a $\mathbf{Z}\{X\}$-module (resp: $\mathbf{Z}\{X\}$-algebra, $K\{X\}$-module, $K\{X\}$-algebra) and then a homomorphism of sheaves of abelian groups (resp: rings, K-modules, K-algebras) on X becomes a $\mathbf{Z}\{X\}$-homomorphism (resp: $\mathbf{Z}\{X\}$-algebra-homomorphism, $K\{X\}$-homomorphism, $K\{X\}$-algebra-homomorphism); and so on.

[7] $\mathring{P}\{X\}(\emptyset) = 0$.

When there is no confusion, $\mathring{P}\{X\}$ and $P\{X\}$ can be denoted simply by $\mathring{P}$ and P respectively.

(41.6) *Germs of homomorphisms.* Let $\mathscr{A}$ be a sheaf of rings on X and let $\mathscr{M}$ and $\mathscr{N}$ be $\mathscr{A}$-modules. For any $\mathscr{A}$-homomorphisms $f, f_1 : \mathscr{M} \to \mathscr{N}$ and any $r \in \mathscr{A}(X)$, the $\mathscr{A}$-homomorphisms $f + f_1 : \mathscr{M} \to \mathscr{N}$ and $rf : \mathscr{M} \to \mathscr{N}$ are defined by taking $(f + f_1)(U)t = f(U)t + f_1(U)t$ and $(rf)(U)t = (r|U)(f(U)t)$ for any open set U in X and any $t \in \mathscr{M}(U)$. Thus the set of all $\mathscr{A}$-homomorphisms of $\mathscr{M}$ into $\mathscr{N}$ becomes an $\mathscr{A}(X)$-module and it is denoted by $\mathrm{Hom}_{\mathscr{A}}(\mathscr{M}, \mathscr{N})$ or $\mathrm{Hom}\,(\mathscr{M}, \mathscr{N})$. For any open sets $U \subset V$ in X and $f \in \mathrm{Hom}_{\mathscr{A}|V}(\mathscr{M}|V, \mathscr{N}|V)$ let $\delta_U^V f = f|(\mathscr{M}|U) \in \mathrm{Hom}_{\mathscr{A}|U}(\mathscr{M}|U, \mathscr{N}|U)$. Then $[\mathrm{Hom}_{\mathscr{A}|U}(\mathscr{M}|U, \mathscr{N}|U), \delta_U^V]$ is an $\mathscr{A}$-module; it is called the sheaf of germs of $\mathscr{A}$-homomorphisms of $\mathscr{M}$ into $\mathscr{N}$ and is denoted by $\mathscr{H}om_{\mathscr{A}}(\mathscr{M}, \mathscr{N})$ or $\mathscr{H}om(\mathscr{M}, \mathscr{N})$, in other words for any open set U in X we take $\mathscr{H}om_{\mathscr{A}}(\mathscr{M}, \mathscr{N})(U) = \mathrm{Hom}_{\mathscr{A}|U}(\mathscr{M}|U, \mathscr{N}|U)$ and for any open sets $U \subset V$ in X we take δ_U^V to be the restriction map belonging to $\mathscr{H}om_{\mathscr{A}}(\mathscr{M}, \mathscr{N})$.

Given any $\mathscr{A}$-homomorphisms $\varphi : \mathscr{M}' \to \mathscr{M}$ and $\psi : \mathscr{N} \to \mathscr{N}'$ they induce the $\mathscr{A}(X)$-homomorphism $\mathrm{Hom}(\varphi, \psi) : \mathrm{Hom}(\mathscr{M}, \mathscr{N}) \to \mathrm{Hom}(\mathscr{M}', \mathscr{N}')$ defined by $\mathrm{Hom}(\varphi, \psi) f = \psi \circ f \circ \varphi$ for all $f \in \mathrm{Hom}(\mathscr{M}, \mathscr{N})$. Furthermore φ and ψ induce the $\mathscr{A}$-homomorphism $\mathscr{H}om(\varphi, \psi) : \mathscr{H}om(\mathscr{M}, \mathscr{N}) \to \mathscr{H}om(\mathscr{M}', \mathscr{N}')$ defined by $\mathscr{H}om(\varphi, \psi)(U) = \mathrm{Hom}(\varphi|U, \psi|U)$ for every open set U in X. Given any other $\mathscr{A}$-homomorphisms $\varphi' : \mathscr{M}'' \to \mathscr{M}'$ and $\psi' : \mathscr{N}' \to \mathscr{N}''$ we obviously have $\mathrm{Hom}(\varphi \circ \varphi', \psi' \circ \psi) = \mathrm{Hom}(\varphi', \psi') \circ \mathrm{Hom}(\varphi, \psi)$. This being the case for the restrictions of $\varphi, \varphi', \psi, \psi'$ to any open set U in X we also get that $\mathscr{H}om(\varphi \circ \varphi', \psi' \circ \psi) = \mathscr{H}om(\varphi', \psi') \circ \mathscr{H}om(\varphi, \psi)$. If $i_{\mathscr{M}}$ and $i_{\mathscr{N}}$ are the identity maps of $\mathscr{M}$ and $\mathscr{N}$, respectively, then $\mathrm{Hom}(i_{\mathscr{M}}, i_{\mathscr{N}})$ is the identity map of $\mathrm{Hom}(\mathscr{M}, \mathscr{N})$. For any open set U in X, $i_{\mathscr{M}}|U$ and $i_{\mathscr{N}}|U$ are the identity maps of $\mathscr{M}|U$ and $\mathscr{N}|U$, respectively, and hence $\mathscr{H}om(i_{\mathscr{M}}, i_{\mathscr{N}})$ is the identity map of $\mathscr{H}om(\mathscr{M}, \mathscr{N})$. The maps $\mathrm{Hom}(\varphi, i_{\mathscr{N}})$ and $\mathscr{H}om(\varphi, i_{\mathscr{N}})$ (resp: $\mathrm{Hom}(i_{\mathscr{M}}, \psi)$ and $\mathscr{H}om(i_{\mathscr{M}}, \psi)$) are said to be induced by φ (resp: ψ). Thus $\mathrm{Hom}_{\mathscr{A}}$ (resp: $\mathscr{H}om_{\mathscr{A}}$) is a functor of two variables, contravariant in the first and covariant in the second, from the category of $\mathscr{A}$-modules into the category of $\mathscr{A}(X)$-modules (resp: $\mathscr{A}$-modules).

It can easily be verified that if

$$\mathscr{M}'' \to \mathscr{M}' \to \mathscr{M} \to 0 \qquad \text{and} \qquad 0 \to \mathscr{N} \to \mathscr{N}' \to \mathscr{N}''$$

are exact sequences of $\mathscr{A}$-homomorphisms, then the induced sequences of $\mathscr{A}(X)$-homomorphisms

$$0 \to \operatorname{Hom}(\mathscr{M}, \mathscr{N}) \to \operatorname{Hom}(\mathscr{M}', \mathscr{N}) \to \operatorname{Hom}(\mathscr{M}'', \mathscr{N}),$$
$$0 \to \operatorname{Hom}(\mathscr{M}, \mathscr{N}) \to \operatorname{Hom}(\mathscr{M}, \mathscr{N}') \to \operatorname{Hom}(\mathscr{M}, \mathscr{N}'')$$

are exact, and this being so for the restrictions of the sheaves to each open set U in X we get that the sequences of $\mathscr{A}$-homomorphisms

$$0 \to \mathscr{H}om(\mathscr{M}, \mathscr{N}) \to \mathscr{H}om(\mathscr{M}', \mathscr{N}) \to \mathscr{H}om(\mathscr{M}'', \mathscr{N}),$$
$$0 \to \mathscr{H}om(\mathscr{M}, \mathscr{N}) \to \mathscr{H}om(\mathscr{M}, \mathscr{N}') \to \mathscr{H}om(\mathscr{M}, \mathscr{N}'')$$

are exact. Thus the functors $\operatorname{Hom}_{\mathscr{A}}$ and $\mathscr{H}om_{\mathscr{A}}$ are left exact.

For any other $\mathscr{A}$-modules $\mathscr{M}'$ and $\mathscr{N}'$ we have natural $\mathscr{A}(X)$-isomorphisms

$$\operatorname{Hom}(\mathscr{M} \oplus \mathscr{M}', \mathscr{N}) \approx \operatorname{Hom}(\mathscr{M}, \mathscr{N}) \oplus \operatorname{Hom}(\mathscr{M}', \mathscr{N}),$$
$$\operatorname{Hom}(\mathscr{M}, \mathscr{N} \oplus \mathscr{N}') \approx \operatorname{Hom}(\mathscr{M}, \mathscr{N}) \oplus \operatorname{Hom}(\mathscr{M}, \mathscr{N}').$$

This being the case for the restrictions of the sheaves to any open set U in X (in which case these are $\mathscr{A}(U)$-isomorphisms) we get the natural $\mathscr{A}$-isomorphisms

$$\mathscr{H}om(\mathscr{M} \oplus \mathscr{M}', \mathscr{N}) \approx \mathscr{H}om(\mathscr{M}, \mathscr{N}) \oplus \mathscr{H}om(\mathscr{M}', \mathscr{N}),$$
$$\mathscr{H}om(\mathscr{M}, \mathscr{N} \oplus \mathscr{N}') \approx \mathscr{H}om(\mathscr{M}, \mathscr{N}) \oplus \mathscr{H}om(\mathscr{M}, \mathscr{N}').$$

Let

$$e_1 = (1, 0, \ldots, 0), \ldots, e_p = (0, \ldots, 0, 1) \in \mathscr{A}^p(X).$$

For any open set U in X, an $\mathscr{A}|U$-homomorphism $f \colon \mathscr{A}^p|U \to \mathscr{M}|U$ is completely determined by the f images $t_1, \ldots, t_p$ of $e_1|U, \ldots, e_p|U$, and $t_1, \ldots, t_p \in \mathscr{M}(U)$ can be assigned arbitrarily; namely, for any open set U' in U we have

$$f(U')(r_1, \ldots, r_p) = r_1 t_1 + \ldots + r_p t_p \in \mathscr{M}(U')$$

for all $(r_1, \ldots, r_p) \in \mathscr{A}^p(U')$.[8] Thus we get a natural $\mathscr{A}(U)$-isomorphism $\operatorname{Hom}(\mathscr{A}^p|U, \mathscr{M}|U) \approx \mathscr{M}(U)^p$. Again this leads to the natural $\mathscr{A}$-isomorphism $\mathscr{H}om(\mathscr{A}^p, \mathscr{M}) \approx \mathscr{M}^p$.

Given $a \in X$ we define the natural $\mathscr{A}_a$-homomorphism

$$\mu : (\mathscr{H}om_{\mathscr{A}}(\mathscr{M}, \mathscr{N}))_a \to \operatorname{Hom}_{\mathscr{A}_a}(\mathscr{M}_a, \mathscr{N}_a)$$

by taking

$$(\mu f_a) t_a = (ft)_a$$

for any neighborhood U of a in X, $f \in \mathscr{H}om_{\mathscr{A}}(\mathscr{M}, \mathscr{N})(U)$

[8] This also holds for presheaves.

$= \operatorname{Hom}_{\mathscr{A}|U}(\mathscr{M}|U, \mathscr{N}|U)$, and $t \in \mathscr{M}(U)$. In general μ is neither a monomorphism nor an epimorphism. In case μ is an isomorphism, we may identify $(\mathscr{H}om_{\mathscr{A}}(\mathscr{M}, \mathscr{N}))_a$ with $\operatorname{Hom}_{\mathscr{A}_a}(\mathscr{M}_a, \mathscr{N}_a)$. For instance this is so for $\mathscr{H}om_{\mathscr{A}}(\mathscr{A}^p, \mathscr{N})$ because then $\mathscr{H}om_{\mathscr{A}}(\mathscr{A}^p, \mathscr{N}) \approx \mathscr{N}^p$ and hence

$$(\mathscr{H}om_{\mathscr{A}}(\mathscr{A}^p, \mathscr{N}))_a \approx \mathscr{N}_a^p \approx \operatorname{Hom}_{\mathscr{A}_a}(\mathscr{A}_a^p, \mathscr{N}_a).$$

In the general case, for any $\mathscr{A}$-homomorphism $\mathscr{N} \to \mathscr{N}'$ the induced diagram

$$\begin{array}{ccc} (\mathscr{H}om_{\mathscr{A}}(\mathscr{M}, \mathscr{N}))_a & \to & (\mathscr{H}om_{\mathscr{A}}(\mathscr{M}, \mathscr{N}'))_a \\ \downarrow & & \downarrow \\ \operatorname{Hom}_{\mathscr{A}_a}(\mathscr{M}_a, \mathscr{N}_a) & \to & \operatorname{Hom}_{\mathscr{A}_a}(\mathscr{M}_a, \mathscr{N}'_a) \end{array}$$

is commutative; and similarly for any $\mathscr{A}$-homomorphism $\mathscr{M}' \to \mathscr{M}$. We define

$$\begin{aligned} \operatorname{Anh}_{\mathscr{A}}\mathscr{M} &= \operatorname{Anh}\mathscr{M} = \textit{annihilator of } \mathscr{M} \text{ (relative to } \mathscr{A}) \\ &= \operatorname{Ker}\alpha \end{aligned}$$

where $\alpha : \mathscr{A} \to \mathscr{H}om(\mathscr{M}, \mathscr{M})$ is the natural $\mathscr{A}$-homomorphism given by taking $\alpha(r)t = rt \in \mathscr{M}(U)$ for any open sets $U \subset V$ in X, $r \in \mathscr{A}(V)$, $t \in \mathscr{M}(U)$. For $a \in X$ let λ be the natural $\mathscr{A}_a$-homomorphism $(\mathscr{H}om_{\mathscr{A}}(\mathscr{M}, \mathscr{M}))_a \to \operatorname{Hom}_{\mathscr{A}_a}(\mathscr{M}_a, \mathscr{M}_a)$; then $\lambda \circ \alpha_a$ is the natural $\mathscr{A}_a$-homomorphism $\mathscr{A}_a \to \operatorname{Hom}_{\mathscr{A}_a}(\mathscr{M}_a, \mathscr{M}_a)$; hence if λ is an isomorphism then

$$(\operatorname{Anh}_{\mathscr{A}}\mathscr{M})_a = \operatorname{Anh}_{\mathscr{A}_a}\mathscr{M}_a.$$

For any $\mathscr{A}$-submodules $\mathscr{P}$ and $\mathscr{Q}$ of $\mathscr{M}$ we define

$$\begin{aligned} \mathscr{P} :_{\mathscr{A}} \mathscr{Q} &= \mathscr{P} : \mathscr{Q} = \textit{transporter of } \mathscr{Q} \textit{ in } \mathscr{P} \text{ (relative to } \mathscr{A}) \\ &= \operatorname{Anh}_{\mathscr{A}}((\mathscr{P} + \mathscr{Q})/\mathscr{P}). \end{aligned}$$

For $a \in X$, if the natural $\mathscr{A}_a$-homomorphism

$$\begin{aligned} &(\mathscr{H}om_{\mathscr{A}}((\mathscr{P} + \mathscr{Q})/\mathscr{P}, (\mathscr{P} + \mathscr{Q})/\mathscr{P}))_a \\ &\to \operatorname{Hom}_{\mathscr{A}_a}(((\mathscr{P} + \mathscr{Q})/\mathscr{P})_a, ((\mathscr{P} + \mathscr{Q})/\mathscr{P})_a) \end{aligned}$$

is an isomorphism then

$$(\mathscr{P} :_{\mathscr{A}} \mathscr{Q})_a = \mathscr{P}_a :_{\mathscr{A}_a} \mathscr{Q}_a.$$

(41.7) *Tensor product.* Let $\mathscr{A} \xrightarrow{\sigma} \mathscr{B} \xrightarrow{\sigma'} \mathscr{B}'$ be homomorphisms of sheaves of rings on X. For any $\mathscr{A}$-modules $\mathscr{M}$ and $\mathscr{N}$, the $\mathscr{A}$-module $\langle \mathscr{M} \mathring{\otimes}_{\mathscr{A}} \mathscr{N} \rangle$ is called the tensor product of $\mathscr{M}$ and $\mathscr{N}$ (over $\mathscr{A}$) and is denoted by $\mathscr{M} \otimes_{\mathscr{A}} \mathscr{N}$ or simply $\mathscr{M} \otimes \mathscr{N}$. For any $a \in X$, by identification we have $(\mathscr{M} \otimes_{\mathscr{A}} \mathscr{N})_a = (\mathscr{M} \mathring{\otimes}_{\mathscr{A}} \mathscr{N})_a = \mathscr{M}_a \otimes_{\mathscr{A}_a} \mathscr{N}_a$. For any

σ-homomorphisms $\varphi : \mathscr{M} \to \mathscr{M}'$ and $\psi : \mathscr{N} \to \mathscr{N}'$, the σ-homomorphism $\langle \varphi \mathring{\otimes} \psi \rangle : \mathscr{M} \otimes_{\mathscr{A}} \mathscr{N} \to \mathscr{M}' \otimes_{\mathscr{B}} \mathscr{N}'$ is called the tensor product of φ and ψ and is denoted by $\varphi \otimes \psi$. Note that for any $a \in X$ we have $(\varphi \otimes \psi)_a = \varphi_a \otimes \psi_a$. If $\varphi' : \mathscr{M}' \to \mathscr{M}''$ and $\psi' : \mathscr{N}' \to \mathscr{N}''$ are any σ'-homomorphisms then $\varphi' \circ \varphi$ and $\psi' \circ \psi$ are $(\sigma' \circ \sigma)$-homomorphisms and $(\varphi' \circ \varphi) \otimes (\psi' \circ \psi) = (\varphi' \otimes \psi') \circ (\varphi \otimes \psi)$. If $i_{\mathscr{M}}$ and $i_{\mathscr{N}}$ are the identity maps of $\mathscr{M}$ and $\mathscr{N}$, respectively, then $i_{\mathscr{M}} \otimes i_{\mathscr{N}}$ is the identity map of $\mathscr{M} \otimes_{\mathscr{A}} \mathscr{N}$; for any $\mathscr{A}$-homomorphisms $\varphi : \mathscr{M} \to \mathscr{M}'$ and $\psi : \mathscr{N} \to \mathscr{N}'$, the $\mathscr{A}$-homomorphisms $\varphi \otimes i_{\mathscr{N}} : \mathscr{M} \otimes_{\mathscr{A}} \mathscr{N} \to \mathscr{M}' \otimes_{\mathscr{A}} \mathscr{N}$ and $i_{\mathscr{M}} \otimes \psi : \mathscr{M} \otimes_{\mathscr{A}} \mathscr{N} \to \mathscr{M} \otimes_{\mathscr{A}} \mathscr{N}'$ are said to be induced by φ and ψ, respectively. Thus $\otimes_{\mathscr{A}}$ is a covariant functor of two variables from the category of $\mathscr{A}$-modules into the category of $\mathscr{A}$-modules. Obviously $\mathscr{M} \otimes_{\mathscr{A}} \mathscr{N} = 0$ if either $\mathscr{M} = 0$ or $\mathscr{N} = 0$. If

$$\mathscr{M} \to \mathscr{M}' \to \mathscr{M}'' \to 0, \qquad \mathscr{N} \to \mathscr{N}' \to \mathscr{N}'' \to 0$$

are exact sequences of $\mathscr{A}$-homomorphisms, then for any $a \in X$ the induced sequences

$$\mathscr{M}_a \to \mathscr{M}'_a \to \mathscr{M}''_a \to 0, \qquad \mathscr{N}_a \to \mathscr{N}'_a \to \mathscr{N}''_a \to 0$$

are exact and hence the sequences

$$\mathscr{M}_a \otimes_{\mathscr{A}_a} \mathscr{N}_a \to \mathscr{M}'_a \otimes_{\mathscr{A}_a} \mathscr{N}_a \to \mathscr{M}''_a \otimes_{\mathscr{A}_a} \mathscr{N}_a \to 0,$$
$$\mathscr{M}_a \otimes_{\mathscr{A}_a} \mathscr{N}_a \to \mathscr{M}_a \otimes_{\mathscr{A}_a} \mathscr{N}'_a \to \mathscr{M}_a \otimes_{\mathscr{A}_a} \mathscr{N}''_a \to 0$$

are exact because $\otimes_{\mathscr{A}_a}$ is right exact; this being so for all $a \in X$ we get that the sequences

$$\mathscr{M} \otimes_{\mathscr{A}} \mathscr{N} \to \mathscr{M}' \otimes_{\mathscr{A}} \mathscr{N} \to \mathscr{M}'' \otimes_{\mathscr{A}} \mathscr{N} \to 0,$$
$$\mathscr{M} \otimes_{\mathscr{A}} \mathscr{N} \to \mathscr{M} \otimes_{\mathscr{A}} \mathscr{N}' \to \mathscr{M} \otimes_{\mathscr{A}} \mathscr{N}'' \to 0$$

of $\mathscr{A}$-homomorphisms are exact. Thus the functor $\otimes_{\mathscr{A}}$ is right exact. Similarly, for any $\mathscr{A}$-modules $\mathscr{M}$, $\mathscr{N}$, $\mathscr{M}'$, $\mathscr{N}'$ we get natural $\mathscr{A}$-isomorphisms

$$\mathscr{M} \otimes_{\mathscr{A}} \mathscr{N} \approx \mathscr{N} \otimes_{\mathscr{A}} \mathscr{M}, \qquad \mathscr{M} \otimes_{\mathscr{A}} \mathscr{A} \approx \mathscr{M},$$
$$(\mathscr{M} \oplus \mathscr{M}') \otimes_{\mathscr{A}} \mathscr{N} \approx (\mathscr{M} \otimes_{\mathscr{A}} \mathscr{N}) \oplus (\mathscr{M}' \otimes_{\mathscr{A}} \mathscr{N}),$$
$$\mathscr{M} \otimes_{\mathscr{A}} (\mathscr{N} \oplus \mathscr{N}') \approx (\mathscr{M} \otimes_{\mathscr{A}} \mathscr{N}) \oplus (\mathscr{M} \otimes_{\mathscr{A}} \mathscr{N}').$$

For any $\mathscr{A}$-module $\mathscr{M}$, $\mathscr{M} \mathring{\otimes}_{\mathscr{A}} \mathscr{B}$ can be considered to be a $\mathscr{B}$-presheaf-module and hence $\mathscr{M} \otimes_{\mathscr{A}} \mathscr{B}$ can be considered to be a $\mathscr{B}$-module; any $\mathscr{A}$-homomorphism $\varphi : \mathscr{M} \to \mathscr{M}'$ induces the $\mathscr{B}$-homomorphism $\mathscr{M} \otimes_{\mathscr{A}} \mathscr{B} \to \mathscr{M}' \otimes_{\mathscr{A}} \mathscr{B}$; and so on.

(**41.8**) *Direct image.* Let Y be a topological space and let $\xi : Y \to X$ be a continuous map of Y into X.

Let $\mathscr{N}$ be a presheaf of abelian groups (resp: rings, K-modules, K-algebras) on Y. For any open set U in X let $\xi_*(\mathscr{N})(U) = \mathscr{N}(\xi^{-1}(U))$. Then $[\xi_*(\mathscr{N})(U),...]$ is a presheaf of abelian groups (resp: rings, K-modules, K-algebras) on X, where for any open sets $U' \subset U$ in X the restriction map $\xi_*(\mathscr{N})(U) \to \xi_*(\mathscr{N})(U')$ is the restriction map $\mathscr{N}(\xi^{-1}(U)) \to \mathscr{N}(\xi^{-1}(U'))$ belonging to $\mathscr{N}$. The presheaf $[\xi_*(\mathscr{N})(U),...]$ on X is called the direct image of $\mathscr{N}$ by ξ and is denoted by $\xi_*(\mathscr{N})$. For any $b \in Y$ let $a = \xi(b)$; then ξ induces a homomorphism $\alpha : (\xi_*(\mathscr{N}))_a \to \mathscr{N}_b$ where for any neighborhood U of a in X and any $f \in \xi_*(\mathscr{N})(U)$ we take $\alpha(f_a) = f_b$. Note that if $\mathscr{N}$ is a sheaf then so is $\xi_*(\mathscr{N})$.

For any homomorphism $\varphi : \mathscr{N} \to \mathscr{N}'$ of presheaves on Y, the direct image of φ by ξ is the homomorphism $\xi_*(\varphi) : \xi_*(\mathscr{N}) \to \xi_*(\mathscr{N}')$ where for any open set U in X and any $f \in \xi_*(\mathscr{N})(U)$ we take $\xi_*(\varphi)(U)f = \varphi(\xi^{-1}(U))f$. For any $b \in Y$ we then have $\varphi_b \circ \alpha = \alpha' \circ (\xi_*(\varphi))_a$ where $a = \xi(b)$ and $\alpha : (\xi_*(\mathscr{N}))_a \to \mathscr{N}_b$ and $\alpha' : (\xi_*(\mathscr{N}'))_a \to \mathscr{N}'_b$ are the homomorphisms induced by ξ. For any other homomorphism $\psi : \mathscr{N}' \to \mathscr{N}''$ of presheaves on Y we have $\xi_*(\psi \circ \varphi) = \xi_*(\psi) \circ \xi_*(\varphi)$.

Given another continuous map $\eta : Z \to Y$ let $\zeta = \xi \circ \eta$. For any presheaf $\mathscr{L}$ on Z we then have $\zeta_*(\mathscr{L}) = \xi_*(\eta_*(\mathscr{L}))$. For any $c \in Z$ let $b = \eta(c)$ and $a = \xi(b)$; then $\gamma = \beta \circ \alpha$ where $\alpha : (\zeta_*(\mathscr{L}))_a \to (\eta_*(\mathscr{L}))_b$, $\beta : (\eta_*(\mathscr{L}))_b \to \mathscr{L}_c$, $\gamma : (\zeta_*(\mathscr{L}))_a \to \mathscr{L}_c$ are the maps induced by ξ, η, ζ, respectively.

If $\mathscr{B}$ is a presheaf of rings on Y and $\mathscr{N}$ is a $\mathscr{B}$-presheaf-module, then $\xi_*(\mathscr{N})$ becomes a $\xi_*(\mathscr{B})$-presheaf-module; if $\varphi : \mathscr{N} \to \mathscr{N}'$ is a $\mathscr{B}$-presheaf-homomorphism, then $\xi_*(\varphi) : \xi_*(\mathscr{N}) \to \xi_*(\mathscr{N}')$ is a $\xi_*(\mathscr{B})$-presheaf-homomorphism; etc.

For presheaves $\mathscr{M}$ and $\mathscr{N}$ on X and Y, respectively, by definition, a ξ-homomorphism $\varphi : \mathscr{M} \to \mathscr{N}$ is simply a homomorphism $\varphi : \mathscr{M} \to \xi_*(\mathscr{N})$ of presheaves on X.

For any presheaf $\mathscr{N}$ on Y, Supp $\xi_*(\mathscr{N})$ is contained in the closure of ξ(Supp $\mathscr{N}$) in X.

If the map $Y \to \xi(Y)$ induced by ξ is a homeomorphism then for any presheaf $\mathscr{N}$ on Y and $b \in Y$ the induced homomorphism $(\xi_*(\mathscr{N}))_{\xi(b)} \to \mathscr{N}_b$ is an isomorphism.

(**41.9**) *Inverse image.* We shall now generalize the construction given in (41.3). Let Y be a topological space and let $\xi : Y \to X$ be a continuous map of Y into X.

Let $\mathscr{M}$ be a presheaf of abelian groups (resp: rings, K-modules, K-algebras) on X. For any nonempty open set V in Y let $\xi^*(\mathscr{M})(V)$ be the set of all functions g on V which to each b in V assign an element $g_{(b)}$ in $\mathcal{M}_{\xi(b)}$ such that: given $b' \in V$ there exist neighborhoods V' and U of b' and $\xi(b')$ in V and X respectively with $V' \subset V \cap \xi^{-1}(U)$ and an element $f \in \mathcal{M}(U)$ such that $g_{(b)} = f_{\xi(b)}$ for all $b \in V'$. In an obvious manner $\xi^*(\mathcal{M})(V)$ is made into an abelian group (resp: ring, K-module, K-algebra). Then $[\xi^*(\mathcal{M})(V),...]$ is a sheaf of abelian groups (resp: rings, K-modules, K-algebras) on Y where for any nonempty open sets $V' \subset V$ in Y the restriction map $\xi^*(\mathcal{M})(V) \to \xi^*(\mathcal{M})(V')$ is the ordinary restriction map.[9] The sheaf $[\xi^*(\mathcal{M})(V),...]$ on Y is called the inverse image of $\mathcal{M}$ by ξ and is denoted by $\xi^*(\mathcal{M})$. Note that for any open set U in X we have $\eta^*(\mathcal{M}|U) = \xi^*(\mathcal{M})|\xi^{-1}(U)$ where $\eta : \xi^{-1}(U) \to U$ is the map induced by ξ. We define a homomorphism $\theta : \mathcal{M} \to \xi_*(\xi^*(\mathcal{M}))$ of presheaves on X as follows (θ is called the natural homomorphism of $\mathcal{M}$ into $\xi_*(\xi^*(\mathcal{M}))$) : for any open set U in X for which $\xi^{-1}(U) \neq \emptyset$ and for any $f \in \mathcal{M}(U)$ let $\theta(U)f \in \xi_*(\xi^*(\mathcal{M}))(U) = \xi^*(\mathcal{M})(\xi^{-1}(U))$ be given by taking $(\theta(U)f)_{(b)} = f_{\xi(b)}$ for all $b \in \xi^{-1}(U)$. For any homomorphism $\varphi : \xi^*(\mathcal{M}) \to \mathcal{N}$ of sheaves on Y, $\xi_*(\varphi) \circ \theta : \mathcal{M} \to \xi_*(\mathcal{N})$ is then a homomorphism of presheaves on X (i.e., it is a ξ-homomorphism $\mathcal{M} \to \mathcal{N}$), and it can be seen that the mapping $\varphi \to \xi_*(\varphi) \circ \theta$ is a 1-1 mapping of the set of all homomorphisms of $\xi^*(\mathcal{M})$ into $\mathcal{N}$ onto the set of all homomorphisms of $\mathcal{M}$ into $\xi_*(\mathcal{N})$.

For any homomorphism $\varphi : \mathcal{M} \to \mathcal{M}'$ of presheaves on X, the inverse image of φ by ξ is the homomorphism $\xi^*(\varphi) : \xi^*(\mathcal{M}) \to \xi^*(\mathcal{M}')$ defined thus: for any nonempty open set V in Y and any $g \in \xi^*(\mathcal{M})(V)$, $\xi^*(\varphi)(V)g \in \xi^*(\mathcal{M}')(V)$ is given by taking $(\xi^*(\varphi)(V)g)_{(b)} = \varphi_{\xi(b)}g_{(b)}$ for all $b \in V$. For any other homomorphism $\psi : \mathcal{M}' \to \mathcal{M}''$ of presheaves on X we have $\xi^*(\psi \circ \varphi) = \xi^*(\psi) \circ \xi^*(\varphi)$.

If $\eta : Z \to Y$ is any other continuous map and $\zeta = \xi \circ \eta$, then for any presheaf $\mathcal{M}$ on X we get a natural isomorphism $\tau : \zeta^*(\mathcal{M}) \to \eta^*(\xi^*(\mathcal{M}))$, where for any nonempty open set W in Z, any $h \in \zeta^*(\mathcal{M})(W)$ and any $c' \in W$, the element $(\tau(W)h)_{(c')} \in (\xi^*(\mathcal{M}))_{\eta(c')}$ is given thus: by definition there exist neighborhoods W' and U of c' and $\zeta(c')$ in W and X respectively with $W' \subset W \cap \zeta^{-1}(U)$ and $f \in \mathcal{M}(U)$ such that $h_{(c)} = f_{\zeta(c)}$ for all $c \in W'$; we get an element $g \in \xi^*(\mathcal{M})(\xi^{-1}(U))$ by taking $g_{(b)} = f_{\xi(b)}$ for all $b \in \xi^{-1}(U)$; take $(\tau(W)h)_{(c')} = g_{\eta(c')}$.

If $\mathcal{A}$ is a presheaf of rings on X and $\mathcal{M}$ is an $\mathcal{A}$-presheaf-module, then $\xi^*(\mathcal{M})$ becomes a $\xi^*(\mathcal{A})$-module; if $\varphi : \mathcal{M} \to \mathcal{M}'$ is an $\mathcal{A}$-presheaf-homomorphism, then $\xi^*(\varphi) : \xi^*(\mathcal{M}) \to \xi^*(\mathcal{M}')$ is a $\xi^*(\mathcal{A})$-homomorphism; etc.

Let $\mathcal{M}$ be a sheaf on X and let $\theta : \mathcal{M} \to \xi_*(\xi^*(\mathcal{M}))$ be the natural homomorphism. For any $b \in Y$ let $a = \xi(b)$ and let $\lambda_{(b)} = \alpha \circ \theta_a$ where

[9] $\xi^*(\mathcal{M})(\emptyset) = 0$.

$\alpha : (\xi_*(\xi^*(\mathscr{M})))_a \to (\xi^*(\mathscr{M}))_b$ is the homomorphism induced by ξ. Then $\lambda_{(b)} : \mathscr{M}_a \to (\xi^*(\mathscr{M}))_b$ is actually an isomorphism and the inverse isomorphism $\lambda_{(b)}^{-1} : (\xi^*(\mathscr{M}))_b \to \mathscr{M}_a$ is described thus: $\lambda_{(b)}^{-1} g_b = g_{(b)}$ for any neighborhood V of b in Y and any $g \in \xi^*(\mathscr{M})(V)$. These isomorphisms are called natural and via them we may sometimes identify $(\xi^*(\mathscr{M}))_b$ with $\mathscr{M}_a$.

(41.10) *Sheaf induced on a subspace.* We shall now recapitulate the formation of inverse image when Y is a subspace of X and $\xi : Y \to X$ is the canonical injection. In this case, for any presheaf $\mathscr{M}$ on X, $\xi^*(\mathscr{M})$ is also called the sheaf induced by $\mathscr{M}$ on Y; and we have the following description. For any open set U in X with $Y \cap U \neq \emptyset$, $\xi^*(\mathscr{M})(Y \cap U)$ is the set of all functions g on $Y \cap U$ which to each $a \in Y \cap U$ assign an element $g_{(a)} \in \mathscr{M}_a$ such that: given $a' \in Y \cap U$ there exists a neighborhood U' of a' in U and $f \in \mathscr{M}(U')$ such that $g_{(a)} = f_a$ for all $a \in Y \cap U'$; for any open set U_1 in X with $U \subset U_1$ the map $\xi^*(\mathscr{M})(Y \cap U_1) \to \xi^*(\mathscr{M})(Y \cap U)$ is the ordinary restriction map. Let $\theta : \mathscr{M} \to \xi_*(\xi^*(\mathscr{M}))$ be the natural homomorphism and let U be any open set in X with $Y \cap U \neq \emptyset$; then for any $f \in \mathscr{M}(U)$ the element $g = \theta(U)f \in \xi_*(\xi^*(\mathscr{M}))(U) = \xi^*(\mathscr{M})(Y \cap U)$ is given by taking $g_{(a)} = f_a$ for all $a \in Y \cap U$; also $\lambda_{(a)} f_a = g_a$ for all $a \in Y \cap U$ where $\lambda_{(a)} : \mathscr{M}_a \to (\xi^*(\mathscr{M}))_a$ is the natural isomorphism.

If $Y = X$ and ξ is the identity map of X then for any presheaf $\mathscr{M}$ on X we simply have: $\xi^*(\mathscr{M}) = \langle \mathscr{M} \rangle$; $\xi_*(\xi^*(\mathscr{M})) = \xi^*(\mathscr{M})$; the above homomorphism $\theta : \mathscr{M} \to \xi_*(\xi^*(\mathscr{M}))$ is the same as the homomorphism $\theta : \mathscr{M} \to \langle \mathscr{M} \rangle$ given in (41.3); and for any $a \in X$ the isomorphism $\lambda_{(a)} : \mathscr{M}_a \to (\xi^*(\mathscr{M}))_a$ is the same as the isomorphism $\theta_a : \mathscr{M}_a \to \langle \mathscr{M} \rangle_a$ given in (41.3).

If Y is a single point a in X and $\xi : a \to X$ is the canonical injection, then for any presheaf $\mathscr{M}$ on X, $\xi^*(\mathscr{M})$ is naturally isomorphic with the simple sheaf $\mathscr{M}_a\{a\}$.

Example. Take $X = \mathbf{C}^n$, let Y be any subset of X (for instance $Y =$ a closed polycylinder) and let $\xi : Y \to X$ be the canonical injection. Call a function $g : Y \to \mathbf{C}$ to be analytic on Y relative to $X \Leftrightarrow$ for each $a \in Y$ there is a neighborhood U of a in X and an analytic function f on U such that $g|Y \cap U = f|Y \cap U$. Then $\xi^*(\mathscr{R}_{X;\mathbf{C}})(Y)$ can be identified with the set of all functions $g : Y \to \mathbf{C}$ which are analytic on Y relative to X.

(41.11) *Extension by putting zero outside a closed set.* Again let Y be a subspace of X and let $\xi : Y \to X$ be the canonical injection. For any sheaf $\mathscr{N}$ of abelian groups (resp: rings, K-modules, K-algebras) on Y, we get a natural isomorphism $\rho : \mathscr{N} \to \xi^*(\xi_*(\mathscr{N}))$ between $\mathscr{N}$ and the sheaf induced by $\mathcal{M} = \xi_*(\mathcal{N})$ on Y thus: for any nonempty open set V in Y and any $g \in \mathcal{N}(V)$, the element $\rho(V)g \in \xi^*(\xi_*(\mathcal{N}))(V)$ is given by taking $(\rho(V)g)_{(a)} = g_a$ for all $a \in V$. *Now assume that Y is closed in X.* Then $\mathcal{M}$ induces the zero sheaf on $X - Y$, or equivalently Supp $\mathcal{M} \subset Y$. If $\mathcal{M}'$ is any other sheaf of abelian groups (resp: rings, K-modules, K-algebras) on X together with an isomorphism $\rho' : \mathcal{N} \to \xi^*(\mathcal{M}')$ such that Supp $\mathcal{M}' \subset Y$, then there exists a unique isomorphism $\sigma : \mathcal{M} \to \mathcal{M}'$ for which we have $\xi^*(\sigma) \circ \rho = \rho'$. Any such sheaf $\mathcal{M}'$ together with the isomorphism $\rho' : \mathcal{N} \to \xi^*(\mathcal{M}')$ may be called an extension of $\mathcal{N}$ by putting zero on $X - Y$; by abuse of language we may say that $\mathcal{M}'$ is an extension of $\mathcal{N}$ by putting zero on $X - Y$ and ρ' is the canonical isomorphism of $\mathcal{N}$ onto $\xi^*(\mathcal{M}')$. Conversely, if $\mathcal{M}_1$ is any sheaf on X such that Supp $\mathcal{M}_1 \subset Y$ then obviously $\mathcal{M}_1$ together with the identity map $\xi^*(\mathcal{M}_1) \to \xi^*(\mathcal{M}_1)$ is an extension of $\xi^*(\mathcal{M}_1)$ by putting zero on $X - Y$. Thus the study of sheaves on Y is essentially the same thing as the study of sheaves on X whose supports are contained in Y.

Example. Assume that K is a complete nondiscrete valued field, take X and Y to be analytic sets in an open set in K^n with $Y \subset X$ and let $\xi : Y \to X$ be the canonical injection. We get a homomorphism $\mu : \mathcal{R}_X \to \xi_*(\mathcal{R}_Y)$ by taking $\mu(U) : \mathcal{R}_X(U) \to \xi_*(\mathcal{R}_Y)(U) = \mathcal{R}_Y(Y \cap U)$ to be the ordinary restriction map $R(U) \to R(Y \cap U)$ for each open set U in X with $Y \cap U \neq \emptyset$. Obviously Ker $\mu_a = \mathfrak{i}(a, Y, X)$ for all $a \in X$ and hence Ker $\mu = \mathcal{I}(Y, X)$. Clearly μ is an epimorphism and hence μ induces an isomorphism $\nu : \xi_*(\mathcal{R}_Y) \to \mathcal{R}_X/\mathcal{I}(Y, X)$ of sheaves of rings on X; *μ is called the natural epimorphism or the restriction epimorphism of $\mathcal{R}_X$ onto $\xi_*(\mathcal{R}_Y)$.* Also Supp $\mathcal{R}_X/\mathcal{I}(Y, X) = Y$ and hence $\mathcal{R}_X/\mathcal{I}(Y, X)$ is an extension of $\mathcal{R}_Y$ by putting zero on $X - Y$.

§42. COHERENT SHEAVES

Let $\mathcal{A}$ be a sheaf of rings on a topological space X.

(42.1) DEFINITION. Let $\mathcal{M}$ be an $\mathcal{A}$-module. For sections $f_1, \ldots, f_p$ of $\mathcal{M}$ on an open set U in X we set

Thus $\mathcal{R}el(f_1, \ldots, f_p) =$ *sheaf of relations between* $f_1, \ldots, f_p$

$$= \operatorname{Ker} \varphi$$

where $\varphi : \mathcal{A}^p|U \to \mathcal{M}|U$ is the $\mathcal{A}|U$-homomorphism given by

$$\varphi(U')(r_1, \ldots, r_p) = r_1 f_1 + \ldots + r_p f_p \in \mathcal{M}(U')$$

for any open set U' in U and any $(r_1, \ldots, r_p) \in \mathcal{A}^p(U')$. Note that

$\mathcal{R}el(f_1,\ldots, f_p)$ is then an $\mathcal{A}|U$-submodule of $\mathcal{A}^p|U$. For any $a \in U$ we obviously have

$$\varphi_a(r_1,\ldots, r_p) = r_1(f_1)_a + \ldots + r_p(f_p)_a$$

for all $(r_1,\ldots, r_p) \in \mathcal{A}^p_a$, and hence

$$(\mathcal{R}el(f_1,\ldots, f_p))_a = \mathrm{Rel}((f_1)_a,\ldots, (f_p)_a).$$

Also note that φ is an epimorphism $\Leftrightarrow f_1,\ldots, f_p$ generate $\mathcal{M}$ on U, i.e., $\Leftrightarrow \mathcal{M}|U = \{f_1,\ldots, f_p\}(\mathcal{A}|U)$.

Consider the following conditions.

1°) Given $a \in X$, there exists an $\mathcal{A}|U$-epimorphism $\mathcal{A}^q|U \to \mathcal{M}|U$ for some neighborhood U of a in X and some positive integer q.

2°) Given $a \in X$, there exists a finite number of sections of $\mathcal{M}$ on a neighborhood U of a in X which generate $\mathcal{M}$ on U.

3°) Given $a \in X$, there exists an exact sequence $\mathcal{A}^q|U \to \mathcal{A}^p|U \to \mathcal{M}|U \to 0$ of $\mathcal{A}|U$-homomorphisms for some neighborhood U of a in X and some positive integers p, q.

Conditions 1°) and 2°) are obviously equivalent. *$\mathcal{M}$ is said to be a finite $\mathcal{A}$-module (or an $\mathcal{A}$-module of finite type) $\Leftrightarrow$ condition* 1°) *holds. $\mathcal{M}$ is said to be a pseudocoherent $\mathcal{A}$-module $\Leftrightarrow$ condition* 3°) *holds.*

The following two conditions are equivalent.

4°) For any open set U in X and any positive integer p, the kernel of any $\mathcal{A}|U$-homomorphism $\mathcal{A}^p|U \to \mathcal{M}|U$ is a finite $\mathcal{A}|U$-module.

5°) For any finite number of sections $f_1,\ldots, f_p$ of $\mathcal{M}$ on any open set U in X, $\mathcal{R}el(f_1,\ldots, f_p)$ is a finite $\mathcal{A}|U$-module.

$\mathcal{M}$ is said to be a coherent $\mathcal{A}$-module $\Leftrightarrow$ $\mathcal{M}$ is a finite $\mathcal{A}$-module and condition 4°) *holds. $\mathcal{A}$ is said to be a coherent sheaf of rings $\Leftrightarrow$ $\mathcal{A}$ is a coherent $\mathcal{A}$-module.* As immediate consequences of these definitions we get the following where 6) follows from (40.11.2).

1) $\mathcal{M}$ is a finite (resp: coherent, pseudocoherent) $\mathcal{A}$-module $\Leftrightarrow$ given $a \in X$, there exists a neighborhood U of a in X such that $\mathcal{M}|U$ is a finite (resp: coherent, pseudocoherent) $\mathcal{A}|U$-module.

2) Assume that $\mathcal{M}$ is of finite type, let $a \in X$, and let $f_1,\ldots, f_p$ be a finite number of sections of $\mathcal{M}$ on a neighborhood U of a in X. If $f_1,\ldots, f_p$ generate $\mathcal{M}$ at a then they generate $\mathcal{M}$ at each point in some neighborhood of a in U.

3) Let $\mathscr{M}$ be an $\mathscr{A}$-module, let $\mathscr{P}$ and $\mathscr{Q}$ be finite $\mathscr{A}$-submodules of $\mathscr{M}$ and let $a \in X$. If $\mathscr{P}_a = \mathscr{Q}_a$ then $\mathscr{P}_b = \mathscr{Q}_b$ for all b in some neighborhood of a in X.

4) If $\mathscr{M}$ is coherent then $\mathscr{M}$ is pseudocoherent.

5) If $\mathscr{M}$ is coherent and $\mathscr{P}$ is an $\mathscr{A}$-submodule of $\mathscr{M}$, then $\mathscr{P}$ is coherent $\Leftrightarrow$ $\mathscr{P}$ is of finite type.

6) If $\mathscr{M}$ is of finite type then Supp $\mathscr{M}$ is closed in X.

7) Obviously $\mathscr{A}$ (and more generally $\mathscr{A}^q$ for any $q > 0$) is a finite $\mathscr{A}$-module. Hence $\mathscr{A}$ is a coherent sheaf of rings (resp: $\mathscr{A}^q$ is a coherent $\mathscr{A}$-module) $\Leftrightarrow$ given $a \in X$ and any finite number of sections $f_1, \ldots, f_p$ of $\mathscr{A}$ (resp: of $\mathscr{A}^q$) on a neighborhood U of a in X, $\mathscr{R}el(f_1, \ldots, f_p)$ is a finite $\mathscr{A}|U$-module.

In virtue of 7), what we have proved in (15.2) can be restated as

(42.2) *Assume that K is a complete nondiscrete valued field and X is an open set in K^n. Then $\mathscr{R}_{X;K}$ is a coherent sheaf of rings on X and $(\mathscr{R}_{X;K})^q$ is a coherent $\mathscr{R}_{X;K}$-module for any $q > 0$.*

Next we prove the following proposition, (X is again any topological space and $\mathscr{A}$ is any sheaf of rings on X).

(42.3) (Serre). *Let $0 \to \mathscr{L} \xrightarrow{\varphi} \mathscr{M} \xrightarrow{\psi} \mathscr{N} \to 0$ be any exact sequences of $\mathscr{A}$-homomorphisms. If any two of the $\mathscr{A}$-modules $\mathscr{L}$, $\mathscr{M}$, $\mathscr{N}$ are coherent then so is the third.*

PROOF. Suppose $\mathscr{M}$ and $\mathscr{N}$ are coherent. Given $a \in X$ we want to show that $\mathscr{L}|U$ is coherent for some neighborhood U of a in X. Since $\mathscr{M}$ is of finite type, there is an epimorphism $\mathscr{A}^p|U \xrightarrow{\tau} \mathscr{M}|U$ where U is some neighborhood of a in X. Let $\sigma = (\psi|U) \circ \tau$ and $\mathscr{P} = \operatorname{Ker} \sigma$. Then $0 \to \mathscr{P} \xrightarrow{\delta} \mathscr{A}^p|U \xrightarrow{\sigma} \mathscr{N}|U \to 0$ is exact where δ is the canonical injection. Since $\mathscr{N}$ is coherent, it follows that $\mathscr{P}$ is of finite type. Hence $\tau(\mathscr{P})$ is of finite type. Since $\tau(\mathscr{P})$ is a submodule of $\mathscr{M}|U$ and $\mathscr{M}$ is coherent, it follows that $\tau(\mathscr{P})$ is coherent. Now $\varphi|U$ maps $\mathscr{L}|U$ isomorphically onto $\tau(\mathscr{P})$ and hence $\mathscr{L}|U$ is coherent.

Suppose $\mathscr{L}$ and $\mathscr{M}$ are coherent. Then in particular $\mathscr{M}$ is of finite type and hence so is $\mathscr{N}$. To show that $\mathscr{N}$ satisfies condition (42.1.5°), let sections $h_1, \ldots, h_p$ of $\mathscr{N}$ on an open set V in X be given. We want to show that, given $a \in V$ there exists a neighborhood U of a in V such that $\mathscr{R}el(h_1|U, \ldots, h_p|U)$ is a finite $\mathscr{A}|U$-module. Since ψ is an epimorphism, we can find sections $g_1',\ldots, g_p'$ of $\mathcal{M}$ on a neighborhood V' of a in V such that $\psi(g_i') = h_i|V'$ for $i = 1,\ldots, p$. Since $\mathcal{L}$ is of finite type, we can find sections $f_1,\ldots, f_q$ of $\mathcal{L}$ on a neighborhood U of a in V' which generate $\mathcal{L}$ on U. Let $g_i = g_i'|U$. Then $g_1,\ldots, g_p, \varphi(f_1),\ldots, \varphi(f_q)$ are sections of $\mathcal{M}$ on U and $\psi(g_i) = h_i|U$ for $i = 1,\ldots, p$. Now $\mathcal{R}el(g_1,\ldots, g_p, \varphi(f_1),\ldots, \varphi(f_q))$ is of finite type because $\mathcal{M}$ is coherent. Therefore, given $b \in U$ we can find sections $(\alpha_{\lambda 1},\ldots, \alpha_{\lambda p}, \beta_{\lambda 1},\ldots, \beta_{\lambda q})$, $(\lambda = 1,\ldots, \Lambda)$, of $\mathcal{A}^{p+q}$ on a neighborhood U' of b in U which generate $\mathcal{R}el(g_1,\ldots, g_p, \varphi(f_1),\ldots, \varphi(f_q))$ on U'. For any $c \in U$ and any $(r_1,\ldots, r_p) \in \mathcal{A}_c^p$ we have:

$$\begin{aligned}
&(r_1,\ldots, r_p) \in (\mathcal{R}el(h_1,\ldots, h_p))_c \\
\Leftrightarrow\ & r_1(g_1)_c + \ldots + r_p(g_p)_c \in \operatorname{Im} \varphi_c \\
\Leftrightarrow\ & \text{there exists } (s_1,\ldots, s_q) \in \mathcal{A}_c^q \quad \text{such that} \\
& r_1(g_1)_c + \ldots + r_p(g_p)_c + s_1(\varphi(f_1))_c + \ldots + s_q(\varphi(f_q))_c = 0 \\
& \text{i.e.,} \\
& (r_1,\ldots, r_p, s_1,\ldots, s_q) \in (\mathcal{R}el(g_1,\ldots, g_p, \varphi(f_1),\ldots, \varphi(f_q)))_c.
\end{aligned}$$

Therefore the sections $(\alpha_{\lambda 1},\ldots, \alpha_{\lambda p})$, $(\lambda = 1,\ldots, \Lambda)$, of $\mathcal{A}^p$ on U' generate $\mathcal{R}el(h_1,\ldots, h_p)$ on U'. This shows that $\mathcal{R}el(h_1|U,\ldots, h_p|U)$ is a finite $\mathcal{A}|U$-module.

Suppose $\mathcal{L}$ and $\mathcal{N}$ are coherent. Then $\mathcal{L}$ and $\mathcal{N}$ are of finite type, and hence given $a' \in X$ we can find sections $x_1,\ldots, x_u$ of $\mathcal{L}$ and sections $z_1,\ldots, z_w$ of $\mathcal{N}$ on a neighborhood Y of a' in X such that these sections generate, respectively, $\mathcal{L}$ and $\mathcal{N}$ on Y. Since ψ is an epimorphism, we can find sections $y_1,\ldots, y_w$ of $\mathcal{M}$ on a neighborhood Z of a' in Y such that $\psi(y_j) = z_j|Z$ for $j = 1,\ldots, w$. Since the given sequence is exact, it follows that $\varphi(x_1)|Z,\ldots, \varphi(x_u)|Z, y_1,\ldots, y_w$ generate $\mathcal{M}$ on Z. This shows that $\mathcal{M}$ is of finite type. To prove that $\mathcal{M}$ satisfies condition (42.1.5°), let sections $g_1,\ldots, g_p$ of $\mathcal{M}$ on an open set V in X be given. We want to show that given $a \in V$ there exists a finite number of sections of $\mathcal{A}^p$ on a neighborhood U of a in V which generate $\mathcal{R}el(g_1,\ldots, g_p)$ on U. Since $\mathcal{N}$ is coherent, we can find sections $(\alpha_{\mu 1},\ldots, \alpha_{\mu p})$, $(\mu = 1,\ldots, m)$, of $\mathcal{A}^p$ on a neighborhood V' of a in V which generate $\mathcal{R}el(\psi(g_1),\ldots, \psi(g_p))$ on V'. Let

$$g_\mu' = \sum_{i=1}^{p} \alpha_{\mu i} g_i \in \mathcal{M}(V'), \qquad (\mu = 1,\ldots, m).$$

Since the given sequence is exact, there exists a neighborhood V'' of a in V' such that $g_\mu'|V'' \in \varphi(\mathcal{L}(V''))$ for $\mu = 1,\ldots, m$. Since $\mathcal{L}$ is coherent and φ is a monomorphism, we can find sections $(\beta_{\nu 1},\ldots, \beta_{\nu m})$, $(\nu = 1,\ldots, n)$, of $\mathscr{A}^m$ on a neighborhood U of a in V'' which generate $\mathscr{R}el(g'_1,\ldots, g'_m)$ on U. Let

$$\gamma_{\nu i} = \sum_{\mu=1}^{m} \beta_{\nu\mu}\alpha_{\mu i} \in \mathscr{A}(U), \qquad (\nu = 1,\ldots, n).$$

We shall show that the sections $(\gamma_{\nu 1},\ldots, \gamma_{\nu p})$, $(\nu = 1,\ldots, n)$, of $\mathscr{A}^p$ on U generate $\mathscr{R}el(g_1,\ldots, g_p)$ on U, and this will complete the proof. So let $b \in U$ be given and let $\bar{g}_i = (g_i)_b$, $\bar{\alpha}_{\mu i} = (\alpha_{\mu i})_b$, $\bar{g}'_\mu = (g'_\mu)_b$, $\bar{\beta}_{\nu\mu} = (\beta_{\nu\mu})_b$, $\bar{\gamma}_{\nu i} = (\gamma_{\nu i})_b$. We have to show that the elements $(\bar{\gamma}_{\nu 1},\ldots, \bar{\gamma}_{\nu p})$, $(\nu = 1,\ldots, n)$, in $\mathscr{A}_b^p$ generate $\operatorname{Rel}(\bar{g}_1,\ldots, \bar{g}_p)$ as an $\mathscr{A}_b$-module. First

$$\sum_{i=1}^{p} \bar{\gamma}_{\nu i}\bar{g}_i = \sum_{\mu=1}^{m}\sum_{i=1}^{p} \bar{\beta}_{\nu\mu}\bar{\alpha}_{\mu i}\bar{g}_i = \sum_{\mu=1}^{m} \bar{\beta}_{\nu\mu}\bar{g}'_\mu = 0$$

and hence

$$(\bar{\gamma}_{\nu 1},\ldots, \bar{\gamma}_{\nu p}) \in \operatorname{Rel}(\bar{g}_1,\ldots, \bar{g}_p) \qquad \text{for} \quad \nu = 1,\ldots, n.$$

Next, let $(r_1,\ldots, r_p) \in \operatorname{Rel}(\bar{g}_1,\ldots, \bar{g}_p)$ be given. Then

$$r_1\bar{g}_1 + \ldots + r_p\bar{g}_p = 0$$

and hence

$$r_1\psi_b(\bar{g}_1) + \ldots + r_p\psi_b(\bar{g}_p) = 0.$$

Therefore we can find $s_1,\ldots, s_m$ in $\mathscr{A}_b$ such that

$$r_i = \sum_{\mu=1}^{m} s_\mu\bar{\alpha}_{\mu i} \qquad \text{for} \quad i = 1,\ldots, p,$$

and then

$$\sum_{\mu=1}^{m} s_\mu\bar{g}'_\mu = \sum_{i=1}^{p}\sum_{\mu=1}^{m} s_\mu\bar{\alpha}_{\mu i}\bar{g}_i = \sum_{i=1}^{p} r_i\bar{g}_i = 0,$$

i.e.,

$$(s_1,\ldots, s_m) \in \operatorname{Rel}(\bar{g}'_1,\ldots, \bar{g}'_m).$$

Hence we can find $t_1,\ldots, t_n$ in $\mathscr{A}_b$ such that

$$s_\mu = \sum_{\nu=1}^{n} t_\nu\bar{\beta}_{\nu\mu} \qquad \text{for} \quad \mu = 1,\ldots, m,$$

and then for $i = 1,\ldots, p$ we get

$$r_i = \sum_{\mu=1}^{m} s_\mu \bar{\alpha}_{\mu i} = \sum_{\mu=1}^{m} \left(\sum_{\nu=1}^{n} t_\nu \bar{\beta}_{\nu\mu} \right) \bar{\alpha}_{\mu i} = \sum_{\nu=1}^{n} t_\nu \bar{\gamma}_{\nu i}.$$

Therefore $(r_1,\ldots, r_p)$ is in the $\mathscr{A}_b$-module generated by the elements $(\bar{\gamma}_{\nu 1},\ldots, \bar{\gamma}_{\nu p})$, $(\nu = 1,\ldots, n)$.

We shall now deduce several corollaries of the above proposition.

(42.4) *The direct sum of any finite number of coherent $\mathscr{A}$-modules is coherent.*

Follows from (42.3).

(42.5) *Let $\varphi : \mathscr{M} \to \mathscr{N}$ be any $\mathscr{A}$-homomorphism. If $\mathscr{M}$ and $\mathscr{N}$ are coherent then so are* Ker φ, Coker φ, Im φ.

PROOF. Since $\mathscr{M}$ is of finite type, so is Im φ. Hence Im φ is coherent because it is a submodule of the coherent module $\mathscr{N}$. The coherence of Ker φ and Coker φ now follows by (42.3) from the exact sequences

$$0 \to \operatorname{Ker} \varphi \to \mathscr{M} \to \operatorname{Im} \varphi \to 0, \qquad 0 \to \operatorname{Im} \varphi \to \mathscr{N} \to \operatorname{Coker} \varphi \to 0.$$

(42.6) *If $\mathscr{P}$ and $\mathscr{Q}$ are coherent submodules of a coherent $\mathscr{A}$-module $\mathscr{M}$, then $\mathscr{P} + \mathscr{Q}$ and $\mathscr{P} \cap \mathscr{Q}$ are coherent.*

PROOF. Since $\mathscr{P}$ and $\mathscr{Q}$ are of finite type, so is $\mathscr{P} + \mathscr{Q}$. Hence $\mathscr{P} + \mathscr{Q}$ is coherent because it is a submodule of the coherent module $\mathscr{M}$. Now $\mathscr{M}/\mathscr{Q}$ is coherent by (42.3) and hence $\mathscr{P} \cap \mathscr{Q}$ is coherent by (42.5) because $\mathscr{P} \cap \mathscr{Q} = \operatorname{Ker}(\tau|\mathscr{P})$ where τ is the natural epimorphism $\mathscr{M} \to \mathscr{M}/\mathscr{Q}$.

(42.7) *If $\mathscr{M}$ and $\mathscr{N}$ are coherent $\mathscr{A}$-modules then so is $\mathscr{M} \otimes \mathscr{N}$.*

PROOF. Since the problem is local and since $\mathscr{M}$ is coherent, in view of (42.1.4) we can assume an exact sequence $\mathscr{A}^q \to \mathscr{A}^p \to \mathscr{M} \to 0$. Since $\otimes$ is right exact, this yields the exact sequence

$$\mathscr{A}^q \otimes \mathscr{N} \xrightarrow{\varphi} \mathscr{A}^p \otimes \mathscr{N} \to \mathscr{M} \otimes \mathscr{N} \to 0$$

and hence $\mathscr{M} \otimes \mathscr{N} \approx \operatorname{Coker} \varphi$. Now $\mathscr{A}^q \otimes \mathscr{N} \approx \mathscr{N}^q$ and $\mathscr{A}^p \otimes \mathscr{N} \approx \mathscr{N}^p$. Also $\mathscr{N}^q$ and $\mathscr{N}^p$ are coherent by (42.4) and hence $\mathscr{M} \otimes \mathscr{N}$ is coherent by (42.5).

(42.8) *If $\mathscr{M}$ and $\mathscr{N}$ are coherent $\mathscr{A}$-modules then so is $\mathscr{H}om(\mathscr{M}, \mathscr{N})$.*

PROOF. Since the problem is local and since $\mathscr{M}$ is coherent, in view of (42.1.4) we can assume an exact sequence $\mathscr{A}^q \to \mathscr{A}^p \to \mathscr{M} \to 0$. Since $\mathscr{H}om$ is left exact, this yields the exact sequence

$$0 \to \mathscr{H}om(\mathscr{M}, \mathscr{N}) \to \mathscr{H}om(\mathscr{A}^p, \mathscr{N}) \xrightarrow{\varphi} \mathscr{H}om(\mathscr{A}^q, \mathscr{N})$$

and hence $\mathscr{H}om(\mathscr{M}, \mathscr{N}) \approx \operatorname{Ker} \varphi$. Now $\mathscr{H}om(\mathscr{A}^p, \mathscr{N}) \approx \mathscr{N}^p$ and $\mathscr{H}om(\mathscr{A}^q, \mathscr{N}) \approx \mathscr{N}^q$. Also $\mathscr{N}^p$ and $\mathscr{N}^q$ are coherent by (42.4) and hence $\mathscr{H}om(\mathscr{M}, \mathscr{N})$ is coherent by (42.5).

(42.9) *Let $\mathscr{M}$ and $\mathscr{N}$ be $\mathscr{A}$-modules. If $\mathscr{M}$ is pseudocoherent, then for any $a \in X$ the natural $\mathscr{A}_a$-homomorphism $(\mathscr{H}om_{\mathscr{A}}(\mathscr{M},\mathscr{N}))_a \to$ $\operatorname{Hom}_{\mathscr{A}_a}(\mathscr{M}_a, \mathscr{N}_a)$ is an isomorphism.*

PROOF. Since the problem is local, we can assume an exact sequence $\mathscr{A}^q \to \mathscr{A}^p \to \mathscr{M} \to 0$. This induces the communative diagram

$$\begin{array}{ccccccc} 0 \to & (\mathscr{H}om_{\mathscr{A}}(\mathscr{M},\mathscr{N}))_a & \to & (\mathscr{H}om_{\mathscr{A}}(\mathscr{A}^p,\mathscr{N}))_a & \to & (\mathscr{H}om_{\mathscr{A}}(\mathscr{A}^q, \mathscr{N}))_a \\ & \downarrow & & \downarrow & & \downarrow \\ 0 \to & \operatorname{Hom}_{\mathscr{A}_a}(\mathscr{M}_a,\mathscr{N}_a) & \to & \operatorname{Hom}_{\mathscr{A}_a}(\mathscr{A}_a^p,\mathscr{N}_a) & \to & \operatorname{Hom}_{\mathscr{A}_a}(\mathscr{A}_a^q, \mathscr{N}_a) \end{array}$$

with exact rows. As remarked in (41.6), the last two vertical arrows are isomorphisms and hence so is the first.

(42.10) *Assume that $\mathscr{A}$ is a coherent sheaf of rings and let $\mathscr{M}$ be an $\mathscr{A}$-module. Then $\mathscr{M}$ is coherent $\Leftrightarrow$ $\mathscr{M}$ is pseudocoherent. If $\mathscr{M}$ is coherent and $f_1, \ldots, f_p$ are any finite number of sections of $\mathscr{M}$ on any open set U in X then $\mathscr{R}el(f_1, \ldots, f_p)$ is a coherent $\mathscr{A}|U$-module.*

PROOF. By (42.4), $\mathscr{A}^p$ is coherent for all $p > 0$. Hence our assertions follow from (42.1.4, 42.5) and (42.1.5), respectively.

(42.11) *Assume that $\mathscr{A}$ is a coherent sheaf of rings and let $\mathscr{M}$ be a coherent $\mathscr{A}$-module. Then* Anh $\mathscr{M}$ *is a coherent $\mathscr{A}$-module and* $(\operatorname{Anh} \mathscr{M})_a = \operatorname{Anh} \mathscr{M}_a$ *for all $a \in X$.*

PROOF. $\mathscr{H}om(\mathscr{M}, \mathscr{M})$ is coherent by (42.8), and hence Anh $\mathscr{M}$ is coherent by (42.5). The second assertion follows from (42.9).

(42.12) *Assume that $\mathscr{A}$ is a coherent sheaf of rings and let $\mathscr{P}$, $\mathscr{Q}$, $\mathscr{M}$ be coherent $\mathscr{A}$-modules where $\mathscr{P}$ and $\mathscr{Q}$ are $\mathscr{A}$-submodules of $\mathscr{M}$. Then $\mathscr{P} : \mathscr{Q}$ is a coherent $\mathscr{A}$-module and $(\mathscr{P} : \mathscr{Q})_a = \mathscr{P}_a : \mathscr{Q}_a$ for all $a \in X$.*

PROOF. $\mathscr{P} + \mathscr{Q}$ is coherent by (42.6) and hence $(\mathscr{P} + \mathscr{Q})/\mathscr{P}$ is coherent by (42.3). Now apply (42.11) to $(\mathscr{P} + \mathscr{Q})/\mathscr{P}$.

(**42.13**) *Let f and g in $\mathscr{A}(X)$ and $a \in X$ be given. Assume that $\mathscr{A}$ is a coherent sheaf of rings and $\mathscr{A}_a$ is noetherian. Then there exists a neighborhood U of a in X such that*

$$(f_b\mathscr{A}_b : g_b^m\mathscr{A}_b) = (f_b\mathscr{A}_b : g_b^n\mathscr{A}_b)$$

for all $m \geqq n$ and for all $b \in U$.

PROOF. Now

$$(f_a\mathscr{A}_a : g_a\mathscr{A}_a) \subset (f_a\mathscr{A}_a : g_a^2\mathscr{A}_a) \subset (f_a\mathscr{A}_a : g_a^3\mathscr{A}_a) \subset \ldots$$

is an increasing sequence of ideals in the noetherian ring $\mathscr{A}_a$ and hence there exists a positive integer n such that

$$(f_a\mathscr{A}_a : g_a^{n+1}\mathscr{A}_a) = (f_a\mathscr{A}_a : g_a^n\mathscr{A}_a)$$

i.e.,

$$((f_a\mathscr{A}_a : g_a^n\mathscr{A}_a) : g_a\mathscr{A}_a) = (f_a\mathscr{A}_a : g_a^n\mathscr{A}_a).$$

Let $\mathscr{P} = (f\mathscr{A} : g^n\mathscr{A})$ and $\mathscr{Q} = (\mathscr{P} : g\mathscr{A})$. Now $f\mathscr{A}$ and $g^n\mathscr{A}$ are coherent $\mathscr{A}$-ideals and hence by (42.12), $\mathscr{P}$ is a coherent $\mathscr{A}$-ideal and

$$\mathscr{P}_b = (f_b\mathscr{A}_b : g_b^n\mathscr{A}_b) \qquad \text{for all} \quad b \in X.$$

Again $g\mathscr{A}$ is a coherent $\mathscr{A}$-ideal and hence by (42.12), $\mathscr{Q}$ is coherent and

$$\mathscr{Q}_b = (\mathscr{P}_b : g_bA_b) \qquad \text{for all} \quad b \in X.$$

Taking $b = a$ we thus get that $\mathscr{Q}_a = \mathscr{P}_a$. Therefore by (42.1.3) there exists a neighborhood U of a in X such that for all $b \in U$ we have $\mathscr{Q}_b = \mathscr{P}_b$ and hence

$$((f_b\mathscr{A}_b : g_b^n\mathscr{A}_b) : g_b\mathscr{A}_b) = (f_b\mathscr{A}_b : g_b^n\mathscr{A}_b).$$

Therefore

$$(f_b\mathscr{A}_b : g_b^m\mathscr{A}_b) = (f_b\mathscr{A}_b : g_b^n\mathscr{A}_b)$$

for all $m \geqq n$ and for all $b \in U$.

(**42.14**) *Assume that $\mathscr{A}$ is a coherent sheaf of rings and let $\mathscr{M}$ be a coherent $\mathscr{A}$-module. Then* Supp $\mathscr{M}$ = Supp $(\mathscr{A}/(0 : \mathscr{M}))$.

PROOF. For any $a \in X$, by (42.12) we have that $(0 : \mathscr{M})_a = (0 : \mathscr{M}_a)$ and hence:

$a \in \operatorname{Supp}(\mathscr{A}/(0 : \mathscr{M})) \Leftrightarrow \mathscr{A}_a/(0 : \mathscr{M}_a) \neq 0 \Leftrightarrow (0 : \mathscr{M}_a) \neq \mathscr{A}_a \Leftrightarrow$
$\mathscr{M}_a \neq 0 \Leftrightarrow a \in \operatorname{Supp} \mathscr{M}$.

(42.15) *Let $\mu : \mathscr{A} \to \bar{\mathscr{A}}$ be an epimorphism of sheaves of rings on X. Assume that $\mathscr{A}$ is a coherent sheaf of rings and* Ker μ *is a coherent $\mathscr{A}$-ideal. Then $\bar{\mathscr{A}}$ is a coherent sheaf of rings. For any $\bar{\mathscr{A}}$-module $\mathscr{M}$, considering $\mathscr{M}_{[\mu]} = \mathscr{M}$ to be an $\mathscr{A}$-module, we have that $\mathscr{M}$ is a finite (resp: coherent) $\bar{\mathscr{A}}$-module $\Leftrightarrow$ $\mathscr{M}$ is a finite (resp: coherent) $\mathscr{A}$-module.*

Proof. Obviously, $\mathscr{M}$ is a finite $\bar{\mathscr{A}}$-module $\Leftrightarrow$ $\mathscr{M}$ is a finite $\mathscr{A}$-module. Since Ker μ is a coherent $\mathscr{A}$-module, by (42.3) it follows that $\bar{\mathscr{A}}$ is a coherent $\mathscr{A}$-module. Now suppose that $\mathscr{M}$ is a coherent $\mathscr{A}$-module. Let any open set U in X and any $\bar{\mathscr{A}}|U$-homomorphism $\varphi : \bar{\mathscr{A}}^p|U \to \mathscr{M}|U$ be given. Let $\nu : \mathscr{A}^p|U \to \bar{\mathscr{A}}^p|U$ be the $\mathscr{A}|U$-epimorphism induced by μ. Then $\varphi \circ \nu : \mathscr{A}^p|U \to \mathscr{M}|U$ is an $\mathscr{A}|U$-homomorphism and hence Ker $\varphi \circ \nu$ is a finite $\mathscr{A}|U$-module. Therefore $\nu(\text{Ker } \varphi \circ \nu)$ is a finite $\bar{\mathscr{A}}|U$-module. Obviously $\nu(\text{Ker } \varphi \circ \nu) = \text{Ker } \varphi$. This shows that $\mathscr{M}$ is a coherent $\bar{\mathscr{A}}$-module. In particular, since $\bar{\mathscr{A}}$ is a coherent $\mathscr{A}$-module, we get that $\bar{\mathscr{A}}$ is a coherent $\bar{\mathscr{A}}$-module, i.e., $\bar{\mathscr{A}}$ is a coherent sheaf of rings. Conversely, suppose that $\mathscr{M}$ is a coherent $\bar{\mathscr{A}}$-module. Given $a \in X$ we can find a neighborhood U of a in X and an exact sequence $\bar{\mathscr{A}}^q|U \to \bar{\mathscr{A}}^p|U \to \mathscr{M}|U \to 0$ of $\bar{\mathscr{A}}|U$-homomorphisms. This can also be regarded as a sequence of $\mathscr{A}|U$-homomorphisms and as such it is still exact. Since $\bar{\mathscr{A}}|U$ is a coherent $\mathscr{A}|U$-module, by (42.4, 42.5) we deduce that $\mathscr{M}|U$ is a coherent $\mathscr{A}|U$-module. This shows that $\mathscr{M}$ is a coherent $\mathscr{A}$-module.

(42.16) *Let Y be a closed subset of X and let $\xi : Y \to X$ be the canonical injection. Let $\mathscr{B}$ be a sheaf of rings on Y and let $\mathscr{N}$ be a $\mathscr{B}$-module. Then $\mathscr{N}$ is a finite (resp: coherent) $\mathscr{B}$-module $\Leftrightarrow$ $\xi_*(\mathscr{N})$ is a finite (resp: coherent) $\xi_*(\mathscr{B})$-module. In particular, taking $\mathscr{B}$ for $\mathscr{N}$ we get that: $\mathscr{B}$ is a coherent sheaf of rings on Y $\Leftrightarrow$ $\xi_*(\mathscr{B})$ is a coherent sheaf of rings on X.*

Proof. Let $\bar{\mathscr{A}} = \xi_*(\mathscr{B})$ and $\mathscr{M} = \xi_*(\mathscr{N})$. Then $\bar{\mathscr{A}}$ as well as $\mathscr{M}$ induce the zero sheaf on $X - Y$ and hence our assertion follows from the following observation. Let U be any open set in X such that $V = Y \cap U \neq \emptyset$, and let $\eta : V \to U$ be the canonical injection. Then: 1°) any $\mathscr{B}|V$-homomorphism $\varphi : (\mathscr{B}|V)^p \to \mathscr{N}|V$ gives the $\bar{\mathscr{A}}|U$-homomorphism $\eta_*(\varphi) : (\bar{\mathscr{A}}|U)^p \to \mathscr{M}|U$ and every $\bar{\mathscr{A}}|U$-homomorphism $(\bar{\mathscr{A}}|U)^p \to \mathscr{M}|U$ is of this form; 2°) φ is an epimorphism $\Leftrightarrow$ $\eta_*(\varphi)$ is an epimorphism; and 3°) $\eta_*(\text{Ker } \varphi) = \text{Ker } \eta_*(\varphi)$.

(42.17) *Assume that $\mathscr{A}$ is a coherent sheaf of rings on X. Let Y be a closed subset of X and let $\xi : Y \to X$ be the canonical injection. Let $\mathscr{B}$ be a sheaf of rings on Y and let $\mu : \mathscr{A} \to \xi_*(\mathscr{B})$ be an epimorphism of sheaves of rings on X such that* Ker μ *is a coherent $\mathscr{A}$-ideal. Then $\mathscr{B}$ is a coherent sheaf of rings on Y; and for any $\mathscr{B}$-module $\mathscr{N}$ we have that: $\mathscr{N}$ is a finite (resp: coherent) $\mathscr{B}$-module $\Leftrightarrow (\xi_*(\mathscr{N}))_{[\mu]}$ is a finite (resp: coherent) $\mathscr{A}$-module.*

PROOF. Follows from (42.15, 42.16) after taking $\xi_*(\mathscr{B})$ for $\bar{\mathscr{A}}$ and $\xi_*(\mathscr{N})$ for $\mathscr{M}$ in (42.15).

Now we are ready to reformulate (33.23) in the language of sheaves.

(42.18) *Assume that K is an algebraically closed complete nondiscrete valued field and X is an open set in K^n. Let Y be any analytic set in X. Then $\mathscr{I}(Y, X)$ a coherent ideal in $\mathscr{R}_{X;K}$ and $\mathscr{R}_{Y;K}$ is a coherent sheaf of rings on Y.*

PROOF. $\mathscr{I}(Y, X)$ is a finite $(\mathscr{R}_{X;K})$-ideal by (33.23), and $\mathscr{R}_{X;K}$ is a coherent sheaf of rings on X by (42.2). Therefore $\mathscr{I}(Y, X)$ a coherent ideal in $\mathscr{R}_{X;K}$ by (42.1.5). Let $\xi : Y \to X$ be the canonical injection. Then $\mathscr{I}(Y, X) = \text{Ker}\,\mu$ where $\mu : \mathscr{R}_{X;K} \to \xi_*(\mathscr{R}_{Y;K})$ is the restriction epimorphism (see 41.11), and hence $\mathscr{R}_{Y;K}$ is a coherent sheaf of rings on Y by (42.17).

CHAPTER VII

Analytic Spaces

In this chapter K will denote a complete nondiscrete valued field. From §44 onward, K will be assumed to be algebraically closed.

In this chapter (as in the previous chapter), for a point a in a topological space X, the germ of F in X at a will be denoted by F_a instead of $\gamma_a F$; (F = a function or a set of functions on a neighborhood of a in X, F = a subset of X, etc.). The points for which we shall use this notation will always be denoted by the letters a, b, c which themselves may carry subscripts and superscripts. These three letters will not be used as ordinary subscripts in the sense of running indices (like i, j, k). However, we shall be allowed to use the letters a, b, c as subscripts in the following sense: not having defined a certain symbol, say λ, we may define λ_a (usually a mapping) for all $a \in X$; this cannot be confused with the germ of λ at a because λ has no independent meaning.

§43. DEFINITIONS

(43.1) *K-space.* A K-space is a topological space X together with a sheaf (called the structure sheaf) $\mathcal{O}_X$ of K-algebras on X which is a subsheaf of the sheaf $\mathcal{E}_X = \mathcal{E}_{X;K}$ of K-algebras on X; we may express this by saying that $(X, \mathcal{O}_X)$ is a K-space. For any open set U in X, $(U, \mathcal{O}_X|U)$ is again a K-space.

Let X and Y be topological spaces and let $\xi: Y \to X$ be a continuous map. Then ξ induces a homomorphism $\hat{\xi}: \mathcal{E}_X \to \xi_*(\mathcal{E}_Y)$ of sheaves of K-algebras on X which is given thus: for any open set U in X with $\xi^{-1}(U) \neq \emptyset$ and any $f \in \mathcal{E}_X(U) = \mathfrak{E}(U)$, $\hat{\xi}(U)f = f \circ (\xi|\xi^{-1}(U)) \in \mathfrak{E}(\xi^{-1}(U)) = \xi_*(\mathcal{E}_Y)(U)$. For any $b \in Y$ let $a = \xi(b)$. The K-algebra-homomorphism $(\xi_*(\mathcal{E}_Y))_a \to (\mathcal{E}_Y)_b = \mathfrak{E}(b, Y)$ induced by ξ is denoted by $\xi'_{(b)}$; see (41.8).

The K-algebra-homomorphism

$$\xi'_{(b)} \circ \hat{\xi}_a : \mathfrak{E}(a, X) = (\mathscr{E}_X)_a \to (\mathscr{E}_Y)_b = \mathfrak{E}(b, Y)$$

is again said to be induced by ξ and is denoted by $\bar{\xi}_{(b)}$. Note that for any neighborhood U of a in X and $f \in \mathfrak{E}(U)$ we simply have: $\bar{\xi}_{(b)}(f_a) = (f \circ (\xi|\xi^{-1}(U)))_b$. For any other continuous map $\eta: Z \to Y$ we have $\hat{\zeta} = \xi_*(\hat{\eta}) \circ \hat{\xi}$ where $\zeta = \xi \circ \eta$; and for any $c \in \eta^{-1}(b)$ we have $\bar{\zeta}_{(c)} = \bar{\eta}_{(c)} \circ \bar{\xi}_{(b)}$.

Let $(X, \mathcal{O}_X)$ and $(Y, \mathcal{O}_Y)$ be K-spaces and let $\xi: Y \to X$ be a map. ξ is said to be permissible for the pair $(\mathcal{O}_Y, \mathcal{O}_X) \Leftrightarrow \xi$ is continuous and $\hat{\xi}(\mathcal{O}_X) \subset \xi_*(\mathcal{O}_Y)$; and then the homomorphism $\mathcal{O}_X \to \xi_*(\mathcal{O}_Y)$ of sheaves of K-algebras on X induced by $\hat{\xi}$ is denoted by $\tilde{\xi}$. Note that if $(V_i)_{i \in I}$ is a covering of Y by nonempty open sets and $(U_i)_{i \in I}$ are open sets in X such that $\xi(V_i) \subset U_i$ for all i in I, then ξ is permissible for $(\mathcal{O}_Y, \mathcal{O}_X) \Leftrightarrow$ for all i in I the map $V_i \to U_i$ induced by ξ is permissible for $(\mathcal{O}_Y|V_i, \mathcal{O}_X|U_i)$. Also note that if ξ is continuous, then ξ is permissible for $(\mathcal{O}_Y, \mathcal{O}_X) \Leftrightarrow$ for all $b \in Y$ we have $\bar{\xi}_{(b)}((\mathcal{O}_X)_a) \subset (\mathcal{O}_Y)_b$ where $a = \xi(b)$. ξ is said to be an isomorphism for $(\mathcal{O}_Y, \mathcal{O}_X)$ (or an isomorphism of K-spaces) $\Leftrightarrow \xi: Y \to X$ is a homeomorphism and $\hat{\xi}(\mathcal{O}_X) = \xi_*(\mathcal{O}_Y)$, i.e., $\Leftrightarrow \xi: Y \to X$ is a homeomorphism which is permissible for $(\mathcal{O}_Y, \mathcal{O}_X)$ and $\tilde{\xi}(\mathcal{O}_X) = \xi_*(\mathcal{O}_Y)$. In other words, an isomorphism $\xi: Y \to X$ of K-spaces is a homeomorphism such that ξ is permissible for $(\mathcal{O}_Y, \mathcal{O}_X)$ and $\omega = \xi^{-1}$ is permissible for $(\mathcal{O}_X, \mathcal{O}_Y)$; and then obviously $\tilde{\xi}: \mathcal{O}_X \to \xi_*(\mathcal{O}_Y)$ and $\tilde{\omega}: \mathcal{O}_Y \to \omega_*(\mathcal{O}_X)$ are isomorphisms of sheaves of K-algebras. Note that if $\mathscr{Q}$ is any other subsheaf of $\mathscr{E}_X$, then the identity map of X is permissible for $(\mathcal{O}_X, \mathscr{Q}) \Leftrightarrow \mathscr{Q}$ is a subsheaf of $\mathcal{O}_X$.

If $(X, \mathcal{O}_X)$, $(Y, \mathcal{O}_Y)$, $(Z, \mathcal{O}_Z)$ are K-spaces and $\xi: Y \to X$ and $\eta: Z \to Y$ are permissible for $(\mathcal{O}_Y, \mathcal{O}_X)$ and $(\mathcal{O}_Z, \mathcal{O}_Y)$, respectively, then obviously $\zeta = \xi \circ \eta: Z \to X$ is permissible for $(\mathcal{O}_Z, \mathcal{O}_X)$ and $\tilde{\zeta} = \xi_*(\tilde{\eta}) \circ \tilde{\xi}$.

(43.2) *Analytic K-space.* A K-space $(X, \mathcal{O}_X)$ is said to be an analytic K-space provided X is a nonempty Hausdorff space and each $a \in X$ has a neighborhood U in X such that $(U, \mathcal{O}_X|U)$ is isomorphic, as a K-space, to $(V, \mathscr{R}_V)$ for some analytic set V in an open set in K^n for some n. A nonempty analytic set V in an open set in K^n is to be regarded as an analytic K-space with structure sheaf $\mathscr{R}_V$. For any analytic K-space $(X, \mathcal{O}_X)$ and any nonempty open set U in X, unless otherwise stated, U is to be regarded as an analytic K-space with structure sheaf $\mathcal{O}_X|U$. For analytic spaces $(X, \mathcal{O}_X)$ and $(Y, \mathcal{O}_Y)$, by definition: an analytic function on a nonempty open set U in X is simply an element of $\mathcal{O}_X(U)$; an analytic map $\xi: Y \to X$ is simply a map which is permissible for $(\mathcal{O}_Y, \mathcal{O}_X)$; and a bianalytic map $\xi: Y \to X$ is simply a map which is an isomorphism for

$(\mathcal{O}_Y, \mathcal{O}_X)$. Thus, for any analytic K-space X and any $a \in X$ there exists a bianalytic map of a neighborhood of a in X onto an analytic set in an open set in K^n. Note that this definition of a bianalytic map agrees with the definition given in (10.9).

Unless otherwise stated, the structure sheaves of analytic K-spaces $X, Y, V, \ldots$ will be denoted by $\mathcal{O}_X, \mathcal{O}_Y, \mathcal{O}_V, \ldots$. An analytic **C**-space may also be called an "analytic complex space" or simply a "complex space".

(**43.3**) *Gluing together analytic K-spaces.*

1) For any open sets V and V' in a K-space $(Y, \mathcal{O}_Y)$ we obviously have $(\mathcal{O}_Y|V)|V \cap V' = (\mathcal{O}_Y|V')|V \cap V'$.

Conversely, let Y be a nonempty topological space, let $(V_i)_{i \in I}$ be an open covering of Y, and let $\mathcal{O}_{V_i}$ be a subsheaf of $\mathcal{E}_{V_i}$ for all i in I, such that $\mathcal{O}_{V_i}|V_i \cap V_j = \mathcal{O}_{V_j}|V_i \cap V_j$ for all i, j in I. Then there exists a unique subsheaf $\mathcal{O}_Y$ of $\mathcal{E}_Y$ such that $\mathcal{O}_Y|V_i = \mathcal{O}_{V_i}$ for all i in I; namely, for each nonempty open set V in Y take

$$\mathcal{O}_Y(V) = \{f \in \mathfrak{E}(V) : f\,|V_i \cap V \in \mathcal{O}_{V_i}(V_i \cap V) \text{ for all } i \text{ in } I\}.$$

If furthermore Y is Hausdorff and $(V_i, \mathcal{O}_{V_i})$ is an analytic K-space for all i in I, then $(Y, \mathcal{O}_Y)$ is an analytic K-space. For an example of this method of defining an analytic K-space, see the definition of a projective space given in (36.8).

2) Let Y be a nonempty topological space and for each $b \in Y$ let a K-subalgebra G_b of $\mathfrak{E}(b, Y)$ be given. We get a subsheaf $\mathcal{H}$ of $\mathcal{E}_Y$ by taking

$$\mathcal{H}(V) = \{f \in \mathfrak{E}(V) : f_b \in G_b \text{ for all } b \in V\}$$

for each nonempty open set V in Y. The following three conditions are obviously equivalent.

i) $\mathcal{H}_b = G_b$ for all $b \in Y$.

ii) Given $b' \in Y$ and $f' \in G_{b'}$ there exists a neighborhood V of b' in Y and $f \in \mathfrak{E}(V)$ such that $f_{b'} = f'$ and $f_b \in G_b$ for all $b \in V$.

iii) There exists a covering $(V_i)_{i \in I}$ of Y by nonempty open sets and for each i in I there exists a subsheaf $\mathcal{H}_i$ of $\mathcal{E}_{V_i}$ such that $(\mathcal{H}_i)_b = G_b$ for all $b \in V_i$.

Note that if condition i) is satisfied then $\mathcal{H}$ is the unique subsheaf of $\mathcal{E}_Y$ satisfying that condition.

Let Y be a topological space, let $(X, \mathcal{O}_X)$ be an analytic K-space, and let $\xi: Y \to X$ be a continuous map. For each $b \in Y$ let a ring homomorphism $\delta_b: Q_a \to \mathfrak{E}(b, Y)$ be given where $a = \xi(b)$ and Q_a is an overring of $(\mathcal{O}_X)_a$ such that $\delta_b|(\mathcal{O}_X)_a = \xi_{(b)}|(\mathcal{O}_X)_a$; and let $G_b = \operatorname{Im} \delta_b$. Let $\mathscr{H}$ be the subsheaf of $\mathscr{E}_Y$ given by taking

$$\mathscr{H}(V) = \{f \in \mathfrak{E}(V): f_b \in G_b \text{ for all } b \in V\}$$

for each nonempty open set V in Y. Then $(Y, \mathscr{H})$ is a K-space and $\xi: Y \to X$ is permissible for $(\mathscr{H}, \mathcal{O}_X)$. Under certain conditions it may happen that $(Y, \mathscr{H})$ is an analytic K-space, and then ξ would be analytic. For examples of this method of defining an analytic K-space see (44.46, 46.31, 46.35).

Recall the following lemma from topology; see Bourbaki [**1**: pp. 36–38].

3) Let $(Y_i)_{i\in I}$ be a family of nonempty topological spaces. For all i, j in I let Y_{ij} be an open set in Y_i such that: $Y_{ij} = \emptyset \Leftrightarrow Y_{ji} = \emptyset$. For all i, j in I for which $Y_{ij} \neq \emptyset$ let $\lambda_{ji}: Y_{ij} \to Y_{ji}$ be a homeomorphism. Assume that:

1′) $Y_{ii} = Y_i$ and $\lambda_{ii} =$ identity map of Y_i for all i in I; and
2′) $\lambda_{ji}(Y_{ij} \cap Y_{ik}) \subset Y_{jk}$ and $\lambda_{ki}|Y_{ij} \cap Y_{ik} = \lambda_{kj} \circ (\lambda_{ji}|Y_{ij} \cap Y_{ik})$ for all i, j, k in I for which $Y_{ij} \cap Y_{ik} \neq \emptyset$.[1]

Then there exists a topological space Y, an open covering $(V_i)_{i\in I}$ of Y, and a homeomorphism $\lambda_i: Y_i \to V_i$ for each i in I, such that

3′) for all i, j in I, $b_i \in Y_i$, $b_j \in Y_j$ we have:

$$\lambda_i(b_i) = \lambda_j(b_j) \Leftrightarrow b_i \in Y_{ij},\ b_j \in Y_{ji}, \text{ and } \lambda_{ji}(b_i) = b_j.$$

Using 1) and 3) we now prove:

4) Let X be a nonempty topological space, let $(X_i)_{i\in I}$ be an open covering of X, let $(Y_i)_{i\in I}$ be a family of nonempty topological spaces, and for each i in I let $\xi_i: Y_i \to X_i$ be a continuous map such that $\xi_i(Y_i) = X_i$. For all i, j, k in I let $Y_{ij} = \xi_i^{-1}(X_i \cap X_j)$ and $Y_{ijk} = \xi_i^{-1}(X_i \cap X_j \cap X_k)$.[2] For all i, j in I for which $Y_{ij} \neq \emptyset$ let $\lambda_{ji}: Y_{ij} \to Y_{ji}$ be a homeomorphism. Assume that

1°) $\xi_i|Y_{ij} = \xi_j \circ \lambda_{ji}$ for all i, j in I for which $Y_{ij} \neq \emptyset$;[3]
2°) $\lambda_{ii} =$ identity map of Y_i for all i in I; and
3°) $\lambda_{ki}|Y_{ijk} = \lambda_{kj} \circ (\lambda_{ji}|Y_{ijk})$ for all i, j, k in I for which $Y_{ijk} \neq \emptyset$.

Then there exists a topological space Y, an open covering $(V_i)_{i\in I}$ of Y, a continuous map $\xi: Y \to X$, and a homeomorphism $\lambda_i: Y_i \to V_i$ for

[1] In view of 1′), taking $k = i$ in 2′) we get that: $\lambda_{ij} = (\lambda_{ji})^{-1}$ for all i, j in I for which $Y_{ij} \neq \emptyset$.
[2] Note that then: $Y_{ii} = Y_i$; $Y_{ijk} = Y_{ikj}$; and $Y_{ij} = \emptyset \Leftrightarrow Y_{ji} = \emptyset$.
[3] Note that for all k in I we then have $\lambda_{ji}(Y_{ijk}) = Y_{jki}$.

each i in I, such that condition 3′) is satisfied and such that for all i in I we have:

$$\xi(V_i) = X_i, \qquad \xi^{-1}(X_i) = V_i, \qquad \text{and} \qquad \xi \circ \lambda_i = \xi_i.$$

If X is Hausdorff and Y_i is Hausdorff for all i in I, then Y is Hausdorff. If X is an analytic K-space, Y_i is an analytic K-space and $\xi_i: Y_i \to X_i$ is analytic for all i in I, and $\lambda_{ji}: Y_{ij} \to Y_{ji}$ is bianalytic for all i, j in I for which $Y_{ij} \neq \emptyset$, then there exists a subsheaf $\mathcal{O}_Y$ of $\mathcal{E}_Y$ such that $(Y, \mathcal{O}_Y)$ is an analytic space, $\xi: Y \to X$ is analytic, and $\lambda_i: Y_i \to V_i$ is bianalytic for all i in I.

Proof. By 3) there exists a topological space Y, an open covering $(V_i)_{i \in I}$ of Y, and a homeomorphism $\lambda_i: Y_i \to V_i$ for all i in I, such that condition 3′) holds. For each i in I let $\eta_i = \xi_i \circ \lambda_i^{-1}$; then $\eta_i: V_i \to X_i$ is continuous and $\eta_i \circ \lambda_i = \xi_i$. By 1°) and 3′) it follows that $\eta_i(b) = \eta_j(b)$ for all i, j in I and $b \in V_i \cap V_j$. Therefore there exists a unique continuous map $\xi: Y \to X$ such that $\xi(b) = \eta_i(b)$ for all i in I and $b \in V_i$. For all i in I we obviously have: $\xi(V_i) = X_i$, $\xi^{-1}(X_i) = V_i$, and $\xi \circ \lambda_i = \xi_i$.

Assume that X is Hausdorff and Y_i is Hausdorff for all i in I. Let b and b' be any two distinct points in Y. Since ξ is continuous and X is Hausdorff, it follows that if $\xi(b) \neq \xi(b')$ then there exist disjoint neighborhoods V and V' of b and b' in Y. Now suppose that $\xi(b) = \xi(b')$. Then there exists i in I such that b and b' are both in V_i. Now V_i is Hausdorff because Y_i is Hausdorff and λ_i is a homeomorphism. Therefore there exist disjoint neighborhoods V and V' of b and b' in V_i. Now V_i is open in Y and hence V and V' are neighborhoods of b and b' in Y. This shows that Y is Hausdorff.

Assume that X is an analytic K-space, Y_i is an analytic K-space and ξ_i is analytic for all i in I, and λ_{ji} is bianalytic for all i, j in I for which $Y_{ij} \neq \emptyset$. For each i in I let

$$\mathcal{O}_{V_i} = (\hat{\lambda}_i)^{-1}((\lambda_i)_*(\mathcal{O}_{Y_i}))$$

where $\mathcal{O}_{Y_i}$ is the structure sheaf of Y_i; then $(V_i, \mathcal{O}_{V_i})$ is an analytic K-space, $\lambda_i: Y_i \to V_i$ is bianalytic, and $\eta_i: V_i \to X_i$ is analytic. Now $\lambda_{ji}: Y_{ij} \to Y_{ji}$ is bianalytic for all i, j in I for which $Y_{ij} \neq \emptyset$. Hence by 3′) it follows that $\mathcal{O}_{V_i}|V_i \cap V_j = \mathcal{O}_{V_j}|V_i \cap V_j$ for all i, j in I. Therefore by 1) there exists a subsheaf $\mathcal{O}_Y$ of $\mathcal{E}_Y$ such that $(Y, \mathcal{O}_Y)$ is an analytic K-space and $\mathcal{O}_Y|V_i = \mathcal{O}_{V_i}$ for all i in I. Since $\eta_i: V_i \to X_i$ is analytic for all i in I, it follows that $\xi: Y \to X$ is analytic.

(43.4) *Analytic set.* Let X be an analytic K-space. In accordance with (29.4) we introduce the following notations and terminology.

For any $a \in X$ we *define*

$$R(a, X) = (\mathcal{O}_X)_a = \text{ ring of analytic function germs on } X \text{ at } a.$$

Note that $R(a, X)$ is a K-algebra as well as a local ring, and the residue class field of $R(a, X)$ can be identified with K.

For any set F of analytic functions on an open set U in X we *define*

$$\mathfrak{V}(F) = \{a \in U : f(a) = 0 \text{ for all } f \in F\}.$$

Let $Y \subset X$. Y is said to be *analytic at* $a \in X \Leftrightarrow$ there exists a finite set F of analytic functions on a neighborhood U of a in X such that $Y \cap U = \mathfrak{V}(F)$. Y is said to be *analytic* (resp: *locally analytic*) *in* $X \Leftrightarrow Y$ is analytic at each point in X (resp: in Y). Thus Y is analytic in $X \Leftrightarrow Y$ is closed and locally analytic in X. Also note that Y is locally analytic in $X \Leftrightarrow Y$ is an analytic set in an open subset of X.

A set germ Z in X at $a \in X$ is said to be *analytic* $\Leftrightarrow Z$ has a representative which is analytic at a; and then each representative of Z is analytic at a.

Let $a \in X$ and let $\mathfrak{a}$ be any ideal in $R(a, X)$. Since $R(a, X)$ is noetherian, we can take a finite set F of analytic functions on a neighborhood U of a in X such that $\mathfrak{a} = F_a R(a, X)$. We *define*

$$\mathfrak{V}(\mathfrak{a}) = (\mathfrak{V}(F))_a.$$

$\mathfrak{V}(\mathfrak{a})$ is then an analytic set germ in X at a and it does not depend on the particular finite set of generators of $\mathfrak{a}$. For any $G \subset R(a, X)$ we *define*

$$\mathfrak{V}(G) = \mathfrak{V}(GR(a, X)).$$

Let Z be an analytic set germ in X at $a \in X$. Z is said to be *reducible* $\Leftrightarrow Z$ can be written in the form $Z = Z_1 \cup Z_2$ where Z_1 and Z_2 are analytic set germs in X at a such that $Z_i \neq Z$ for $i = 1, 2$. Z is said to be *irreducible* $\Leftrightarrow Z$ is not reducible. An analytic set germ Z' in X at a is said to be an *irreducible component of* $Z \Leftrightarrow$ i) $\emptyset \neq Z' \subset Z$, ii) Z' is irreducible, and iii) there does not exist any irreducible analytic set germ Z^* in X at a such that $Z' \subset Z^* \subset Z$ and $Z' \neq Z^*$. An analytic set Y in X is said to be *reducible* (resp: *irreducible*) *at* $a \Leftrightarrow Y_a$ is reducible (resp: irreducible).

For $Y \subset X$ and $a \in X$ we *define*

$$\begin{aligned}\mathfrak{i}(a, Y, X) &= \mathfrak{i}(a, Y_a, X) = \mathfrak{i}(Y_a, X)\\ &= \{f \in R(a, X) : f(Y_a) = 0\}.\end{aligned}$$

Note that $\mathfrak{i}(a, Y, X)$ is an ideal in $R(a, X)$ which is its own radical; and we have: $\mathfrak{i}(a, Y, X) = R(a, X) \Leftrightarrow a \notin \text{cl}_X Y$. Taking

$$\mathscr{I}(Y, X)(U) = \{f \in \mathcal{O}_X(U) : f(Y \cap U) = 0\}$$

for each nonempty open set U in X we get an ideal $\mathscr{I}(Y, X)$ in $\mathscr{O}_X$; this ideal is called the *ideal of Y in X* and it will always be denoted by $\mathscr{I}(Y, X)$. Note that $(\mathscr{I}(Y, X))_a = \mathfrak{i}(a, Y, X)$ for all $a \in X$. If $a \in Y$ then we *define*

$$R(a, Y) = \text{image of } R(a, X) \quad \text{under the restriction map}$$
$$\mathfrak{E}(a, X) \to \mathfrak{E}(a, Y).$$

The corresponding epimorphism $R(a, X) \to R(a, Y)$ is again called the *restriction map*; note that the kernel of this epimorphism is $\mathfrak{i}(a, Y, X)$. If Y is analytic at a then we *define*

$$\begin{aligned}\dim_a Y &= \text{dimension of } Y \text{ at } a\\ &= \dim Y_a = \text{dimension of } Y_a\\ &= \begin{cases}\dim R(a, Y) & \text{if } a \in Y\\ -1 & \text{if } a \notin Y.\end{cases}\end{aligned}$$

Let Y be an analytic set in X. For any nonempty open set V in Y we *define*

$$R(V) = \{f \in \mathfrak{E}(V) : f_a \in R(a, Y) \text{ for all } a \in V\},$$

and for any open set V' in Y with $V \subset V'$ the map $R(V') \to R(V)$ induced by the restriction map $\mathfrak{E}(V') \to \mathfrak{E}(V)$ is again called the *restriction map*. Finally we *define*

$$\dim V = \text{dimension of } V = \begin{cases}\max\limits_{a \in V} \dim_a V & \text{if } V \neq \emptyset\\ -1 & \text{if } V = \emptyset.\end{cases}$$

(**43.5**) *Analytic subspace.* Let $(X, \mathscr{O}_X)$ be any analytic K-space and let Y be any nonempty analytic set in X. We get a subsheaf $\mathscr{O}_Y$ of $\mathscr{E}_Y$ by taking $\mathscr{O}_Y(V) = R(V)$ for each nonempty open set V in Y; and then $(Y, \mathscr{O}_Y)$ is an analytic K-space and the canonical injection $\xi: Y \to X$ is an analytic map. Clearly the meanings of $R(a, Y)$, $\dim_a Y$, $R(V)$, and $\dim Y$ are the same whether Y is regarded as an analytic set in X or as an analytic K-space with the said structure sheaf $\mathscr{O}_Y$; unless otherwise stated, we shall regard Y as an analytic K-space with this structure sheaf, and we may then say that Y is an analytic subspace of X.

Now $\xi: \mathscr{O}_X \to \xi_*(\mathscr{O}_Y)$ is obviously an epimorphism and hence it induces an isomorphism $\nu: \xi_*(\mathscr{O}_Y) \to \mathscr{O}_X/\mathscr{I}(Y, X)$; *$\xi$ may be called the restriction epimorphism or the natural epimorphism of $\mathscr{O}_X$ onto $\xi_*(\mathscr{O}_Y)$*. Note that ξ_a is the restriction map $R(a, X) \to R(a, Y)$ for all $a \in Y$. Also $\operatorname{Ker} \xi_a = \mathfrak{i}(a, Y, X)$ for all $a \in X$ and hence $\operatorname{Ker} \xi = \mathscr{I}(Y, X)$. Furthermore,

Supp $\mathcal{O}_X/\mathcal{I}(Y, X) = Y$ and hence $\mathcal{O}_X/\mathcal{I}(Y, X)$ is an extension of $\mathcal{O}_Y$ by putting zero on $X - Y$; see (41.11).

For any $\emptyset \neq Z \subset Y$ we obviously have that Z is analytic in $Y \Leftrightarrow Z$ is analytic in X; and then the two ways of considering Z as an analytic K-space coincide. Finally note that for any analytic set Z in Y we have: $\xi(\mathcal{I}(Z, X)) = \xi_*(\mathcal{I}(Z, Y))$, and for any $a \in Z$ the restriction map $R(a, X) \to R(a, Z)$ is the composition of the restriction maps $R(a, X) \to R(a, Y) \to R(a, Z)$.

(43.6) *Decomposition of an analytic set germ.* Let X be an analytic K-space and let $a \in X$. Since $R(a, X)$ is noetherian, the proofs of (30.1) to (30.11) carry over *verbatim* when we replace K^n by X. The corresponding results are summarized below.

1) For any ideal $\mathfrak{a}$ in $R(a, X)$ we have: $\mathfrak{V}(\mathfrak{a}) = \mathfrak{V}(\text{rad}\, \mathfrak{a})$. For any set germ Y in X at a we have: $Y \subset \mathfrak{V}(\mathfrak{i}(a, Y, X))$; and furthermore, Y is analytic $\Leftrightarrow Y = \mathfrak{V}(\mathfrak{i}(a, Y, X))$.

2) For any finite number of ideals $\mathfrak{a}_1, \ldots, \mathfrak{a}_t$ in $R(a, X)$ we have the following.

i) $\mathfrak{a}_1 \supset \mathfrak{a}_2 \Leftrightarrow \mathfrak{V}(\mathfrak{a}_1) \subset \mathfrak{V}(\mathfrak{a}_2)$.

ii) $\mathfrak{V}\left(\bigcap_{i=1}^{t} \mathfrak{a}_i\right) = \mathfrak{V}\left(\prod_{i=1}^{t} \mathfrak{a}_i\right) = \bigcup_{i=1}^{t} \mathfrak{V}(\mathfrak{a}_i)$.

iii) $\mathfrak{V}\left(\sum_{i=1}^{t} \mathfrak{a}_i\right) = \bigcap_{i=1}^{t} \mathfrak{V}(\mathfrak{a}_i)$.

3) For any finite number of analytic set germs $Y, Y_1, \ldots, Y_t$ in X at a we have the following.

i) $Y_1 = Y_2 \Leftrightarrow \mathfrak{i}(a, Y_1, X) = \mathfrak{i}(a, Y_2, X)$.

ii) $Y_1 \subset Y_2 \Leftrightarrow \mathfrak{i}(a, Y_1, X) \supset \mathfrak{i}(a, Y_2, X)$.

iii) $Y = \bigcup_{i=1}^{t} Y_i \Leftrightarrow \mathfrak{i}(a, Y, X) = \bigcap_{i=1}^{t} \mathfrak{i}(a, Y_i, X)$.

4) Finite unions and arbitrary intersections of analytic set germs in X at a are again analytic set germs in X at a. Every strictly descending chain of analytic set germs in X at a is finite. Given any nonempty set Ω of ideals in $R(a, X)$, there exists a nonempty finite subset Ω^* of Ω such that

$$\sum_{\mathfrak{a} \in \Omega} \mathfrak{a} = \sum_{\mathfrak{a} \in \Omega^*} \mathfrak{a}$$

and

$$\bigcap_{\mathfrak{a}\in\Omega} \mathfrak{V}(\mathfrak{a}) = \mathfrak{V}\left(\sum_{\mathfrak{a}\in\Omega} \mathfrak{a}\right) = \bigcap_{\mathfrak{a}\in\Omega^*} \mathfrak{V}(\mathfrak{a}).$$

5) An analytic set germ Y in X at a is irreducible $\Leftrightarrow$ $\mathfrak{i}(a, Y, X)$ is either prime or the unit ideal.

6) Every analytic set germ Y in X can uniquely be expressed as an irredundant finite union of irreducible analytic set germs in X at a: $Y = Y_1 \cup ... \cup Y_t$, $(t = 0 \Leftrightarrow Y = \emptyset)$. Furthermore, $Y_1,..., Y_t$ are exactly all the distinct irreducible components of Y.

DEFINITION. The above expression $Y = Y_1 \cup ... \cup Y_t$ is called the *normal decomposition of* Y.

Without using the language of germs, 6) can be reformulated thus.

7) Given an analytic set Y in a neighborhood U of a in X there exist analytic sets $Y_1,..., Y_t$ in a neighborhood U' of a in U such that:

i) $Y_1,..., Y_t$ are irreducible at a;
ii) $Y \cap U' = Y_1 \cup ... \cup Y_t$; and
iii) for any neighborhood U'' of a in U' and for $i = 1,..., t$ we have $Y_i \cap U'' \not\subset \bigcup_{j\neq i} (Y_j \cap U'')$.

Furthermore, if in any other neighborhood U^* of a in X we have any other such decomposition, then the two decompositions coincide in some neighborhood of a in $U' \cap U^*$.

§44. RECAPITULATION OF PROPERTIES OF ANALYTIC SPACES[1]

§44A. *Local properties*

Let X be an analytic K-space and let $a \in X$. Many of the properties given in §30 and §33, being of a local nature, carry over to X. For further reference we shall reproduce them here.

(44.1) RÜCKERT NULLSTELLENSATZ. *For any ideal* $\mathfrak{a}$ *in* $R(a, X)$ *we have* $\mathfrak{i}(a, \mathfrak{V}(\mathfrak{a}), X) = \operatorname{rad} \mathfrak{a}$.

The problem being local we may assume that X is an analytic set in an open set D in K^n. Let $\mu: R(a, D) \to R(a, X)$ be the restriction epimorphism. As an analytic set germ in D at a, $\mathfrak{V}(\mathfrak{a})$ can be defined by $\mu^{-1}(\mathfrak{a})$, i.e.,

[1] Henceforth, K is assumed to be algebraically closed.

$\mathfrak{V}(\mathfrak{a}) = \mathfrak{V}(\mu^{-1}(\mathfrak{a}))$. Given $f \in \mathfrak{i}(a, \mathfrak{V}(\mathfrak{a}), X)$, take $g \in \mu^{-1}(f)$. Then $g(\mathfrak{V}(\mathfrak{a})) = 0$ and hence $g^p \in \mu^{-1}(\mathfrak{a})$ for some $p > 0$ by (30.12). Therefore $f^p \in \mathfrak{a}$ and hence $f \in \operatorname{rad} \mathfrak{a}$.

Again in virtue of (43.6) and (44.1), the ideal theory in $R(a, X)$ can effectively be used to study analytic set germs in X at a. For instance, corresponding to (30.13, 30.14, 30.15) we get (44.2, 44.3).

(**44.2**) *The mapping* $\mathfrak{a} \to \mathfrak{V}(\mathfrak{a})$ *maps the set of all ideals in* $R(a, X)$ *which are their own radicals (i.e., which are intersections of a finite number of prime ideals) in a one to one inclusion reversing manner onto the set of all analytic set germs in* X *at* a; *in particular* $\operatorname{rad}\{0\} = \{0\}$, $\mathfrak{V}(\{0\}) = X_a$, *and* $\mathfrak{V}(R(a, X)) = \emptyset$. *For any ideal* $\mathfrak{a}$ *in* $R(a, X)$, $\mathfrak{V}(\mathfrak{p}_1) \cup \ldots \cup \mathfrak{V}(\mathfrak{p}_t)$ *is the normal decomposition of* $\mathfrak{V}(\mathfrak{a})$ *where* $\mathfrak{p}_1, \ldots, \mathfrak{p}_t$ *are exactly all the distinct minimal prime ideals of* $\mathfrak{a}$. *In particular,* $\mathfrak{V}(\mathfrak{q}_1) \cup \ldots \cup \mathfrak{V}(\mathfrak{q}_s)$ *is the normal decomposition of* X_a *where* $\mathfrak{q}_1, \ldots, \mathfrak{q}_s$ *are exactly all the distinct prime ideals of height zero in* $R(a, X)$.

(**44.3**) *For any finite number of analytic set germs* $Y_1, \ldots, Y_t$, $(t > 0)$, *in* X *at* a *we have the following.*

i) $\dim \bigcup_{i=1}^{t} Y_i = \max_{1 \leq i \leq t} \dim Y_i$.

ii) *If* Y' *is an irreducible component of* $\bigcup_{i=1}^{t} Y_i$, *then* Y' *is an irreducible component of* Y_i *for some* i.

iii) *If* $Y_1 \subsetneq Y_2$ *and* Y_2 *is irreducible, then* $\dim Y_1 < \dim Y_2$.

iv) *If* $Y_1 \subset Y_2$ *and* Y' *is an irreducible component of* Y_1, *then* Y' *is contained in some irreducible component of* Y_2.

(**44.4**) To note some further consequences of the Nullstellensatz, *let* Y *be any nonempty analytic set germ in* X *at* a. *Then we have the following.*

i) $\dim Y = \dim R(a, X)/\mathfrak{i}(a, Y, X) = \operatorname{dpt}_{R(a,X)} \mathfrak{i}(a, Y, X)$
$= \max e$ *such that there exist nonempty irreducible analytic set germs* $Y_0, \ldots, Y_e$ *in* X *at* a *for which* $Y_0 \subsetneq Y_1 \subsetneq \ldots \subsetneq Y_e \subset Y$.

ii) *If* Y *is irreducible then:*
$\operatorname{hgt}_{R(a,X)} \mathfrak{i}(a, Y, X)$
$= \max e$ *such that there exist irreducible analytic set germs* $Y_0, \ldots, Y_e$ *in* X *at* a *for which* $Y \subset Y_0 \subsetneq Y_1 \subsetneq \ldots \subsetneq Y_e$.

iii) *If* X_a *is irreducible then by* (23.8) *we get*:
$\operatorname{hgt}_{R(a,X)} \mathfrak{i}(a, Y, X) = \dim_a X - \dim Y.$

By (33.2) we get

(**44.5**) $\dim X_b \leqq \dim X_a$ *for all* b *in some neighborhood of* a *in* X.

(**44.6**) DEFINITION. In accordance with (30.16) we make the following definitions.

1) X is *pure* e *dimensional at* $a \Leftrightarrow X_a$ is *pure* e *dimensional* $\Leftrightarrow$ every irreducible component of X_a is e dimensional, i.e., $\Leftrightarrow$ every prime ideal of zero in $R(a, X)$ has depth e. Note that for any analytic set Y in X with $a \in Y$ we have: Y is pure e dimensional at $a \Leftrightarrow Y_a$ is pure e dimensional $\Leftrightarrow \dim R(a, X)/\mathfrak{p} = e$ for every prime ideal $\mathfrak{p}$ of $\mathfrak{i}(a, Y, X)$.

2) An analytic set Y in X is *pure e dimensional* $\Leftrightarrow Y \neq \emptyset$ and $\dim_b Y = e$ for all $b \in Y$.

3) Let Y be an analytic set in X. Then $Z \subset Y$ is a *thin subset of* $Y \Leftrightarrow$ given $b \in Y$, there exists an analytic set Z^* in a neighborhood Y^* of b in Y such that $Z \cap Y^* \subset Z^*$ and $\dim Z^*_c < \dim Y_c$ for all $c \in Y^*$.

4) a is a *simple point of* $X \Leftrightarrow X$ is *simple at* $a \Leftrightarrow X_a$ is *simple* $\Leftrightarrow R(a, X)$ is a regular local ring.
a is a *singular point of* $X \Leftrightarrow X$ is *singular at* $a \Leftrightarrow X_a$ is *singular* $\Leftrightarrow X_a$ is not simple.

$$\mathbf{S}(X) = \text{singular locus of } X = \{b \in X\colon X_b \text{ is singular}\}.$$
$$\mathbf{S}(X_a) = \text{singular locus of } X_a = (\mathbf{S}(X))_a.$$

X is *nonsingular* $\Leftrightarrow \mathbf{S}(X) = \emptyset$.

5) a is a *normal point of* $X \Leftrightarrow X$ is *normal at* $a \Leftrightarrow X_a$ is *normal* $\Leftrightarrow R(a, X)$ is normal.

$$\mathbf{N}(X) = \text{nonnormal locus of } X = \{b \in X\colon X_b \text{ is not normal}\}.$$
$$\mathbf{N}^*(X) = \{b \in X\colon X_b \text{ is reducible}\}.$$

X is *normal* $\Leftrightarrow \mathbf{N}(X) = \emptyset$.

By (19.9, 21.5.1) we get

(**44.7**) $\mathbf{N}^*(X) \subset \mathbf{N}(X) \subset \mathbf{S}(X)$.

By (30.17, 33.3, 33.4, 33.10) we get

(**44.8**) *X is pure e dimensional $\Leftrightarrow X_b$ is pure e dimensional for all $b \in X$. If X_a is pure e dimensional, then X_b is pure e dimensional for all b in some neighborhood of a in X. If X_a has an e dimensional irreducible component and Z is a nowhere dense subset of X (for instance $Z = \emptyset$), then there exists a nonempty open subset X' of X such that X' is pure e dimensional and $Z \cap X' = \emptyset$. If Z is a thin subset of X, then Z is nowhere dense in X.*

By (33.6, 33.7, 33.8) we get

(**44.9**) *Let Y and Z be analytic sets in X.*

1) *If $a \in Y$ and Y_a is irreducible, then $Y_a \subset Z_a \Leftrightarrow Y_a \subset Z^*$ for some irreducible component Z^* of Z_a.*

2) *If $Y^* \not\subset Z_a$ for each irreducible component Y^* of Y_a, then there exists a neighborhood U of a in X such that for every $b \in U$ and every irreducible component Y' of Y_b we have $Y' \not\subset Z_b$.*

3) *The following five conditions are equivalent.*

i) $\dim_b(Y \cap Z) < \dim_b Y$ *for all $b \in Y$.*
ii) *For every $b \in X$ and every irreducible component Y' of Y_b we have $Y' \not\subset Z_b$.*
iii) *$Z \cap Y$ is nowhere dense in Y.*
iv) *$Z \cap Y$ is a thin subset of Y.*
v) *$Y - Z$ is everywhere dense in Y.*

(**44.10**) *Let Y and Z be any analytic sets in X. Then $\mathrm{cl}_X(Y - Z)$ is analytic in X.*

PROOF. $\mathrm{cl}_X(Y - Z)$ is obviously analytic at each point in $X - Z$. To show that $\mathrm{cl}_X(Y - Z)$ is analytic at each point in Z as well, let $b \in Z$ be given. Let $Y_1, \ldots, Y_t$ be all the distinct irreducible components of Y_b labeled so that $Y_i \not\subset Z_b$ for $i \leqq k$ and $Y_i \subset Z_b$ for $i > k$. Take analytic sets Y' and Y'' in a neighborhood U of b in X such that $Y \cap U = Y' \cup Y''$, $Y'_b = Y_1 \cup \ldots \cup Y_k$, and $Y''_b = Y_{k+1} \cup \ldots \cup Y_t$. Then $Y''_b \subset Z_b$ and hence there exists a neighborhood V of b in U such that $Y'' \cap V \subset Z$. By (44.9) there exists a neighborhood W of b in V such that $\mathrm{cl}_W((Y' - Z) \cap W) = Y' \cap W$. Now

$$W \cap \mathrm{cl}_X(Y - Z) = \mathrm{cl}_W((Y - Z) \cap W) = \mathrm{cl}_W((Y' - Z) \cap W) = Y' \cap W.$$

Therefore $\mathrm{cl}_X(Y - Z)$ is analytic at b.

By (33.11) we get

(**44.11**) *Let* $X_1, \ldots, X_\lambda$ *be analytic sets in* X *such that* $(X_1)_a, \ldots, (X_\lambda)_a$ *are the distinct irreducible components of* X_a. *Then there exists a neighborhood* U *of* a *in* X *such that for any* $b \in U$ *letting* $X'_{i1}, \ldots, X'_{ip_i}$ *to be the distinct irreducible components of* $(X_i)_b$ *we have the following.*

i) *The* $p_1 + \ldots + p_\lambda$ *elements* X'_{ik} *are all distinct and they are exactly all the irreducible components of* X_b.

ii) *For all* i, k *we have* $X'_{ik} \not\subset [\bigcap_{j \neq j'} (X_j \cap X_{j'})]_b$, *and hence in particular*

$$\dim[\bigcap_{j \neq j'} (X_j \cap X_{j'})]_b < \dim X_b.$$

(**44.12**) Definition. Let $Y \subset X$ be such that $a \in Y$ and Y_a is analytic. Let $Y_1, \ldots, Y_\lambda$ be the distinct irreducible components of Y_a. Let $X_1, \ldots, X_\mu$ be the distinct irreducible components of X_a labeled so that for $j \leqq k$: $Y_i \subset X_j$ for some i (depending on j), and for $j > k$: $Y_i \not\subset X_j$ for $i = 1, \ldots, \lambda$. We *define*

$$\mathfrak{J}[a, Y, X] = \mathfrak{J}[a, Y_a, X] = X_1 \cup \ldots \cup X_k.$$

By (33.12) we get

(**44.13**) *Given an analytic set* Y *in* X *with* $a \in Y$, *let* $Y_1, \ldots, Y_\lambda$ *be the distinct irreducible components of* Y_a. *Then*

$$\mathfrak{i}(a, \mathfrak{J}[a, Y, X], X) = \bigcap_{i=1}^{\lambda} \mathfrak{i}(a, \mathfrak{J}[a, Y_i, X], X)$$

$$= \mathfrak{j}_{R(a,X)}[\mathfrak{i}(a, Y, X)] = \bigcap_{i=1}^{\lambda} \mathfrak{j}_{R(a,X)}[\mathfrak{i}(a, Y_i, X)].$$

Let f *be any analytic function on* X *such that* $f_a \in \mathfrak{j}_{R(a,X)}[\mathfrak{i}(a, Y, X)]$. *Then there exists a neighborhood* U *of* a *in* X *such that for all* $b \in Y \cap U$ *we have*: $f_b \in \mathfrak{j}_{R(b,X)}[\mathfrak{i}(b, Y, X)]$ *or equivalently* $f_b \in \mathfrak{j}_{R(b,X)}[\mathfrak{i}(b, Y', X)]$ *for every irreducible component* Y' *of* Y_b.

(**44.14**) *Let* Y *be an analytic set in* X *such that* $a \in Y$ *and* Y_a *is irreducible. Then there exists a neighborhood* U *of* a *in* X *such that for every* $b \in Y \cap U$ *and every irreducible component* Y' *of* Y_b *we have*:

$$\dim \mathfrak{J}[b, Y', X] = \dim \mathfrak{J}[a, Y, X].$$

PROOF. Take analytic sets $X_1, \ldots, X_\mu$ in a neighborhood V of a in X such that $(X_1)_a, \ldots, (X_\mu)_a$ are the distinct irreducible components of X_a, and $V = X_1 \cup \ldots \cup X_\mu$. Label $X_1, \ldots, X_\mu$ so that $: Y_a \not\subset (X_j)_a$ for $j > k$, $Y_a \subset (X_j)_a$ for $j \leqq k$, and $\dim(X_j)_a \leqq e$ for $j \leqq k$ where $e = \dim(X_k)_a$. Then $\mathfrak{J}[a, Y, X] = (X_1 \cup \ldots \cup X_k)_a$ and hence $\dim \mathfrak{J}[a, Y, X] = e$. Upon replacing V by a smaller neighborhood of a in X we can arrange that $Y \cap V \subset X_k$. By (44.5, 44.8, 44.11) we can find a neighborhood W of a in V such that $X_k \cap W$ is pure e dimensional, $\dim(X_j \cap W) \leqq e$ for all j $\leqq k$, and

1°) for any $b \in V$ letting $X_{j1}, \ldots, X_{jp_j}$ to be the distinct irreducible components of $(X_j)_b$ we have that the $p_1 + \ldots + p_\mu$ elements X_{jt} are exactly all the distinct irreducible components of X_b.

By (44.9) there exists a neighborhood U of a in W such that for every $b \in U$ and every irreducible component Y' of Y_b we have $Y' \not\subset (X_j)_b$ for all $j > k$. Given $b \in Y \cap U$ let the notation be as in 1°) and let Y' be any irreducible component of Y_b. Then

$$\mathfrak{J}[b, Y', X] \subset \bigcup_{j=1}^{k} (X_j)_b.$$

Since $Y \cap V \subset X_k$ we must have $Y' \subset X_{kt}$ for some t and hence $X_{kt} \subset \mathfrak{J}[b, Y', X]$. Now

$$\dim X_{kt} = e \leqq \dim \left(\bigcup_{j=1}^{k} X_j \right)_b$$

and hence $\dim \mathfrak{J}[b, Y', X] = e$.

By (33.13) we get

(**44.15**) *For any analytic function f on X we have the following.*

1) *The following four conditions are equivalent.*

i) *f_a is a nonzerodivisor in $R(a, X)$.*
ii) *$f_a \notin \mathfrak{i}(a, X', X)$ for each irreducible component X' of X_a.*
iii) *$X' \not\subset (\mathfrak{V}(f))_a$ for each irreducible component X' of X_a.*
iv) *There exists a neighborhood U of a in X such that $\mathfrak{V}(f) \cap U$ is nowhere dense in U.*

2) *If f_a is a nonzerodivisor in $R(a, X)$ then f_b is a nonzerodivisor in $R(b, X)$ for all b in some neighborhood of a in X.*

By (33.14) we get

(**44.16**) *Any element in* $R(a, X)$ *which is a nonzerodivisor in* $R(a, X)$ *remains a nonzerodivisor in* $\mathfrak{E}(a, X)$, *and hence the total quotient ring of* $R(a, X)$ *can be considered to be a subring of the total quotient ring of* $\mathfrak{E}(a, X)$.

By (33.15) we get

(**44.17**) Open Map Theorem. *For any analytic function* f *on* X *we have the following.*

1) f_a *is nonconstant* $\Leftrightarrow (f - f(a))_a \neq 0 \Leftrightarrow$ *the map* $f\colon X \to K$ *is open at* a.

2) $f_a | X'$ *is nonconstant*[2] *for each irreducible component* X' *of* $X_a \Leftrightarrow (f - f(a))_a$ *is a nonzerodivisor in* $R(a, X)$.

3) $(f - f(b))_b$ *is a nonzerodivisor in* $R(b, X)$ *for all* $b \in X \Leftrightarrow$ *the map* $f\colon X \to K$ *is open.*

4) $(f - f(a))_a$ *is a nonzerodivisor in* $R(a, X) \Leftrightarrow$ *the map* $f | U\colon U \to K$ *is open for some neighborhood* U *of* a *in* X.

By (33.16) we get

(**44.18**) *Let* $X_1,\ldots, X_\lambda$ *be the distinct irreducible components of* X_a. *Then*

$$\mathbf{S}(X_a) = \left[\bigcup_{i=1,\ldots,\lambda} \mathbf{S}(X_i)\right] \cup \left[\bigcup_{\substack{i,\, j=1,\ldots,\lambda \\ i \neq j}} (X_i \cap X_j)\right].$$

By applying (33.18) twice we get

(**44.19**) *Let* $\dim X_a = n$. *Then* a *is a simple point of* $X \Leftrightarrow R(a, X)$ *is* K*-algebra-isomorphic to the convergent power series ring in* n *variables over* $K \Leftrightarrow$ *some neighborhood of* a *in* X *can be mapped bianalytically onto an open set in* K^n.

Let Y *be an analytic set in* X *with* $a \in Y$, *and let* $\dim Y_a = m$. *Then* a *is a simple point of* Y *as well as of* $X \Leftrightarrow$ *there exists a bianalytic map* ξ *of a neighborhood* U *of* a *in* X *onto a neighborhood* D *of the origin in* $K^n\{x_1,\ldots, x_n\}$ *such that* $\xi(a)$ *is at the origin and*

$$\xi(Y \cap U) = \{x \in D\colon x_1 = \ldots = x_{n-m} = 0\}.$$

By (33.20, 33.24) we get

[2] That is, $(f | \tilde{X})_a$ is a nonconstant for a representative $\tilde{X}$ of X'.

(**44.20**) $\mathbf{S}(X)$ *is a nowhere dense analytic set in* X.

(**44.21**) *Assume that* X_a *is irreducible.*[3] *Then there exists an analytic function* Δ *on a neighborhood* U *of* a *in* X *such that*: Δ_b *is a nonzerodivisor in* $R(b, X)$ *and* $\Delta_b \in \mathfrak{c}(R(b, X))$ *for all* $b \in U$.

In virtue of the Nullstellensatz (44.1), this follows from (44.8) and (26.3).

§44B. *Coherence of the structure sheaf and definition of meromorphic functions*

Let X be an analytic K-space.

(**44.22**) Cartan Coherence. $\mathcal{O}_X$ *is a coherent sheaf of rings on* X. *For any analytic set* Y *in* X, $\mathcal{I}(Y, X)$ *is a coherent* $\mathcal{O}_X$*-ideal. Now assume that* $Y \neq \emptyset$, *let* $\xi: Y \to X$ *be the canonical injection, let* $\mu = \tilde{\xi}$, *and let* $\mathcal{N}$ *be any* $\mathcal{O}_Y$*-module. Then* $\mathcal{N}$ *is a finite (resp: coherent)* $\mathcal{O}_Y$*-module* $\Leftrightarrow (\xi_*(\mathcal{N}))_{[\mu]}$ *is a finite (resp: coherent)* $\mathcal{O}_X$*-module.*

Proof. Now $\mu: \mathcal{O}_X \to \xi_*(\mathcal{O}_Y)$ is an epimorphism and $\operatorname{Ker} \mu = \mathcal{I}(Y, X)$; hence in virtue of (42.17) we only have to prove the first two assertions. The problem being local we may assume that X is an analytic set in an open set D in K^n. Then by (42.18), $\mathcal{O}_X = \mathcal{R}_X$ is a coherent sheaf of rings on X, and $\mathcal{I}(Y, D)$ and $\mathcal{I}(X, D)$ are coherent $\mathcal{O}_D$-ideals. Let $\eta: X \to D$ be the canonical injection. Then $\tilde{\eta}(\mathcal{I}(Y, D)) = \eta_*(\mathcal{I}(Y, X))$. Since $\mathcal{I}(Y, D)$ is a finite $\mathcal{O}_D$-ideal, we get that $\eta_*(\mathcal{I}(Y, X))$ is a finite $\eta_*(\mathcal{O}_X)$-ideal. By (42.16), $\eta_*(\mathcal{O}_X)$ is a coherent sheaf of rings on D and hence $\eta_*(\mathcal{I}(Y, X))$ is a coherent $\eta_*(\mathcal{O}_X)$-ideal. Therefore again by (42.16), $\mathcal{I}(Y, X)$ is a coherent $\mathcal{O}_X$-ideal.

(**44.23**) *For any set* F *of analytic functions on* X *we have* $\operatorname{Supp}(\mathcal{O}_X/F\mathcal{O}_X) = \mathfrak{V}(F)$. *If furthermore* F *is a finite set then* $(\operatorname{Supp}(\mathcal{O}_X/F\mathcal{O}_X))_a = \mathfrak{V}(F_a)$ *for all* $a \in X$, *and hence* $\operatorname{Supp}(\mathcal{O}_X/F\mathcal{O}_X)$ *is an analytic set in* X.

Proof. For any $a \in X$ we have: $a \in \operatorname{Supp}(\mathcal{O}_X/F\mathcal{O}_X) \Leftrightarrow F_aR(a, X) \neq R(a, X) \Leftrightarrow a \in \mathfrak{V}(F)$. Therefore $\operatorname{Supp}(\mathcal{O}_X/F\mathcal{O}_X) = \mathfrak{V}(F)$. If F is a finite set then obviously $(\mathfrak{V}(F))_a = \mathfrak{V}(F_a)$ for all $a \in X$, and hence $\operatorname{Supp}(\mathcal{O}_X/F\mathcal{O}_X)$ is an analytic set in X.

(**44.24**) *For any coherent* $\mathcal{O}_X$*-ideal* $\mathcal{P}$ *we have that*: $\operatorname{Supp}(\mathcal{O}_X/\mathcal{P})$ *is an analytic set in* X; $\operatorname{Supp}(\mathcal{O}_X/\mathcal{P}) = \{a \in X: \mathcal{P}_a \neq R(a, X)\}$; *and* $(\operatorname{Supp}(\mathcal{O}_X/\mathcal{P}))_a = \mathfrak{V}(\mathcal{P}_a)$ *for all* $a \in X$.

[3] In (46.28) we shall remove this assumption.

PROOF. The problem being local, our assertion follows from (44.23).

(44.25) *Let $\mathscr{P}$, $\mathscr{Q}$, $\mathscr{M}$ be coherent $\mathscr{O}_X$-modules where $\mathscr{P}$ and $\mathscr{Q}$ are $\mathscr{O}_X$-submodules of $\mathscr{M}$. Then* $\operatorname{Supp}(\mathscr{O}_X/(\mathscr{P}:\mathscr{Q}))$ *is an analytic set in X and* $\operatorname{Supp}(\mathscr{O}_X/(\mathscr{P}:\mathscr{Q})) = \{a \in X: (\mathscr{P}_a:\mathscr{Q}_a) \neq R(a, X)\}$.

PROOF. By (42.12, 44.22), $\mathscr{P}:\mathscr{Q}$ is a coherent $\mathscr{O}_X$-ideal and $(\mathscr{P}:\mathscr{Q})_a = \mathscr{P}_a:\mathscr{Q}_a$ for all $a \in X$. Now our assertion follows from (44.24).

(44.26) *For any coherent $\mathscr{O}_X$-module $\mathscr{M}$,* $\operatorname{Supp} \mathscr{M}$ *is an analytic set in X.*

PROOF. Follows from (42.14, 44.22, 44.25).

(44.27) DEFINITION. For any $a \in X$ we *define*

$$M(a, X) = \text{set of all nonzerodivisors in } R(a, X).$$

For any nonempty open set U in X we *define*

$$M(U) = \{f \in R(U): f_a \in M(a, X) \text{ for all } a \in U\}.$$

By (44.15) *it follows that*

$$M(U) = \{f \in R(U): \mathfrak{B}(f) \text{ is nowhere dense in } U\}.$$

Let $f \in R(U)$ be a zerodivisor in $R(U)$, i.e., $fg = 0$ for some $0 \neq g \in R(U)$; then there exists a nonempty open set U' in U such that $g(b) \neq 0$ for all $b \in U'$ and hence $f(b) = 0$ for all $b \in U'$; therefore $\mathfrak{B}(f)$ is not nowhere dense in U and hence $f \notin M(U)$. Thus $M(U)$ is a multiplicative set in $R(U)$ not containing any zerodivisors of $R(U)$.[4]

Consequently, the quotient ring $R(U)_{M(U)}$ is a subring of the total quotient ring of $R(U)$. We set

$$\mathring{\mathfrak{R}}(U) = \textit{ring of premeromorphic functions on } U = R(U)_{M(U)}.$$

For any open set V in X with $U \subset V$, letting $\delta_U^V: R(V) \to R(U)$ to be the restriction map, we obviously have $\delta_U^V(M(V)) \subset M(U)$; consequently by (18.4), δ_U^V induces a unique ring homomorphism $\tau_U^V: \mathring{\mathfrak{R}}(V) \to \mathring{\mathfrak{R}}(U)$ such that $\tau_U^V(f) = \delta_U^V(f)$ for all $f \in R(V)$; τ_U^V is again called the restriction map of $\mathring{\mathfrak{R}}(V)$ into $\mathring{\mathfrak{R}}(U)$. Obviously τ_U^U = identity map of $\mathring{\mathfrak{R}}(U)$ and $\tau_U^V \circ \tau_V^W = \tau_U^W$ for any open set W in X with $V \subset W$. The resulting presheaf of K-algebras on X is called *the presheaf of premeromorphic functions*

[4] See the example at the end of (44.27).

on X and is denoted by $\mathring{\mathscr{K}}_X$; i.e., $\mathring{\mathscr{K}}_X(U) = \mathring{\mathfrak{K}}(U)$ for every nonempty open set U in X and the restriction maps belonging to $\mathring{\mathscr{K}}_X$ are the maps τ_U^V.[5]

For any $a \in X$ we *define*

$$\mathfrak{K}(a, X) = \text{total quotient ring of } R(a, X).$$

By (44.15) it follows that we get an isomorphism $\sigma: (\mathring{\mathscr{K}}_X)_a \to \mathfrak{K}(a, X)$ where for any neighborhood U of a in X, $f \in R(U)$, $g \in M(U)$ we take $\sigma((f/g)_a) = f_a/g_a$. *We identify $(\mathring{\mathscr{K}}_X)_a$ with $\mathfrak{K}(a, X)$ via this isomorphism, i.e., we take $(f/g)_a = f_a/g_a$.*

We *define*

$$\mathscr{K}_X = \textit{sheaf of germs of meromorphic functions on } X = \langle \mathring{\mathscr{K}}_X \rangle$$

and for any open set U in X we *define*

$$\mathfrak{K}(U) = \textit{ring of meromorphic functions on } U = \mathscr{K}_X(U).$$

For any open sets $U \subset V$ in X, the restriction map $\mathscr{K}_X(V) \to \mathscr{K}_X(U)$ belonging to $\mathscr{K}_X$ is again called the restriction map of $\mathfrak{K}(V)$ into $\mathfrak{K}(U)$. It is clear that $\theta(U): \mathring{\mathfrak{K}}(U) \to \mathfrak{K}(U)$ is a monomorphism for every open set U in X, where $\theta: \mathring{\mathscr{K}}_X \to \langle \mathring{\mathscr{K}}_X \rangle$ is the natural map; via θ *we identify $\mathring{\mathscr{K}}_X$ with a subpresheaf of $\mathscr{K}_X$*. By general convention: $(\mathscr{K}_X)_a = (\mathring{\mathscr{K}}_X)_a = \mathfrak{K}(a, X)$ for all $a \in X$.

Alternatively: A meromorphic "function" h on a nonempty open set U in X is a function on U which to each $a \in U$ associates an element h_a in $\mathfrak{K}(a, X)$ such that: given $a' \in U$ there exists a neighborhood U' of a' in U and elements $f \in R(U')$, $g \in M(U')$ such that $h_a = f_a/g_a$ for all $a \in U'$. The meromorphic function h on U is said to be a premeromorphic function provided there exist $f \in R(U)$ and $g \in M(U)$ such that $h_a = f_a/g_a$ for all $a \in U$. The set of all meromorphic functions on U is the K-algebra $\mathfrak{K}(U)$ and the set of all premeromorphic functions on U is the K-subalgebra $\mathring{\mathfrak{K}}(U)$ of $\mathfrak{K}(U)$. The sheaf $\mathscr{K}_X$ (resp: the presheaf $\mathring{\mathscr{K}}_X$) of K-algebras on X is defined by taking $\mathscr{K}_X(U) = \mathfrak{K}(U)$ (resp: $\mathring{\mathscr{K}}_X(U) = \mathring{\mathfrak{K}}(U)$) for every nonempty open set U in X and taking the obvious restriction maps. For any nonempty open set U in X, $\mathscr{O}_X(U) = R(U)$ is a K-subalgebra of $\mathring{\mathscr{K}}_X(U) = \mathring{\mathfrak{K}}(U)$ and $\mathring{\mathscr{K}}_X(U) = \mathring{\mathfrak{K}}(U)$ is a K-subalgebra of $\mathscr{K}_X(U) = \mathfrak{K}(U)$. As presheaves of K-algebras on X, $\mathscr{O}_X$ is a subpresheaf of $\mathring{\mathscr{K}}_X$ and $\mathring{\mathscr{K}}_X$ is a subpresheaf of $\mathscr{K}_X$. We regard $\mathscr{K}_X$ as an $\mathscr{O}_X$-algebra with the canonical injection $\mathscr{O}_X \to \mathscr{K}_X$ as the underlying homomorphism.

[5] We take $\mathring{\mathscr{K}}_X(\emptyset) = \mathring{\mathfrak{K}}(\emptyset) = 0$.

Finally we *define*:

$\mathring{R}'(a, X)$ = integral closure of $R(a, X)$ in $\mathfrak{R}(a, X)$ for any $a \in X$.
$\mathring{R}'(U)$ = integral closure of $R(U)$ in $\mathring{\mathfrak{R}}(U)$ for any nonempty open set U in X.
$\mathring{\mathcal{O}}'_X$ = subpresheaf of $\mathring{\mathcal{K}}_X$ given by taking $\mathring{\mathcal{O}}'_X(U) = \mathring{R}'(U)$ for every nonempty open set U in X.
$\mathcal{O}'_X$ = the subsheaf $\langle \mathring{\mathcal{O}}'_X \rangle$ of $\mathcal{K}_X$.
$R'(U)$ = $\mathcal{O}'_X(U)$ for any nonempty open set U in X.

Note that for any $a \in X$ we then have:

$$R'(a, X) = (\mathcal{O}'_X)_a = (\mathring{\mathcal{O}}'_X)_a;$$

and for any nonempty open set U in X we have:

$$R'(U) = \{f \in \mathfrak{R}(U) : f_a \in R'(a, X) \text{ for all } a \in U\}.$$

Again for any nonempty open set U in X we have:

$$\mathring{\mathcal{K}}_X(U) = \mathring{\mathcal{K}}_U(U), \qquad \mathcal{K}_X(U) = \mathcal{K}_U(U), \qquad \mathring{\mathcal{O}}'_X(U) = \mathring{\mathcal{O}}'_U(U),$$
$$\mathcal{O}'_X(U) = \mathcal{O}'_U(U);$$

and hence there is no ambiguity in the notations $\mathring{\mathfrak{R}}(U)$, $\mathfrak{R}(U)$, $\mathring{R}'(U)$, $R'(U)$.

1) Remark. For each $a \in X$ identify $\mathfrak{R}(a, X)$ with a subring of the total quotient ring of $\mathfrak{C}(a, X)$; see (44.16). For any nonempty open set U in X and any $f \in \mathfrak{C}(U)$ we then clearly have: $f_a \in R'(a, X)$ for all $a \in U$ $\Leftrightarrow$ there exists $g \in R'(U)$ such that $f_a = g_a$ for all $a \in U$; (if g exists then it is obviously unique).

2) *Example.* As the following example shows, for some nonempty open set U in X it can happen that $R(U)$ contains nonzerodivisors which are not in $M(U)$. Let X consist of a complex affine line A and a complex projective line B such that A and B meet in exactly one point p; for instance take the union of two projective lines in a complex projective plane and remove a point different from their intersection point. Take $U = X$. Now $R(B)$ contains only constant functions, and $\alpha: R(U) \to R(A)$ is an isomorphism where $\alpha(f) = f|A$ for all $f \in R(U)$; note that $f(b) = f(p)$ for all $b \in B$. Take any nonzero element $h \in R(A)$ such that $h(p) = 0$, and let $f = \alpha^{-1}(h)$. Then f is a nonzerodivisor in $R(U)$, but f_b is a zero-divisor in $R(b, X)$ for all $b \in U - A$ because actually $f_b = 0$.

(44.28) *For any $\mathcal{O}_X$-algebra $\mathcal{P}$ we have the following.*

1) *If* $\mathscr{P}_a$ *is* $R(a, X)$*-algebra-isomorphic to an* $R(a, X)$*-subalgebra of* $\mathfrak{R}(a, X)$ *for all* $a \in X$*, then* $\mathscr{P}$ *is* $\mathcal{O}_X$*-algebra-isomorphic to an* $\mathcal{O}_X$*-subalgebra of* $\mathscr{K}_X$.

2) *Let* $\mathscr{Q}$ *be an* $\mathcal{O}_X$*-subalgebra of* $\mathscr{K}_X$*. Then* $\mathscr{P}$ *is* $\mathcal{O}_X$*-algebra-isomorphic to* $\mathscr{Q} \Leftrightarrow \mathscr{P}_a$ *is* $R(a, X)$*-algebra-isomorphic to* $\mathscr{Q}_a$ *for all* $a \in X$.

3) *If* $\mathscr{Q}$ *and* $\mathscr{Q}'$ *are* $\mathcal{O}_X$*-subalgebras of* $\mathscr{K}_X$ *and* $\mu: \mathscr{P} \to \mathscr{Q}$ *and* $\mu': \mathscr{P} \to \mathscr{Q}'$ *are* $\mathcal{O}_X$*-algebra-isomorphisms, then* $\mathscr{Q} = \mathscr{Q}'$ *and* $\mu = \mu'$.

Proof of 1). Let $\varphi: \mathcal{O}_X \to \mathscr{P}$ be the underlying homomorphism of the $\mathcal{O}_X$-algebra $\mathscr{P}$. For each $a \in X$ let $\mathfrak{L}(a)$ be the total quotient ring of $\mathscr{P}_a$, (obviously $\mathscr{P}_a$ is a nonnull ring). By (18.5.5) there exists a ring isomorphism $\psi_a: \mathfrak{R}(a, X) \to \mathfrak{L}(a)$ such that $\psi_a(r) = \varphi_a(r)$ for all $r \in R(a, X)$. Suppose we have proved the following.

1°) Given any nonempty open set U in X and any $f \in \mathscr{P}(U)$, there exists a unique meromorphic function $\bar{f}$ on U such that $\psi_a(\bar{f}_a) = f_a$ for all $a \in U$.

For each nonempty open set U in X and $f \in \mathscr{P}(U)$ take $\lambda(U)f = \bar{f} \in \mathfrak{R}(U)$. Then $\lambda: \mathscr{P} \to \mathscr{K}_X$ is obviously an $\mathcal{O}_X$-algebra-homomorphism. Also for each $a \in X$ and $s \in \mathscr{P}_a$ we have $\lambda_a(s) = \psi_a^{-1}(s)$; and hence λ_a is a monomorphism. Therefore λ is a monomorphism and hence $\mathscr{P}$ is $\mathcal{O}_X$-algebra-isomorphic to the $\mathcal{O}_X$-subalgebra $\operatorname{Im} \lambda$ of $\mathscr{K}_X$.

To prove 1°), first note that $\bar{f}$ is unique because ψ_a is an isomorphism. To prove that $\bar{f}$ exists, what we have to show is that the "function" $a \to \psi_a^{-1}(f_a)$ is an element of $\langle \mathring{\mathscr{K}}_X \rangle(U)$, i.e., given $b \in U$ there exists a neighborhood U' of b in U, $g \in R(U')$, $h \in M(U')$, such that for all $a \in U'$ we have: $g_a/h_a = \psi_a^{-1}(f_a)$, i.e., $f_a = \psi_a(g_a)/\psi_a(h_a)$. Since $\psi_b^{-1}(f_b)$ is an element of $\mathfrak{R}(b, X)$, we can find a neighborhood U^* of b in U and elements $G \in R(U^*)$ and $H \in M(U^*)$ such that $\psi_b^{-1}(f_b) = G_b/H_b$, i.e., $f_b = \psi_b(G_b)/\psi_b(H_b)$, i.e., $f_b\psi_b(H_b) = \psi_b(G_b)$, i.e., $f_b\varphi_b(H_b) = \varphi_b(G_b)$. Now $f_b\varphi_b(H_b) = \varphi_b(G_b)$ implies that there exists a neighborhood U' of b such that for all $a \in U'$ we have: $f_a\varphi_a(H_a) = \varphi_a(G_a)$, i.e., $f_a\psi_a(H_a) = \psi_a(G_a)$, i.e., $f_a = \psi_a(G_a)/\psi_a(H_a)$. Take $g = G|U' \in R(U')$ and $h = H|U' \in M(U')$.

Proof of 2). If $\mathscr{P}$ is $\mathcal{O}_X$-algebra-isomorphic to $\mathscr{Q}$ then obviously $\mathscr{P}_a$ is $R(a, X)$-algebra-isomorphic to $\mathscr{Q}_a$ for all $a \in X$. Conversely suppose that $\mathscr{P}_a$ is $R(a, X)$-algebra-isomorphic to $\mathscr{Q}_a$ for all $a \in X$. Then by 1), $\mathscr{P}$ is $\mathcal{O}_X$-algebra-isomorphic to some $\mathcal{O}_X$-subalgebra $\mathscr{Q}'$ of $\mathscr{K}_X$, and hence $\mathscr{P}_a$ is $R(a, X)$-algebra-isomorphic to $\mathscr{Q}'_a$ for all $a \in X$. By the uniqueness statement in (18.5.5) we must then have $\mathscr{Q}_a = \mathscr{Q}'_a$ for all $a \in X$, and hence $\mathscr{Q} = \mathscr{Q}'$.

Proof of 3). For each $a \in X$, $\mathcal{Q}_a$ and $\mathcal{Q}'_a$ are $R(a, X)$-subalgebras of $\mathfrak{R}(a, X)$ and $\mu_a: \mathcal{P}_a \to \mathcal{Q}_a$ and $\mu'_a: \mathcal{P}_a \to \mathcal{Q}'_a$ are $R(a, X)$-algebra-isomorphisms; therefore $\mathcal{Q}_a = \mathcal{Q}'_a$ and $\mu_a = \mu'_a$ by (18.5.5). Now $\mathcal{Q} = \mathcal{Q}'$ because $\mathcal{Q}_a = \mathcal{Q}'_a$ for all $a \in X$. For any nonempty open set U in X and any $f \in \mathcal{P}(U)$ we have: $(\mu(U)f)_a = \mu_a(f_a) = \mu'_a(f_a) = (\mu'(U)f)_a$ for all $a \in U$; and hence $\mu(U)f = \mu'(U)f$. Therefore $\mu = \mu'$.

§44C. *Connectivity properties of complex spaces*

By (34.2) we get

(44.29) *Let a be a point in a complex space X and let $X'_1, \ldots, X'_\lambda$ be analytic sets in a neighborhood U' of a in X such that $(X'_1)_a, \ldots, (X'_\lambda)_a$ are exactly all the distinct irreducible components of X_a and $U' = X'_1 \cup \ldots \cup X'_\lambda$. Let $Y \subset X$ be such that Y_a is analytic and $(X'_i)_a \not\subset Y_a$ for $i = 1, \ldots, \lambda$; (for instance $Y = \emptyset$). Then there exists a neighborhood basis $\mathbf{U}$ of a in U' such that for any $U \in \mathbf{U}$ upon letting $X_i = X'_i \cap U$ for $i = 1, \ldots, \lambda$ we have the following.*

i) *$X_1 - \mathbf{S}(X) - Y, \ldots, X_\lambda - \mathbf{S}(X) - Y$ are exactly all the distinct connected components of $U - \mathbf{S}(X) - Y$.*

ii) *$X_i = \mathrm{cl}_U(X_i - \mathbf{S}(X) - Y)$ and $\mathbf{S}(X_i) \subset \mathbf{S}(X)$* for $i = 1, \ldots, \lambda$.

iii) *For any $i \leqq \lambda$, any point $\alpha \in X_i$ can be joined to a point in $X_i - \mathbf{S}(X) - Y$ by a simple arc in X_i meeting $\mathbf{S}(X) \cup Y$ at most in α.*

iv) *U is arcwise connected.*[6]

v) *X_i, $X_i - \mathbf{S}(X)$, and $X_i - \mathbf{S}(X) - Y$ are arcwise connected for* $i = 1, \ldots, \lambda$.

vi) *If X_a is irreducible, i.e., $\lambda = 1$, then U, $U - \mathbf{S}(X)$ and $U - \mathbf{S}(X) - Y$ are arcwise connected.*

By (34.3) we get

(44.30) *For any point a in a complex space X the following three conditions are equivalent.*

i) *X_a is irreducible.*

ii) *$\mathbf{S}(X)$ does not disconnect X at a.*

iii) *If $Y' \subset Y \subset X$ are such that Y_a is analytic and $Y_a \neq X_a$, then Y' does not disconnect X at a.*

(44.31) DEFINITION. Let X be a complex space. X is said to be *reducible* $\Leftrightarrow$ there exist nonempty analytic sets X' and X'' in X such that

[6] Hence in particular, every complex space is locally arcwise connected.

$X = X' \cup X''$ and $X' \neq X \neq X''$. X is said to be *irreducible* $\Leftrightarrow$ X is not reducible. $Y \subset X$ is said to be an *irreducible component of* X $\Leftrightarrow$ Y is a nonempty irreducible analytic set in X and there does not exist any irreducible analytic set Y' in X such that $Y \underset{\neq}{\subset} Y'$. The proofs of (34.5) to (34.20) were based only on the local statements (33.8, 33.16, 33.20, 34.2, 34.3). Therefore (34.5) to (34.20) remain valid for an arbitrary complex space. The resulting assertions are summarized in (44.32) and (44.33).

(44.32) *Let X be a complex space and let $(X_i)_{i \in I}$ be the distinct irreducible components of X. Then we have the following.*

1) $X = \bigcup_{i \in I} X_i$. *For any $\emptyset \neq J \subset I$, $\bigcup_{i \in J} X_i$ is an analytic set in X and $(X_i)_{i \in J}$ are exactly all the distinct irreducible components of $\bigcup_{i \in J} X_i$. For any $J \underset{\neq}{\subset} I$ we have $X \neq \bigcup_{i \in J} X_i$.*

2) *Given any $a \in X$ let $J = \{i \in I : a \in X_i\}$ and for each $i \in J$ let $X'_{i1}, \ldots, X'_{ip_i}$ be the distinct irreducible components of $(X_i)_a$. Then J is finite and the $\sum_{i \in J} p_i$ elements X'_{ij} are all distinct and they are exactly all the irreducible components of X_a.*

3) $\dim X = \max_{i \in I} \dim X_i$. *$X$ is pure e dimensional $\Leftrightarrow$ X_i is pure e dimensional for all $i \in I$. If X is irreducible then X is pure e dimensional for some $e < \infty$.*

4) $$\mathbf{S}(X) = \left[\bigcup_{i \in I} \mathbf{S}(X_i)\right] \cup \left[\bigcup_{\substack{i, j \in I \\ i \neq j}} (X_i \cap X_j)\right].$$

5) *For any $Y \subset X$ we have: Y is a thin subset of $X \Leftrightarrow X_i \cap Y$ is a thin subset of X_i for all $i \in I$. For any analytic set Y in X we have: Y is nowhere dense in $X \Leftrightarrow X_i \cap Y$ is nowhere dense in X_i for all $i \in I \Leftrightarrow Y \not\subset X_i$ for all $i \in I$.*

6) *The following six conditions are equivalent.*[7]

i) *X is irreducible.*

ii) *X has only one irreducible component.*

iii) *$X - \mathbf{S}(X)$ is connected.*

iv) *If Y is any analytic set in X such that $Y \neq X$, then Y is nowhere dense in X.*

[7] In view of i) $\Leftrightarrow$ iii), in the situation of (44.29) we get that: $X_1, \ldots, X_\lambda$ are irreducible; and if X_a is irreducible then U is irreducible.

v) *If* Y *is any analytic set in* X *such that* $Y \neq X$, *then* $X - Y$ *is connected.*
vi) *If* Y *is any thin subset of* X, *then* $X - Y$ *is connected.*

7) *If* X *is connected and* X_a *is irreducible for all* $a \in X$, *then* X *is irreducible.*

8) *Let* Y *be any thin subset of* X. *Then* $X_i - Y$ *is connected and* $X_i = \mathrm{cl}_X(X_i - Y)$ *for all* $i \in I$. *If furthermore* $\mathbf{S}(X) \subset Y$, *then* $(X_i - Y)_{i \in I}$ *are exactly all the distinct connected components of* $X - Y$.

9) *If* X *has a countable basis of open sets, then* I *is countable.*

(**44.33**) Identity Theorem for Analytic Sets. *Let* Y *and* Z *be nonempty analytic sets in a complex space* X *such that* Y *is irreducible. Then we have the following.*

1) *The following three conditions are equivalent.*

i) $Y \subset Z$.
ii) $Y \subset Z^*$ *for some irreducible component* Z^* *of* Z.
iii) *There exists* $a \in Y$ *and an irreducible component* Y' *of* Y_a *such that* $Y' \subset Z_a$.

2) *The following three conditions are equivalent.*

i′) Y *is an irreducible component of* Z.
ii′) *There exists* $a \in Y$ *and an irreducible component* Y' *of* Y_a *such that* Y' *is an irreducible component of* Z_a.
iii′) *For every* $a \in Y$ *each irreducible component of* Y_a *is an irreducible component of* Z_a.

(**44.34**) *For any nonempty analytic sets* Y *and* Z *in a complex space* X *we have the following.*

1) *The following three conditions are equivalent.*

i) Y *is the union of a certain number of irreducible components of* Z.
ii) *Every irreducible component of* Y *is an irreducible component of* Z.
iii) *For every* $a \in Y$ *each irreducible component of* Y_a *is an irreducible component of* Z_a.

2) *If* $\dim Z = e < \infty$, Y *is pure* e *dimensional, and* $Y \subset Z$, *then* Y *is the union of a certain number of irreducible components of* Z.

Proof. 1) follows from (44.32.1, 44.32.2, 44.33.2). 2) follows from 1).

(**44.35**) REMARK. Let Y be a nonempty irreducible analytic set in a complex space X. For each $a \in Y$ and each irreducible component Y^* of Y_a, by (44.11) we can find an analytic set $Z(Y^*)$ in a neighborhood $V(Y^*)$ of a in X such that: $(Z(Y^*))_a = Y^*$, and for each $b \in Z(Y^*)$ every irreducible component of $(Z(Y^*))_b$ is an irreducible component of Y_b.

Let H be a set. For each $a \in Y$ and each irreducible component Y^* of Y_a let there be assigned an element $\varphi(Y^*)$ in H. Assume that for each $a \in Y$ and each irreducible component Y^* of Y_a there exists a neighborhood $U(Y^*)$ of a in $V(Y^*)$ such that: for every $b \in Z(Y^*) \cap U(Y^*)$ and every irreducible component Y' of $(Z(Y^*))_b$ we have $\varphi(Y') = \varphi(Y^*)$.

We claim that then there exists $h \in H$ such that for every $a \in Y$ and every irreducible component Y^* of Y_a we have $\varphi(Y^*) = h$, i.e., $\varphi(Y^*)$ does not depend on which $a \in Y$ and which irreducible component Y^* of Y_a we take.

PROOF. Take the discrete topology on H, and for each $c \in Y - \mathbf{S}(Y)$ let $\psi(c) = \varphi(Y_c)$. Then ψ: $Y - \mathbf{S}(Y) \to H$ is continuous. $Y - \mathbf{S}(Y)$ is connected by (44.32.6), and hence ψ is constant on $Y - \mathbf{S}(Y)$, i.e., there exists $h \in H$ such that $\varphi(Y_c) = h$ for all $c \in Y - \mathbf{S}(Y)$. Since $\mathbf{S}(Y)$ is nowhere dense in Y, given any $a \in Y$ and any irreducible component Y^* of Y_a there exists $b \in (Z(Y^*)) \cap U(Y^*) - \mathbf{S}(Y)$; and then $\varphi(Y^*) = \varphi(Y_b) = h$.

(**44.36**) DEFINITION. Let X be a complex space and let $(X_i)_{i \in I}$ be the distinct irreducible components of X. We *define*

$$\mathbf{N}'(X) = \bigcup_{\substack{i, j \in I \\ i \neq j}} (X_i \cap X_j).$$

The following proposition sharpens (44.32.7, 44.32.8).

(**44.37**) *For any complex space X, $\mathbf{N}'(X)$ is a nowhere dense analytic set in X and $\mathbf{N}'(X) \subset \mathbf{N}^*(X)$. Let $(X_i)_{i \in I}$ be the distinct irreducible components of X and let Y be any thin subset of X. Then $\mathrm{cl}_X(X_i - Y) = X_i$ for all $i \in I$. If furthermore $\mathbf{N}'(X) \subset Y$ then $(X_i - Y)_{i \in I}$ are exactly all the distinct connected components of $X - Y$. In particular, taking $Y = \mathbf{N}^*(X)$ we get the following.*

$(X_i - \mathbf{N}^*(X))_{i \in I}$ are exactly all the distinct connected components of $X - \mathbf{N}^*(X)$. If X_a is irreducible for all $a \in X$, then $(X_i)_{i \in I}$ are exactly all the distinct connected components of X. If X is connected and X_a is irreducible for all $a \in X$, then X is irreducible.

PROOF. By (44.9, 44.32.2) it follows that $\mathbf{N}'(X)$ is a nowhere dense analytic set in X and $\mathbf{N}'(X) \subset \mathbf{N}^*(X)$. For any $i \in I$ let

$$X_i' = \bigcup_{\substack{j \in I \\ j \neq i}} X_j.$$

By (44.32.1, 44.32.5, 44.32.6) it follows that: $X_i - Y$ is connected; $X_i = \mathrm{cl}_X(X_i - Y)$; $X_i - Y$ and $X_i' - Y$ are closed sets in $X - Y$; and $X - Y = (X_i - Y) \cup (X_i' - Y)$. If $\mathbf{N}'(X) \subset Y$, then obviously $(X_i - Y) \cap (X_i' - Y) = \emptyset$ and hence $X_i - Y$ must be a connected component of $X - Y$.

(44.38) *For any analytic function f on a complex space X and any $a \in X$ we have the following.*

1) OPEN MAP THEOREM. *The following eight conditions are equivalent.*

α) (resp: $\alpha_1, \alpha_2, \alpha_3$). f_a (resp: $(|f|)_a$, $(\mathbf{Re}\, f)_a$, $(\mathbf{Im}\, f)_a$) *is nonconstant.*
β) (resp: $\beta_1, \beta_2, \beta_3$). *The map f* (resp: $|f|$, $\mathbf{Re}\, f$, $\mathbf{Im}\, f$) *of X into* $\mathbf{C}$ (resp: $\mathbf{R}_+$, $\mathbf{R}$, $\mathbf{R}$) *is open at a.*

2) MAXIMUM PRINCIPLE. *If any one of the following five conditions is satisfied then* f_a, $(|f|)_a$, $(\mathbf{Re}\, f)_a$, *and* $(\mathbf{Im}\, f)_a$ *are constant.*

i) $|f(a)| = \sup |f(X)|$.
ii) $\mathbf{Re}\, f(a) = \sup \mathbf{Re}\, f(X)$. iii) $\mathbf{Re}\, f(a) = \inf \mathbf{Re}\, f(X)$.
ii′) $\mathbf{Im}\, f(a) = \sup \mathbf{Im}\, f(X)$. iii′) $\mathbf{Im}\, f(a) = \inf \mathbf{Im}\, f(X)$.

PROOF. Same as the proof of (34.22).

(44.39) *For any irreducible complex space X we have the following.*

1) IDENTITY THEOREM. *Let f and g be any analytic functions on X such that $f \neq g$, and let $Y = \{a \in X : f(a) = g(a)\}$. Then $Y = \emptyset$ or Y is a pure $e - 1$ dimensional analytic set in X where $e =$* dim X; *in either case Y is nowhere dense in X.*

2) OPEN MAP THEOREM. *For any analytic function f on X the following twelve conditions are equivalent.*

α) (resp: $\alpha_1, \alpha_2, \alpha_3$). f_a (resp: $(|f|)_a$, $(\mathbf{Re}\, f)_a$, $(\mathbf{Im}\, f)_a$) *is nonconstant for some $a \in X$.*
β) (resp: $\beta_1, \beta_2, \beta_3$). f (resp: $|f|$, $\mathbf{Re}\, f$, $\mathbf{Im}\, f$) *is nonconstant.*
γ) (resp: $\gamma_1, \gamma_2, \gamma_3$). f (resp: $|f|$, $\mathbf{Re}\, f$, $\mathbf{Im}\, f$) *is an open map of X into* $\mathbf{C}$ (resp: $\mathbf{R}_+$, $\mathbf{R}$, $\mathbf{R}$).

3) MAXIMUM PRINCIPLE. *For any analytic function f on X the following ten conditions are equivalent, and if any one of them is satisfied then f, $|f|$, $\mathbf{Re}\, f$, and $\mathbf{Im}\, f$ are constant.*

i) $|f(a)| = \sup |f(X)|$ *for some* $a \in X$.
ii) $|f(a)| = \sup |f(U)|$ *for some neighborhood* U *of some point* $a \in X$.
iii) $\mathbf{Re}\, f(a) = \sup \mathbf{Re}\, f(X)$ for *some* $a \in X$.
iv) $\mathbf{Re}\, f(a) = \sup \mathbf{Re}\, f(U)$ *for some neighborhood* U *of some point* $a \in X$.
v) $\mathbf{Re}\, f(a) = \inf \mathbf{Re}\, f(X)$ *for some* $a \in X$.
vi) $\mathbf{Re}\, f(a) = \inf \mathbf{Re}\, f(U)$ *for some neighborhood* U *of some point* $a \in X$.
iii′, iv′, v′, vi′) *Same as* iii, iv, v, vi) *with* **Im** *replacing* **Re**.

PROOF. In the proof of (34.23) replace the reference to (34.10, 34.11, 34.22) by reference to (44.32.6, 44.32.3, 44.38), respectively.

(**44.40**) HARTOGS EXTENSION THEOREM. *Let Y be an analytic set in a complex space X such that $Y \cap \mathbf{S}(X) = \emptyset$ and* $\dim Y_a \leqq (\dim X_a) - 2$ *for all $a \in Y$.*[8] *Let f be any analytic function on $X - Y$. Then f has a unique analytic extension to X.*

PROOF. Uniqueness is obvious because Y is nowhere dense in X by (44.9). Suppose for each $a \in X$ we have found an analytic function $f^{(a)}$ on a neighborhood $U(a)$ of a in X such that $f^{(a)}|U(a) - Y = f|U(a) - Y$. Let $g(a) = f^{(a)}(a)$ for all $a \in X$. Then $g|U(a) = f^{(a)}$ for all $a \in X$, and hence g is an analytic function on X and $g|X - Y = f$.

To prove our supposition, let $a \in X$ be given. If $a \notin Y$ then we have nothing to show. Now assume that $a \in Y$. By (44.5, 44.19) there exists a neighborhood $U(a)$ of a in X such that $\dim Y \cap U(a) \leqq n - 2$ and $U(a)$ can be mapped bianalytically onto an open set in $\mathbf{C}^n$ where $n = \dim X_a$. By (33.21), $f|U(a) - Y$ has an analytic extension to $U(a)$.

(**44.41**) *Let X be a complex space. For $a \in X$ let*

$R''(a, X) =$ *integral closure of $R(a, X)$ in $\mathfrak{E}(a, X)$;*
$R_1''(a, X) = \{r \in \mathfrak{E}(a, X)$: *there exists a closed thin subset Z in a neighborhood U of a in X and $f \in \mathfrak{E}(U)$ such that $f_a = r$ and $f|U - Z \in R(U - Z)\}$;*
$R_2''(a, X) = \{r \in \mathfrak{E}(a, X)$: *there exists a neighborhood U of a in X and $f \in \mathfrak{E}(U)$ such that $f_a = r$ and $f|U - \mathbf{S}(X) \in R(U - \mathbf{S}(X))\}$.*

[8] By (44.32), these assumptions are satisfied if X is nonsingular and connected, and $\dim Y \leqq (\dim X) - 2$.

Then we have the following.[9]

1) *If X_a is pure dimensional then $R_1''(a, X) = R_2''(a, X) = R''(a, X) \subset R'(a, X)$. If X_b is irreducible for all b in some neighborhood of a in X then $R''(a, X) = R'(a, X)$.*

2) *Let Ω be a nowhere dense analytic set in X such that $\mathbf{N}(X) \subset \Omega$, and let U be a nonempty open set in X such that X_b is irreducible for all $b \in U$.*[10] *Then for any $f \in \mathfrak{E}(U)$ the following three conditions are equivalent.*

i) *$f_b \in R'(b, X)$ for all $b \in U$.*[11]
ii) *$f | U - \Omega \in R(U - \Omega)$.*
iii) *$f | U - Z \in R(U - Z)$ for some closed thin subset Z of U.*

3) *Assume that X_b is irreducible for all b in some neighborhood of a in X. Then the following three conditions are equivalent.*

1°) *X_a is normal.*
2°) *If Z is any closed thin subset in any neighborhood U of a in X and f is any element in $\mathfrak{E}(U)$ such that $f | U - Z \in R(U - Z)$, then $f_a \in R(a, X)$.*
3°) *If U is any neighborhood of a in X and f is any element in $\mathfrak{E}(U)$ such that $f | U - \mathbf{S}(X) \in R(U - \mathbf{S}(X))$, then $f_a \in R(a, X)$.*

PROOF. 1) and 3) follow from (36.6), and 2) follows from 1).

(**44.42**) RIEMANN EXTENSION THEOREM. *Let X be a complex space and let Z be a closed thin subset of X. Then we have the following.*

1) *Assume that X_a is irreducible for all $a \in X$ and let $f \in R(X - Z)$ be such that $|f|$ is bounded in the neighborhood of each point of Z. Then there exists a unique $g \in \mathfrak{E}(X)$ such that $g|X - Z = f$.*

2) *Assume that X is normal and let $f \in \mathfrak{E}(X)$ be such that $r|X - Z \in R(X - Z)$. Then $f \in R(X)$.*

3) *Assume that X is normal, let Y be a complex space, and let $\mu : X \to Y$ be a continuous map such that $\mu|X - Z: X - Z \to Y$ is analytic. Then μ is analytic.*

PROOF. 1) follows from (36.5). 2) follows from (44.41.3). To prove 3) what we have to show is that: $\bar{\mu}_{(a)}(R(b, Y)) \subset R(a, X)$ for all $a \in X$ where

[9] In 1) and 2), for each $b \in X$ we are considering $\mathfrak{R}(b, X)$ to be a subring of the total quotient ring of $\mathfrak{E}(b, X)$; see (44.16).

[10] For instance $\Omega = \mathbf{S}(X)$. In (45.28) we shall show that $\mathbf{N}(X)$ is closed in X and in (46.28) we shall show that $\mathbf{N}(X)$ is analytic in X. In (46.34.2) we shall remove the assumption that X_b is irreducible for all $b \in U$.

[11] See (44.27.1).

$b = \mu(a)$. Given any element in $R(b, Y)$ we can write it in the form h_b where h is an analytic function on a neighborhood V of b in Y. Let $U = \mu^{-1}(V)$ and let $f = h \circ (\mu|U)$. Then $f \in \mathfrak{C}(U)$, $h_{b'} \in R(b', Y)$, and $\bar{\mu}_{(a')}(h_{b'}) = f_{a'}$ for all $a' \in U$ where $b' = \mu(a')$. Since $\mu|X - Z$ is analytic for all $a' \in U - Z$ we have $\bar{\mu}_{(a')}(R(\mu(a'), Y)) \subset R(a', X)$ and hence $f_{a'} \in R(a', X)$. Thus $f|U - Z \in R(U - Z)$ and hence $f_a \in R(a, X)$ by 2).

(**44.43**) REMMERT–STEIN–THULLEN THEOREM ON ESSENTIAL SINGULARITIES OF COMPLEX ANALYTIC SETS. *Let X be a complex space, let Z be an analytic set in X, let Y be an analytic set in $X - Z$, and let $\bar{Y} = \mathrm{cl}_X Y$.*

A point $a \in X$ is said to be *ordinary relative to* $Y \Leftrightarrow \bar{Y}$ is analytic at a. A point $a \in X$ is said to be an *essential singularity of* $Y \Leftrightarrow \bar{Y}$ is not analytic at a. We make the following observations (1° to 7°).

1°) The set of points of Z which are ordinary relative to Y is an open subset of Z.

2°) $\bar{Y} - Y =$ (boundary of Y in $\bar{Y}$) $\subset Z$.

3°) If $a \in X$ is an essential singularity of Y, then $a \in \bar{Y} - Y$.

4°) $\bar{Y}$ is analytic in $X \Leftrightarrow$ every point of Z is ordinary relative to Y.

5°) If Y is pure e dimensional and $\bar{Y}$ is analytic at $a \in \bar{Y}$, then $\bar{Y}_a$ is pure e dimensional by (44.5, 44.8).

6°) Let ξ be a bianalytic map of a nonempty open set U in X onto an analytic set V in a complex space X', let $Z' = \xi(Z \cap U)$ and $Y' = \xi(Y \cap U)$. Then Z' is an analytic set in X', Y' is an analytic set in $X' - Z'$, and $\mathrm{cl}_{X'} Y' = \xi(\bar{Y} \cap U)$. Therefore $Q = \xi(P \cap U)$ where P is the set of all essential singularities of Y in X and Q is the set of all essential singularities of Y' in X'.

7°) Given $a \in X$, there exists a bianalytic map ξ of a neighborhood U of a in X onto an analytic set V in an open set X' in $\mathbf{C}^n$ for some n.

The said theorem asserts the following.

1) *If* $\dim Z < \dim Y_b$ *for all $b \in Y$, then $\bar{Y}$ is analytic in X.*

2) *Assume that Y is pure e dimensional and let Z_1 be an e dimensional irreducible component of Z. If $\bar{Y}$ is analytic at some point of Z_1 then $\bar{Y}$ is analytic at every point of Z_1 which is not in any other irreducible component of Z.*

3) *Assume that* $\dim Z \leqq \dim Y$, *and Y is pure e dimensional. Then we have the following.*

i) *Let P be the set of all the essential singularities of Y in X. Then P is either empty or P is a pure e dimensional analytic set in Z, and P is the union of a certain number of irreducible components of Z.*

ii) *If every irreducible component of Z contains an essential singularity of Y which is not in any other irreducible component of Z, then every point of Z is an essential singularity of Y, and Z is either empty or pure e dimensional.*

iii) *If every e dimensional irreducible component of Z contains a point which is ordinary relative to Y, then $\bar{Y}$ is a pure e dimensional analytic set in X.*

These assertions can be proved by making a few changes in the proof of (37.1, 37.2, 37.3), or they can be deduced from (37.1, 37.3.1) in the following manner.

Proof of 1). Given $a \in X$ we want to show that $\bar{Y}$ is analytic at a. In virtue of 6°) and 7°), upon replacing X, Y, Z by X', Y', Z', we may assume that X is an open set in $\mathbf{C}^n$ and then we are reduced to (37.1).

Proof of 3). In virtue of (5°, 44.32.1, 44.32.3), ii) and iii) follow from i). If we showed that P is either empty or a pure e dimensional analytic set in Z then by (44.34.2) it would follow that P is the union of a certain number of irreducible components of Z and that would prove i). To prove that P is either empty or a pure e dimensional analytic set in Z what we have to show is that: given $a \in P$, P_a is analytic and pure e dimensional. To prove the last statement, in virtue of 6°) and 7°) we may assume that X is an open set in $\mathbf{C}^n$ and then we are reduced to (37.3.1).

Proof of 2). Let Z_2 be the union of all the irreducible components of Z other than Z_1, let $X^* = X - Z_2$, $Z^* = Z - Z_2$, and $\bar{Y}^* = \mathrm{cl}_{X^*} Y$. By (1°, 44.32), Z^* is an e dimensional irreducible analytic set in X^* and Z^* contains a point at which $\bar{Y}^*$ is analytic. Therefore by 3.iii), $\bar{Y}^*$ is analytic at every point of Z^*, i.e., $\bar{Y}$ is analytic at every point of Z^*.

(**44.44**) *Let X be a connected, locally arcwise connected and locally simply connected topological space. Let Z be a closed nowhere dense subset of X such that each $a \in X$ has a connected neighborhood $U(a)$ in X for which $U(a) - Z$ is connected and simply connected. Given any covering map $\eta: Y' \to X - Z$, there exists a covering map $\xi: Y \to X$ and a homeomorphism $\delta: \xi^{-1}(X - Z) \to Y'$ such that $\xi | \xi^{-1}(X - Z) = \eta \circ \delta$. If furthermore Z disconnects X nowhere, then the natural map $\pi_1(X - Z) \to \pi_1(X)$ is an isomorphism.*

Proof. By assumption there exists a covering $(X_i)_{i \in I}$ of X by nonempty open subsets such that $X_i - Z$ is connected and simply connected for all i in I. For each i in I let A_i be the set of all distinct connected components of $\eta^{-1}(X_i - Z)$, let $Y_i = A_i \times X_i$ have the product topology where A_i is given the discrete topology, and let $\xi_i: Y_i \to X_i$ be the natural projection. For all i, j, k in I let $X_{ij} = X_i \cap X_j$, $Y_{ij} = \xi_i^{-1}(X_{ij}) = A_i \times X_{ij}$,

$X_{ijk} = X_i \cap X_j \cap X_k$, $Y_{ijk} = \xi_i^{-1}(X_{ijk}) = A_i \times X_{ijk}$. For each $i \in I$ and $P \in A_i$ the map $P \to X_i - Z$ induced by η is a homeomorphism because $X_i - Z$ is simply connected. Therefore for any i, j in I for which $X_{ij} \neq \emptyset$ we get a one to one onto map $\alpha_{ji}\colon A_i \to A_j$ defined by the condition

$$P \cap \alpha_{ji}(P) \neq \emptyset;$$

this yields a homeomorphism $\lambda_{ji}\colon Y_{ji} \to Y_{ij}$ defined by

$$\lambda_{ji}(P, a) = (\alpha_{ji}(P), a) \qquad \text{for all} \quad P \in A_i \quad \text{and} \quad a \in X_{ij};$$

and we obviously have

$$\xi_i | Y_{ij} = \xi_j \circ \lambda_{ji}.$$

For all i in I, α_{ii} is the identity map of A_i and hence λ_{ii} is the identity map of Y_i. For all i, j, k in I for which $X_{ijk} \neq \emptyset$ we clearly have $\alpha_{ki} = \alpha_{kj} \circ \alpha_{ji}$ and hence

$$\lambda_{ki} | Y_{ijk} = \lambda_{kj} \circ (\lambda_{ji} | Y_{ijk}).$$

Therefore by (43.3.4) there exists a topological space Y, an open covering $(V_i)_{i \in I}$ of Y, a continuous map $\xi\colon Y \to X$, and a homeomorphism $\lambda_i\colon Y_i \to V_i$ for each i in I such that

1°) $\xi(V_i) = X_i$, $\xi^{-1}(X_i) = V_i$, and $\xi \circ \lambda_i = \xi_i$ for all i in I;

and

2°) for all i, j in I, $\quad b_i \in Y_i, \quad b_j \in Y_j$:

$$\lambda_i(b_i) = \lambda_j(b_j) \Leftrightarrow b_i \in Y_{ij},\ b_j \in Y_{ji}, \text{ and } \lambda_{ji}(b_i) = b_j.$$

Obviously $\xi_i\colon Y_i \to X_i$ is a covering map for all i in I, and hence $\xi\colon Y \to X$ is a covering map by 1°). For each $i \in I$, $P \in A_i$, $a \in X_i - Z$ let $\delta_i(\lambda_i(P, a)) = P \cap \eta^{-1}(a)$. Then $\delta_i\colon \xi^{-1}(X_i - Z) \to \eta^{-1}(X_i - Z)$ is a homeomorphism and $\xi | \xi^{-1}(X_i - Z) = \eta \circ \delta_i$ for all i in I. By 2°) it follows that $\delta_i(b) = \delta_j(b)$ for all i, j in I, and $b \in \xi^{-1}(X_{ij} - Z)$. Therefore there exists a unique continuous map $\delta\colon \xi^{-1}(X - Z) \to Y'$ such that $\delta(\xi^{-1}(X - Z)) = Y'$ and such that $\delta(b) = \delta_i(b)$ for all $i \in I$ and $b \in \xi^{-1}(X_i - Z)$. By 2°) it follows that δ is one to one. Therefore $\delta\colon \xi^{-1}(X - Z) \to Y'$ is a homeomorphism and $\xi | \xi^{-1}(X - Z) = \eta \circ \delta$.

Since $\xi\colon Y \to X$ is a covering map, it follows that $\xi^{-1}(Z)$ is a closed nowhere dense subset of Y; hence if Y' is connected then Y is connected. Now assume that Z disconnects X nowhere. Then $\xi^{-1}(Z)$ disconnects Y nowhere. Take $\eta\colon Y' \to X - Z$ to be a universal covering of $X - Z$.

Then $Y - \xi^{-1}(Z)$ is connected and simply connected. Therefore Y is connected, and by (39.4), Y is simply connected. Thus $\xi: Y \to X$ is a universal covering of X and the map $Y - \xi^{-1}(Z) \to X - Z$ induced by ξ is a universal covering of $X - Z$. Therefore the natural map $\pi_1(X - Z) \to \pi_1(X)$ is an isomorphism.

(44.45) *Let X be a connected nonsingular complex space and let Z be an analytic set in X such that* $\dim Z \leqq (\dim X) - 2$. *Given any covering map $\eta: Y' \to X - Z$, there exists a covering map $\xi: Y \to X$ and a homeomorphism $\delta: \xi^{-1}(X - Z) \to Y'$ such that $\xi | \xi^{-1}(X - Z) = \eta \circ \delta$. Furthermore, the natural map $\pi_1(X - Z) \to \pi_1(X)$ is an isomorphism; hence in particular, X is simply connected $\Leftrightarrow$ $X - Z$ is simply connected.*

Proof. By (44.32), X is pure n dimensional for some n. By (44.19), every point in X has a neighborhood which can be mapped bianalytically onto an open set in $\mathbf{C}^n$. Therefore our assertion follows from (39.8) and (44.44).

(44.46) Remark. Let X be a connected complex space, let Y be a topological space and let $\xi: Y \to X$ be a covering map. Let $\mathcal{O}_Y$ be the subsheaf of $\mathcal{E}_Y$ given by taking

$$\mathcal{O}_Y(V) = \{f \in \mathfrak{E}(V): f_b \in \xi_{(b)}(R(\xi(b), X)) \text{ for all } b \in V\}$$

for each nonempty open set V in Y. Since ξ is a covering map, we can find a covering $(V_j)_{j \in J}$ of Y by nonempty open sets such that the map $\mu_j: V_j \to \xi(V_j)$ induced by ξ is a homeomorphism for all j in J. It follows that $(Y, \mathcal{O}_Y)$ is a complex space, $\xi: Y \to X$ is analytic, and $\mu_j: V_j \to \xi(V_j)$ is bianalytic for all j in J.

Let X' be a nonempty connected open set in X, let Y' be a topological space, let $\eta: Y' \to X'$ be a covering map, and let $\delta: \xi^{-1}(X') \to Y'$ be a homeomorphism such that $\xi | \xi^{-1}(X') = \eta \circ \delta$. Convert Y' into a complex space in the above manner. It can easily be seen that $\delta: \xi^{-1}(X') \to Y'$ is then a bianalytic map.

§45. INVARIANCE OF ORDER AND RANK[1]

Let X be an analytic K-space, let $a \in X$, and let Y be an analytic set in X with $a \in Y$ such that Y_a is irreducible.

(45.1) Definition. For any $Z \subset X$ such that $a \in Z$ and Z is analytic at a we *define*

[1] This section is based on Abhyankar [3]. For corrections to this paper see (45.30).

$$
\begin{aligned}
R(a, Z, X) &= R(a, Z_a, X) \\
&= \textit{quotient ring of } Z \textit{ at } a \textit{ (or of } Z_a\textit{) in } X \\
&= R(a, X)_{\mathfrak{i}(a, Z, X)}.
\end{aligned}
$$

Note the following: 1°) $R(a, Z, X)$ is a semilocal ring with maximal ideals $\mathfrak{i}(a, Z_1, X)R(a, Z, X), \dots, \mathfrak{i}(a, Z_\mu, X)R(a, Z, X)$ where $Z_1, \dots, Z_\mu$ are the irreducible components of Z_a. 2°) $R(a, X, X) = \mathfrak{R}(a, X)$. 3°) $R(a, \{a\}, X) = R(a, X)$.

Now assume that Z_a is irreducible. Then $R(a, Z, X)$ is a local ring with maximal ideal $\mathfrak{i}(a, Z, X)R(a, Z, X)$. We *define*

$$\mathfrak{m}(a, Z, X) = \mathfrak{m}(a, Z_a, X) = \mathfrak{i}(a, Z, X)R(a, Z, X).$$

For any nonempty subset F of $R(a, Z, X)$ we *define*

$$\mathrm{ord}_{a, Z, X}F = \mathrm{ord}_{a, Z_a, X}F = \mathrm{ord}_{R(a, Z, X)}F$$

and in case $F \subset \mathfrak{m}(a, Z, X)$ we *define*

$$\mathrm{rnk}_{a, Z, X}F = \mathrm{rnk}_{a, Z_a, X}F = \mathrm{rnk}_{R(a, Z, X)}F.$$

For any nonempty set F of analytic functions on a neighborhood of a in X we *define*

$$\mathrm{ord}_{a, Z, X}F = \mathrm{ord}_{a, Z_a, X}F = \mathrm{ord}_{a, Z, X}F_a$$

and in case $F_a \subset \mathfrak{i}(a, Z, X)$ we *define*

$$\mathrm{rnk}_{a, Z, X}F = \mathrm{rnk}_{a, Z_a, X}F = \mathrm{rnk}_{a, Z, X}F_a.$$

(**45.2**) $\dim R(a, Y, X) = \dim \mathfrak{J}[a, Y, X] - \dim Y_a$. *In particular, if* X_a *is pure dimensional then* $\dim R(a, Y, X) = \dim X_a - \dim Y_a$.

PROOF. Follows from (44.4) in view of the fact that $\dim R(a, Y, X) = \mathrm{hgt}_{R(a,X)}\mathfrak{i}(a, Y, X)$. Alternatively, let $X_1, \dots, X_\mu$ be the irreducible components of X_a labeled so that $Y_a \subset X_j$ for $j \leqq k$ and $Y_a \not\subset X_j$ for $j > k$. Let $\mathfrak{p} = \mathfrak{i}(a, Y, X)$. Then $\mathfrak{i}(a, X_1, X) \cap \dots \cap \mathfrak{i}(a, X_\mu, X)$ is the normal decomposition of $\{0\}$ in $R(a, X)$, $\mathfrak{i}(a, X_j, X) \subset \mathfrak{p}$ for $j \leqq k$, and $\mathfrak{i}(a, X_j, X) \not\subset \mathfrak{p}$ for $j > k$. Therefore

$$\dim R(a, Y, X) = \mathrm{hgt}_{R(a, X)}\mathfrak{p} = \max_{j \leqq k} \mathrm{hgt}_{S_j}\varphi_j(\mathfrak{p})$$

where $\varphi_j: R(a, Y, X) \to S_j = R(a, X)/\mathfrak{i}(a, X_j, X)$ is the natural epimorphism. For any $j \leqq k$, obviously

$$\mathrm{dpt}_{S_j}\varphi_j(\mathfrak{p}) = \mathrm{dpt}_{R(a, X)}\mathfrak{p} = \dim R(a, X)/\mathfrak{p} = \dim R(a, Y) = \dim Y_a$$

and by (23.8)

$$\operatorname{dpt}_{S_j}\varphi_j(\mathfrak{p}) + \operatorname{hgt}_{S_j}\varphi_j(\mathfrak{p}) = \dim S_j.$$

Therefore

$$\operatorname{hgt}_{S_j}\varphi_j(\mathfrak{p}) = \dim S_j - \dim Y_a \quad \text{for} \quad j = 1,\dots, k.$$

Now it suffices to note that

$$\dim S_j = \dim X_j, \qquad \text{and} \qquad \dim \mathfrak{J}[a, Y, X] = \max_{j \leq k} \dim X_j.$$

(45.3) *Let Z be any analytic subspace of X with $Y \subset Z$. Then $R(a, Y, Z) \approx R(a, Y, X)/\mathfrak{i}(a, Z, X)R(a, Y, X)$.*

PROOF. Follows from (18.5.2).

(45.4) *Let F be a finite set of analytic functions on X such that $Y \subset \mathfrak{V}(F)$. Then*

$$\dim R(a, Y, X)/F_a R(a, Y, X) = \dim \mathfrak{J}[a, Y, \mathfrak{V}(F)] - \dim Y_a.$$

PROOF. By the Nullstellensatz

$$\dim R(a, Y, X)/F_a R(a, Y, X) = \dim R(a, Y, X)/\mathfrak{i}(a, \mathfrak{V}(F), X)R(a, Y, X)$$

and hence by (45.3)

$$\dim R(a, Y, X)/F_a R(a, Y, X) = \dim R(a, Y, \mathfrak{V}(F)).$$

Our assertion now follows by taking $\mathfrak{V}(F)$ for X in (45.2).

(45.5) *There exists a neighborhood U of a in X such that for every $b \in U$ and every irreducible component Y' of Y_b we have*: $\dim R(a, Y, X) = \dim R(b, Y', X)$.

PROOF. By (44.8) there exists a neighborhood V of a in X such that $Y \cap V$ is pure dimensional. By (44.14) there exists a neighborhood U of a in V such that for every $b \in U$ and every irreducible component Y' of Y_b we have: $\dim \mathfrak{J}[b, Y', X] = \dim \mathfrak{J}[a, Y, X]$. Now invoke (45.2).

In virtue of (44.19), if a is a simple point of Y as well as of X then the significance of $\operatorname{ord}_{a,Y,X}$ and $\operatorname{rnk}_{a,Y,X}$ is explained by (21.11). For instance, for rnk we have the following.

(45.6) *Suppose that X is an open set in $K^n\{x_1,\dots, x_n\}$ and $Y = \{x \in X: x_1 = a_1,\dots, x_e = a_e\}$. Let $F = \{f_1,\dots, f_p\}$ be a nonempty finite set of* *analytic functions on X such that $F_a \subset \mathfrak{i}(a, Y, X)$. Then*

$$\operatorname{rnk}_{a, Y, X} F = \operatorname{rnk}\left(\frac{J(f_1,\ldots, f_p)}{J(x_1,\ldots, x_e)}(a_1,\ldots, a_e, x_{e+1},\ldots, x_n)\right)_a .$$

PROOF. Upon replacing $x_1,\ldots, x_n$ by $x_1 - a_1,\ldots, x_e - a_e, x_{e+1},\ldots, x_n$ we may assume that $a_1 = \ldots = a_e = 0$; and then upon replacing $f_1,\ldots, f_p$ by their Taylor expansions around a we may assume that a is at the origin and we may identify $R(a, X)$ with $R = K[\langle x_1,\ldots, x_n\rangle]$. Now $\mathfrak{p} = \{x_1,\ldots, x_e\}R$ is a prime ideal in R and hence $\mathfrak{i}(a, Y, X) = \mathfrak{p}$ by the Nullstellensatz. Thus we are reduced to (21.11.2.1°).

(**45.7**) Lower semicontinuity of order. *Given a finite nonempty set $F = \{f_1,\ldots, f_p\}$ of analytic functions on X, there exists a neighborhood U of a in X such that for every $b \in U$ and every irreducible component Y' of Y_b we have*: $\operatorname{ord}_{a,Y,X} F \leqq \operatorname{ord}_{b,Y',X} F$.

PROOF. Let $\operatorname{ord}_{a,Y,X} F = e$. For $e = \infty$ the assertion follows from (44.13). Now assume that $e < \infty$. Take analytic functions $w_1,\ldots, w_\nu$ on a neighborhood V of a in X such that $\{(w_1)_a,\ldots, (w_\nu)_a\}R(a, X) = \mathfrak{i}(a, Y, X)$ and $w_1(b) = \ldots = w_\nu(b) = 0$ for all $b \in Y \cap V$. By (21.2.1) there exist analytic functions $r_j, r_{ji_1\ldots i_\nu}$ on a neighborhood V_1 of a in V such that for $j = 1,\ldots, p$ we have

$$(r_j)_a \notin \mathfrak{i}(a, Y, X),$$

and

$$r_j f_j = \sum_{i_1+\cdots+i_\nu=e} r_{ji_1\cdots i_\nu} w_1^{i_1}\ldots w_\nu^{i_\nu} \qquad \text{about } a.$$

Take a neighborhood V_2 of a in V_1 such that the above equations hold on V_2 for $j = 1,\ldots, p$. By (44.15) there exists a neighborhood U of a in V_2 such that for every $b \in U$ and every irreducible component Y' of Y_b we have

$$(r_j)_b \notin \mathfrak{i}(b, Y', X) \qquad \text{for} \quad j = 1,\ldots, p.$$

Now again invoke (21.2.1).

(**45.8**) Upper semicontinuity of rank. *Given a finite nonempty set $F = \{f_1,\ldots, f_p\}$ of analytic functions on X with $F_a \subset \mathfrak{i}(a, Y, X)$, there exists a neighborhood U of a in X such that for every $b \in U$ and every irreducible component Y' of Y_b we have*: $F_b \subset \mathfrak{i}(b, Y', X)$ *and* $\operatorname{rnk}_{a,Y,X} F \geqq \operatorname{rnk}_{b,Y',X} F$.

PROOF. Label the elements $f_1,\ldots, f_p$ so that $(f_1)_a,\ldots, (f_e)_a$ form a basis of F_a mod $\mathfrak{m}(a, Y, X)^2$. Take analytic functions $w_1,\ldots, w_\nu$ on a neighborhood V of a in X such that $\{(w_1)_a,\ldots, (w_\nu)_a\}R(a, X) = \mathfrak{i}(a, Y, X)$ and $w_1(b) = \ldots = w_\nu(b) = 0$ for all $b \in Y \cap V$. By (21.2.3) there exist analytic functions $r_j, r_{ji}, r_{ji_1\ldots i_\nu}$ on a neighborhood V_1 of a in V such that for $j = 1,\ldots, p$ we have

$$(r_j)_a \notin \mathfrak{i}(a, Y, X),$$

and

$$r_j f_j = \sum_{j=1}^{e} r_{ji} f_i + \sum_{i_1+\ldots+i_\nu=2} r_{ji_1\ldots i_\nu} w_1^{i_1}\ldots w_\nu^{i_\nu} \quad \text{about } a.$$

Take a neighborhood V_2 of a in V_1 such that the above equations hold on V_2 for $j = 1\ldots, p$ and such that $f_1(b) = \ldots = f_p(b) = 0$ for all $b \in Y \cap V_2$. By (44.15) there exists a neighborhood U of a in V_2 such that for every $b \in U$ and every irreducible component Y' of Y_b we have

$$(r_j)_b \notin \mathfrak{i}(b, Y', X) \quad \text{for} \quad j = 1,\ldots, p.$$

Now again invoke (21.2.3).

(45.9) *Let $u_1,\ldots, u_\lambda$ be analytic functions on a neighborhood W of a in X such that $\{(u_1)_a,\ldots, (u_\lambda)_a\}R(a, Y, X) = \mathfrak{m}(a, Y, X)$. Then there exists a neighborhood U of a in W such that for every b in U and every irreducible component Y' of Y_b we have: $\{(u_1)_b,\ldots, (u_\lambda)_b\}R(b, Y', X) = \mathfrak{m}(b, Y', X)$, i.e., $(u_1)_b,\ldots, (u_\lambda)_b$ generate $\mathfrak{m}(b, Y', X)$* mod $\mathfrak{m}(b, Y', X)^2$.

PROOF. We can take neighborhood V of a in W such that $u_1(b) = \ldots = u_\lambda(b) = 0$ for all $b \in Y \cap V$. By coherence (44.22) there exist analytic functions $v_1,\ldots, v_\mu$ on a neighborhood V_1 of a in V such that for every $b \in V_1$ we have $\{(v_1)_b,\ldots, (v_\mu)_b\}R(b, X) = \mathfrak{i}(b, Y, X)$. For any $b \in V_1$ and any irreducible component Y' of Y_b, denoting the other irreducible components of Y_b by $Y'_1,\ldots, Y'_\nu$ we have

$$\mathfrak{i}(b, Y, X) = \mathfrak{i}(b, Y', X) \cap \mathfrak{i}(b, Y'_1, X) \cap \ldots \cap \mathfrak{i}(b, Y'_\nu, X)$$

and

$$\mathfrak{i}(b, Y'_k, X) \not\subset \mathfrak{i}(b, Y', X) \quad \text{for} \quad k = 1,\ldots, \nu;$$

and hence $\{(v_1)_b,\ldots, (v_\mu)_b\}R(b, Y', X) = \mathfrak{m}(b, Y', X)$.

Now $(v_j)_a \in \mathfrak{i}(a, Y, X)$ and hence there exist analytic functions r_j, r_{ji} on a neighborhood V_2 of a in V_1 such that for $j = 1,\ldots, \mu$ we have

$$(r_j)_a \notin \mathfrak{i}(a, Y, X),$$

and

$$r_j v_j = \sum_{i=1}^{\lambda} r_{ji} u_i \quad \text{about } a.$$

Take a neighborhood V_3 of a in V_2 such that the above equations hold on V_3 for $j = 1,\dots,\mu$. By (44.15) there exists a neighborhood U of a in V_3 such that for every $b \in U$ and every irreducible component Y' of Y_b we have

$$(r_j)_b \notin \mathfrak{i}(b, Y', X) \qquad \text{for} \quad j = 1,\dots,\mu;$$

and hence

$$\{(u_1)_b,\dots,(u_\lambda)_b\}R(b, Y', X) = \{(v_1)_b,\dots,(v_\mu)_b\}R(b, Y', X) = \mathfrak{m}(b, Y', X).$$

(**45.10**) Continuity of rank and embedding dimension. *Given a finite nonempty set $F = \{f_1,\dots,f_p\}$ of analytic functions on X with $F_a \subset \mathfrak{i}(a, Y, X)$, there exists a neighborhood U of a in X such that for every $b \in U$ and every irreducible component Y' of Y_b we have*: $F_b \subset \mathfrak{i}(b, Y', X)$ *and*

i) $\operatorname{emdim} R(a, Y, X)/F_aR(a, Y, X) = \operatorname{emdim} R(b, Y', X)/F_bR(b, Y', X)$,
ii) $\operatorname{emdim} R(a, Y, X) = \operatorname{emdim} R(b, Y', X)$,
iii) $\operatorname{rnk}_{a,Y,X}F = \operatorname{rnk}_{b,Y',X}F$.

PROOF. ii) follows from i) by taking $F = \{0\}$; and then in virtue of (21.1.2), iii) follows from i) and ii). Consequently it is enough to prove i).

The problem being local, upon replacing X by a small enough neighborhood of a in X we may assume that: X is an analytic set in an open set D in K^n for some n, f_j is the restriction to X of an analytic function g_j on D for $j = 1,\dots,p$, and $g_1(b) = \dots = g_p(b) = 0$ for all $b \in Y$. By coherence (44.22), upon replacing D by a neighborhood of a in D, we can find analytic functions $g_{p+1},\dots,g_q$ on D such that for all $b \in D$ we have $\{(g_{p+1})_b,\dots,(g_q)_b\}R(b, D) = \mathfrak{i}(b, X, D)$. Let $G = \{g_1,\dots,g_q\}$. Given any $b \in Y$ and any irreducible component Y' of Y_b let $\varphi\colon R = R(b, D) \to R(b, X) = S$ be the restriction epimorphism and let $\mathfrak{a} = \mathfrak{i}(b, X, D)$, $\mathfrak{b} = G_bR(b, D)$, $\mathfrak{P} = \mathfrak{i}(b, Y', D)$. Then

$$\operatorname{Ker}\varphi = \mathfrak{a} \subset \mathfrak{b} \subset \mathfrak{P}$$

and hence

$$S_{\varphi(\mathfrak{P})}/\varphi(\mathfrak{b})S_{\varphi(\mathfrak{P})} \approx R_{\mathfrak{P}}/\mathfrak{b}R_{\mathfrak{P}}$$

by (18.5.3). Now

$$S_{\varphi(\mathfrak{P})} = R(b, Y', X), \qquad \varphi(\mathfrak{b})S_{\varphi(\mathfrak{P})} = F_bR(b, Y', X),$$
$$R_{\mathfrak{P}} = R(b, Y', D), \qquad \mathfrak{b}R_{\mathfrak{P}} = G_bR(b, Y', D)$$

and hence

$$R(b, Y', X)/F_bR(b, Y', X) \approx R(b, Y', D)/G_bR(b, Y', D).$$

Therefore it suffices to prove our assertion with D replacing X and G replacing F, i.e., *without loss of generality we may assume that X is an open set in K^n.*

Upon replacing X by a smaller neighborhood of a in X we may assume that $f_1(b) = ... = f_p(b) = 0$ for all $b \in Y$; and in view of (44.8) we may also assume that Y is pure dimensional. Since X is an open set in K^n, in view of (25.6, 21.6.1), what we have to show is the existence of a neighborhood U of a in X such that for every $b \in U$ and every irreducible component Y' of Y_b the equality $\text{rnk}_{a,Y,X}F = \text{rnk}_{b,Y',X}F$ holds. In view of (45.8), it is enough to obtain the inequality $\text{rnk}_{a,Y,X}F \leqq \text{rnk}_{b,Y',X}F$.

Let $\text{rnk}_{a,Y,X}F = e$. Relabel the elements $f_1,..., f_p$ so that $(f_1)_a,..., (f_e)_a$ form a basis of $F_a \bmod \mathfrak{m}(a, Y, X)^2$. We can find analytic functions $f'_1,..., f'_{e'}$ on a neighborhood V of a in X such that $(f_1)_a,..., (f_e)_a, (f'_1)_a,..., (f'_{e'})_a$ form a basis of $\mathfrak{m}(a, Y, X) \bmod \mathfrak{m}(a, Y, X)^2$. By (45.9) there exists a neighborhood U of a in V such that for every $b \in U$ and every irreducible component Y' of Y_b we have that $(f_1)_b,..., (f_e)_b, (f'_1)_b,..., (f'_{e'})_b$ generate $\mathfrak{m}(b, Y', X) \bmod \mathfrak{m}(b, Y', X)^2$. Since Y is pure dimensional, by (25.6) we get that $\text{emdim}\, R(a, Y, X) = \text{emdim}\, R(b, Y', X)$. Also by construction, $\text{emdim}\, R(a, Y, X) = e + e'$. Therefore $(f_1)_b,..., (f_e)_b, (f'_1)_b,..., (f'_{e'})_b$ are linearly independent mod $\mathfrak{m}(b, Y', X)^2$, and hence in particular so are $(f_1)_b,..., (f_e)_b$. Therefore $\text{rnk}_{a,Y,X}F \leqq \text{rnk}_{b,Y',X}F$.

(45.11) *Criterion for a simple subspace.*[2]

$$Y_a \not\subset \mathbf{S}(X_a) \Leftrightarrow R(a, Y, X) \text{ is regular.}$$

Proof of "$\Rightarrow$".[3] The problem being local, we may assume that X is an analytic set in an open set D in K^n. By (45.3), $R(a, Y, X)$ is isomorphic to $R(a, Y, D)/\mathfrak{i}(a, X, D)R(a, Y, D)$ and hence what we have to show is that the dim and emdim of $R(a, Y, D)/\mathfrak{i}(a, X, D)R(a, Y, D)$ are equal. By (25.6), $R(a, Y, D)$ is a regular local ring and $\dim R(a, Y, D) = n - \dim Y_a$. Hence by (21.6.1)

$$\text{emdim}\, R(a, Y, D)/\mathfrak{i}(a, X, D)R(a, Y, D)$$
$$= n - \dim Y_a - \text{rnk}_{a,Y,D}\mathfrak{i}(a, X, D).$$

By (45.4)

$$\dim R(a, Y, D)/\mathfrak{i}(a, X, D)R(a, Y, D) = \dim \mathfrak{J}[a, Y, X] - \dim Y_a.$$

[2] This is the analytic analogue of Zariski's criterion in algebraic geometry; see Zariski [**4**].

[3] By a slight modification, the use of (45.10) in this proof can be avoided; see Abhyankar [**3**: §9].

Thus our assertion reduces to showing that

1°) $$\operatorname{rnk}_{a, Y, D}\mathfrak{i}(a, X, D) = n - \dim \mathfrak{J}[a, Y, X].$$

By (44.14) and, in view of coherence (44.22), by (45.10) we can find a neighborhood D' of a in D such that for every $b \in D'$ and every irreducible component Y' of Y_b we have

2°) $$\operatorname{rnk}_{a, Y, D}\mathfrak{i}(a, X, D) = \operatorname{rnk}_{b, Y', D}\mathfrak{i}(b, X, D)$$

and

3°) $$\dim \mathfrak{J}[a, Y, X] = \dim \mathfrak{J}[b, Y', X].$$

Since $Y_a \not\subset \mathbf{S}(X_a)$, we can take $b \in Y \cap D'$ such that b is a simple point of X. Take any irreducible component Y' of Y_b. By (45.3), $R(b, Y', D)/\mathfrak{i}(b, X, D)R(b, Y', D)$ is isomorphic to $R(b, Y', X)$, and by (25.6), $R(b, Y', D)$ and $R(b, Y', X)$ are regular local rings of dimension $(n - \dim Y')$ and $(\dim X_b - \dim Y')$, respectively. Therefore by (21.6.2)

$$\begin{aligned}\operatorname{rnk}_{b, Y', D}\mathfrak{i}(b, X, D) &= \dim R(b, Y', D) - \dim R(b, Y', X)\\ &= n - \dim X_b.\end{aligned}$$

Now X_b is irreducible and hence

$$\mathfrak{J}[b, Y', X] = X_b.$$

Therefore

4°) $$\operatorname{rnk}_{b, Y', D}\mathfrak{i}(b, X, D) = n - \dim \mathfrak{J}[b, Y', X].$$

Now 1°) follows from (2°, 3°, 4°).

Proof of "$\Leftarrow$". We want to show that, given any neighborhood W of a in X there exists $b \in Y \cap W$ such that $b \notin \mathbf{S}(X)$. By (45.5) there exists a neighborhood V of a in W such that for every $a' \in V$ and every irreducible component Y' of $Y_{a'}$ we have: $\dim R(a', Y', X) = \dim R(a, Y, X)$. In view of coherence (44.22), by (45.10) there exists a neighborhood V_1 of a in V such that for every $a' \in V_1$ and every irreducible component Y' of $Y_{a'}$ we have: $\operatorname{emdim} R(a', Y', X) = \operatorname{emdim} R(a, Y, X)$. Since $R(a, Y, X)$ is given to be regular, it follows that $R(a', Y', X)$ is regular for every $a' \in V_1$ and every irreducible component Y' of $Y_{a'}$. Now $\mathbf{S}(Y)$ is a nowhere dense closed subset of Y and hence there exists $a^* \in Y \cap V_1$ and a neighborhood V_2 of a^* in V_1 such that every point in $Y \cap V_2$ is a simple point of Y. Since $R(a^*, Y, X)$ is regular, it is an integral domain; and hence from the definition of a quotient ring it follows that only one irreducible component of X_{a^*} contains Y_{a^*}. Therefore by (44.8) there exists $a' \in Y \cap V_2$ and a neighborhood X' of a' in V_2 such that X' is pure dimensional. Now $X' \subset W$ and $R(a', Y, X)$ is regular. Thus *without loss of generality*, upon replacing X by X' and a by a', *we may assume that a is a simple point of Y and X is pure dimensional.*

Given any neighborhood X^* of a in X we want to show that there exists $b \in Y \cap X^*$ such that $b \notin \mathbf{S}(X)$. Since a is a simple point of Y, upon replacing X by a neighborhood of a in X^*, by (44.19) we may assume that: X is an analytic set in an open set D in $K^n\{x_1,\ldots, x_n\}$ for some n, a is at the origin in K^n, and $Y = \{x \in D: x_1 = \ldots = x_e = 0\}$ where $e = n - \dim Y_a$. By (21.6 or 25.6), $R(a, Y, D)$ is a regular local ring and $\dim R(a, Y, D) = n - \dim Y_a$; by (45.2, 45.3), $R(a, Y, X) \approx R(a, Y, D)/\mathfrak{i}(a, X, D)R(a, Y, D)$ and $\dim R(a, Y, X) = \dim X_a - \dim Y_a$; and by assumption $R(a, Y, X)$ is a regular local ring. Therefore by (21.6.2)

$$\begin{aligned} \operatorname{rnk}_{a, Y, D}\mathfrak{i}(a, X, D) &= \dim R(a, Y, D) - \dim R(a, Y, X) \\ &= n - \dim X_a. \end{aligned}$$

Therefore there exist analytic functions $f_1,\ldots, f_p$ on a neighborhood D_1 of a in D where $p = n - \dim X_a$ such that: $f_1(b) = \ldots = f_p(b) = 0$ for all $b \in X \cap D_1$ and

$$\operatorname{rnk}_{a, Y, D}\{f_1,\ldots, f_p\} = p.$$

By (45.6)

$$\operatorname{rnk}\left(\frac{J(f_1,\ldots, f_p)}{J(x_1,\ldots, x_e)}(0,\ldots, 0, x_{e+1},\ldots, x_n)\right)_a = p.$$

Hence $p \leqq e$ and upon relabeling $x_1,\ldots, x_e$ we can arrange that

$$\left(\frac{\partial(f_1,\ldots, f_p)}{\partial(x_1,\ldots, x_p)}(0,\ldots, 0, x_{e+1},\ldots, x_n)\right)_a \neq 0.$$

Therefore there exists $b \in Y \cap D_1$ such that

$$\frac{\partial(f_1,\ldots, f_p)}{\partial(x_1,\ldots, x_p)}(b) \neq 0,$$

and hence

$$\operatorname{rnk} \frac{J(f_1,\ldots, f_p)}{J(x_1,\ldots, x_n)}(b) = p.$$

Now $p = n - \dim X_b$ because X is pure dimensional; and hence b is a simple point of X by (33.18).

Using (45.11) we now strengthen (45.7).

(45.12) Continuity of order along a simple subspace. *Assume that* $Y_a \not\subset \mathbf{S}(X_a)$. *Let* F *be any nonempty finite set of analytic functions on* X. *Then there exists a neighborhood* U *of* a *in* X *such that for every* $b \in U$ *and every irreducible component* Y' *of* Y_b *we have*: $\operatorname{ord}_{a,Y,X}F = \operatorname{ord}_{b,Y',X}F$.

PROOF. In view of (45.7) it is enough to obtain the inequality $\operatorname{ord}_{a,Y,X}F \geqq \operatorname{ord}_{b,Y,X'}F$. Let $e = \operatorname{ord}_{a,Y,X}F$. The case $e = \infty$ is trivial and the case $e = 0$ follows from (44.15). Now assume that $e \neq 0, \infty$. Fix $f \in F$ such that $\operatorname{ord}_{a,Y,X}f = e$. Take analytic functions $u_1, \ldots, u_\lambda$ on a neighborhood V of a in X such that $(u_1)_a, \ldots, (u_\lambda)_a$ form a basis of $\mathfrak{m}(a, Y, X) \bmod \mathfrak{m}(a, Y, X)^2$. Let $v_1, \ldots, v_\mu$ be all the monomials in $u_1, \ldots, u_\lambda$ of degree e, where

$$\mu = \binom{\lambda + e - 1}{e}.$$

Then there exist analytic functions r, r_i on a neighborhood V_1 of a in V such that

$$r_a \notin \mathfrak{i}(a, Y, X),$$

and

$$r_a f_a = (r_1)_a(v_1)_a + \ldots + (r_\mu)_a(v_\mu)_a.$$

Now $(r_i)_a \notin \mathfrak{i}(a, Y, X)$ for some i, and hence upon relabeling $v_1, \ldots, v_\mu$ we can arrange that $(r_1)_a \notin \mathfrak{i}(a, Y, X)$. We can take a neighborhood V_2 of a in V_1 such that

$$r_b f_b = (r_1)_b(v_1)_b + \ldots + (r_\mu)_b(v_\mu)_b \qquad \text{for all} \quad b \in V_2.$$

By (44.15, 45.5, 45.9) there exists a neighborhood V_3 of a in V_2 such that for every $b \in V_3$ and every irreducible component Y' of Y_b we have:

$$r_b \notin \mathfrak{i}(b, Y', X), \qquad (r_1)_b \notin \mathfrak{i}(b, Y', X);$$

and

$$\dim R(a, Y, X) = \dim R(b, Y', X);$$

and

$$(u_1)_b, \ldots, (u_\lambda)_b \quad \text{generate} \quad \mathfrak{m}(b, Y', X) \bmod \mathfrak{m}(b, Y', X)^2.$$

Now $\mathbf{S}(X)$ is an analytic set in X and by assumption $Y_a \not\subset (\mathbf{S}(X))_a$. Therefore by (44.9) there exists a neighborhood U of a in V_3 such that for every $b \in U$ and every irreducible component Y' of Y_b we have: $Y' \not\subset \mathbf{S}(X_b)$. By (45.11), $R(a, Y, X)$ and $R(b, Y', X)$ are regular local rings. Therefore $(u_1)_b, \ldots, (u_\lambda)_b$ is a basis of $\mathfrak{m}(b, Y', X) \bmod \mathfrak{m}(b, Y', X)^2$. Since $(r_1)_b$

$\notin \mathfrak{i}(b, Y', X)$, by (21.3.1) we get that $\mathrm{ord}_{b,Y',X} rf = e$. Since $r_b \notin \mathfrak{i}(b, Y', X)$, we must have $\mathrm{ord}_{b,Y',X} f = e$. Therefore

$$\mathrm{ord}_{a,Y,X} F = e = \mathrm{ord}_{b,Y',X} f \geqq \mathrm{ord}_{b,Y',X} F.$$

(**45.13**) REMARK. Referring to the proof of (45.12), without the assumption that $Y_a \not\subset \mathbf{S}(X_a)$, by (45.9, 45.10) we can still arrange matters so that $(u_1)_b, \ldots, (u_\lambda)_b$ is a basis of $\mathfrak{m}(b, Y', X) \bmod \mathfrak{m}(b, Y', X)^2$. However, if $Y_a \subset \mathbf{S}(X)_a$ then $Y' \subset \mathbf{S}(X_b)$ for b near a. Consequently by (45.11), $R(b, Y', X)$ is not regular and hence we cannot invoke (21.3.1) to conclude that $\mathrm{ord}_{b,Y',X} rf = e$. At present the following question remains open.

1) Does (45.12) hold without assuming $Y_a \not\subset \mathbf{S}(X_a)$?

(45.10.ii) suggests the following question concerning the dimensions of the "higher tangent spaces" $\mathfrak{m}(a, Y, X)^n/\mathfrak{m}(a, Y, X)^{n+1}$ of Y in X at a.

2) Does there exist a neighborhood U of a in X such that for every $b \in U$, for every irreducible component Y' of Y_b, and for every $n > 0$, the dimension of $\mathfrak{m}(a, Y, X)^n/\mathfrak{m}(a, Y, X)^{n+1}$ as a vector space over $R(a, Y, X)/\mathfrak{m}(a, Y, X)$ equals the dimension of $\mathfrak{m}(b, Y', X)^n/\mathfrak{m}(b, Y', X)^{n+1}$ as a vector space over $R(b, Y', X)/\mathfrak{m}(b, Y', X)$?

In (45.10) we have answered this affirmatively for $n = 1$ and in (45.5, 45.11) we have answered it affirmatively for all n in case $Y_a \not\subset \mathbf{S}(X_a)$.

(**45.14**) *If* X_a *is pure dimensional and* $\dim X_a > 0$ *then*: $\dim \mathbf{S}(X_a) \leqq (\dim X_a) - 2 \Leftrightarrow R(a, X)_{\mathfrak{P}}$ *is regular for every prime ideal* $\mathfrak{P}$ *in* $R(a, X)$ *of height one.*

PROOF. Let Ω' be the set of all prime ideals in $R(a, X)$ of height one, and let Ω be the set of all $e - 1$ dimensional irreducible analytic set germs in X at a where $e = \dim X_a$. Since X_a is pure e dimensional, we get that $\Omega' = \{\mathfrak{i}(a, Z, X): Z \in \Omega\}$ and hence our assertion follows from (45.11).

(**45.15**) *If* X_a *is normal and* $\dim X_a > 0$ *then* $\dim \mathbf{S}(X_a) \leqq (\dim X_a) - 2$.

PROOF. By (19.12), the quotient ring of a normal integral domain with respect to any prime ideal is normal; and by (21.4), a one dimensional local integral domain is regular if and only if it is normal. Therefore our assertion follows from (45.14).

(**45.16**) *Complete intersections.*

1) DEFINITION. X is said to be a *formal complete intersection at* $a \Leftrightarrow$ there exists an exact sequence $0 \to \mathfrak{a} \to R \to R(a, X) \to 0$ where R is a regular local ring and $\mathfrak{a}$ is an ideal in R generated by $(\dim R - \dim X_a)$ elements. X is said to be a *complete intersection at* $a \Leftrightarrow$ there exists a bianalytic map ξ of a neighborhood X^* of a in X onto an analytic set in an open set D in K^n for some n, such that $\mathfrak{i}(\xi(a), \xi(X^*), D)$ is generated by $(n - \dim X_a)$ elements.

2) *If X is a formal complete intersection at a and* $\dim X_a > 0$ *then we have the following.*

i) *X_a is normal* $\Leftrightarrow \dim \mathbf{S}(X_a) \leqq (\dim X_a) - 2$.
ii) *X_a is pure dimensional.*
iii) *If X_a is reducible then there exist two distinct irreducible components X' and X'' of X_a such that* $\dim (X' \cap X'') = (\dim X_a) - 1$.

PROOF. Follows from (21.7, 45.2, 45.14, 45.15).

3) Generalization of a lemma of Oka.[4] *If X is a complete intersection at a and* $\dim X_a > 0$ *then we have the following.*

i) *X is a formal complete intersection at a.*
ii) *X is a complete intersection at every point in some neighborhood of a in X.*
iii) *X_a is pure dimensional.*
iv) *If X_a is reducible then there exist two distinct irreducible components X' and X'' of X_a such that* $\dim (X' \cap X'') = (\dim X_a) - 1$.
v) *X_a is normal* $\Leftrightarrow \dim \mathbf{S}(X_a) \leqq (\dim X_a) - 2$.
vi) *X_a is normal $\Rightarrow$ X_b is normal for all b in some neighborhood of a in X.*

PROOF. The problem being local, by definition, upon replacing X by a neighborhood of a in X, we may assume that X is an analytic set in an open set D in K^n and there exist analytic functions $u_1, \ldots, u_k$ on D such that $\{(u_1)_a, \ldots, (u_k)_a\}R(a, D) = \mathfrak{i}(a, X, D)$ where $k = n - \dim X_a$. Now $R(a, X) \approx R(a, D)/\mathfrak{i}(a, X, D)$ and $R(a, D)$ is a regular local ring of dimension n. Therefore X is a formal complete intersection at a. This proves i) and now iii), iv), v) follow from 2). By coherence (44.22) there exists a neighborhood D_1 of a in D such that $\{(u_1)_b, \ldots, (u_k)_b\}R(b, D) = \mathfrak{i}(b, X, D)$ for all $b \in D_1$. Now X_a is pure $n - k$ dimensional by iii) and hence by (44.8) there exists a neighborhood D_2 of a in D_1 such that X_b is pure $n - k$ dimensional for all $b \in X \cap D_2$. Therefore X is a complete intersection at every point in $X \cap D_2$. This proves ii). By (44.5) there exists a neighborhood D_3 of a in D_2 such that for any $b \in X \cap D_3$ we have

[4] Proved in Oka [**8**: Lemma 1 on p. 261] when X is a hypersurface in $\mathbf{C}^n$.

$\dim \mathbf{S}(X_b) \leqq \dim \mathbf{S}(X_a)$ and hence $\dim \mathbf{S}(X_b) \leqq (\dim X_b) - 2$; consequently X_b is normal by v). This proves vi).

(**45.17**) DEFINITION. Let $Z \subset X$ be such that Z is analytic at a, Z_a is irreducible, and $Z_a \not\subset \mathbf{S}(X_a)$. By (45.11), $R(a, Z, X)$ is a regular local ring. Hence by (21.8), $\operatorname{ord}_{R(a,Z,X)}F$ is defined for any $\emptyset \neq F \subset \mathfrak{R}(a, X)$, and *we set*

$$\operatorname{ord}_{a,Z,X}F = \operatorname{ord}_{a,Z_a,X}F = \operatorname{ord}_{R(a,Z,X)}F.$$

Note that for $F \subset R(a, Z, X)$ this coincides with the previous definition. For any nonempty set F of meromorphic functions on a neighborhood of a in X *we set*

$$\operatorname{ord}_{a,Z,X}F = \operatorname{ord}_{a,Z_a,X}F = \operatorname{ord}_{a,Z,X}F_a.$$

Again, this coincides with the previous definition if the elements in F are analytic. Denoting the natural homomorphism of $\mathfrak{R}(a, X)$ into the quotient field of $R(a, Z, X)$ by φ, for any $\emptyset \neq F \subset \mathfrak{R}(a, X)$, by (21.8.3°, 21.8.4°) we get the following.

1) $$F \subset \varphi^{-1}(R(a, Z, X)) \Rightarrow \operatorname{ord}_{a,Z,X}F \geqq 0.$$

2) If $\dim R(a, Z, X) = 1$ then:

$$F \subset \varphi^{-1}(R(a, Z, X)) \Leftrightarrow \operatorname{ord}_{a,Z,X}F \geqq 0.$$

(**45.18**) Continuity of order of meromorphic functions along a simple subspace. *Assume that $Y_a \not\subset \mathbf{S}(X_a)$ and let F be any nonempty finite set of meromorphic functions on X. Then there exists a neighborhood U of a in X such that for every $b \in U$ and every irreducible component Y' of Y_b we have: $Y' \not\subset \mathbf{S}(X_b)$ and $\operatorname{ord}_{b,Y',X}F = \operatorname{ord}_{a,Y,X}F$.*

PROOF. Follows from (44.9) and (45.12).

(**45.19**) REMARK. Take $K = \mathbf{C}$ and assume that Y is irreducible. In view of (44.35), by (45.10) we get 1) and 2) and by (45.18) we get 3).

1) For every $b \in Y$ and every irreducible component Y' of Y_b we have: $\operatorname{emdim} R(b, Y', X) = \operatorname{emdim} R(a, Y, X)$.

2) If F is any nonempty finite set of analytic functions on X such that $F_a \subset \mathfrak{i}(a, Y, X)$, then for every $b \in Y$ and every irreducible component Y' of Y_b we have: $F_b \subset \mathfrak{i}(b, Y', X)$; $\operatorname{emdim} R(b, Y', X)/F_bR(b, Y', X) = \operatorname{emdim} R(a, Y, X)/F_aR(a, Y, X)$; and $\operatorname{rnk}_{b,Y',X}F = \operatorname{rnk}_{a,Y,X}F$. More generally, if $\mathscr{F}$ is any coherent $\mathcal{O}_X$-ideal such that $\mathscr{F}_a \subset \mathfrak{i}(a, Y, X)$, then for every $b \in Y$ and every irreducible component Y' of Y_b we have: $\mathscr{F}_b \subset \mathfrak{i}(b, Y', X)$; $\operatorname{emdim} R(b, Y', X)/\mathscr{F}_b R(b, Y', X) =$ $\operatorname{emdim} R(a, Y, X)/\mathscr{F}_a R(a, Y, X)$; and $\operatorname{rnk}_{b,Y',X}\mathscr{F}_b = \operatorname{rnk}_{a,Y,X}\mathscr{F}_a$.

3) Assume that $Y_a \not\subset \mathbf{S}(X_a)$. Then for every $b \in Y$ and every irreducible component Y' of Y_b we have: $Y' \not\subset \mathbf{S}(X_b)$. If F is any nonempty finite set of meromorphic functions on X, then for every $b \in Y$ and every irreducible component Y' of Y_b we have: $\operatorname{ord}_{b,Y',X}F = \operatorname{ord}_{a,Y,X}F$. More generally, if every $\mathscr{F}$ is any coherent $\mathcal{O}_X$-submodule of $\mathscr{K}_X$, then for every $b \in Y$ and irreducible component Y' of Y_b we have: $\operatorname{ord}_{b,Y',X}\mathscr{F}_b = \operatorname{ord}_{a,Y,X}\mathscr{F}_a$.

(45.20) *Let Ω be the set of all irreducible analytic set germs Z in X at a such that* $\dim Z = (\dim X_a) - 1$.[5] *Assume that X_a is pure dimensional,* $\dim X_a > 0$, *and* $\dim \mathbf{S}(X_a) \leqq (\dim X_a) - 2$. *Then for any $\emptyset \neq F \subset \mathfrak{R}(a, X)$ we have:*

$$F \subset R'(a, X) \Leftrightarrow \operatorname{ord}_{a,Z,X}F \geqq 0 \textit{ for all } Z \in \Omega.$$

PROOF. Follows from (24.3.5).

(45.21) *Assume that X_a is pure dimensional,* $\dim X_a > 0$, *and* $\dim \mathbf{S}(X_a) \leqq (\dim X_a) - 2$. *Then for any meromorphic function f on X the following three conditions are equivalent.*

i) $f_a \in R'(a, X)$.
ii) *There exists a neighborhood U of a in X such that $f_b \in R(b, X)$ for all $b \in U - \mathbf{S}(X)$.*
iii) *There exists an analytic set W in a neighborhood U of a in X such that* $\dim W_a \leqq (\dim X_a) - 2$ *and $f_b \in R'(b, X)$ for all $b \in U - W$.*

PROOF. i) $\Rightarrow$ ii) because $R(b, X) = R'(b, X)$ for all $b \in X - \mathbf{S}(X)$. ii) $\Rightarrow$ iii) is obvious. Now assuming iii) we want to show that $f_a \in R'(a, X)$. By (45.20) it suffices to show that if Z is any analytic set in any neighborhood V of a in U such that Z_a is irreducible and $\dim Z_a = (\dim X_a) - 1$, then $\operatorname{ord}_{a,Z,X}f \geqq 0$. By (45.18) there exists a neighborhood V' of a in V such that for every $b \in V'$ and every irreducible component Z' of Z_b we

[5] If $\dim_a X > 0$ then: $\dim \mathbf{S}(X_a) \leqq (\dim X_a) - 2 \Rightarrow Z \not\subset \mathbf{S}(X_a)$ for all $Z \in \Omega$. If X_a is pure dimensional then by (45.2), Ω is the set of all irreducible analytic set germs Z in X at a such that $\dim R(a, Z, X) = 1$. Consequently, if X_a is pure dimensional and $\dim \mathbf{S}(X_a) \leqq (\dim X_a) - 2$ then by (45.11) it follows that $R(a, Z, X)$ is a one dimensional regular local ring for all $Z \in \Omega$. Also note that if X_a is normal and $\dim X_a > 0$ then by (44.7, 45.15) it follows that X_a is pure dimensional and $\dim \mathbf{S}(X_a) \leqq (\dim X_a) - 2$.

have: $Z' \not\subset \mathbf{S}(X_b)$ and $\operatorname{ord}_{a,Z,X} f = \operatorname{ord}_{b,Z',X} f$. Now $Z_a \not\subset W_a \cup \mathbf{S}(X_a)$ and hence $(Z \cap V') - (W \cup \mathbf{S}(X)) \neq \emptyset$. Take $b \in Z \cap V'$ with $b \notin W \cup \mathbf{S}(X)$, and take an irreducible component Z' of Z_b. Then $f_b \in R'(b, X) = R(b, X)$ and hence $\operatorname{ord}_{b,Z',X} f \geqq 0$. Therefore $\operatorname{ord}_{a,Z,X} f \geqq 0$.

(**45.22**) *Let Ω be the set of all irreducible analytic set germs Z in X at a such that* $\dim Z = (\dim X_a) - 1$.[5] *Assume that X_a is pure dimensional,* $\dim X_a > 0$, *and* $\dim \mathbf{S}(X_a) \leqq (\dim X_a) - 2$. *Then the following four conditions are equivalent.*

i) *X_a is normal.*

ii) *If f is any element in $\mathfrak{R}(a, X)$ such that $\operatorname{ord}_{a,Z,X} f \geqq 0$ for all $Z \in \Omega$, then $f \in R(a, X)$.*

iii) *If f is any meromorphic function on any neighborhood U of a in X such that $f_b \in R(b, X)$ for all $b \in U -$ $\mathbf{S}(X)$, then $f_a \in R(a, X)$.*

iv) *If f is any meromorphic function on any neighborhood U of a in X and W is any analytic set in U such that* $\dim W_a \leqq (\dim X_a) - 2$ *and $f_b \in R'(b, X)$ for all $b \in U - W$, then $f_a \in R(a, X)$.*

PROOF. Follows from (45.20, 45.21).

(**45.23**) $\mathfrak{B}(\mathfrak{c}(R(a, X))) \subset \mathbf{S}(X_a)$.

PROOF. Given any irreducible component Z of $\mathfrak{B}(\mathfrak{c}(R(a, X)))$ we want to show that $Z \subset \mathbf{S}(X_a)$. Now $\mathfrak{c}(R(a, X)) \subset \mathfrak{i}(a, Z, X)$ and $R(a, Z, X) = R(a, X)_{\mathfrak{i}(a,Z,X)}$. Therefore by (24.3.4), $R(a, Z, X)$ is not normal. Therefore $R(a, Z, X)$ is not regular, and hence $Z \subset \mathbf{S}(X_a)$ by (45.11).

(**45.24**) *Given $t \in \mathfrak{i}(a, \mathbf{S}(X), X)$ there exists a positive integer n such that $t^n \in \mathfrak{c}(R(a, X))$.*

PROOF. Follows from (45.23) in virtue of the Nullstellensatz.

(**45.25**) *Let t and Δ be analytic functions on X such that* $t(\mathbf{S}(X)) = 0$ *and Δ_b is a nonzerodivisor in $R(b, X)$ for all $b \in X$. Then there exists a positive integer n and a neighborhood U of a in X such that*

$$(R(b, X) \cap \Delta_b R'(b, X)) \subset (\Delta_b R(b, X) : t_b^n R(b, X))$$

for all $b \in U$.[6]

[6] The transporters are relative to $R(b, X)$.

PROOF. For each $b \in X$, by (45.24) there exists a positive integer $n(b)$ depending on b such that $t_b^{n(b)} \in \mathfrak{c}(R(b, X))$ and hence $t_b^m \in \mathfrak{c}(R(b, X))$ for all $m \geqq n(b)$. For any $m \geqq n(b)$ and any $f \in R(b, X) \cap \Delta_b R'(b, X)$ we then have: $f/\Delta_b \in R'(b, X)$ and hence $(f/\Delta_b)t_b^m \in R(b, X)$, i.e., $ft_b^m \in \Delta_b R(b, X)$, and hence $f \in (\Delta_b R(b, X) : t_b^m R(b, X))$. Thus for any $b \in X$ and $m \geqq n(b)$ we have

$$(R(b, X) \cap \Delta_b R'(b, X)) \subset (\Delta_b R(b, X) : t_b^m R(b, X)).$$

By (42.13) there exists a positive integer n and a neighborhood U of a in X such that for all $b \in U$ and for all $m \geqq n$ we have

$$(\Delta_b R(b, X) : t_b^m R(b, X)) = (\Delta_b R(b, X) : t_b^n R(b, X)).$$

Given $b \in U$, upon taking $m = \max(n, n(b))$, we get that

$$(R(b, X) \cap \Delta_b R'(b, X)) \subset (\Delta_b R(b, X) : t_b^n R(b, X)).$$

(45.26) *Let Δ be an analytic function on X such that Δ_b is a nonzero-divisor in $R(b, X)$ for all $b \in X$. Assume that X is pure dimensional and* $\dim \mathbf{S}(X) \leqq (\dim X) - 2$. *Then $\mathcal{O}_X \cap \Delta\mathcal{O}'_X$ is a coherent $\mathcal{O}_X$-ideal.*

PROOF. Take analytic functions $t_1, \ldots, t_p$ on a neighborhood X' of a in X such that $X' \cap \mathbf{S}(X) = \{b \in X' : t_1(b) = \ldots = t_p(b) = 0\}$. By (45.25) there exist positive integers $n_1, \ldots, n_p$ and a neighborhood X^* of a in X' such that for $i = 1, \ldots, p$ we have

$$(R(b, X) \cap \Delta_b R'(b, X)) \subset (\Delta_b R(b, X) : (t_i^{n_i})_b R(b, X)) \text{ for all } b \in X^*.$$

Let $s_i = t_i^{n_i}$. Then $X^* \cap \mathbf{S}(X) = \{b \in X^* : s_1(b) = \ldots = s_p(b) = 0\}$, and for $i = 1, \ldots, p$ we have

$$(R(b, X) \cap \Delta_b R'(b, X)) \subset (\Delta_b R(b, X) : (s_i)_b R(b, X)) \text{ for all } b \in X^*.$$

Since the problem is local and since a is an arbitrary point of X, we may replace X by X^* and $\Delta, s_1, \ldots, s_p$ by $\Delta|X^*, s_1|X^*, \ldots, s_p|X^*$, respectively. Then $\Delta, s_1, \ldots, s_p$ are analytic functions on X, Δ_b is a nonzero-divisor in $R(b, X)$ for all $b \in X$,

1°) $$\mathbf{S}(X) = \{b \in X : s_1(b) = \ldots = s_p(b) = 0\},$$

2°) $$(R(b, X) \cap \Delta_b R'(b, X)) \subset \bigcap_{i=1}^{p} (\Delta_b R(b, X) : (s_i)_b R(b, X)) \text{ for all } b \in X;$$

and we want to show that $\mathcal{O}_X \cap \Delta\mathcal{O}'_X$ is a coherent $\mathcal{O}_X$-ideal. Suppose we have shown that

3°) $$\bigcap_{i=1}^{p} (\Delta_b R(b, X) : (s_i)_b R(b, X)) \subset (R(b, X) \cap \Delta_b R'(b, X)) \text{ for all } b \in X.$$

Now $\mathcal{O}_X$ is a coherent sheaf of rings on X and hence $\Delta\mathcal{O}_X$ and $s_i\mathcal{O}_X$ are coherent $\mathcal{O}_X$-ideals. Therefore by (42.12), $(\Delta\mathcal{O}_X: s_i\mathcal{O}_X)$ is a coherent $\mathcal{O}_X$-ideal and

$$(\Delta\mathcal{O}_X: s_i\mathcal{O}_X)_b = (\Delta_b R(b, X): (s_i)_b R(b, X)) \qquad \text{for all} \quad b \in X.$$

This being so for $i = 1,\ldots, p$, by (42.6) we get that $\bigcap_{i=1}^{p} (\Delta\mathcal{O}_X: s_i\mathcal{O}_X)$ is a coherent $\mathcal{O}_X$-ideal and

$$\left(\bigcap_{i=1}^{p} (\Delta\mathcal{O}_X: s_i\mathcal{O}_X)\right)_b = \bigcap_{i=1}^{p} (\Delta_b R(b, X): (s_i)_b R(b, X)) \qquad \text{for all} \quad b \in X.$$

Therefore $\mathcal{O}_X \cap \Delta\mathcal{O}'_X$ is a coherent $\mathcal{O}_X$-ideal by (2°, 3°).

To prove 3°), let any $b \in X$ and any analytic function f on any neighborhood V of b in X be given such that

$$f_b \in \bigcap_{i=1}^{p} (\Delta_b R(b, X): (s_i)_b R(b, X)).$$

We can then find analytic functions $g_1,\ldots, g_p$ on a neighborhood U of b in V such that

$$fs_i = \Delta g_i \quad \text{on } U, \qquad \text{for} \quad i = 1,\ldots, p.$$

Given $c \in U - \mathbf{S}(X)$, by 1°) there exists i such that $s_i(c) \neq 0$ and hence $f_c/\Delta_c = (g_i)_c/(s_i)_c \in R(c, X)$. Thus $f_c/\Delta_c \in R(c, X)$ for all $c \in U - \mathbf{S}(X)$. Therefore $f_b/\Delta_b \in R'(b, X)$ by (45.21), and hence

$$f_b \in (R(b, X) \cap \Delta_b R'(b, X)).$$

(45.27) *Assume that X_a is irreducible and* $\dim \mathbf{S}(X_a) \leqq (\dim X_a) - 2$. *Then $\mathcal{O}'_U$ is a coherent $\mathcal{O}_U$-module for some neighborhood U of a in X.*

Proof. By (44.5, 44.8), there exists a neighborhood V of a in X such that V is pure dimensional and $\dim \mathbf{S}(V) \leqq (\dim V) - 2$. By (44.21), there exists an analytic function Δ on a neighborhood U of a in X such that for all $b \in U$ we have that Δ_b is a nonzerodivisor in $R(b, U)$ and $\Delta_b \in \mathfrak{c}(R(b, U))$. We define an $\mathcal{O}_U$-homomorphism $\varphi: \mathcal{O}'_U \to \mathcal{O}'_U$ thus: for any nonempty open set U^* in U and any $f \in \mathcal{O}'_U(U^*)$ let $\varphi(U^*)f = (\Delta|U^*)f$. For any $b \in U$ we then have: $\varphi_b f = \Delta_b f$ for all $f \in R'(b, U)$, and hence

$$\operatorname{Im} \varphi_b = \Delta_b R'(b, U) = R(b, U) \cap \Delta_b R'(b, U) = (\mathcal{O}_U \cap \Delta\mathcal{O}'_U)_b$$

because $\Delta_b \in \mathfrak{c}(R(b, U))$; furthermore, φ_b is a monomorphism because Δ_b is a nonzerodivisor in $R(b, U)$. This being so for all $b \in U$, it follows that $\operatorname{Im}\varphi = \Delta\mathcal{O}'_U = \mathcal{O}_U \cap \Delta\mathcal{O}'_U$ and that φ is a monomorphism. Therefore, φ induces an $\mathcal{O}_U$-isomorphism: $\mathcal{O}'_U \approx (\mathcal{O}_U \cap \Delta\mathcal{O}'_U)$. By (45.26), $(\mathcal{O}_U \cap \Delta\mathcal{O}'_U)$ is a coherent $\mathcal{O}_U$-ideal and hence $\mathcal{O}'_U$ is a coherent $\mathcal{O}_U$-module.

(**45.28**) *If X is normal at a then X is normal at every point in some neighborhood of a in X. In other words,* $\mathbf{N}(X)$ *is a closed subset of X.*

PROOF. The assertion is trivial if $\dim X_a = 0$. So assume that $\dim X_a > 0$. Then by (44.7, 45.15), X_a is irreducible and $\dim \mathbf{S}(X_a) \leqq (\dim X_a) - 2$. Therefore by (45.27) there exists a neighborhood V of a in X such that $\mathcal{O}'_V$ is a coherent $\mathcal{O}_V$-module. Since X_a is normal, $(\mathcal{O}'_V)_a = R'(a, X) = R(a, X) = (\mathcal{O}_V)_a$. Therefore by (42.1.3) there exists a neighborhood U of a in V such that for all $b \in U$ we have: $(\mathcal{O}'_V)_b = (\mathcal{O}_V)_b$, i.e., $R'(b, X) = R(b, X)$, i.e., X_b is normal.

(**45.29**) *In the case of $K = \mathbf{C}$ the following three conditions are equivalent.*

i) *X_a is normal.*

ii) *If Z is any closed thin subset in any neighborhood U of a in X and f is any analytic function on $U - Z$ such that $|f|$ is bounded on $U - Z$, then there exists a neighborhood V of a in U and $g \in \mathfrak{E}(V)$ such that $g|V - Z = f|V - Z$ and $g_a \in R(a, X)$.*

iii) *If U is any neighborhood of a in X and f is any analytic function on $U - \mathbf{S}(X)$ such that $|f|$ is bounded on $U - \mathbf{S}(X)$, then there exists a neighborhood V of a in U and $g \in \mathfrak{E}(V)$ such that $g|V - \mathbf{S}(X) = f|V - \mathbf{S}(X)$ and $g_a \in R(a, X)$.*

PROOF. Follows from (36.6.4, 36.6.5) and (45.28).

(**45.30**) *Corrections* to Abhyankar [**3**]. Referring to this paper as C we take this opportunity to list the following corrections. The assertion at the end of the first paragraph of C§2 should read "We note that if a local ring is normal and has no nonzero nilpotent elements then it is an integral domain"; see (19.9, 19.11). In the proof of C(2.2) the argument given to show that F is well defined is faulty but it can easily be corrected; for a slightly different proof of C(2.2) see (18.5.2). The alternative proof of C(5.2c) given in C(9.4) is faulty. The statement and the proof of C(13.6) are wrong; however the lemma is true if A^* is generated by $g_1(y_1), \ldots, g_n(y_n)$ where $g_i(y_i)$ is a distinguished polynomial in y_i with coefficients in S; this assumption is satisfied in C(13.13) and C(13.15) which were the only places where C(13.6) was used; for a proof of the corrected version of C(13.6) see (25.4). In C(5.3) line 6, replace P' by p'. In C(7.1) line 10, replace α by $\alpha_{j(p)}$.

§46. BIMEROMORPHIC MAPS AND NORMALIZATIONS[1]

(46.1) DEFINITION. Let X and Y be analytic K-spaces and let $\xi: Y \to X$ be an analytic map.

The homomorphism $\mathcal{O}_X \to \xi_*(\mathcal{O}_Y)$ of sheaves of K-algebras on X induced by ξ is denoted by $\bar{\xi}$; see (43.1). We consider $\xi_*(\mathcal{O}_Y)$ to be an $\mathcal{O}_X$-algebra with $\bar{\xi}$ as the underlying homomorphism. For any $a \in X$, $(\xi_*(\mathcal{O}_Y))_a$ is then an $R(a, X)$-algebra with underlying homomorphism $\bar{\xi}_a$.

Let $b \in Y$ and $a = \xi(b)$. The K-algebra-homomorphism $(\xi_*(\mathcal{O}_Y))_a \to (\mathcal{O}_Y)_b$ induced by ξ is denoted by ξ'_b; see (41.8). The K-algebra-homomorphism

$$\xi'_b \circ \bar{\xi}_a: R(a, X) = (\mathcal{O}_X)_a \to (\mathcal{O}_Y)_b = R(b, Y)$$

is again said to be induced by ξ and is denoted by $\bar{\xi}_b$. We consider $R(b, Y)$ as an $R(a, X)$-algebra with $\bar{\xi}_b$ as the underlying homomorphism. Note that $\xi'_b: (\xi_*(\mathcal{O}_Y))_a \to R(b, Y)$ is then an $R(a, X)$-algebra-homomorphism. Also note that $\bar{\xi}_{(b)}(R(a, X)) \subset R(b, Y)$ and $\bar{\xi}_{(b)}(r) = \bar{\xi}_b(r)$ for all $r \in R(a, X)$. In other words, if f is any analytic function on any neighborhood U of a in X then $f \circ (\xi|\xi^{-1}(U))$ is an analytic function on the neighborhood $\xi^{-1}(U)$ of b in Y and $\bar{\xi}_b(f_a) = (f \circ (\xi|\xi^{-1}(U))_b$.

For any $Z \subset X$ such that Z_a is analytic, the analytic set germ $\mathfrak{V}(\bar{\xi}_b(\mathfrak{i}(a, Z, X)))$ in Y at b is denoted by $\xi_{\mathfrak{w}b}(Z)$ or $\xi_{\mathfrak{w}b}(Z_a)$. Thus $\xi_{\mathfrak{w}b}$ maps the set of all analytic set germs in X at a into the set of all analytic set germs in Y at b.

For any $Z \subset Y$ such that Z_b is analytic, the analytic set germ $\mathfrak{V}(\bar{\xi}_b^{-1}(\mathfrak{i}(b, Z, Y)))$ in X at a is denoted by $\xi_{\mathfrak{v}b}(Z)$ or $\xi_{\mathfrak{v}b}(Z_b)$. Thus $\xi_{\mathfrak{v}b}$ maps the set of all analytic set germs in Y at b into the set of all analytic set germs in X at a.

(46.2) *Properties of the maps* $\xi_{\mathfrak{w}b}$ *and* $\xi_{\mathfrak{v}b}$. Let X and Y be analytic K-spaces, let $\xi : Y \to X$ be an analytic map, let $b \in Y$ and let $a = \xi(b)$.

1) *If F is any set of analytic functions on a neighborhood U of a in X then $\bar{\xi}(F)$ is a set of analytic functions on the neighborhood $\xi^{-1}(U)$ of b in Y and $\xi^{-1}(\mathfrak{V}(F)) = \mathfrak{V}(\bar{\xi}(F))$; furthermore, if F is finite then $(\xi^{-1}(\mathfrak{V}(F)))_b = \mathfrak{V}(\bar{\xi}_b(F_a))$. Given any $Z \subset X$ such that Z_a is analytic, taking F to be a*

[1] This section can be read immediately after §44B; especially see (44.27, 44.28). From §44C we shall only use (44.37, 44.42) in the proofs of (46.22, 46.33, 46.34, 46.35.1, 46.35.3). From §45 we shall only use (45.28), and that not until the proof of (46.26).

finite set of analytic functions on a neighborhood U of a in X such that $Z \cap U = \mathfrak{B}(F)$ and $F_a R(a, X) = \mathfrak{i}(a, Z, X)$, we see that: $\xi_{\mathfrak{w}b}(Z) = \mathfrak{B}(\xi_b(F_a)) = (\xi^{-1}(Z))_b$.

Proof is obvious.

2) *Consider the following conditions.*

i) $\xi_b(M(a, X)) \subset M(b, Y)$.

ii) *If Z is any analytic set germ in X at a such that Z does not contain any irreducible component of X_a, then $\xi_{\mathfrak{w}b}(Z)$ does not contain any irreducible component of Y_b.*

iii) $\xi_{b'}(M(\xi(b'), X)) \subset M(b', Y)$ *for all* $b' \in Y$.

iv) *If Z is any thin subset of X then $\xi^{-1}(Z)$ is a thin subset of Y.*

v) *There exists a nowhere dense analytic set Ω in X such that $\xi^{-1}(\Omega)$ is nowhere dense in Y and the map $Y - \xi^{-1}(\Omega) \to X - \Omega$ induced by ξ is a homeomorphism.*

Then we have: i) $\Leftrightarrow$ ii); iii) $\Rightarrow$ iv); *and* v) $\Rightarrow$ iii).

Proof of i) $\Rightarrow$ ii). Let $\mathfrak{p}_1, \ldots, \mathfrak{p}_q$ be the distinct prime ideals of $\{0\}$ in $R(a, X)$. Then $\mathfrak{i}(a, Z, X) \not\subset \mathfrak{p}_j$ for $j = 1, \ldots, q$ and hence $\mathfrak{i}(a, Z, X) \not\subset \mathfrak{p}_1 \cup \ldots \cup \mathfrak{p}_q$ by (18.6). Therefore there exists $f \in \mathfrak{i}(a, Z, X) \cap M(a, X)$. By assumption, $\xi_b(f) \in M(b, Y)$ and hence by (44.15), $\mathfrak{B}(\xi_b(f))$ does not contain any irreducible component of Y_b. Obviously $\xi_{\mathfrak{w}b}(Z) \subset \mathfrak{B}(\xi_b(f))$.

Proof of ii) $\Rightarrow$ i). Let $f \in M(a, X)$. By (44.15), $\mathfrak{B}(f)$ does not contain any irreducible component of X_a. Hence by assumption, $\xi_{\mathfrak{w}b}(\mathfrak{B}(f))$ does not contain any irreducible component of Y_b. Obviously $\xi_{\mathfrak{w}b}(\mathfrak{B}(f)) = \mathfrak{B}(\xi_b(f))$, and hence $\xi_b(f) \in M(b, Y)$ by (44.15).

Proof of iii) $\Rightarrow$ iv). Given any $b' \in Y$ let $a' = \xi(b')$. By (44.9) there exists an analytic set Z' in a neighborhood U of a' in X such that $Z \cap U \subset Z'$ and $Z'_{a'}$ does not contain any irreducible component of $X_{a'}$. Because of "i) $\Rightarrow$ ii)", we get that $\xi_{\mathfrak{w}b'}(Z')$ does not contain any irreducible component of $Y_{b'}$. Now $\xi^{-1}(Z')$ is an analytic set in $\xi^{-1}(U)$ and $\xi_{\mathfrak{w}b'}(Z') = (\xi^{-1}(Z'))_{b'}$. Therefore by (44.9) there exists a neighborhood V' of b' in $\xi^{-1}(U)$ such that $\xi^{-1}(Z') \cap V'$ is a thin subset of V'. Now $\xi^{-1}(Z) \cap V' \subset \xi^{-1}(Z') \cap V'$ and hence $\xi^{-1}(Z) \cap V'$ is a thin subset of V'. Since b' was an arbitrary point of Y, we conclude that $\xi^{-1}(Z)$ is a thin subset of Y.

Proof of v) $\Rightarrow$ iii). Because of "ii) $\Rightarrow$ i)", it suffices to show that: if b' is any point in Y and Z' is any analytic set germ in X at $a' = \xi(b')$ such that Z' does not contain any irreducible component of $X_{a'}$, then $\xi_{\mathfrak{w}b'}(Z')$ does not contain any irreducible component of $Y_{b'}$. By (44.9) there exists a nowhere dense analytic set Z in a neighborhood U of a' in X such that $Z_{a'} = Z'$. Now $Z \cap (U - \Omega)$ is nowhere dense in $U - \Omega$, and hence $\xi^{-1}(Z) \cap \xi^{-1}(U - \Omega)$ is nowhere dense in $\xi^{-1}(U - \Omega)$ because $\xi^{-1}(U - \Omega) \to U - \Omega$ is a homeomorphism. Also $\xi^{-1}(U \cap \Omega)$ is nowhere dense in $\xi^{-1}(U)$. Thus $\xi^{-1}(Z)$ is a nowhere dense analytic set in $\xi^{-1}(U)$. Therefore by (44.9), $(\xi^{-1}(Z))_{b'}$ does not contain any irreducible component of $Y_{b'}$. Obviously $\xi_{\mathfrak{w}b'}(Z') = (\xi^{-1}(Z))_{b'}$.

3) *Let Z be an analytic set in a neighborhood V of b in Y such that $b \in Z$. Let $\eta: Z \to Y$ be the canonical injection and let $\zeta = \xi \circ \eta$. Then $\zeta: Z \to X$ is analytic and $\bar{\xi}_b^{-1}(\mathfrak{i}(b, Z, Y)) = \operatorname{Ker} \bar{\zeta}_b$, and hence $\xi_{\mathfrak{v}b}(Z) = \zeta_{\mathfrak{v}b}(Z) = \mathfrak{V}(\operatorname{Ker} \bar{\zeta}_b)$. In particular, $\xi_{\mathfrak{v}b}(Y) = \mathfrak{V}(\operatorname{Ker} \bar{\xi}_b)$.*

Proof is obvious.

4) *For any finite family $(Z_i)_{i \in I}$ of analytic set germs in Y at b we have*

$$\bar{\xi}_b^{-1}(\mathfrak{i}(b, \bigcup_{i \in I} Z_i, Y)) = \bigcap_{i \in I} \bar{\xi}_b^{-1}(\mathfrak{i}(b, Z_i, Y))$$

and hence

$$\bigcup_{i \in I} \xi_{\mathfrak{v}b}(Z_i) = \xi_{\mathfrak{v}b}(\bigcup_{i \in I} Z_i).$$

Proof. Follows from (43.6.2, 43.6.3).

5) *For any $Z \subset Y$ such that Z_b is analytic, we have the following.*

1°) *The ideal $\bar{\xi}_b^{-1}(\mathfrak{i}(b, Z, Y))$ in $R(a, X)$ is its own radical.*

2°) $\bar{\xi}_b^{-1}(\mathfrak{i}(b, Z, Y)) = \mathfrak{i}(a, \xi_{\mathfrak{v}b}(Z), X) = \bigcup \mathfrak{i}(a, \xi(Z \cap V), X) = \Sigma\, \mathfrak{i}(a, \xi(Z \cap V), X)$ *where $\bigcup$ and Σ are taken over all neighborhoods V of b in Y.*

3°) $\xi_{\mathfrak{v}b}(Z) = \bigcap \mathfrak{V}(\mathfrak{i}(a, \xi(Z \cap V), X))$ *where $\bigcap$ is taken over all neighborhoods V of b in Y.*[2]

4°) *There exists a neighborhood V^* of b in Y such that for every neighborhood V of b in V^* we have: $\mathfrak{V}(\mathfrak{i}(a, \xi(Z \cap V), X)) = \xi_{\mathfrak{v}b}(Z)$.*

5°) *Given any $Z' \subset X$ such that $Z'_a = \xi_{\mathfrak{v}b}(Z)$, there exists a neighborhood V' of b in Y such that $\xi(Z \cap V') \subset Z'$.*

6°) $\xi_{\mathfrak{v}b}(Z) = \emptyset \Leftrightarrow Z_b = \emptyset$.

7°) *If Z_b is nonempty and irreducible, then $\bar{\xi}_b^{-1}(\mathfrak{i}(b, Z, Y))$ is prime and hence $\xi_{\mathfrak{v}b}(Z)$ is irreducible.*

Proof. 1°) is obvious. In view of the Nullstellensatz, by 1°) we get that $\bar{\xi}_b^{-1}(\mathfrak{i}(b, Z, Y)) = \mathfrak{i}(a, \xi_{\mathfrak{v}b}(Z), X)$. Given any element in $R(a, X)$ we

[2] Note that $\mathfrak{V}(\mathfrak{i}(a, \xi(Z \cap V), X))$ is the smallest analytic set germ in X at a containing $(\xi(Z \cap V))_a$.

can write it in the form f_a where f is an analytic function on a neighborhood U of a in X. If $f_a \in \xi_b^{-1}(\mathfrak{i}(b, Z, Y))$, i.e., if $\xi_b(f_a) \in \mathfrak{i}(b, Z, V)$, then there exists a neighborhood V of b in Y such that $f(U \cap \xi(Z \cap Y)) = 0$ and hence $f_a \in \mathfrak{i}(a, \xi(Z \cap V), X)$. Conversely, if $f_a \in \mathfrak{i}(a, \xi(Z \cap V), X)$ for some neighborhood V of b in Y, then $f(U' \cap \xi(Z \cap V)) = 0$ for some neighborhood U' of a in U and hence $\xi_b(f_a) \in \mathfrak{i}(b, Z, Y)$, i.e., $f_a \in \xi_b^{-1}(\mathfrak{i}(b, Z, Y))$. Thus $\xi_b^{-1}(\mathfrak{i}(b, Z, Y)) = \bigcup \mathfrak{i}(a, \xi(Z \cap V), X)$ where $\bigcup$ is taken over all neighborhoods V of b in Y, and hence $\xi_b^{-1}(\mathfrak{i}(b, Z, Y)) = \Sigma\, \mathfrak{i}(a, \xi(Z \cap V), X)$ where Σ is taken over all neighborhoods V of b in Y. This proves 2°). 3°) and 4°) follow from 2°) by (43.6.4). 5°) follows from 4°). 6°) and 7°) are now obvious.

6) *Let $Z \subset Y$ be such that Z_b is analytic and $b \in \mathrm{cl}_Z(Z - \xi^{-1}(\mathbf{N}^*(X)))$. Then $\xi_{\mathfrak{v}b}(Z)$ is contained in at most one irreducible component of X_a, i.e., $\xi_b^{-1}(\mathfrak{i}(b, Z, Y))$ contains at most one prime ideal of $\{0\}$ in $R(a, X)$. Consequently, if Z_b is also irreducible then $\xi_{\mathfrak{v}b}(Z)$ is contained in exactly one irreducible component of X_a, i.e., the prime ideal $\xi_b^{-1}(\mathfrak{i}(b, Z, Y))$ contains exactly one prime ideal of $\{0\}$ in $R(a, X)$.*

Proof. In view of 3), it suffices to consider the case of $Z = Y$. If X_a is irreducible then we have nothing to show. So suppose that X_a is reducible. By (44.11) we can take analytic sets $X_1, \ldots, X_q$ in a neighborhood U of a in X such that: $U = X_1 \cup \ldots \cup X_q$; $(X_1)_a, \ldots, (X_q)_a$ are exactly all the distinct irreducible components of X_a; and $\Gamma \subset \mathbf{N}^*(X)$ where

$$\Gamma = \bigcup_{\substack{i \neq j \\ i, j = 1, \ldots, q}} (X_i \cap X_j).$$

By 5) we can find an analytic set Z' in a neighborhood U' of a in U and a neighborhood V of b in Y such that $\xi(V) \subset Z'$ and $Z'_a = \xi_{\mathfrak{v}b}(Y)$. Suppose if possible that $\xi_{\mathfrak{v}b}(Y) \subset (X_i)_a \cap (X_j)_a$ for some $i \neq j$. Then $Z'_a \subset \Gamma_a$ and hence $Z' \cap U'' \subset \Gamma \cap U''$ for some neighborhood U'' of a in U'. Let $V^* = V \cap \xi^{-1}(U'')$. Then V^* is a neighborhood of b in Y, and $\xi(V^*) \subset Z' \cap U'' \subset \Gamma \cap U'' \subset \mathbf{N}^*(X)$, i.e., $V^* \cap (Y - \xi^{-1}(\mathbf{N}^*(X))) = \emptyset$. This contradicts the assumption that $b \in \mathrm{cl}_Y(Y - \xi^{-1}(\mathbf{N}^*(X)))$.

7) *Assume that $\xi^{-1}(\mathbf{N}^*(X))$ is nowhere dense in Y. Then for any irreducible component Y' of Y_b we have that $\xi_{\mathfrak{v}b}(Y')$ is contained in exactly one irreducible component of X_a; or equivalently, for any prime ideal $\mathfrak{q}$ of $\{0\}$ in $R(b, Y)$ we have that the prime ideal $\xi_b^{-1}(\mathfrak{q})$ contains exactly one prime ideal of $\{0\}$ in $R(a, X)$.*

Proof. By (44.9) we can take analytic sets Z and Z^* in a neighborhood V of b in Y such that: $Z_b = Y'$, $V = Z \cup Z^*$, and $Z \cap Z^*$ is nowhere dense in Z. It follows that $Z \cap \xi^{-1}(\mathbf{N}^*(X))$ is nowhere dense in Z, and hence $b \in \mathrm{cl}_Z(Z - \xi^{-1}(\mathbf{N}^*(X))$. Now apply 6).

(46.3) *Let X and Y be Hausdorff spaces, let $\xi\colon Y \to X$ be a proper continuous map, let a be a point in X having a countable basis of neighborhoods in X, and let V be any neighborhood of $\xi^{-1}(a)$ in Y. Then there exists a neighborhood U of a in X such that $\xi^{-1}(U) \subset V$.*

PROOF. Let $U_1 \supset U_2 \supset \ldots$ be a countable basis of neighborhoods of a in X. Suppose if possible that $\xi^{-1}(U) \not\subset V$ for every neighborhood U of a in X. Then in particular $\xi^{-1}(U_i) \not\subset V$ for $i = 1, 2, \ldots$. Take $\beta_i \in \xi^{-1}(U_i) - V$ and let $\alpha_i = \xi(\beta_i)$. Then $\lim\limits_{i\to\infty} \alpha_i = a$ and hence $\{a, \alpha_1, \alpha_2, \ldots\}$ is a compact set in X. Therefore $\xi^{-1}\{a, \alpha_1, \alpha_2, \ldots\}$ is compact and hence the sequence $\beta_1, \beta_2, \ldots$ contains a convergent subsequence $\beta_{t_1}, \beta_{t_2}, \ldots$. Let $b = \lim\limits_{n\to\infty} \beta_{t_n}$. Then $\xi(b) = a$ and hence $b \in \xi^{-1}(a)$. Since V is a neighborhood of $\xi^{-1}(a)$, we must have $\beta_{t_n} \in V$ for some n. Contradiction.

(46.4) *Let X and Y be analytic K-spaces, let $\xi\colon Y \to X$ be a proper analytic map such that $\xi(Y) = X$, and let $a \in X$ be such that $\xi^{-1}(a)$ contains only a finite number of distinct points $b_1, \ldots, b_p$, $(p > 0)$. Then $(\mathrm{Ker}\, \bar{\xi}_{b_1}) \cap \ldots \cap (\mathrm{Ker}\, \bar{\xi}_{b_p}) = \{0\}$.*

PROOF. Take analytic sets $X_1, \ldots, X_p$ in a neighborhood U^* of a in X such that $(X_i)_a = \xi_{\mathfrak{v}b_i}(Y)$ for $i = 1, \ldots, p$. By (46.2.5) there exists a neighborhood V_i^* of b_i in Y such that $\xi(V_i^*) \subset X_i$ and $\mathfrak{V}(\mathfrak{i}(a, \xi(V_i), X)) = (X_i)_a$ for every neighborhood V_i of b_i in V_i^*. By (46.3) there exists a neighborhood U of a in U^* such that $\xi^{-1}(U) \subset V_1^* \cup \ldots \cup V_p^*$. Let $V_i = V_i^* \cap \xi^{-1}(U)$ for $i = 1, \ldots, p$. By assumption $\xi(Y) = X$ and hence $\xi(V_1 \cup \ldots \cup V_p) = U$. For $i = 1, \ldots, p$ we have that $(X_i)_a$ is the smallest analytic set germ in X at a containing $(\xi(V_i))_a$. Therefore $(X_1 \cup \ldots \cup X_p)_a$ is the smallest analytic set germ in X at a containing $(\xi(V_1) \cup \ldots \cup \xi(V_p))_a$. Now $\xi(V_1) \cup \ldots \cup \xi(V_p) = U$ and hence $(\xi(V_1) \cup \ldots \cup \xi(V_p))_a = U_a = X_a$. Therefore $(X_1 \cup \ldots \cup X_p)_a = X_a$ and hence

$$(\mathrm{Ker}\, \bar{\xi}_{b_1}) \cap \ldots \cap (\mathrm{Ker}\, \bar{\xi}_{b_p}) = \mathfrak{i}(a, X_1 \cup \ldots \cup X_p, X) = \{0\}.$$

(46.5) *Let X and Y be analytic K-spaces, let $\xi\colon Y \to X$ be a proper analytic map, and let $a \in X$ be such that $\xi^{-1}(a)$ contains only a finite number of distinct points $b_1, \ldots, b_p$, $(p > 0)$. Then*

$$\xi'_{b_1} \oplus \ldots \oplus \xi'_{b_p} : (\xi_*(\mathcal{O}_Y))_a \to R(b_1, Y) \oplus \ldots \oplus R(b_p, Y)$$

is an isomorphism of $R(a, X)$-algebras.

PROOF. Y being Hausdorff, we can find pairwise disjoint neighborhoods $V_1^*,\ldots, V_p^*$ of $b_1,\ldots, b_p$ in Y.

Given any element in $R(b_1, Y) \oplus\ldots\oplus R(b_p, Y)$ we can write it in the form $((f_1)_{b_1},\ldots, (f_p)_{b_p})$ where f_i is an analytic function on a neighborhood V_i of b_i in V_i^*. By (46.3) there exists a neighborhood U of a in X such that $\xi^{-1}(U) \subset V_1 \cup\ldots\cup V_p$. Now $\xi^{-1}(U) \cap V_1,\ldots, \xi^{-1}(U) \cap V_p$ are pairwise disjoint open sets in Y and their union is $\xi^{-1}(U)$. Consequently we get an analytic function g on $\xi^{-1}(U)$ by setting $g = f_i$ on $\xi^{-1}(U) \cap V_i$ for $i = 1,\ldots, p$. Thus $g \in (\xi_*(\mathcal{O}_Y))(U)$, $g_a \in (\xi_*(\mathcal{O}_Y))_a$, and clearly $\xi'_{b_i}(g_a) = (f_i)_{b_i}$ for $i = 1,\ldots, p$. This shows that $\xi'_{b_1} \oplus\ldots\oplus \xi'_{b_p}$ is an epimorphism.

Given any element in $(\xi_*(\mathcal{O}_Y))_a$ we can write it in the form h_a where h is an analytic function on $\xi^{-1}(U^*)$ where U^* is a neighborhood of a in X. Suppose that $\xi'_{b_i}(h_a) = 0$ for $i = 1,\ldots, p$. Then there exists a neighborhood V'_i of b_i in $\xi^{-1}(U^*) \cap V_i^*$ such that $h(V'_i) = 0$ for $i = 1,\ldots, p$. By (46.3) there exists a neighborhood U' of a in U^* such that $\xi^{-1}(U') \subset V'_1 \cup\ldots\cup V'_p$, and then $h(\xi^{-1}(U')) = 0$ and hence $h_a = 0$. This shows that $\xi'_{b_1} \oplus\ldots\oplus \xi'_{b_p}$ is a monomorphism.

(**46.6**) DEFINITION. Let X and Y be analytic K-spaces. A *bimeromorphic map* $\xi: Y \to X$ is a closed analytic map such that $\xi^{-1}(a)$ is a nonempty finite set for all $a \in X$ and $\xi_*(\mathcal{O}_Y)$ is $\mathcal{O}_X$-algebra-isomorphic to an $\mathcal{O}_X$-subalgebra of $\mathcal{O}'_X$; by (44.28) it follows that the said subalgebra and the isomorphism of $\xi_*(\mathcal{O}_Y)$ onto it are then uniquely determined by ξ. A *normalization map* $\xi: Y \to X$ is a closed analytic map such that $\xi^{-1}(a)$ is a nonempty finite set for all $a \in X$ and $\xi_*(\mathcal{O}_Y)$ is $\mathcal{O}_X$-algebra-isomorphic to $\mathcal{O}'_X$; this may also be expressed by saying that Y is a *normalization* of X and ξ is the corresponding map of Y onto X.

Note that, in view of the following remark, *a bimeromorphic map* (*hence in particular, a normalization map*) *is always proper.*

Remark on proper maps. Let X and Y be Hausdorff spaces and let $\xi: Y \to X$ be a map. According to the definition given in §1: φ is proper $\Leftrightarrow$ for every compact subset X' of X, $\xi^{-1}(X')$ is compact. This definition does not agree with the latest definition given in Bourbaki [**1**: §10]. However, letting "B-proper" to stand for "proper in the sense of Bourbaki", by Bourbaki [**1**: Theorem 1 and Propositions 6 and 7 of §10] we get: 1°) If ξ is continuous, then ξ is B-proper $\Leftrightarrow$ ξ is closed and $\xi^{-1}(a)$ is compact for all $a \in X$. 2°) If ξ is B-proper then ξ is proper. 3°) If ξ is continuous and X is locally compact, then ξ is B-proper $\Leftrightarrow$ ξ is proper.

We have used the notion of "proper" only in (12.5.2, 30.21, 31.7, 32.1.1, 35.10.3). In all these propositions the map was continuous and the inverse map was finitely valued, and it was shown that the map was proper and closed. In view of 1°) and 2°), in these instances "proper" actually follows from "closed"; however the proofs of these propositions depended only on (12.5.2) where the direct proof of "proper" was trivial.

In any case, by 1°) and 2°) we get

1) A bimeromorphic map is always proper.

Since a complex space is obviously locally compact, by 1°) and 3°) we get

2) Let X and Y be complex spaces and let $\xi: Y \to X$ be continuous. Then ξ is proper $\Leftrightarrow$ ξ is closed and $\xi^{-1}(a)$ is compact for all $a \in X$.

(**46.7**) *Let X and Y be analytic K-spaces, and let $\xi: Y \to X$ be a closed analytic map such that $\xi^{-1}(a)$ is a nonempty finite set for all $a \in X$. Then for each $a \in X$ the following three conditions are equivalent where $b_1,\ldots, b_p$ are the distinct points in $\xi^{-1}(a)$.*

i) *$(\xi_*(\mathcal{O}_Y))_a$ is $R(a, X)$-algebra-isomorphic to an $R(a, X)$-subalgebra of $R'(a, X)$.*

ii) *$R(b_1, Y) \oplus\ldots\oplus R(b_p, Y)$ is $R(a, X)$-algebra-isomorphic to an $R(a, X)$-subalgebra of $R'(a, X)$.*

iii) *For $i = 1,\ldots, p$ there exists a ring homomorphism $\psi_i: \mathfrak{R}(a, X) \to \mathfrak{R}(b_i, Y)$ for which $\psi_i(r) = \xi_{b_i}(r)$ for all $r \in R(a, X)$, such that $\psi_1 \oplus\ldots\oplus \psi_p : \mathfrak{R}(a, X) \to \mathfrak{R}(b_1, Y) \oplus\ldots\oplus \mathfrak{R}(b_p, Y)$ is a ring isomorphism and $R(b_1, Y) \oplus\ldots\oplus R(b_p, Y) \subset (\psi_1 \oplus\ldots\oplus \psi_p)(R'(a, X))$.*

Furthermore, ξ is bimeromorphic $\Leftrightarrow$ $(\xi_*(\mathcal{O}_Y))_a$ is $R(a, X)$-algebra-isomorphic to an $R(a, X)$-subalgebra of $R'(a, X)$ for all $a \in X$.

Proof. i) $\Leftrightarrow$ ii) by (46.5). Considering $\mathfrak{R}(b_1, Y) \oplus\ldots\oplus \mathfrak{R}(b_p, Y)$ to be the total quotient ring of $R(b_1, Y) \oplus\ldots\oplus R(b_p, Y)$, by (18.5.5) we see that ii) is equivalent to : ii') there exists a ring isomorphism $\psi: \mathfrak{R}(a, X) \to \mathfrak{R}(b_1, Y) \oplus\ldots\oplus \mathfrak{R}(b_p, Y)$ such that $\psi(r) = (\xi_{b_1} \oplus\ldots\oplus \xi_{b_p})(r)$ for all $r \in R(a, X)$ and $R(b_1, Y) \oplus\ldots\oplus R(b_p, Y) \subset \psi(R'(a, X))$. Obviously ii') $\Leftrightarrow$ iii). The final assertion follows from (44.28) and (18.5.5).

(**46.8**) *Let X and Y be analytic K-spaces, let $\xi: Y \to X$ be a closed analytic map such that $\xi^{-1}(a)$ is a nonempty finite set for all $a \in X$, and let $\mathfrak{Q}$ be an $\mathcal{O}_X$-subalgebra of $\mathcal{O}'_X$. Then for each $a \in X$ the following four conditions are equivalent where $b_1,\ldots, b_p$ are the distinct points in $\xi^{-1}(a)$.*

i) *$(\xi_*(\mathcal{O}_Y))_a$ is $R(a, X)$-algebra-isomorphic to $\mathfrak{Q}_a$.*

ii) *$R(b_1, Y) \oplus\ldots\oplus R(b_p, Y)$ is $R(a, X)$-algebra-isomorphic to $\mathfrak{Q}_a$.*

iii) *For $i = 1,\ldots, p$ there exists a ring homomorphism $\psi_i: \mathfrak{R}(a, X) \to \mathfrak{R}(b_i, Y)$ for which $\psi_i(r) = \xi_{b_i}(r)$ for all $r \in R(a, X)$, such that $\psi_1 \oplus\ldots\oplus \psi_p: \mathfrak{R}(a, X)$*

$\to \mathfrak{R}(b_1, Y) \oplus ... \oplus \mathfrak{R}(b_p, Y)$ *is a ring isomorphism and* $(\psi_1 \oplus ... \oplus \psi_p)(\mathcal{Q}_a) = R(b_1, Y) \oplus ... \oplus R(b_p, Y)$.

iv) *For* $i = 1, ..., p$: $\xi_{b_i}(M(a, X)) \subset M(b_i, Y)$ *and* $\psi_i(\mathcal{Q}_a) = R(b_i, Y)$ *where* $\psi_i: \mathfrak{R}(a, X) \to \mathfrak{R}(b_i, Y)$ *is induced by* ξ_{b_i}; *and for all* $i \neq j$, $(i, j = 1, ..., p)$: *there exists* $h_{ij} \in \mathcal{Q}_a$ *such that* $(\psi_i(h_{ij}))(b_i) \neq 0$ *and* $\psi_j(h_{ij}) = 0$.[3]

Furthermore, $\xi_*(\mathcal{O}_Y)$ *is* $\mathcal{O}_X$*-algebra-isomorphic to* $\mathcal{Q} \Leftrightarrow (\xi_*(\mathcal{O}_Y))_a$ *is* $R(a, X)$*-algebra-isomorphic to* $\mathcal{Q}_a$ *for all* $a \in X$.

PROOF. i) $\Leftrightarrow$ ii) by (46.5). Considering $\mathfrak{R}(b_1, Y) \oplus ... \oplus \mathfrak{R}(b_p, Y)$ to be the total quotient ring of $R(b_1, Y) \oplus ... \oplus R(b_p, Y)$, by (18.5.5) we see that ii) is equivalent to: ii′) there exists a ring isomorphism $\psi: \mathfrak{R}(a, X) \to \mathfrak{R}(b_1, Y) \oplus ... \oplus \mathfrak{R}(b_p, Y)$ such that $\psi(r) = (\bar{\xi}_{b_1} \oplus ... \oplus \bar{\xi}_{b_p})(r)$ for all $r \in R(a, X)$ and $\psi(\mathcal{Q}_a) = R(b_1, Y) \oplus ... \oplus R(b_p, Y)$. Obviously ii′) $\Leftrightarrow$ iii). Now $(\operatorname{Ker} \bar{\xi}_{b_1}) \cap ... \cap (\operatorname{Ker} \bar{\xi}_{b_p}) = \{0\}$ by (46.4); and for any $b \in Y$ and any $h \in R(b, Y)$ we obviously have: h is a unit in $R(b, Y) \Leftrightarrow h(b) \neq 0$. Therefore ii) $\Leftrightarrow$ iv) by (18.5.8). The final assertion follows from (44.28).

(**46.9**) *Let* X *and* Y *be analytic K-spaces and let* $\xi: Y \to X$ *be a bimeromorphic map. Then for each* $a \in X$ *the following three conditions are equivalent.*

i) $(\xi_*(\mathcal{O}_Y))_a$ *is* $R(a, X)$*-algebra-isomorphic to* $R'(a, X)$.

ii) $R(b_1, Y) \oplus ... \oplus R(b_p, Y)$ *is* $R(a, X)$*-algebra-isomorphic to* $R'(a, X)$ *where* $b_1, ..., b_p$ *are the distinct points in* $\xi^{-1}(a)$.

iii) Y_b *is normal for all* $b \in \xi^{-1}(a)$.

Furthermore, ξ *is a normalization map* $\Leftrightarrow$ Y *is normal.*

PROOF. i) $\Leftrightarrow$ ii) by (46.5). Since ξ is bimeromorphic, by (46.5) and (18.5.5) we get that $R(b_1, Y) \oplus ... \oplus R(b_p, Y)$ is $R(a, X)$-algebra-isomorphic to a unique $R(a, X)$-subalgebra of $R'(a, X)$. Therefore ii) is equivalent to saying that $R(b_1, Y) \oplus ... \oplus R(b_p, Y)$ is normal. By (19.22), $R(b_1, Y) \oplus ... \oplus R(b_p, Y)$ is normal $\Leftrightarrow R(b_i, Y)$ is normal for $i = 1, ..., p$. Thus ii) $\Leftrightarrow$ iii). By (46.8), ξ is a normalization map $\Leftrightarrow$ i) holds for all $a \in X$. Therefore by "i) $\Leftrightarrow$ iii)" we get that, ξ is a normalization map $\Leftrightarrow$ Y is normal.

(**46.10**) *Let* X *and* Y *be analytic K-spaces and let* $\xi: Y \to X$ *be a bimeromorphic map. If* X_a *is irreducible for all* $a \in X$*, then* ξ *is a homeomorphism. If* X *is normal, then* ξ *is bianalytic.*

[3] Note that for $i = 1, ..., p$ we then have: the map ψ_i in iii) is the same as the map ψ_i in iv); $\mathfrak{R}(b_i, Y)$ is the total quotient ring of $\bar{\xi}_{b_i}(R(a, X))$; and $R(b_i, Y)$ is integral over $\bar{\xi}_{b_i}(R(a, X))$.

PROOF. For any $a \in X$ let $b_1, \ldots, b_p$ be the distinct points in $\xi^{-1}(a)$. By (46.7), $\mathfrak{R}(b_1, Y) \oplus \ldots \oplus \mathfrak{R}(b_p, Y)$ is ring isomorphic to $\mathfrak{R}(a, X)$. If X_a is irreducible then $\mathfrak{R}(a, X)$ is a field and hence $p = 1$. Thus if X_a is irreducible for all $a \in X$, then ξ is a one to one continuous map of Y onto X, and by (46.3), ξ is open; whence ξ is a homeomorphism.

Now assume that X is normal. For any $a \in X$ we then have $R'(a, X) = R(a, X)$ and hence $(\xi_*(\mathcal{O}_Y))_a$ is $R(a, X)$-algebra-isomorphic to $R(a, X)$; therefore the underlying homomorphism ξ_a of the $R(a, X)$-algebra $(\xi_*(\mathcal{O}_Y))_a$ must be a ring isomorphism. This being so for all $a \in X$, we get that $\xi(\mathcal{O}_X) = \xi_*(\mathcal{O}_Y)$ and hence ξ is bianalytic.

(46.11) *Let X and Y be analytic K-spaces, and let $\xi: Y \to X$ be a bimeromorphic map. If Ω is any thin subset of X, then $\xi^{-1}(\Omega)$ is thin subset of Y and in particular $\xi^{-1}(\Omega)$ is nowhere dense in Y. Furthermore, for any closed subset Ω of X, with $\Omega \neq X$, we have the following: if $\mathbf{N}^*(X) \subset \Omega$ then the map $Y - \xi^{-1}(\Omega) \to X - \Omega$ induced by ξ is a homeomorphism; if $\mathbf{N}(X) \subset \Omega$ then the map $Y - \xi^{-1}(\Omega) \to X - \Omega$ induced by ξ is bianalytic; if $\mathbf{S}(X) \subset \Omega$ then $\mathbf{S}(Y) \subset \xi^{-1}(\Omega)$.*

PROOF. By (46.8), $\xi_b(M(\xi(b), X)) \subset M(b, Y)$ for all $b \in Y$. Therefore by (46.2.2) we get that if Ω is any thin subset of X, then $\xi^{-1}(\Omega)$ is a thin subset of Y and hence $\xi^{-1}(\Omega)$ is nowhere dense in Y. The rest follows from (46.10).

(46.12) *Let X and Y be analytic K-spaces and let $\xi: Y \to X$ be a bimeromorphic map. For any $a \in X$ let $b_1, \ldots, b_p$ the distinct points in $\xi^{-1}(a)$ and let $\mathfrak{q}_{i1}, \ldots, \mathfrak{q}_{i\delta_i}$ be the distinct prime ideals of $\{0\}$ in $R(b_i, Y)$. Then the $\delta_1 + \ldots + \delta_p$ ideals $\xi_{b_i}^{-1}(\mathfrak{q}_{ij})$ are all distinct and they are exactly all the prime ideals of $\{0\}$ in $R(a, X)$. In other words, letting $Y'_{i1}, \ldots, Y'_{i\delta_i}$ to be the distinct irreducible components of Y_{b_i} we have that the $\delta_1 + \ldots + \delta_p$ elements $\xi_{\mathfrak{v}b_i}(Y'_{ij})$ are all distinct and they are exactly all the irreducible components of X_a. Furthermore, $\xi_{\mathfrak{v}b_i}(Y'_{i1}), \ldots, \xi_{\mathfrak{v}b_i}(Y'_{i\delta_i})$ are exactly all the distinct irreducible components of $\xi_{\mathfrak{v}b_i}(Y)$.*

PROOF. By (46.7) we get a ring isomorphism $\lambda_1 \oplus \ldots \oplus \lambda_p: R^* \to R(b_1, Y) \oplus \ldots \oplus R(b_p, Y)$ where R^* is a subring of $R'(a, X)$ such that $R(a, X) \subset R^*$ and $\lambda_i: R^* \to R(b_i, Y)$ is a ring homomorphism such that $\lambda_i | R(a, X) = \xi_{b_i}$ for $i = 1, \ldots, p$. Now $\xi_{b_i}^{-1}(\mathfrak{q}_{ij}) = R(a, X) \cap \lambda_i^{-1}(\mathfrak{q}_{ij})$ and hence by (18.8, 18.9.3) we get that the $\delta_1 + \ldots + \delta_p$ ideals $\xi_{b_i}^{-1}(\mathfrak{q}_{ij})$ are exactly all the distinct prime ideals of $\{0\}$ in $R(a, X)$. This proves the first assertion. The second assertion is simply a reformulation of the first. The third assertion follows from the second by (46.2.4).

(46.13) *Let X and Y be analytic K-spaces and let $\xi: Y \to X$ be a normalization map. For any $a \in X$ let $b_1, \ldots, b_p$ be the distinct points in $\xi^{-1}(a)$. For $i = 1, \ldots, p$ we then have $\xi_{b_i}(M(a, X)) \subset M(b_i, Y)$ and $\psi_i(R'(a, X)) = R(b_i, Y)$ where $\psi_i: \mathfrak{R}(a, X) \to \mathfrak{R}(b_i, Y)$ is induced by ξ_{b_i}; also $\xi_{(b_i)}(M(a, X)) \subset$ (the set of all nonzerodivisors in $\mathfrak{E}(b_i, Y)$) and $\varphi_i(r) = \psi_i(r)$ for all $r \in R'(a, X)$ where $\varphi_i: \mathfrak{R}(a, X) \to$ (the total quotient ring of $\mathfrak{E}(b_i, Y)$) is induced by $\xi_{(b_i)} | R(a, X)$. Let $\lambda_i: R'(a, X) \to R(b_i, Y)$ be given by taking $\lambda_i(r) = \psi_i(r)$ for all $r \in R'(a, X)$, let $\mathfrak{m}_i$ be the maximal ideal in $R(b_i, Y)$, and let $\mathfrak{n}_i = \lambda_i^{-1}(\mathfrak{m}_i)$, $\mathfrak{p}_i' =$ Ker λ_i, $\mathfrak{p}_i =$ Ker ξ_{b_i}. Then $\psi_1 \oplus \ldots \oplus \psi_p: \mathfrak{R}(a, X) \to \mathfrak{R}(b_1, Y) \oplus \ldots \oplus \mathfrak{R}(b_p, Y)$ and $\lambda_1 \oplus \ldots \oplus \lambda_p: R'(a, X) \to R(b_1, Y) \oplus \ldots \oplus R(b_p, Y)$ are ring isomorphisms; $\mathfrak{n}_1, \ldots, \mathfrak{n}_p$ are exactly all the distinct maximal ideals in $R'(a, X)$; $\mathfrak{p}_1', \ldots, \mathfrak{p}_p'$ are exactly all the distinct prime ideals of $\{0\}$ in $R'(a, X)$; $\{0\} = \mathfrak{p}_1' \cap \ldots \cap \mathfrak{p}_p'$ is the unique normal decomposition of $\{0\}$ in $R'(a, X)$; $\mathfrak{p}_1, \ldots, \mathfrak{p}_p$ are exactly all the distinct prime ideals of $\{0\}$ in $R(a, X)$; $\mathfrak{p}_i \subset \mathfrak{p}_i' \subset \mathfrak{n}_i$ and $\mathfrak{p}_i = \mathfrak{p}_i' \cap R(a, X)$ for all i; and $\mathfrak{p}_j \not\subset \mathfrak{p}_i$ and $\mathfrak{p}_j' \not\subset \mathfrak{n}_i$ for all $j \neq i$.*

PROOF. Everything except the assertion concerning $\xi_{(b_i)}$ follows from (46.8) and (24.3.3). The assertion concerning $\xi_{(b_i)}$ follows from (44.16).

(46.14) *Let X and Y be analytic K-spaces, let $\xi: Y \to X$ be a bimeromorphic map, let $a \in X$ and let $b_1, \ldots, b_p$ be the distinct points in $\xi^{-1}(a)$. Let any $Y_{ij} \subset Y$ and $X_{ij} \subset X$ be given such that $(Y_{i1})_{b_i}, \ldots, (Y_{i\delta_i})_{b_i}$ are the distinct irreducible components of Y_{b_i} for $i = 1, \ldots, p$, and $(X_{ij})_a = \xi_{\mathfrak{v}b_i}(Y_{ij})$ for all i, j. Let $X_i = \bigcup_j X_{ij}$. Also let neighborhoods $V_1^*, \ldots, V_p^*$ of $b_1, \ldots, b_p$ in Y and a neighborhood U^* of a in X be given. Then there exist pairwise disjoint neighborhoods $V_1, \ldots, V_p$ of $b_1, \ldots, b_p$ in $V_1^*, \ldots, V_p^*$ and a neighborhood U of a in U^* such that we have the following.*

i) $\xi^{-1}(U) = V_1 \cup \ldots \cup V_p$.

ii) *$X_{ij} \cap U$ is analytic in U for all i, j and $U = \bigcup_{i,j} (X_{ij} \cap U)$.*

iii) *$Y_{ij} \cap V_i$ is analytic in V_i for all i, j and $V_i = \bigcup_j (Y_{ij} \cap V_i)$ for all i.*

iv) *$\xi(Y_{ij} \cap V_i) = X_{ij} \cap U$ for all i, j and $\xi(V_i) = X_i$ for all i.*

v) *$(X_i)_{a'} = \bigcup_{b' \in V_i \cap \xi^{-1}(a')} \xi_{\mathfrak{v}b'}(Y)$ for all $a' \in U$ for $i = 1, \ldots, p$.*

vi) *For any $a' \in U$ let $X'_{ij1}, \ldots, X'_{ij\mu_{ij}}$ be the distinct irreducible components of $(X_{ij})_{a'}$. Then the $\sum_{i,j} \mu_{ij}$ elements X'_{ijk} are exactly all the distinct irreducible components of $X_{a'}$.*

PROOF. By (46.2.5) there exists a neighborhood $\tilde{V}_{ij}$ of b_i in V_i^* such that

1°) $$\xi(Y_{ij} \cap \tilde{V}_{ij}) \subset X_{ij}.$$

Since Y is Hausdorff, we can take pairwise disjoint neighborhoods $\tilde{V}_1, \ldots, \tilde{V}_p$ of $b_1, \ldots, b_p$ in $\bigcap_{j=1}^{\delta_1} \tilde{V}_{1j}, \ldots, \bigcap_{j=1}^{\delta_p} \tilde{V}_{pj}$. We can obviously take neighborhoods $\bar{V}_1, \ldots, \bar{V}_p$ of $b_1, \ldots, b_p$ in $\tilde{V}_1, \ldots, \tilde{V}_p$ such that $Y_{ij} \cap \bar{V}_i$ is analytic in $\bar{V}_i$ for all i, j, and $\bar{V}_i = \bigcup_j (Y_{ij} \cap \bar{V}_i)$ for all i.

By (46.12), the $\delta_1 + \ldots + \delta_p$ elements $(X_{ij})_a$ are exactly all the distinct irreducible components of X_a and hence by (44.11) there exists a neighborhood $\tilde{U}$ of a in U^* such that: $X_{ij} \cap \tilde{U}$ is analytic in $\tilde{U}$ for all i, j; $\tilde{U} = \bigcup_{i,j} (X_{ij} \cap \tilde{U})$; and for all $a' \in \tilde{U}$ we have the following.

2°) Let $X'_{ij1}, \ldots, X'_{ij\mu_{ij}}$ be the distinct irreducible components of $(X_{ij})_{a'}$. Then the $\sum_{i,j} \mu_{ij}$ elements X'_{ijk} are exactly all the distinct irreducible components of $X_{a'}$.

For any i, j let

$$Z_{ij} = \bigcup_{(i',j') \neq (i,j)} X_{i'j'}$$

where the union is over $(\delta_1 + \ldots + \delta_p) - 1$ elements. Then $(X_{ij})_a \not\subset (Z_{ij})_a$ and hence by (44.9) there exists a neighborhood $\bar{U}_{ij}$ of a in $\tilde{U}$ such that $X_{ij} \cap \bar{U}_{ij}$ is the closure of $(X_{ij} \cap \bar{U}_{ij}) - Z_{ij}$ in $\bar{U}_{ij}$. Let $\bar{U} = \bigcap_{i,j} \bar{U}_{ij}$. Then for every neighborhood U of a in $\bar{U}$ we have

4°) $$X_{ij} \cap U = \mathrm{cl}_U((X_{ij} \cap U) - Z_{ij}) \qquad \text{for all} \quad i, j.$$

By (46.3) there exists a neighborhood U of a in $\bar{U}$ such that $\xi^{-1}(U) \subset \bar{V}_1 \cup \ldots \cup \bar{V}_p$. Let $V_i = \bar{V}_i \cap \xi^{-1}(U)$. Then $V_1, \ldots, V_p$ are pairwise disjoint neighborhoods of $b_1, \ldots, b_p$ in $V_1^*, \ldots, V_p^*$ and we have i), ii), iii), and vi). By i), ii), iii) we get 5°) and 6°).

5°) $$\bigcup_{i,j} \xi(Y_{ij} \cap V_i) = \bigcup_{i,j} (X_{ij} \cap U) = U.$$

6°) $$Y_{ij} \cap V_i \text{ is a closed subset of } \xi^{-1}(U) \qquad \text{for all} \quad i, j.$$

By 1°) we get

7°) $$\xi(Y_{ij} \cap V_i) \subset X_{ij} \cap U \qquad \text{for all} \quad i, j.$$

By (3°, 5°, 7°) we get

8°) $$(X_{ij} \cap U) - Z_{ij} \subset \xi(Y_{ij} \cap V_i) \subset X_{ij} \cap U \qquad \text{for all} \quad i, j.$$

By 4°) and 8°) we get

9°) $$\mathrm{cl}_U \xi(Y_{ij} \cap V_i) = X_{ij} \cap U \qquad \text{for all} \quad i, j.$$

Now $\xi\colon Y \to X$ is a closed map and hence by 6°) and 9°) we get that

$$\xi(Y_{ij} \cap V_i) = X_{ij} \cap U \qquad \text{for all} \quad i, j$$

and hence

$$\xi(V_i) = X_i \cap U \qquad \text{for all} \quad i.$$

This proves iv).

To prove v) let $a' \in U$ be given. Let $b'_{i1},\ldots, b'_{i\lambda_i}$ be the distinct points in $V_i \cap \xi^{-1}(a')$. By (46.2.5) there exists a neighborhood V'_{is} of b'_{is} in V_i such that $\xi_{\mathfrak{v}b'_{is}}(Y)$ is the smallest analytic set germ in X at a' containing $\xi(V'_{is})$. Now

$$\bigcup_{s=1}^{\lambda_i} \xi(V'_{is}) \subset \xi(V_i) \subset X_i \cap U$$

and hence

10°) $$\bigcup_{s=1}^{\lambda_i} \xi_{\mathfrak{v}b'_{is}}(Y) \subset (X_i)_{a'} \qquad \text{for} \quad i = 1,\ldots, p.$$

Now $V_1,\ldots, V_p$ are pairwise disjoint and hence the $\lambda_1 + \ldots + \lambda_p$ points b'_{is} are exactly all the distinct points in $\xi^{-1}(a')$. Therefore applying (46.12) at a' we get the following.

11°) Let $X''_{i1},\ldots, X''_{i\nu_i}$ be the distinct irreducible components of $\bigcup_{s=1}^{\lambda_i} \xi_{\mathfrak{v}b'_{is}}(Y)$. Then the $\nu_1 + \ldots + \nu_p$ elements X''_{it} are exactly all the distinct irreducible components of $X_{a'}$.

Now $X_i = X_{i1} \cup \ldots \cup X_{i\delta_i}$ and hence by (2°, 10°, 11°) we deduce that

$$\bigcup_{s=1}^{\lambda_i} \xi_{\mathfrak{v}b'_{is}}(Y) = (X_i)_{a'} \qquad \text{for} \quad i = 1,\ldots, p.$$

This proves v).

(46.15) *Let X and Y be analytic K-spaces, let $\xi\colon Y \to X$ be a bimeromorphic map, let $a \in X$ and let $b_1,\ldots, b_p$ be the distinct points in $\xi^{-1}(a)$. Let neighborhoods $V_1^*,\ldots, V_p^*$ of $b_1,\ldots, b_p$ in Y and a neighborhood U^* of a in X be given. Then there exist pairwise disjoint neighborhoods $V_1,\ldots, V_p$ of $b_1,\ldots, b_p$ in $V_1^*,\ldots, V_p^*$ and analytic sets $X_1,\ldots, X_p$ in a neighborhood U of a in U^* such that we have the following.*

i) $\xi^{-1}(U) = V_1 \cup \ldots \cup V_p$; $\quad U = X_1 \cup \ldots \cup X_p$; $\quad \xi(V_i) = X_i$ *for* $i = 1,\ldots, p$.

ii) $(X_i)_{a'} = \bigcup_{b' \in V_i \cap \xi^{-1}(a')} \xi_{\mathfrak{v}b'}(Y)$ *for all* $a' \in U$, *for* $i = 1,\ldots, p$.

iii) *For any* $a' \in U$ *let* $X'_{i1},\ldots, X'_{i\nu_i}$ *be the distinct irreducible components of* $(X_i)_{a'}$. *Then the* $\nu_1 + \ldots + \nu_p$ *elements* X'_{ij} *are exactly all the distinct irreducible components of* $X_{a'}$.

Proof. Follows from (46.14).

(46.16) *Let* X *and* Y *be analytic K-spaces, let* $\xi\colon Y \to X$ *be a bimeromorphic map, and assume that* Y_b *is irreducible for all* $b \in Y$. *Let* X' *be any analytic set in any nonempty open set* U^* *in* X *such that for each* $a \in X'$ *every irreducible component of* X'_a *is an irreducible component of* X_a. *Let*

$$V = \bigcup_{a\in X'} \{b \in \xi^{-1}(a)\colon \xi_{\mathfrak{v}b}(Y) \text{ is an irreducible component of } X'_a\}.$$

Then V *is open in* Y.

Proof. Given any $b_1 \in V$ let $a = \xi(b_1)$ and let $b_2,\ldots, b_p$ be the remaining points in $\xi^{-1}(a)$. By (46.12), $\xi_{\mathfrak{v}b_1}(Y),\ldots, \xi_{\mathfrak{v}b_p}(Y)$ are exactly all the distinct irreducible components of X_a. Label $b_2,\ldots, b_p$ so that $\xi_{\mathfrak{v}b_2}(Y),\ldots, \xi_{\mathfrak{v}b_q}(Y)$ are the remaining irreducible components of X'_a. Take $V_1^* = \ldots = V_p^* = Y$ and let $V_1,\ldots, V_p, X_1,\ldots, X_p, U$ be as found in (46.15). Then $(X_1)_a,\ldots, (X_q)_a$ are exactly all the distinct irreducible components of X'_a. Therefore there exists a neighborhood U' of a in U such that $X' \cap U' = (X_1 \cup\ldots\cup X_q) \cap U'$. For all $a' \in X' \cap U'$ we then have

$$X'_{a'} = \bigcup_{i=1}^{q} \bigcup_{b'\in V_i \cap \xi^{-1}(a')} \xi_{\mathfrak{v}b'}(Y)$$

and hence $V_1 \cup\ldots\cup V_q \subset V$ by (46.12). Thus V is a neighborhood of each point in it, i.e., V is open in Y.

(46.17) *Let* X *and* Y *be analytic K-spaces and let* $\xi\colon Y \to X$ *be a bimeromorphic map. If* Y' *is any analytic set in* Y *such that for all* $b \in Y'$ *each irreducible component of* Y'_b *is an irreducible component of* Y_b, *then* $\xi(Y')$ *is an analytic set in* X *and for all* $a \in \xi(Y')$ *each irreducible component of* $(\xi(Y'))_a$ *is an irreducible component of* X_a. *If* Y'' *is another analytic set in* Y *such that for all* $b \in Y''$ *each irreducible component of* Y''_b *is an irreducible component of* Y_b *and no irreducible component of* Y''_b *is contained in* Y'_b, *then for all* $a \in \xi(Y'')$ *we have that no irreducible component of* $(\xi(Y''))_a$ *is contained in* $(\xi(Y'))_a$.

Proof. Follows from (46.14).

(46.18) *Let X, Y, Z be analytic K-spaces, let $\xi\colon Y \to X$ be a bimeromorphic map, and let $\zeta\colon Z \to X$ be an analytic map.*

1) *Assume that $\mathbf{N}^*(Z) = \emptyset$, and $\zeta^{-1}(\mathbf{N}^*(X))$ is nowhere dense in Z. Then there exists a unique continuous map $\eta\colon Z \to Y$ such that $\zeta = \xi \circ \eta$.*

2) *Assume that Z is normal and $\bar{\zeta}_c(M(\zeta(c), X)) \subset M(c, Z)$ for all $c \in Z$.*[4]

Let $\eta\colon Z \to Y$ be any continuous map such that $\zeta = \xi \circ \eta$. Then η is analytic.

Proof of 1). Given $c \in Z$, by (46.2.7), $\zeta_{\mathfrak{v}c}(Z)$ is contained in a unique irreducible component X' of X_a where $a = \zeta(c)$. By (46.12) there exists a unique point b in $\xi^{-1}(a)$ such that $X' \subset \xi_{\mathfrak{v}b}(Y)$. We define: $\eta(c) = b$. By (46.12) it follows that $b = \eta(c)$ *is the unique point in* $\xi^{-1}(\zeta(c))$ *for which* $\zeta_{\mathfrak{v}c}(Z) \subset \xi_{\mathfrak{v}b}(Y)$.

Obviously $\zeta = \xi \circ \eta$. To show that η is continuous, let $c \in Z$ and a neighborhood V^* of $b = \eta(c)$ in Y be given. By (46.15) there exists a neighborhood V of b in V^* and an analytic set X^* in a neighborhood U of $a = \xi(b)$ in X such that: $\xi(V) = X^*$, $\xi_{\mathfrak{v}b}(Y) = X^*_a$, and

$$1^\circ) \qquad X^*_{a'} = \bigcup_{b' \in V \cap \xi^{-1}(a')} \xi_{\mathfrak{v}b'}(Y) \qquad \text{for all} \quad a' \in U.$$

Now $\zeta_{\mathfrak{v}c}(Z) \subset X^*_a$, and hence by (46.2.5) there exists a neighborhood W of c in Z such that $\zeta(W) \subset X^*$. Given any $c' \in W$ let $a' = \zeta(c')$. Since W is a neighborhood of c' in Z, by (46.2.5) we get that $\zeta_{\mathfrak{v}c'}(Z) \subset X^*_{a'}$. Now $\zeta_{\mathfrak{v}c'}(Z)$ is irreducible and hence by 1°) there exists $b' \in V \cap \xi^{-1}(a')$ such that $\zeta_{\mathfrak{v}c'}(Z) \subset \xi_{\mathfrak{v}b'}(Y)$; and then we must have $b' = \eta(c')$. Thus $\eta(W) \subset V \subset V^*$. This shows that η is continuous.

To prove uniqueness, let $\lambda\colon Z \to Y$ be any continuous map such that $\zeta = \xi \circ \lambda$, let c be any point in Z and let $b = \lambda(c)$ and $a = \xi(b)$. We want to show that $b = \eta(c)$, i.e., we want to show that $\zeta_{\mathfrak{v}c}(Z) \subset \xi_{\mathfrak{v}b}(Y)$. By (46.2.5) there exists a neighborhood V of b in Y and an analytic set X^* in a neighborhood U of a in X such that $\xi_{\mathfrak{v}b}(Y) = X^*_a$ and $\xi(V) \subset X^*$. Since λ is continuous, there exists a neighborhood W of c in Z such that $\lambda(W) \subset V$. Now $\zeta(W) \subset \xi(V) \subset X^*$ and hence $\zeta_{\mathfrak{v}c}(Z) \subset X^*_a$ by (46.2.5).

Proof of 2). Given any $c \in Z$ let $b = \eta(c)$ and $a = \xi(b)$. We want to show that $\bar{\eta}_{(c)}(R(b, Y)) \subset R(c, Z)$. By (46.8), $\bar{\xi}_b(M(a, X)) \subset M(b, Y)$ and $\psi(R^*) = R(b, Y)$ where $\psi\colon \mathfrak{R}(a, X) \to \mathfrak{R}(b, X)$ is induced by $\bar{\xi}_b$, and R^* is a subring of $\mathfrak{R}(a, X)$ such that $R(a, X) \subset R^*$ and R^* is integral over $R(a, X)$. Given $s \in R(b, Y)$ there exist $u \in R(a, X)$ and $v \in M(a, X)$

[4] Concerning the last assumption see (46.2.2).

such that $u/v \in R^*$ and $\psi(u/v) = s$. Let $t = \bar{\eta}_{(c)}(s)$. We want to show that $t \in R(c, Z)$. Now

$$\bar{\xi}_{(b)}(u) = \bar{\xi}_b(u) = \psi(u) = \psi(u/v)\psi(v) = s\psi(v) = s\bar{\xi}_b(v) = s\bar{\xi}_{(b)}(v),$$

$$\bar{\zeta}_c(u) = \bar{\zeta}_{(c)}(u) = \bar{\eta}_{(c)}(\bar{\xi}_{(b)}(u)),$$

and

$$t\bar{\zeta}_c(v) = t\bar{\zeta}_{(c)}(v) = \bar{\eta}_{(c)}(s)\bar{\eta}_{(c)}(\bar{\xi}_{(b)}(v)) = \bar{\eta}_{(c)}(s\bar{\xi}_{(b)}(v)).$$

Therefore

$$\bar{\zeta}_c(u) = t\bar{\zeta}_c(v).$$

By assumption $\bar{\zeta}_c(M(a, X)) \subset M(c, Z)$, and hence in particular $\bar{\zeta}_c(v) \in M(c, Z)$. Let $\varphi: \mathfrak{R}(a, X) \to \mathfrak{R}(c, Z)$ be induced by $\bar{\zeta}_c$. By (44.16) we can consider $\mathfrak{R}(c, Z)$ to be a subring of the total quotient ring of $\mathfrak{E}(c, Z)$, and then $t = \bar{\zeta}_c(u)/\bar{\zeta}_c(v) \in \mathfrak{R}(c, Z)$ and hence $t = \varphi(u/v)$. Now u/v is integral over $R(a, X)$ and hence t is integral over $\varphi(R(a, X))$. Also $\varphi(R(a, X)) = \bar{\zeta}_c(R(a, X)) \subset R(c, Z)$ and hence t is integral over $R(c, Z)$. Therefore $t \in R(c, Z)$ because $R(c, Z)$ is integrally closed in $\mathfrak{R}(c, Z)$.

(46.19) *Let X, Y, X', Z be analytic K-spaces, let $\xi: Y \to X$ and $\mu: Z \to X'$ be bimeromorphic maps, and let $\lambda: X' \to X$ be an analytic map.*

1) *Assume that $\mathbf{N}^*(Z) = \emptyset$, and $\lambda^{-1}(\mathbf{N}(X))$ is a thin subset of X'. Then there exists a unique continuous map $\eta: Z \to Y$ such that $\lambda \circ \mu = \xi \circ \eta$.*

2) *Assume that Z is normal and $\bar{\lambda}_{a'}(M(\lambda(a'), X)) \subset M(a', X')$ for all $a' \in X'$.*[4] *Let $\eta: Z \to Y$ be any continuous map such that $\lambda \circ \mu = \xi \circ \eta$. Then η is analytic.*

Proof of 1). Let $\zeta = \lambda \circ \mu: Z \to X$. By (46.11), $\zeta^{-1}(\mathbf{N}^*(X))$ is nowhere dense in Z and hence we are reduced to (46.18.1).

Proof of 2). Let $\zeta = \lambda \circ \mu: Z \to X$. For any $c \in Z$ let $a' = \mu(c)$ and $a = \lambda(a')$. Then $\bar{\zeta}_c = \bar{\mu}_c, \circ \bar{\lambda}_{a'}$ and by (46.8), $\bar{\mu}_c(M(a', X')) \subset M(c, Z)$. Therefore $\bar{\zeta}_c(M(a, X)) \subset M(c, Z)$. Thus we are reduced to (46.18.2).

(46.20) *Let X, Y, Z be analytic K-spaces, let $\xi: Y \to X$ be a bimeromorphic map, and let $\zeta: Z \to X$ be a normalization map. Then there exists a unique continuous map $\eta: Z \to Y$ such that $\zeta = \xi \circ \eta$. Furthermore η is actually analytic. Now assume that ξ is also a normalization map, i.e., Y is normal. Then η is bianalytic, and $\eta^{-1} = \delta$ where $\delta: Y \to Z$ is the unique continuous map such that $\xi = \zeta \circ \delta$.*

PROOF. The first two assertions follow from (46.19) by taking λ to be the identity map of X. Now assume that Y is normal. Then $\delta \circ \eta: Z \to Z$ is continuous and $\zeta \circ (\delta \circ \eta) = \zeta$. Therefore by the uniqueness part of the first assertion, $\delta \circ \eta$ must be the identity map of Z. Similarly $\eta \circ \delta$ must be identity map of Y. Therefore η is bianalytic and $\eta^{-1} = \delta$.

(**46.21**) *Let X, Y, Z be analytic K-spaces, let $\xi: Y \to X$ and $\eta: Z \to Y$ be bimeromorphic maps, and let $\zeta = \xi \circ \eta$. Then $\zeta : Z \to X$ is a bimeromorphic map. If furthermore η is a normalization map, then ζ is a normalization map and $\eta: Z \to Y$ is the only continuous map such that $\zeta = \xi \circ \eta$.*

PROOF. The second assertion follows from the first by (46.9, 46.20). Since ξ and η are bimeromorphic, it follows that ζ is a closed analytic map and $\zeta^{-1}(a)$ is a nonempty finite set for all $a \in X$. Given any $a \in X$ let $b_1,..., b_p$ be the distinct points in $\xi^{-1}(a)$ and let $c_{i1},..., c_{iq_i}$ be the distinct points in $\eta^{-1}(b_i)$. By (46.7) there exist ring homomorphisms $\psi_i: \mathfrak{R}(a, X) \to \mathfrak{R}(b_i, Y)$ and $\varphi_{ij}: \mathfrak{R}(b_i, Y) \to \mathfrak{R}(c_{ij}, Z)$ such that: $\psi_i(r) = \bar{\xi}_{b_i}(r)$ for all i and for all $r \in R(a, X)$; $\varphi_{ij}(s) = \bar{\eta}_{c_{ij}}(s)$ for all i, j and for all $s \in R(b_i, Y)$; $\bigoplus_i \psi_i: \mathfrak{R}(a, X) \to \bigoplus_i \mathfrak{R}(b_i, Y)$ is a ring isomorphism and $\bigoplus_i R(b_i, Y) \subset (\bigoplus_i \psi_i)(R'(a, X))$; $\bigoplus_j \varphi_{ij}: \mathfrak{R}(b_i, Y) \to \bigoplus_j \mathfrak{R}(c_{ij}, Z)$ is a ring isomorphism and $\bigoplus_j R(c_{ij}, Z) \subset (\bigoplus_j \varphi_{ij})(R'(b_i, Y))$ for all i. Let $\lambda_{ij} = \varphi_{ij} \circ \psi_i$. Then $\lambda_{ij}(r) = \bar{\zeta}_{c_{ij}}(r)$ for all i, j and for all $r \in R(a, X)$; and $\bigoplus_{i,j} \lambda_{ij}: \mathfrak{R}(a, X) \to \bigoplus_{i,j} \mathfrak{R}(c_{ij}, Z)$ is a ring isomorphism. Now $\bigoplus_i R(b_i, Y) \subset (\bigoplus_i \psi_i)(R'(a, X))$; $(\bigoplus_i \psi_i)(R'(a, X))$ is integrally closed in $\bigoplus_i \mathfrak{R}(b_i, Y)$; and by (19.22), $\bigoplus_i R'(b_i, Y)$ is integral over $\bigoplus_i R(b_i, Y)$. Therefore $\bigoplus_i R'(b_i, Y) \subset (\bigoplus_i \psi_i)(R'(a, X))$ and hence $\bigoplus_{i,j} R(c_{ij}, Z) \subset (\bigoplus_{i,j} \lambda_{ij})(R'(a, X))$. This being so for all $a \in X$, by (46.7) we conclude that ζ is bimeromorphic.

(**46.22**) Special properties in the complex case.[5]

1) *Let X and Y be complex spaces, let $\xi: Y \to X$ be a bimeromorphic map, and let $(Y_i)_{i \in I}$ be the distinct irreducible components of Y. Then $(\xi(Y_i))_{i \in I}$ are exactly all the distinct irreducible components of X. If Y_b is irreducible for all $b \in Y$, then $(Y_i)_{i \in I}$ are exactly all the distinct connected components of Y.*

2) *Let X and Y be complex spaces, let $\xi: Y \to X$ be a normalization map, and let Ω be a closed thin subset of X such that $\mathbf{N}(X) \subset \Omega$. Then*

[5] Compare (46.22.1, 46.22.3, 46.22.4) with (46.17, 46.18.2, 46.19.2), respectively.

$\xi_{(b)}(R(\xi(b), X)) = R(b, Y)$ for all $b \in Y - \xi^{-1}(\Omega)$, and for each nonempty open set V in Y we have

$$\mathcal{O}_Y(V) = \{f \in \mathfrak{E}(V): f_b \in R(b, Y) \text{ for all } b \in V - \xi^{-1}(\Omega)\}.$$

3) *Let X, Y, Z be complex spaces, let $\xi: Y \to X$ be a bimeromorphic map, let $\zeta: Z \to X$ be an analytic map, and let $\eta: Z \to Y$ be a continuous map such that $\zeta = \xi \circ \eta$. Assume that Z is normal, and there exists a closed subset Ω of X such that $\mathbf{N}(X) \subset \Omega$ and $\zeta^{-1}(\Omega)$ is a thin subset of Z. Then η is analytic.*

4) *Let X, Y, X', Z be complex spaces, let $\xi: Y \to X$ be a bimeromorphic map, let $\mu: Z \to X'$ be a normalization map, let $\lambda: X' \to X$ be an analytic map, and let $\eta: Z \to Y$ be a continuous map such that $\lambda \circ \mu = \xi \circ \eta$. Assume that there exists a closed subset Ω of X such that $\mathbf{N}(X) \subset \Omega$ and $\lambda^{-1}(\Omega)$ is a thin subset of X'. Then η is analytic.*

5) *Let X and Y be complex spaces and let $\xi: Y \to X$ be a proper analytic map such that $\xi^{-1}(a)$ is a nonempty finite set for all $a \in X$. Assume that X is normal, and there exists a closed thin subset Ω of X such that $\xi^{-1}(\Omega)$ is nowhere dense in Y and the map $Y - \xi^{-1}(\Omega) \to X - \Omega$ induced by ξ is bianalytic. Then ξ is bianalytic.*

Proof of 1). By (46.11), $\xi^{-1}(\mathbf{S}(X))$ is a nowhere dense analytic set in Y and $\mathbf{S}(Y) \subset \xi^{-1}(\mathbf{S}(X))$. Therefore by (44.37), $(Y_i - \xi^{-1}(\mathbf{S}(X)))_{i \in I}$ are exactly all the distinct connected components of $Y - \xi^{-1}(\mathbf{S}(X))$ and $Y_i = \mathrm{cl}_Y(Y_i - \xi^{-1}(\mathbf{S}(X)))$ for all $i \in I$. By (46.11), the map $Y - \xi^{-1}(\mathbf{S}(X)) \to X - \mathbf{S}(X)$ induced by ξ is a homeomorphism, and obviously $\xi(Y_i - \xi^{-1}(\mathbf{S}(X))) = \xi(Y_i) - \mathbf{S}(X)$ for all $i \in I$. Therefore $(\xi(Y_i) - \mathbf{S}(X))_{i \in I}$ are exactly all the distinct connected components of $X - \mathbf{S}(X)$. Let $X_i = \mathrm{cl}_X(\xi(Y_i) - \mathbf{S}(X))$. Then by (44.37), $(X_i)_{i \in I}$ are exactly all the distinct irreducible components of X. Since $\xi: Y \to X$ is a closed continuous map, we get that $X_i = \xi(Y_i)$ for all $i \in I$. The second assertion is proved in (44.37).

Proof of 2). By (46.11), $\xi_{(b)}(R(\xi(b), X)) = R(b, Y)$ for all $b \in Y - \xi^{-1}(\Omega)$, and $\xi^{-1}(\Omega)$ is a closed thin subset of Y. Therefore the second assertion follows from (44.42.2).

Proof of 3). The map $Y - \xi^{-1}(\Omega) \to X - \Omega$ induced by ξ is bianalytic by (46.11), and hence the map $\eta | Z - \zeta^{-1}(\Omega): Z - \zeta^{-1}(\Omega) \to Y$ is analytic. Therefore $\eta: Z \to Y$ is analytic by (44.42.3).

Proof of 4). Let $\zeta = \lambda \circ \mu: Z \to X$. Then $\zeta^{-1}(\Omega)$ is a thin subset of Z by (46.11), and thus we are reduced to 3).

Proof of 5). For any $a \in X$ let $b_1, \ldots, b_p$ be the distinct points in $\xi^{-1}(a)$. Then $\operatorname{Ker} \bar{\xi}_a = \{0\}$ and $(\xi_*(\mathcal{O}_Y))_a$ is $R(a, X)$-algebra-isomorphic to $R(b_1, Y) \oplus \ldots \oplus R(b_p, Y)$ by (46.4, 46.5). Given any element in $(\xi_*(\mathcal{O}_Y))_a$ we can write it in the form h_a where h is an analytic function on $\xi^{-1}(U)$ where U is some neighborhood of a in X. We get a unique element $f \in R(U - \Omega)$ such that $h|\xi^{-1}(U - \Omega) = f \circ (\xi|\xi^{-1}(U - \Omega))$. Given any $a' \in \Omega \cap U$ we can take $U' \subset U^* \subset U$ such that U^* is compact and U' is a neighborhood of a' in X. Since ξ is proper, $\xi^{-1}(U^*)$ is compact and hence $|h|$ is bounded on $\xi^{-1}(U^*)$. Therefore $|f|$ is bounded on $U' - \Omega$. Thus $|f|$ is bounded in the neighborhood of every point of $\Omega \cap U$. Therefore by (44.42) there exists $g \in R(U)$ such that $g|U - \Omega = f$. Let $t = g \circ (\xi|\xi^{-1}(U))$. Then t is an analytic function on $\xi^{-1}(U)$ and $t|\xi^{-1}(U - \Omega) = h|\xi^{-1}(U - \Omega)$. Therefore $t = h$. Now $g_a \in R(a, X)$ and $\bar{\xi}_a(g_a) = t_a = h_a$. Thus we have shown that $\operatorname{Im}\bar{\xi}_a = (\xi_*(\mathcal{O}_Y))_a$. Therefore $\bar{\xi}_a$ is an isomorphism, and hence $\bar{\xi}_{b_1} \oplus \ldots \oplus \bar{\xi}_{b_p}: R(a, X) \to R(b_1, Y) \oplus \ldots \oplus R(b_p, Y)$ is an isomorphism. Since $R(a, X)$ is an integral domain, we conclude that $p = 1$ and $\bar{\xi}_{b_1}: R(a, X) \to R(b_1, Y)$ is an isomorphism. In particular ξ is a one to one continuous map of Y onto X, and by (46.3), ξ is open. Therefore ξ is a homeomorphism and $\bar{\xi}(\mathcal{O}_X) = \xi_*(\mathcal{O}_Y)$, i.e., ξ is bianalytic.

(46.23) *Let Y be a nonempty open set in $K^e\{y\} = K^e\{y_1, \ldots, y_e\}$, let $Z = K^m\{z\} = K^m\{z_1, \ldots, z_m\}$, and let $\pi: Y \times Z \to Y$ be the natural projection. Let*

$$g_i(y, z_i) = z_i^{d_i} + \sum_{j=0}^{d_i - 1} r_{ij} z_i^j, \qquad d_i > 0, \qquad (i = 1, \ldots, m),$$

where r_{ij} are analytic functions on Y. Let

$$W = \{(b, c) \in Y \times Z : g_i(b, c_i) = 0 \text{ for } i = 1, \ldots, m\}.$$

Then we have the following.

1) *If $(a^{(n)})_{n=1,2,\ldots}$ is any sequence in W such that the sequence $(\pi a^{(n)})$ contains a subsequence converging to a point in Y, then the sequence $(a^{(n)})$ contains a subsequence converging to a point in W.*

2) *If W' is any nonempty closed subset of W, then $\pi|W': W' \to Y$ is a proper closed map.*

3) *Let U be a nonempty analytic set in Y, and let $f_1, \ldots, f_m$ be elements in $R'(U)$ such that for $i = 1, \ldots, m$ we have*

$$f_i^{d_i} + \sum_{j=0}^{d_i - 1} (r_{ij}|U) f_i^j = 0 \in R'(U)$$

and $f_i = (s_i|U)/(\Delta|U)$ *where* s_i *and* Δ *are analytic functions on* Y *such that* $\Omega = \{b \in U: \Delta(b) = 0\}$ *is nowhere dense in* U. *Let*

$$W^* = \{(b, c) \in U \times Z: s_i(b) = \Delta(b)c_i \text{ for } i = 1,\ldots, m\},$$

let

$$V = \mathrm{cl}_{Y\times Z}(W^* - \pi^{-1}(\Omega)),$$

and let $\xi: V \to U$ *be the map induced by* π. *Then* V *is an analytic set in* $Y \times Z$, $\xi: V \to U$ *is a bimeromorphic map, and* $\xi_*(\mathcal{O}_V)$ *is* $\mathcal{O}_U$*-algebra-isomorphic to* $\mathcal{O}_U[f_1,\ldots,f_m]$.

PROOF. 1) follows from (12.5.1), and 2) follows from 1) as in the proof of (12.5.2). Now proceed to prove 3).

W^* and $\pi^{-1}(\Omega)$ are analytic sets in $Y \times Z$, and hence V is an analytic set in $Y \times Z$ by (44.10). The map $\xi: V \to U$ is obviously analytic. Furthermore $V - \xi^{-1}(\Omega)$ is everywhere dense in V and hence $\xi^{-1}(\Omega)$ is nowhere dense in V by (44.9). Also the map $V - \xi^{-1}(\Omega) \to U - \Omega$ induced by ξ is a homeomorphism because $V - \xi^{-1}(\Omega) = W^* - \pi^{-1}(\Omega)$. Therefore by (46.2.2), $\bar{\xi}_a(M(b, U)) \subset M(a, V)$ for all $a = (b, c) \in V$. In particular $\bar{\xi}_a((\Delta|U)_b) \in M(a, V)$ because $(\Delta|U)_b \in M(b, U)$. Let $\psi: \mathfrak{R}(b, U) \to \mathfrak{R}(a, V)$ be induced by $\bar{\xi}_a$. Now $V \subset W^*$ and hence

$$\bar{\xi}_a((s_i|U)_b) = (\bar{\xi}_a((\Delta|U)_b))((z_i|V)_a).$$

Therefore

$$\psi((f_i)_b) = \psi((s_i|U)_b/(\Delta|U)_b) = (z_i|V)_a.$$

Thus we have proved

1°) For any $a = (b, c) \in V$ with $b \in U$ and $c \in Z$ we have $\bar{\xi}_a(M(b, U)) \subset M(a, V)$ and $\psi((f_i)_b) = (z_i|V)_a$ for $i = 1,\ldots, m$ where $\psi: \mathfrak{R}(b, U) \to \mathfrak{R}(a, V)$ is induced by $\bar{\xi}_a$.

Clearly $W^* - \pi^{-1}(\Omega) \subset W$, and hence $V \subset W$. Therefore $\xi: V \to U$ is a proper closed map by 2). Since $\xi(V - \xi^{-1}(\Omega)) = U - \Omega$ and $U = \mathrm{cl}_U(U - \Omega)$, we get that $\xi(V) = U$. Now $W \cap \pi^{-1}(b)$ is a finite set for all $b \in Y$, and hence $\xi^{-1}(b)$ is a nonempty finite set for all $b \in U$.

Let $a = (b, c)$ be any point in V with $b \in U$ and $c \in Z$, and let $\psi: \mathfrak{R}(b, U) \to \mathfrak{R}(a, V)$ be induced by $\bar{\xi}_a$. Let $w_i = (z_i)_a \in R(a, Y \times Z)$. Let $\nu: R(b, Y) \to R(b, U)$ and $\mu: R(a, Y \times Z) \to R(a, V)$ be the restriction epimorphisms. Now $\bar{\pi}_a: R(b, Y) \to R(a, Y \times Z)$ is a monomorphism and $\mathrm{Ker}\, \mu = \mathfrak{i}(a, V, Y \times Z)$. Since $V \subset W$, by (23.3) we get that

$$R(a, V) = \mu((\bar{\pi}_a R(b, Y))[w_1,\ldots, w_m]).$$

By 1°) we have

$$\mu(w_i) = \psi((f_i)_b) \qquad \text{for} \quad i = 1,\ldots, m,$$

and obviously

$$\mu \circ \bar{\pi}_a = \xi_a \circ \nu.$$

Therefore

$$\begin{aligned}\mu((\bar{\pi}_a R(b, Y))[w_1,\dots, w_m]) &= (\xi_a R(b, U))[\psi((f_1)_b),\dots, \psi((f_m)_b)] \\ &= \psi((R(b, U))[(f_1)_b,\dots, (f_m)_b])\end{aligned}$$

and hence

$$\begin{aligned}R(a, V) &= \psi((R(b, U))[(f_1)_b,\dots, (f_m)_b]) \\ &= \psi((\mathcal{O}_U[f_1,\dots, f_m])_b).\end{aligned}$$

In virtue of (46.8), it only remains to prove that: given any $b \in U$ and any two distinct points $a = (b, c)$ and $a' = (b, c')$ in V, there exists $h \in (R(b, U))[(f_1)_b,\dots, (f_m)_b]$ such that $(\psi(h))(a) \neq 0$ and $\psi'(h) = 0$ where $\psi\colon \mathfrak{R}(b, U) \to \mathfrak{R}(a, V)$ and $\psi'\colon \mathfrak{R}(b, U) \to \mathfrak{R}(a', V)$ are induced by ξ_a and $\xi_{a'}$ respectively. Since $a \neq a'$, we must have $c_i \neq c'_i$ for some i; say $c_1 \neq c'_1$. Since $V \subset W$, we get that $g_1(b, c_1) = 0 = g_1(b, c'_1)$. By Hensel's lemma (12.2), we can write

$$g_1(y, z_1) = H(y, z_1)\bar{H}(y, z_1) \qquad \text{on} \quad \hat{Y} \times Z$$

where $H(y, z_1)$ and $\bar{H}(y, z_1)$ are monic polynomials in z_1 with coefficients which are analytic functions on a neighborhood $\hat{Y}$ of b in Y, and

$$H(b, c_1) \neq 0, \qquad \bar{H}(b, c'_1) \neq 0.$$

We can take neighborhoods $\tilde{Y}$ and $\tilde{Z}$ of b and c' in $\hat{Y}$ and Z respectively such that

$$\bar{H}(\tilde{b}, \tilde{c}_1) \neq 0 \qquad \text{for all} \qquad (\tilde{b}, \tilde{c}) \in (\tilde{Y} \times \tilde{Z}).$$

Since $V \subset W$, we have

$$g_1(\tilde{b}, \tilde{c}_1) = 0 \qquad \text{for all} \qquad (\tilde{b}, \tilde{c}) \in (\tilde{Y} \times \tilde{Z}) \cap V$$

and hence

$$(H(y, z_1)|\hat{V})_{a'} = 0 \qquad \text{where} \qquad \hat{V} = (\hat{Y} \times Z) \cap V.$$

Let

$$H(y, z_1) = z_1^d + t_1 z_1^{d-1} + \dots + t_d$$

be the expression of $H(y, z_1)$ as a polynomial in z_1 with coefficients $t_1,\dots, t_d$ which are analytic functions on $\hat{Y}$. Let

$$h = (f_1^d)_b + (t_1)_b(f_1^{d-1})_b + \dots + (t_d)_b \in R'(b, U).$$

Then

$$h \in (R(b, U))[(f_1)_b] \subset (R(b, U))[(f_1)_b, \dots, (f_m)_b]$$

and by 1°)

$$\psi(h) = (H(y, z_1)|\hat{V})_a \qquad \text{and} \qquad \psi'(h) = (H(y, z_1)|\hat{V})_{a'}.$$

Therefore

$$(\psi(h))(a) \neq 0 \qquad \text{and} \qquad \psi'(h) = 0.$$

(46.24) *Let X be an analytic K-space, let $a \in X$, and let F be a nonempty finite subset of $R'(X)$. Then there exists a neighborhood U of a in X, an analytic K-space V, and a bimeromorphic map $\xi\colon V \to U$ such that $\xi_*(\mathcal{O}_V)$ is $\mathcal{O}_U$-algebra-isomorphic to $\mathcal{O}_U[F]$.*

Proof. Let $\bar{f}_1, \dots, \bar{f}_m$ be the elements in F. We can find analytic functions $\bar{r}_{ij}, \bar{s}_i, \bar{\Delta}$ on a neighborhood $\bar{U}$ of a in X such that $\mathfrak{V}(\bar{\Delta})$ is nowhere dense in $\bar{U}$ and such that for $i = 1, \dots, m$ we have

$$\bar{f}_i^{d_i} + \sum_{j=0}^{d_i-1} \bar{r}_{ij}\, \bar{f}_i^j = 0 \quad \text{on } \bar{U},$$

and $\bar{f}_i = \bar{s}_i/\bar{\Delta}$ on $\bar{U}$. The problem being local, we may assume that a certain neighborhood U of a in $\bar{U}$ is an analytic set in an open set Y in K^e for some e and

$$\bar{r}_{ij}|U = r_{ij}|U, \qquad \bar{s}_i|U = s_i|U, \qquad \bar{\Delta}|U = \Delta|U$$

where r_{ij}, s_i, Δ are analytic functions on U. Let $f_i = \bar{f}_i|U$. Then

$$f_i^{d_i} + \sum_{j=0}^{d_i-1} (r_{ij}|U) f_i^j = 0 \in R'(U) \qquad \text{for} \quad i = 1, \dots, m.$$

Now we are reduced to (46.23.3).

(46.25) *Let X be an analytic K-space, let F be a finite nonempty subset of $R'(X)$ and let $a \in X$ be such that $(R(a, X))[F_a] = F_a R(a, X)$. Then there exists a neighborhood U of a in X such that $\mathcal{O}_U[F] = F\mathcal{O}_U$.*

Proof. Let $f_1, \dots, f_m$ be the elements in F. Then there exist analytic functions r_{ij} on a neighborhood U' of a in X and positive integers d_i such that

$$f_i^{d_i} + \sum_{j=0}^{d_i-1} r_{ij} f_i^j = 0 \qquad \text{on } U', \quad \text{for} \quad i = 1, \dots, m.$$

By division algorithm we can write

$$f_i^k = \sum_{j=0}^{d_i-1} r_{ijk} f_i^j \qquad \text{on } U', \quad \text{for} \quad i = 1,\dots, m \quad \text{and all} \quad k \geqq d_i$$

where r_{ijk} are analytic functions on U'. Since $(R(a, X))[F_a] = F_a R(a, X)$, there exist analytic functions s_{ijk} on a neighborhood U of a in U' such that

$$f_i^j = \sum_{k=1}^{m} s_{ijk} f_k \qquad \text{on } U, \quad \text{for} \quad i = 1,\dots, m \quad \text{and} \quad j = 0,\dots, d_i - 1.$$

Therefore

$$f_i^j = \sum_{k=1}^{m} t_{ijk} f_k \quad \text{on } U, \quad \text{for} \quad i = 1,\dots, m \quad \text{and all} \quad j \geqq 0$$

where t_{ijk} are analytic functions on U. Consequently $\mathcal{O}_U[F] = F\mathcal{O}_U$.

(46.26) *Let X and Y be analytic K-spaces, let $\xi: Y \to X$ be a bimeromorphic map, and let $a \in X$ be such that Y_b is normal for all $b \in \xi^{-1}(a)$. Then there exists a neighborhood U of a in X such that Y_b is normal for all $b \in \xi^{-1}(U)$.*

PROOF. Let $b_1,\dots, b_p$ be the distinct points in $\xi^{-1}(a)$. By (45.28) there exists a neighborhood V_i of b_i in Y such that Y_b is normal for all $b \in V_i$. By (46.3) there exists a neighborhood U of a in X such that $\xi^{-1}(U) \subset V_1 \cup \dots \cup V_p$.

(46.27) *Let X be an analytic K-space and let $a \in X$ be given. Then there exists a neighborhood U of a in X, an analytic K-space V and a normalization map $\xi: V \to U$.*

PROOF. By (24.3.2), $R'(a, X)$ is a finite $R(a, X)$-module. Hence there exists a neighborhood U'' of a in X and a nonempty finite subset F of $R'(U'')$ such that $F_a R(a, X) = R'(a, X)$. By (46.24) there exists a neighborhood U' of a in U'', an analytic K-space V' and a bimeromorphic map $\eta: V' \to U'$ such that $\eta_*(\mathcal{O}_{V'})$ is $\mathcal{O}_{U'}$-algebra-isomorphic to $\mathcal{O}_{U'}[F]$. Now $(\mathcal{O}_{U'}[F])_a = R'(a, X)$ and hence by (46.9), Y_b is normal for all $b \in \eta^{-1}(a)$. Therefore by (46.26) there exists a neighborhood U of a in X such that V is normal where $V = \eta^{-1}(U)$. By (46.9) the map $\xi: V \to U$ induced by η is a normalization map.

Now $\xi_*(\mathcal{O}_V)$ is $\mathcal{O}_U$-algebra-isomorphic to $\mathcal{O}_U[F]$ as well as to $\mathcal{O}'_U$. Therefore $\mathcal{O}'_U = \mathcal{O}_U[F]$ by (44.28). Hence by (46.25) there exists a neighborhood U^* of a in U such that $\mathcal{O}'_{U^*} = F\mathcal{O}_{U^*}$. Since a was an arbitrary point of X, *we conclude that* $\mathcal{O}'_X$ *is a finite* $\mathcal{O}_X$*-module.*

(**46.28**) *For any analytic K-space X we have the following.*

1) $\mathcal{O}'_X$ *is a coherent* $\mathcal{O}_X$*-module.* $\mathcal{O}_X\colon \mathcal{O}'_X$ *is a coherent* $\mathcal{O}_X$*-ideal, and* $(\mathcal{O}_X\colon \mathcal{O}'_X)_a = \mathfrak{c}(R(a, X))$ *for all* $a \in X$.

2) $\text{Supp}(\mathcal{O}_X/(\mathcal{O}_X\colon \mathcal{O}'_X)) = \mathbf{N}(X)$. $\mathbf{N}(X)$ *is an analytic set in* X, *and* $(\mathbf{N}(X))_a = \mathfrak{V}(\mathfrak{c}(R(a, X)))$ *for all* $a \in X$.

3) *Given* $a \in X$ *there exists an analytic function* Δ *on a neighborhood* U *of* a *in* X *such that* $\Delta_{a^*} \in M(a^*, X) \cap \mathfrak{c}(R(a^*, X))$ *for all* $a^* \in U$.[6]

4) *Given an analytic function* Δ *on an open set* U' *in* X *and given* $a \in U'$ *such that* $\Delta_a \in \mathfrak{c}(R(a, X))$, *there exists a neighborhood* U^* *of* a *in* U' *such that* $\Delta_{a^*} \in \mathfrak{c}(R(a^*, X))$ *for all* $a^* \in U^*$. *If furthermore* $\Delta_a \in M(a, X)$, *then there exists a neighborhood* U *of* a *in* U' *such that* $\Delta_{a^*} \in M(a^*, X)$ *for all* $a^* \in U$.

PROOF. We just proved that $\mathcal{O}'_X$ is a finite $\mathcal{O}_X$-module. Therefore, given $a \in X$ there exists a neighborhood U^* of a in X and a finite number of elements $f_1,\dots,f_m$ in $R'(U^*)$ such that $R'(a^*, X) = \{(f_1)_{a^*},\dots,(f_m)_{a^*}\}R(a^*, X)$ for all $a^* \in U$. We can find analytic functions $\Delta, s_1,\dots, s_m$ on a neighborhood U of a in U^* such that for all $a^* \in U$ we have $\Delta_{a^*} \in M(a^*, X)$ and $(f_i)_{a^*} = (s_i)_{a^*}/\Delta_{a^*}$ for $i = 1,\dots, m$. It follows that $\Delta_{a^*} \in \mathfrak{c}(R(a^*, X))$ for all $a^* \in X$, and hence we get an $\mathcal{O}_U$-homomorphism $\varphi\colon \mathcal{O}'_U \to \mathcal{O}_U$ by taking $\varphi(\hat{U})f = (\Delta|\hat{U})f$ for every nonempty open set $\hat{U}$ in U and every $f \in R'(\hat{U})$. φ is a monomorphism because $\Delta_{a^*} \in M(a^*, X)$ for all $a^* \in U$. Therefore φ induces an $\mathcal{O}_U$-isomorphism of $\mathcal{O}'_U$ onto the $\mathcal{O}_U$-ideal $\text{Im}\,\varphi$. Now $\mathcal{O}'_U$ is a finite $\mathcal{O}_U$-module and hence $\text{Im}\,\varphi$ is a finite $\mathcal{O}_U$-module. Since $\mathcal{O}_U$ is a coherent sheaf of rings, it follows that $\text{Im}\,\varphi$ is a coherent $\mathcal{O}_U$-ideal. Therefore $\mathcal{O}'_U$ is a coherent $\mathcal{O}_U$-module. Since a was an arbitrary point of X, we conclude that $\mathcal{O}'_X$ is a coherent $\mathcal{O}_X$-module. By (42.12) it now follows that $\mathcal{O}_X\colon \mathcal{O}'_X$ is a coherent $\mathcal{O}_X$-ideal and $(\mathcal{O}_X\colon \mathcal{O}'_X)_a = \mathfrak{c}(R(a, X))$ for all $a \in X$. This proves 1) and 3). In virtue of (44.24), 2) follows from 1) because for any $a \in X$ we obviously have: $\mathfrak{c}(R(a, X)) = R(a, X) \Leftrightarrow R'(a, X) = R(a, X)$. In virtue of (44.15), 4) also follows from 1).

(**46.29**) *Given any analytic K-space X, there exists an analytic K-space Y and a normalization map* $\xi\colon Y \to X$.

[6] See (46.30).

PROOF. By (46.27) we can find a covering $(X_i)_{i \in I}$ of X by nonempty open sets, a family $(Y_i)_{i \in I}$ of analytic K-spaces, and a normalization map $\xi_i\colon Y_i \to X_i$ for each i in I. For all i, j, k in I let $Y_{ij} = \xi_i^{-1}(X_i \cap X_j)$ and $Y_{ijk} = \xi_i^{-1}(X_i \cap X_j \cap X_k)$. For all i, j in I for which $X_i \cap X_j \neq \emptyset$, the maps $Y_{ij} \to X_i \cap X_j$ and $Y_{ji} \to X_i \cap X_j$ induced respectively by ξ_i and ξ_j are obviously normalization maps and hence by (46.20) there exists a bianalytic map $\lambda_{ji}\colon Y_{ij} \to Y_{ji}$ such that $\xi_i | Y_{ij} = \xi_j \circ \lambda_{ji}$. By the uniqueness part of (46.20) it follows that λ_{ii} = identity map of Y_i for all i in I. For any i, j, k in I for which $X_i \cap X_j \cap X_k \neq \emptyset$ we now have that the maps

$$Y_{ijk} \to X_i \cap X_j \cap X_k \qquad \text{and} \qquad Y_{kji} \to X_i \cap X_j \cap X_k$$

induced respectively by ξ_i and ξ_k are both normalization maps,

$$\lambda_{ki} | Y_{ijk}\colon Y_{ijk} \to Y_{kji} \qquad \text{and} \qquad \lambda_{kj} \circ (\lambda_{ji} | Y_{ijk})\colon Y_{ijk} \to Y_{kji}$$

are both bianalytic maps, and

$$\xi_k \circ (\lambda_{ki} | Y_{ijk}) = \xi_i | Y_{ijk} = \xi_k \circ (\lambda_{kj} \circ (\lambda_{ji} | Y_{ijk}));$$

therefore again by the uniqueness part of (46.20) it follows that $\lambda_{ki} | Y_{ijk} = \lambda_{kj} \circ (\lambda_{ji} | Y_{ijk})$. Consequently by (43.3.4), there exists an analytic K-space Y, an analytic map $\xi\colon Y \to X$, an open covering $(V_i)_{i \in I}$ of Y, and a bianalytic map $\lambda_i\colon Y_i \to V_i$ for each i in I, such that for each i in I we have

$$\xi(V_i) = X_i, \qquad \xi^{-1}(X_i) = V_i, \qquad \text{and} \qquad \xi \circ \lambda_i = \xi_i.$$

Since $\xi_i\colon Y_i \to X_i$ is a normalization map, it follows that the map $\eta_i\colon V_i \to X_i$ induced by ξ is a normalization map. Since $(X_i)_{i \in I}$ is an open covering of X and the map η_i is closed for all i in I, it follows that ξ is closed. Since η_i is normalization map for all i in I, by (46.8) it follows that ξ is a normalization map.

(46.30) REMARK ON (46.28.3). Let Δ be an analytic function on an analytic K-space X. Consider the following conditions.

1°) $\Delta_a \in \mathfrak{c}(R(a, X))$ for all $a \in X$.
2°) $\Delta_a \in M(a, X)$ for all $a \in X$.
1′) $(\Delta | U)f \in R(U)$ for any nonempty open set U in X and $f \in R'(U)$.

1) *Conditions* 1°) *and* 1′) *are obviously equivalent. Therefore if* 1°) *and* 2°) *hold, then for any nonempty open set* U *in* X *and* $f \in R'(U)$ *we get* $f = s/(\Delta | U)$ *where* $s = (\Delta | U)f \in R(U)$.

Now let $\xi\colon Y \to X$ be a normalization map and let $\mu\colon \mathcal{O}'_X \to \xi_*(\mathcal{O}_Y)$ be the unique $\mathcal{O}_X$-algebra-isomorphism; by (46.29) we know that ξ exists.

Note that for any nonempty open set U in X we have : $\xi_*(\mathcal{O}_Y)(U) = R(\xi^{-1}(U))$; $\mu(U): R'(U) \to R(\xi^{-1}(U))$ is an isomorphism; and $\mu(s) = \xi(s) = s \circ (\xi|\xi^{-1}(U))$ for all $s \in R(U)$. Thus 1′) is equivalent to

1″) Given any nonempty open set U in X and $g \in R(\xi^{-1}(U))$, there exists $s \in R(U)$ such that: $\xi(s) = \xi(\Delta|U)g$, i.e., $s(\xi(b)) = \Delta(\xi(b))g(b)$ for all $b \in \xi^{-1}(U)$.

By (46.8), 2°) $\Rightarrow (\xi(\Delta))_b \in M(b, Y)$ for all $b \in Y$, and hence by 1) we get

2) *Assume* 1°) *and* 2°). *Let U be any nonempty open set in X and let g be any analytic function on $\xi^{-1}(U)$. Then there exists an analytic function s on U such that*: $g = \xi(s)/\xi(\Delta|U) = \mu(s/(\Delta|U))$.

Since 1°) and 1″) are equivalent, by (44.42.2, 46.11) we get

3) *Take* $K = \mathbf{C}$ *and assume* 1°). *Let U be any nonempty open set in X, let Ω be any closed thin subset of U and let f be any element in $\mathfrak{E}(U)$ such that $f|U - \Omega \in R(U - \Omega)$. Then there exists $s \in R(U)$ such that*: $s(a) = \Delta(a)f(a)$ *for all* $a \in U$.

For $K = \mathbf{C}$, in Cartan [**5**] any analytic function Δ on X satisfying 1°) and 2°) is called a *universal denominator on* X, and in Oka [**8**] it is called a (W)*-function on* X.

(**46.31**) *Let X be an analytic K-space. For each $a \in X$ identify $\mathfrak{R}(a, X)$ with a subring of the total quotient ring of $\mathfrak{E}(a, X)$.*[7]

If $a \in X$ is such that $X_{a'}$ is irreducible for all a' in some neighborhood of a in X, then $R'(a, X) \subset \mathfrak{E}(a, X)$.[8]

Now assume that X_a is irreducible for all $a \in X$. Let α be the identity map of X, and let $\mathscr{H}$ be the subsheaf of $\mathscr{E}_X$ given by taking

$$\mathscr{H}(U) = \{f \in \mathfrak{E}(U): f_a \in R'(a, X) \text{ for all } a \in U\}$$

for each nonempty open set U in X.[9] *Then $(X, \mathscr{H})$ is a normal analytic K-space, $\mathscr{H}_a = R'(a, X)$ for all $a \in X$, and $\alpha: (X, \mathscr{H}) \to (X, \mathcal{O}_X)$ is a normalization map. Let $\beta: \mathscr{H} = \alpha_*(\mathscr{H}) \to \mathcal{O}'_X$ be the corresponding unique $\mathcal{O}_X$-algebra-isomorphism. Then β_a is the identity map of $R'(a, X)$ for all $a \in X$; and for any nonempty open set U in X and any $f \in \mathscr{H}(U)$ we have*

[7] See (44.16).

[8] For the complex case, in (44.41.1) we have already proved this and have given a function theoretic interpretation of $R'(a, X)$.

[9] For the complex case, in (44.41.2) we have given a function theoretic interpretation of $\mathscr{H}(U)$.

$(\beta(U)f)_a = f_a$ *for all* $a \in U$.[10] *Finally, if* $\xi\colon Y \to (X, \mathcal{O}_X)$ *is any normalization map then* $\xi\colon Y \to (X, \mathscr{H})$ *is bianalytic.*

PROOF. The first assertion being local, from the beginning we may assume that X_a is irreducible for all $a \in X$. Let $\xi\colon Y \to (X, \mathcal{O}_X)$ be any normalization map; by (46.29) we know that it exists. By (46.10), $\hat{\xi}\colon Y \to X$ is a homeomorphism. Let $\mathscr{G} = (\hat{\xi})^{-1}(\xi_*(\mathcal{O}_Y))$. Then $(X, \mathscr{G})$ is a normal analytic K-space, $\alpha\colon (X, \mathscr{G}) \to (X, \mathcal{O}_X)$ is a normalization map, and $\xi\colon Y \to (X, \mathscr{G})$ is bianalytic. For any $b \in Y$ let $a = \xi(b)$. Then $\xi_{(b)}\colon \mathfrak{E}(a, X) \to \mathfrak{E}(b, Y)$ is an isomorphism, $\mathscr{G}_a = (\xi_{(b)})^{-1}(R(b, Y))$, and by (46.13) there exists an isomorphism $\lambda\colon R'(a, X) \to R(b, Y)$ such that $\lambda(r) = \xi_{(b)}(r)$ for all $r \in R(a, X)$. For any $s \in R(b, Y)$ let $u = \lambda^{-1}(s)$ and $v = (\xi_{(b)})^{-1}(s)$; we can take $m \in M(a, X)$ such that $mu \in R(a, X)$, and then

$$\xi_{(b)}(mu) = \lambda(mu) = \lambda(m)s = \xi_{(b)}(m)s = \xi_{(b)}(mv);$$

therefore $mu = mv$ and hence $u = v$ because m is a nonzerodivisor in the total quotient ring of $\mathfrak{E}(a, X)$. This shows that $\mathscr{G}_a = R'(a, X)$ for all $a \in X$, and hence $\mathscr{H} = \mathscr{G}$. The assertions concerning β are now obvious.

Here is a converse of (46.20).

(46.32) *Let X and Z be analytic K-spaces and let $\zeta\colon Z \to X$ be a bimeromorphic map. Assume that for each bimeromorphic map $\xi\colon Y \to X$ there exists a unique analytic map $\eta\colon Z \to Y$ such that $\zeta = \xi \circ \eta$. Then ζ is a normalization map, i.e., Z is normal.*

PROOF. By (46.29) we can take ξ to be a normalization map. By (46.20) there exists an analytic map $\delta\colon Y \to Z$ such that $\xi = \zeta \circ \delta$. By uniqueness, $\delta \circ \eta$ must be the identity map of Z and $\eta \circ \delta$ must be the identity map of Y. Therefore η is bianalytic and hence Z is normal.

Here is a converse of (46.11) in the complex case.

(46.33) *Let X and Z be complex spaces and let $\zeta\colon Z \to X$ be a proper analytic map such that $\zeta^{-1}(a)$ is a nonempty finite set for all $a \in X$. Assume that Z is normal, and there exists a nowhere dense analytic set Ω in X such that $\zeta^{-1}(\Omega)$ is nowhere dense in Z and the map $Z - \zeta^{-1}(\Omega) \to X - \Omega$ induced by ζ is bianalytic. Then ζ is a normalization map.*

PROOF. By (46.29) there exists a normalization map $\xi\colon Y \to X$. Let $\Omega' = \mathbf{S}(X) \cup \Omega$. Then Ω' is a nowhere dense analytic set in X, $\mathbf{N}(X) \subset \Omega'$, $\zeta^{-1}(\Omega')$ is a nowhere dense analytic set in Z, and the map $Z - \zeta^{-1}(\Omega') \to X - \Omega'$ induced by ζ is bianalytic. By (46.18.1, 46.22.3) there exists an

[10] Compare with (44.27.1).

analytic map $\eta: Z \to Y$ such that $\zeta = \xi \circ \eta$. By (46.11), the map $Y - \xi^{-1}(\Omega') \to X - \Omega'$ induced by ξ is bianalytic and hence the map $Z - \eta^{-1}(\xi^{-1}(\Omega')) \to Y - \xi^{-1}(\Omega')$ induced by η is bianalytic. Also $\xi^{-1}(\Omega')$ is a closed thin subset of Y by (46.11). Therefore η is bianalytic by (46.22.5), and hence ζ is a normalization map.

(46.34) *Let X be a complex space.*

1) *Let Ω be a closed thin subset of X and let $f \in R(X - \Omega)$ be such that $|f|$ is bounded in the neighborhood of each point of Ω. Then there exists $g \in R'(X)$ such that $g|X - \Omega = f$.*

2) [11]*For each $a \in X$ identify $\mathfrak{R}(a, X)$ with a subring of the total quotient ring of $\mathfrak{C}(a, X)$.*[7] *Then for any $f \in \mathfrak{C}(X)$ the following four conditions are equivalent.*

i) *There exists $g \in R'(X)$ such that $f_a = g_a$ for all $a \in X$.*
ii) *$f_a \in R'(a, X)$ for all $a \in X$.*
iii) *$f|X - \mathbf{N}(X) \in R(X - \mathbf{N}(X))$.*
iv) *$f|X - \Omega \in R(X - \Omega)$ for some closed thin subset Ω of X.*

Proof of 1). By (46.29) there exists a normalization map $\xi: Y \to X$. Let $\nu: \xi_*(\mathcal{O}_Y) \to \mathcal{O}'_X$ be the corresponding $\mathcal{O}_X$-algebra-isomorphism. Let $h = f \circ (\xi|Y - \xi^{-1}(\Omega))$. Then h is an analytic function on $Y - \xi^{-1}(\Omega)$ and $|h|$ is bounded in the neighborhood of each point of $\xi^{-1}(\Omega)$. By (46.11), $\xi^{-1}(\Omega)$ is a closed thin subset of Y, and hence by (44.42) there exists $t \in R(Y)$ such that $t|Y - \xi^{-1}(\Omega) = h$. Let $g = \nu(t)$. Then $g \in R'(X)$ and $g|X - \Omega = f$.

Proof of 2). Obviously i) $\Rightarrow$ ii) $\Rightarrow$ iii) $\Rightarrow$ iv). Now assume iv). By (46.29) there exists a normalization map $\xi: Y \to X$. Let $\nu: \xi_*(\mathcal{O}_Y) \to \mathcal{O}'_X$ be the corresponding $\mathcal{O}_X$-algebra-isomorphism. Let $h = f \circ \xi$. Then $h \in \mathfrak{C}(Y)$ and $h|Y - \xi^{-1}(\Omega) \in R(Y - \xi^{-1}(\Omega))$. By (46.11), $\xi^{-1}(\Omega)$ is a closed thin subset of Y, and hence $h \in R(Y)$ by (44.42.2). Let $g = \nu(h)$. Then $g \in R'(X)$ and $g|X - \Omega = f|X - \Omega$. Given $a \in X$ we can find a neighborhood U of a in X, $r \in R(U)$, and $s \in M(U)$, such that $sg = r$ on U. Then $sf = r$ on $U - \Omega$ and hence $sf = r$ on U. Therefore $f_a = r_a/s_a = g_a$.

(46.35) *Canonical normalization.* Let X be an analytic K-space. Let Y be the set of all irreducible components of X_a as a varies in X, and let ξ be the map of Y onto X given by: $\xi^{-1}(a)$ = set of all irreducible components of X_a. For any nonempty open set U in X let $\sigma(U)$ be the set of all analytic sets X' in U such that for each $a \in X'$ every irreducible component

[11] In (44.41.2) we proved this under the assumption that X_a is irreducible for all $a \in X$.

of X'_a is an irreducible component of X_a; and for each such X' let $\tau(X')$ be the set of all irreducible components of X'_a as a varies in X'. Let $\mathfrak{T}$ be the set of all subsets of Y of the form $\bigcup_{i \in I} \tau(X_i)$ where $(U_i)_{i \in I}$ is any family of nonempty open subsets of X and X_i is any element in $\sigma(U_i)$. We claim that $\mathfrak{T}$ is a topology on Y. It suffices to show that given any nonempty open subsets U' and U'' of X, $X' \in \sigma(U')$, $X'' \in \sigma(U'')$, $a \in U' \cap U''$, and an irreducible component $\bar{X}$ of X_a such that $\bar{X}$ is an irreducible component of X'_a as well as of X''_a, there exists a neighborhood U^* of a in $U' \cap U''$ and $X^* \in \sigma(U^*)$ such that $\bar{X} \in \tau(X^*) \subset \tau(X') \cap \tau(X'')$. This however follows from (44.11). Topologize Y with the topology $\mathfrak{T}$. By (44.11) it follows that $\xi: Y \to X$ is continuous.

Let $\zeta: Z \to X$ be any normalization map; by (46.29) we know that it exists. Upon taking $\eta(c) = \zeta_{\mathfrak{v}c}(Z)$ for all $c \in Z$, by (46.12) we get a one to one map η of Z onto Y such that $\zeta = \xi \circ \eta$. By (46.15, 46.16) it follows that η is a homeomorphism. Therefore by (46.22.1) we get

1) *Take $K = \mathbf{C}$ and let $(Y_i)_{i \in I}$ be the distinct connected components of Y. Then $(\xi(Y_i))_{i \in I}$ are exactly all the distinct irreducible components of X.*

REMARK. For $K = \mathbf{C}$, in Cartan [**4** and **5**] Y is called the parameter space of X, it is directly proved that Y is locally compact, and the above property is taken as the definition of irreducible components of X.

Going back to the general case of any K, let $\mathscr{G} = \hat{\eta}^{-1}(\eta_*(\mathscr{O}_Z))$. It follows that $(Y, \mathscr{G})$ is a normal analytic K-space and $\xi: Y \to X$ is a normalization map. Therefore, in virtue of (46.13) we can paraphrase (46.29) in the following form.

2) *For each $b \in Y$, $\xi_{(b)}(M(\xi(b), X)) \subset$ (the set of all nonzerodivisors in $\mathfrak{E}(b, Y)$) and $\varphi_b(R'(\xi(b), X)) \subset \mathfrak{E}(b, Y)$ where $\varphi_b: \mathfrak{R}(\xi(b), X) \to$ (the total quotient ring of $\mathfrak{E}(b, Y)$) is induced by $\xi_{(b)}|R(\xi(b), X)$.[12] Let $\mathscr{H}$ be the subsheaf of $\mathscr{E}_Y$ given by taking*

$$\mathscr{H}(V) = \{f \in \mathfrak{E}(V): f_b \in \varphi_b(R'(\xi(b), X)) \text{ for all } b \in V\}$$

for each nonempty open subset V of Y. Then $(Y, \mathscr{H})$ is a normal analytic K-space, $\xi: (Y, \mathscr{H}) \to X$ is a normalization map, and $\mathscr{H}_b = \varphi_b(R'(\xi(b), Y))$ for all $b \in Y$.

DEFINITION. $(Y, \mathscr{H})$ may be called the *canonical normalization of* X and $\xi: (Y, \mathscr{H}) \to X$ may be called the *canonical normalization map*.

In virtue of (46.22.2), by 2) we get

[12] That is, φ_b is the unique ring homomorphism of $\mathfrak{R}(\xi(b), X)$ into the total quotient ring of $\mathfrak{E}(b, Y)$ such that $\varphi_b(r) = \bar{\xi}_{(b)}(r)$ for all $r \in R(\xi(b), X)$.

3) *Take* $K = \mathbf{C}$ *and let* Ω *be any closed thin subset of* X *such that* $\mathbf{N}(X) \subset \Omega$. *Let* $\mathscr{P}$ *be the subsheaf of* $\mathscr{E}_Y$ *given by taking*

$$\mathscr{P}(V) = \{f \in \mathfrak{E}(V) : f_b \in \xi_{(b)}(R(\xi(b), X)) \text{ for all } b \in V - \xi^{-1}(\Omega)\}$$

for each nonempty open subset V *of* Y. *Then* $\mathscr{P} = \mathscr{H}$ *where* $\mathscr{H}$ *is as in* 2), *and hence* $(Y, \mathscr{P})$ *is a normal complex space,* $\xi: (Y, \mathscr{P}) \to X$ *is a normalization map, and* $\mathscr{P}_b = \xi_{(b)}(R(\xi(b), X))$ *for all* $b \in Y - \xi^{-1}(\Omega)$.

REMARK. For $K = \mathbf{C}$, the theorem that $(Y, \mathscr{P})$ is a normal complex space was first proved by Oka; see Oka [**8**]. In Cartan's exposition of Oka's work, the theorem is given in the equivalent form: "$\xi_*(\mathscr{P})$ is a coherent $\mathscr{O}_X$-module"; see Cartan [**5**]. We arrived at our treatment (first announced at a meeting of The American Mathematical Society in 1960) of the theory of normalization which works for any K, by noticing the following two points.

1°) In the Oka–Cartan treatment the so called "favorable case" is first dealt with; one is in the favorable case at $a \in X$ means: X_a is irreducible and $\dim \mathbf{S}(X_a) \leqq (\dim X_a) - 2$. The following lemma is used, Cartan [**5**: lemma 2 of exposé X]: in the favorable case, any analytic function on $X - \mathbf{S}(X)$ has a continuous extension to Y in the neighborhood of $\xi^{-1}(a)$; this is proved by using the Rückert–Weierstrass parametrization and applying Hartogs' theorem (44.40). For the case of general K, this lemma is obviously false. However, the purely formal statement (45.21) serves the same purpose.

2°) In the Oka–Cartan treatment, the procedure for passing from the favorable case to the general case is something like this. Take the Rückert–Weierstrass parametrization of X in the neighborhood of the point under consideration. Adjoin an nth root of the discriminant for suitable n. There results a complex space X^* which is in the favorable case, and a "branched analytic covering" $\delta: X^* \to X$ which roughly means that locally the "function field" $\mathscr{K}_{X^*}$ is a finite extension of the "function field" $\mathscr{K}_X$. Now use the theorem on the coherence of the direct image of a coherent analytic sheaf under a finite proper map. Copying from Zariski's theory of normalization in algebraic geometry,[13] one realizes that the same thing can be achieved without leaving $\mathscr{K}_X$; see (46.23).

Finally it should be noted that Kuhlmann has also given a treatment of the normalization problem in his recent paper Kuhlmann [**1**]. Although Kuhlmann's treatment is restricted to the complex case, his method seems to be somewhat similar to ours.

[13] Zariski [**2** and **3**].

Bibliography

S. Abhyankar

[1] "Ramification Theoretic Methods in Algebraic Geometry." Princeton Univ. Press, Princeton, New Jersey, 1959.

[2] Über die endliche Erzeugung der Fundamentalgruppe einer komplex-algebraischen Mannigfaltigkeit, *Math. Ann.* **139** (1960), pp. 265–274.

[3] Concepts of order and rank on a complex space and a condition for normality, *Math. Ann.* **141** (1960), pp. 171–192.

M. Auslander and D. A. Buchsbaum

[1] Homological dimension in local rings, *Trans. AMS* **85** (1957), pp. 390–405.

H. Behnke and F. Sommer

[1] "Theorie der analytischen Funktionen einer komplexen Veränderlichen." Springer Verlag, Berlin, 1955.

H. Behnke and K. Stein

[1] Die Konvexität in der Funktionentheorie mehrerer komplexer Veränderlichen, *Festschr. math. Ges. Hamburg*, Part II (1940), pp. 34–81.

H. Behnke and P. Thullen

[1] Theorie der Funktionen mehrerer komplexer Veränderlichen, *Ergeb. Math. u. Grenzgebiete* **3,** No. 3 (1934).

S. Bochner and W. T. Martin

[1] "Several Complex Variables." Princeton Univ. Press, Princeton, New Jersey, 1948.

N. Bourbaki

[1] "Topologie Générale," Chapters I and II, 3rd edition. Hermann, Paris, 1961.

H. Cartan

[1] Sur les matrices holomorphes de n variables complexes, *J. Math.* 9e Ser. **19** (1940), pp. 1–26.

[2] Idéaux de fonctions analytiques de n variables complexes, *Ann. Sci. Ecole Norm. Sup.* (3), **61** (1944), pp. 149–197.

[3] Idéaux et modules de fonctions analytiques de variables complexes, *Bull. Soc. Math. France* **78** (1950), pp. 29–64.

[4, 5] Seminaire: 1951–52, 1953–54.

[6] Variétés analytiques complexes et cohomologie, *Colloque de Bruxelles* (1953), pp. 41–55.

H. Cartan and P. Thullen

[1] Zur Theorie der Singularitäten der Funktionen mehrerer komplexer Veränderlichen. Die Regularitäts- und Konvergenzbereiche, *Math. Ann.* **106** (1932), pp. 617–647.

C. Carathéodory

[1] "Funktionentheorie," Vol. II. Akademie Verlag, Basel, 1950.

C. Chevalley

[1] On the theory of local rings, *Ann. Math.* **44** (1943), pp. 690–708.
[2] Some properties of ideals in rings of power series, *Trans. AMS* **55** (1944), pp. 68–84.
[3] Intersections of algebraic and algebroid varieties, *Trans. AMS* **57** (1945), pp. 1–85.

W. L. Chow

[1] On compact analytic varieties, *Am. J. Math.* **71** (1949), pp. 893–914.

I. S. Cohen and A. Seidenberg

[1] Prime ideals and integral dependence, *Bull. AMS* **52** (1946), pp. 252–261.

S. Eilenberg and N. Steenrod

[1] "Foundations of Algebraic Topology." Princeton Univ. Press, Princeton, New Jersey, 1952.

R. Godement

[1] "Théorie des faisceaux." Hermann, Paris, 1958.

H. Grauert and R. Remmert

[1] Plurisubharmonische Funktionen in komplexen Räumen, *Math. Z.* **61** (1956), pp. 175–194.
[2] Komplexe Räume, *Math. Ann.* **136** (1958), pp. 245–318.

A. Grothendieck

[1] Sur quelques points d'algèbre homologique, *Tohoku Math. J.* **9** (1957), pp. 119–221.
[2] Elements de géométrie algébrique I, Institut des Hautes Études Scientifiques, Paris, 1960.

H. Hasse

[1] "Zahlentheorie." Akademie-Verlag, Berlin, 1949.

E. Heinz

[1] Ein elementarer Beweis des Satzes von Radó–Behnke–Stein–Cartan über analytische Funktionen, *Math. Ann.* **131** (1956), pp. 258–259.

W. Hurewicz and H. Wallman

[1] "Dimension Theory." Princeton Univ. Press, Princeton, New Jersey, 1948.

W. Krull

[1] Zum Dimensionsbegriff der Idealtheorie, *Math. Z.* **42** (1937), pp. 745–766.

N. Kuhlmann

[1] Die Normalisierung komplexer Räume, *Math. Ann.* **144** (1961), pp. 110–125.

M. Nagata

[1] On the theory of Henselian rings, *Nagoya Math. J.* **5** (1953), pp. 45–57.
[2] Some remarks on local rings, II, *Mem. Coll. Sci., Univ. Kyoto* **28** (1953), pp. 109–120.
[3] On the chain problem of prime ideals, *Nagoya Math. J.* **10** (1956), pp. 51–64.
[4] On the purity of branch loci in regular local rings, *Illinois J. Math.* **3** (1959), pp. 328–333.

D. G. Northcott

[1] "Ideal Theory." Cambridge Univ. Press, Cambridge, 1953.

K. Oka

[1 to 9] Sur les fonctions analytiques de plusieurs variables:
I. Domaines convexes par rapport aux fonctions rationelles, *J. Sci. Hiroshima Univ.* **6** (1936), pp. 245–255.
II. Domaines d'holomorphie, *J. Sci. Hiroshima Univ.* **7** (1937), pp. 115–130.
III. Deuxième problème de Cousin, *J. Sci. Hiroshima Univ.* **9** (1939), pp. 7–19.
IV. Domaines d'holomorphie et domaines rationellement convexes, *Japanese J. Math.* **17** (1941), pp. 517–521.
V. L'intégrale de Cauchy, *Japanese J. Math.* **17** (1942), pp. 523–531.
VI. Domaines pseudoconvexes, *Tohoku Math. J.* **49** (1942), pp. 15–52.
VII. Sur quelques notions arithmétiques, *Bull. Soc. Math. France* **78** (1950), pp. 1–27.
VIII. Lemme fondamental, *J. Math. Soc. Japan* **3** (1951), pp. 204–214 and 259–278.
IX. Domaines finis sans point critique intérieur, *Japanese J. Math.* **27** (1953), pp. 97–155.

W. F. Osgood

[1] "Lehrbuch der Funktionentheorie," Vol. II 1. Teubner, Leipzig, 1929.

A. Ostrowski

[1] Über einige Lösungen der Funktionalgleichung $\varphi(x)\varphi(y) = \varphi(xy)$, *Acta Math.* **41** (1918), pp. 271–284.

T. Radó

[1] Über eine nicht fortsetzbare Riemannsche Mannigfaltigkeit, *Math. Ann.* **20** (1924), pp. 1–6.

R. Remmert and K. Stein

[1] Über die wesentlichen Singularitäten analytischer Mengen, *Math. Ann.* **126** (1953), pp. 263–306.

W. Rückert

[1] Zum Eliminationsproblem der Potenzreihenideale, *Math. Ann.* **107** (1933), pp. 259–281.

J. P. Serre

[1] Faisceaux algébriques cohérents, *Ann. Math.* **61** (1955), pp. 197–278.
[2] Géométrie algébrique et géométrie analytique, *Ann. Inst. Fourier* **6** (1956), pp. 1–42.
[3] Algèbre locale—Multiplicités, Mimeographed notes of a course, Collège de France, Paris, 1957–1958.

H. Späth

[1] Der Weierstrassche Vorbereitungssatz, *Crelle J.* **161** (1929), pp. 95–100.

N. Steenrod

[1] "The Topology of Fibre Bundles." Princeton Univ. Press, Princeton, New Jersey, 1951.

P. Thullen

[1] Über die wesentlichen Singularitäten analytischer Funktionen und Flächen im Raume von *n* komplexen Veränderlichen, *Math. Ann.* **111** (1935), pp. 137–157.

B. L. van der Waerden

[1, 2] "Modern Algebra," Vols. I and II. Frederick Unger Publ. Co., New York, 1949–1950.

O. Zariski

[1] A theorem on the Poincaré group of an algebraic hypersurface, *Ann. Math.* **38** (1937), pp. 131–141.
[2] Some results in the arithmetic theory of algebraic varieties, *Am. J. Math.* **61** (1939), pp. 249–294.
[3] Foundations of a general theory of birational correspondences, *Trans. AMS* **53** (1943), pp. 430–542.
[4] The concept of a simple point of an abstract algebraic variety, *Trans. AMS* **62** (1947), pp. 1–52.
[5] On the purity of the branch locus of algebraic functions, *Proc. Natl. Acad. Sci. U.S.A.* **44** (1958), pp. 791–796.

O. Zariski and P. Samuel

[1, 2] "Commutative Algebra," Vols. I and II. Van Nostrand, Princeton, New Jersey, 1959–1961.

Index of Notation

We shall not include the notation which is introduced in a particular section and is used only in that section.

The following notation is meant to be generic. For example: $|a|$ denotes the absolute value of a, and so for instance $|b|$ will denote the absolute value of b; R_M denotes the quotient ring of R with respect to M, and so for instance S_N will denote the quotient ring of S with respect to N.

Subject Index

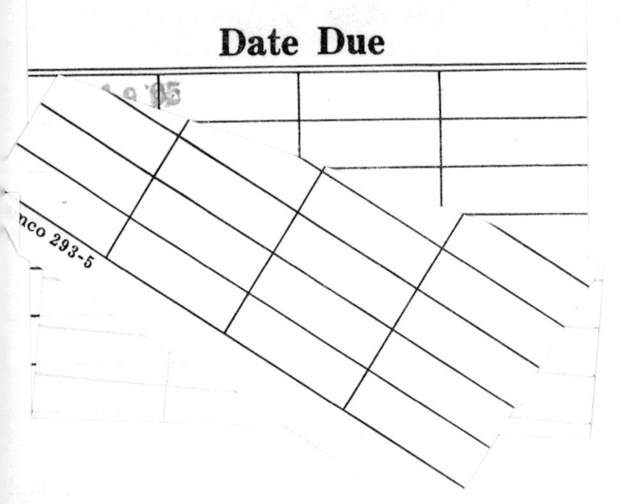
Date Due
'95
nco 293-5